HANDBOOK OF MARINE SCIENCE

VOLUME I

Handbook of Marine Science

Volume I

EDITOR

F. G. Walton Smith, Ph.D., A.R.C.S.

Dean Emeritus, School of Marine and
Atmospheric Science
University of Miami
President, International Oceanographic Foundation
Miami, Florida

published by:

18901 Cranwood Parkway, Cleveland, Ohio 44128

HANDBOOK OF MARINE SCIENCE

VOLUME I

This book presents data obtained from authentic and highly regarded sources. Reprinted material is quoted with permission, and sources are indicated. A wide variety of references are listed. Every reasonable effort has been made to give reliable data and information, but the editors and the publisher cannot assume responsibility for the validity of all materials or for the consequences of their use.

International Standard Book Number (ISBN)
Complete Set 0-87819-388-X
Volume I 0-87819-389-8

THE EDITOR

F. G. Walton Smith is Dean Emeritus of the Rosenstiel School of Marine and Atmospheric Science, University of Miami, Florida, and President of the International Oceanographic Foundation.

Dr. Smith received his B.Sc., (Honors) degree from the University of London and the A.R.C.S. from the Royal College of Science, London, in 1931; in 1934 he was awarded a Ph.D. degree from the University of London. His honorary degrees are D.Sc. from Memorial University of Newfoundland in 1967 and D.Sc. from the University of Miami in 1974.

Several awards were won by Dr. Smith during his undergraduate days. He was also given the Achievement Medal and Gold Medal Award by the Florida Academy of Science in 1942 and 1969, respectively, and the Naval Ordnance Development Award for Exceptional Service by the U.S. Navy in 1945.

Dr. Smith has held various positions in the field of marine science, mostly at the University of Miami. He is a member of numerous organizations in the federal and local government and holds memberships in many societies both in the United States and abroad.

He is the author of *Atlantic Reef Corals*, University of Miami Press; *The Spiny Lobster Industry of the Caribbean and Florida*, Caribbean Research Council; co-author of *Sea Turtles and the Turtle Industry*, University of Miami Press; co-author of *The Ocean River*, Scribner's; and co-author of *The Sun, the Sea, and Tomorrow*, Scribner's. His latest book, *The Seas in Motion*, was recently published by Crowell. Dr. Smith has also made numerous contributions to scientific journals, reports, etc.

ADVISORY BOARD

PREFACE

Oceanography is essentially interdisciplinary in its nature. Rather than the elucidation of basic principles of chemistry, physics, biology, or other scientific disciplines, it is the application of these principles towards an understanding of the nature of the ocean environment. The ocean is a complicated system of energy pathways, both within it and across its boundaries, air-sea, ocean-land, seafloor, and internal boundaries of biological membranes of living organisms in the sea. Associated with the energy pathways are the chemical transformations which take place.

In view of the foregoing, the oceanographer is more likely than most scientists to be involved in more than one discipline. This is the justification for preparing a special handbook of constants, tables, and properties covering all of the major disciplines as they relate to the ocean within one or two volumes.

Quite clearly, since there exist a number of handbooks for the basic disciplines and the CRC *Handbook of Chemistry and Physics* alone is a very bulky volume today in its 55th edition, the task of assembling a handbook for oceanographers becomes largely a question of elimination rather than compilation. Here the guideline has been to identify those tables that are most frequently used by the oceanographer. There will be many occasions that he will need to consult handbooks of chemistry and physics and the like, but it is hoped the present compilation will be of especial value.

Volume I covers chemical oceanography, physical oceanography, atmospheric science (relation between ocean and atmosphere), marine geology, ocean engineering, and a number of tables of conversions and constants most used by oceanographers. Successive volumes will be concerned with biological and fisheries data.

The editor was greatly assisted, not only by the section editors but also by numerous persons who supplied tables or assisted in assembling the material. Particular thanks go to Mrs. Monica Abbott, Mrs. Eloise Zakevich, and Mr. Charles L. Fleming.

TABLE OF CONTENTS

Section 1

Chemical Oceanography

Donald Hood, Ph.D., Richard M. Pytkowicz, Ph.D.

1.1 PERIODIC TABLE OF THE ELEMENTS

KEY TO CHART

Atomic Number → **50** +2 ← Oxidation States
Symbol → Sn +4
Atomic Weight → 118.69
18 18 4 ← Electron Configuration

1a	2a	3b	4b	5b	6b	7b	8	8	8	1b	2b	3a	4a	5a	6a	7a	0	Orbit
1 +1 −1 H 1.0079 1																	**2** 0 He 4.00260 2	K
3 +1 Li 6.94_1 2–1	**4** +2 Be 9.01218 2–2											**5** +3 B 10.81 2–3	**6** +2 +4 −4 C 12.011 2–4	**7** +1 +2 +3 +4 +5 −1 −2 −3 N 14.0067 2–5	**8** −2 O 15.9994 2–6	**9** −1 F 18.99840 2–7	**10** 0 Ne 20.17_9 2–8	K–L
11 +1 Na 22.98977 2–8–1	**12** +2 Mg 24.305 2–8–2	Transition Elements					Group 8			Transition Elements		**13** +3 Al 26.98154 2–8–3	**14** +2 +4 −4 Si 28.086 2–8–4	**15** +3 +5 −3 P 30.97376 2–8–5	**16** +4 +6 −2 S 32.06 2–8–6	**17** +1 +5 +7 −1 Cl 35.453 2–8–7	**18** 0 Ar 39.948 2–8–8	K–L–M
19 +1 K 39.09_8 –8–8–1	**20** +2 Ca 40.08 –8–8–2	**21** +3 Sc 44.9559 –8–9–2	**22** +2 +3 +4 Ti 47.90 –8–10–2	**23** +2 +3 +4 +5 V 50.941_4 –8–11–2	**24** +2 +3 +6 Cr 51.996 –8–13–1	**25** +2 +3 +4 +7 Mn 54.9380 –8–13–2	**26** +2 +3 Fe 55.847 –8–14–2	**27** +2 +3 Co 58.9332 –8–15–2	**28** +2 +3 Ni 58.71 –8–16–2	**29** +1 +2 Cu 63.546 –8–18–1	**30** +2 Zn 65.38 –8–18–2	**31** +3 Ga 69.72 –8–18–3	**32** +2 +4 Ge 72.59 –8–18–4	**33** +3 +5 −3 As 74.9216 –8–18–5	**34** +4 +6 −2 Se 78.96 –8–18–6	**35** +1 +5 −1 Br 79.904 –8–18–7	**36** 0 Kr 83.80 –8–18–8	–L–M–N
37 +1 Rb 85.467_8 –18–8–1	**38** +2 Sr 87.62 –18–8–2	**39** +3 Y 88.9059 –18–9–2	**40** +4 Zr 91.22 –18–10–2	**41** +3 +5 Nb 92.9064 –18–12–1	**42** +6 Mo 95.94 –18–13–1	**43** +4 +6 +7 Tc 98.9062 –18–13–2	**44** +3 Ru 101.07 –18–15–1	**45** +3 Rh 102.9055 –18–16–1	**46** +2 +4 Pd 106.4 –18–18–0	**47** +1 Ag 107.868 –18–18–1	**48** +2 Cd 112.40 –18–18–2	**49** +3 In 114.82 –18–18–3	**50** +2 +4 Sn 118.69 –18–18–4	**51** +3 +5 −3 Sb 121.75 –18–18–5	**52** +4 +6 −2 Te 127.60 –18–18–6	**53** +1 +5 +7 −1 I 126.9045 –18–18–7	**54** 0 Xe 131.30 –18–18–8	–M–N–O
55 +1 Cs 132.9054 –18–8–1	**56** +2 Ba 137.34 –18–8–2	**57*** +3 La 138.9055 –18–9–2	**72** +4 Hf 178.49 –32–10–2	**73** +5 Ta 180.947_9 –32–11–2	**74** +6 W 183.85 –32–12–2	**75** +4 +6 +7 Re 186.2 –32–13–2	**76** +3 +4 Os 190.2 –32–14–2	**77** +3 +4 Ir 192.22 –32–15–2	**78** +2 +4 Pt 195.09 –32–16–2	**79** +1 +3 Au 196.9665 –32–18–1	**80** +1 +2 Hg 200.59 –32–18–2	**81** +1 +3 Tl 204.37 –32–18–3	**82** +2 +4 Pb 207.2 –32–18–4	**83** +3 +5 Bi 208.9808 –32–18–5	**84** +2 +4 Po (209) –32–18–6	**85** At (210) –32–18–7	**86** 0 Rn (222) –32–18–8	–N–O–P
87 +1 Fr (223) –18–8–1	**88** +2 Ra 226.0254 –18–8–2	**89**** +3 Ac (227) –18–9–2	**104** — –32–10–2	**105** —														O P Q

																Orbit
*Lanthanides	**58** +3 +4 Ce 140.12 –20–8–2	**59** +3 Pr 140.9077 –21–8–2	**60** +3 Nd 144.24 –22–8–2	**61** +3 Pm (145) –23–8–2	**62** +2 +3 Sm 150.4 –24–8–2	**63** +2 +3 Eu 151.96 –25–8–2	**64** +3 Gd 157.25 –25–9–2	**65** +3 Tb 158.9254 –27–8–2	**66** +3 Dy 162.50 –28–8–2	**67** +3 Ho 164.9304 –29–8–2	**68** +3 Er 167.26 –30–8–2	**69** +3 Tm 168.9342 –31–8–2	**70** +2 +3 Yb 173.04 –32–8–2	**71** +3 Lu 174.97 –32–9–2		N O P
**Actinides	**90** +4 Th 232.0381 –18–10–2	**91** +5 +4 Pa 231.0359 –20–9–2	**92** +3 +4 +5 +6 U 238.029 –21–9–2	**93** +3 +4 +5 +6 Np 237.0482 –22–9–2	**94** +3 +4 +5 +6 Pu (244) –24–8–2	**95** +3 +4 +5 +6 Am (243) –25–8–2	**96** +3 Cm (247) –25–9–2	**97** +3 +4 Bk (247) –27–8–2	**98** +3 Cf (251) –28–8–2	**99** Es (254) –29–8–2	**100** Fm (257) –30–8–2	**101** Md (256) –31–8–2	**102** No (254) –32–8–2	**103** Lr –32–9–2	**104** (257)	O P Q

Note: Numbers in parentheses are mass numbers of most stable isotope of that element.

(From *CRC Handbook of Chemistry and Physics*, 53rd Ed., Weast, R. C., Ed., CRC Press, Cleveland, 1972. With permission.)

1.2 Composition and Related Properties of Sea Water

Table 1.2–1

CONCENTRATION OF THE MAJOR IONS IN SEA WATER (g/kg SEA WATER) NORMALIZED TO 35°/₀₀ SALINITY

Ion	Average value	Range	Reference
Chloride	19.353		
Sodium	10.76	10.72 – 10.80	Culkin and Cox (1966)
	10.79	10.76 – 10.80	Riley and Tongudai (1967)
Magnesium	1.297	1.292 – 1.301	Culkin and Cox (1966)
	1.292	1.296 – 1.287	Riley and Tongudai (1967)
Sulfate	2.712	2.701 – 2.724	Morris and Riley (1966)
Calcium	0.4119	0.4098 – 0.4134	Culkin and Cox (1966)
	0.4123	0.4088 – 0.4165	Riley and Tongudai (1967)
Potassium	0.399	0.393 – 0.405	Culkin and Cox (1966) Riley and Tongudai (1967)
Bicarbonate*	0.145	0.137 – 0.153	Koczy (1956); Postma (1964) Park (1966)
Bromide	0.0673	0.0666 – 0.0680	Morris and Riley (1966)
Boron	0.0046	0.0043 – 0.0051	Culkin (1965)
Strontium	0.0078	0.0074 – 0.0079	Culkin and Cox (1966)
	0.0081	0.0078 – 0.0085	Riley and Tongudai (1967)
Fluoride	0.0013	0.0012 – 0.0017	Greenhalgh and Riley (1963) Riley (1965)

* The values reported for bicarbonate are actually titration alkalinities.

(Compiled by D. R. Kester, Graduate School of Oceanography, University of Rhode Island.)

REFERENCES

1. Culkin, F., The major constituents of sea water, in *Chemical Oceanography,* Vol. 1, Riley, J. P. and Skirrow, G., Eds., Academic Press, London, 1965, 121-161.
2. Culkin, F. and Cox, R. A., Sodium, potassium, magnesium, calcium, and strontium in seawater, *Deep-Sea Res. Oceanogr. Abstr.,* 13, 789, 1966.
3. Greenhalgh, R. and Riley, J. P., Occurrence of abnormally high fluoride concentrations at depth in the oceans, *Nature,* 197, 371, 1963.
4. Koczy, F. F., The specific alkalinity, *Deep-Sea Res. Oceanogr. Abstr.,* 3, 279, 1956.
5. Morris, A. W. and Riley, J. P., The bromide/chlorinity and sulphate/chlorinity ratio in sea water, *Deep-Sea Res. Oceanogr. Abstr.,* 3, 699, 1966.
6. Park, Kilho, Deep-sea pH, *Science,* 154, 1540, 1966.
7. Postma, H., The exchange of oxygen and carbon dioxide between the ocean and the atmosphere, *Neth. J. Sea Res.,* 2, 258, 1964.
8. Riley, J. P., The occurrence of anomalously high fluoride concentrations in the North Atlantic, *Deep-Sea Res. Oceanogr. Abstr.,* 12, 219, 1965.
9. Riley, J. P. and Tongudai, M., The major cation/chlorinity ratios in sea water, *Chem. Geol.,* 2, 263, 1967.

Table 1.2–2

MOLALITY OF THE MAJOR CONSTITUENTS IN SEA WATER AT VARIOUS SALINITIES

Constituent	Salinity		
	30.0°/oo	34.8°/oo	40.0°/oo
Cl^-	0.48243	0.56241	0.64997
Na^+	0.41417	0.48284	0.55801
Mg^{2+}	0.04666	0.05440	0.06287
SO_4^{2-}	0.02495	0.02909	0.03362
Ca^{2+}	0.00909	0.01059	0.01224
K^+	0.00902	0.01052	0.01215
HCO_3^-	0.00211	0.00245	0.00284
Br^-	0.00074	0.00087	0.00100
$B(OH)_3$	0.00038	0.00044	0.00051
Sr^{2+}	0.00008	0.00009	0.00011

Note: These molalities are based on the concentrations in Table 1.2–1. The average of the two sets of analyses was used for Mg, Ca, K, and Sr. The Na^+ was calculated to preserve electroneutrality; the resulting value is within 0.1% of the analytical values of Na^+ reported in the previous table.

(Compiled by D. R. Kester, Graduate School of Oceanography, University of Rhode Island.)

Table 1.2–3

MAJOR CONSTITUENT CONCENTRATION-TO-CHLORINITY RATIOS FOR VARIOUS OCEANS AND SEAS

Ocean or Sea	Na °/₀₀ *Cl*	Mg °/₀₀ *Cl*	K °/₀₀ *Cl*	Ca °/₀₀ *Cl*	Sr °/₀₀ *Cl*	SO_4 °/₀₀ *Cl*	Br °/₀₀ *Cl*
N. Atlantic	–	–	0.02026	–	–	–	0.00337 – 0.00341
Atlantic	0.5544 – 0.5567	0.0667	0.01953 – 0.0263	0.02122 – 0.02126	0.000420	0.1393	0.00325 – 0.0038
N. Pacific	0.5553	0.06632 – 0.06695	0.02096	0.02154	–	0.1396 – 0.1397	0.00348
W. Pacific	0.5497 – 0.5561	0.06627 – 0.0676	0.02125	0.02058 – 0.02128	0.000413 – 0.000420	0.1399	0.0033
Indian	–	–	–	0.02099	0.000445	0.1399	0.0038
Mediterranean	0.5310 – 0.5528	0.06785	0.02008	–	–	0.1396	0.0034 – 0.0038
Baltic	0.5536	0.06693	–	0.02156	–	0.1414	0.00316 – 0.00344
Black	0.55184	–	0.0210	–	–	–	–
Irish	0.5573	–	–	–	–	0.1397	0.0033
Puget Sound	0.5495 – 0.5562	–	0.0191	–	–	–	–
Siberian	0.5484	–	0.0211	–	–	–	–
Antarctic	–	–	–	0.02120	0.000467	–	0.00347
Tokyo Bay	–	0.0676	–	0.02130	–	0.1394	–
Barents	–	0.06742	–	0.02085	–	–	–
Arctic	–	–	–	–	0.000424	–	–
Red	–	–	–	–	–	0.1395	0.0043
Japan	–	–	–	–	–	–	0.00327 – 0.00347
Bering	–	–	–	–	–	–	0.00341
Adriatic	–	–	–	–	–	–	0.00341

(From Culkin, F. and Cox, R. A., *Deep-Sea Research,* 13, 789, 1966. With permission.)

Table 1.2–4

THE MAJOR CHEMICAL SPECIES IN SEA WATER

Constituent	Percentage of the constituent present as each species at 25°C, 19.375°/₀₀ chlorinity, 1 atm, and pH 8.0
Chloride	–
Sodium	Na^+ (97.7%); $NaSO_4^-$ (2.2%); $NaHCO_3^\circ$ (0.03%)
Magnesium	Mg^{2+} (89%); $MgSO_4^\circ$ (10%); $MgHCO_3^+$ (0.6%); $MgCO_3^\circ$ (0.1%)
Sulfate	SO_4^{2-} (39%); $NaSO_4^-$ (37%); $MgSO_4^\circ$ (19%); $CaSO_4^\circ$ (4%)
Calcium	Ca^{2+} (88%); $CaSO_4^\circ$ (11%); $CaHCO_3^+$ (0.6%); $CaCO_3^\circ$ (0.1%)
Potassium	K^+ (98.8%); KSO_4^- (1.2%)
Bicarbonate	HCO_3^- (64%) $MgHCO_3^+$ (16%); $NaHCO_3^\circ$ (8%); $CaHCO_3^+$ (3%); CO_3^{2-} (0.8%); $MgCO_3^\circ$ (6%); $NaCO_3^-$ (1%); $CaCO_3^\circ$ (0.5%)
Bromide	–
Boron	$B(OH)_3$ (84%); $B(OH)_4^-$ (16%)
Strontium	–
Fluoride	F^- (50-80%); MgF^+ (20-50%)

(From Pytkowicz, R. M. and Kester, D. R., The physical chemistry of seawater, in *Oceanogr. Mar. Biol. Ann. Rev.*, Barnes, H., Ed., in press. With permission of George Allen and Unwin, Ltd., London.)

Table 1.2–5

EFFECT OF TEMPERATURE AND PRESSURE ON THE DISTRIBUTION OF SULFATE SPECIES IN SEA WATER

Percentage of Total Sulfate as Each Species

T(°C)	P(atm)	SO_4^{2-}	$NaSO_4^-$	$MgSO_4^\circ$	$CaSO_4^\circ$
25	1	39	38	19	4
2	1	28	47	21	4
2	1000	39	32	24	5

(From Kester, D. R. and Pytkowicz, R. M., *Geochim. Cosmochim. Acta,* 34, 1039, 1970. With permission.)

Table 1.2–6
MOLALITY OF CHEMICAL SPECIES AND IONIC STRENGTH OF SEA WATER AT VARIOUS PRESSURES, TEMPERATURES, SALINITIES, AND pH = 8.0*

Pressure	1 atm				500 atm	1000 atm
Temperature	25°C			2°C	2°C	2°C
Salinity	30.0°/oo	34.8°/oo	40.0°/oo	34.8°/oo	34.8°/oo	34.8°/oo
Cl^-	0.48243	0.56241	0.64997	0.56241	0.56241	0.56241
Na^+	0.40556	0.47178	0.54384	0.46911	0.47098	0.47282
Mg^{2+}	0.04131	0.04831	0.05611	0.04795	0.04792	0.04801
SO_4^{2-}	0.01041	0.01136	0.01216	0.00828	0.01009	0.01201
$NaSO_4^-$	0.00845	0.01085	0.01391	0.01351	0.01165	0.00982
K^+	0.00892	0.01039	0.01200	0.01043	0.01041	0.01039
Ca^{2+}	0.00800	0.00936	0.01088	0.00928	0.00928	0.00930
$MgSO_4^\circ$	0.00498	0.00561	0.00614	0.00599	0.00602	0.00592
HCO_3^-	0.00131	0.00143	0.00154	0.00155	0.00147	0.00138
$CaSO_4^\circ$	0.00102	0.00115	0.00126	0.00123	0.00123	0.00121
Br^-	0.00074	0.00087	0.00100	0.00087	0.00087	0.00087
$MgHCO_3^+$	0.00028	0.00036	0.00045	0.00039	0.00037	0.00035
$B(OH)_3$	0.00032	0.00037	0.00042	0.00040	0.00036	0.00032
$NaHCO_3^\circ$	0.00015	0.00020	0.00024	0.00021	0.00020	0.00019
KSO_4^-	0.00010	0.00012	0.00015	0.00009	0.00011	0.00013
Sr^{2+}	0.00008	0.00009	0.00011	0.00009	0.00009	0.00009
μ	0.5736	0.6675	0.7701	0.6605	0.6640	0.6681

* Ionic strength of sea water is given by the empirical expression: $\mu = 0.0054 + 0.01840\ (S°/oo) + 1.78 \times 10^{-5}\ (S°/oo)^2 - 3.0 \times 10^{-4}\ (25 - t°C) + 7.6 \times 10^{-6}\ (P\ atm - 1)$ for $30°/oo \leq S°/oo \leq 40°/oo$.

(Based on Kester, D. R. and Pytkowicz, R. M., *Limnol. Oceanogr.*, 14, 686, 1969 and *Geochim. Cosmochim. Acta,* 34, 1039, 1970.)

Table 1.2–7
STOICHIOMETRIC ASSOCIATION CONSTANTS, $K^*_{MA} = \frac{[MA]}{[M]\ [A]}$ †

Pressure	1 atm				500 atm	1000 atm	
Temperature	25°C			2°C	2°C	2°C	
Salinity	30.0°/oo	34.8°/oo	40.0°/oo	34.8°/oo	34.8°/oo	34.8°/oo	Ref.
$NaSO_4^-$	2.00	2.02	2.09	3.45	2.43	1.70	1–4
$MgSO_4^\circ$	11.8	10.2	8.9	14.7	13.5	12.5	1–4
$CaSO_4^\circ$	12.4	10.8	9.5	15.3	14.1	13.1	1–4
KSO_4^-	1.03	1.03	1.03	1.03	1.03	1.03	5
$NaHCO_3^\circ$	0.29	0.29	0.29	0.29	0.29	0.29	6
$MgHCO_3^+$	5.22	5.22	5.22	5.22	5.22	5.22	5
$CaHCO_3^+$	5.10	5.10	5.10	5.10	5.10	5.10	5
$NaCO_3^-$	1.58	1.58	1.58	1.58	1.58	1.58	6
$MgCO_3^\circ$	160	160	160	160	160	160	5
$CaCO_3^\circ$	78	78	78	78	78	78	5

† Used in the calculation of the major chemical species in sea water at various pressures, temperatures, and salinities.

TABLE 1.2–7 (*Continued*)

REFERENCES

1. **Pytkowicz, R. M. and Kester, D. R.,** *Am. J. Sci.,* 267, 217, 1969.
2. **Kester, D. R. and Pytkowicz, R. M.,** *Limnol. Oceanogr.,* 13, 670, 1968.
3. **Pytkowicz, R. M. and Kester, D. R.,** *Limnol. Oceanogr.,* 14, 686, 1969.
4. **Pytkowicz, R. M. and Kester, D. R.,** *Geochim. Cosmochim. Acta,* in press.
5. **Garrels, R. M. and Thompson, M. E.,** *Am. J. Sci.,* 260, 57, 1962.
6. **Butler, J. N. and Huston, R.,** *J. Phys. Chem.,* 74, 2976, 1970.

Table 1.2–8
MINOR CONSTITUENTS OF SEA WATER EXCLUDING THE DISSOLVED GASES*

Element	Concentration μg/l		References on the distribution in the oceans
	Average	Range	
Lithium	185 (2, 18, 29, 52, 62)	180–195 (2, 18, 29, 52, 62)	(2, 18, 29, 52, 62)
Beryllium	5.7×10^{-4} (48)		
Nitrogen	280 (82)	0–560 (82)	(82)
Aluminum	2 (65, 70, 10, 31)	0–7 (65, 70)	(65)
Silicon	2000 (5)	0–4900 (5)	(5)
Phosphorus	30 (4)	0–90 (4)	(4)
Scandium	0.04 (31)		
	<0.004 (68)	$0.1–18 \times 10^{-4}$ (37)	
	9.6×10^{-4} (37)		
Titanium	1 (34)		
Vanadium	2.5 (11, 12)	2.0–3.0 (11, 12)	(11)
Chromium	0.3 (30)	0.23–0.43 (30)	
	0.05 (41)	0.04–0.07 (41)	
Manganese	1.5 (64)	0.2–8.6 (64)	(64, 78)
	0.9 (78)	0.7–1.3 (78)	
		3.0–4.4 (28)	
Iron	6.6 (78)	0.1–62 (78)	(3, 7, 22, 78)
	2.6 (70)	8–13 (22)	
	0.2 (7)	0–7 (28, 70)	
		0.03–2.56 (7)	
Cobalt	0.27 (68)	0.035–4.1 (68)	(68, 69, 78)
	0.032 (78)	<0.005–0.092 (78)	
Nickel	5.4 (68)	0.43–43 (22, 68)	(68, 69, 73)
	1.7 (73)	0.8–2.4 (73)	
		0.13–0.37 (28)	
Copper	2 (28, 80)	0.2–4 (28, 73, 78, 80)	(1, 73, 78, 80)
	1.2 (78)	0.5–27 (1, 9, 22, 38)	
	0.7 (73)		

* The numbers in parentheses refer to the citations listed after the table. The concentrations represent the dissolved and particulate forms of the elements.

(Based on compilations of Pytkowicz, R. M. and Kester, D. R., The physical chemistry of seawater, in *Oceanogr. Mar. Biol. Ann. Rev.,* Barnes, H., Ed., in press. With permission of George Allen and Unwin, Ltd., London.)

Table 1.2–8 (*Continued*)
MINOR CONSTITUENTS OF SEA WATER EXCLUDING THE DISSOLVED GASES

Element	Concentration μg/l Average	Range	References on the distribution in the oceans
Zinc	12.3 (78)	3.9–48.4 (78)	(64, 73, 78, 80)
	6.5 (64, 80)	2–18 (64, 80)	
	2 (73)	1–8 (73)	
		29–50 (9)	
Gallium	0.03 (23)	0.023–0.037 (23)	
Germanium	0.05 (12, 27)	0.05–0.06 (12)	
Arsenic	4 (39)	3–6 (39)	
	0.46 (41)	2–35 (61)	
Selenium	0.2 (15, 68)	0.34–0.50 (15)	(68)
		0.052–0.12 (68)	
Rubidium	120 (8, 52, 63, 71)	112–134 (8, 52, 63, 71)	(8, 29, 52, 71)
		86–119 (29)	
Yttrium	0.03 (31)	0.0112–0.0163 (37)	
	0.0133 (37)		
Zirconium	2.6×10^{-2} (88)		
Niobium	0.01 (13)	0.01–0.02 (13)	
Molybdenum	10 (41)	0.24–12.2 (9, 85)	
	1 (9)		
Technetium			
Ruthenium	0.0007 (88)		
Rhodium			
Palladium			
Silver	0.29 (68)	0.055–1.5 (68)	(68, 69)
	0.04 (31)		
Cadmium	0.113 (53)	0.02–0.25 (53)	
Indium	<20 (31)		
Tin	0.8 (31)		
Antimony	0.33 (68)	0.18–1.1 (68)	(68)
Tellurium			
Iodine	63 (6)	48–80 (6)	(6)
	44 (41)		
Cesium	0.4 (8, 63)	0.27–0.33 (8)	(8)
		0.48–0.58 (63)	
Barium	20 (8, 17, 19, 81)	5–93 (8, 17, 19, 81)	(19, 81)
Lanthanum	3×10^{-3} (33, 37)	$1-6 \times 10^{-3}$ (37)	(35–37)
Cerium	14×10^{-3} (14)	$4-850 \times 10^{-3}$ (14)	(35–37)
	1×10^{-3} 37)	$0.6-2.8 \times 10^{-3}$ (37)	
Praseodymium	6.4×10^{-4} (33, 37)	$4.1-15.8 \times 10^{-4}$ (37)	(35–37)
Neodymium	23×10^{-4} (33)	$13-65 \times 10^{-4}$ (37)	(35–37)
	28×10^{-4} (37)		
Promethium			
Samarium	4.2×10^{-4} (33)	$2.6-10 \times 10^{-4}$ (37)	(35–37)
	4.5×10^{-4} (37)		
Europium	1.14×10^{-4}	$0.9-7.9 \times 10^{-4}$ (37)	(35–37)
	1.3×10^{-4} (37)		

Table 1.2–8 (*Continued*)
MINOR CONSTITUENTS OF SEA WATER EXCLUDING THE DISSOLVED GASES

Element	Concentration μg/l		References on the distribution in the oceans
	Average	Range	
Gadolinium	6.0×10^{-4} (33) 7.0×10^{-4} (37)	$5.2–11.5 \times 10^{-4}$ (37)	(35–37)
Terbium	1.4×10^{-4} (37)	$0.6–3.6 \times 10^{-4}$ (37)	(35–37)
Dysprosium	7.3×10^{-4} (33) 9.1×10^{-4} (37)	$5.2–14.0 \times 10^{-4}$ (37)	(35–37)
Holmium	2.2×10^{-4} (33, 37)	$1.2–7.2 \times 10^{-4}$ (33, 37)	(33, 35–37)
Erbium	6.1×10^{-4} (33) 8.7×10^{-4} (37)	$6.6–12.4 \times 10^{-4}$ (37)	(35–37)
Thulium	1.3×10^{-4} (33) 1.7×10^{-4} (37)	$0.9–3.7 \times 10^{-4}$ (37)	(35–37)
Ytterbium	5.2×10^{-4} (33) 8.2×10^{-4} (37)	$4.8–28 \times 10^{-4}$ (33, 37)	(33, 35–37)
Lutetium	2.0×10^{-4} (33) 1.5×10^{-4} (37)	$1.2–7.5 \times 10^{-4}$ (33, 37)	(33, 35–37)
Hafnium	80×10^{-4} (68)		
Tantalum	25×10^{-4} (68)		
Tungsten	0.1 (41)		
Rhenium	8.4×10^{-3} (66)		
Osmium			
Indium	1×10^{-4} (88)		
Platinum			
Gold	0.068 (86)	0.004–0.027 (68)	
Mercury	0.03 (31)		
Thallium	<0.01 (31)		
Lead	0.05 (19)	0.02–0.4 (19, 76, 77)	(19, 76, 77)
Bismuth	0.02 (56)	0.015–0.033 (56)	
Polonium			
Astatine			
Francium			
Radium	8×10^{-8} (55)	$4–15 \times 10^{-8}$ (45, 49, 75)	(45, 49, 75)
Actinium			
Thorium	0.05 (31) 0.02 (55) 6×10^{-4} (51, 72) $<7 \times 10^{-5}$ (42)	$2–40 \times 10^{-4}$ (51, 72)	
Protactinium	2×10^{-6} (31) 5×10^{-8} (55)		
Uranium	3 (50, 55, 79)	2–4.7 (50, 55, 79)	(50, 55, 79)

Table 1.2–8 (*Continued*)

REFERENCES

1. **Alexander, J. E. and Corcoran, E. F.,** *Limnol. Oceanogr.,* 12, 236, 1967.
2. **Angino, E. E. and Billings, G. K.,** *Geochim. Cosmochim. Acta,* 30, 153, 1966.
3. **Armstrong, F. A. J.,** *J. Mar. Biol. Assoc. U.K.,* 36, 509, 1957.
4. **Armstrong, F. A. J.,** in *Chemical Oceanography,* Vol. 1, Riley, J. P. and Skirrow, G., Eds., Academic Press, London, 1965, 323-364.
5. **Armstrong, F. A. J.,** in *Chemical Oceanography,* Vol. 1, Riley, J. P. and Skirrow, G., Eds., Academic Press, London, 1965, 409-432.
6. **Barkley, R. A. and Thompson, T. G.,** *Deep Sea Res.,* 7, 24, 1960.
7. **Betzer, P. and Pilson, M. E. Q.,** *J. Mar. Res.,* 28, 251, 1970.
8. **Bolter, E., Turekian, K. K., and Schutz, D. F.,** *Geochim. Cosmochim. Acta,* 28, 1459, 1964.
9. **Brooks, R. R.,** *Geochim. Cosmochim. Acta,* 29, 1369, 1965.
10. **Burton, J. D.,** *Nature,* 212, 976, 1966.
11. **Burton, J. D. and Krishnamurty, K.,** *Rep. Challenger Soc.,* 3, 24, 1967.
12. **Burton, J. D. and Riley, J. P.,** *Nature,* 181, 179, 1958.
13. **Carlisle, D. B. and Hummerstone, L. G.,** *Nature,* 181, 1002, 1958.
14. **Carpenter, J. H. and Grant, V. E.,** *J. Mar. Res.,* 25, 228, 1967.
15. **Chau, Y. K. and Riley, J. P.,** *Anal. Chim. Acta,* 33, 36, 1965.
16. **Chester, R.,** *Nature,* 206, 884, 1965.
17. **Chow, T. J. and Goldberg, E. D.,** *Geochim. Cosmochim. Acta,* 20, 192, 1960.
18. **Chow, T. J. and Goldberg, E. D.,** *J. Mar. Res.,* 20, 163, 1962.
19. **Chow, T. J. and Patterson, C. C.,** *Earth and Planet. Sci. Lett.,* 1, 397, 1966.
20. **Chow, T. J. and Tatsumoto, M.,** in *Recent Researches in the Fields of Hydrosphere, Atmosphere, and Nuclear Geochemistry,* Miyake, Y. and Koyama, T., Eds., Maruzen Co., Tokyo, 1964, 179-183.
21. **Chuecas, L. and Riley, J. P.,** *Anal. Chim. Acta,* 35, 240, 1966.
22. **Corcoran, E. F. and Alexander, J. E.,** *Bull. Mar. Sci. Gulf Caribbean,* 14, 594, 1964.
23. **Culkin, F. and Riley, J. P.,** *Nature,* 181, 180, 1958.
24. **Curl, H., Cutshall, N., and Osterberg, C.,** *Nature,* 205, 275, 1965.
25. **Cutshall, N., Johnson, V., and Osterberg, C.,** *Science,* 152, 202, 1966.
26. **Duursma, E. K. and Sevenhuysen, W.,** *Neth. J. Sea Res.,* 3, 95, 1966.
27. **El Wardani, S. A.,** *Geochim. Cosmochim. Acta,* 15, 237, 1958.
28. **Fabricand, B. P., Sawyer, R. R., Ungar, S. G., and Adler, S.,** *Geochim. Cosmochim. Acta,* 26, 1023, 1962.
29. **Fabricand, B. P., Imbimbo, E. S., Brey, M. E., and Weston, J. A.,** *J. Geophys. Res.,* 71, 3917, 1966.
30. **Fukai, R.,** *Nature,* 213, 901, 1967.
31. **Goldberg, E. D.,** in *Chemical Oceanography,* Vol. 1, Riley, J. P. and Skirrow, G., Eds., Academic Press, London, 1965, 163-196.
32. **Goldberg, E. D. and Arrhenius, G. S.,** *Geochim. Cosmochim. Acta,* 13, 153, 1958.
33. **Goldberg, E. D., Koide, M., Schmitt, R. A., and Smith, R. H.,** *J. Geophys. Res.,* 68, 4209, 1963.
34. **Griel, J. V. and Robinson, R. J.,** *J. Mar. Res.,* 11, 173, 1952.
35. **Høgdahl, O.,** Semi Annual Progress Report No. 5, NATO Scientific Affairs Div., Brussels, 1967.
36. **Høgdahl, O.,** Semi Annual Progress Report No. 6, NATO Scientific Affairs Div., Brussels, 1968.
37. **Høgdahl, O., Melsom, S., and Bowen, V. T.,** Trace inorganics in water, in *Advances in Chemistry Series,* No. 73, American Chemical Society, Washington, D.C., 1968, 308-325.
38. **Hood, D. W.,** in *Oceanogr. Mar. Biol. Annu. Rev.,* Vol. 1, Barnes, H., Ed., George Allen and Unwin, Ltd., London, 1963, 129-155.
39. **Ishibashi, M.,** *Rec. Oceanogr. Works Jap.,* 1, 88, 1953.
40. **Johnson, V., Cutshall, N., and Osterberg, C.,** *Water Resour. Res.,* 3, 99, 1967.
41. **Kappanna, A. N., Gadre, G. T., Bhavnagary, H. M., and Joshi, J. M.,** *Curr. Sci. (India),* 31, 273, 1962.
42. **Kaufman, A.,** *Geochim. Cosmochim. Acta,* 33, 717, 1969.
43. **Kester, D. R. and Pytkowicz, R. M.,** *Limnol. Oceanogr.,* 12, 243, 1967.
44. **Kharkar, D. P., Turekian, K. K., and Bertine, K. K.,** *Geochim. Cosmochim. Acta,* 32, 285, 1968.
45. **Koczy, F. F.,** *Proc. Second U.N. Internat. Conf. Peaceful Uses Atomic Energy,* 18, 351, 1958.

46. **Krauskopf, K. B.,** *Geochim. Cosmochim. Acta,* 9, 1, 1956.
47. **Menzenl, D. W. and Ryther, J. H.,** *Deep Sea Res.,* 7, 276, 1961.
48. **Merrill, J. R., Lyden, E. F. X., Honda, M., and Arnold, J.,** *Geochim. Cosmochim. Acta,* 18, 108, 1960.
49. **Miyake, Y. and Sugimura, Y.,** in *Studies on Oceanography,* Yoshida, K., Ed., Univ. of Washington Press, Seattle, 1964, 274.
50. **Miyake, Y., Sugimura, Y., and Uchida, T.,** *J. Geophys. Res.,* 71, 3083, 1966.
51. **Moore, W. S. and Sackett, W. M.,** *J. Geophys. Res.,* 69, 5401, 1964.
52. **Morozov, N. P.,** *Oceanology,* 8, 169, 1968.
53. **Mullin, J. B. and Riley, J. P.,** *J. Mar. Res.,* 15, 103, 1956.
54. **Peshchevitskiy, B. I., Anoshin, G. N., and Yereburg, A. M.,** *Dokl. Earth Sci. Sect.,* 162, 205, 1965.
55. **Picciotto, E. E.,** in *Oceanography,* Sears, M., Ed., Amer. Assoc. Adv. Sci., Washington, D.C., 1961, 367.
56. **Portmann, J. E. and Riley, J. P.,** *Anal. Chim. Acta,* 34, 201, 1966.
57. **Putnam, G. L.,** *J. Chem. Educ.,* 30, 576, 1953.
58. **Pytkowicz, R. M.,** *J. Oceanogr. Soc. Jap.,* 24, 21, 1968.
59. **Pytkowicz, R. M. and Kester, D. R.,** *Deep Sea Res.,* 13, 373, 1966.
60. **Pytkowicz, R. M. and Kester, D. R.,** *Limnol. Oceanogr.,* 12, 714, 1967.
61. **Richards, F. A.,** in *Physics and Chemistry of the Earth,* Vol. 2, Ahrens, L. H., Press, F., Rankama, K., and Runcorn, S. K., Eds., Pergamon Press, New York, 1957, 77-128.
62. **Riley, J. P. and Tongudai, M.,** *Deep Sea Res.,* 11, 563, 1964.
63. **Riley, J. P. and Tongudai, M.,** *Chem. Geol.,* 1, 291, 1966.
64. **Rona, E., Hood, D. W., Muse, L., and Buglio, B.,** *Limnol. Oceanogr.,* 7, 201, 1962.
65. **Sackett, W. and Arrhenius, G.,** *Geochim. Cosmochim. Acta,* 26, 955, 1962.
66. **Scadden, E. M.,** *Geochim. Cosmochim. Acta,* 33, 633, 1969.
67. **Schink, D. R.,** *Geochim. Cosmochim. Acta,* 31, 987, 1967.
68. **Schutz, D. F. and Turekian, K. K.,** *Geochim. Cosmochim. Acta,* 29, 259, 1965.
69. **Schutz, D. F. and Turekian, K. K.,** *J. Geophys. Res.,* 70, 5519, 1965.
70. **Simmons, L. H., Monaghan, P. H., and Taggart, M. S.,** *Anal. Chem.,* 25, 989, 1953.
71. **Smith, R. C., Pillai, K. C., Chow, T. J., and Folson, T. R.,** *Limnol. Oceanogr.,* 10, 226, 1965.
72. **Somayajulu, B. L. K. and Goldberg, E. D.,** *Earth Planet. Sci. Lett.,* 1, 102, 1966.
73. **Spencer, D. W. and Brewer, P. G.,** *Geochim. Cosmochim. Acta,* 33, 325, 1969.
74. **Sugawara, K. and Terada, K.,** *Nature,* 182, 250, 1958.
75. **Szabo, B. J.,** *Geochim. Cosmochim. Acta,* 31, 1321, 1967.
76. **Tatsumoto, M. and Patterson, C. C.,** *Nature,* 199, 350, 1963.
77. **Tatsumoto, M. and Patterson, C. C.,** in *Earth Sciences and Meteoritics,* Geiss, J. and Goldberg, E. D., Compilers, North Holland Publ. Co., Amsterdam, 1963, 74-89.
78. **Topping, G.,** *J. Mar. Res.,* 27, 318, 1969.
79. **Torii, T. and Murata, S.,** in *Recent Researches in the Fields of Hydrosphere, Atmosphere, and Nuclear Geochemistry,* Miyake, Y. and Koyama, T., Eds., Maruzen Co., Tokyo, 1964.
80. **Torii, T. and Murata, S.,** *J. Oceanogr. Soc. Jap.,* 22, 56, 1966.
81. **Turekian, K. K. and Johnson, D. G.,** *Geochim. Cosmochim. Acta,* 30, 1153, 1966.
82. **Vaccaro, R. F.,** in *Chemical Oceanography,* Vol. 1, Riley, J. P. and Skirrow, G., Eds., Academic Press, London, 1965, 365-408.
83. **Veeh, H. H.,** *Earth and Planet. Sci. Lett.,* 3, 145, 1967.
84. **Wangersky, P. J. and Gordon, D. C., Jr.,** *Limnol. Oceanogr.,* 10, 544, 1965.
85. **Weiss, H. V. and Lai, M. G.,** *Talanta,* 8, 72, 1961.
86. **Weiss, H. V. and Lai, M. G.,** *Anal. Chim. Acta,* 28, 242, 1963.
87. **Williams, P. M.,** *Limnol. Oceanogr.,* 14, 156, 1969.
88. **Riley, J. P. and Chester, R.,** *Introduction to Marine Chemistry,* Academic Press, London, 1971.

Table 1.2–9
VALUES OF K'_1 FOR PHOSPHORIC ACID (x 10^2) IN SEA WATER AND EQUATIONS TO CALCULATE THE SPECIATION*

	Salinity (°/oo)								
Temp (°C)	29	30	31	32	33	34	35	36	37
0	2.84	2.87	2.87	2.86	2.85	2.84	2.83	2.82	2.81
1	2.80	2.83	2.83	2.82	2.82	2.82	2.81	2.81	2.80
2	2.74	2.77	2.77	2.78	2.78	2.78	2.79	2.79	2.80
3	2.69	2.72	2.73	2.74	2.75	2.76	2.77	2.78	2.78
4	2.63	2.66	2.68	2.69	2.71	2.72	2.74	2.76	2.77
5	2.58	2.61	2.63	2.66	2.68	2.70	2.73	2.75	2.77
6	2.53	2.56	2.58	2.61	2.64	2.66	2.69	2.73	2.75
7	2.46	2.50	2.54	2.58	2.61	2.64	2.68	2.72	2.75
8	2.40	2.44	2.49	2.54	2.58	2.62	2.66	2.70	2.74
9	2.34	2.38	2.42	2.48	2.54	2.59	2.64	2.68	2.73
10	2.30	2.35	2.40	2.46	2.51	2.56	2.62	2.67	2.72
11	2.34	2.39	2.44	2.49	2.53	2.58	2.64	2.70	2.76
12	2.44	2.48	2.52	2.56	2.61	2.66	2.72	2.79	2.87
13	2.57	2.60	2.63	2.67	2.72	2.77	2.84	2.92	3.10
14	2.67	2.69	2.72	2.76	2.81	2.87	2.93	3.01	3.13
15	2.70	2.72	2.75	2.78	2.83	2.89	2.96	3.05	3.15
16	2.70	2.71	2.74	2.77	2.81	2.85	2.90	3.00	3.08
17	2.70	2.70	2.70	2.71	2.72	2.73	2.74	2.75	2.80
18	2.70	2.66	2.64	2.63	2.58	2.56	2.54	2.52	2.50
19	2.69	2.62	2.55	2.49	2.42	2.39	2.37	2.30	2.32
20	2.68	2.58	2.49	2.41	2.35	2.31	2.28	2.26	2.25
21	2.60	2.54	2.48	2.45	2.37	2.33	2.31	2.27	2.23
22	2.52	2.50	2.47	2.46	2.40	2.36	2.33	2.30	2.24
23	2.42	2.45	2.46	2.47	2.44	2.40	2.36	2.33	2.26
24	2.34	2.41	2.45	2.48	2.48	2.46	2.41	2.35	2.27
25	2.26	2.36	2.44	2.50	2.52	2.50	2.45	2.37	2.28
26	2.22	2.32	2.40	2.51	2.55	2.52	2.46	2.39	2.30
27	2.18	2.28	2.39	2.52	2.59	2.56	2.50	2.42	2.32
28	2.15	2.23	2.38	2.53	2.62	2.59	2.53	2.44	2.36
29	2.13	2.19	2.37	2.54	2.65	2.62	2.55	2.46	2.38
30	2.10	2.15	2.36	2.55	2.68	2.65	2.57	2.48	2.40

$$K'_1 = \frac{a_H [H_2PO_4^-]}{[H_3PO_4]} \qquad K'_2 = \frac{a_H [HPO_4^{2-}]}{[H_2PO_4^-]} \qquad K'_3 = \frac{a_H [PO_4^{3-}]}{[HPO_4^{2-}]}$$

$$[H_3PO_4] = \frac{a_H^{3\,*}}{a_H^3 + a_H^2 K'_1 + a_H K'_1 K'_2 + K'_1 K'_2 K'_3} \; T(PO_4)^{**}$$

$$[H_2PO_4^-] = \frac{a_H^2 K'_1}{a_H^3 + a_H^2 K'_1 + a_H K'_1 K'_2 + K'_1 K'_2 K'_3} \; T(PO_4)$$

* $a_H = 10^{-pH}$
** $T(PO_4)$ = Total inorganic phosphate.

Table 1.2–9 (*Continued*)

$$[HPO_4^{2-}] = \frac{a_H K'_1 K'_2}{a_H^3 + a_H^2 K'_1 + a_H K'_1 K'_2 + K'_1 K'_2 K'_3} T(PO_4)$$

$$[PO_4^{3-}] = \frac{K'_1 K'_2 K'_3}{a_H^3 + a_H^2 K'_1 + a_H K'_1 K'_2 + K'_1 K'_2 K'_3} T(PO_4)$$

(From Kester, D. R. and Pytkowicz, R. M., *Limnol. Oceanogr.*, 12, 243, 1967. With permission.)

Table 1.2–10
VALUES OF K'_2 FOR PHOSPHORIC ACID (x 10^6) IN SEA WATER

	Salinity (°/oo)								
Temp (°C)	29	30	31	32	33	34	35	36	37
0	0.48	0.50	0.52	0.54	0.56	0.58	0.59	0.60	0.62
1	0.49	0.51	0.53	0.55	0.57	0.59	0.61	0.62	0.64
2	0.50	0.52	0.54	0.56	0.58	0.60	0.62	0.63	0.65
3	0.51	0.53	0.55	0.57	0.60	0.62	0.63	0.64	0.66
4	0.53	0.55	0.57	0.59	0.61	0.63	0.65	0.66	0.68
5	0.54	0.56	0.58	0.60	0.62	0.64	0.66	0.67	0.69
6	0.55	0.57	0.59	0.61	0.63	0.65	0.67	0.68	0.70
7	0.56	0.58	0.60	0.62	0.64	0.66	0.68	0.69	0.71
8	0.57	0.59	0.61	0.63	0.66	0.68	0.69	0.71	0.72
9	0.59	0.61	0.63	0.65	0.67	0.69	0.70	0.72	0.73
10	0.60	0.62	0.64	0.66	0.68	0.70	0.71	0.73	0.73
11	0.61	0.63	0.65	0.67	0.69	0.71	0.72	0.73	0.74
12	0.62	0.64	0.66	0.68	0.70	0.71	0.72	0.74	0.74
13	0.63	0.65	0.67	0.69	0.70	0.72	0.73	0.74	0.75
14	0.63	0.65	0.67	0.69	0.71	0.72	0.73	0.75	0.76
15	0.64	0.66	0.68	0.70	0.72	0.73	0.74	0.75	0.76
16	0.65	0.67	0.69	0.72	0.75	0.76	0.77	0.78	0.79
17	0.65	0.68	0.72	0.76	0.79	0.81	0.83	0.85	0.87
18	0.65	0.69	0.74	0.79	0.83	0.86	0.90	0.94	0.98
19	0.65	0.70	0.76	0.81	0.86	0.91	0.96	1.01	1.05
20	0.65	0.71	0.77	0.82	0.88	0.93	0.98	1.03	1.07
21	0.68	0.72	0.76	0.81	0.87	0.92	0.97	1.01	1.05
22	0.70	0.72	0.75	0.80	0.85	0.90	0.95	0.99	1.03
23	0.71	0.73	0.75	0.79	0.83	0.88	0.93	0.97	1.02
24	0.72	0.73	0.75	0.78	0.81	0.85	0.90	0.95	1.01
25	0.73	0.74	0.75	0.76	0.79	0.83	0.87	0.93	1.00
26	0.73	0.74	0.75	0.76	0.77	0.81	0.85	0.91	0.98
27	0.74	0.75	0.75	0.75	0.75	0.79	0.83	0.89	0.96
28	0.75	0.75	0.75	0.74	0.73	0.77	0.81	0.87	0.94
29	0.76	0.76	0.74	0.73	0.71	0.75	0.79	0.85	0.92
30	0.78	0.77	0.74	0.71	0.69	0.73	0.77	0.83	0.90

(From Kester, D. R. and Pytkowicz, R. M., *Limnol. Oceanogr.*, 12, 243, 1967. With permission.)

Table 1.2–11
VALUES OF K'_3 FOR PHOSPHORIC ACID (x 10^9) IN SEA WATER

Temp (°C)	Salinity (°/oo)								
	29	30	31	32	33	34	35	36	37
0	0.16	0.20	0.26	0.30	0.34	0.30	0.26	0.20	0.16
1	0.17	0.21	0.27	0.32	0.36	0.33	0.29	0.24	0.20
2	0.18	0.22	0.28	0.34	0.38	0.35	0.31	0.28	0.25
3	0.19	0.23	0.29	0.36	0.41	0.38	0.35	0.32	0.29
4	0.20	0.24	0.30	0.38	0.43	0.41	0.38	0.36	0.34
5	0.20	0.25	0.32	0.40	0.46	0.44	0.42	0.40	0.38
6	0.21	0.26	0.33	0.42	0.49	0.48	0.46	0.44	0.42
7	0.22	0.28	0.36	0.45	0.52	0.51	0.51	0.48	0.46
8	0.23	0.29	0.38	0.47	0.54	0.53	0.52	0.51	0.49
9	0.23	0.31	0.41	0.51	0.58	0.59	0.57	0.54	0.51
10	0.24	0.34	0.44	0.54	0.61	0.60	0.59	0.58	0.57
11	0.25	0.36	0.48	0.58	0.67	0.65	0.62	0.59	0.56
12	0.26	0.39	0.55	0.67	0.73	0.69	0.65	0.61	0.55
13	0.26	0.43	0.60	0.71	0.79	0.74	0.69	0.62	0.54
14	0.27	0.47	0.65	0.77	0.86	0.81	0.73	0.64	0.53
15	0.27	0.52	0.76	0.90	0.95	0.92	0.82	0.66	0.49
16	0.42	0.62	0.80	0.95	1.01	0.94	0.83	0.70	0.58
17	0.60	0.75	0.90	1.04	1.09	1.01	0.90	0.77	0.64
18	0.84	0.94	1.02	1.11	1.17	1.10	0.99	0.86	0.73
19	1.04	1.11	1.17	1.22	1.26	1.21	1.12	1.00	0.88
20	1.18	1.26	1.31	1.35	1.37	1.34	1.28	1.20	1.11
21	1.31	1.37	1.43	1.49	1.55	1.55	1.54	1.54	1.53
22	1.37	1.47	1.58	1.69	1.80	1.82	1.84	1.85	1.86
23	1.43	1.58	1.73	1.94	2.05	2.09	2.13	2.16	2.19
24	1.48	1.68	1.88	2.08	2.28	2.35	2.42	2.48	2.54
25	1.56	1.79	2.03	2.29	2.50	2.63	2.73	2.80	2.86
26	1.59	1.89	2.19	2.48	2.74	2.87	2.99	3.11	3.23
27	1.69	1.99	2.30	2.65	2.97	3.12	3.27	3.42	3.57
28	1.80	2.09	2.44	2.88	3.20	3.34	3.48	3.73	3.87
29	1.90	2.19	2.62	3.08	3.44	3.64	3.84	4.04	4.24
30	2.00	2.29	2.70	3.17	3.67	3.90	4.13	4.35	4.58

(From Kester, D. R. and Pytkowicz, R. M., *Limnol. Oceanogr.*, 12, 243, 1967. With permission.)

Table 1.2–12
FIRST APPARENT DISSOCIATION CONSTANT OF CARBONIC ACID* IN SEA WATER (EXPRESSED AS $pK'_L{}^1$)

	t(°C)							
Cl(°/₀₀)	0°	5°	10°	15°	20°	25°	30°	35°
0	6.58	6.52	6.47	6.42	6.38	6.35	6.33	6.31
1	6.47	6.42	6.37	6.33	6.29	6.26	6.24	6.23
4	6.36	6.32	6.28	6.24	6.21	6.18	6.16	6.15
9	6.27	6.23	6.19	6.15	6.13	6.10	6.08	6.07
16	6.18	6.14	6.11	6.07	6.05	6.03	6.01	5.99
17	6.17	6.13	6.10	6.06	6.04	6.02	6.00	5.98
18	6.16	6.12	6.09	6.06	6.03	6.01	5.99	5.97
19	6.15	6.11	6.08	6.05	6.02	6.00	5.98	5.97
20	6.14	6.10	6.07	6.04	6.01	5.99	5.97	5.96
21	6.13	6.09	6.06	6.03	6.00	5.98	5.96	5.95
25	6.09	6.05	6.02	6.00	5.97	5.95	5.93	5.92
36	6.00	5.97	5.94	5.92	5.89	5.87	5.86	5.84
49	5.92	5.88	5.86	5.84	5.82	5.80	5.78	5.77
64	5.84	5.80	5.78	5.76	5.74	5.72	5.71	5.70

* Values based on the N.B.S. pH scale.

(From Lyman, J., Buffer Mechanism of Seawater, Ph.D. thesis, University of California, Los Angeles, 1956. With permission.)

Table 1.2–13
SECOND APPARENT DISSOCIATION CONSTANT OF CARBONIC ACID* IN SEA WATER (EXPRESSED AS pK'_2)

	t(°C)							
Cl(°/₀₀)	0°	5°	10°	15°	20°	25°	30°	35°
0	10.62	10.55	10.49	10.43	10.38	10.33	10.29	10.25
1	10.06	9.99	9.93	9.87	9.81	9.76	9.71	9.66
4	9.78	9.72	9.67	9.61	9.54	9.49	9.43	9.38
9	9.64	9.58	9.52	9.46	9.40	9.34	9.27	9.21
16	9.46	9.40	9.35	9.29	9.23	9.17	9.10	9.02
17	9.44	9.38	9.32	9.27	9.21	9.15	9.08	9.00
18	9.42	9.36	9.30	9.25	9.19	9.12	9.06	8.98
19	9.40	9.34	9.28	9.23	9.17	9.10	9.02	8.95
20	9.38	9.32	9.26	9.21	9.15	9.08	9.01	8.92
21	9.36	9.30	9.25	9.19	9.13	9.06	8.98	8.89
25	9.29	9.23	9.17	9.11	9.05	8.98	8.91	8.82
36	9.12	9.06	8.99	8.93	8.86	8.79	8.72	8.63
49	8.95	8.89	8.82	8.75	8.68	8.61	8.53	8.43
64	8.77	8.71	8.64	8.57	8.50	8.42	8.34	8.23

* Values based on the N.B.S. pH scale.

(From Lyman, J., Buffer Mechanism of Seawater, Ph.D. thesis, University of California, Los Angeles, 1956. With permission.)

Table 1.2–14
FIRST APPARENT DISSOCIATION CONSTANT OF BORIC ACID* IN SEA WATER (EXPRESSED AS pK'_B)

	t°C							
Cl(°/oo)	0°	5°	10°	15°	20°	25°	30°	35°
0	9.50	9.44	9.38	9.33	9.28	9.24	9.20	9.16
1	9.40	9.34	9.28	9.23	9.18	9.14	9.10	9.06
4	9.28	9.22	9.16	9.11	9.06	9.02	8.98	8.94
9	9.14	9.08	9.03	8.98	8.93	8.88	8.85	8.82
16	9.00	8.95	8.89	8.84	8.80	8.76	8.72	8.69
17	8.98	8.93	8.88	8.83	8.78	8.74	8.70	8.67
18	8.96	8.91	8.86	8.81	8.76	8.72	8.69	8.66
19	8.95	8.90	8.85	8.80	8.75	8.71	8.67	8.64
20	8.94	8.88	8.83	8.78	8.74	8.69	8.65	8.63
21	8.92	8.87	8.82	8.77	8.72	8.68	8.64	8.61
25	8.85	8.80	8.75	8.70	8.66	8.62	8.59	8.56
36	8.71	8.66	8.61	8.57	8.53	8.49	8.46	8.43
49	8.56	8.52	8.47	8.43	8.39^5	8.36	8.33	8.30
64	8.41	8.37	8.33	8.30	8.26^5	8.23	8.20	8.17

* Values based on the N.B.S. pH scale.

(From Lyman, J., Buffer Mechanism of Seawater, Ph.D. thesis, University of California, Los Angeles, 1956. With permission.)

Table 1.2–15
PERCENTAGE DISTRIBUTION OF CARBONIC ACID SPECIES IN SEA WATER AS A FUNCTION OF pH, TEMPERATURE, AND SALINITY

pH	S°/oo	0°C			10°C			20°C			30°C		
		CO_2	HCO_3	CO_3	CO_2	HCO_3	CO_3	CO_2	HCO_3	CO_3	CO_2	HCO_3	CO_3
7.5	30.7	4.42	94.5	1.09	3.77	94.8	1.44	3.29	94.9	1.85	2.99	94.5	2.49
	34.3	4.22	94.6	1.19	3.60	94.8	1.58	3.14	94.8	2.03	2.85	94.3	2.85
	37.9	4.04	94.7	1.31	3.44	94.9	1.69	3.00	94.8	2.22	2.71	94.2	3.12
7.6		3.53	95.1	1.38	3.01	95.2	1.82	2.62	95.0	2.34	2.37	94.5	3.13
		3.37	95.1	1.51	2.87	95.1	1.99	2.50	94.9	2.56	2.26	94.2	3.58
		3.22	95.1	1.66	2.74	95.1	2.13	2.38	94.8	2.80	2.15	93.9	3.92
7.7		2.82	95.4	1.73	2.40	95.3	2.28	2.08	95.0	2.93	1.88	94.2	3.92
		2.70	95.4	1.90	2.29	95.2	2.50	1.99	94.8	3.20	1.79	93.7	4.48
		2.57	95.3	2.08	2.18	95.1	2.67	1.89	94.6	3.51	1.70	93.4	4.89
7.8		2.25	95.6	2.18	1.91	95.2	2.87	1.65	94.7	3.67	1.49	93.6	4.90
		2.14	95.5	2.39	1.82	95.0	3.14	1.57	94.4	4.01	1.41	93.0	5.59
		2.05	95.3	2.62	1.73	94.9	3.35	1.50	94.1	4.39	1.34	92.6	6.10
7.9		1.78	95.5	2.75	1.51	94.9	3.61	1.30	94.1	4.61	1.17	92.7	6.12
		1.70	95.3	3.01	1.43	94.6	3.94	1.24	93.7	5.03	1.11	91.9	6.97
		1.62	95.1	3.30	1.37	94.4	4.21	1.18	93.3	5.49	1.05	91.4	7.59
8.0		1.41	95.1	3.45	1.19	94.3	4.52	1.02	93.2	5.75	0.91	91.5	7.61
		1.34	94.9	3.78	1.13	93.9	4.93	0.97	92.8	6.27	0.86	90.5	8.64
		1.28	94.6	4.13	1.08	93.7	5.26	0.92	92.2	6.84	0.82	89.8	9.40
8.1		1.10	94.6	4.34	0.93	93.4	5.66	0.80	92.0	7.19	0.71	89.8	9.46
		1.05	94.2	4.75	0.88	92.9	6.18	0.76	91.4	7.82	0.67	88.6	10.71
		1.00	93.8	5.19	0.84	92.6	6.59	0.72	90.8	8.51	0.63	87.7	11.63
8.2		0.87	93.7	5.40	0.73	92.3	7.01	0.63	90.5	8.86	0.55	87.8	11.60
		0.83	93.3	5.89	0.69	91.7	7.64	0.59	89.8	9.63	0.52	86.4	13.09
		0.79	92.8	6.44	0.66	91.2	8.14	0.56	89.0	10.47	0.49	85.3	14.18
8.3		0.68	92.6	6.72	0.57	90.7	8.69	0.49	88.6	10.93	0.43	85.4	14.21
		0.65	92.0	7.33	0.54	90.0	9.45	0.46	87.7	11.86	0.40	83.6	15.97
		0.62	91.4	7.99	0.51	89.4	10.05	0.43	86.7	12.85	0.38	82.4	17.25
8.4		0.54	91.2	8.28	0.45	88.9	10.65	0.38	86.3	13.31	0.33	82.5	17.16
		0.51	90.5	9.00	0.42	88.0	11.55	0.36	85.2	14.41	0.31	80.5	19.21
		0.48	89.7	9.80	0.40	87.3	12.27	0.34	84.1	15.58	0.29	79.0	20.69

(Calculated from Lyman, J., Buffer Mechanism of Seawater, Ph.D. thesis, University of California, Los Angeles, 1956. With permission.)

Table 1.2–16
VALUES OF THE PRESSURE COEFFICIENTS OF THE APPARENT DISSOCIATION CONSTANTS*

Pressure (atm)	Temp (°C) 0	5	10
		$(K_1')_p/(K_1')_1$	
100	1.12	1.11	1.11
200	1.25	1.24	1.23
300	1.39	1.38	1.36
400	1.55	1.53	1.50
500	1.73	1.69	1.66
600	1.92	1.88	1.84
700	2.13	2.08	2.03
800	2.37	2.30	2.23
900	2.62	2.54	2.46
1000	2.91	2.80	2.70
		$(K_2')_p/(K_2')_1$	
100	1.07	1.07	1.07
200	1.15	1.15	1.15
300	1.24	1.23	1.23
400	1.34	1.33	1.32
500	1.44	1.42	1.41
600	1.55	1.53	1.51
700	1.66	1.64	1.62
800	1.79	1.76	1.73
900	1.93	1.89	1.86
1000	2.07	2.03	1.99
		$(K_B')_p/(K_B')_1$	
100	1.14	1.13	1.13
200	1.30	1.28	1.27
300	1.47	1.45	1.43
400	1.67	1.64	1.61
500	1.90	1.85	1.81
600	2.14	2.09	2.03
700	2.42	2.35	2.28
800	2.73	2.64	2.55
900	3.07	2.96	2.85
1000	3.45	3.31	3.18

* Interpolated values of the pressure coefficients should be accurate to ± 2%.

(From Culberson, C. and Pytkowicz, R. M., Effect of pressure on carbonic acid, boric acid and the pH in seawater, *Limnol. Oceanogr.*, 13, 403, 1968. With permission.)

Table 1.2–17
CHANGE IN pH OF SEA WATER FOR RISE OF 1°C

	Cl °/oo = 10			Cl °/oo = 15		
pH	0–20°	10–20°	20–30°	0–20°	10–20°	20–30°
7.4	–0.0087	– 0.0084	– 0.0069	– 0.0088	– 0.0087	– 0.0076
7.6	92	92	79	95	96	83
7.8	100	101	89	103	105	90
8.0	108	109	94	110	112	94
8.2	114	115	98	115	117	96
8.4	117	117	99	118	118	98

	Cl °/oo = 19.5			Cl °/oo = 21		
pH	0–20°	10–20°	20–30°	0–20°	10–20°	20–30°
7.4	– 0.0089	– 0.0087	– 0.0081	– 0.0092	– 0.0089	– 0.0079
7.6	95	95	91	97	98	88
7.8	104	104	98	106	108	93
8.0	110	109	102	112	114	96
8.2	114	112	103	116	116	98
8.4	116	114	104	118	119	100

Note: The table contains some irregular values.

(From Buch, K. and Nynäs, O., Studien über neuere pH-Methodik mit besonderer Berücksichtigung des Meerwassers, *Acta Academiae Aboensis,* Ser. B, 12, 1939. With permission.)

Table 1.2–18
EFFECT OF PRESSURE ON THE pH OF SEA WATER

Calculated Values of ($pH_1 - pH_p$) at 34.8°/oo Salinity

		pH at atmospheric pressure				
Temp (°C)	Pressure (atm)	7.6	7.8	8.0	8.2	8.4
0	250	0.112	0.107	0.103	0.100	0.098
	500	0.222	0.213	0.205	0.200	0.196
	750	0.330	0.318	0.308	0.300	0.294
	1,000	0.437	0.422	0.409	0.399	0.391
5	250	0.107	0.102	0.098	0.096	0.094
	500	0.212	0.203	0.197	0.192	0.189
	750	0.316	0.304	0.294	0.288	0.283
	1,000	0.417	0.402	0.391	0.383	0.376
10	250	0.102	0.098	0.094	0.092	0.091
	500	0.203	0.195	0.189	0.185	0.182
	750	0.302	0.291	0.283	0.277	0.272
	1,000	0.401	0.387	0.376	0.369	0.362

(From Culberson, C. and Pytkowicz, R. M., Effect of pressure on carbonic acid, boric acid, and the pH in seawater, *Limnol. Oceanogr.*, 13, 403, 1968. With permission.)

Table 1.2–19
RECIPES FOR ARTIFICIAL SEA WATER (19.00°/oo CHLORINITY)*

From McClendon, Gault, and Mulholland (1917)

NaCl	26.726 g	H_3BO_3	0.088 g
$MgCl_2$	2.260	Na_2SiO_3	0.0024
$MgSO_4$	3.248	$Na_2Si_4O_9$	0.0015
$CaCl_2$	1.153	H_3PO_4	0.0002
KCl	0.721	Al_2Cl_6	0.013
$NaHCO_3$	0.198	NH_3	0.002
NaBr	0.058	$LiNO_3$	0.0013

Add water to make a total weight of 1000 g.

From Subow (1941)

NaCl	26.518 g	$CaCl_2$	0.725 g
$MgCl_2$	2.447	$NaHCO_3$	0.202
$MgSO_4$	3.305	NaBr	0.083

Add water to make a total weight of 1000 g.

From Lyman and Fleming (1940)

NaCl	23.476 g	$NaHCO_3$	0.192 g
$MgCl_2$	4.981	KBr	0.096
Na_2SO_4	3.917	H_3BO_3	0.026
$CaCl_2$	1.102	$SrCl_2$	0.024
KCl	0.664	NaF	0.003

Add water to make a total weight of 1000 g.

From Kalle (1945)

NaCl	28.014 g	$CaCO_3$	0.1221 g
$MgCl_2$	3.812	KBr	0.1013
$MgSO_4$	1.752	$SrSO_4$	0.0282
$CaSO_4$	1.283	H_3BO_3	0.0277
K_2SO_4	0.8163		

Add water to make a total weight of 1000 g.

From Kester, Duedall, Conners, and Pytkowicz (1967)

NaCl	23.926 g	53.27 ml of a 1.0 *M* $MgCl_2$ solution
Na_2SO_4	4.008	10.33 ml of a 1.0 *M* $CaCl_2$ solution
KCl	0.677	0.90 ml of a 0.1 *M* SrO_2 solution
$NaHCO_3$	0.196	
KBr	0.098	
H_3BO_3	0.026	
NaF	0.003	

* After equilibration and aeration the pH should be 7.9–8.3.

(From Horne, R. A., *Marine Chemistry,* Wiley-Interscience, New York, 1969.)

Table 1.2–19 (*Continued*)

REFERENCES

1. **McClendon, Gault, and Mulholland,** Carnegie Institution of Washington, Publ. No. 251, 1917.
2. **Subow,** *Oceanographic Tables,* USSR Oceanographic Institute, Moscow, 1941.
3. **Lyman and Fleming,** *J. Mar. Res.,* 3, 134, 1967.
4. **Kalle,** *Probleme Der Kosmischem Physik,* Vol. 23, Akademische Verlagsgesellschaft, Becker und Erler, Leipzig, 1945.
5. **Kester,** *Limnol. Oceanogr.,* 12, 176, 1967.

Table 1.2–20

STABILITY CONSTANTS OF INORGANIC ASSOCIATION

Expressed by K_1 at 25°C

The format of this table has been adopted in part from Riley and Chester (1971). Values have been selected with the help of "Stability Constants" (Sillén and Martell, 1964, 1971) and are valid in a noncomplexing medium of ionic strength similar to that of sea water. A dash indicates that there is no or little evidence for complex formation; + indicates that there is evidence for complex formation. The value given is underlined when a significant part of the cation is present in that form. ~ means order of magnitude of constant. * indicates that these metals tend to form polynuclear hydroxo complexes – especially in concentrated solutions.

Ligand	F^-	OH^-	CO_3^{2-}	SO_4^{2-}	Cl^-	NH_3	HS^-
– log concentration of the ligand in sea water	4.4	5.8	4.9	1.9	0.3	–	–
Be^{2+}	5	~7*	–	0.7	~1	–	–
Mg^{2+}	1.3	1.5	2.2	1.0	0.2	–0.1	–
Ca^{2+}	0.6	0.8	1.9	1.0	–	–	–
Al^{3+}	6.4	~9*	–	1.1	–		–
Sc^{3+}	6.2	~8.6*	–	2.6	1.1	+	–
Y^{3+}	3.6	5.4*	–	~2	0.4	–	–
Th^{4+}	7.6	10.5*	–	3.3	0.2	–	–
UO_2^{2+}	4.5	8.0	+	1.8	~0.3	–	–
Fe^{3+}	5.0	11	–	2.3	0.5	–	–
Mn^{2+}	–	3	–	~1	–	–	+
Co^{2+}	–	3.9	–	1.2	~0	2	+
Cu^{2+}	0.7	~7*	5.5	1.2	~0.7	4.2	+
Pb^{2+}	0.3	~6.8	6.2		~0.8	–	+
Zn^{2+}	0.7	~4.7	~4	1.2	~0	~2	+
Ag^+	–0.2	1.8	–	0.4	3.5	3.6	13.3
Cd^{2+}	0.5	~4	~4	1.2	1.5	2.7	7.6
Hg^{2+}	1.0	10	+	1.3	6.7	~8.0	+
H^+	2.9	13.7	9.1	1.4	–7	9.4	6.9

(Compiled by Professor W. V. Stumm, Swiss Federal Institute for Water Research and Water Pollution Control, Dübendorf-Zürich, Switzerland, and Dr. P. Brauner, Chemistry Dept., Simmons College, Boston, Mass. From Riley, J. P. and Chester, R., *Chemical Oceanography,* Academic Press, London, in press. With permission.)

REFERENCES

Riley, J. P. and Chester, R., *Introduction to Marine Chemistry,* Academic Press, London, 1971.
Sillen, L. G., Stability Constants, Chem. Soc., Spec. Publ. 17, 1964.
Sillen, L. G., Stability Constants, Chem. Soc., Spec. Publ. 25, 1971.

Table 1.2–21
PHASES FORMED DURING THE PROGRESSIVE EVAPORATION OF SEA WATER

Stage no.	Density of brine	Weight % of liquid remaining	Principal solid phases deposited	% Total dissolved solids
I	1.026	100	Calcium carbonate and dolomite	1
II	1.140	50	Gypsum ($CaSO_4 \cdot 2H_2O$)	3
III	1.214	10	Halite (NaCl)	70
IV	1.236	3.9	Sodium-magnesium-potassium sulfates and chlorides	26

(From Riley, J. P. and Chester, R., *Introduction to Marine Chemistry,* Academic Press, London, 1971. With permission.)

Table 1.2–22
FACTORS FOR CONVERSION OF NUTRIENT AND OXYGEN CONCENTRATIONS IN SEA WATER

To convert	to	multiply by
To convert μg Si/kg	to μg - at Si/kg	0.03560
	ppb SiO_2	2.1392
	μg Si/l	ρ_{SW}*
	μg - at Si/l	0.03560 ρ_{SW}
To convert μg NO_3–N/kg	to μg - at NO_3–N/kg	0.07138
	ppb NO_3	4.4261
	μg - NO_3–N/l	ρ_{SW}
	μg - at NO_3–N/l	0.07138 ρ_{SW}
To convert μg PO_4–P/kg	to μg - at PO_4–P/kg	0.03229
	ppb PO_4	3.0665
	μg PO_4–P/l	ρ_{SW}
	μg - at PO_4–P/l	0.03229 ρ_{SW}
To convert ml O_2/l	to μmol O_2/kg	44.643/ρ_{SW}
	μg - at O/kg	89.286/ρ_{SW}
	ppm O_2	1.4286/ρ_{SW}
To convert mol/kg	to mol/l	ρ_{SW}
	molality	1/1 - 0.001 S ‰

* ρ_{SW} is the density of sea water.

(Compiled by C. Culberson, Department of Oceanography, Oregon State University.)

Table 1.2–23
THE DISSOLVED ORGANIC CONSTITUENTS OF SEA WATER

Specific Dissolved Organic Compounds Identified in Sea Water*

Name of compound and chemical formula	Concentration				Author(s)	Locality
I. Carbohydrates						
Pentoses $C_5H_{10}O_5$		0–8	mg/l		Collier et al. (1950, 1956)	Gulf of Mexico
Pentoses $C_5H_{10}O_5$		0.5	μg/l		Degens et al. (1964)	Pacific off California
Hexoses		14–36	μg/l		Degens et al. (1964)	Pacific off California
Rhamnosides $C_6H_{12}O_5$		0.1–0.4	mg/l		Lewis and Rakestraw (1955)	Pacific Ocean coast U.S.A.
Rhamnosides						
Dehydroascorbic acid COCOCOCHCH(OH)CH_2OH (ring through O)		0.1	mg/l		Wangersky (1952)	Gulf of Mexico inshore water
II. Proteins and Their Derivatives						
Peptides C:N ratio = 13.8:1					Jeffrey and Hood (1958)	Gulf of Mexico
Polypeptides and polycondensates of:	(a) μg/l	(b) μg/l	(c) μg/l	(d) μg/l		
Glutamic acid COOH$(CH_2)_2$CH(NH_2)COOH		8–13	8–13	0.1–1.8	(a) Park et al. (1962) (by ion-exchange)	Gulf of Mexico
Lysine $NH_2(CH_2)_4$CH(NH_2)COOH	<1	?	trace–3	0.1–0.9	(b) Tatsumoto et al. (1961) (by paper chromatography)	Gulf of Mexico
Glycine NH_2CH_2COOH		–	trace–3	1.2–3.7	(c) Tatsumoto et al. (1961) (by ion-exchange)	Gulf of Mexico
Aspartic acid COOHCH_2CH(NH_2)COOH		3–8	trace–3	0.1–1.0	(d) Degens et al. (1964)	Pacific off California

* det = detected.
tr. = trace.
– = not detected.
? = possibly present.

(From Duursma, E. K., in *Chemical Oceanography,* Vol. 1, Riley, J. P. and Skirrow, G., Eds., Academic Press, London, 1965, 450. With permission.)

Table 1.2–23 (*Continued*)

Specific Dissolved Organic Compounds Identified in Sea Water*

Name of compound and chemical formula	Concentration				Author(s)	Locality
Serine $CH_2OHCH(NH_2)COOH$		?	trace–3	1.8–5.6		
Alanine $CH_3CH(NH_2)COOH$		3–8	trace–3	0.7–3.1	(a) Park et al. (1962) (by ion-exchange)	Gulf of Mexico
Leucine $(CH_3)_2CHCH_2CH(NH_2)COOH$	0.5–1	8–13	trace–3	0.9–3.8	(b) Tatsumoto et al. (1961) (by paper chromatography)	Gulf of Mexico
Valine $(CH_3)_2CHCH(NH_2)COOH$		trace–3	trace–3	0.1–1.7	(c) Tatsumoto et al. (1961) (by ion-exchange)	Gulf of Mexico
Cystine $[SCH_2CH(NH_2)COOH]_2$		trace–3	–	0.0–3.8	(d) Degens et al. (1964)	Pacific off California
Isoleucine $CH_3CH_2CH(CH_3)CH(NH_2)COOH$		8–13	trace–3	–		
Leucine $(CH_3)_2CHCH_2CH(NH_2)COOH$		–	–	0.9–3.8		
Ornithine $NH_2(CH_2)_3CH(NH_2)COOH$		–	trace–3	0.2–2.4		
Methionine sulphoxide $CH_3S(:O)CH_2CH_2CH(NH_2)COOH$				–		
Threonine $CH_3CHOHCH(NH_2)COOH$		–	3–8	0.3–1.3		
Tyrosine $HOC_6H_4CH_2CH(NH_2)COOH$		–	trace–3	tr.–0.5		
Phenylalanine $C_6H_5CH_2CH(NH_2)COOH$	<0.5	–	–	0.1–0.9		
Histidine $C_3H_3N_2CH_2CH(NH_2)COOH$		?	trace–3	tr.–2.4		
Arginine $NH_2C(:NH)NH(CH_2)_3CH(NH_2)COOH$		?	trace–3	0.1–0.6		
Proline C_4H_8NCOOH		?	–	0.3–1.4		
Methionine $CH_3SCH_2CH_2CH(NH_2)COOH$		–	trace–3	tr.–0.4		
Tryptophan $C_8H_6NCH_2CH(NH_2)COOH$		–	trace–3	–		

(In the first concentration column, 0.5–1 is bracketed across Serine through Isoleucine, and <0.5 across Ornithine through Proline.)

* tr. = trace.
– = not detected.
? = possibly present.

Table 1.2–23 (*Continued*)
Specific Dissolved Organic Compounds Identified in Sea Water*

Name of compound and chemical formula	Concentration		Author(s)	Locality
Glucosamine $C_6H_{13}NO_5$	–	trace–3		
Free amino acids	(e)	(f) μg/l		
Cystine $[SCH_2CH(NH_2)COOH]_2$	det	–	(e) Palmork (1963a)	Norwegian coastal water
Lysine $NH_2(CH_2)_4CH(NH_2)COOH$	det.	0.2–3.1	(f) Degens et al. (1964)	Pacific off California
Histidine $C_3H_3N_2CH_2CH(NH_2)COOH$	det.	0.5–1.7		
Arginine $NH_2C(:NH)NH(CH_2)_3CH(NH_2)COOH$	det.	0.0		
Serine $CH_2OHCH(NH_2)COOH$	det.	2.3–28.4		
Aspartic acid $COOHCH_2CH(NH_2)COOH$	det.	tr.–9.6		
Glycine NH_2CH_2COOH	det.	tr.–37.6		
Hydroxyproline $C_4H_7N(OH)COOH$	det.	tr.–2.8		
Glutamic acid $COOH(CH_2)_2CH(NH_2)COOH$	det.	1.4–6.8		
Threonine $CH_3CHOHCH(NH_2)COOH$	det.	2.8–11.8		
α-Alanine $CH_3CH(NH_2)COOH$	det.			
Proline C_4H_8NCOOH	det.	0.0		
Tyrosine $HOC_6H_4CH_2CH(NH_2)COOH$	det.	tr.–5.0		
Tryptophan $C_8H_6NCH_2CH(NH_2)COOH$	det.	–		

* det = detected.
tr. = trace.
– = not detected.

Table 1.2–23 (*Continued*)

Specific Dissolved Organic Compounds Identified in Sea Water*

Name of compound and chemical formula		Concentration	Author(s)	Locality
Methionine	det.	–		
$CH_3SCH_2CH_2CH(NH_2)COOH$				
Valine	det.	0.3–2.7		
$(CH_3)_2CHCH(NH_2)COOH$				
Phenylalanine	det.	tr.–2.4		
$C_6H_5CH_2(NH_2)COOH$				
Isoleucine	det.	–		
$CH_3CH_2CH(CH_3)CH(NH_2)COOH$				
Leucine	det.	0.5–5.5		
$(CH_3)_2CHCH_2CH(NH_2)COOH$				
Free compounds				
Uracil		det.	Belser (1959, 1963)	Pacific coast near La Jolla
NHCONHCOCH:CH				
Isoleucine		det.		
$CH_3CH_2CH(CH_3)CH(NH_2)COOH$				
Methionine		det.		
$CH_3SCH_2CH_2CH(NH_2)COOH$				
Histidine		det.		
$C_3H_3N_2CH_2CH(NH_2)COOH$				
Adenine		det.		
$C_5H_3N_4NH_2$				
Peptone		det.		
Threonine		det.		
$CH_3CHOHCH(NH_2)COOH$				
Tryptophan		det.		
$C_8H_6NCH_2CH(NH_2)COOH$				
Glycine		det.		
NH_2CH_2COOH				
Purine		det.		
$C_5H_4N_4$				
Urea		det.	Degens et al. (1964)	Pacific off California
CH_4ON_2				

* det. = detected.
tr. = trace.
– = not detected.

Table 1.2–23 (*Continued*)

Specific Dissolved Organic Compounds Identified in Sea Water

Name of compound and chemical formula	Concentration			Author(s)	Locality
III. Aliphatic Carboxylic and Hydroxycarboxylic Acids					
	mg/l (0–200 m)	mg/l (200–600 m)	mg/l (>600 m)		
Lauric acid $CH_3(CH_2)_{10}COOH$	0.01–0.32	0.01–0.28	0–0.28	Slowey et al. (1962)	Coastal waters of Gulf of Mexico
Myristic acid $CH_3(CH_2)_{12}COOH$	0.01–0.10	0.01–0.05	0–0.07		
Myristoleic acid $CH_3(CH_2)_3CH{:}CH(CH_2)_7COOH$	traces–0.02	0.01–0.03	0–0.05		
Palmitic acid $CH_3(CH_2)_{14}COOH$	0.01–0.17	0.03–0.42	0–0.38		
Palmitoleic acid $CH_3(CH_2)_5CH{:}CH(CH_2)_7COOH$	0.02–0.16	0.02–0.16	0–0.21		
Stearic acid $CH_3(CH_2)_{16}COOH$	0.04–0.09	0.02–0.13	0–0.10		
Oleic acid $CH_3(CH_2)_7CH{:}CH(CH_2)_7COOH$	0.01	0.02	0		
Linoleic acid $CH_3(CH_2)_4CH{:}CHCH_2CH{:}CH(CH_2)_7COOH$	0.01	0.01	0		
		mg/l (1000–2500 m)			
Fatty acids with:					
12 C-atoms		0.0003–0.02		Williams (1961)	Pacific Ocean coastal water
14 C-atoms		0.0004–0.043			
16 C-atoms		0.0027–0.0209			
16 C-atoms + 1 double bond		0.0003–0.003			
18 C-atoms		0.0037–0.0222			
18 C-atoms + 1 double bond		0.0083			
18 C-atoms + 2 double bonds		0.0000–0.0029			
20 C-atoms		traces–0.0081			
22 C-atoms		traces–0.0014			

Table 1.2–23 (*Continued*)
Specific Dissolved Organic Compounds Identified in Sea Water

Name of compound and chemical formula	Concentration		Author(s)	Locality
	mg/l			
Acetic acid CH_3COOH	<1.0		Koyama and Thompson (1959)	Pacific Ocean
Lactic acid $CH_3CH(OH)COOH$				
Glycolic acid $HOCH_2COOH$				
Malic acid $HOOCCH(OH)CH_2COOH$	0.28		Creac'h (1955)	Atlantic coastal water
Citric acid $HOOCCH_2C(OH)(COOH)CH_2COOH$	0.14			
Carotenoids and brownish-waxy or fatty matter	2.5		Johnston (1955)	North Sea
			Wilson and Armstrong (1955)	English Channel
IV. Biologically Active Compounds (see also Provasoli, 1963)				
Organic Fe compound(s)	3.4–1.6	mμg/l	Harvey (1925)	Deep sea water
Vitamin B_{12} (Cobalamin) $C_{63}H_{88}O_{14}N_{14}PCo$			Vishniak and Riley (1961)	Long Island Sound
Vitamin B_{12}	0.2	mμg/l (summer)	Cowey (1956)	Oceanic surface water
	2.0	mμg/l (winter)		
Vitamin B_{12}	0.2–5.0	mμg/l	Daisley and Fisher (1958)	
Vitamin B_{12}	0–2.6	mμg/l	Kashiwada et al. (1957)	North Pacific Ocean
Vitamin B_{12}	0–0.03	mμg/l	Menzel and Spaeth (1962)	Sargasso Sea 0–05 m.
Thiamine (Vitamin B_1) $C_{12}H_{17}ON_4SCl_2$	0–20	mμg/l	Cowey (1956)	Surface water, possibly from land drainage
Plant hormones (auxins)	3.41	mμg/l	Bentley (1960)	North Sea near Scotland
V. Humic Acids				
"Gelbstoffe" (Yellow substances) Melanoidin-like			Kalle (1949, 1962)	Coastal waters
			Jerlov (1955)	
			Armstrong and Boalch (1961a,b)	

Table 1.2–23 (*Continued*)

Specific Dissolved Organic Compounds Identified in Sea Water

Name of compound and chemical formula	Concentration	Author(s)	Locality
	VI. Phenolic Compounds		
p-Hydroxybenzoic acid HOC_6H_5COOH	1–3 μg/l	Degens et al. (1964)	Pacific off California
Vanillic acid $CH_3(HO)C_6H_3COOH$	1–3 μg/l		
Syringic acid $(CH_3O)_2(HO)C_6H_2COOH$	1–3 μg/l		
	VII. Hydrocarbons		
Pristane: (2, 6, 10, 14-tetramethylpentadecane)	trace	Blumer et al. (1963)	Cape Cod Bay

Table 1.2–23 (*Continued*)

REFERENCES

1. **Armstrong, F. A. J. and Boalch, G. T.,** *Nature (Lond.),* 192, 858, 1961a.
2. **Armstrong, F. A. J. and Boalch, G. T.,** *J. Mar. Biol. Assoc. U.K.,* 41, 591, 1961b.
3. **Belser, W. L.,** *Proc. Natl. Acad. Sci., Wash.,* 45, 1533, 1959.
4. **Belser, W. L.,** in *The Sea,* Hill, M. N., Ed., Vol. II, Wiley-Interscience, New York, 1963, 220-231.
5. **Bentley, Joyce A.,** *J. Mar. Biol. Assoc. U.K.,* 39, 433, 1960.
6. **Blumer, M., Mullin, M. M., and Thomas, D. W.,** *Science,* 140, 974, 1963.
7. **Collier, A.,** *Spec. Sci. Rep. U.S. Fish Wildl.,* 178, 7, 1956.
8. **Collier, A., Ray, S. M., and Magnitzky, A. W.,** *Science,* 111, 151, 1950.
9. **Cowey, C. B.,** *J. Mar. Biol. Assoc. U.K.,* 35, 609, 1956.
10. **Creac'h, P.,** *C. R. Acad. Sci., (Paris),* 240, 2551, 1955.
11. **Daisley, K. W. and Fisher, L. R.,** *J. Mar. Biol. Assoc. U.K.,* 37, 683, 1958.
12. **Degens, E. T., Reuter, J. H., and Shaw, K. N. F.,** *Geochim. Cosmochim. Acta,* 28, 45, 1964.
13. **Harvey, H. W.,** *J. Mar. Biol. Assoc. U.K.,* 13, 953, 1925.
14. **Jeffrey, L. M. and Hood, D. W.,** *J. Mar. Res.,* 17, 247, 1958.
15. **Jerlov, N. G.,** *Göteb. Vetensk Samh. Handl.,* F.6. B.6. (14), 1955.
16. **Johnston, R.,** *J. Mar. Biol. Assoc. U.K.,* 34, 185, 1955.
17. **Kalle, K.,** *Dtsch. Hydrogr. Z.,* 2, 117, 1949.
18. **Kalle, K.,** *Kiel. Meeresforsch.,* 18, 128, 1962.
19. **Kashiwada, K., Kakimoto, D., Morita, T., Kanazawa, A., and Kawagoe, K.,** *Bull. Jap. Soc. Sci. Fish.,* 22, 637,1957.
20. **Koyama, T. and Thompson, T. G.,** *Preprints International Oceanographic Congress, 1959,* American Association for Advancement of Science, Washington, D.C., 1959, 925.
21. **Lewis, G. J. and Rakestraw, N. W.,** *J. Mar. Res.,* 14, 253, 1955.
22. **Menzel, D. W. and Spaeth, J. P.,** *Limnol. Oceanogr.,* 7, 151, 1962.
23. **Palmork, K. H.,** *Acta Chem. Scand.,* 17, 1456, 1963a.
24. **Park, K., Williams, W. T., Prescott, J. M., and Hood, D. W.,** *Science,* 138, 531, 1962.
25. **Provasoli, L.,** in *The Sea,* Hill, M. N., Ed., Vol. II, Wiley-Interscience, New York, 1963, 165-219.
26. **Slowey, J. F., Jeffrey, L. M., and Hood, D. W.,** *Geochim. Cosmochim. Acta,* 26, 607, 1962.
27. **Tatsumoto, M., Williams, W. T., Prescott, J. M., and Hood, D. W.,** *J. Mar. Res.,* 19, 89, 1961.
28. **Vishniac, H. S. and Riley, G. A.,** *Limnol. Oceanogr.,* 6, 36, 1961.
29. **Wangersky, P. J.,** *Science,* 115, 685, 1952.
30. **Williams, P. M.,** *Nature (Lond.),* 189, 219, 1961.
31. **Wilson, D. P. and Armstrong, F. A. J.,** *J. Mar. Biol. Assoc. U.K.,* 31, 335, 1952.

Table 1.2–24
VALUES OF THE FREE ACTIVITY COEFFICIENTS OF THE MAJOR IONS IN SEA WATER*

Ion	Free activity coefficient
Na^+	0.71
K^+	0.63
Mg^{2+}	0.29
Ca^{2+}	0.26
Sr^{2+}	0.24
Cl^-	0.63
Br^-	0.65
SO_4^{2-}	0.21
F^-	0.68
HCO_3^-	0.68
CO_3^{2-}	0.20

* 34.8°/₀₀ salinity, 25°C; based on the MacInnes assumption ($\gamma_K = \gamma_{Cl}$).

(Compiled by D. R. Kester, Graduate School of Oceanography, University of Rhode Island.)

TABLE 1.2–25
VALUES OF THE TOTAL ACTIVITY COEFFICIENTS OF THE MAJOR IONS IN SEA WATER*

Ion	Total activity coefficient	Ref.
Na^+	0.67	1
K^+	0.62	3
Mg^{2+}	0.33	4
Ca^{2+}	0.21	2
Sr^{2+}	0.21	3
Cl^-	0.63	3
Br^-	0.65	3
$SO_4{}^{2-}$	0.082	3
F^-	0.34	5
$HCO_3{}^-$	0.55	2
$CO_3{}^{2-}$	0.022	2

* 34.8°/₀₀ salinity, 25°C.

(Compiled by D. R. Kester, Graduate School of Oceanography, University of Rhode Island.)

REFERENCES

1 **Platford, R. F.,** *J. Fish. Res. Board Can.,* 22, 885, 1965.
2 **Berner, R. A.,** *Geochim. Cosmochim. Acta,* 29, 947, 1965.
3 Calculated by D. R. Kester.
4 **Thompson, M. E.,** *Science,* 153, 966, 1966.
5 **Elgquist, B.,** Rep. Chem. Sea Water, No. 7, Univ. Göteborg, Sweden, 1969.

Table 1.2–26
APPARENT DISSOCIATION CONSTANTS

HF and HSO_4^- and the H^+ Species in Sea Water at 25°C and 1 atm

Salinity (°/₀₀)	$K'_{HF} \times 10^3$	$K'_{HSO_4^-} \times 10^2$
26.7	2.06 ± 0.03	6.68 ± 0.01
34.6	2.47 ± 0.05	8.16 ± 0.13

Note: $K'_{HF} = {}^aH \times [F^-]/[HF]$ $K'_{HSO_4} = {}^aH \times [SO_4^{2-}]/[HSO_4^-]$

at 34.6°/₀₀ salinity $[H^+]_{free} = 0.74\,[H^+]_{total}$

$[HSO_4^-] = 0.24\,[H^+]_{total}$

$[HF] = 0.02\,[H^+]_{total}$.

(Based on Culberson, C., Pytkowicz, R. M., and Hawley, J. E., *J. Mar. Res.,* 28, 15, 1970. With permission.)

Table 1.2–27
RESIDENCE TIMES OF THE ELEMENTS IN SEA WATER

Element	Years	Element	Years	Element	Years
Li	2.0×10^7	Zm	1.8×10^5	Nd	270
Be	150	Ga	1.4×10^3	Sm	180
Na	2.6×10^8	Ge	7.0×10^3	Eu	300
Mg	4.5×10^7	Rb	2.7×10^5	Gd	260
Al	100	Sr	1.9×10^7	Dy	460
Si	8.0×10^3	Y	7.5×10^3	Ho	530
K	1.1×10^7	Nb	300	Er	690
Ca	8.0×10^6	Mo	5.0×10^5	Tm	1800
Sc	5.6×10^3	Ag	2.1×10^6	Yb	530
Ti	160	Cd	5.0×10^5	Lu	450
V	1.0×10^4	Sm	1.0×10^5	W	1000
Cr	350	Sb	3.5×10^5	Au	5.6×10^5
Mm	1400	Cs	4.0×10^4	Hg	4.2×10^4
Fe	140	Ba	8.4×10^4	Pb	2000
Co	1.8×10^4	La	440	Bi	4.5×10^4
Ni	1.8×10^4	Ce	80	Th	350
Cu	5.0×10^4	Pr	320	U	5.0×10^5

(From Goldberg, E. P., in *Chemical Oceanography,* Vol. 1, Riley, J. P. and Skirrow, G., Eds., Academic Press, London, 1965, 163. With permission.)

Table 1.2–28
FRACTION OF INORGANIC PHOSPHATE

A. Pure Water

pH	$H_2PO_4^-$	HPO_4^{2-}	PO_4^{3-}
7.2	0.503	0.479	0.000
7.6	0.287	0.713	0.000
8.0	0.138	0.862	0.000
8.4	0.060	0.940	0.000

B. 0.68 Molar NaCl

pH	$H_2PO_4^-$	HPO_4^{2-}	PO_4^{3-}
7.2	0.133	0.867	0.000
7.6	0.058	0.942	0.000
8.0	0.024	0.975	0.001
8.4	0.010	0.988	0.002

C. 33°/oo Salinity Sea Water

pH	$H_2PO_4^-$	HPO_4^{2-}	PO_4^{3-}
7.2	0.066	0.915	0.020
7.6	0.026	0.923	0.050
8.0	0.010	0.871	0.119
8.4	0.003	0.741	0.255

Note: As each species in A. the absence of ionic interactions, B. the presence of ionic strength effects, and C. the presence of complexes and ionic strength of sea water.

(From Kester, D. R. and Pytkowicz, R. M., *Limnol. Oceanogr.,* 12, 243, 1967. With permission.)

Table 1.2–29
CHEMICAL SPECIES IN SEA WATER

Element	Chemical form	Reference
Hydrogen	H_2O	8
Helium	He(g)	8
Lithium	Li^+	19
Beryllium		19
Boron	$B(OH)_3$, $B(OH)_4^-$	3, 14
Carbon	HCO_3^-, CO_3^{2-}, CO_2, $MgHCO_3^+$, $NaHCO_3°$, $MgCO_3°$, organic coumpounds	3, 4, 7, 12, 14
Nitrogen	NO_3^-, NO_2^-, NH_3, N_2 (g), organic compounds	20
Oxygen	H_2O, O_2 (g), SO_4^{2-}, organic compounds	8
Fluorine	F^-, MgF^+, CaF^+	6
Neon	Ne(g)	8
Sodium	Na^+, $NaSO_4^-$, $NaHCO_3°$	12, 13, 17
Magnesium	Mg^{2+}, $MgSO_4°$, $MgHCO_3^+$, $MgCO_3°$	7, 16, 18
Aluminum	$Al(OH)_3$	19
Silicon	$Si(OH)_4$, $SiO(OH)_3^-$	1
Phosphorus	$H_2PO_4^-$, HPO_4^{2-}, PO_4^{3-}	11
Sulfur	SO_4^{2-}, $NaSO_4^-$, $MgSO_4°$, $CaSO_4°$	12, 13, 17
Chlorine	Cl^-	12, 13
Argon	Ar(g)	8
Potassium	K^+, KSO_4^-	7, 12, 13
Calcium	Ca^{2+}, $CaSO_4°$, $CaHCO_3^+$	7, 12, 13
Scandium		19
Titanium	$Ti(OH)_4$	19
Vandium	$VO_2(OH)_3^{2-}$	19
Chromium	$Cr(OH)_2^+$, $CrOH^{2+}$, CrO_2^-, CrO_4^{2-}, $HCrO_4^-$, H_2CrO_4	5
Manganese	Mn^{2+}, $MnSO_4°$, $Mn(OH)_{3,4}$	8, 19
Iron	$Fe(OH)_3$, $Fe(OH)_2^+$	10
Cobalt	Co^{2+}, $CoSO_4°$	8
Nickel	Ni^{2+}, $NiSO_4°$	8
Copper	Cu^{2+}, $CuSO_4°$, $CuOH^+$	8, 19
Zinc	Zn^{2+}, $ZnSO_4°$, $ZnOH^+$	2, 8
Gallium	–	
Germanium	$Ge(OH)_4°$, $GeO(OH)_3^-$	8
Arsenic	$H_3AsO_4^-$, $H_2AsO_4^-$, $HAsO_4^{2-}$, AsO_4^{3-}	8
Selenium	SeO_4^{2-}	19
Bromine	Br^-	8
Krypton	Kr(g)	8
Rubidium	Rb^+	19
Strontium	Sr^{2+}, $SrSO_4°$	8
Yttrium	–	
Zirconium	–	
Niobium	–	
Molybdenum	MoO_4^{2-}	19
Technetium	–	
Ruthenium	–	
Rhodium	–	

(Compiled by D. R. Kester, Graduate School of Oceanography, University of Rhode Island.)

Table 1.2–29 (*Continued*)
CHEMICAL SPECIES IN SEA WATER

Element	Chemical form	Reference
Palladium	–	
Silver	$AgCl_2^-$, $AgCl_3^{2-}$	8
Cadmium	$CdCl^+$, Cd^{2+}, $CdSO_4{}^\circ$	2, 9
Indium	–	
Tin	–	
Antimony	–	
Tellurium	–	
Iodine	IO_3^-, I^-	8
Zenon	Xe(g)	8
Cesium	Cs^+	19
Barium	Ba^{2+}, $BaSO_4{}^\circ$	8
Lanthanum	La^{3+}, $La(OH)^{2+}$	19
Cerium	–	
Praseodymium	–	
Neodymium	–	
Promethium	–	
Samarium	–	
Europium	–	
Gadolinium	–	
Terbium	–	
Dysprosium	–	
Holmium	–	
Erbium	–	
Thulium	–	
Ytterbium	–	
Lutetium	–	
Hafnium	–	
Tantalum	–	
Tungsten	WO_4^{2-}	19
Rhenium	–	
Osmium	–	
Iridium	–	
Platinum	–	
Gold	$AuCl_4^-$, $AuCl_2^-$	8, 15, 19
Mercury	$HgCl_3^-$, $HgCl_4^{2-}$	8
Thallium	Tl^+	8
Lead	Pb^{2+}, $PbSO_4{}^\circ$, $PbOH^+$	8, 19
Bismuth	–	
Polonium	–	
Astatine	–	
Radon	Rn(g)	8
Francium	–	
Radium	Ra^{2+}, $RaSO_4{}^\circ$	8
Actinium	–	
Thorium	–	
Protactinium	–	
Uranium	$UO_2(CO_3)_3^{4-}$	8

Table 1.2–29 (*Continued*)

REFERENCES

1. **Armstrong, F. A. J.,** in *Chemical Oceanography,* Vol. 1, Riley, J. P. and Skirrow, G., Eds., Academic Press, London, 1965, 409.
2. **Branica, M., Barić, M., and Jeftić, L.,** *Rapp. P.-V. Reun. Cons. Perm. Int. Explor. Scient. Mer Médit.,* 19, 929, 1969.
3. **Culberson, C. and Pytkowicz, R. M.,** *Limnol. Oceanogr.,* 13, 403, 1968.
4. **Duursma, E. K.,** in *Chemical Oceanography,* Vol. 1, Riley, J. P. and Skirrow, G., Eds., Academic Press, London, 1965, 433-475.
5. **Elderfield, H.,** *Earth Planet. Sci. Lett.,* 9, 10, 1970.
6. **Elgquist, B.,** Rep. Chem. Seawater, No. 7, Univ. Göteborg, Sweden, 1969.
7. **Garrels, R. M. and Thompson, M.,** *Am. J. Sci.,* 260, 57, 1962.
8. **Goldberg, E. D.,** in *The Sea,* Vol. 2, Hill, M. N., Ed., Wiley-Interscience, New York, 1963, 3-25.
9. **Goldberg, E. D.,** in *Chemical Oceanography,* Vol. 1, Riley, J. P. and Skirrow, G., Eds., Academic Press, London, 1965, 163-196.
10. **Horne, R. A.,** *Marine Chemistry,* John Wiley & Sons, New York, 1969.
11. **Kester, D. R. and Pytkowicz, R. M.,** *Limnol. Oceanogr.,* 12, 243, 1967.
12. **Kester, D. R. and Pytkowicz, R. M.,** *Limnol. Oceanogr.,* 14, 686, 1969.
13. **Kester, D. R. and Pytkowicz, R. M.,** *Geochim. Cosmochim. Acta,* 34, 1039, 1970.
14. **Lyman, J.,** Buffer Mechanism of Seawater, Ph.D. Thesis, University of California, Los Angeles, 1956.
15. **Peshchevitskiy, B. I., Anoshin, G. N., and Yereberg, A. M.,** *Dokl. Earth Sci. Sect.,* 162, 205, 1963.
16. **Pytkowicz, R. M. and Gates, R.,** *Science,* 161, 690, 1968.
17. **Pytkowicz, R. M. and Kester, D. R.,** *Am. J. Sci.,* 267, 217, 1969.
18. **Pytkowicz, R. M. and Kester, D. R.,** *Oceanogr. Mar. Biol. Annu. Rev.,* Barnes, H., Ed., George Allen and Unwin, London, in press.
19. **Sillen, L. G.,** in *Oceanography,* Sears, M., Ed., Assoc. Adv. Sci., Washington, D.C., 1959, 549-581.
20. **Vaccaro, R. F.,** in *Chemical Oceanography,* Vol. 1, Riley J. P. and Skirrow, G., Eds., Academic Press, London, 1965, 365-408.

1.3 Solubilities of Gases in Sea Water

Table 1.3–1
INTERPOLATED VALUES OF OXYGEN SOLUBILITY (ml/l)*

Temp (°C)	Chlorinity (°/₀₀) 0.0	2.0	4.0	6.0	8.0	10.0	12.0	14.0	16.0	18.0	20.0
0.5	10.10	9.84	9.59	9.35	9.12	8.89	8.67	8.46	8.26	8.06	7.87
1.0	9.96	9.71	9.47	9.24	9.01	8.79	8.57	8.36	8.16	7.96	7.77
2.0	9.68	9.45	9.22	9.00	8.78	8.57	8.37	8.16	7.96	7.77	7.58
3.0	9.41	9.19	8.98	8.77	8.56	8.36	8.16	7.96	7.77	7.58	7.40
4.0	9.16	8.95	8.74	8.54	8.34	8.15	7.95	7.76	7.58	7.40	7.22
5.0	8.91	8.71	8.51	8.32	8.13	7.94	7.75	7.57	7.39	7.22	7.04
6.0	8.68	8.49	8.29	8.11	7.92	7.74	7.56	7.39	7.21	7.04	6.88
7.0	8.46	8.27	8.09	7.90	7.73	7.55	7.38	7.21	7.04	6.88	6.72
8.0	8.26	8.07	7.89	7.71	7.54	7.37	7.20	7.04	6.88	6.72	6.57
9.0	8.06	7.88	7.70	7.53	7.36	7.19	7.03	6.87	6.72	6.57	6.42
10.0	7.88	7.70	7.53	7.36	7.19	7.03	6.87	6.72	6.57	6.42	6.28
11.0	7.71	7.53	7.36	7.19	7.03	6.87	6.72	6.57	6.42	6.28	6.15
12.0	7.54	7.37	7.20	7.03	6.87	6.72	6.57	6.42	6.28	6.15	6.02
13.0	7.39	7.21	7.04	6.88	6.72	6.57	6.43	6.28	6.15	6.02	5.89
14.0	7.23	7.06	6.90	6.74	6.58	6.43	6.29	6.15	6.02	5.89	5.77
15.0	7.07	6.91	6.75	6.60	6.45	6.30	6.16	6.03	5.90	5.78	5.66
16.0	6.92	6.76	6.61	6.46	6.31	6.18	6.04	5.91	5.78	5.66	5.55
17.0	6.77	6.62	6.47	6.33	6.19	6.05	5.92	5.80	5.67	5.55	5.44
18.0	6.62	6.48	6.34	6.20	6.07	5.94	5.81	5.69	5.57	5.45	5.34
19.0	6.49	6.35	6.21	6.08	5.95	5.82	5.70	5.58	5.46	5.35	5.24
20.0	6.36	6.22	6.09	5.96	5.84	5.71	5.59	5.48	5.37	5.26	5.15
21.0	6.23	6.10	5.97	5.85	5.72	5.61	5.49	5.38	5.27	5.16	5.06
22.0	6.11	5.98	5.86	5.74	5.62	5.50	5.39	5.28	5.17	5.07	4.97
23.0	6.00	5.87	5.75	5.63	5.51	5.40	5.29	5.18	5.08	4.98	4.89
24.0	5.88	5.76	5.64	5.52	5.41	5.30	5.19	5.09	4.99	4.90	4.80
25.0	5.77	5.65	5.54	5.42	5.31	5.21	5.10	5.00	4.90	4.81	4.72
26.0	5.67	5.55	5.44	5.33	5.22	5.11	5.01	4.91	4.82	4.73	4.64
27.0	5.57	5.45	5.34	5.23	5.13	5.02	4.92	4.83	4.74	4.65	4.56
28.0	5.47	5.36	5.25	5.14	5.04	4.94	4.84	4.75	4.65	4.57	4.48
29.0	5.37	5.26	5.16	5.05	4.95	4.85	4.76	4.66	4.57	4.49	4.40
30.0	5.28	5.17	5.07	4.97	4.87	4.77	4.68	4.59	4.50	4.41	4.33
31.0	5.19	5.09	4.98	4.88	4.79	4.69	4.60	4.51	4.43	4.34	4.26
32.0	5.11	5.00	4.90	4.80	4.71	4.62	4.53	4.44	4.36	4.27	4.20
33.0	5.02	4.92	4.82	4.73	4.63	4.54	4.45	4.37	4.29	4.21	4.13
34.0	4.94	4.84	4.74	4.65	4.56	4.47	4.38	4.30	4.22	4.14	4.07
35.0	4.85	4.76	4.67	4.57	4.49	4.40	4.32	4.23	4.16	4.08	4.00
36.0	4.77	4.68	4.59	4.50	4.41	4.33	4.25	4.17	4.09	4.02	3.94

* From an atmosphere of 20.94% O_2 and 100% relative humidity.

(From Carpenter, J. H., New measurements of oxygen solubility in pure and natural water, *Limnol. Oceanogr.*, 11, 264, 1966. With permission.)

Table 1.3–2
INTERPOLATED VALUES OF OXYGEN SOLUBILITY (μg-at./l)*

Temp (°C)	Chlorinity (°/₀₀) 0.0	2.0	4.0	6.0	8.0	10.0	12.0	14.0	16.0	18.0	20.0
0.5	902	879	857	835	814	794	774	756	737	720	703
1.0	889	867	846	825	804	785	765	747	729	711	694
2.0	864	844	823	804	784	765	747	729	711	694	677
3.0	840	821	802	783	764	746	728	711	694	677	660
4.0	817	799	780	762	745	727	710	693	677	660	644
5.0	796	778	760	743	725	709	692	676	660	644	629
6.0	775	758	741	724	707	691	675	659	644	629	614
7.0	756	739	722	706	690	674	659	643	629	614	600
8.0	737	721	704	689	673	658	643	628	614	600	586
9.0	720	704	688	672	657	642	628	614	600	586	573
10.0	703	688	672	657	642	627	613	600	586	573	561
11.0	688	672	657	642	627	613	600	586	573	561	549
12.0	674	658	643	628	614	600	586	573	561	549	537
13.0	659	644	629	614	600	587	574	561	549	537	526
14.0	645	630	616	601	588	574	562	549	538	526	515
15.0	631	617	603	589	576	563	550	538	527	516	505
16.0	618	603	590	577	564	551	539	528	516	506	495
17.0	604	591	578	565	553	540	529	517	507	496	486
18.0	591	578	566	554	542	530	519	508	497	487	477
19.0	579	567	555	543	531	520	509	498	488	478	468
20.0	568	556	544	532	521	510	499	489	479	469	460
21.0	556	545	533	522	511	500	490	480	470	461	452
22.0	546	534	523	512	501	491	481	471	462	453	444
23.0	535	524	513	502	492	482	472	463	454	445	436
24.0	525	514	504	493	483	473	464	455	446	437	429
25.0	516	505	494	484	474	465	455	447	438	430	421
26.0	506	496	485	475	466	457	447	439	430	422	414
27.0	497	487	477	467	458	448	440	431	423	415	407
28.0	488	478	468	459	450	441	432	424	415	408	400
29.0	480	470	460	451	442	433	425	416	408	401	393
30.0	471	462	453	443	435	426	418	410	402	394	387
31.0	464	454	445	436	427	419	411	403	395	388	381
32.0	456	447	438	429	420	412	404	396	389	382	375
33.0	448	439	430	422	414	406	398	390	383	376	369
34.0	441	432	423	415	407	399	391	384	377	370	363
35.0	433	425	417	408	400	393	385	378	371	364	358
36.0	426	418	410	402	394	387	379	372	365	359	352

* From an atmosphere of 20.94% O_2 and 100% relative humidity.

(From Carpenter, J. H., New measurements of oxygen solubility in pure and natural water, *Limnol. Oceanogr.*, 11, 264, 1966. With permission.)

Table 1.3–3
INTERPOLATED VALUES OF NITROGEN SOLUBILITY

Temp (°C)	Chlorinity (°/∘∘) 0	2	4	6	8	10	12	14	16	18	20
−2	–	–	–	–	–	–	–	–	–	–	14.74
−1	–	–	–	–	–	–	16.13	15.69	15.26	14.82	14.39
0	18.39	17.89	17.45	17.01	16.58	16.16	15.73	15.31	14.89	14.47	14.05
1	17.92	17.43	17.00	16.58	16.16	15.76	15.35	14.93	14.53	14.13	13.72
2	17.48	16.99	16.57	16.17	15.76	15.37	14.97	14.58	14.18	13.79	13.41
3	17.05	16.57	16.17	15.77	15.38	15.00	14.62	14.24	13.86	13.48	13.11
4	16.64	16.17	15.78	15.39	15.01	14.65	14.28	13.90	13.54	13.18	12.81
5	16.25	15.78	15.41	15.03	14.66	14.31	13.95	13.59	13.24	12.89	12.53
6	15.88	15.42	15.05	14.68	14.33	13.98	13.63	13.29	12.94	12.61	12.27
7	15.51	15.07	14.71	14.35	14.01	13.67	13.34	13.00	12.67	12.34	12.01
8	15.17	14.73	14.37	14.03	13.70	13.37	13.05	12.72	12.40	12.08	11.76
9	14.84	14.41	14.06	13.73	13.40	13.09	12.77	12.45	12.14	11.84	11.53
10	14.52	14.09	13.75	13.44	13.12	12.81	12.50	12.20	11.90	11.59	11.29
11	14.21	13.80	13.47	13.16	12.85	12.55	12.25	11.95	11.66	11.37	11.08
12	13.91	13.51	13.19	12.88	12.58	12.29	12.01	11.71	11.43	11.15	10.87
13	13.63	13.23	12.92	12.62	12.33	12.05	11.77	11.49	11.21	10.94	10.66
14	13.36	12.97	12.67	12.37	12.09	11.81	11.54	11.27	11.00	10.73	10.47
15	13.10	12.71	12.41	12.13	11.85	11.59	11.32	11.06	10.79	10.53	10.27
16	12.84	12.47	12.18	11.90	11.63	11.37	11.11	10.85	10.60	10.35	10.09
17	12.60	12.23	11.95	11.68	11.42	11.16	10.91	10.65	10.41	10.16	9.91
18	12.37	12.00	11.73	11.47	11.21	10.96	10.71	10.46	10.23	9.98	9.75
19	12.14	11.79	11.51	11.26	11.01	10.76	10.53	10.28	10.05	9.82	9.58
20	11.92	11.57	11.31	11.06	10.82	10.58	10.34	10.11	9.88	9.65	9.42
21	11.71	11.37	11.11	10.87	10.63	10.40	10.17	9.94	9.71	9.49	9.26
22	11.51	11.17	10.92	10.69	10.45	10.22	9.99	9.77	9.55	9.33	9.12
23	11.31	10.99	10.74	10.50	10.27	10.05	9.83	9.61	9.40	9.19	8.97
24	11.12	10.80	10.56	10.33	10.10	9.90	9.67	9.46	9.25	9.04	8.83
25	10.94	10.62	10.39	10.16	9.94	9.73	9.52	9.31	9.11	8.90	8.70
26	10.76	10.45	10.22	10.00	9.78	9.58	9.37	9.17	8.96	8.77	8.56
27	10.59	10.28	10.06	9.84	9.64	9.43	9.23	9.03	8.83	8.63	8.44
28	10.41	10.13	9.90	9.69	9.49	9.28	9.09	8.89	8.70	8.50	8.31
29	10.25	9.97	9.75	9.54	9.35	9.14	8.96	8.76	8.57	8.38	8.19
30	10.09	9.82	9.60	9.40	9.20	9.01	8.82	8.63	8.45	8.26	8.07
31	9.94	9.67	9.46	9.26	9.07	8.88	8.69	8.51	8.32	8.14	7.96
32	9.79	9.53	9.32	9.12	8.94	8.75	8.57	8.39	8.21	8.03	7.85
33	9.65	9.39	9.19	8.99	8.81	8.63	8.45	8.27	8.09	7.92	7.74
34	9.51	9.25	9.06	8.87	8.69	8.51	8.33	8.15	7.98	7.81	7.64

* In ml/l from an atmosphere of 78.08% N_2 and 100% relative humidity.

(From Murray, C. N., Riley, J. P., and Wilson, T. R. S., Solubility of gases in distilled water and sea water – I Nitrogen, *Deep Sea Res.*, 16, 297, 1969. With permission.)

Table 1.3–4
SOLUBILITY OF CARBON DIOXIDE IN PURE WATER AND IN SEA WATER*

Temp °C / Cl °/₀₀	0	2	4	6	8	10	12	14	16	18	20	22	24	26
0	771	713	661	614	572	535	499	467	440	413	389	367	347	328 x 10^{-4}
15	670	620	576	536	500	468	437	409	385	364	344	325	308	291
16	664	615	571	531	496	464	433	406	382	360	341	322	305	289
17	658	609	565	526	491	460	429	402	378	357	338	319	303	287
18	652	603	559	521	486	455	425	398	374	354	335	316	300	284
19	645	597	554	515	481	450	421	394	371	350	332	313	297	281
20	638	591	548	510	476	445	416	390	367	347	328	310	294	278

* In mole/liter/atmosphere.

(From Murray, C. N. and Riley, J. P., *Deep Sea Res.*, 18, 533, 1971. With permission.)

Table 1.3–5
SOLUBILITY OF ARGON (ml AT S.T.P./l) RELATIVE TO AN ATMOSPHERE CONTAINING 0.934% OF ARGON AND HAVING A RELATIVE HUMIDITY OF 100%

Temp (°C)	Chlorinity (°/₀₀) 0	2	4	6	8	10	12	14	16	18	20
−2	–	–	–	–	–	–	–	–	–	–	0.4082
−1	–	–	–	–	–	–	0.4285	0.4280	0.4176	0.4072	0.3968
0	0.4984	0.4811	0.4698	0.4589	0.4483	0.4377	0.4273	0.4170	0.4067	0.3964	0.3863
1	0.4834	0.4681	0.4571	0.4466	0.4363	0.4261	0.4161	0.4061	0.3962	0.3863	0.3765
2	0.4697	0.4561	0.4455	0.4353	0.4253	0.4154	0.4057	0.3960	0.3863	0.3768	0.3674
3	0.4572	0.4447	0.4343	0.4245	0.4147	0.4052	0.3958	0.3865	0.3771	0.3679	0.3588
4	0.4451	0.4337	0.4236	0.4139	0.4044	0.3954	0.3864	0.3774	0.3684	0.3595	0.3506
5	0.4336	0.4234	0.4137	0.4045	0.3955	0.3864	0.3773	0.3684	0.3598	0.3512	0.3426
6	0.4230	0.4119	0.4025	0.3935	0.3848	0.3762	0.3677	0.3592	0.3509	0.3426	0.3343
7	0.4127	0.4016	0.3924	0.3837	0.3752	0.3669	0.3586	0.3505	0.3424	0.3344	0.3264
8	0.4030	0.3917	0.3827	0.3743	0.3661	0.3580	0.3501	0.3421	0.3344	0.3266	0.3189
9	0.3934	0.3821	0.3734	0.3651	0.3573	0.3494	0.3418	0.3341	0.3265	0.3190	0.3116
10	0.3842	0.3730	0.3645	0.3565	0.3488	0.3411	0.3337	0.3264	0.3191	0.3117	0.3045
11	0.3755	0.3644	0.3561	0.3484	0.3409	0.3336	0.3263	0.3192	0.3121	0.3050	0.2980
12	0.3672	0.3563	0.3483	0.3407	0.3335	0.3263	0.3193	0.3124	0.3054	0.2986	0.2918
13	0.3593	0.3485	0.3406	0.3333	0.3264	0.3194	0.3127	0.3060	0.2993	0.2924	0.2857
14	0.3515	0.3410	0.3333	0.3263	0.3195	0.3128	0.3062	0.2997	0.2931	0.2865	0.2800
15	0.3442	0.3337	0.3264	0.3195	0.3129	0.3064	0.3001	0.2938	0.2873	0.2809	0.2746
16	0.3369	0.3265	0.3194	0.3126	0.3062	0.3000	0.2937	0.2874	0.2812	0.2752	0.2690
17	0.3300	0.3196	0.3126	0.3062	0.3000	0.2939	0.2879	0.2817	0.2758	0.2698	0.2639
18	0.3234	0.3131	0.3062	0.2998	0.2938	0.2879	0.2820	0.2762	0.2705	0.2646	0.2589
19	0.3169	0.3068	0.2999	0.2939	0.2879	0.2822	0.2765	0.2709	0.2654	0.2598	0.2540
20	0.3106	0.3007	0.2938	0.2881	0.2823	0.2768	0.2712	0.2659	0.2605	0.2551	0.2493
21	0.3047	0.2946	0.2882	0.2824	0.2769	0.2714	0.2661	0.2608	0.2557	0.2503	0.2450
22	0.2990	0.2888	0.2826	0.2770	0.2716	0.2663	0.2612	0.2561	0.2512	0.2460	0.2409

Table 1.3–5 (continued)

23	0.2935	0.2832	0.2772	0.2717	0.2665	0.2614	0.2564	0.2514	0.2467	0.2418	0.2368
24	0.2881	0.2777	0.2720	0.2665	0.2615	0.2565	0.2517	0.2469	0.2423	0.2378	0.2330
25	0.2829	0.2724	0.2667	0.2616	0.2566	0.2519	0.2473	0.2428	0.2383	0.2339	0.2292
26	0.2777	0.2676	0.2617	0.2566	0.2519	0.2473	0.2427	0.2383	0.2339	0.2296	0.2250
27	0.2727	0.2627	0.2568	0.2517	0.2472	0.2427	0.2383	0.2339	0.2296	0.2254	0.2210
28	0.2676	0.2579	0.2520	0.2469	0.2426	0.2382	0.2338	0.2297	0.2254	0.2213	0.2171
29	0.2627	0.2531	0.2474	0.2422	0.2381	0.2338	0.2296	0.2255	0.2213	0.2172	0.2132
30	0.2582	0.2485	0.2428	0.2376	0.2336	0.2295	0.2254	0.2213	0.2173	0.2133	0.2094
31	0.2536	0.2447	0.2390	0.2340	0.2300	0.2261	0.2220	0.2181	0.2142	0.2103	0.2066
32	0.2496	0.2410	0.2355	0.2307	0.2268	0.2227	0.2188	0.2149	0.2112	0.2074	0.2037
33	0.2454	0.2374	0.2320	0.2273	0.2236	0.2195	0.2157	0.2120	0.2082	0.2046	0.2011
34	0.2414	0.2338	0.2286	0.2241	0.2204	0.2165	0.2127	0.2090	0.2055	0.2020	0.1984
35	0.2375	0.2302	0.2252	0.2208	0.2172	0.2135	0.2097	0.2061	0.2026	0.1994	0.1958
36	0.2337	0.2269	0.2221	0.2179	0.2140	0.2103	0.2067	0.2033	0.1999	0.1965	0.1933
37	0.2299	0.2237	0.2190	0.2146	0.2108	0.2071	0.2037	0.2003	0.1971	0.1938	0.1907
38	0.2263	0.2204	0.2157	0.2113	0.2076	0.2041	0.2007	0.1975	0.1942	0.1911	0.1880

(From Murray, C. N. and Riley, J. P., Solubility of gases in distilled water and sea water – III. Argon, *Deep Sea Res.*, 17, 203, 1970. With permission.)

Table 1.3–6
SOLUBILITIES OF NOBLE GASES IN SEA WATER*

Temp (°C)	He		Ne		Ar		Kr		Xe	
	Pure	Air	Pure	Air	Pure	Air	Pure	Air	Pure	Air
0 ± 1	–	–	9.37	171×10^{-6}	–	–	71.5	81.5×10^{-6}	136	11.70×10^{-6}
1 ± 1	7.91	41.4×10^{-6}	–	–	38.5	0.359	–	–	–	–
5 ± 1	–	–	9.02	164×10^{-6}	35.3	0.329	63.9	72.8×10^{-6}	115	9.89×10^{-6}
10 ± 1	7.40	38.8×10^{-6}	8.67	158×10^{-6}	32.8	0.306	58.2	66.3×10^{-6}	103	8.86×10^{-6}
15 ± 0.5	6.95	36.4×10^{-6}	8.35	152×10^{-6}	30.2	0.282	51.6	58.5×10^{-6}	90.0	7.74×10^{-6}
17.5 ± 0.5	–	–	–	–	–	–	50.2	57.2×10^{-6}	–	–
20 ± 0.5	7.00	36.7×10^{-6}	8.20	149×10^{-6}	26.3	0.245	44.8	51.1×10^{-6}	80.0	6.88×10^{-6}
22.8 ± 0.5	–	–	–	–	–	–	44.2	50.4×10^{-6}	–	–
24 ± 0.5	–	–	–	–	–	–	42.9	48.9×10^{-6}	–	–
25 ± 0.5	–	–	8.07	147×10^{-6}	–	–	–	–	70.2	6.04×10^{-6}

* Equilibrated with 760 torr of each of the gases and calculated for equilibrium with air containing 5.24×10^{-6} atm of He, 1.82×10^{-5} atm of Ne, 9.32×10^{-3} atm of Ar, 1.14×10^{-6} atm of Kr, and 8.6×10^{-8} atm of Xe, respectively. The units are ml (S.T.P.)/kg water.

(From König, H., Über die Löslichkeit der Edelgase in Meerwasser, *Z. Naturforsch.*, 18A, 363, 1963. With permission.)

Table 1.3–7
SOLUBILITY OF CARBON MONOXIDE IN SEA WATER

Temp °C	Chlorinity 15	16	17	18	19	20	21
				a, Carbon monoxide			
–2	0.03162	0.03124	0.03084	0.03044	0.03004	0.02966	0.02926
–1	0.03090	0.03052	0.03014	0.02976	0.02938	0.02900	0.02862
0	0.03024	0.02986	0.02948	0.02910	0.02872	0.02835	0.02797
1	0.02949	0.02913	0.02878	0.02842	0.02807	0.02772	0.02736
2	0.02880	0.02846	0.02811	0.02776	0.02743	0.02709	0.02675
3	0.02812	0.02779	0.02746	0.02713	0.02680	0.02648	0.02614
4	0.02750	0.02717	0.02684	0.02652	0.02620	0.02588	0.02556
5	0.02686	0.02656	0.02625	0.02594	0.02564	0.02532	0.02501
6	0.02632	0.02602	0.02572	0.02541	0.02510	0.02480	0.02450
7	0.02578	0.02548	0.02519	0.02490	0.02460	0.02432	0.02402
8	0.02524	0.02496	0.02468	0.02440	0.02412	0.02384	0.02356
9	0.02475	0.02448	0.02421	0.02394	0.02366	0.02339	0.02312
10	0.02428	0.02402	0.02376	0.02350	0.02322	0.02296	0.02270
11	0.02385	0.02359	0.02334	0.02308	0.02282	0.02256	0.02230
12	0.02343	0.02318	0.02292	0.02267	0.02242	0.02216	0.02192
13	0.02302	0.02278	0.02252	0.02228	0.02202	0.02178	0.02153
14	0.02262	0.02238	0.02213	0.02188	0.02164	0.02140	0.02116
15	0.02224	0.02200	0.02176	0.02152	0.02128	0.02104	0.02080
16	0.02187	0.02164	0.02140	0.02116	0.02092	0.02070	0.02046
17	0.02152	0.02129	0.02106	0.02082	0.02059	0.02036	0.02014
18	0.02118	0.02094	0.02072	0.02048	0.02026	0.02002	0.01980

(From Douglas, E., Carbon monoxide solubilities in seawater, *J. Phys. Chem.*, 71, 1931, 1967. With permission of the American Chemical Society.)

1.4 Mineral Solubilities in Sea Water

Table 1.4–1
SOLUBILITY OF CALCIUM CARBONATE IN SEA WATER AT ATMOSPHERIC PRESSURE

Calcite	$K'_{sp} = [Ca^{2+}][CO_3^{2-}] = (0.69 - 0.0063\ t°C) \times 10^{-6} \times S\ (°/_{oo})/34.3$
Aragonite	$K'_{sp} = [Ca^{2+}][CO_3^{2-}] = 0.90 \times 10^{-6}$ at 19°/oo Cl and t = 25°C $\Delta K'_{sp}/\Delta t°C = 0.0078 \times 10^{-6}/°C$ at 19°/oo Cl from 0 to 40°C

Note: $K'_{sp} = [Ca^{2+}]\ [CO_3^{2-}]$, the concentration product.

(From MacIntyre, W. G., Fisheries Res. Bd. of Canada, Oceanographic and Limnological Series, Manuscript Rep. Ser. 200, Dartmouth, Nova Scotia, 1965. With permission.)

Table 1.4–2
EFFECT OF PRESSURE ON THE SOLUBILITY OF CALCIUM CARBONATE IN SEA WATER*

Mineral	t°C	$(K'_{sp})_{500}/(K'_{sp})_1$	$(K'_{sp})_{1000}/(K'_{sp})_1$
Aragonite	2	2.11 ± 0.06	4.23 ± 0.27
	22	1.80 ± 0.01	3.16 ± 0.02
Calcite	2	2.18	4.79
	22	1.88	3.56

Note: $K'_{sp} = [Ca^{2+}]\ [CO_3^{2-}]$

*The subscripts 1, 500, and 1000 refer to the pressure (atm).

(From Hawley, J. and Pytkowicz, R. M., *Geochim. Cosmochim. Acta,* 33, 1557, 1969. With permission.)

Table 1.4–3
SOLUBILITY OF SOME MINERALS IN SEA WATER*

Mineral	Temperature	Cl (°/oo)	K′sp	Reference	Comments
$Ca_5(PO_4)_3F$	25°C	ca. 19	$0.16–16 \times 10^{-32}$	1	
$Mg(OH)_2$	25°C	19.3	$(2.4±0.2 \times 10^{-11}$	2	
SiO_2	0°C	?	58–80 mg/l	3	
SiO_2	22-27°C	?	100–110 mg/l	3	
$MgCO_3$	?	?	3×10^{-4}	4	
$ZmCO_3$	?	?	1.4×10^{-8}	5	Rough estimate**
$CuCO_3$	?	?	1.75×10^{-8}	5	Rough estimate**
$PbCO_3$	?	?	1.05×10^{-11}	5	Rough estimate**
BiOCl	?	?	1.4×10^{-8}	5	Rough estimate**
Cd(OH)Cl	?	?	5.1×10^{-10}	5	Rough estimate**
$Ni(OH)_2$	?	?	2.6×10^{-15}	5	Rough estimate**
$CoCO_3$ } $Co(OH)_3$ }	?	?	5.6×10^{-11}	5	Rough estimate**
$CaCrO_4$ (?)			5×10^{-2}	5	Rough estimate**
$V_2O_5 \cdot nH_2O$	?	?	10^{-3}	5	Rough estimate**
$MgCO_3 \cdot H_2O$	?	?	7×10^{-4}	5	Rough estimate**
$SrCO_3$	?	?	$2.1–11.2 \times 10^{-8}$	5	Rough estimate**
$BaSO_4$	?	?	7×10^{-9}	5	Rough estimate**

*At atmospheric pressure, expressed as K′sp, the concentration solubility products, except where otherwise stated.

**Obtained by multiplying thermodynamic solubility products by estimated activity coefficients as recommended by Krauskopf. These coefficients only reflect the ionic strength and may not be correct if there is a significant extent of ion pair or complex formation.

REFERENCES

1. **Pytkowicz, R. M. and Kester, D. R.,** *Limnol. Oceanogr.,* 12, 714, 1967.
2. **Pytkowicz, R. M. and Gates, R.,** *Science,* 161, 690, 1968.
3. **Krauskopf, K. B.,** *Geochim. Cosmochim. Acta,* 10, 1, 1956.
4. **Wattenberg, H. and Timmerman, E.,** Ann. Hydrogr., Berl., U.S.W. p. 23.
5. Based upon **Krauskopf, K. B.,** *Geochim. Cosmochim. Acta,* 9, 1, 1956.

Table 1.4–4
MEASURED CONCENTRATIONS OF METALS AT SATURATION IN SEA WATER*

Metal	Saturation concentration (ppm)	Metal	Saturation concentration (ppm)
Zn	1.2–2.5	Cr	high
Cu	0.4–0.8	Mo	25–750
Pb	0.3–0.7	W	2–200
Bi	0.04	V^{IV}	4–150
Cd	4–1000	V^{V}	>400
Ni	20–450	Mg	36,000
Co	25–200	Ca	100–480
Hg	100–1000	Sr	22
Ag	2.0–2.5	Ba	0.11

*t = 18–23°C, pH = 7.8–8.2, S ≅ 30°/oo.

(From Krauskopf, K. B., *Geochim. Cosmochim. Acta,* 9, 1, 1956. With permission.)

Table 1.4–5

CONCENTRATIONS OF METALS AT EQUILIBRIUM WITH SULFIDE AT pH 7 AND $[H_2S] = 5 \times 10^{-3}$ *M*

Metal	Concentration (ppm)
Zn	0.008–0.07
Cu	<0.003
Pb	<0.02
Ni	0.06–0.2
Co	0.02–0.6
Hg	<0.005
Ag	<0.006
Cr	<0.004
Mo	6
V	1

(From Krauskopf, K. B., *Geochim. Cosmochim. Acta,* 9, 1, 1956. With permission.)

1.5 Physicochemical Properties of Water and Sea Water

Table 1.5–1

THE FREEZING POINT LOWERING OF SEA WATER (°C)

Table A

Cl °/oo	Knudsen (1903)	Miyake (1939)
5	0.483	0.514
10	0.969	1.027
15	1.466	1.541
17	1.668	1.746
19	1.872	1.951
21	2.078	2.157

Table B

Salinity, °/oo	Murray et al.	Salinity, °/oo	Murray et al.
5	0.268	33	1.791
10	0.535	34	1.849
15	0.801	35	1.906
20	1.068	36	1.964
25	1.341	37	2.018
30	1.621	38	2.079
31	1.678	39	2.138
32	1.734	40	2.196

1. **Knudsen, M.,** *J. Cons. Cons. Perm. Int. Explor. Mer.,* 5, 11, 1903.
2. **Miyake, Y.,** *Bull. Chem. Soc. Jap.,* 14b, 58, 1939.
3. **Murray, C. N., Murray, L. A., and Riley, J. P.,** unpublished results.

Table 1.5–2
THE VAPOR PRESSURE LOWERING OF SEA WATER (mm Hg)

	Ref. 1	Ref. 2		
Cl °/₀₀	25°C	25°C	15°C	5°C
5	–	0.10	0.06	0.03
10	0.225	0.20	0.11	0.06
15	0.340	0.31	0.17	0.09
17	0.387	0.35	0.19	0.10
19	0.435	0.40	0.22	0.11
21	0.484	0.45	0.24	0.13

1. **Robinson, R. A.,** *J. Mar. Biol. Assoc. U.K.,* 33, 449, 1954.
2. **Arons, A. B. and Kientzler, C. F.,** *Trans. Am. Geophys. Union,* 35, 722, 1954.

Table 1.5–3
BOILING POINT OF WATER
(Hydrogen Scale)

Pressure, mm	Tenths of millimeters .0	.1	.2	.3	.4	.5	.6	.7	.8	.9
700	97.714	718	722	725	729	733	737	741	745	749
701	753	757	761	765	769	773	777	781	785	789
702	792	796	800	804	808	812	816	820	824	828
703	832	836	840	844	847	851	855	859	863	867
704	871	875	879	883	887	891	895	899	902	906
705	97.910	914	918	922	926	930	934	938	942	946
706	949	953	957	961	965	969	973	977	981	985
707	989	993	996	000	004	008	012	016	020	024
708	98.028	032	036	040	043	047	051	055	059	063
709	067	071	075	079	082	086	090	094	098	102
710	98.106	110	114	118	121	125	129	133	137	141
711	145	149	153	157	160	164	168	172	176	180
712	184	188	192	195	199	203	207	211	215	219
713	223	227	230	234	238	242	246	250	254	258
714	261	265	269	273	277	281	285	289	292	296
715	98.300	304	308	312	316	320	323	327	331	335
716	339	343	347	351	355	358	362	366	370	374
717	378	382	385	389	393	397	401	405	409	412
718	416	420	424	428	432	436	440	443	447	451
719	455	459	463	467	470	474	478	482	486	490
720	98.493	497	501	505	509	513	517	520	524	528
721	532	536	540	544	547	551	555	559	563	567
722	570	574	578	582	586	590	593	597	601	605
723	609	613	617	620	624	628	632	636	640	643
724	647	651	655	659	662	666	670	674	678	682
725	98.686	689	693	697	701	705	709	712	716	720
726	724	728	732	735	739	743	747	751	755	758
727	762	766	770	774	777	781	785	789	793	797
728	800	804	808	812	816	819	823	827	831	835
729	838	842	846	850	854	858	861	865	869	873

Table 1.5–3 (*Continued*)

Pressure, mm	Tenths of millimeters .0	.1	.2	.3	.4	.5	.6	.7	.8	.9
730	98.877	880	884	888	892	896	899	903	907	911
731	915	918	922	926	930	934	937	941	945	949
732	953	956	960	964	968	972	975	979	983	987
733	991	994	998	002	006	010	013	017	021	025
734	99.029	032	036	040	044	048	051	055	059	063
735	99.067	070	074	078	082	085	089	093	097	101
736	104	108	112	116	119	123	127	131	135	138
737	142	146	150	153	157	161	165	169	172	176
738	180	184	187	191	195	199	203	206	210	214
739	218	221	225	229	233	236	240	244	248	252
740	99.255	259	263	267	270	274	278	282	285	289
741	293	297	300	304	308	312	316	319	323	327
742	331	334	338	342	346	349	353	357	361	364
743	368	372	376	379	383	387	391	394	398	402
744	406	409	413	417	421	424	428	432	436	439
745	99.443	447	451	454	458	462	466	469	473	477
746	481	484	488	492	495	499	503	507	510	514
747	518	522	525	529	533	537	540	544	548	551
748	555	559	563	566	570	574	578	581	585	589
749	592	596	600	604	607	611	615	619	622	626
750	99.630	633	637	641	645	648	652	656	659	663
751	667	671	674	678	682	686	689	693	697	700
752	704	708	712	715	719	723	726	730	734	738
753	741	745	749	752	756	760	764	767	771	775
754	778	782	786	790	793	797	801	804	808	812
755	99.815	819	823	827	830	834	838	841	845	849
756	852	856	860	863	867	871	875	878	882	886
757	889	893	897	900	904	908	911	915	919	923
758	926	930	934	937	941	945	948	952	956	959
759	963	967	970	974	978	982	985	989	993	996
760	100.000	004	007	011	015	018	022	026	029	033
761	037	040	044	048	052	055	059	063	066	070
762	074	077	081	085	088	092	096	099	103	107
763	110	114	118	121	125	129	132	136	140	143
764	147	151	154	158	162	165	169	173	176	180
765	100.184	187	191	195	198	202	206	209	213	216
766	220	224	227	231	235	238	242	246	249	253
767	257	260	264	268	271	275	279	283	286	290
768	293	297	300	304	308	311	315	319	322	326
769	330	333	337	341	344	348	352	355	359	363
770	100.366	370	373	377	381	384	388	392	395	399
771	403	406	410	414	417	421	424	428	432	435
772	439	442	446	450	453	457	461	464	468	472
773	475	479	483	486	490	493	497	501	504	508
774	511	515	519	522	526	530	533	537	540	544
775	100.548	551	555	559	562	566	569	573	577	580
776	584	588	591	595	598	602	606	609	613	616
777	620	624	627	631	634	638	642	645	649	653
778	656	660	663	667	671	674	678	681	685	689
779	692	696	699	703	707	710	714	718	721	725

Table 1.5–3 (*Continued*)

Pressure, mm	Tenths of millimeters .0	.1	.2	.3	.4	.5	.6	.7	.8	.9
780	100.728	732	735	739	743	746	750	753	757	761
781	764	768	772	775	779	782	786	789	793	797
782	800	804	807	811	815	818	822	825	829	833
783	836	840	843	847	851	854	858	861	865	869
784	872	876	879	883	886	890	894	897	901	904
785	100.908	912	915	919	922	926	929	933	937	940
786	944	947	951	954	958	962	965	969	972	976
787	979	983	987	990	994	997	001	005	008	012
788	101.015	019	022	026	029	033	037	040	044	047
789	051	054	058	062	065	069	072	076	079	083
790	101.087	090	094	097	101	104	108	112	115	119
791	122	126	129	133	136	140	144	147	151	154
792	158	161	165	168	172	176	179	183	186	190
793	193	197	200	204	207	211	215	218	222	225
794	229	232	236	239	243	246	250	254	257	261
795	101.264	268	271	275	278	282	286	289	293	296
796	300	303	307	310	314	317	321	324	328	332
797	335	339	342	346	349	353	356	360	363	367
798	370	374	377	381	385	388	392	395	399	402
799	406	409	413	416	420	423	427	430	434	437
800	101.411	–	–	–	–	–	–	–	–	–

(From *CRC Handbook of Chemistry and Physics,* 53rd ed., Weast, R. C., Ed., Chemical Rubber Company, Cleveland, 1970. With permission.)

Table 1.5-4

BOILING POINT ELEVATION FOR SEA WATER

Table A

		Temperature								
		°C, 20	40	60	80	100	120	140	160	180
Cl °/oo	S °/oo	°F, 68	104	140	176	212	248	284	320	356
19.00	34.46	0.30	0.34	0.40	0.47	0.53	0.59	0.66	0.71	0.77
22.80	41.35	0.36	0.42	0.49	0.57	0.67	0.72	0.80	0.87	0.93
26.61	48.24	0.43	0.50	0.58	0.68	0.77	0.86	0.95	1.03	1.10
30.41	55.13	0.51	0.58	0.68	0.79	0.89	1.00	1.10	1.19	1.28
34.21	62.03	0.57	0.67	0.79	0.90	1.01	1.14	1.26	1.36	1.46
38.01	68.92	0.65	0.75	0.88	1.02	1.16	1.29	1.42	1.54	1.65
41.81	75.81	0.72	0.85	0.98	1.13	1.27	1.44	1.58	1.72	1.84
45.61	82.70	0.81	0.94	1.07	1.26	1.43	1.59	1.75	1.90	2.04
49.41	89.59	0.89	1.04	1.21	1.39	1.59	1.75	1.92	2.09	2.24
53.21	96.48	0.98	1.13	1.32	1.52	1.70	1.91	2.10	2.28	2.45
57.01	103.38	1.06	1.23	1.44	1.66	1.86	2.08	2.28	2.48	2.66

(From Fabuss, B. M. and Korosi, A., *J. Chem. Eng. Data,* 11, 606, 1966. With permission of the American Chemical Society.)

Table B

		Wt % sea salt									
T°C	p_O, atm	2.0	3.45[a]	4.0	6.0	8.0	12.0	16.0	20.0	25.0	28.0
25	0.031	0.177	0.312	0.366	0.570	0.795	1.324	1.991	2.858	4.36	5.58
30	0.042	0.184	0.325	0.380	0.594	0.829	1.381	2.077	2.977	4.52	5.77
40	0.073	0.198	0.350	0.410	0.642	0.898	1.497	2.250	3.216	4.86	6.16
50	0.122	0.214	0.377	0.442	0.692	0.969	1.616	2.426	3.458	5.19	6.56
60	0.197	0.229	0.405	0.474	0.744	1.041	1,737	2.604	3.704	5.53	6.96
70	0.309	0.245	0.433	0.508	0.797	1.115	1.860	2.786	3.952	5.88	7.36
80	0.469	0.262	0.463	0.542	0.851	1.191	1.986	2.969	4.202	6.22	7.77
90	0.694	0.279	0.493	0.578	0.907	1.269	2.113	3.155	4.454	6.57	8.18
100	1.003	0.296	0.524	0.615	0.964	1.348	2.242	3.342	4.708	6.92	8.60
110	1.418	0.315	0.556	0.652	1.022	1.429	2.374	3.532	4.963	7.27	9.01
120	1.965	0.334	0.590	0.691	1.082	1.512	2.508	3.723	5.22	7.62	9.43
130	2.673	0.354	0.624	0.731	1.144	1.597	2.643	3.917	5.48	7.98	9.86
140	3.577	0.375	0.660	0.773	1.208	1.684	2.782	4.113	5.74	8.34	10.28
150	4.711	0.396	0.697	0.816	1.274	1.774	2.923	4.311	6.00	8.70	10.71
160	6.119	0.418	0.735	0.861	1.341	1.866	3.066	4.511	6.27	9.06	11.15
180	9.931	0.466	0.817	0.955	1.484	2.057	3.361	4.920	6.81	9.79	12.03
200	15.407	0.519	0.906	1.058	1.637	2.261	3.670	5.342	7.36	10.54	12.94
220	22.993	0.577	1.003	1.170	1.802	2.480	3.995	5.777	7.92	11.30	13.87
240	33.184	0.642	1.111	1.293	1.983	2.715	4.338	6.231	8.49	12.08	14.84
260	46.520	0.716	1.232	1.431	2.181	2.971	4.703	6.700	9.08	12.88	15.83

[a] Standard sea water.

(From Stoughton, R. W. and Lietzke, M. H., *J. Chem. Eng. Data,* 12, 101, 1967. With permission of the American Chemical Society.)

Table 1.5-5
SPECIFIC HEAT OF WATER
Heat capacity of Air-free Water 0°-100°C at 1 Atmosphere Pressure

Temp °C.	Thermal Capacity		Enthalpy		Temp °C	Thermal Capacity		Enthalpy	
	Cal /g/°C	Joules/g/°C	Cal /g	Joules/g		Cal/g/°C	Joules/g/°C	Cal/g	Joules/g
0	1.00738	4.2177	0.0245	0.1026	50	.99854	4.1807	50.0079	209.3729
1	1.00652	4.2141	1.0314	4.3184	51	.99862	4.1810	51.0065	213.5538
2	1.00571	4.2107	2.0376	8.5308	52	.99871	4.1814	52.0051	217.7350
3	1.00499	4.2077	3.0429	12.7400	53	.99878	4.1817	53 0039	221.9166
4	1.00430	4.2048	4.0475	16.9462	54	.99885	4.1820	54.0027	226.0984
5	1.00368	4.2022	5.0515	21.1498	55	.99895	4.1824	55.0016	230.2806
6	1.00313	4.1999	6.0549	25.3508	56	.99905	4.1828	56.0006	234.4632
7	1.00260	4.1977	7.0578	29.5496	57	.99914	4.1832	56.9997	238.6462
8	1.00213	4.1957	8.0602	33.7463	58	.99924	4.1836	57.9989	242.8296
9	1.00170	4.1939	9.0621	37.9410	59	.99933	4.1840	58.9982	247.0134
10	1.00129	4.1922	10.0636	42.1341	60	.99943	4.1844	59.9975	251.1976
11	1.00093	4.1907	11.0647	46.3255	61	.99955	4.1849	60.9970	255.3822
12	1.00060	4.1893	12.0654	50.5155	62	.99964	4.1853	61.9966	259.5673
13	1.00029	4.1880	13.0659	54.7041	63	.99976	4.1858	62.9963	263.7529
14	1.00002	4.1869	14.0660	58.8916	64	.99988	4.1863	63.9962	267.9390
15	.99976	4.1858	15.0659	63 0779	65	1.00000	4.1868	64.9961	272.1256
16	.99955	4.1849	16.0655	67.2632	66	1.00014	4.1874	65.9962	276.3127
17	.99933	4.1840	17.0650	71.4476	67	1.00026	4.1879	66.9964	280.5003
18	.99914	4.1832	18.0642	75.6312	68	1.00041	4.1885	67.9967	284.6885
19	.99897	4.1825	19.0633	79.8141	69	1.00053	4.1890	68.9972	288.8772
20	.99883	4.1819	20.0622	83.9963	70	1.00067	4.1896	69.9977	293.0665
21	.99869	4.1813	21.0609	88.1778	71	1.00081	4.1902	70.9985	297.2564
22	.99857	4.1808	22.0596	92.3589	72	1.00096	4.1908	71.9994	301.4460
23	.99847	4.1804	23.0581	96.5395	73	1.00112	4.1915	73.0004	305.6381
24	.99838	4.1800	24.0565	100.7196	74	1.00127	4.1921	74.0016	309.8299
25	.99828	4.1796	25.0548	104.8994	75	1.00143	4.1928	75.0030	314.0224
26	.99821	4.1793	26.0530	109.0788	76	1.00160	4.1935	76.0045	318.2155
27	.99814	4.1790	27.0512	113.2580	77	1.00177	4.1942	77.0062	322.4094
28	.99809	4.1788	28.0493	117.4369	78	1.00194	4.1949	78.0080	326.6039
29	.99804	4.1786	29.0474	121.6157	79	1.00213	4.1957	79.0101	330.7992
30	.99802	4 1785	30.0455	125 7943	80	1.00229	4.1964	80 0123	334.9952
31	.99799	4.1784	31.0435	129.9727	81	1.00248	4.1972	81.0147	339.1920
32	.99797	4.1783	32.0414	134.1510	82	1.00268	4.1980	82.0172	343.3897
33	.99797	4.1783	33.0394	138.3293	83	1.00287	4.1988	83.0200	347.5881
34	.99795	4.1782	34.0374	142.5076	84	1.00308	4.1997	84.0230	351.7873
35	.99795	4.1782	35.0353	146.6858	85	1.00327	4.2005	85.0262	355.9874
36	.99797	4.1783	36.0333	150.8641	86	1.00349	4.2014	86.0295	360.1883
37	.99797	4.1783	37.0312	155.0423	87	1.00370	4.2023	87.0331	364.3902
38	.99799	4.1784	38.0292	159.2207	88	1.00392	4.2032	88.0369	368.5929
39	.99802	4.1785	39.0272	163.3991	89	1.00416	4.2042	89.0410	372.7966
40	.99804	4.1786	40.0253	167.5777	90	1.00437	4.2051	90.0452	377.0012
41	.99807	4.1787	41.0233	171.7563	91	1.00461	4.2061	91.0497	381.2068
42	.99811	4.1789	42.0214	175.9351	92	1.00485	4.2071	92.0545	385.4135
43	.99816	4.1791	43.0195	180.1141	93	1.00509	4.2081	93.0594	389.6211
44	.99819	4.1792	44.0177	184.2933	94	1.00535	4.2092	94.0647	393.8297
45	.99826	4.1795	45.0159	188.4726	95	1.00561	4.2103	95.0701	398.0395
46	.99830	4.1797	46.0142	192.6522	96	1.00588	4.2114	96.0759	402.2503
47	.99835	4.1799	47.0125	196.8320	97	1.00614	4.2125	97.0819	406.4622
48	.99842	4.1802	48.0109	201.0120	98	1.00640	4.2136	98.0882	410.6753
49	.99847	4.1804	49.0094	205.1923	99	1.00669	4.2148	99.0947	414.8895
					100	1.00697	4.2160	100.1015	419.1049

*The heat capacity of air-free water is given in international steam table calories per gram and in absolute joules per gram. (1 absolute joule – 0.238846 I.T. cal.)

**The enthalpy or heat content is given for air-free water in I.T. Cal per gram and in absolute joules per gram.

(From Osborne, Stimson, and Ginnings, *J. of Res. of the NBS,* 23, 338, 1939.)

Table 1.5-6
ENTHALPY OF AIR-SATURATED WATER
1 Atmosphere Pressure 0–100°C

Temp	Enthalpy		Temp	Enthalpy	
°C	cal/g	J/g	°C	cal/g	J/g
0	0	0	50	49.9896	209.2964
5	5.0276	21.0496	55	54.9842	230.2077
10	10.0402	42.0363	60	59.9811	251.1289
15	15.0431	62.9826	65	64.9808	272.0619
20	20.0400	83.9034	70	69.9839	293.0087
25	25.0332	104.8089	75	74.9907	313.9712
30	30.0244	125.7063	80	80.0019	334.9519
35	35.0149	146.6003	85	85.0180	355.9532
40	40.0055	167.4949	90	90.0395	376.9773
45	44.9968	188.3928	95	95.0671	398.0270
			100	100.1016	419.1053

(From *CRC Handbook of Chemistry and Physics*, 53rd ed., Weast, R. C. Ed., CRC Press, Cleveland, 1972. With permission.)

Table 1.5-7
SPECIFIC HEAT OF WATER ABOVE 100°C

Temp °C	Specific heat mean* 0-t°C	Heat content 0-t** J/g	Temp °C	Specific heat mean* 0-t°C	Heat content 0-t** J/g
100	1.0008	418.75	190	1.0153	807.15
110	1.0015	460.97	200	1.0181	852.02
120	1.0025	503.36	210	1.0212	897.35
130	1.0037	545.93	220	1.0247	943.24
140	1.0050	588.71	230	1.0285	989.75
150	1.0067	631.75	240	1.0326	1036.97
160	1.0083	675.06	250	1.0376	1084.97
170	1.0103	718.66	260	1.0423	1133.87
180	1.0127	762.72	270	1.0483	1184.32

*Mean specific heat of water in 15°C calories between 0°C and the temperature stated.

**Heat content (Enthalpy) in joules/gram between 0°C and the temperature stated.

(From Osborne, N. S., Stimson, H. F., and Fiock, E. F., *J. of Res. of the NBS*, 5, 411, 1930.)

Table 1.5-8
SPECIFIC HEAT OF SUPER-HEATED STEAM*

Temp °C	Pressure in atmospheres 1	2	4	6	8	10	12
110							
110	0.481						
120	0.477	0.498					
130	0.475	0.494					
140	0.473	0.489					
150	0.472	0.486	0.519				
160	0.471	0.483	0.512	0.549			
170	0.470	0.481	0.507	0.538			
180	0.469	0.479	0.502	0.528	0.561	0.602	
190	0.469	0.478	0.498	0.522	0.549	0.583	0.625
200	0.469	0.478	0.495	0.515	0.539	0.567	0.601
210	0.470	0.477	0.493	0.510	0.531	0.555	0.584
220	0.470	0.477	0.491	0.506	0.524	0.545	0.569
230	0.471	0.477	0.489	0.504	0.519	0.537	0.557
240	0.472	0.477	0.488	0.501	0.515	0.530	0.548
250	0.473	0.477	0.488	0.499	0.512	0.525	0.540
260	0.474	0.478	0.487	0.498	0.509	0.521	0.534
270	0.474	0.478	0.487	0.497	0.507	0.518	0.529
280	0.475	0.479	0.487	0.496	0.505	0.515	0.525
290	0.476	0.480	0.487	0.495	0.504	0.513	0.523
300	0.477	0.481	0.488	0.495	0.503	0.511	0.519
310	0.478	0.482	0.488	0.495	0.502	0.510	0.518
320	0.480	0.483	0.489	0.496	0.502	0.509	0.516
330	0.482	0.484	0.490	0.496	0.502	0.508	0.515
340	0.483	0.485	0.491	0.496	0.502	0.507	0.513
350	0.484	0.486	0.492	0.497	0.502	0.507	0.512
360	0.485	0.487	0.492	0.497	0.502	0.507	0.511
370	0.486	0.488	0.493	0.408	0.503	0.507	0.511
380	0.488	0.490	0.494	0.498	0.503	0.507	0.511
390	0.489	0.491	0.495	0.499	0.503		
400	0.490	0.492	0.496	0.500	0.504		
410	0.492	0.494	0.497	0.501	0.505		
420	0.494	0.496	0.498	0.502	0.506		
430	0.495	0.497	0.500	0.504	0.507		
440	0.497	0.499	0.501	0.505	0.508		
450	0.498	0.500	0.503	0.506	0.509		
460	0.500	0.501	0.505	0.507	0.510		
470	0.502	0.503	0.506	0.508	0.512		
480	0.504	0.505	0.507	0.509	0.513		
490	0.505	0.506	0.509	0.511	0.514		
500	0.506	0.508	0.510	0.512	0.515		

*Specific heat of steam under constant pressure given in atmospheres and at temperatures above saturation in cal/g/°C.

(From *CRC Handbook of Chemistry and Physics,* 53rd ed., Weast, R.C., Ed., CRC Press, Cleveland, 1972. With permission.)

Table 1.5-9
SPECIFIC HEAT OF ICE – cal/g/°C

Temp °C	Specific heat	Observer	Temp °C	Specific heat	Observer
−252 to − 188	.146	Dieterici, 1903	−31.8	.4454	Dickinson-Osborne, 1915
−250	.0361		−23.7	.4599	Dickinson-Osborne, 1915
−200	.162	Mean	−24.5	.4605	Dickinson-Osborne, 1915
−188 to − 78	.285	Dieterici, 1903	−20.8	.4668	Dickinson-Osborne, 1915
−180	.199	Nernst, 1910	−14.8	.4782	Dickinson-Osborne, 1915
−160	.230	Nernst, 1910	−14.6	.4779	Dickinson-Osborne, 1915
−150	.246		−11.0	.4861	Dickinson-Osborne, 1915
−140	.262	Nernst, 1910	− 8.1	.4896	Dickinson-Osborne, 1915
−100	.329	Mean	− 4.3	.4989	Dickinson-Osborne, 1915
−78 to − 18	.463	Dieterici, 1903	− 4.5	.4984	Dickinson-Osborne, 1915
−60	.392		− 4.9	.4932	Dickinson-Osborne, 1915
−38.3	.4346	Dickinson-Osborne, 1915	− 2.6	.5003	Dickinson-Osborne, 1915
−34.3	.4411	Dickinson-Osborne, 1915	− 2.2	.5018	Dickinson-Osborne, 1915
−30.6	.4488	Dickinson-Osborne, 1915			
Water Below 0°C					
−6	1.0119	Martinetti, 1890	−3	1.0102	Martinetti, 1890
−5	1.0155	Barnes, 1902	−2	1.0097	Martinetti, 1890
−5	1.0113	Martinetti, 1890	−1	1.0092	Martinetti, 1890
−4	1.0105	Martinetti, 1890			

(From *CRC Handbook of Chemistry and Physics,* 53rd ed., Weast, R. C., Ed., CRC Press, Cleveland, 1972. With permission.)

Table 1.5-10
COMPUTED VALUES FOR SPECIFIC HEAT OF SEA WATER AT CONSTANT PRESSURE*

Salinity (g/kg)	Temperature (°C) −2	−1	0	1	2	5	10	15	20	25	30
0	–	–	4.217	4.214	4.210	4.202	4.192	4.186	4.182	4.179	4.178
5	–	–	4.179	4.176	4.174	4.168	4.161	4.157	4.154	4.153	4.152
10	–	–	4.142	4.140	4.138	4.135	4.130	4.128	4.126	4.126	4.126
15	–	–	4.107	4.106	4.105	4.103	4.100	4.099	4.098	4.099	4.100
20	–	4.075	4.074	4.074	4.073	4.072	4.071	4.071	4.071	4.072	4.074
25	–	4.043	4.043	4.043	4.042	4.042	4.042	4.043	4.045	4.046	4.048
30	–	4.013	4.013	4.013	4.013	4.014	4.015	4.016	4.018	4.020	4.023
32	–	4.001	4.002	4.002	4.002	4.003	4.004	4.006	4.008	4.010	4.013
34	–	3.990	3.990	3.991	3.991	3.992	3.993	3.995	3.998	4.000	4.003
35	3.984	3.984	3.985	3.985	3.985	3.986	3.988	3.990	3.993	3.995	3.999
36	3.979	3.979	3.979	3.980	3.980	3.981	3.983	3.985	3.988	3.991	3.994
38	3.968	3.968	3.968	3.968	3.969	3.970	3.972	3.975	3.978	3.981	3.985
40	3.957	3.957	3.957	3.958	3.958	3.959	3.962	3.965	3.968	3.972	3.976

* In absolute joules per gram.

(From Cox, R. A. and Smith, N. D., The specific heat of sea water, *Proc. R. Soc. Lond. A.,* 252, 51, 1959. With permission of the Royal Society.)

Table 1.5-11
SPECIFIC HEAT OF SEA ICE

The specific heat of pure ice depends upon its temperature and varies within narrow limits but that of sea ice is a much more variable property, depending upon the salt or brine content and the temperature. Changing the temperature of sea ice will generally involve either melting or freezing, and the amount of heat required will depend upon the salinity of the ice, as shown in the table. It should be noted that the specific heat of pure ice is less than half that of pure water. Near the initial freezing point, the extremely high specific heat of ice of high salinity is, of course, due to the formation of ice from the enclosed brine or its melting[1]

Salinity	Temperature (°C)										
°/oo	-2°	-4°	-6°	-8°	-10°	-12°	-14°	-16°	-18°	-20°	-22°
2	2.57	1.00	0.73	0.63	0.57	0.55	0.54	0.53	0.53	0.52	0.52
4	4.63	1.50	0.96	0.76	0.64	0.59	0.57	0.57	0.56	0.55	0.54
6	6.70	1.99	1.20	0.88	0.71	0.64	0.61	0.60	0.58	0.57	0.56
8	8.76	2.49	1.43	1.01	0.78	0.68	0.64	0.64	0.61	0.60	0.58
10	10.83	2.99	1.66	1.14	0.85	0.73	0.68	0.67	0.64	0.62	0.60
15	16.01	4.24	2.24	1.46	1.02	0.85	0.77	0.76	0.71	0.68	0.65

(From *Smithsonian Meteorological Tables,* Smithsonian Miscellaneous Collection, V.114, 6th ed., 1966.)

REFERENCE

1. **Sverdrup, H. U., Johnson, M. W., and Fleming, R. H.,** *The Oceans, Their Physics, Chemistry, and General Biology,* Prentice-Hall, Inc., Englewood Cliffs, N.J., © 1942, renewed 1970.

Table 1.5-12
LATENT HEAT OF MELTING OF SEA ICE

Let S be the salinity of the ice and t_8 the freezing point of a sea water with the salinity S. If the temperature t lies in the neighborhood of 0 °C, the heat of fusion of pure ice between t and t_8 can be considered constant and equal to 80 gram calories. The amount of heat required to melt the sea ice is then the sum of the heat required to melt all the pure ice in one gram of sea ice $(80[1-S(1-A_t)])$ and the amount of heat required to increase the temperature of the pure ice and brine from t to t_8 (approximately=0.5 (t_8-t), where A_t is the weight of all the pure ice in 1 gram of sea ice with salinity 1°/oo and temperature t and is equal to $1-1/S_t$ where S_t is the salinity of the brine at t. Thus

$$U = 80(1 - \frac{S}{S_t}) + 0.5(t_8 - t;)$$

where U = number of calories required to melt 1 g sea ice of the temperature t and the salinity S.

Temperature	Salinity (°/oo)						
	0	2	4	6	8	10	15
°C	cal	cal	cal	cal	cal	cal	cal
–1	80	72	63	55	46	37	16
–2	81	77	72	68	63	59	48

(From Malmgren, F., On the properties of sea ice, *The Norwegian North Polar Expedition with the Maud, 1918-1925,* Scientific Results, Vol. I, No. 5, 1927. With permission.)

Table 1.5-13
THERMAL CONDUCTIVITY OF WATER*

Temperature °C	Thermal conductivity cal cm^{-1} sec^{-1} °C^{-1}	Temperature °C	Thermal conductivity cal cm^{-1} sec^{-1} °C^{-1}
0	0.00132	60	0.00156
10	.00138	70	.00159
20	.00143	80	.00160
30	.00147	90	.00161
40	.00151	100	.00162
50	.00154		

*Compiled by Dorsey from the investigation of Schmidt and Sellschopp. All values are for a pressure of one atmosphere.

(From *Smithsonian Meteorological Tables,* Smithsonian Miscellaneous Collection. V. 114, 6th ed., 1966.)

REFERENCES

1. **Dorsey, N. E.,** *Properties of Ordinary Water Substance,* © 1940 by Litton Educational Publishings, Inc.
2. **Schmidt, E. and Sellschopp, W.,** *Forsch., Gebiete Ingenieurw.,* 3, 277, 1932.

Table 1.5-14
THERMAL CONDUCTIVITY OF SEA WATER AT 17.5°C AND ATMOSPHERIC PRESSURE

Thermal conductivity x1000	Salinity (°/₀₀)				
	0	10	20	30	40
(cal·cm^{-1}·sec^{-1}·°C^{-1})	1.400	1.367	1.353	1.346	1.337

(From Krümmel, Otto, *Handbuch der Ozeanographie: Vol. I, Die räumlich, chemischen und physikalischen Verhältnisse des Meeres,* J. Engelhornverlag GmbH, Stuttgart, 1907. With permission.)

Table 1.5-15
RELATIVE DENSITY AND VOLUME OF WATER*

Temp °C	Density	Volume	Temp °C	Density	Volume
-10	0.99815	1.00186	+35	0.99406	1.00598
-9	843	157	36	371	633
-8	869	131	37	336	669
-7	892	108	38	299	706
-6	912	088	39	262	743
-5	0.99930	1.00070	40	0.99224	1.00782
-4	945	055	41	186	821
-3	958	042	42	147	861
-2	970	031	43	107	901
-1	979	021	44	066	943
+0	0.99987	1.00013	45	0.99025	1.00985
1	993	007	46	0.98982	1.01028
2	997	003	47	940	072
3	999	001	48	896	116
4	1.00000	1.00000	49	852	162
5	0.99999	1.00001	50	0.98807	1.01207
6	997	003	51	762	254
7	993	007	52	715	301
8	988	012	53	669	349
9	981	019	54	621	398
10	0.99973	1.00027	55	0.98573	1.01448
11	963	037	60	324	705
12	952	048	65	059	979
13	940	060	70	0.97781	1.02270
14	927	073	75	489	576
15	0.99913	1.00087	80	0.97183	1.02899
16	897	103	85	0.96865	1.03237
17	880	120	90	534	590
18	862	138	95	192	959
19	843	157	100	0.95838	1.04343
20	0.99823	1.00177	110	0.9510	1.0515
21	802	198	120	0.9434	1.0601
22	780	221	130	0.9352	1.0693
23	756	244	140	0.9264	1.0794
24	732	268	150	0.9173	1.0902
25	0.99707	1.00294	160	0.9075	1.1019
26	681	320	170	0.8973	1.1145
27	654	347	180	0.8866	1.1279
28	626	375	190	0.8750	1.1429
29	597	405	200	0.8628	1.1590
30	0.99567	1.00435	210	0.850	1.177
31	537	466	220	0.837	1.195
32	505	497	230	0.823	1.215
33	473	530	240	0.809	1.236
34	440	563	250	0.794	1.259

* The mass of one cubic centimeter of water at 4°C is taken as unity. The values given are numerically equal to the absolute density in grams per milliliter.

(From *Handbook of Chemistry and Physics,* 39th ed., Hodgman, C. D., Ed., The Chemical Rubber Co., Cleveland, 1957, 1994. With permission.)

Table 1.5-16

ABSOLUTE DENSITY OF WATER*

Degrees	0	1	2	3	4	5	6	7	8	9
0	0.999841	847	854	860	866	872	878	884	889	895
1	900	905	909	914	918	923	927	930	934	938
2	941	944	947	950	953	955	958	960	962	964
3	965	967	968	969	970	971	972	972	973	973
4	973	973	973	972	972	972	970	969	968	966
5	965	963	961	959	957	955	952	950	947	944
6	941	938	935	931	927	924	920	916	911	907
7	902	898	893	888	883	877	872	866	861	855
8	849	843	837	830	824	817	810	803	796	789
9	781	774	766	758	751	742	734	726	717	709
10	700	691	682	673	664	654	645	635	625	615
11	605	595	585	574	564	553	542	531	520	509
12	498	486	475	463	451	439	427	415	402	390
13	377	364	352	339	326	312	299	285	272	258
14	244	230	216	202	188	173	159	144	129	114
15	099	084	069	054	038	023	007	*991	*975	*959
16	0.998943	926	910	893	877	860	843	826	809	792
17	774	757	739	722	704	686	668	650	632	613
18	595	576	558	539	520	501	482	463	444	424
19	405	385	365	345	325	305	285	265	244	224
20	203	183	162	141	120	099	078	056	035	013
21	0.997992	970	948	926	904	882	860	837	815	792
22	770	747	724	701	678	655	632	608	585	561
23	538	514	490	466	442	418	394	369	345	320
24	296	271	246	221	196	171	146	120	095	069
25	044	018	*992	*967	*941	*914	*888	*862	*836	*809
26	0.996783	756	729	703	676	649	621	594	567	540
27	512	485	457	429	401	373	345	317	289	261
28	232	204	175	147	118	089	060	031	002	*973
29	0.995944	914	885	855	826	796	766	736	706	676
30	646	616	586	555	525	494	464	433	402	371

* Density in grams per cubic centimeter, computed from the relative values by Thiesen, Scheel and Disselhorst (1900), and the absolute value at 3.98°C by the International Bureau of Weights and Measures (1910).

(From *Handbook of Chemistry and Physics,* 39th ed., Hodgman, C. D., Ed., The Chemical Rubber Co., Cleveland, 1957, 1993. With permission.)

Figure 1.5–1
SEA WATER DENSITY AT VARIOUS TEMPERATURES

The purpose of this graph is to provide the density of sea water at any temperature apt to be encountered when the density at the standard temperature of 59°F(15°C) is known. To convert a density at 59°F(15°C) to density at another temperature, enter the graph horizontally from the left with the known density and downward from the top or upward from the bottom with the desired temperature; the position of the point of intersection with respect to the curves gives the density at the desired temperature. Interpolate between curves when necessary. For example, by this method, water having a density of 1.0162 at 59°F is found to have a density of 1.0124 at 85°F. The densities are referred to the density of fresh water at 4°C(39.2°F) as unity. (From Surface Water Temperature and Density, *Shore and Beach,* 40, 42, 1972. Original source: National Ocean Survey, National Oceanic and Atmospheric Administration, Rockville, Maryland. With permission.)

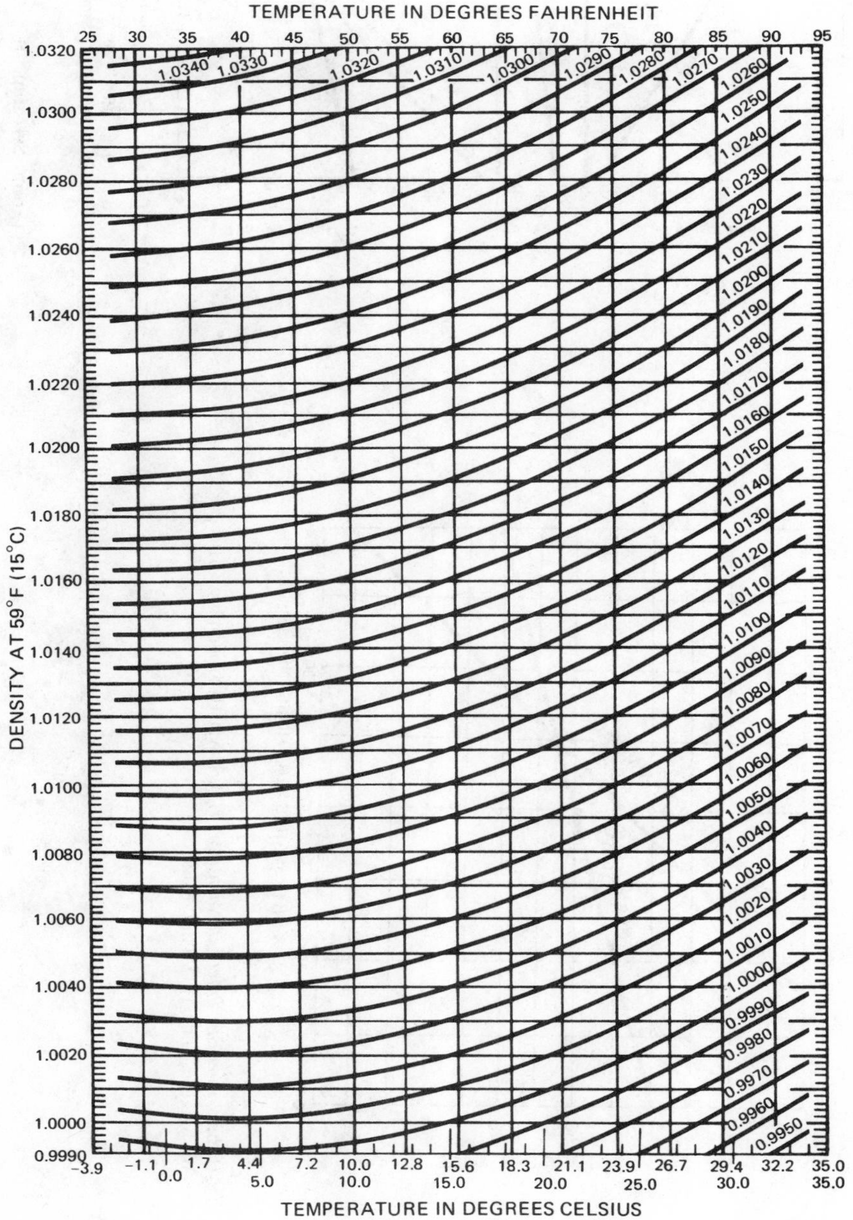

(From National Ocean Survey, National Oceanic and Atmospheric Administration, Rockville, Maryland. With permission.)

Figure 1.5-2
RELATIONSHIP BETWEEN TEMPERATURE OF MAXIMUM DENSITY AND FREEZING POINT FOR WATER OF VARYING SALINITY

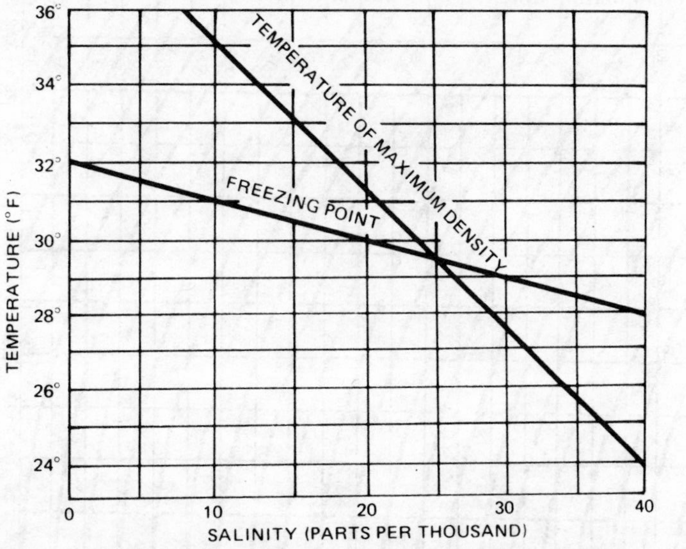

(From *American Practical Navigator,* U.S. Naval Hydrographic Office, Washington, D.C., H.O. Publ. No.9.)

Figure 1.5-3
COLLIGATIVE PROPERTIES OF SEA WATER

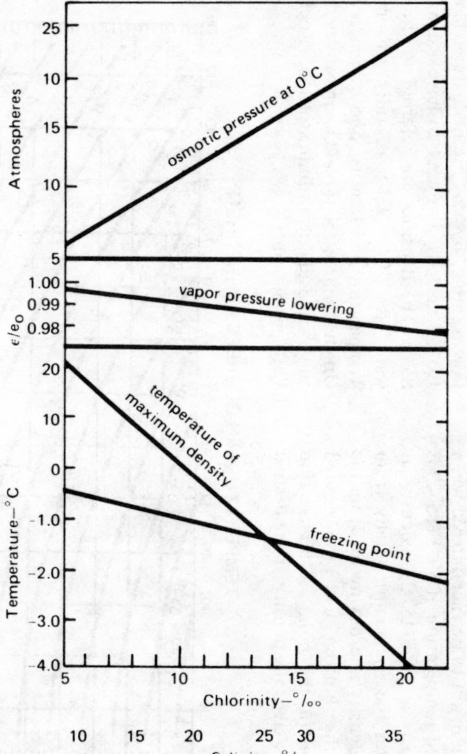

(From Sverdrup, H. U., Johnson, M. W., and Fleming, R. H., *The Oceans, Their Physics, Chemistry, and General Biology,* Prentice-Hall, Inc., Englewood Cliffs, N.J., © 1942, renewed 1970. With permission.)

Table 1.5-17
RATIO OF THE DRAFT OF ICE HAVING VERTICAL WALLS TO THE HEIGHT OF ICE ABOVE WATER

Density of ice	0.60	0.65	0.70	0.75	0.80	0.85	0.90	0.95
Density of water								
1.00	1.5	1.9	2.3	3.0	4.0	5.7	9.0	19.0
1.01	1.5	1.8	2.3	2.9	3.8	5.3	8.2	15.2
1.02	1.4	1.8	2.2	2.8	3.6	5.0	7.5	13.6
1.03	1.4	1.7	2.1	2.7	3.5	4.7	7.0	11.9

(From Zubov, N. N., *Oceanological Tables,* Hydrometerological Institute, Leningrad, USSR, 1957. With permission.)

Table 1.5-18
MEAN COMPRESSIBILITY OF SEA WATER OF SALINITY 34.85°/₀₀, (k x 10^8)

p (bars)	Temperature (°C) 0	5	10	15	20	25	30
0	4659	4531	4427	4345	4281	4233	4197
100	4582	4458	4357	4278			
200	4508	4388	4291				
400	4368	4256					
1000	4009	3916					

(From Sverdrup, H. U., Johnson, M. W., and Fleming, R. H., *The Oceans, Their Physics, Chemistry, and General Biology,* Prentice-Hall, Englewood Cliffs, N.J., ©1942, renewed 1970. With permission.)

Table 1.5-19
THE OSMOTIC PRESSURE OF SEA WATER (atm) CALCULATED FROM OTHER COLLIGATIVE PROPERTIES

	Robinson (1954)	Wilson and Arons (1955)			
Cl °/₀₀	25°C	25°C	15°C	5°C	0°C
5	–	5.7	6.2	5.8	5.4
10	12.87	11.5	11.4	11.8	10.9
15	19.55	18.0	17.5	17.5	16.4
17	22.28	20.7	20.1	19.9	18.6
19	25.06	23.3	22.6	22.2	20.8
21	27.89	26.1	25.2	24.7	23.0

REFERENCES

1. **Robinson, R. A.,** *J. Mar. Biol. Assoc. U.K.,* 33, 449, 1954.
2. **Wilson, K. G. and Arons, A. B.,** *J. Mar. Res.,* 14, 195, 1955. With permission.)

Table 1.5-20
RELATIVE VISCOSITY OF SEA WATER
At 1 atm[a]

Temp °C	5°/₀₀	10°/₀₀	20°/₀₀	30°/₀₀	40°/₀₀
0	1.009	1.017	1.032	1.056	1.054
5	0.855	0.863	0.877	0.891	0.905
10	0.738	0.745	0.785	0.772	0.785
15	0.643	0.649	0.662	0.675	0.688
20	0.568	0.574	0.586	0.599	0.611
25	0.504	0.510	0.521	0.533	0.545
30	0.454	0.460	0.470	0.481	0.491

[a] $\eta/\eta o$, where ηo is the viscosity of pure water at 0°C (1.787 centipoise).

(From Dorsey, N. E., *Properties of Ordinary Water Substance,* © 1940 by Litton Educational Publishing, Inc. With permission of Van Nostrand Reinhold Co.)

Table 1.5-21
RELATIVE VISCOSITY OF 19.374°/₀₀ CHLORINITY IAPO STANDARD SEA WATER FOR VARIOUS TEMPERATURES AND PRESSURES

Pressure, kg/cm²	η_ρ/η_1 at -0.024°C	η_ρ/η_1 at 2.219°C	η_ρ/η_1 at 6.003°C	η_ρ/η_1 at 10.013°C	η_ρ/η_1 at 15.018°C	η_ρ/η_1 at 20.013°C	η_ρ/η_1 at 29.953°C
176	0.9828	0.9849	0.9891	0.9908	0.9961	0.9972	1.0010
	0.9828	0.9855	0.9890	0.9929	0.9946	0.9985	0.9983
				0.9911	0.9941	0.9976	0.9999
352	0.9707	0.9742	0.9810	0.9881	0.9924	0.9961	1.0017
	0.9711	0.9747	0.9818	0.9872	0.9917	0.9984	0.9995
		0.9737			0.9938	0.9973	0.9992
527	0.9623	0.9667	0.9762	0.9843	0.9900	0.9969	1.0037
	0.9616	0.9674	0.9770	0.9843	0.9875	0.9992	1.0023
					0.9923	0.9973	1.0033
703	0.9559	0.9622	0.9729	0.9817	0.9916	1.0013	1.0072
	0.9562	0.9629	0.9740	0.9825	0.9909	0.9994	1.0069
					0.9919	0.9987	1.0073
878	0.9528	0.9594	0.9730	0.9834	0.9937	1.0044	1.0143
	0.9538	0.9603	0.9736	0.9837	0.9928	1.0043	1.0114
					0.9933	1.0015	1.0142
1055	0.9519	0.9592	0.9754	0.9875	0.9969	1.0077	1.0174
	0.9536	0.9606	0.9744	0.9872	0.9961	1.0076	1.0183
					0.9964	1.0056	1.0179
1230	0.9527	0.9631	0.9781	0.9904	1.0025	1.0116	1.0253
	0.9540	0.9643	0.9752	0.9899	1.0009	1.0099	1.0235
					1.0009	1.0106	
1406	0.9553	0.9670	0.9825	0.9956	1.0099	1.0177	1.0323
	0.9565	0.9676	0.9817	0.9965	1.0058	1.0168	1.0303
					1.0064	1.0154	

(From Stanley, E. M. and Batten, R. C., Viscosity of sea water at moderate temperatures and pressures, *J. Geophys. Res.*, 74, 3415, 1969. With permission of American Geophysical Union.)

Figure 1.5–4
PRESSURE OF MINIMUM RELATIVE VISCOSITY P_m, FOR STANDARD SEA WATER AND PURE WATER AS A FUNCTION OF TEMPERATURE

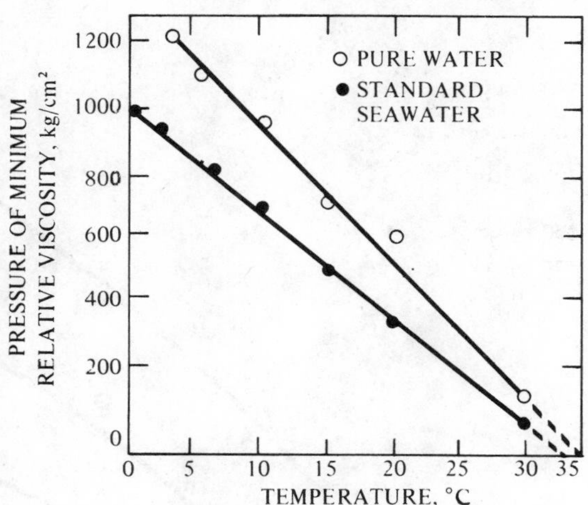

Note: Dashed lines indicate extrapolated values.

(From Stanley, E. M. and Batten, R. C., Viscosity of sea water at moderate temperatures and pressures, *J. Geophys. Res.*, 74, 3415, 1969. With permission of American Geophysical Union.)

Figure 1.5–5
DIFFERENTIAL RELATIVE VISCOSITY AS A FUNCTION OF TEMPERATURE

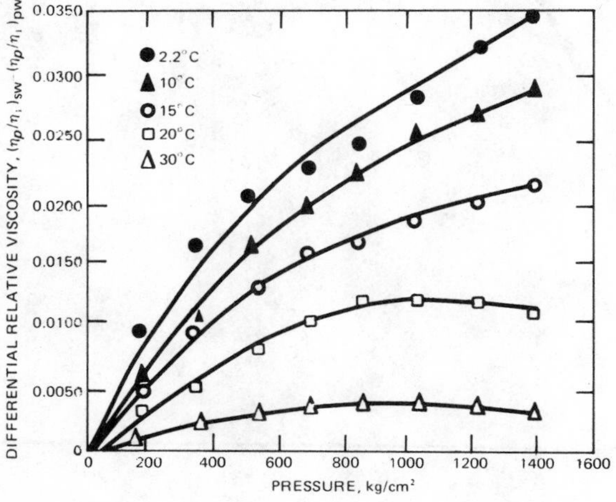

(From Stanley, E. M. and Batten, R. C., Viscosity of sea water at moderate temperatures and pressures, *J. Geophys. Res.*, 74, 3415, 1969. With permission of American Geophysical Union.)

Figure 1.5–6

ISOBARS OF RELATIVE VISCOSITY OF STANDARD SEA WATER AS A FUNCTION OF TEMPERATURE

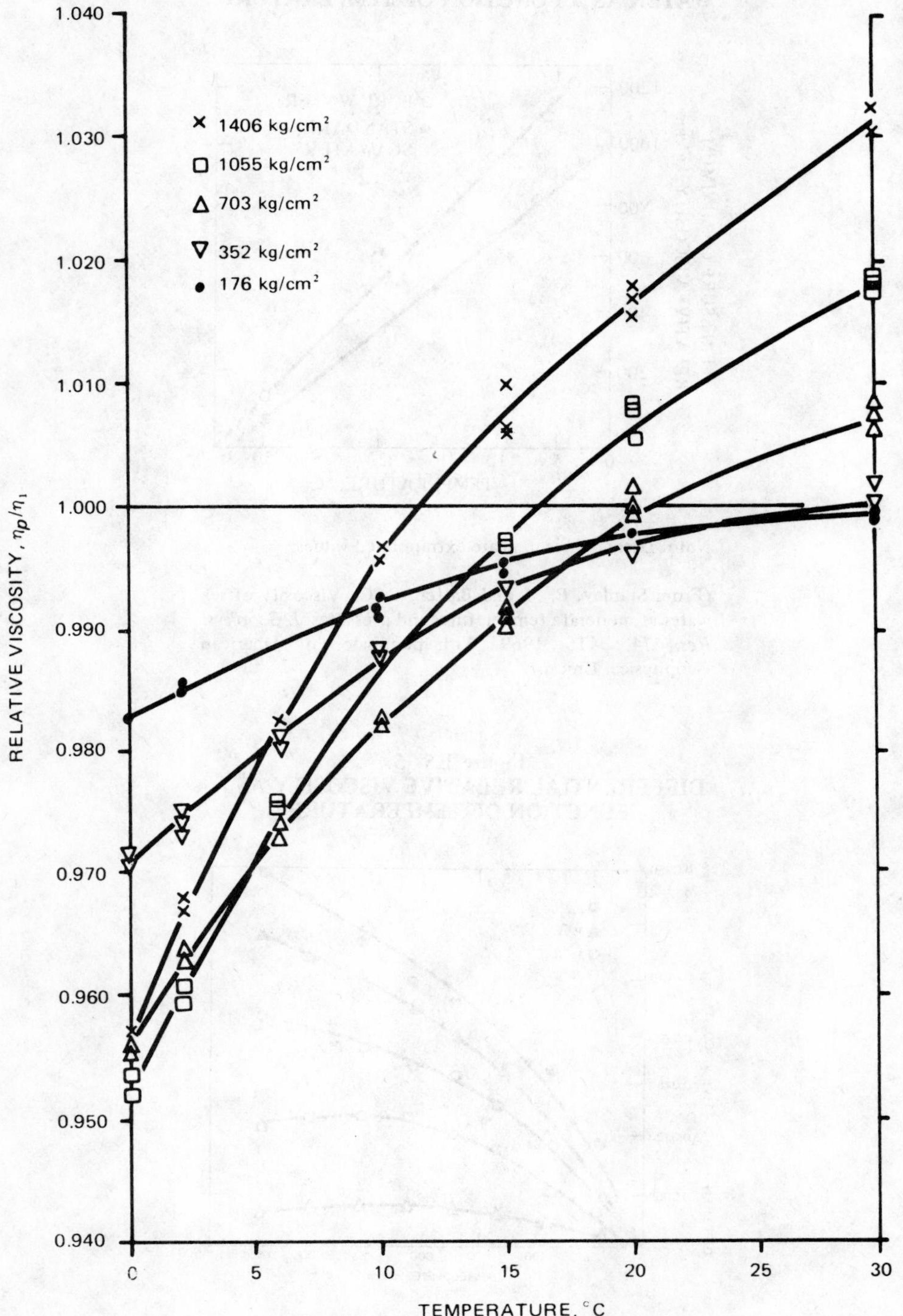

(From Stanley, E. M. and Batten, R. C., Viscosity of sea water at moderate temperatures and pressures, *J. Geophys. Res.*, 74, 3415, 1969. With permission of American Geophysical Union.)

Table 1.5-22

REFRACTIVE INDEX OF SEA WATER*

S°/oo	Temperature (°C) 0	5	10	15	20	25
0	1.3 3395	1.3 3385	1.3 3370	1.3 3340	1.3 3300	1.3 3250
5	3500	3485	3465	3435	3395	3345
10	3600	3585	3565	3530	3485	3435
15	3700	3685	3660	3625	3580	3525
20	3795	3780	3750	3715	3670	3620
25	3895	3875	3845	3805	3760	3710
30	3991	3966	3935	3898	3851	3798
31	4011	3985	3954	3916	3869	3816
32	4030	4004	3973	3934	3886	3834
33	4049	4023	3992	3953	3904	3851
34	4068	4042	4011	3971	3922	3868
35	4088	4061	4030	3990	3940	3886
36	4107	4080	4049	4008	3958	3904
37	4127	4099	4068	4026	3976	3922
38	4146	4118	4086	4044	3994	3940
39	4166	4139	4105	4062	4012	3958
40	(4185)	(4157)	(4124)	(4080)	(4031)	(3976)
41	(4204)	(4176)	(4143)	(4098)	(4049)	(3944)

*For sodium D light.

(From Utterback, C. L., Thompson, T. G., and Thomas, B. D., Refractivity-chlorinity-temperature relationships of ocean waters, *J. Cons. Cons. Perm. Int. Explor. Mer.*, 9, 35, 1934. With permission.)

Table 1.5-23

SPECIFIC CONDUCTIVITY OF SEA WATER*

S°/oo	Temperature (°C) 30	25	20	15	10	5	0
10	(19.127)	17.345	15.628	13.967	12.361	10.816	9.341
20	(35.458)	32.188	29.027	25.967	23.010	20.166	17.456
30	(50.856)	46.213	41.713	37.351	33.137	29.090	25.238
31	(52.360)	47.584	42.954	38.467	34.131	29.968	26.005
32	(53.859)	48.951	44.192	39.579	35.122	30.843	26.771
33	(55.352)	50.314	45.426	40.688	36.110	31.716	27.535
34	(56.840)	51.671	46.656	41.794	37.096	32.588	28.298
35	(58.323)	53.025	47.882	42.896	38.080	33.457	29.060
36	(59.801)	54.374	(49.105)	(43.996)	(39.061)	(34.325)	(29.820)
37	(61.274)	55.719	(50.325)	(45.093)	(40.039)	(35.190)	(30.579)
38	(62.743)	57.061	(51.541)	(46.187)	(41.016)	(36.055)	(31.337)
39	(64.207)	58.398	(52.754)	(47.278)	(41.990)	(36.917)	(32.094)
40	(65.667)	(59.732)	(53.963)	(48.367)	(42.962)	(37.778)	(32.851)

* Conductivity in mmol/cm. Values are calculated from an equation presented by Weyl based on the conductivity data of Thomas, Thompson, and Utterback.

(From Cox, R. A., The physical properties of sea water, in *Chemical Oceanography,* Vol. 1, Riley, J. P. and Skirrow, G., Eds., Academic Press, London, 1965. With permission.)

Table 1.5-23 (continued)

REFERENCES

1. **Weyl, P. K.,** On the change in electrical conductance of seawater with temperature, *Limnol. Oceanogr.*, 9, 75, 1964.
2. **Thomas, B. D., Thompson, T. G., and Utterback, C. L.,** The electrical conductivity of seawater, *J. Cons. Cons. Perm. Int. Explor. Mer.*, 9, 28, 1934.

Table 1.5-24
RELATIVE CONDUCTIVITY OF SEA WATER AT 15° AND 20°C

S %	R_{15}	R_{20}
31	0.89704	0.89732
32	0.92296	0.92327
33	0.94876	0.94890
34	0.97443	0.97450
35	1.00000	1.00000
36	1.02545	1.02537
37	1.05078	1.05062
38	1.07600	1.07577
39	1.10112	1.10080
40	1.12613	1.12572

(From *International Oceanographic Tables,* Vol. 1, National Institute of Oceanography of Great Britain, Wormley, England, and UNESCO, Paris, France, ©1966, reprinted 1971. With permission.)

Table 1.5-25
EFFECT OF TEMPERATURE ON CONDUCTIVITY RATIO EXPRESSED AS CONDUCTIVITY RATIO ANOMALY Δ_t

$R_{15} = R_t + \Delta_t$

R_t	10°	15°	20°	25°
0.875	36	0	−32	−59
0.900	30	0	−26	−49
0.925	23	0	−20	−38
0.950	16	0	−14	−26
0.975	8	0	−7	−13
1.000	0	0	0	0
1.025	−8	0	7	14
1.050	−17	0	15	28
1.075	−27	0	23	43
1.100	−37	0	32	59
1.125	−47	0	41	75

(Values of Δ_t were taken from *International Oceanographic Tables,* Vol. 1, National Institute of Oceanography of Great Britian, Wormley, England and UNESCO, Paris, France, © 1966, reprinted 1971. With permission.)

Table 1.5-26
EFFECT OF PRESSURE ON THE CONDUCTIVITY OF SEA WATER*

		S°/oo				S°/oo		
	Pressure (db)	31	35	39		31	35	39
	1000	1.599	1.556	1.512		1.032	1.008	0.985
	2000	3.089	3.006	2.922		1.996	1.951	1.906
	3000	4.475	4.354	4.233		2.895	2.830	2.764
	4000	5.759	5.603	5.448		3.731	3.646	3.562
0°C	5000	6.944	6.757	6.569	15°C	4.506	4.403	4.301
	6000	8.034	7.817	7.599		5.221	5.102	4.984
	7000	9.031	8.787	8.543		5.879	5.745	5.612
	8000	9.939	9.670	9.401		6.481	6.334	6.187
	9000	10.761	10.469	10.178		7.031	6.871	6.711
	10000	11.499	11.188	10.877		7.529	7.358	7.187
	1000	1.368	1.333	1.298		0.907	0.888	0.868
	2000	2.646	2.578	2.510		1.755	1.718	1.680
	3000	3.835	3.737	3.639		2.546	2.492	2.438
	4000	4.939	4.813	4.686		3.282	3.212	3.142
5°C	5000	5.960	5.807	5.655	20°C	3.964	3.879	3.795
	6000	6.901	6.724	6.547		4.594	4.496	4.399
	7000	7.764	7.565	7.366		5.174	5.064	4.954
	8000	8.552	8.333	8.114		5.706	5.585	5.464
	9000	9.269	9.031	8.794		6.192	6.060	5.929
	10000	9.915	9.661	9.408		6.633	6.492	6.351
	1000	1.183	1.154	1.125		0.799	0.783	0.767
	2000	2.287	2.232	2.177		1.547	1.516	1.485
	3000	3.317	3.237	3.157		2.245	2.200	2.156
	4000	4.273	4.170	4.067		2.895	2.837	2.780
10°C	5000	5.159	5.034	4.910	25°C	3.498	3.429	3.359
	6000	5.976	5.832	5.688		4.056	3.976	3.896
	7000	6.728	6.565	6.402		4.571	4.481	4.390
	8000	7.415	7.236	7.057		5.045	4.945	4.845
	9000	8.041	7.847	7.652		5.478	5.369	5.261
	10000	8.608	8.400	8.192		5.872	5.756	5.640

*Percentage increase compared with the conductivity at one atmosphere.

(From Bradshaw, A. and Schleicher, K. E., The effect of pressure on the electrical conductance of seawater, *Deep-Sea Res.*, 12, 151, 1965. With permission.)

Table 1.5–27
PARTIAL EQUIVALENT CONDUCTANCE OF ELECTROLYTES IN SEA WATER (Ω^{-1} cm^2 cq^{-1}) at 35°/oo and 23°C

Electrolyte	$\bar{\lambda}_i$ Revised values	$\bar{\lambda}_i$ Equation 5	$\bar{\lambda}_i$* Park (1964)[a]
NaCl	76.9	76.8	90
KCl	99.0	99.2	116
KBr	102.8		120
½$MgCl_2$	60.9	61.5	72
½$CaCl_2$	66.6	66.6	78
½$SrCl_2$	68.1		80
½Na_2SO_4	44.9	45.1	52
½K_2SO_4	67.0	67.0	78
½$MgSO_4$	29.1	29.2	34
$NaHCO_3$	39.8	40.4	47
$KHCO_3$	61.8	62.3	73
½Na_2CO_3	20.7		23
½K_2CO_3	42.0		49
KH_2PO_4	48.5		57
HCl	268		310

[a] Park used his partial equivalent conductance data to determine the specific conductance of sea water at 35·00°/oo and 23°C. The equation he used,

$$1000\,K = \sum_i c_i \bar{\lambda} i^*$$

where c_i is equivalents/l, can be rewritten with c_i in equivalents/g and the 0·855 correction multiplied out of the $\bar{\lambda} i^*$'s as:

$$0.855\,\nu K = \sum_i c_i \bar{\lambda} i^*.$$

(From Connors, D. N. and Park, K., The partial equivalent conductances of electrolytes in seawater: a revision, *Deep-Sea Res.*, 14, 481, 1967. With permission.)

Table 1.5–28
DIFFUSION COEFFICIENTS OF SOME SEA WATER ELECTROLYTES AT 25°C

Concentration, *M*	NaCl	KCl	CsCl	$CaCl_2$	$SrCl_2$	Na_2SO_4	$MgSO_4$
				cm²/sec x 10⁵			
0.005	1.560	1.934	1.978	1.179	1.219	1.123	0.710
0.01	1.545	1.917	1.958	–	–	–	–
0.05	1.507	1.864	–	1.121	–	–	–
0.10	1.483	1.844	1.871	1.110	–	–	–
0.50	1.474	1.850	1.860	1.140	–	–	–
1.00	1.484	1.892	1.902	1.203	–	–	–
1.50	1.495	1.943	–	1.263	–	–	–

(From Horne, R. A., *Marine Chemistry*, Wiley-Interscience, New York, 1969.)

REFERENCE

1. **Robinson, R. A. and Stokes, R. H.,** *Electrolyte Solutions,* Butterworths, London, 1969.

Section 2

Physical Oceanography

Joseph Reid, Ph.D.

2.1 Topographic Data

Table 2.1–1
DEPTH DISTRIBUTION OF WORLD OCEAN

	Area				Cumulative area (Shallower than deeper limit of depth interval)		
	10^6 km²		Percent		10^6 km²	Percent	
Depth, km	**Menard and Smith**	**Kossinna**	**Menard and Smith**	**Kossinna**	**Menard and Smith**	**Menard and Smith**	**Kossinna**
0–0.2	27.123	27.491	7.49	7.6	27.123	7.49	7.6
0.2–1	16.012	15.437	4.42	4.3	43.135	11.91	11.9
1–2	15.844	15.184	4.38	4.2	58.978	16.29	16.1
2–3	30.762	24.347	8.50	6.8	89.740	24.79	22.9
3–4	75.824	70.800	20.94	19.6	165.565	45.73	42.5
4–5	114.725	119.092	31.69	33.0	280.289	77.42	75.5
5–6	76.753	84.317	21.20	23.3	357.042	98.62	98.8
6–7	4.461	3.919	1.23	1.1	361.503	99.85	99.9
7–8	0.380	0.328	0.10		361.883	99.96	
8–9	0.115	0.126	0.03		361.998	99.99	
9–10	0.032	0.018	0.01	0.1	362.031	100.00	100.0
10–11	0.002		0.00		362.033	100.00	

(From Menard, H. W. and Smith, S. M., Hypsometry of ocean basin provinces, *J. Geophys. Res.*, 71, 4305, 1966. With permission of American Geophysical Union.)

REFERENCE

Kossinna, E., Die Tiefen des Weltmeeres, *Inst. Meereskunde, Veroff., Georg.-naturwiss.*, 9, 70, 1921.

Table 2.1–2
AREA, VOLUME, AND MEAN DEPTH OF THE OCEANS

Oceans and adjacent seas	Area, 10^6 km^2	Volume, 10^6 km^3	Mean depth, m: Menard and Smith	Mean depth, m: Kossinna (our boundaries)
Pacific	166.241	696.189	4188	4282
Asiatic Mediterranean	9.082	11.366	1252	1182
Bering Sea	2.261	3.373	1492	1437
Sea of Okhotsk	1.392	1.354	973	838
Yellow and East China seas	1.202	0.327	272	188
Sea of Japan	1.013	1.690	1667	1350
Gulf of California	0.153	0.111	724	813
Pacific and adjacent seas, total	181.344	714.410	3940	4013
Atlantic	86.557	323.369	3736	3805
American Mediterranean	4.357	9.427	2164	2216
Mediterranean	2.510	3.771	1502	1487
Black Sea	0.508	0.605	1191	1115
Baltic Sea	0.382	0.038	101	55
Atlantic and adjacent seas, total	94.314	337.210	3575	3641
Indian	73.427	284.340	3872	3963
Red Sea	0.453	0.244	538	491
Persian Gulf	0.238	0.024	100	25
Indian and adjacent seas, total	74.118	284.608	3840	3929
Arctic	9.485	12.615	1330	1240
Arctic Mediterranean	2.772	1.087	392	277
Arctic and adjacent seas, total	12.257	13.702	1117	1020
Totals and mean depths	362.033	1349.929	3729	3814

(From Menard, H. W. and Smith, S. M., Hypsometry of ocean basin provinces, *J. Geophys. Res.*, 71, 4305, 1966. With permission of American Geophysical Union.)

REFERENCE

Kossinna, E., Die Tiefen des Weltmeeres, *Inst. Meereskunde, Veroff., Georg.-naturwiss.*, 9, 70, 1921.

Table 2.1–3
DEPTH ZONES IN THE OCEANS*

Table A

Ocean	Depth interval in kilometers												Total area
	0–0.2	0.2–1	1–2	2–3	3–4	4–5	5–6	6–7	7–8	8–9	9–10	10–11	(ocean)
Pacific Ocean	2.712	4.294	5.403	11.397	36.233	58.162	44.691	2.896	0.313	0.105	0.032	0.002	166.241
Asiatic Mediterranean	4.715	0.841	0.948	1.104	0.608	0.707	0.149	0.007	0.005	0	0	0	9.082
Bering Sea	1.050	0.135	0.172	0.234	0.670	0	0	0	0	0	0	0	2.261
Sea of Okhotsk	0.368	0.549	0.311	0.047	0.115	0	0	0	0	0	0	0	1.392
Yellow and East China seas	0.977	0.137	0.072	0.015	0.001	0	0	0	0	0	0	0	1.202
Sea of Japan	0.238	0.154	0.199	0.204	0.218	0	0	0	0	0	0	0	1.013
Gulf of California	0.071	0.032	0.040	0.010	0	0	0	0	0	0	0	0	0.153
Atlantic Ocean	6.080	4.474	3.718	7.436	16.729	28.090	19.324	0.639	0.058	0.010	0	0	86.557
American Mediterranean	1.021	0.465	0.589	0.667	0.906	0.586	0.112	0.008	0.002	0	0	0	4.357
Mediterranean	0.513	0.564	0.437	0.766	0.224	0.006	0	0	0	0	0	0	2.510
Black Sea	0.177	0.064	0.117	0.149	0	0	0	0	0	0	0	0	0.508
Baltic Sea	0.381	0.001	0	0	0	0	0	0	0	0	0	0	0.382
Indian Ocean	2.622	1.971	2.628	7.364	18.547	26.906	12.476	0.911	0.001	0	0	0	73.427
Red Sea	0.188	0.195	0.068	0.003	0	0	0	0	0	0	0	0	0.453
Persian Gulf	0.238	0	0	0	0	0	0	0	0	0	0	0	0.238
Arctic Ocean	3.858	1.569	0.968	1.249	1.573	0.269	0	0	0	0	0	0	9.485
Arctic Mediterranean	1.913	0.567	0.174	0.118	0	0	0	0	0	0	0	0	2.772
Total each depth	27.123	16.012	15.844	30.762	75.824	114.725	76.753	4.461	0.380	0.115	0.032	0.002	362.033

*Area in millions of square kilometers.

(From Menard, H. W. and Smith, S. M., Hypsometry of ocean basin provinces, *J. Geophys. Res.*, 71, 4305, 1966. With permission of American Geophysical Union.)

Table 2.1–3
DEPTH ZONES IN THE OCEANS*

Table B

Ocean	Depth interval in kilometers												Percent of world ocean in each ocean
	0–0.2	0.2–1	1–2	2–3	3–4	4–5	5–6	6–7	7–8	8–9	9–10	10–11	
Pacific Ocean	1.631	2.583	3.250	6.856	21.796	34.987	26.884	1.742	0.188	0.063	0.019	0.001	45.919
Asiatic Mediterranean	51.913	9.255	10.433	12.151	6.698	7.780	1.636	0.076	0.058	0	0	0	2.509
Bering Sea	46.443	5.975	7.623	10.330	29.629	0	0	0	0	0	0	0	0.625
Sea of Okhotsk	26.475	39.479	22.383	3.403	8.260	0	0	0	0	0	0	0	0.384
Yellow and East China seas	81.305	11.427	5.974	1.239	0.055	0	0	0	0	0	0	0	0.332
Sea of Japan	23.498	15.176	19.646	20.096	21.551	0.033	0	0	0	0	0	0	0.280
Gulf of California	46.705	20.848	25.891	6.556	0	0	0	0	0	0	0	0	0.042
Atlantic Ocean	7.025	5.169	4.295	8.590	19.327	32.452	22.326	0.738	0.067	0.012	0	0	23.909
American Mediterranean	23.443	10.674	13.518	15.313	20.796	13.440	2.572	0.193	0.051	0	0	0	1.203
Mediterranean	20.436	22.475	17.413	30.515	8.940	0.221	0	0	0	0	0	0	0.693
Black Sea	34.965	12.587	23.077	29.371	0	0	0	0	0	0	0	0	0.140
Baltic Sea	99.832	0.168	0	0	0	0	0	0	0	0	0	0	0.105
Indian Ocean	3.570	2.685	3.580	10.029	25.259	36.643	16.991	1.241	0.001	0	0	0	20.282
Red Sea	41.454	43.058	14.920	0.568	0	0	0	0	0	0	0	0	0.125
Persian Gulf	100.000	0	0	0	0	0	0	0	0	0	0	0	0.066
Arctic Ocean	40.673	16.539	10.209	13.167	16.580	2.834	0	0	0	0	0	0	2.620
Arctic Mediterranean	69.013	20.454	6.274	4.260	0	0	0	0	0	0	0	0	0.766
Percent of world ocean in each depth interval	7.492	4.423	4.376	8.497	20.944	31.689	21.201	1.232	0.105	0.032	0.009	0.001	

*Area in percent of each ocean.

(From Menard, H. W. and Smith, S. M., Hypsometry of ocean basin provinces, *J. Geophys. Res.*, 71, 4305, 1966. With permission of American Geophysical Union.)

HYPSOMETRY OF OCEAN BASIN PROVINCES

Physiographic provinces – These 'provinces' are regions or groups of features that have distinctive topography and usually characteristic structures and relations to other provinces. Province boundaries are based on detailed physiographic diagrams where available [Heezen and Tharp, 1961, 1964; Heezen et al., 1959; Menard, 1964] supplemented by more generalized physiographic and bathymetric charts. Provinces do not overlap nor are they superimposed in this study. Thus the area of a volcano rising from an ocean basin is included only in province VOLCANO and excluded from province OCEAN BASIN. The provinces identified in this study, the capitalized province names used in the text, the abbreviations used in data processing, and the corresponding numbers appearing in illustrations are

1. Continental SHELF AND SLOPE (CONS), the whole region from the shoreline to the base of the steep continental slope. Shelf and slope are grouped because they are merely the top and front of the margins of continental blocks.
2. CONTINENTAL RISE and partially filled sedimentary basins (CNRI). Gently sloping or almost flat, they appear to have characteristic features resulting from the accumulation of a thick fill of sediment eroded from an adjacent continent and overlying an otherwise relatively normal oceanic crust. In this respect, the Gulf of Mexico and the western basin of the Mediterranean differ from the continental rise off the eastern United States only because they are relatively enclosed.
3. OCEAN BASIN (OCBN), the remainder after removing all other provinces. Abyssal plains and abyssal hills and archipelagic aprons are common features of low relief.
4. Oceanic RISE AND RIDGE (RISE), commonly called "mid-ocean ridges" despite the fact that they continue across ocean margins. They form one worldwide system with many branches. Boundaries are taken in most places as outer limit of essentially continuous slopes from crest.
5. RIDGE NOT KNOWN TO BE VOLCANIC (RIDG), relatively long and narrow and with steep sides. Most have unknown structure and some or most may be volcanic.
6. Individual VOLCANO (VOLC), with a boundary defined as the base of steep side slopes.
7. Island ARC AND TRENCH (TNCH), includes whole system of low swells and swales subparallel to trenches. Continental equivalents or extensions of island arcs, such as Japan, are excluded.
8. Composite VOLCANIC RIDGE (VRCM), formed by overlapping volcanoes and with a boundary at the base of steep side slopes.
9. POORLY DEFINED ELEVATION (BLOB), with nondescript side slopes and length no more than about twice width. Crustal structure unknown; may be thin continental type.

Tabulation of data and measuring procedure – Data were tabulated by 10° squares of latitude and longitude. Squares containing more than one ocean were split, and each ocean was treated separately. Within a square, the areas between the depth intervals 0–200 m, 200–1,000 m, and between 1-km contours down to 11-km were compiled for each physiographic province.

The polar planimeters (Keuffel and Esser models 4236 and 4242) used for measuring areas were read to the nearest unit on the vernier scale, and measurements were tabulated directly for card punching. These values were converted to square kilometers during computer processing by a scale factor derived from a measurement of the total number of units in the square. The area of a square was calculated assuming a spherical earth with a radius of 6,371.22 km.

(From Menard, H. W. and Smith, S. M., Hypsometry of ocean basin provinces, *J. Geophys. Res.,* 71, 4305, 1966. With permission of American Geophysical Union.)

REFERENCES

Heezen, B. C. and Tharp, M., Physiographic diagram of the South Atlantic, Geological Society of America, N.Y., 1961.

Heezen, B. C. and Tharp, M., Physiographic diagram of the Indian Ocean, Geological Society of America, N.Y., 1964.

Heezen, B. C., Tharp, M., and Ewing, M., The floors of the oceans, 1, the North Atlantic, Geological Society of America, Special paper 65, 1959.

Menard, H. W., *Marine Geology of the Pacific,* McGraw-Hill, New York, 1964.

Table 2.1–4
PROVINCE AREAS IN EACH OCEAN AND TOTAL AREAS OF PROVINCES AND OCEANS (10^6 km^2)*

Oceans and adjacent seas	RISE	OCBN	VOLC	CONS	TNCH	CNRI	VRCM	RIDG	BLOB	Total are of each ocean
Pacific Ocean	65.109	77.951	2.127	11.299	4.757	2.690	1.589	0.494	0.227	166.241
Asiatic Mediterranean	0	0	0.003	7.824	0.023	1.233	0	0	0	9.082
Bering Sea	0	0	0	1.286	0.281	0.694	0	0	0	2.261
Sea of Okhotsk	0	0	0	1.254	0.023	0.115	0	0	0	1.392
Yellow and East China seas	0	0	0	1.119	0.082	0	0	0	0	1.202
Sea of Japan	0	0	0.005	0.798	0	0.210	0	0	0	1.013
Gulf of California	0.042	0	0	0.111	0	0	0	0	0	0.153
Atlantic Ocean	30.519	35.728	0.882	12.658	0.447	5.381	0	0.412	0.530	86.557
American Mediterranean	0	1.346	0.060	1.889	0.201	0.861	0	0	0	4.357
Mediterranean	0	0	0	1.465	0	1.046	0	0	0	2.510
Black Sea	0	0	0	0.263	0	0.245	0	0	0	0.508
Baltic Sea	0	0	0	0.382	0	0	0	0	0	0.382
Indian Ocean	22.426	36.426	0.358	6.097	0.256	4.212	0.407	2.567	0.679	73.427
Red Sea	0	0.070	0	0	0.383	0	0	0	0	0.453
Persian Gulf	0	0	0	0.238	0	0	0	0	0	0.238
Arctic Ocean	0.513	0	0	5.874	0	2.267	0.302	0	0.528	9.485
Arctic Mediterranean	0	0	0	2.483	0	0.289	0	0	0	2.772
Total area each province	118.607	151.522	3.435	55.421	6.070	19.242	2.298	3.473	1.965	362.033

* Abbreviations are defined in text preceding this table.

(From Menard, H. W. and Smith, S. M., Hypsometry of ocean basin provinces, *J. Geophys. Res.*, 71, 4305, 1966. With permission c American Geophysical Union.)

Table 2.1–5
PERCENT OF PROVINCES IN OCEANS AND ADJACENT SEAS*

Oceans and adjacent seas	RISE	OCBN	VOLC VRCM RIDG BLOB	CONS	TNCH	CNRI	Percent of world ocean in each ocean group
Pacific and adjacent seas	35.9	43.0	2.5	13.1	2.9	2.7	50.1
Atlantic and adjacent seas	32.3	39.3	2.0	17.7	0.7	8.0	26.0
Indian and adjacent seas	30.2	49.2	5.4	9.1	0.3	5.7	20.5
Arctic and adjacent seas	4.2	0	6.8	68.2	0	20.8	3.4
Percent of world ocean in each province	32.7	41.8	3.1	15.3	1.7	5.3	

* Abbreviations are defined in text preceding Table 2.1–4.

(From Menard, H. W. and Smith, S. M., Hypsometry of ocean basin provinces, *J. Geophys. Res.*, 71, 4305, 1966. With permission of American Geophysical Union.)

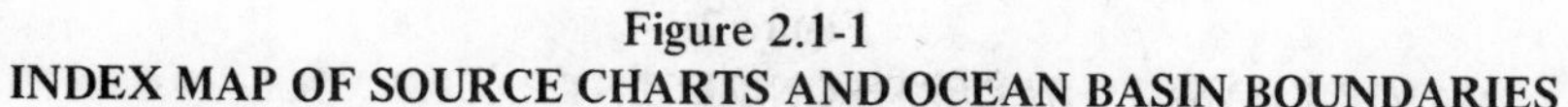

Figure 2.1-1
INDEX MAP OF SOURCE CHARTS AND OCEAN BASIN BOUNDARIES

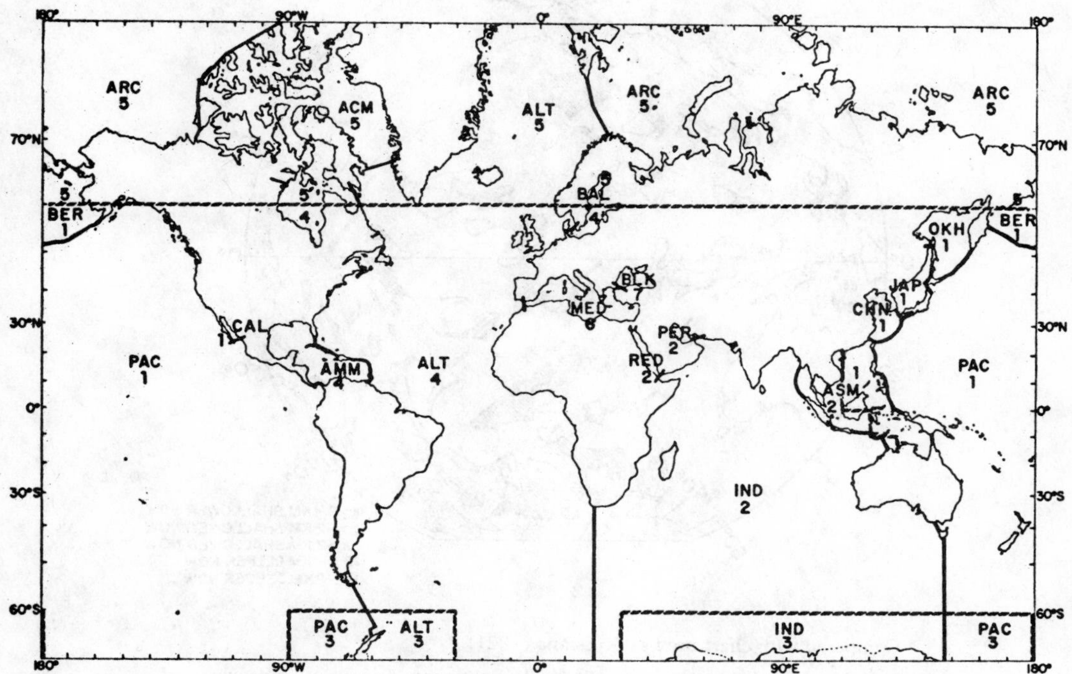

FIGURE 2.1–1. Source charts are bounded by dashed lines. Ocean abbreviations are explained in the text, and their boundaries (solid lines) are shown in more detail in Figures 2.1–4 to 2.1–7.

(From Menard, H. W. and Smith, S. M., Hypsometry of ocean basin provinces, *J. Geophys. Res.,* 71, 4305, 1966. With permission of American Geophysical Union.)

Figure 2.1-2
MAJOR CHANGES IN DEPTH ON RECENT PACIFIC OCEAN CHART*

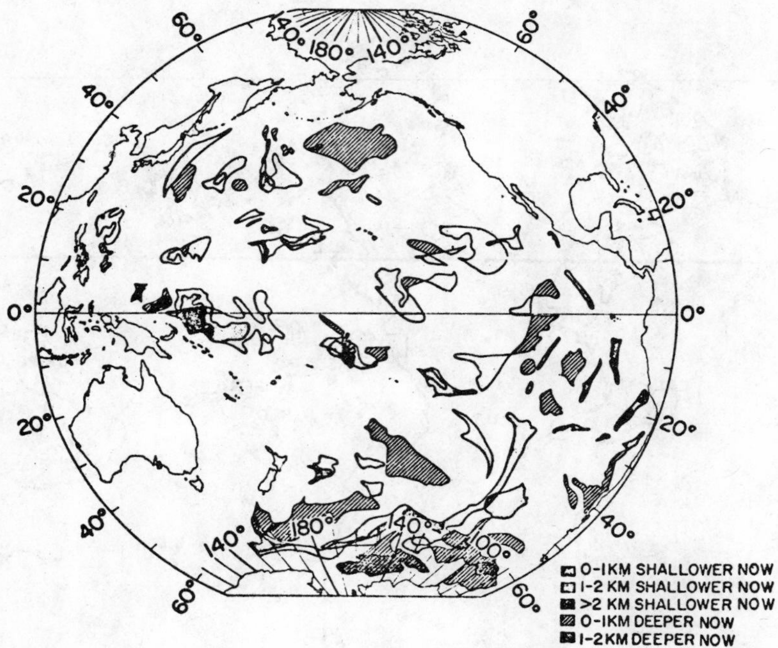

* Compared with chart used by Kossinna (1921).

(From Menard, H. W. and Smith, S. M., Hypsometry of ocean basin provinces, *J. Geophys. Res.*, 71, 4305, 1966. With permission of American Geophysical Union.)

REFERENCE

Kossinna, E., Die Tiefen des Weltmeeres, *Inst. Meereskunde, Veroff., Georg.-naturwiss.*, 9, 70, 1921.

Figure 2.1–3
MAJOR CHANGES IN DEPTH ON RECENT ATLANTIC AND INDIAN OCEAN CHARTS*

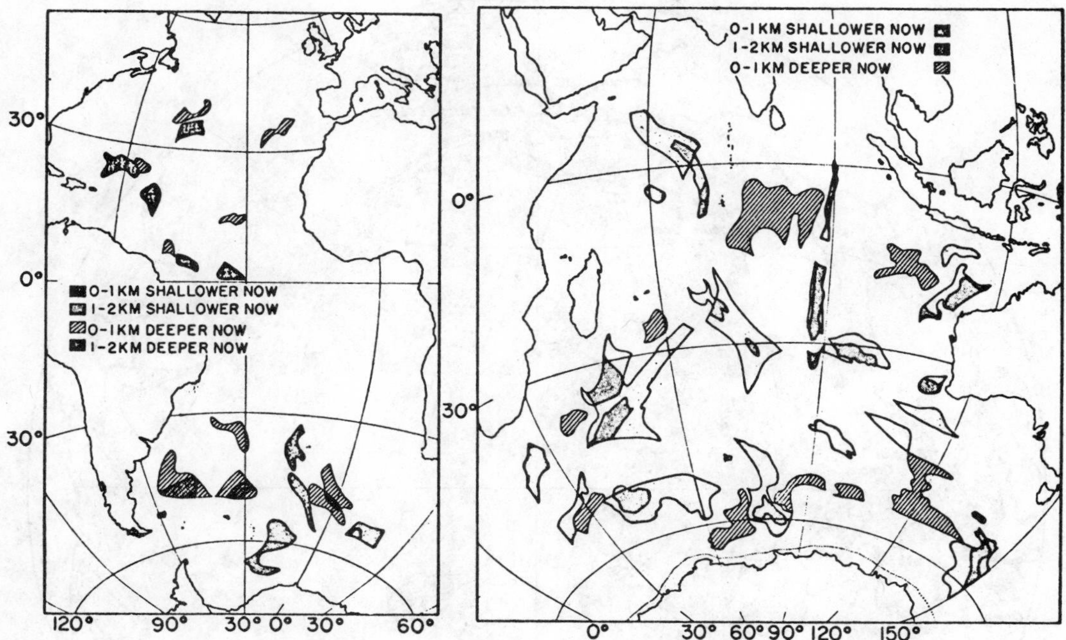

* Compared with charts used by Kossinna (1921).

(From Menard, H. W. and Smith, S. M., Hypsometry of ocean basin provinces, *J. Geophys. Res.*, 71, 4305, 1966. With permission of American Geophysical Union.)

REFERENCE

Kossinna, E., Die Tiefen des Weltmeeres, *Inst. Meereskunde, Veroff., Georg.-naturwiss.*, 9, 70, 1921.

Figure 2.1–4
PACIFIC OCEAN – PHYSIOGRAPHIC PROVINCES

FIGURE 2.1–4. Text contains key to province numbers. Individual volcanoes (VOLC) in black.

(From Menard, H. W. and Smith, S. M., Hypsometry of ocean basin provinces, *J. Geophys. Res.*, 71, 4305, 1966. With permission of American Geophysical Union.)

Figure 2.1–5
ATLANTIC OCEAN – PHYSIOGRAPHIC PROVINCES

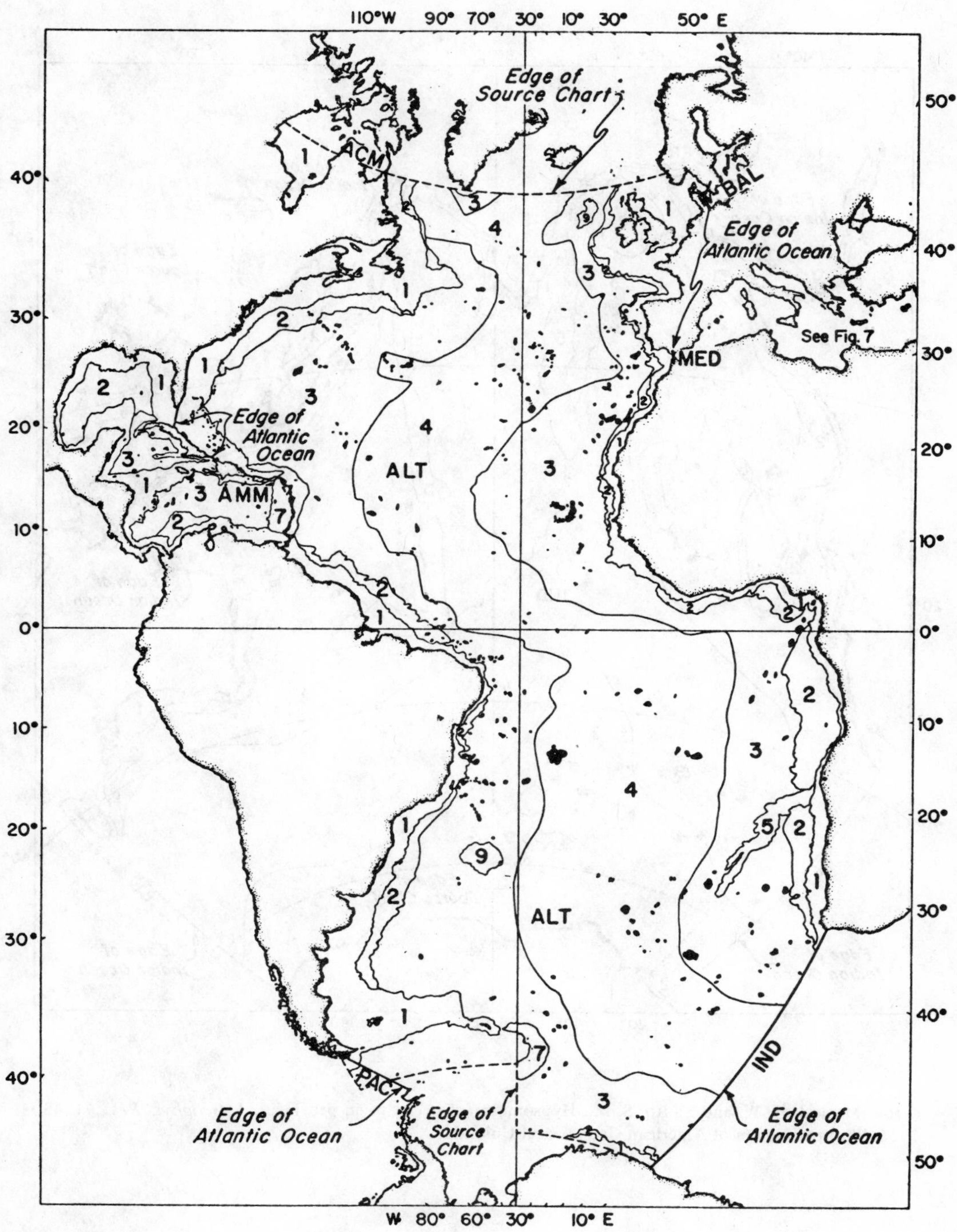

(From Menard, H. W. and Smith, S. M., Hypsometry of ocean basin provinces, *J. Geophys. Res.*, 71, 4305, 1966. With permission of American Geophysical Union.)

Figure 2.1–6
INDIAN OCEAN – PHYSIOGRAPHIC PROVINCES

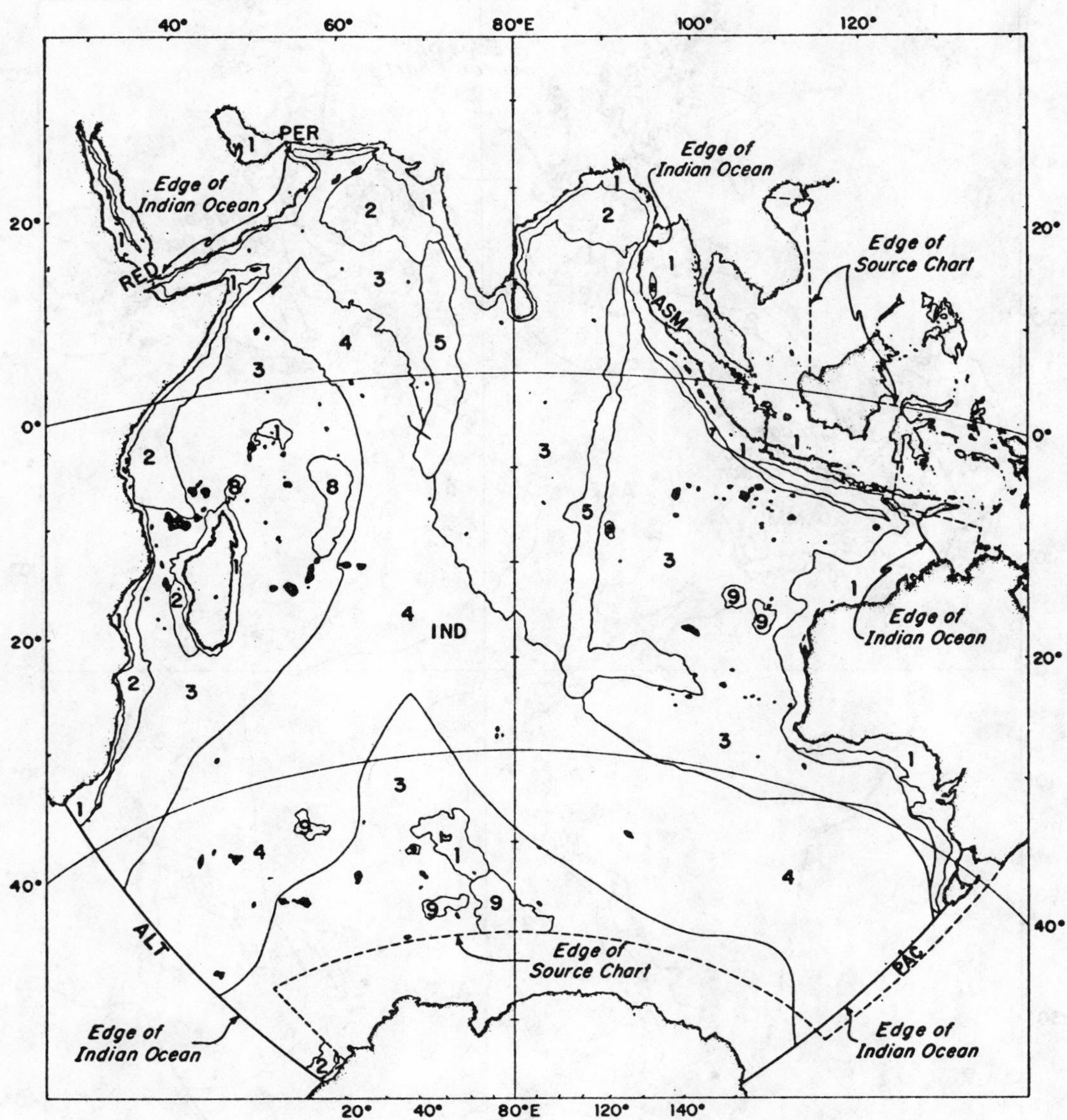

(From Menard, H. W. and Smith, S. M., Hypsometry of ocean basin provinces, *J. Geophys. Res.*, 71, 4305, 1966. With permission of American Geophysical Union.)

Figure 2.1–7
SMALLER OCEANS AND SEAS – PHYSIOGRAPHIC PROVINCES

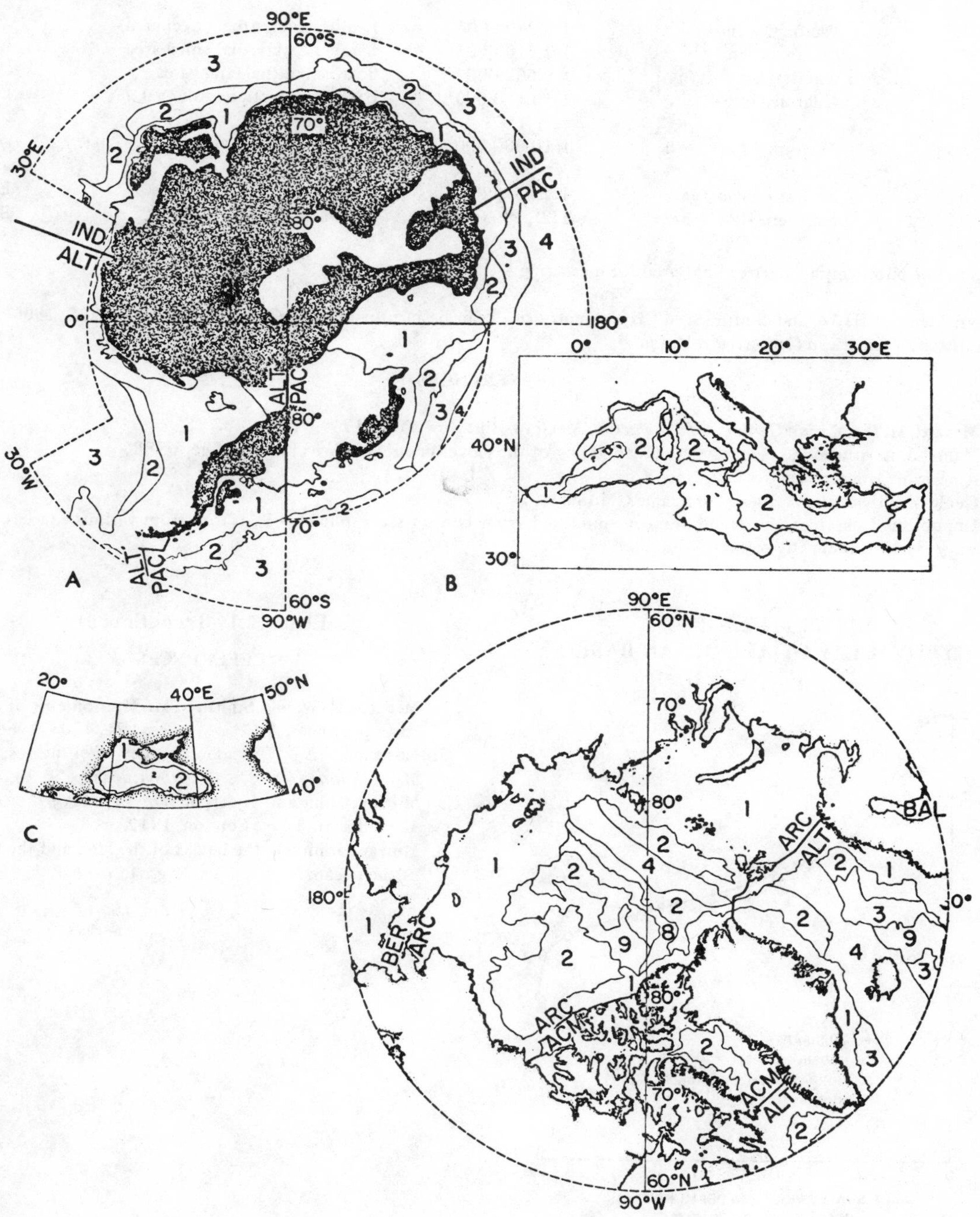

FIGURE 2.1–7. Antarctic sub-ice in white is below sea level.

(From Menard, H. W. and Smith, S. M., Hypsometry of ocean basin provinces, *J. Geophys. Res.*, 71, 4305, 1966. With permission of American Geophysical Union.)

Table 2.1–6
BATHYMETRIC CHARTS USED FOR HYPSOMETRIC CALCULATIONS

Source No.	Title	Scale	Projection	Reference
1	Pacific Ocean	1:7,270,000*	Lambert azimuthal equal-area	A
2	Indian Ocean	1:7,510,000*	Lambert azimuthal equal-area	B
3	Antarctica	1:9,667,000	Polar azimuthal equal-area	C
4	Atlantic Ocean	1:10,150,000*	Lateral projection with oval isoclines	B
5	Tectonic Chart of the Arctic	1:10,000,000	Polar azimuthal equal-area	D
6	Mediterranean Sea	1:2,259,000	Mercator	E
7	Northern Hemisphere	1:25,000,000	Polar azimuthal equal-area	B

* Scale of photographic enlargement used for measuring.

(From Menard, H. W. and Smith, S. M., Hypsometry of ocean basin provinces, *J. Geophys. Res.*, 71, 4305, 1966. With permission of American Geophysical Union.)

REFERENCES

A. **Menard, H. W.,** *Marine Geology of the Pacific,* McGraw-Hill, New York, 1964.
B. Main Administration in Geodesy and Cartography of the Government Geological Committee, USSR.
C. American Geographical Society, New York.
D. Geological Institute, Academy of Science, Moscow.
E. Unpublished chart of the Mediterranean, modified from contours compiled by R. Nason from various sources. U.S. Navy Hydrographic Office chart 4300 used as base.

Figure 2.1–8
HYPSOMETRY OF ALL OCEAN BASINS*

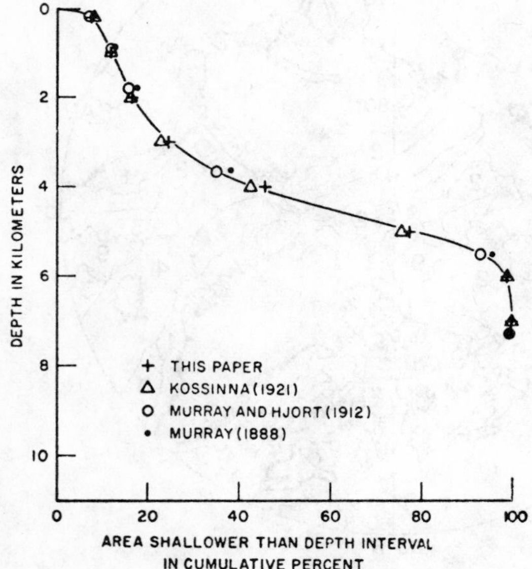

* According to various studies.

(From Menard, H. W. and Smith, S. M., Hypsometry of ocean basin provinces, *J. Geophys. Res.*, 71, 4305, 1966. With permission of American Geophysical Union.)

Figure 2.1–8 (continued)

REFERENCES

1. **Menard, H. W. and Smith, S. M.,** Hypsometry of ocean basin provinces, *J. Geophys. Res.*, 71, 4305, 1966.
2. **Kossinna, E.,** Die Tiefen des Weltmeeres, *Inst. Meereskunde, Veroff., Geogr.-naturwiss.*, 9, 70, 1921.
3. **Murray, John and Hjort, J.,** *The Depths of the Ocean,* Macmillan and Co., London, 1912.
4. **Murray, John,** On the height of the land and the depth of the ocean, *Scot. Geogr. Mag.*, 4, S. 1, 1888.

Figure 2.1–9
HYPSOMETRY OF INDIVIDUAL MAJOR OCEAN BASINS

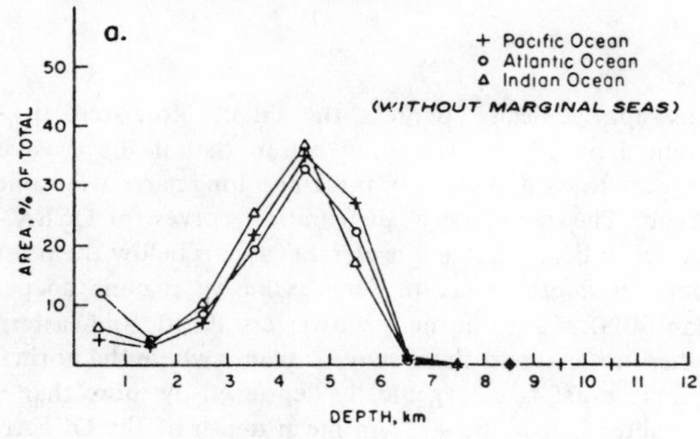

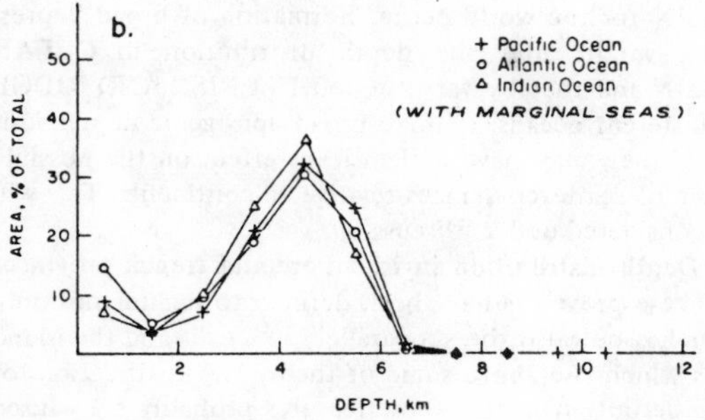

(From Menard, H. W. and Smith, S. M., Hypsometry of ocean basin provinces, *J. Geophys. Res.*, 71, 4305, 1966. With permission of American Geophysical Union.)

Figure 2.1–10
HYPSOMETRY OF ALL OCEAN BASINS*

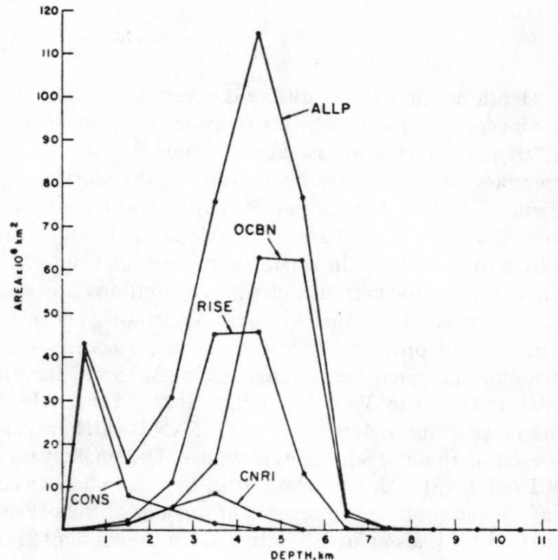

FIGURE 2.1–10. This diagram is for all provinces combined (ALLP) and for individual major provinces.

* Abbreviations are identified in the text preceding Table 2.1–4.

(From Menard, H. W. and Smith, S. M., Hypsometry of ocean basin provinces, *J. Geophys. Res.*, 71, 4305, 1966. With permission of American Geophysical Union.)

Figure 2.1–11
HYPSOMETRY OF OCEAN BASINS PLOTTED CUMULATIVELY BY PROVINCES*

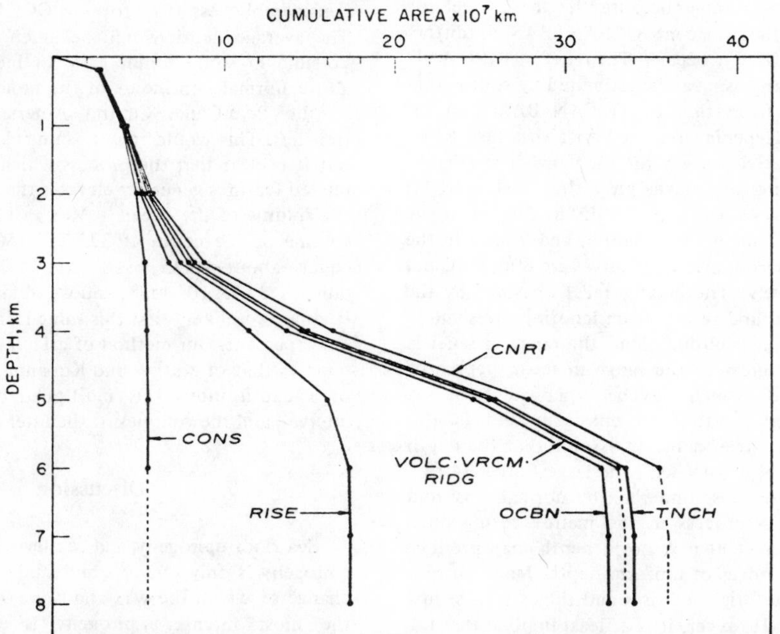

* Abbreviations are identified in the text preceding Table 2.1–4.

(From Meynard, H. W. and Smith, S. M., Hypsometry of ocean basin provinces, *J. Geophys. Res.*, 71, 4305, 1966. With permission of American Geophysical Union.)

HYPSOMETRY OF OCEAN BASIN PROVINCES (*Continued*)

Depth distribution in different oceans as a function of provinces – The depth distribution in provinces in different ocean basins, as seen in Figure 2.1–14, closely resembles the composite distribution in the world ocean (Figure 2.1–10). The sum of the depth distribution of all provinces in an ocean basin is double peaked, but for the individual provinces it is single peaked and relatively symmetrical. However, the depth distributions are sufficiently different to warrant some discussion. The mean depths of all provinces in the three major ocean basins, including marginal seas, range from 3575 m for the Atlantic Ocean to 3940 m for the Pacific (Table 2.1–7). The range of mean depths of the OCEAN BASIN province in each of these ocean basins is similar. The smallest mean OCEAN BASIN depth of 4530 m in the Indian Ocean may be the result of epirogenic movement of the oceanic crust, but it is also partially attributable to sedimentation. The eastern and southwestern parts of the Indian Ocean are deeper than 5000 m and are thus below the mean depth of the world ocean. The northwestern and southeastern parts, however, are exceptionally shallow. Seismic stations and topography show that the northwestern region has been shoaled by deposition of turbidites spreading from the mouths of the great Indian and east African rivers [Menard, 1961; Heezen and Tharp, 1964].

The mean depths of RISE AND RIDGE have a limited range – from 3945 m in the Indian Ocean to 4008 m in the Atlantic Ocean (Table 2.1–7). This uniformity seems remarkable considering the widespread and diverse evidence that oceanic rises and ridges are tectonically among the more unstable features of the surface of the earth. It is all the more remarkable because the local relief, or elevation above the adjacent OCEAN BASIN, differs substantially in different oceans. The relief of RISE AND RIDGE in an ocean basin can be estimated by subtracting the mean depth from that of OCEAN BASIN or by determining the deepening required to give a best fit of individual hypsometric curves for each province (Figure 2.1–15). Comparing the means gives the relief of RISE AND RIDGE ABOVE OCEAN BASIN as 585 m in the Indian Ocean, 662 m in the Atlantic, and 928 m in the Pacific. The reliefs from matching curves are 800, 900, and 1200 m, respectively. The greater relief obtained by the curve-matching method results from ignoring the shallow tails of the depth distribution. Thus the range in relief is about 6 times as great as the range in mean depths of RISE AND RIDGE, which may be explained if the sea floor is not only elevated by epirogeny but is also depressed. It seems reasonable to assume that the depth intervals in OCEAN BASIN with the largest areas (4 to 5 and 5 to 6 km) are those underlain by normal crust and mantle. A uniform process in the mantle acting on a uniform oceanic crust at a uniform depth may produce oceanic rises and ridges of uniform depth. Many current hypotheses for the origin of rises and ridges suggest just such an elevation. However, it is at least implicit that the mantle under the ocean basins cannot become denser and thus epirogenically depress the crust. Moreover, it is assumed by advocates of convection that if the crust is dragged down dynamically it forms a long narrow oceanic trench. The symmetrical distribution curves for OCEAN BASIN indicate that a considerable area is below the most common depth interval. Very extensive regions deeper than 6000 m exist in the northwestern Pacific and eastern Indian oceans, and there may be places where the normal oceanic crust is epirogenically depressed by more than a kilometer below the 4753-m mean depth of the OCEAN BASIN for the world ocean. Formation of broad depressions would alter the depth distribution in OCEAN BASIN and thereby vary the relief of RISE AND RIDGE in different oceans. If these broad epirogenic depressions exist, they may have a significant effect on the possible range of sea level changes relative to continents. This will be considered under 'Discussion.'

Depth distribution in island arc and trench provinces – These provinces have been defined to include not only trenches but also the subparallel low swells and the island arcs which rise above some of them. The justification for this definition is that these features probably are caused by the same process; one question that can be answered by this type of study is whether the process elevates or depresses the sea floor. The volcanoes, some capped with limestone, which form most islands in this province, have a rather minor volume and have hardly any effect on the hypsometry.

Figure 2.1–12 shows that the median depth for island ARC AND TRENCH is somewhat less than 4 km, which is less than the median depth for all ocean basins and considerably less than for the OCEAN BASIN province. The average depth would be much shallower if it were possible in some simple way to include the elevations above normal continents of the mountain ranges parallel to the Peru-Chile, Central America, Japan, and Java trenches. This would require some elaborate assumptions, but it is clear that the process which forms trenches and related features generally elevates the crust.

Volume of the ocean – Murray [1888] calculated the volume of the ocean at 323,722,150 cubic miles, which equals about 1.325×10^9 km^3. Kossinna [1921] obtained 1.370×10^9 km^3, and we obtain 1.350×10^9 km^3. It appears unlikely that this value is in error by more than a few percent. Our method of calculation is essentially the same as that of Murray and Kossinna. The midpoint value of a depth interval is multiplied by the area of that interval, and the volumes of the intervals are summed.

Discussion

Sea floor epirogeny and sea level changes – Sea floor epirogeny is only one of a multitude of causes of sea level change of which the wax and wane of glaciers is probably the most intense. Epirogeny is especially important because it may have occurred at any time in the history of the earth in contrast to relatively brief periods of glaciation. That eustatic changes in sea level have occurred during geological time is suggested by widespread epicontinental seas alternating with apparently high continents.

The hypothesis that oceanic rises are ephemeral [Menard, 1958] provides a basis for quantitative estimates of epirogenic effects on sea level. If the approximate volume of existing rises and ridges is compared with the area of the oceans, it appears that uplift of the existing rises has elevated the sea level 300 m. Likewise, subsidence of the ancient Darwin rise has lowered it by 100 m [Menard, 1964].

The present study suggests that the sea floor may be depressed epirogenically in places where this movement does not merely restore the equilibrium disturbed by a previous uplift. The argument derives from the fact that the mean depth in the OCEAN BASIN province is about 4700 m. Considering that the crust has about the same thickness everywhere in the province, variations from this depth generally are caused by differences in density in the upper mantle. (We assume that where the mean depth of the crust is "normal" it is underlain by a "normal" mantle.) Thus the deeper regions, which are roughly 70 million km^2 in area, have been depressed by a density increase in the mantle. If large areas of the sea floor can be depressed as well as elevated, the resulting changes in sea level would be highly complex.

Only the most general conclusions can be drawn from this analysis, but they may be significant. First, a plausible mechanism is available to explain the eustatic changes in sea level observed in the geological record. At present, the mechanism places no constraints on the sign of a change but appears to limit the amount to a few hundred meters. Second, in large regions the upper mantle may possibly become denser than normal. Substantial evidence exists that it is less dense than normal under rises and ridges [Le Pichon et al., 1965]. If it can also be more dense than normal in large regions, these facts can provide very useful clues regarding the composition of the upper mantle and processes acting below the crust. The implications of possible densification of normal mantle can be avoided by defining the 'normal' depth as the deepest that is at all widespread. If this definition is accepted as reasonable (it does not appear so to us), small decreases in density of the upper mantle occur under most of the world ocean. The volume of ocean basin elevated above normal is consequently large, and the possible range of sea level changes is thus at least 1 km.

Sea floor spreading and continental drift – Several aspects of our data appear to have some bearing on modern hypotheses of global tectonics. The relationships are not definitive, however, and at this time we prefer merely to indicate some of the questions which have arisen.

1. The proportion of RISE AND RIDGE to OCEAN BASIN in a basin could range from zero to infinity, but it is 0.84 for the Pacific, 0.82 for the Atlantic, and 0.61 for the Indian Ocean. The sample is very small, and consequently the similarity of the proportions may be coincidental. However, it suggests that the area of RISE AND RIDGE is proportional to the whole area of an ocean basin. This in turn suggests that the size of the basin is related to the existence of rises and ridges.

2. The proportion of SHELF AND SLOPE to OCEAN BASIN plus RISE AND RIDGE is relatively constant for large ocean basins and quite different from the proportion for small ocean basins. This relationship may require modification of at least many of the details of the hypothesis that the Atlantic Ocean basin was formed when an ancient continent split. When the supposed splitting began, the whole basin was SHELF AND SLOPE. Consequently, the proportion of SHELF AND SLOPE has since decreased. In the Pacific basin, on the other hand, the proportion of SHELF AND SLOPE to OCEAN BASIN plus RISE AND RIDGE was smaller than now and has since increased. If the Atlantic split apart at a constant rate and is still splitting as the Pacific contracts, the present equality of the proportions of SHELF AND SLOPE in the two ocean basins requires a striking coincidence. No coincidence is necessary if the splitting occurred relatively rapidly until it reached some dynamic equilibrium state, perhaps when the proportion of RISE AND RIDGE to OCEAN BASIN in each ocean basin reached about 0.8 to 0.9.

Acknowledgments – Some of these data were compiled by Isabel Taylor, Surendra Mathur, and Sarah Buffington. We wish especially to thank Mrs. Taylor for her careful rechecking of the measurements. We are indebted to Dr. G. B. Udintsev for providing Russian bathymetric charts from the first press runs.

This research was supported by Office of Naval Research Long Range Research Contract 2216(12) and National Science Foundation Grant NSF gp-4235.

REFERENCES

Heezen, B. C. and Tharp, M., Physiographic diagram of the Indian Ocean, Geological Society of America, N.Y., 1964.

Heezen, B. C., Tharp, M., and Ewing, M., The floors of the oceans, 1, the North Atlantic, Geological Society of America, Special paper 65, 1959.

Kossinna, E., Die Tiefen des Weltmeeres, *Inst. Meereskunde, Veroff., Georg.-naturwiss.*, 9, 70, 1921.

Le Pichon, X., Houtz, R. E., Drake, C. L., and Nafe, J. E., Crustal structure of the mid-ocean ridges, 1, Seismic refraction measurements, *J. Geophys. Res.*, 70(2), 319, 1965.

Menard, H. W., Development of median elevations in ocean basins, *Bull. Geol. Soc. Am.*, 69(9), 1179, 1958.

Menard, H. W., *Marine Geology of the Pacific*, McGraw-Hill, New York, 1964.

Menard, H. W., Some rates of regional erosion, *J. Geol.*, 69(2), 154, 1961.

Murray, John, On the height of the land and the depth of the ocean, *Scot. Geogr. Mag.*, 4, S. 1, 1888.

Figure 2.1–12
HYPSOMETRY OF ALL ARC AND TRENCH PROVINCES AND OF SOME GROUPS OF ARCS AND TRENCHES

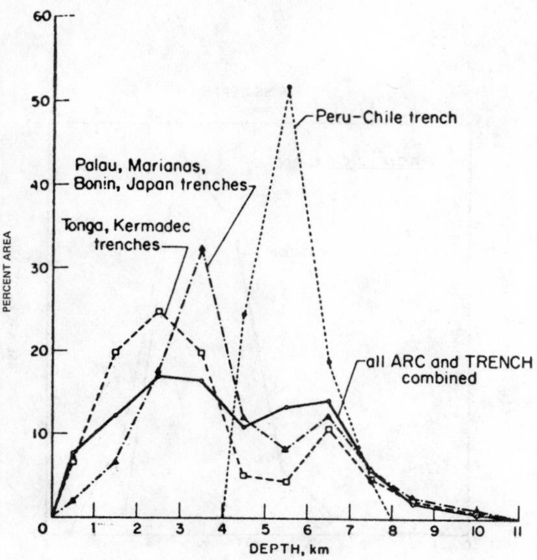

(From Menard, H. W. and Smith, S. M., Hypsometry of ocean basin provinces, *J. Geophys. Res.*, 71, 4305, 1966. With permission of American Geophysical Union.)

Figure 2.1–13
HYPSOMETRIC CURVE OF OCEAN BASINS

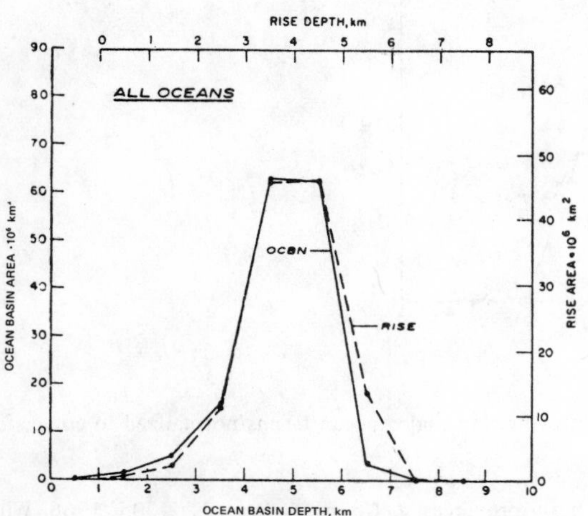

FIGURE 2.1–13. Hypsometric curve of all ocean basins for RISE AND RIDGE province normalized to curve for OCEAN BASIN province to show close similarity.

(From Menard, H. W. and Smith, S. M., Hypsometry of ocean basin provinces, *J. Geophys. Res.*, 71, 4305, 1966. With permission of American Geophysical Union.)

Figure 2.1–14
HYPSOMETRY OF ALL PROVINCES (ALLP) AND INDIVIDUAL PROVINCES IN MAJOR BASINS

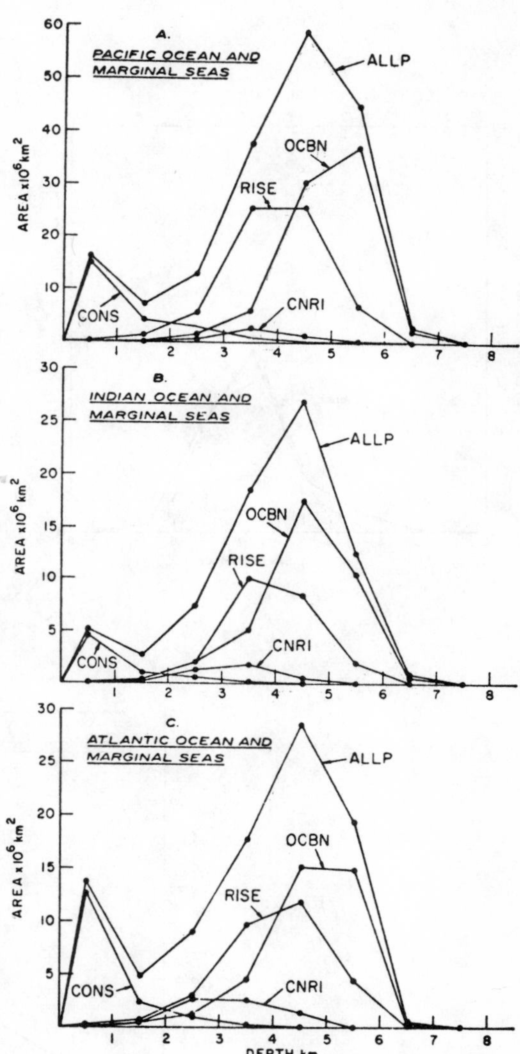

(From Menard, H. W. and Smith, S. M., Hypsometry of ocean basin provinces, *J. Geophys. Res.*, 71, 4305, 1966. With permission of American Geophysical Union.)

Figure 2.1–15

HYPSOMETRIC CURVES FOR RISE AND RIDGE PROVINCES

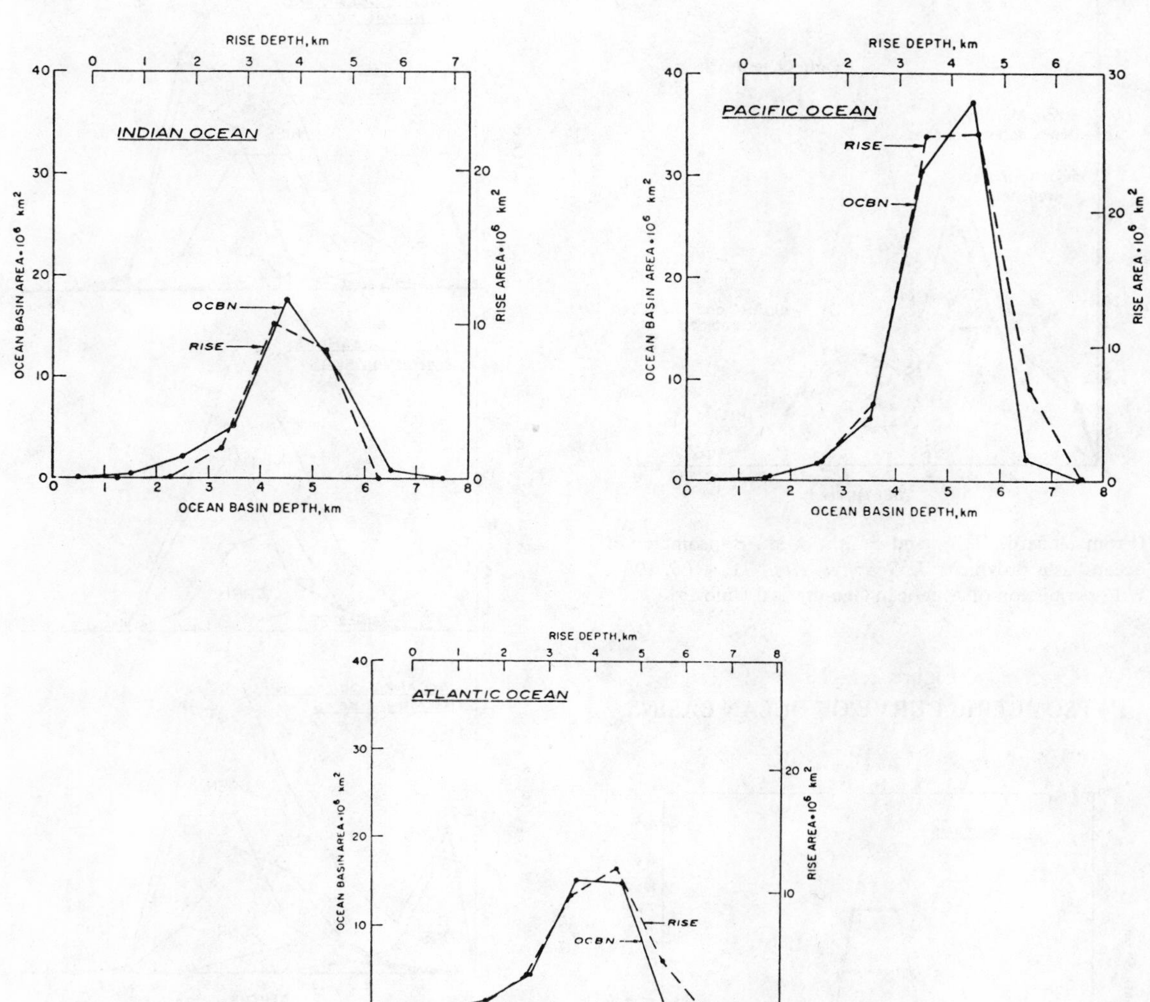

FIGURE 2.1–15. Hypsometric curves for RISE AND RIDGE provinces in major ocean basins normalized to curves for OCEAN BASIN provinces.

(From Menard, H. W. and Smith, S. M., Hypsometry of ocean basin provinces, *J. Geophys. Res.*, 71, 4305, 1966. With permission of American Geophysical Union.)

Table 2.1–7
CHARACTERISTICS OF OCEANIC RISES

	Mean depth, m			Relief, m	
	All provinces	OCBN (1)	RISE (2)	Mean (1) –Mean (2)	Shift of distribution curves*
World ocean	3729	4753	3970	783	1000
Pacific Ocean and marginal seas	3940	4896	3968	928	1100
Atlantic Ocean and marginal seas	3575	4670	4008	662	900
Indian Ocean and marginal seas	3840	4530	3945	585	800

* See text and Figure 2.1–13.

(From Menard, H. W. and Smith, S. M., Hypsometry of ocean basin provinces, *J. Geophys. Res.*, 71, 4305, 1966. With permission of American Geophysical Union.)

Table 2.1–8
MAJOR DEEPS AND THEIR LOCATION, SIZE, AND DEPTHS

Trench	Max depths, m	Ref.
Marianas Trench	11,034 ± 50	5
(specifically Challenger Deep)	10,915 ± 20[a]	
	10,915 ±	8
	10,863 ± 35	1
	10,850 ± 20[a]	
Tonga	10,882 ± 50	5
	10,800 ± 100	4
Kuril–Kamchatka	10,542 ± 100	13
	9,750 ± 100[b]	2
Philippine		
(vicinity of Cape Johnson Deep)	10,497 ± 100	6
	10,265 ± 45	16
	10,030 ± 10[a]	
Kermadec	10,047 ±	14
Idzu–Bonin		
(includes "Ramapo Deep" of the Japan Trench)	9,810	13
(vicinity of Ramapo Depth)	9,695	11
Puerto Rico	9,200 ± 20	9
New Hebrides (North)	9,165 ± 20[a]	
North Solomons (Bougainville)	9,103 ±	14
	8,940 ± 20[a]	
Yap (West Caroline)	8,527 ±	7
New Britain	8,320 ±	14
	8,245 ± 20[a]	
South Solomons	8,310 ± 20[a]	
South Sandwich	8,264	10
Peru–Chile	8,055 ± 10	3
Palau	8,054 ±	14
	8,050 ± 10[a]	

[a] These soundings were taken during Proa Expedition, April–June, 1962, aboard R.V. *Spencer F. Baird.* A Precision Depth Recorder was employed, and the ship's track crossed over (within the limits of celestial navigation) points from which maximum depths had been reported.

[b] This is the maximum sounding obtained in the vicinity of the Vitiaz Depth (Udintsev, 1959) by French and Japanese vessels in connection with dives of the bathyscaph *Archimède,* July, 1962.

Table 2.1–8 (*Continued*)

Trench	Max depths, m	Ref.
Aleutian (uncorrected, taken with nominal sounding velocity of 1,500 m/sec)	7,679	
Nansei Shoto (Ryuku)	7,507	
Java	7,450	15
New Hebrides (South)	7,070 ± 20[a]	
Middle America	6,662 ± 10	

[a] These soundings were taken during Proa Expedition, April–June, 1962, aboard R.V. *Spencer F. Baird.* A Precision Depth Recorder was employed, and the ship's track crossed over (within the limits of celestial navigation) points from which maximum depths had been reported.

REFERENCES

1. **Carruthers, J.N. and Lawford, A.L.,** The deepest oceanic sounding, *Nature,* 169, 601, 1952.
2. **Delauze,** personal communication, 1962.
3. **Fisher, R.L.,** in *Preliminary Report on Expedition Downwind,* I.G.Y. General Report Ser., 2, I.G.Y. World Data Center A, Washington, 1958.
4. **Fisher, R.L. and Revelle, R.,** A deep sounding from the southern hemisphere, *Nature,* 174, 469, 1954.
5. **Hanson, P.P., Zenkevich, N.L., Sergeev, U.V., and Udintsev, G.B.,** Maximum depths of the Pacific Ocean, *Priroda (Mosk),* 6, 84, 1959 (in Russian).
6. **Hess, H.H. and Buell, M.W.,** The greatest depth in the oceans, *Trans. Am. Geophys. Un.,* 31, 401, 1950.
7. **Kanaev, V.F.,** New data on the bottom relief of the western part of the Pacific Ocean, *Oceanological Researches,* 2, 33, 1960 (in Russian).
8. **Lyman, J.,** personal communication, 1960.
9. **Lyman, J.,** The deepest sounding in the North Atlantic, *Proc. R. Soc. Lond.,* A222, 334, 1954.
10. **Maurer, H. and Stocks, T.,** *Die Echolötungen des Meteor. Wiss. Ergebn. Deut. Atlant. Exped. 'Meteor,' 1925–27,* 2, 1, 1933.
11. **Nasu, N., Iijima, A., and Kagami, H.,** Geological results in the Japanese Deep Sea Expedition in 1959, *Oceanog. Mag.,* 11, 201, 1960.
12. **Udintsev., G.B.,** Discovery of a deep-sea trough in the western part of the Pacific Ocean, *Priroda (Mosk),* 7, 85, 1958 (in Russian).
13. **Udintsev, G.B.,** Relief of abyssal trenches in the Pacific Ocean (abst.), *Intern. Oceanog. Cong. Preprints,* Am.Assoc. Adv. Sci., Washington, 1959.
14. **Udintsev, G.B.,** Bottom relief of the western part of the Pacific Ocean, *Oceanological Researches,* 2, 5, 1960 (in Russian).
15. **van Riel, P.M.,** The bottom configuration in relation to the flow of bottom water, *The 'Snellius' Exped.,* E.J. Brill, Leiden Neth., 2(2), Ch. 2, 1933.
16. **Wiseman, J.D.H. and Ovey, C.D.,** Proposed names of features on the deep-sea floor, *Deep-Sea Res.,* 2, 93, 1955.

(From Hill, M. N., Ed., *The Sea,* Vol. III, Wiley-Interscience, New York, 1963. With permission. In part after the compilation of Wiseman and Ovey,[16] 1955.)

Figure 2.1–16
TOPOGRAPHY OF THE DEEPEST BASIN IN THE PHILIPPINE TRENCH, IN THE VICINITY OF THE CAPE JOHNSON AND GALATHEA DEPTHS

See special foldout section at back of the book, p. 615.

(From Hill, M. N., Ed., *The Sea,* Vol. III, Wiley-Interscience, New York, 1963. With permission.)

Figure 2.1–17
BATHYMETRIC EXPLORATION OF THE CHALLENGER DEEP, MARIANAS TRENCH

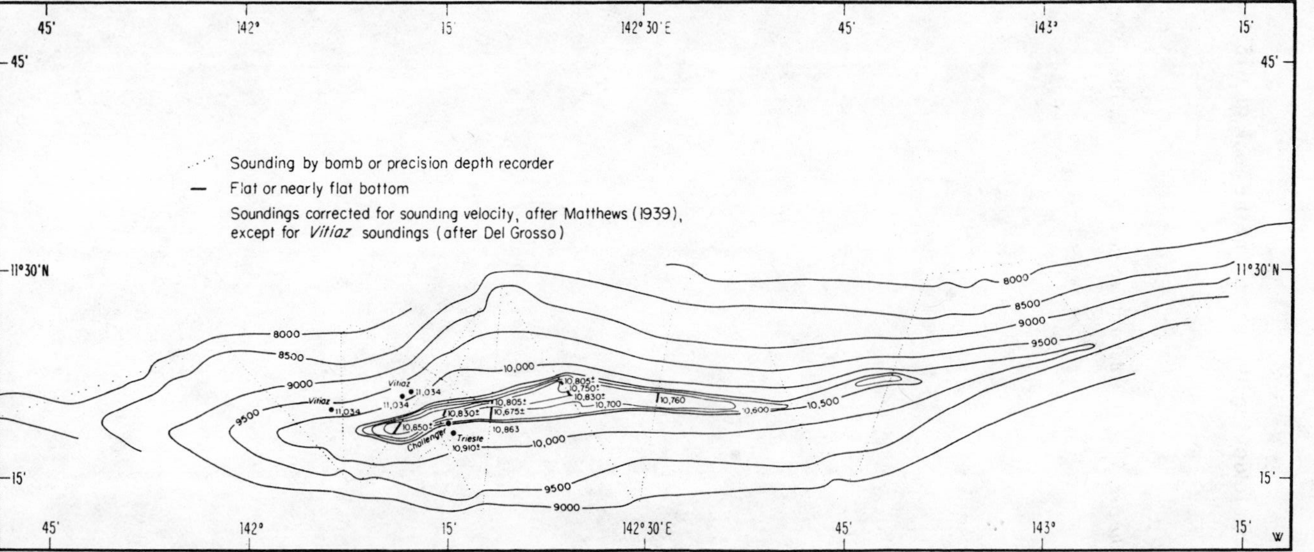

Note: By S.I.O. R.V. *Stranger*, Naga Expedition, July, 1959.

(From Hill, M. N., Ed., *The Sea*, Vol. III, Wiley-Interscience, New York, 1963. With permission.)

Figure 2.1–18
EXPLORATION OF THE CENTRAL PORTION OF THE PHILIPPINE TRENCH

See special foldout section at back of the book, p. 616.

Note: By R.V. *Stranger*, Naga Expedition, August, 1959.

(From Hill, M.N., Ed., *The Sea,* Vol. III, Wiley-Interscience, New York, 1963. With permission.)

Figure 2.1–19
CROSS SECTIONS OF THE PHILIPPINE TRENCH

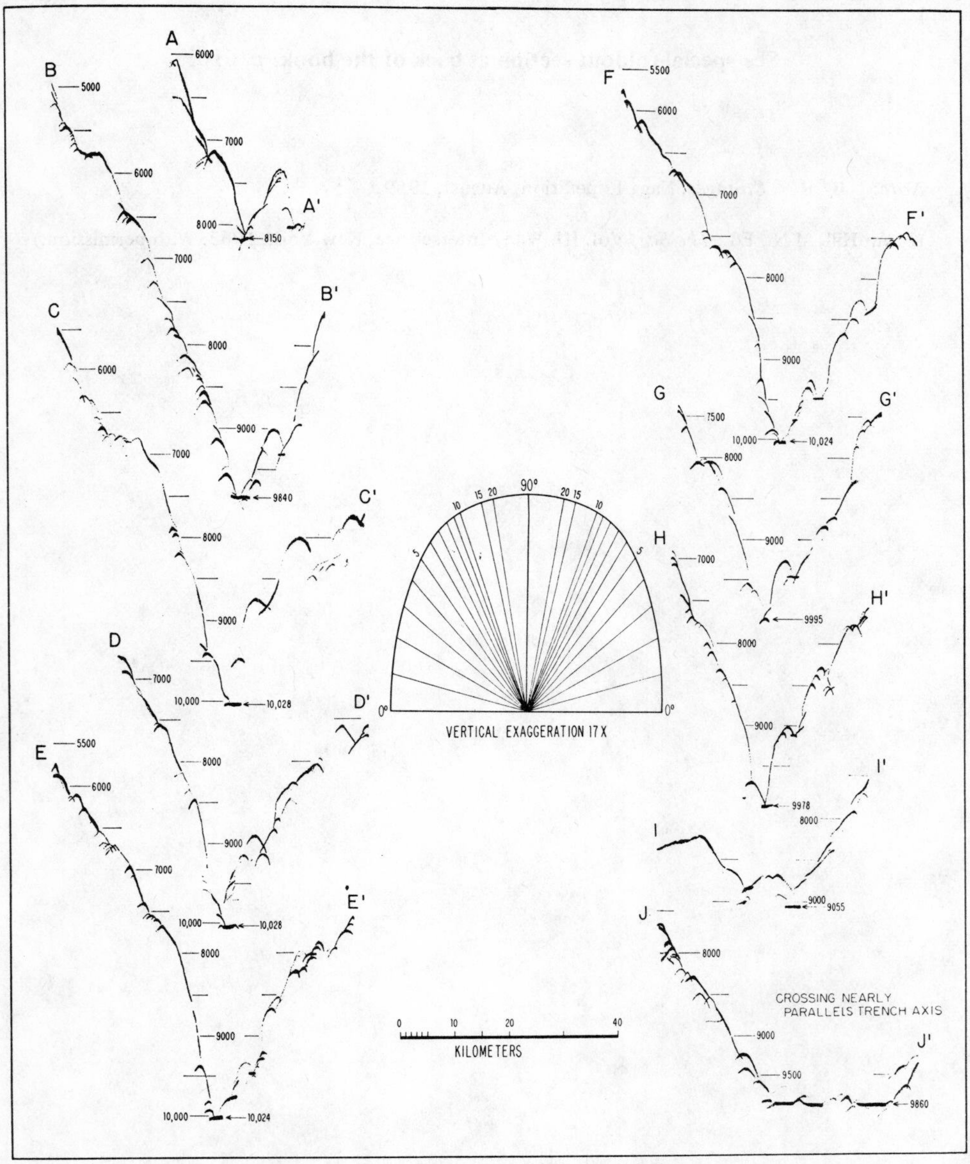

FIGURE 2.1–19. Traced from R. V. *Stranger* Precision Depth Recorder tapes. Sounding scales corrected after Matthews (1939). (See Figure 2.1–18 for location of the sections.)

Note: Since a wide-beam sounder was employed, many side echoes appear as early, late, or faint returns. The upper surface, ordinarily accepted as the sounding trace, is actually the envelope of minimum reflection times.

(From Hill, M. N., Ed., *The Sea,* Vol. III, Wiley-Interscience, New York, 1963. With permission.)

REFERENCE

Matthews, D. J., Tables of the velocity of sound in pure water and sea water for use in echo-sounding and sound-ranging, *Brit. Admiralty Hydrog. Dep. Pub.,* H.D. 282, 2nd ed.

Figure 2.1–20
TOPOGRAPHY OF THE MIDDLE AMERICA TRENCH

See special foldout section at back of the book, p. 616.

Note: Based chiefly on soundings from Scripps Institution investigations, 1952–1959.

(From Hill, M.N., Ed., *The Sea*, Vol. III, Wiley-Interscience, New York 1963. With permission.)

Figure 2.1–21
CROSS SECTIONS OF THE MIDDLE AMERICA TRENCH

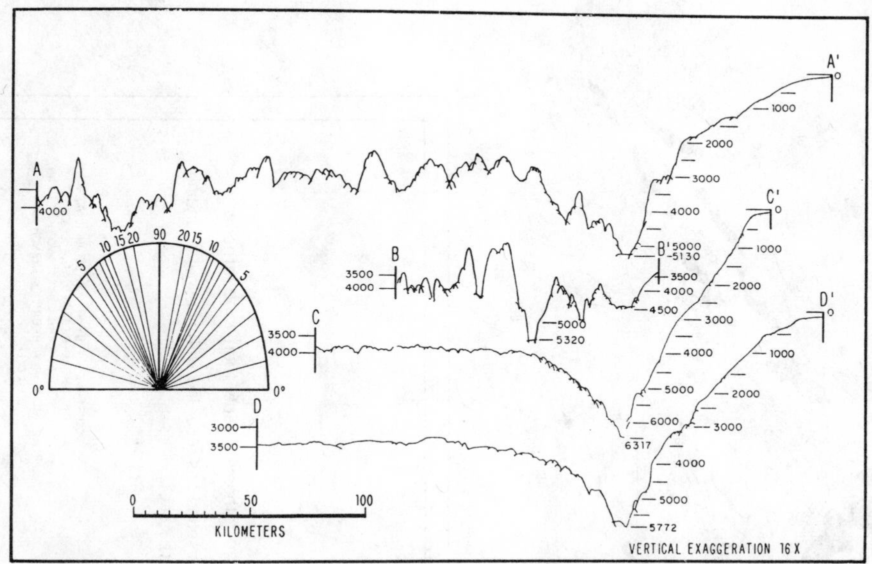

FIGURE 2.1–21. Traced from continuous-sounding records. Sounding scales corrected after Matthews (1939). (See Figure 2.1–20 for location of the sections.)

(From Hill, M. N., Ed., *The Sea,* Vol. III, Wiley-Interscience, New York, 1963. With permission.)

REFERENCE

Matthews, D. J., Tables of the velocity of sound in pure water and sea water for use in echo-sounding and sound-ranging, *Brit. Admiralty Hydrog. Dep. Pub.*, H.D. 282, 2nd ed.

Figure 2.1–22

SUBMARINE TOPOGRAPHY OF THE NEW BRITAIN-NEW HEBRIDES REGION, SOUTHWEST PACIFIC*

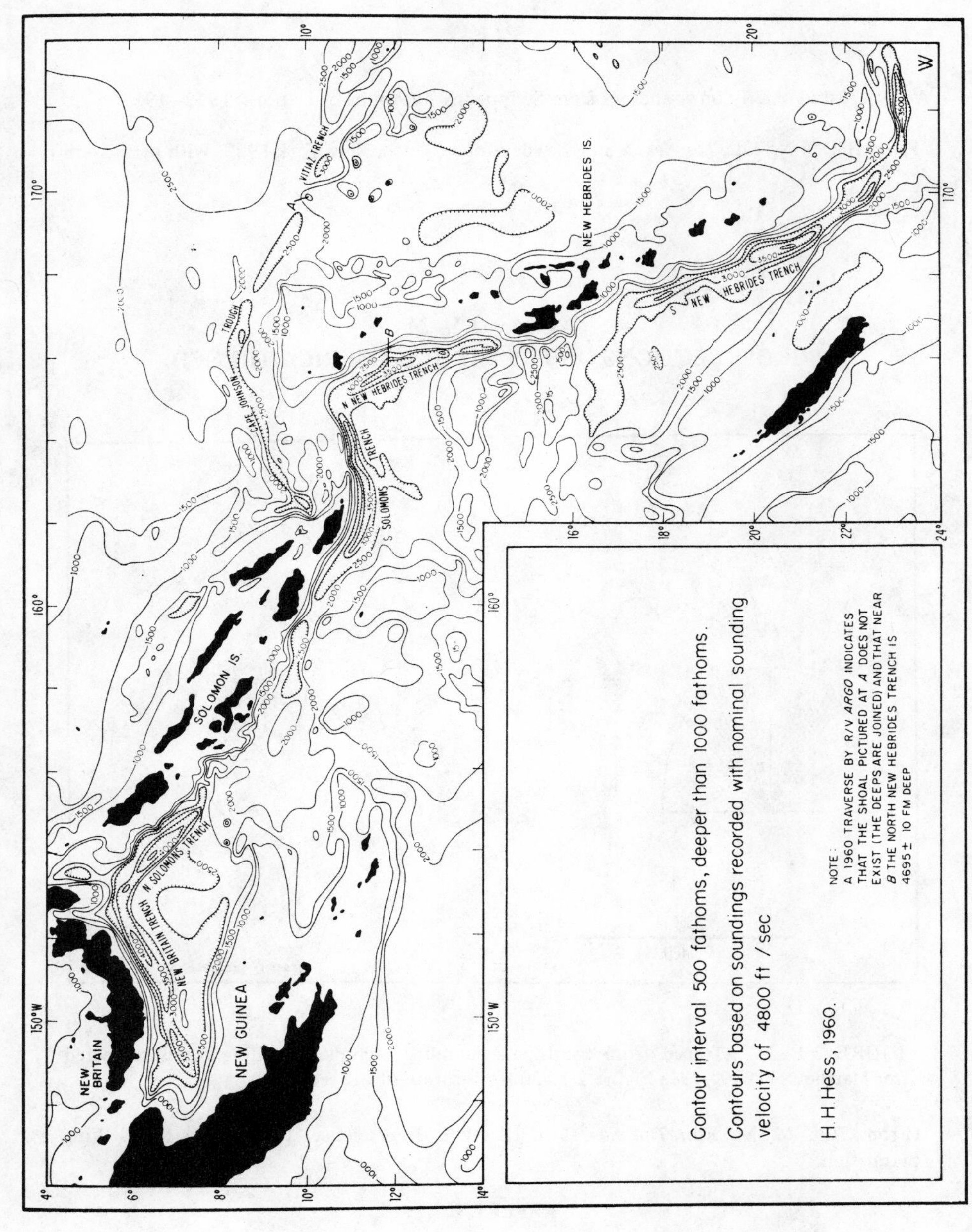
NEW BRITAIN
NEW GUINEA
SOLOMON IS.
NEW HEBRIDES IS.
NEW BRITAIN TRENCH
N SOLOMONS TRENCH
S SOLOMONS TRENCH
N NEW HEBRIDES TRENCH
S NEW HEBRIDES TRENCH
VITIAZ TRENCH
CAPE JOHNSON TROUGH
Contour interval 500 fathoms, deeper than 1000 fathoms.
Contours based on soundings recorded with nominal sounding velocity of 4800 ft /sec
H.H Hess, 1960.
NOTE:
A 1960 TRAVERSE BY R/V ARGO INDICATES THAT THE SHOAL PICTURED AT A DOES NOT EXIST (THE DEEPS ARE JOINED) AND THAT NEAR B THE NORTH NEW HEBRIDES TRENCH IS 4695 ± 10 FM DEEP

* Near 10°S, 170°E; *B* in North New Hebrides Trench.

(From Hill, M. N., Ed., *The Sea,* Vol. III, Wiley-Interscience, New York, 1963. With permission.)

Figure 2.1–23

ISLAND ARC AND CONTINENTAL MARGIN STRUCTURE SECTIONS DEDUCED FROM SEISMIC-REFRACTION DATA

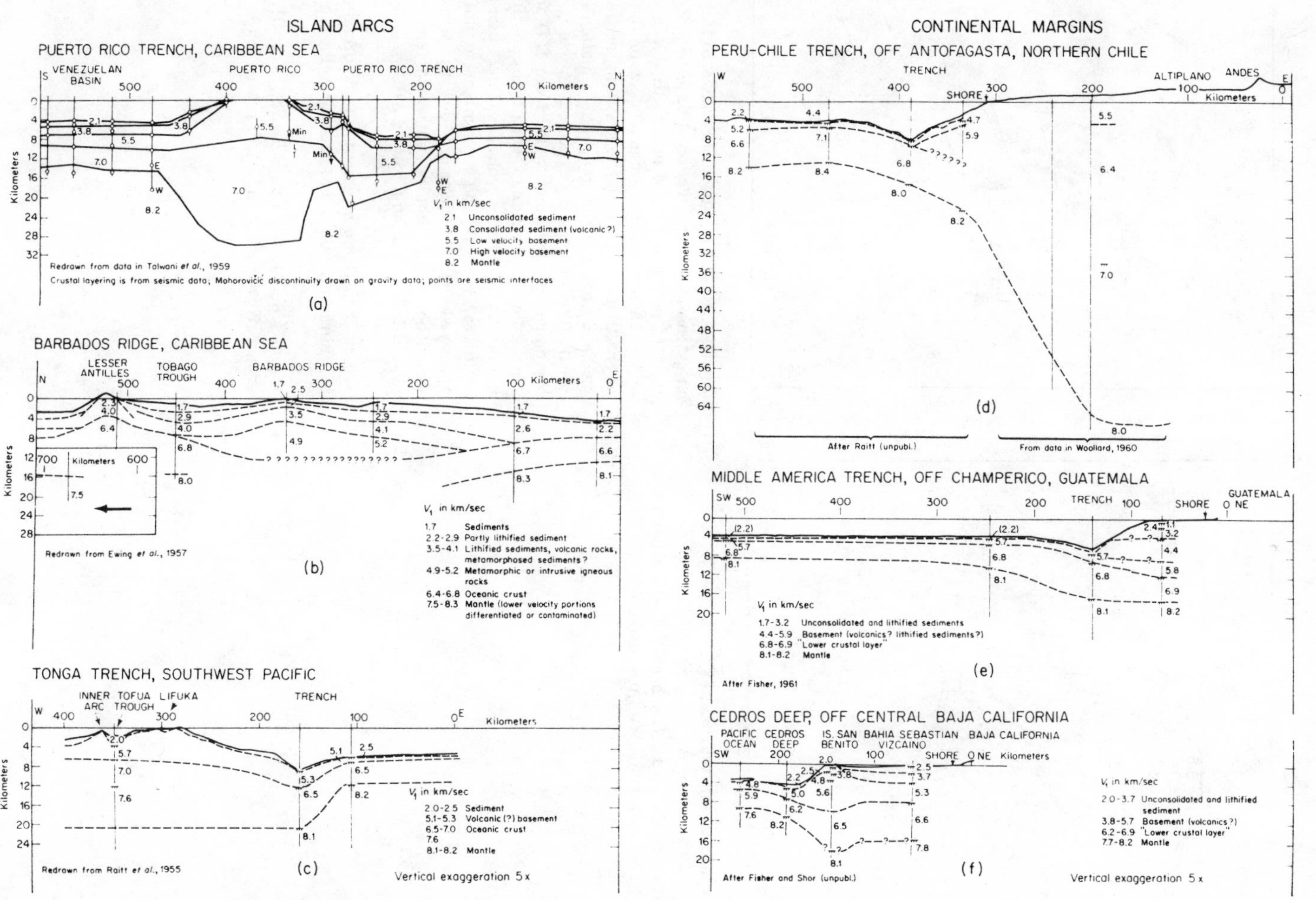

(From Hill, M. N., Ed., *The Sea,* Vol. III, Wiley-Interscience, New York, 1963. With permission.)

Figure 2.1–24
SUPPOSED STRUCTURE FOR A HYPOTHETICAL TRENCH-ISLAND ARC ASSOCIATION*

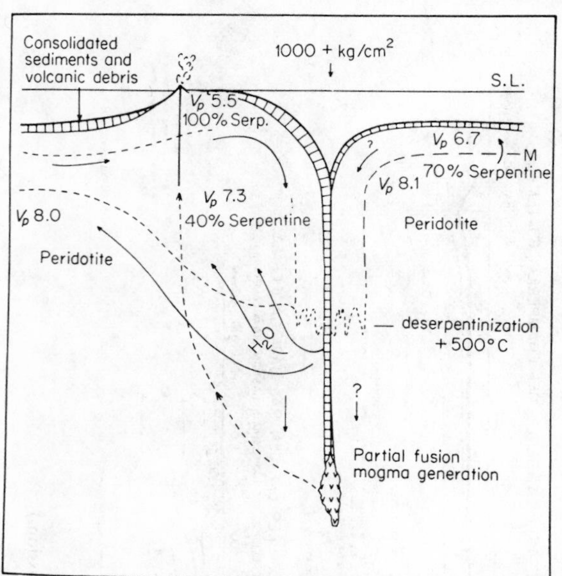

* With typical seismic velocities (V_p in km/sec).

(From Hill, M. N., Ed., *The Sea,* Vol. III, Wiley-Interscience, New York, 1963. With permission.)

Figure 2.1–25
POSTULATED MECHANICAL SITUATION WHERE THE CRUST MOVES INTO A CURVED TRENCH

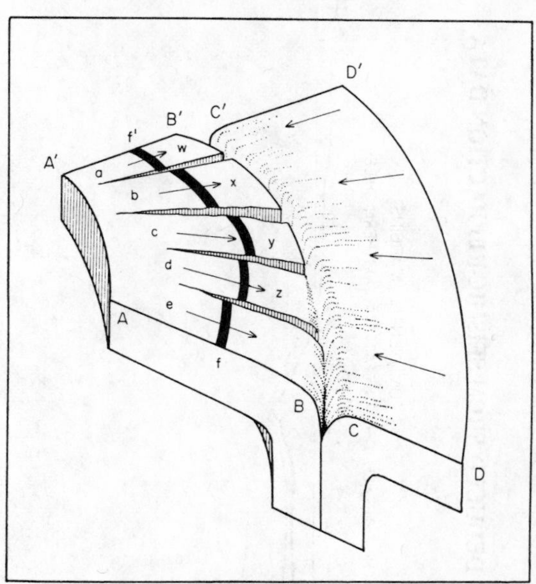

FIGURE 2.1–25. Movement of A′A to B′B would result in extension in the direction B′B, providing potential fissures to permit escape of magma to volcanoes at w, x, y, and z. These volcanoes are in all cases on the concave side of the trench and about 180 km from the trench axis. Immediately beneath the trench, deformation is severe, and plastic flow might be expected to close the fissures. Movement on the convex side from D′D to C′C would cause compression along C′C so that open fissures would not form and hence volcanoes are absent. Individual sectors a, b, c, d, and e might move differentially as portrayed by the displaced bed f′f. Strike-slip faults would bound the sectors and would tend to be sinistral toward A′B′ and dextral toward AB.

Note: This figure represents the deformation of a layer of arbitrary thickness, not necessarily the crust.

(From Hill, M. N., Ed., *The Sea,* Vol. III, Wiley-Interscience, New York, 1963. With permission.)

Table 2.1–9

SUBMARINE CANYONS: LOCATION, SIZE, DEPTH

Symbols

1. Length of canyon measured along axis (nautical miles)
2. Depth at canyon head (feet)
3. Depth at canyon terminus (feet)
4. Character of coast inside canyon head
   - A. Heads in estuary
   - B. Heads off embayment
   - C. Heads off straight beach or barrier
   - D. Heads off relatively straight cliff
   - E. Uncertain
5. Relation of canyon head to points of land
   - A. On upcurrent side of point
   - B. Relatively near upcurrent side of point
   - C. No relation to point
6. Relation of canyon head to river valleys
   - A. Probable connection
   - B. No connection
   - C. Uncertain
7. Source of sediments to canyon head
   - A. Receives good supply
   - B. Supply restricted now, greater during lowered sea level stages
   - C. Little known supply of sediment because of depth
8. Gradient of axis in meters per kilometer
9. Nature of longitudinal profile
   - A. Generally concave upward
   - B. Generally convex upward
   - C. Relatively even slope
   - D. Local step-like steepening along axis
10. Maximum height of walls in feet
11. Channel curvature
    - A. Straight
    - B. Slightly curving
    - C. Twisting or winding
    - D. Meandering
    - E. One meandering bend
    - F. Right-angled bends
12. Abundance of tributaries
    - A. As common as typical land valleys
    - B. Less common than typical land valleys
    - C. Confined to canyon head
    - D. No known tributaries
13. Character of transverse profile
    - A. Predominantly V-shaped
    - B. V-shaped inner canyon, trough-shaped outer canyon
    - C. Predominantly trough-shaped
    - D. Uncertain
14. Nature of canyon wall material
    - A. Crystalline rock dredged
    - B. Rock dredged, but all sedimentary
    - C. Mud only dredged on wall
    - D. Unknown
15. Nature of core sediment from axis
    - A. Includes sand layers
    - B. Includes sand and gravel layers
    - C. Mud cores only
    - D. Unknown

Table 2.1–9 (*Continued*)
SUBMARINE CANYONS: LOCATION, SIZE, DEPTH

	1	2	3	4	5	6	7	8
Canyon name and location	Canyon length	Depth at canyon head	Depth at canyon terminus	Coast character	Relation to points	Relation to river valleys	Sediment sources at head	Gradient in m/km
California								
Coronado	8.0	240	5,580	C	C	C	B	58
La Jolla	7.3	50	1,800	C	B	A	A	40
Scripps (tributary)	1.45	60	900	D	C	A	A	97
Redondo	8.0	30	1,920	C	B	B	A	39
Dume	3.0	120	1,860	C	A	A	A	97
Mugu	8.0	40	2,400	C	B	C	A	49
Sur Partington	49.0	300	10,200	D	C	C	A	34
Carmel (tributary)	15.0	30	6,600	A	A	A	A	73
Monterey	60.0	50?	9,600?	C	C	B	A	26.5
Delgada	55.0	90	8,400	D	C	B	A	25
Mattole	16.0	60	5,720	B	B	A	A	59
Eel	27.0	250	8,500	C	C	A	B	51
Total or Average (12)	21.5	110	5,290	1A, 1B, 7C, 3D	2A, 4B, 6C	6A, 3B, 3C	10A, 2B	54
Oregon-Washington								
Columbia	37.0?	360	6,130?	B	B	A	C	26
Willapa	60.0	500+	7,000	B	C	A	C	24
Gray	30.0	500	6,440	B	C	A	C	33
Quinault	25.0	500±	5,750	C	C	A	C	35
Juan de Fuca	31.0+	800±	4,520+	B	B	C	C	20
Total or Average (5)	36.6	532	5,968	4B, 1C	2B, 3C	4A, 1C	5C	27.6
Bering Sea								
Umnak	160.0	900	10,850	B	C	C	C	10.4
Bering	220.0	600±	11,160	B	C	C	C	8
Pribilof	86.0	500±	10,700	C?	C	C	C	20
Total or Average (3)	155.3	667	10,903	2B, 1C	3C	3C	3C	12.8

Table 2.1–9 (*Continued*)
SUBMARINE CANYONS: LOCATION, SIZE, DEPTH

	1	2	3	4	5	6	7	8
Canyon name and location	Canyon length	Depth at canyon head	Depth at canyon terminus	Coast character	Relation to points	Relation to river valleys	Sediment sources at head	Gradient in m/km
U.S. East Coast								
Corsair	14+	360	5,400	E	C	C	B	23
Lydonia	16+	370	4,400+	E	C	C	B	42
Gilbert	20+	480	7,680+	E	C	C	C	60
Oceanographer	17+	600+	7,230+	E	C	C	C	65
Welker	27+	400	6,450+	E	C	C	B	38
Hydrographer	27+	450+	6,600+	E	C	C	B	37
Hudson	50	300	7,000	B	C	A	B	25
Wilmington	23+	320	6,940+	E	C	C	B	48
Baltimore	28+	400	6,110+	B?	C	C	B	34
Washington	28+	360	6,740+	E	C	C	B	38
Norfolk	38	320	8,300	E	C	C	B	35
Total or Average (11)	26.2	395	6,623	2B, 9E	11C	1A, 10C	9B, 2C	40
Hawaiian-Molokai								
Halawai	6.0+	300±	3,540+	B	C	A	B	90
Naiwa	7.5	380	4,880	D	C	A	B	100
Waikolu	9.0	<600	6,540	B	C	A	B	110
Pelekunu	10.0	<320	6,320	B	C	A	A	100
Hawaiian-Kauai								
Hanakapiai	6.0+	280	7,480	D	C	A	B	200
Hanakoa	3.7	600±	4,820	D	C	C	C	190
Hanopu	3.6	300	5,100	D	C	C	B	220
Total or Average (7)	6.5	397	5,526	3B, 4D	7C	5A, 2C	1A, 5B, 1C	144
Western Europe								
Shamrock	30+	1,200±	14,400	B?	C	C	C	28
Black Mud	30+	900±	12,200	E	C	C	B	57
Audierne	27	600±	10,500	B	C	C	C	60
Cap Ferret	50+	800	11,647	C	C	C	C	31
Cap Breton	135 or 70	400±	13,100	D	C	C	B	58
Aviles	65	60±	8,000	C	B	A (old river)	A	20 or 16

Table 2.1–9 (*Continued*)
SUBMARINE CANYONS: LOCATION, SIZE, DEPTH

	1	2	3	4	5	6	7	8
Canyon name and location	Canyon length	Depth at canyon head	Depth at canyon terminus	Coast character	Relation to points	Relation to river valleys	Sediment sources at head	Gradient in m/km
Llanes	38	450	13,300	D	B	C	B	45
Nazare	93	200±	14,764	C	A	A	A	36
Lisbon	21	400	6,450	B	B	A?	B	48
Setubal	33+	350	6,880	C	C	A	B	33
Total or Average (10)	52.2 or 45.7	536	11,224	3B, 4C, 2D	1A 3B, 5C	4A, 5C	2A, 4B, 3C	41.6 or 41.2
Mediterranean mainland								
Grand Rhone	15+	600±	5,550	C	C	A	C	55
Marseille	20+	600±	6,840±	B	C	C	C	52
Canon de la Cassidaigne	19+	360	6,630+	B	B	A	B	55
Toulon	12+	260	6,600	A	C	C	B	110
Stoechades	17+	300	4,380+	borderline A	C	C	A	40
St. Topez	25+	60?	5,750	A	C	A	A	38
Cannes	17+	100?	6,600?	borderline C or A	C	B	A	65
Var	15	160	6,550	D	A	A	A	71
Nice	12	150	5,840	delta D	C	B	A	79
Cap d'Ail	14	320	6,870	B	C	C	B	78
Nervia	16	330	6,280	C	C	A	B	62
Taggia	12	300±	7,500	C	C	A	B	100
Mele	31	200	6,150	C	C	B	B	32
Noli	14	120	4,990	curving D	C	A?	A	58
Polcevera	49	300	8,830	curving C	C	A?	B	29
Genoa	20	260	6,260	B	C	A	B	50
Total or Average (16)	17.4	276.5	6,351	3A, 4B, 5C, 3D	1A, 1B, 14C	9A, 3B, 4C	7A, 7B, 2C	60.9
Mediterranean Islands								
Crete	4	<300	3,300	B?	C	A	A	200

Table 2.1–9 (*Continued*)
SUBMARINE CANYONS: LOCATION, SIZE, DEPTH

Canyon name and location	1 Canyon length	2 Depth at canyon head	3 Depth at canyon terminus	4 Coast character	5 Relation to points	6 Relation to river valleys	7 Sediment sources at head	8 Gradient in m/km
West Corsica								
St. Florent	25	150±	7,850	A	A	A	A	51
Calvi	13	200±	7,800	B	C	A	B	97
Porto	20	150±	8,200	A	C	A	A	67
Sagone	29	150±	6,200	A	C	A	A	35
Ajaccio	34	150±	8,200	A	C	A	A	39
Valinco	35	150±	8,000	A	C	A	A	37
Total or Average (7)	22.8	178	7,078	5A, 2B	1A, 6C	7A	6A, 1B	75
Baja, California								
San Pablo	20+	<400	8,400+	D	A	B	A	67
Cardonal	16+	<450	7,500+	C	B	B	B	73
Vigia	10	?	7,200	C + D	C	A or B	A	115
San Lucas –	19	30	6,900?	A-bay	C	A	A	70
Santa Maria	(24)		8,000					56
San Jose	32	50	7,200?	C	C	A?	A	41
Vinorama – Salado	9	200	6,300	C	A	A	B	113
Los Frailes	9.5	10	5,200	A-bay	A	A	A	91
					(S. wind)			
Saltito	6	1,200	5,100	B?	C	B	C	108
Palmas –	13	100?	5,300	C	A	C	A	65 or 91
Pescadero	9.3				(S. wind)			
Total or Average (9)	15.2	305	6,710	2A, 1B,	4A, 1B,	4½A, 3½B,	6A, 2B,	
				4½C, 1½D	4C	1C	1C	81
East Honshu								
Ninomiya	4.8	400	2,600	C	C	C	B	77
Sagami	5.0	310	3,300	C	C	C	B	100
Enoshima	6.7	450	3,250	E	C	C	B	70
Hayama	13	300		E	C	C	B	54
			4,600					
Miura	15	173		E	C	C	B	48
Misaki	14.5	330	4,600	E	C	C	B	49

Table 2.1–9 (*Continued*)
SUBMARINE CANYONS: LOCATION, SIZE, DEPTH

	1	2	3	4	5	6	7	8
Canyon name and location	**Canyon length**	**Depth at canyon head**	**Depth at canyon terminus**	**Coast character**	**Relation to points**	**Relation to river valleys**	**Sediment sources at head**	**Gradient in m/km**
Jogashima	10	330		E	C	C	B	71
Tokyo	30	300	4,900	A	C	C	B	26
Mera	20	190	5,500	B (bay)	B	C	B	44
Kamogawa	25	200	9,100	B	C	A	B	59
Total or Average (10)	29.25	298	4,731	1A, 2B, 2C, 5E	1B, 9C	1A, 9C	10B	60
Miscellaneous								
Great Bahama	125	4,800	14,060	B	C	C	C	13
Congo	120	80	7,000	A	C	A	A	96
Ceylon Trincomalee	20+	30+	9,500+	A	A?	A	A	79
Manila	31+	300	7,800+	B	C	A	B	40
Bacarra NW Luzon	15	300	6,000+	C + D	C	A	B	63
San Antonio, Chile	20+	<150	2,700+	C?	C	A?	A	32
Total or Average (6)	55	943	7,843	2A, 2B, 1½C, ½D	1A, 5C	5A, 1C	3A, 2B, 1C	54

(From Shepard, F. P. and Dill, R. F., *Submarine Canyons and Other Sea Valleys,* Rand McNally & Co., Chicago, 1966. With permission.)

Table 2.1–9 (*Continued*)
SUBMARINE CANYONS: LOCATION, SIZE, DEPTH

Canyon name and location	9 Nature of long profile	10 Max wall heights to nearest 1000 ft	11 Channel curvature	12 Abundance of tributaries	13 Transverse profile character	14 Name of canyon wall material	15 Sediment found in axial cores	16 Relation to fan-valleys
California								
Coronado	A	1,000	C	B	A	B	A	A
La Jolla	A	1,000	C	A	A	B	B	A
Scripps (tributary)	A	<1,000	B	C	A	B	B	B
Redondo	A	1,000	C	B	C	B	A	A
Dume	A	1,000	C	B	A	A	D	C
Mugu	A	<1,000	D	A	A	B	A	C
Sur Partington	A	2,000	C	A	A	B	D	C
Carmel (tributary)	A	2,000	C	A	A	A	A	B
Monterey	A + D	6,000	C or D	A	B	A	B	A
Delgada	A	2,000	D	B	A	D	D	A
Mattole	A	3,000	C	B	A	B	D	C
Eel	B	4,000	E	B	A	D	D	C
Total or Average (12)	10A, 1B, 1D	2,083	½B, 8½C, 2½D, 1E	5A, 6B 1C	10A, 1B, 1C	3A, 7B, 2D	4A, 3B, 5D	5A, 2B, 5C
Orgeon-Washington								
Columbia	A	2,000	C	B	D	D	D	C
Willapa	A	2,000	C	A	D	B	A	C
Gray	A	1,000	C	A	D	D	D	C
Quinault	A	3,000	C	A	D	D	D	C
Juan de Fuca	A	2,000	C	D	D	D	D	C
Total or Average (5)	5A	2,400	5C	3A, 1B, 1D	5D	4D, 1B	4D, 1A	5C
Bering Sea								
Umnak	A	4,000	C	A	D	D	D	C
Bering	A + D	6,000	C	A	A	B?	D	C
Pribilof	A	7,000	C	A	D	D	D	C
Total or Average (3)	2½A ½D	5,667	3C	3A	1A, 2D	1B, 2D	3D	3C

Table 2.1–9 (*Continued*)
SUBMARINE CANYONS: LOCATION, SIZE, DEPTH

Canyon name and location	9 Nature of long profile	10 Max wall heights to nearest 1000 ft	11 Channel curvature	12 Abundance of tributaries	13 Transverse profile character	14 Nature of canyon wall material	15 Sediment found in axial cores	16 Relation to fan-valleys
U.S. East Coast								
Corsair	A	2,000	B	B	A	B	D	C
Lydonia	A	3,000	B	B	A	B	C	C
Gilbert	A + D	3,000	B	A	A	B	D	C
Oceanographer	A	2,000	B	B	A	D	D	C
Welker	A + D	4,000	B	B	A	B	A	C
Hydrographer	A + D	3,000	B	B	A	C	A	A
Hudson	A + D	4,000	B	A	A	B	A	A
Wilmington	A	3,000	C	A	A	C	C	C
Baltimore	A + D	3,000	B	B	A	C	C	C
Washington	A + D	2,000	B	A	A	C	C	C
Norfolk	A + D	3,000	B	B	A	B	A	C
Total or Average (11)	7½A, 3½D	2,900	10B, 1C	4A, 7B	11A	6B, 4C, 1D	4A, 4C, 3D	2A, 9C
Hawaiian-Molokai								
Halawai	C	1,000	C	D	A	D	D	C
Naiwa	C	1,000	B	D	A	A	A	B
Waikolu	A	2,000	B	B	A	A	B	A
Pelekunu	A	1,000	C	B	A	D	D	B
Hawaiian-Kauai								
Hanakapiai	B + D	1,000	B	B?	A	A	D	C
Hanakoa	B	1,000	B	B?	A	A	A	C
Hanopu	B + D	2,000	B	B?	A	B	A	A
Total or Average (7)	2A, 2B 2C, 1D	1,286	5B, 2C	5B, 2D	7A	4A, 1B, 2D	3A, 1B, 3D	2A, 2B, 3C
Western Europe								
Shamrock	C + D	3,000	B	B?	D	D	D	C
Black Mud	D	3,000	B	B	B	B	A	A
Audierne	D	4,000	B	D	D	D	D	C
Cap Ferret	A	3,000	C	A	D	D	D	A

Table 2.1–9 (*Continued*)
SUBMARINE CANYONS: LOCATION, SIZE, DEPTH

	9	10	11	12	13	14	15	16
Canyon name and location	Nature of long profile	Max wall heights to nearest 1000 ft	Channel curvature	Abundance of tributaries	Transverse profile character	Nature of canyon wall material	Sediment found in axial cores	Relation to fan-valleys
Cap Breton	A	6,000	B	B	D	D	D	C
Aviles	C + D	5,000 or 6,000	B	A?	B	B	D	A?
Llanes	C	5,000	C	A	D	D	D	C
Nazare	D	5,000	F	B	D	A?	D	C
Lisbon	B + D	4,000	B	D	D	B	D	C
Setubal	C?	2,000	C?	B	D	B?	D	C
Total or Average (10)	2A, ½B, 3C, 3½D	4,000	5B, 3C, 1F	3A, 4B, 2D	1B, 8D	1A, 3B, 5D	9D	2A, 7C
Mediterranean mainland								
Grand Rhone	C?	2,000	B	C	A	D	D	C
Marseille	A + D	2,000	C	A	A	D	D	C
Canon de la Cassidaigne	D	3,000	C	B	A	D	D	C
Toulon	D?	4,000	B	A	A	D	D	C
Stoechades	A	4,000	B	A	A	B?	D	C
St. Topez	C?	3,000	C	A	A	D	D	C
Cannes	A	3,000	C	A	A	D	D	C
Var	A	3,000	C?	A	B	D	B	A
Nice	A + D	2,000	C?	A	B	B?	B	A
Cap d'Ail	D	1,000	B	B	B	D	D	A
Nervia	D	2,000	B	B	B	D	B	A
Taggia	A	2,000	C	B	A	D	D	A
Mele	A + D	1,000	C	B	B	D	D	B
Noli	A	2,000	C	B	B	D	D	B
Polcevera	A + D	3,000	B	B	B	D	D	C
Genoa	D	2,000	B	B	C?	D	D	B
Total or Average (16)	7A, 2C, 7D	2,400	7B, 9C	7A, 8B, 1C	8A, 7B, 1C	2B, 15D	3B, 13D	4A, 3B, 8C
Mediterranean Islands								
Crete	D	1,000	C	B	A	D	B	A

Table 2.1–9 (*Continued*)
SUBMARINE CANYONS: LOCATION, SIZE, DEPTH

	9	10	11	12	13	14	15	16
Canyon name and location	Nature of long profile	Max wall heights to nearest 1000 ft	Channel curvature	Abundance of tributaries	Transverse profile character	Nature of canyon wall material	Sediment found in axial cores	Relation to fan-valleys
West Corsica								
St. Florent	A	3,000	C	A	A	D	A	A?
Calvi	A + D	3,000	C	Bor A	A	D	D	A
Porto	A	4,000	C	A	A	A?	D	C
Sagone	A	3,000	C	A	A	D	D	A?
Ajaccio	A	4,000	B	A	A	D	D	B?
Valinco	A + D	4,000	B	A	A	D	D	C
Total or Average (7)	6A, 1D	3,100	2B, 5C	5½A, 1½B	7A	1A, 6D	1A, 1B, 5D	4A, 1B, 2C
Baja, California								
San Pablo	B + D	3,000	C	B	A	B	D?	C
Cardonal	A + D	3,000	C	A	A	B	D	C
Vigia	A	3,000	B	C	B	A	B	A
San Lucas – Santa Maria	A + D	3,000	C	A	A	A	B	A
San Jose	A + D	3,000	C	A	A	A (sed.)	B	A
Vinorama – Salado	A	1,000	C	A	A	A	B	A
Los Frailes	A + D	2,000	C	C	A	A	B	B
Saltito	A	1,000	C?	A	A	A	D	A
Palmas – Pescadero	A	2,000	C	A	A	A	A	A
Total or Average (9)	6A, ½B, 2½D	2,333	1B, 8C	6A, 1B, 2C	8A, 1B	7A, 2B	1A, 5B, 3D	6A, 1B, 2C
East Honshu								
Ninomiya	A	<1,000	B	C	A	B	D	C
Sagami	A	<1,000	C	A	B	B	D	C
Enoshima	A	<1,000	B	C	A	B	B	C
Hayama	A	2,000	C	B	A	A	D	C
Miura	A	2,000	C	B	A	B	B	C
Misaki	A	2,000	C	A	A	B	B	C
Jogashima	D	1,000	C	A	A	B	A	C
Tokyo	A + D	3,000	C	A	B	A	D	C

Table 2.1–9 (*Continued*)
SUBMARINE CANYONS: LOCATION, SIZE, DEPTH

Canyon name and location	9 Nature of long profile	10 Max wall heights to nearest 1000 ft	11 Channel curvature	12 Abundance of tributaries	13 Transverse profile character	14 Nature of canyon wall material	15 Sediment found in axial cores	16 Relation to fan-valleys
Mera	C + D	2,000	C	A	A	B	B	C
Kamogawa	A + D	5,000	B	B	B	B	A	C
Total or Average (10)	7A, ½C, 2½D	2,000	3B, 7C	5A, 3B, 2C	7A, 3B	3A, 7B	2A, 4B, 4D	1A, 9C
Miscellaneous								
Great Bahama	A	14,000	C	A	A	C	B	A
Congo	A	4,000	B	C	A?	D	A sand	A
Ceylon Trincomalee	A	4,000	F	A	A	A?	D	C
Manila	A + D	6,000	C	A	D	D	D	C
Bacarra NW Luzon	C	3,000	C	A	B?	D	D	C
San Antonio, Chile	A	3,000	B + C	B	D	D	D	C
Total or Average (6)	4½A, 1C, ½D	5,666	1½B, 3½C, 1F	4A, 1B, 1C	3A, 1B, 2D	1A, 1C, 4D	1A, 1B, 4D	4½A, 1C, ½D

(From Shepard, F. P. and Dill, R. F., *Submarine Canyons and Other Sea Valleys,* Rand McNally & Co., Chicago, 1966. With permission.)

Table 2.1–10
MARSDEN SQUARE NUMBERS (1 DEGREE)

	10°				West Long						0°					East Long					10°	
10°	00	09	08	07	06	05	04	03	02	01	00	00	01	02	03	04	05	06	07	08	09	00	10°
	90	99	98	97	96	95	94	93	92	91	90	90	91	92	93	94	95	96	97	98	99	90	
	80	89	88	87	86	85	84	83	82	81	80	80	81	82	83	84	85	86	87	88	89	80	
	70	79	78	77	76	75	74	73	72	71	70	70	71	72	73	74	75	76	77	78	79	70	
	60	69	68	67	66	65	64	63	62	61	60	60	61	62	63	64	65	66	67	68	69	60	
North	50	59	58	57	56	55	54	53	52	51	50	50	51	52	53	54	55	56	57	58	59	50	North
Lat.	40	49	48	47	46	45	44	43	42	41	40	40	41	42	43	44	45	46	47	48	49	40	Lat.
	30	39	38	37	36	35	34	33	32	31	30	30	31	32	33	34	35	36	37	38	39	30	
	20	29	28	27	26	25	24	23	22	21	20	20	21	22	23	24	25	26	27	28	29	20	
	10	19	18	17	16	15	14	13	12	11	10	10	11	12	13	14	15	16	17	18	19	10	
0°	00	09	08	07	06	05	04	03	02	01	00	00	01	02	03	04	05	06	07	08	09	00	0°
	00	09	08	07	06	05	04	03	02	01	00	00	01	02	03	04	05	06	07	08	09	00	
	10	19	18	17	16	15	14	13	12	11	10	10	11	12	13	14	15	16	17	18	19	10	
	20	29	28	27	26	25	24	23	22	21	20	20	21	22	23	24	25	26	27	28	29	20	
	30	39	38	37	36	35	34	33	32	31	30	30	31	32	33	34	35	36	37	38	39	30	
South	40	49	48	47	46	45	44	43	42	41	40	40	41	42	43	44	45	46	47	48	49	40	South
Lat.	50	59	58	57	56	55	54	53	52	51	50	50	51	52	53	54	55	56	57	58	59	50	Lat.
	60	69	68	67	66	65	64	63	62	61	60	60	61	62	63	64	65	66	67	68	69	60	
	70	79	78	77	76	75	74	73	72	71	70	70	71	72	73	74	75	76	77	78	79	70	
10°	80	89	88	87	86	85	84	83	82	81	80	80	81	82	83	84	85	86	87	88	89	80	10°
	90	99	98	97	96	95	94	93	92	91	90	90	91	92	93	94	95	96	97	98	99	90	
	00	09	08	07	06	05	04	03	02	01	00	00	01	02	03	04	05	06	07	08	09	00	
	10°																					10°	

(From *Handbook of Oceanographic Tables,* SP-68, Bialek, E. L., Compiler, U.S. Naval Oceanographic Office, Washington, D.C., 1966.)

Table 2.1–11
AREAS OF QUADRILATERALS OF EARTH'S SURFACE OF 10° EXTENT IN LATITUDE AND LONGITUDE*

Middle latitude of quadrilateral	Area in square miles
0°	474,653
5	472,895
10	467,631
15	458,891
20	446,728
25	431,213
30	412,442
35	390,533
40	356,627
45	337,890
50	307,514
55	274,714
60	239,730
65	202,823
70	164,279
75	124,400
80	83,504
85	41,924

*Statute miles.

(From Smithsonian Institution, *Smithsonian Geographical Tables,* miscellaneous collection 854, 3rd ed., 2nd printing, Washington, D.C., 1929.)

2.2 Temperature, Salinity, and Density Distribution

Figure 2.2–1
MEAN ANNUAL MAXIMUM SALINITY

See special foldout section at back of the book, p. 617.

(From Grabham, A. L., Harbor Analog Systems: Salinity, Density, Conductivity, Informal manuscript report 0-H-65, U.S. Naval Oceanographic Office, Washington, D.C., 1965.)

Figure 2.2–2

AVERAGE SURFACE TEMPERATURE, SALINITY, AND DENSITY VARIATION WITH LATITUDE FOR ALL OCEANS

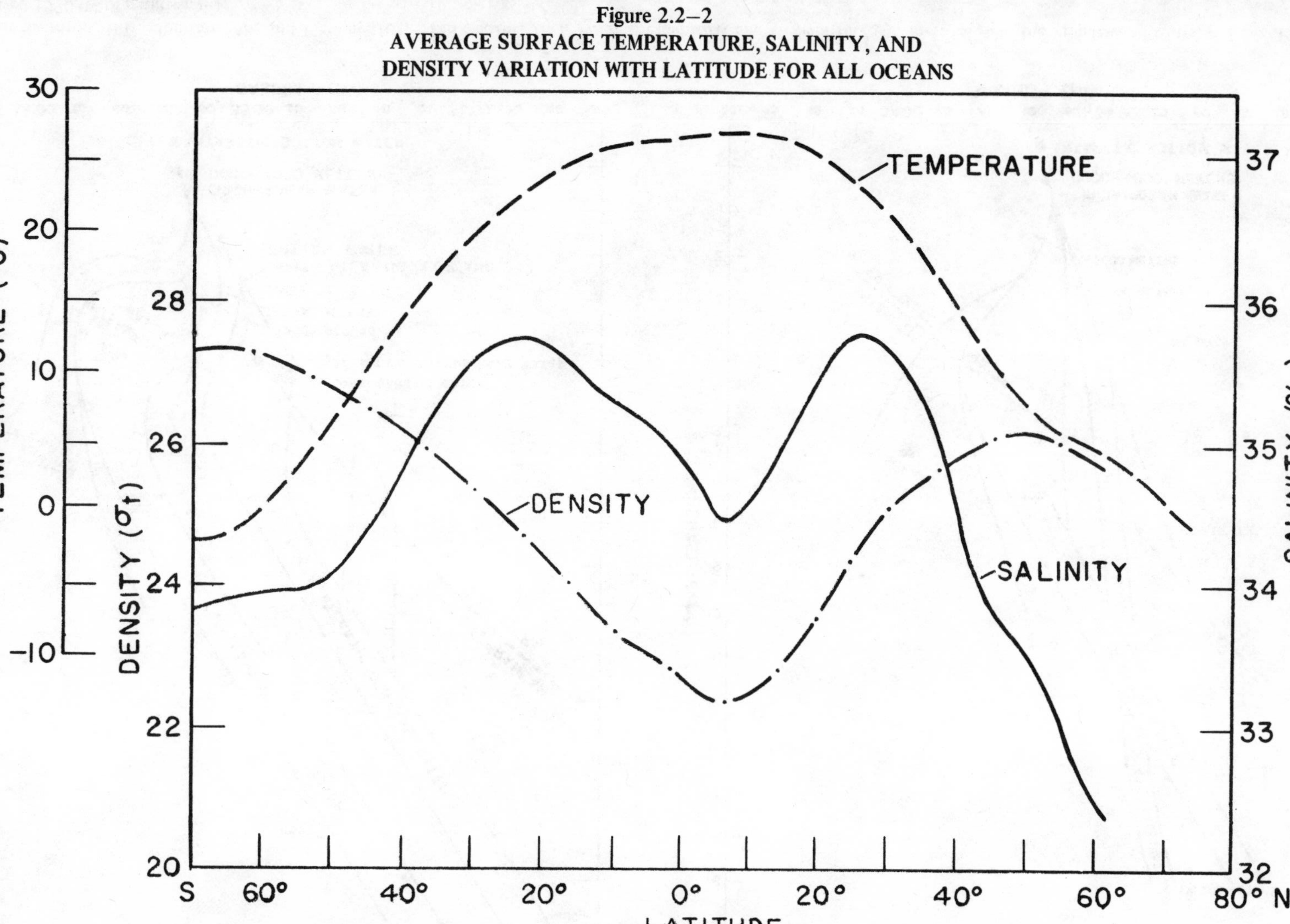

(From Pickard, G.L., *Descriptive Physical Oceanography,* Pergamon Press, New York, 1964. With permission.)

Figure 2.2–3
TEMPERATURE-SALINITY RELATIONS OF PRINCIPAL WATER MASSES OF OCEANS

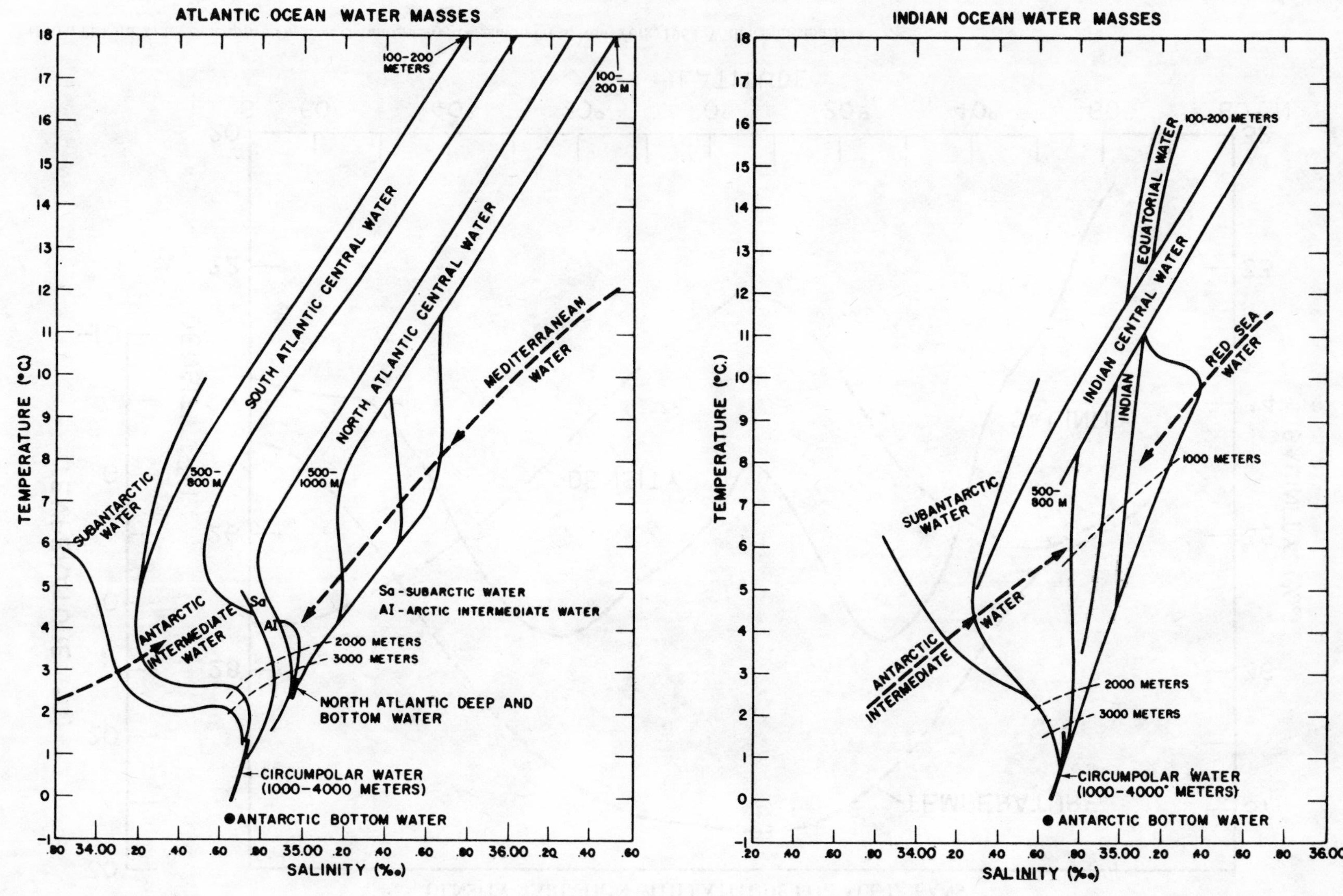

(From Sverdrup, H.U., Johnson, M., and Fleming, R.H., *The Oceans, Their Physics, Chemistry, and General Biology*, Prentice-Hall, Inc., Englewood Cliffs, N.J., © 1942, renewed 1970. With permission.)

Figure 2.2–4

TEMPERATURE-SALINITY RELATIONS OF PRINCIPAL WATER MASSES OF OCEANS

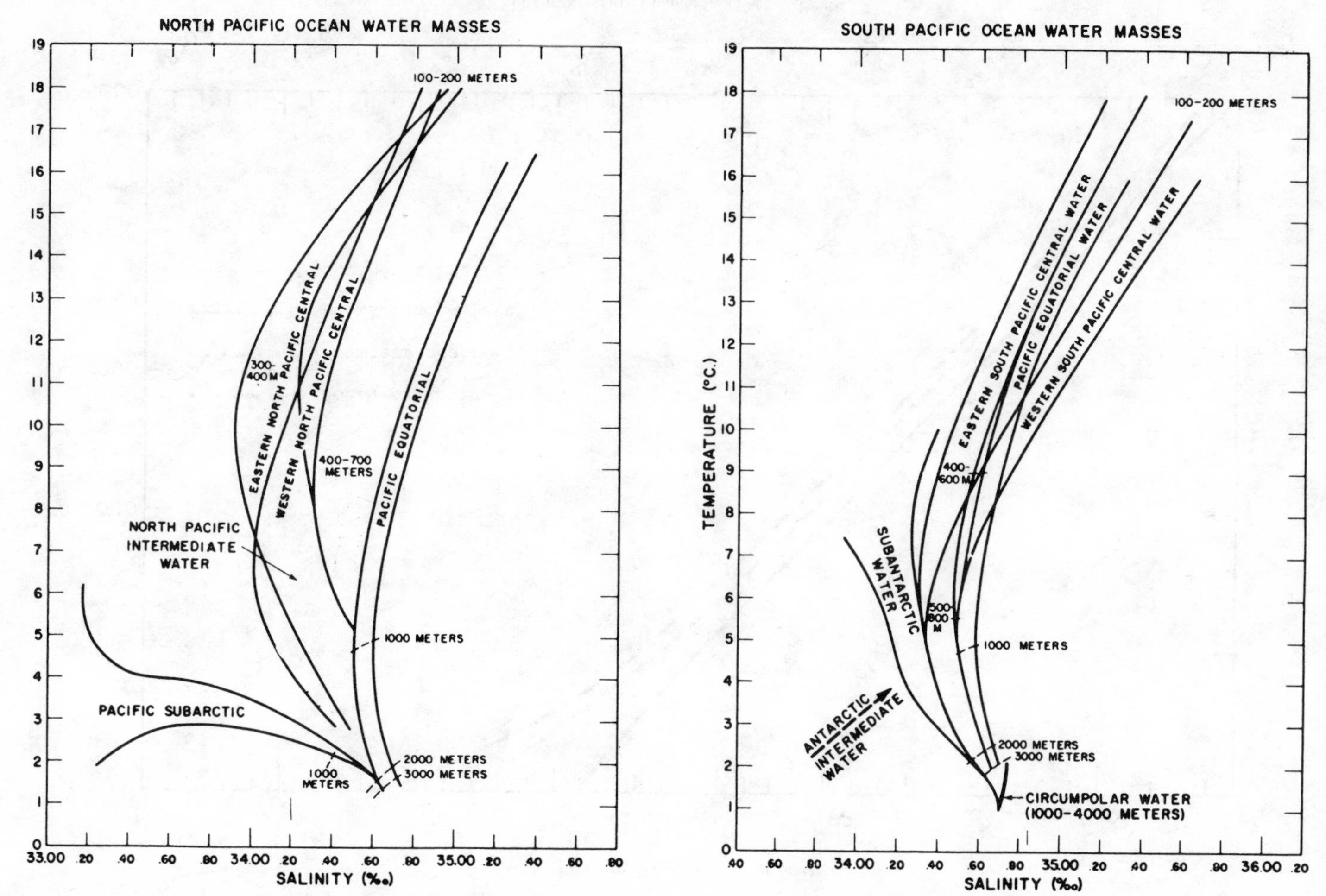

(From Sverdrup, H.U., Johnson, M., and Fleming, R.H., *The Oceans, Their Physics, Chemistry, and General Biology*, Prentice-Hall, Inc., Englewood Cliffs, N.J., © 1942, renewed 1970. With permission.)

Figure 2.2—5
PRESSURE CHANGES WITH DEPTH

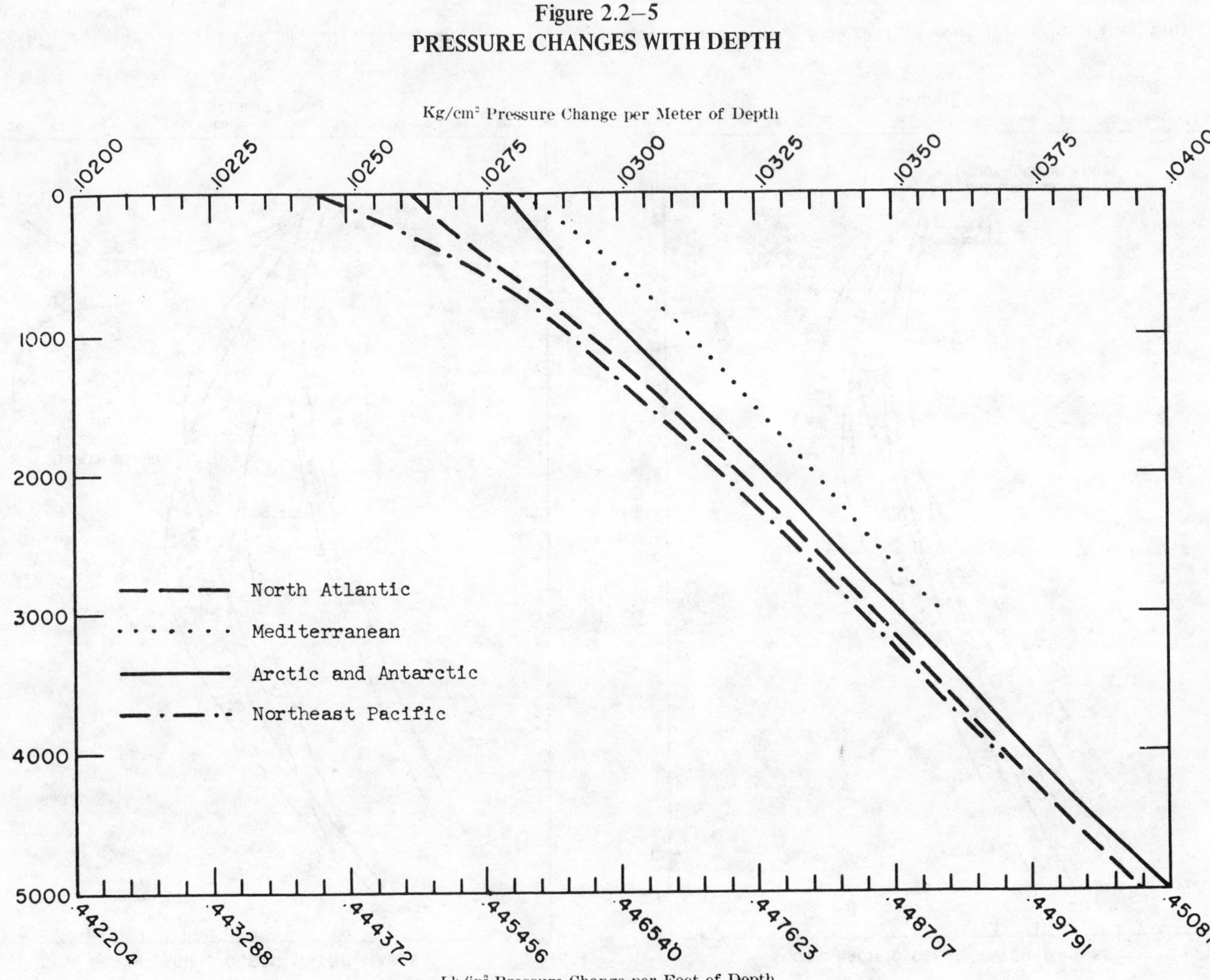

(From Bialek, E. L., Errors in the determination of depth, *Int. Hydrograph. Rev.*, 43, 1966. With permission.)

Table 2.2–1
MEAN VERTICAL TEMPERATURE (°C) DISTRIBUTION IN THE THREE OCEANS BETWEEN 40°N. AND 40°S.

	Atlantic Ocean		Indian Ocean		Pacific Ocean		Mean	
Depth (m)	°C	Δ°C/100 m	°C	Δ°C/100 m	°C	Δ°C/100 m	°C	Δ°C/100 m
0	20.0		22.2		21.8		21.3	
		2.2		3.3		3.1		2.8
100	17.8		18.9		18.7		18.5	
		4.4†		4.7†		4.4†		4.5†
200	13.4		14.3		14.3		14.0	
		1.8		1.6		2.6		2.0
400	9.9		11.0		9.0		10.0	
		1.5		1.2		1.2		1.3
600	7.0		8.7		6.4		7.4	
		0.7		0.9		0.65		0.75
800	5.6		6.9		5.1		5.9	
		0.35		0.7		0.4		0.5
1000	4.9		5.5		4.3		4.9	
		0.20		0.4		0.4		0.35
1200	4.5		4.7		3.5		4.2	
		0.15		0.3		0.2		0.22
1600	3.9		3.4		2.6		3.3	
		0.12		0.15		0.1		0.12
2000	3.4		2.8		2.15		2.8	
		0.08		0.09		0.05		0.07
3000	2.6		1.9		1.7		2.1	
		0.08		0.03		0.03		0.05
4000	1.8		1.6		1.45		1.6	

† Maximum.

(From Defant, A., *Physical Oceanography,* Vol. II, Pergamon Press, New York, 1961. With permission.)

Table 2.2–2
RAPID COMPUTATION OF POTENTIAL TEMPERATURE

Adiabatic cooling in 0.01°C when sea water (S°/₀₀ = 34.85°/₀₀, δ_0 = 28.0), which has a temperature of t_m at the depth of m meters, is raised from that depth to the surface.

m/tm	−2°	−1°	0°	1°	2°	3°	4°	5°	6°	7°	8°	9°	10°
	–	–	–	–	–	–	–	–	–	–	–	–	–
1000	2.6	3.5	4.4	5.3	6.2	7.0	7.8	8.6	9.5	10.2	11.0	11.7	12.4
2000	7.2	8.9	10.7	12.4	14.1	15.7	17.2	18.8	20.4	21.9	23.3	24.8	26.2
3000	13.6	16.1	18.7	21.2	23.6	25.9	28.2	30.5	32.7	34.9	37.1	39.2	41.2
4000	21.7	25.0	28.4	31.6	34.7	37.7	40.6	43.5	46.3	49.1	51.9	54.6	57.2
5000	31.5	35.5	39.6	43.4	47.2	50.9	54.4						
6000	42.8	47.5	52.2	56.7	61.1	65.3	69.4						
7000			66.2	71.3	76.2	80.9	85.5						
8000			81.5	87.1	92.5	97.7	102.7						
9000			98.1	104.1	109.9	115.6	121.0						
10000			115.7	122.1	128.3	134.4	140.2						

(From Wüst, G., *Table for Rapid Computation of Potential Temperature,* Technical Report CU-9-61 AT(30-1) 1808 Geol., Lamont Geological Observatory, Palisades, New York, 1961. With permission.)

Table 2.2–3
RAPID COMPUTATION OF POTENTIAL TEMPERATURE

Adiabatic heating in 0.01°C when sea water (S°/₀₀ = 34.85°/₀₀, δ_0 = 28.0), which has a temperature of t_o at the surface, sinks from the surface to a depth of m meters

m/t_o	−2°	−1°	0°	1°	2°	3°	4°	5°	6°	7°	8°	9°	10°
	+	+	+	+	+	+	+	+	+	+	+	+	+
1000	2.6	3.6	4.5	5.4	6.2	7.1	7.9	8.7	9.5	10.3	11.1	11.8	12.5
2000	7.3	9.1	10.9	12.7	14.3	16.0	17.5	19.1	20.7	22.2	23.7	25.1	26.5
3000	13.9	16.6	19.2	21.8	24.2	26.7	28.9	31.2	33.4	35.6	37.8	39.9	41.9
4000	22.4	25.9	29.3	32.6	35.8	39.0	41.9	44.8	47.7	50.5	53.4	56.1	58.7
5000	32.8	37.0	41.2	45.1	49.0	52.8	56.4						
6000	44.9	49.8	54.7	59.3	63.8	68.1	72.3						
7000		64.3	69.8	75.0	80.0	84.8	89.5						
8000		80.4	86.4	92.1	97.6	102.9							
9000		97.9	104.4	110.5	116.5	122.2							
10000		116.7	123.7	130.2	136.6	142.7							

(From Wüst, G., *Tables for Rapid Computation of Potential Temperature,* Technical Report CU-9-61 AT(30-1) 1808 Geol., Lamont Geological Observatory, Palisades, New York, 1961. With permission.)

Table 2.2–4
RAPID COMPUTATION OF POTENTIAL TEMPERATURE

Adiabatic variations of temperature in 0.01°C for the upper 1000 m of sea water at different salinities

S°/oo	0°C	2°	4°	6°	8°	10°	12°	14°	16°	18°	20°	22°
30.0	3.5	5.3	7.0	8.7	10.3	11.8	13.2	14.7	16.1	17.6	18.9	20.3
32.0	3.9	5.7	7.3	9.0	10.6	12.1	13.5	15.0	16.4	17.8	19.1	20.5
34.0	4.3	6.0	7.7	9.4	10.9	12.4	13.8	15.3	16.6	18.0	19.3	20.7
36.0	4.7	6.4	8.1	9.7	11.2	12.7	14.1	15.5	16.9	18.3	19.6	20.9
38.0	5.1	6.8	8.4	10.0	11.6	13.0	14.4	15.8	17.2	18.5	19.8	21.1

(From Wüst, G., *Tables for Rapid Computation of Potential Temperature,* Technical Report CU-9-61 AT(30-1) 1808 Geol., Lamont Geological Observatory, Palisades, New York, 1961. With permission.)

Table 2.2–5

RAPID COMPUTATION OF POTENTIAL TEMPERATURE

Adiabatic variations of temperature in 0.01°C in Mediterranean sea water of (S°/oo = 38.57°/oo, δ_0 31.0)

	t_m (raising)			t_o (sinking)		
m	12°	13°	14°	12°	13°	14°
	−	−	−	+	+	+
1000	14.4	15.1	15.8	14.5	15.3	16.0
2000	30.0	31.4	32.7	30.4	31.8	33.1
3000	46.6	48.6	50.6	47.4	49.4	51.4
4000	64.2	66.7	69.2	65.7	68.3	70.8

(From Wüst, G., *Tables for Rapid Computation of Potential Temperature,* Technical Report, CU-9-61 AT(30-1– 1808 Geol., Lamont Geological Observatory, Palisades, New York, 1961. With permission.)

2.3 Currents and Transport Charts

Figure 2.3–1
SURFACE CURRENTS OF OCEANS IN JULY

See special fold out section at back of the book, p. 618 .

(From Vietrick, O. O., Ocean currents, in *McGraw-Hill Encyclopedia of Science and Technology,* Vol. 9, McGraw-Hill, New York, 1971. With permission.)

Figure 2.3–2
TRANSPORT CHART OF THE NORTH PACIFIC

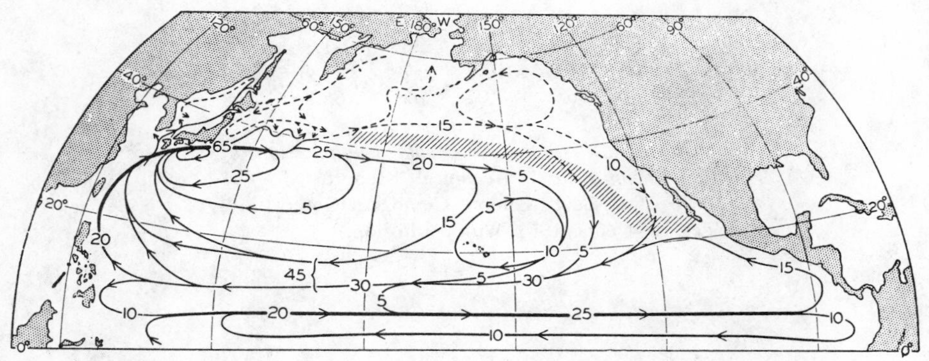

Note: The lines with arrows indicate the approximate direction of the transport above 1500 m, and the inserted numbers indicate the transported volumes in mil m³/sec. Dashed lines show cold currents; full-drawn lines show warm currents.

(From Sverdrup, H.U., Johnson, M.W., and Fleming, R.H., *The Oceans, Their Physics, Chemistry, and General Biology,* Prentice-Hall, Inc., Engelwood Cliffs, N.J., © 1942, renewed 1970. With permission.)

Figure 2.3–3
TRANSPORT LINES AROUND THE ANTARCTIC CONTINENT

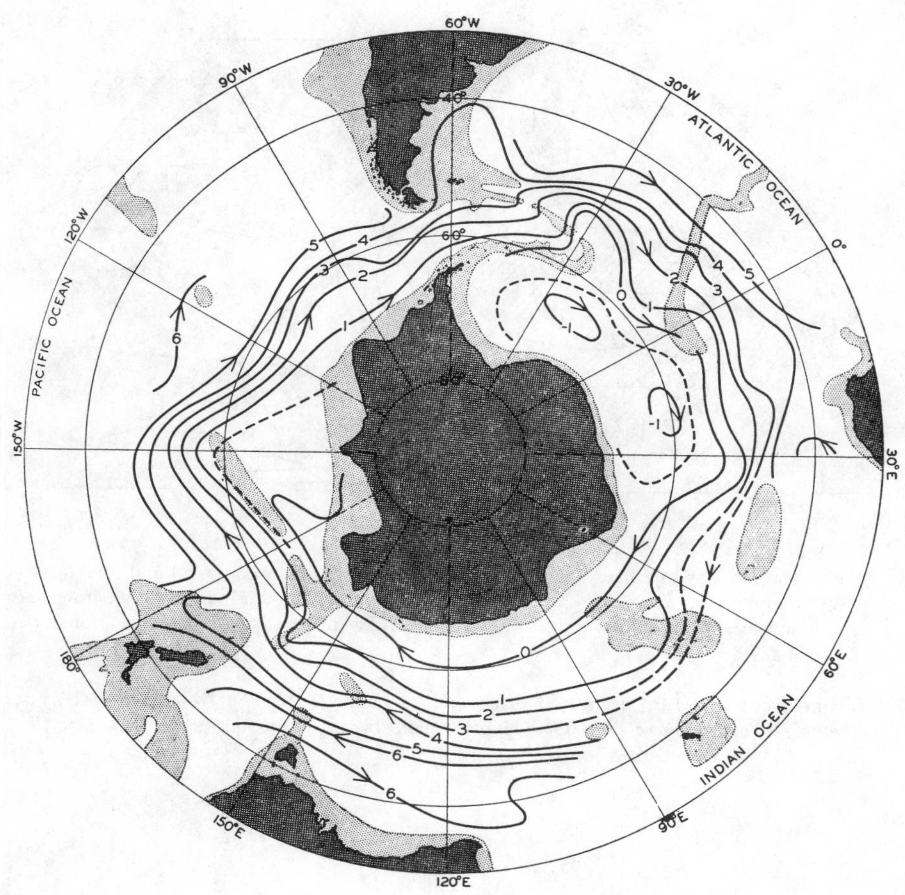

Note: Between two lines the transport relative to the 3000-decibar surface is about 20 mil m^3/sec.

(From Sverdrup, H.U., Johnson, M.W., and Fleming, R.H., *The Oceans, Their Physics, Chemistry, and General Biology*, Prentice-Hall, Inc., Englewood Cliffs, N.J., © 1942, renewed 1970. With permission.)

Figure 2.3–4
TRANSPORT OF CENTRAL WATER AND SUBARCTIC WATER IN THE ATLANTIC OCEAN

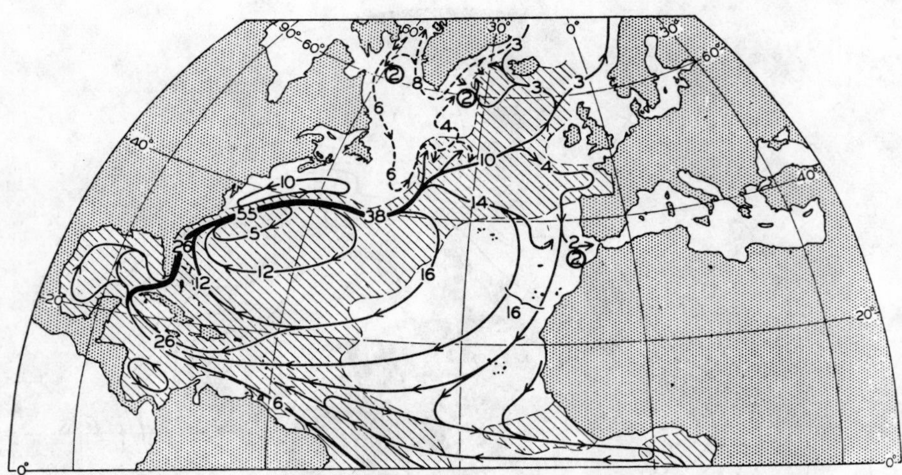

Note: The lines with arrows indicate the direction of the transport, and the inserted numbers indicate the transported volumes in mil m^3/sec. Full-drawn lines show warm currents; dashed lines show cold currents. Areas of positive temperature anomaly are shaded.

(From Sverdrup, H.U., Johnson, M.W., and Fleming, R.H., *The Oceans, Their Physics, Chemistry, and General Biology,* Prentice-Hall, Inc., Englewood Cliffs, N.J., © 1942, renewed 1970. With permission.)

2.4 Underwater Energy Transmission

Tables 2.4–1 to 2.4–7
SOUND SPEED TABLES*

Table 2.4–1 – Sound speed, V_o (1449.1 m/sec), corrected for changes in Pressure (kg/cm²), V_p.
Table 2.4–2 – Sound speed, V_o (1449.1 m/sec), corrected for changes in Depth (meters), (pressures derived assuming 35°/₀₀, 0°C) V_p.
Table 2.4–3 – Correction to sound speed, V_o (1449.1 m/sec), for changes in Latitude-Depth, V_ϕ.
Table 2.4–4 – Correction to sound speed, V_o (1449.1 m/sec), for changes in Salinity (°/₀₀), V_s.
Table 2.4–5 – Correction to sound speed, V_o (1449.1 m/sec), for changes in Temperature (°C), V_t.
Table 2.4–6 – Correction to sound speed, V_o (1449.1 m/sec), for simultaneous changes in Salinity, Temperature, and Pressure, V_{stp}.
Table 2.4–7 – Sound speed conversion – Meters/second to feet/second.

Example A: Determine sound speed (in situ pressure known)

Given: Pressure = 83.5 kg/cm², Latitude = 60°, Salinity = 32.71°/₀₀, Temperature 4.52°C.

From Table 2.4–1, under 83.5 kg/cm²	$1449.1 + V_p$ = 1462.6 m/sec
From Table 2.4–3, under 60° lat	V_ϕ = 0.0 m/sec
From Table 2.4–4, under 32.71°/₀₀	V_s = –3.2 m/sec
From Table 2.4–5, under 4.52°C	V_t = 19.7 m/sec
From Table 2.4–6, under 83.5 kg/cm², 32.71°/₀₀, 4.52°C	V_{stp} = 0.0 m/sec

Sound Speed, $V = 1449.1 + V_p + V_\phi + V_s + V_t + V_{stp}$ = 1479.1 m/sec

Example B: Determine sound speed (assume a water column of 35°/₀₀, 0°C for depth-pressure correction)

Given: Depth-pressure = 2,000 m, latitude = 50°, salinity 35.20°/₀₀, Temperature 5.66°C

From Table 2.4–2, under 2000 m	$1449.1 + V_p$ = 1482.8 m/sec
From Table 2.4–7, under 50°lat.	V_ϕ = 0.1 m/sec
From Table 2.4–4, under 35.20°/₀₀	V_s = 0.3 m/sec
From Table 2.4–5, under 5.66°C	V_t = 24.4 m/sec
From Table 2.4–6, under 2000 m, 35.20°/₀₀, 5.66°C	V_{stp} = –0.2 m/sec

Sound speed, $V = 1449.1 + V_p + V_\phi + V_s + V_{stp}$ = 1507.4 m/sec

* (Based on Wilson's equation, *J. Acoust. Soc. Am.,* 32 (10), 1357, 1960.)

(From *Tables of Sound Speed in Sea Water,* SP-58, U.S. Naval Oceanographic Office, Washington, D.C., 1962.)

Table 2.4–1
SOUND SPEED, V_o (1449.1 m/sec), CORRECTED FOR CHANGES IN PRESSURE (kg/cm^2), V_p

p kg/cm^2	1449.1 + V_p	p kg/cm^2	1449.1 + V_p	p kg/cm^2	1449.1 + V_p	p kg/cm^2	1449.1 + V_p	p kg/cm^2	1449.1 + V_p	p kg/cm^2	1449.1 + V_p	p kg/cm^2	1449.1 + V_p	p kg/cm^2	1449.1 + V_p	p kg/cm^2	1449.1 + V_p
1.03	1449.3	70	1460.4	220	1484.9	370	1510.0	520	1535.5	670	1561.5	820	1587.9	970	1614.5	1120	1641.2
2.00	1449.5	80	1462.0	230	1486.6	380	1511.6	530	1537.2	680	1563.3	830	1589.7	980	1616.3	1130	1643.0
3.00	1449.6	90	1463.6	240	1488.2	390	1513.3	540	1538.9	690	1565.0	840	1591.4	990	1618.1	1140	1644.7
4.00	1449.8	100	1465.3	250	1489.9	400	1515.0	550	1540.7	700	1566.8	850	1593.2	1000	1619.8	1150	1646.5
5.00	1449.9	110	1466.9	260	1491.6	410	1516.7	560	1542.4	710	1568.5	860	1595.0	1010	1621.6	1160	1648.3
6.00	1450.1	120	1468.5	270	1493.2	420	1518.4	570	1544.1	720	1570.3	870	1596.7	1020	1623.4	1170	1650.1
7.00	1450.3	130	1470.2	280	1494.9	430	1520.1	580	1545.9	730	1572.0	880	1598.5	1030	1625.2	1180	1651.8
8.00	1450.4	140	1471.8	290	1496.5	440	1521.8	590	1547.6	740	1573.8	890	1600.3	1040	1627.0	1190	1653.6
9.00	1450.6	150	1473.4	300	1498.2	450	1523.5	600	1549.3	750	1575.5	900	1602.1	1050	1628.7	1200	1655.4
10.00	1450.7	160	1475.1	310	1499.9	460	1525.2	610	1551.1	760	1577.3	910	1603.8	1060	1630.5	1210	1657.1
20.00	1452.3	170	1476.7	320	1501.6	470	1526.9	620	1552.8	770	1579.1	920	1605.6	1070	1632.3	1220	1658.9
30.00	1454.0	180	1478.3	330	1503.2	480	1528.6	630	1554.5	780	1580.8	930	1607.4	1080	1634.1	1230	1660.7
40.00	1455.6	190	1480.0	340	1504.9	490	1530.4	640	1556.3	790	1582.6	940	1609.2	1090	1635.9	1240	1662.4
50.00	1457.2	200	1481.6	350	1506.6	500	1532.1	650	1558.0	800	1584.4	950	1610.9	1100	1637.6	1250	1664.2
60.00	1458.8	210	1483.3	360	1508.3	510	1533.8	660	1559.8	810	1586.1	960	1612.7	1110	1639.4	1260	1666.0

(From *Tables of Sound Speed in Sea Water,* SP-58, U.S. Naval Oceanographic Office, Washington, D.C., 1962.)

Table 2.4–2

SOUND SPEED, V_0 (1449.1 m/sec), CORRECTED FOR CHANGES IN DEPTH (METERS)*

Depth m	1449.1 + V_p	Depth m	1449.1 + V_p	Depth m	1449.1 + V_p	Depth m	1449.1 + V_p	Depth m	1449.1 + V_p	Depth m	1449.1 + V_p	Depth m	1449.1 + V_p	Depth m	1449.1 + V_p
0	1449.3	80	1450.6	900	1464.3	2500	1491.5	4300	1523.1	6000	1553.8	7700	1585.4	9400	1617.5
1	1449.3	90	1450.8	950	1465.1	2600	1493.2	4400	1524.8	6100	1555.6	7800	1587.2	9500	1619.3
2	1449.3	100	1451.0	1000	1465.9	2700	1494.9	4500	1526.6	6200	1557.5	7900	1589.1	9600	1621.3
3	1449.4	150	1451.8	1050	1466.8	2800	1496.7	4600	1528.4	6300	1559.3	8000	1591.0	9700	1623.2
4	1449.4	200	1452.6	1100	1467.6	2900	1498.4	4700	1530.2	6400	1561.2	8100	1592.9	9800	1625.1
5	1449.4	250	1453.4	1200	1469.3	3000	1500.1	4800	1532.0	6500	1563.0	8200	1594.8	9900	1627.0
6	1449.4	300	1454.3	1300	1471.0	3100	1501.9	4900	1533.8	6600	1564.9	8300	1596.6	10000	1628.9
7	1449.4	350	1455.1	1400	1472.7	3200	1503.6	5000	1535.6	6700	1566.7	8400	1598.5	10100	1630.8
8	1449.4	400	1455.9	1500	1474.4	3300	1505.4	5100	1537.4	6800	1568.6	8500	1600.4	10200	1632.7
9	1449.5	450	1456.7	1600	1476.1	3400	1507.1	5200	1539.2	6900	1570.4	8600	1602.3	10300	1634.6
10	1449.5	500	1457.6	1700	1477.8	3500	1508.9	5300	1541.0	7000	1572.3	8700	1604.2	10400	1636.5
20	1449.6	550	1458.4	1800	1479.5	3600	1510.6	5400	1542.9	7100	1574.1	8800	1606.1	10500	1638.3
30	1449.8	600	1459.2	1900	1481.1	3700	1512.4	5500	1544.7	7200	1576.0	8900	1608.0	10600	1640.2
40	1450.0	650	1460.1	2000	1482.8	3800	1514.2	5600	1546.5	7300	1577.9	9000	1609.9	10700	1642.1
50	1450.1	700	1460.9	2100	1484.6	3900	1515.9	5700	1548.3	7400	1579.7	9100	1611.8	10800	1644.0
60	1450.3	750	1461.8	2200	1486.3	4000	1517.7	5800	1550.1	7500	1581.6	9200	1613.7	10900	1645.9
70	1450.5	800	1462.6	2300	1488.0	4100	1519.5	5900	1552.0	7600	1583.5	9300	1615.6	11000	1647.8
75	1450.5	850	1463.4	2400	1489.7	4200	1521.3								

*Pressures derived assuming 35°/∘∘, 0°C, V_p.

(From *Tables of Sound Speed in Sea Water,* SP-58, U.S. Naval Oceanographic Office, Washington, D.C., 1962.)

Table 2.4–3
CORRECTION TO SOUND SPEED, V_o (1449.1 m/sec), FOR CHANGES IN LATITUDE-DEPTH, V_ϕ

Depth m	Latitude 0°	10°	20°	30°	40°	50°	60°	70°	80°	90°
0	0	0	0	0	0	0	0	0	0	0
1000	-.1	0	0	0	0	0	0	.1	.1	.1
2000	-.1	-.1	-.1	0	0	.1	.1	.1	.1	.1
3000	-.1	-.1	-.1	0	0	.1	.1	.1	.2	.2
4000	-.1	-.1	-.1	0	0	.1	.2	.2	.3	.3
5000	-.2	-.1	-.1	0	-.1	.1	.2	.3	.3	.3
6000	-.2	-.2	-.1	0	-.1	.2	.2	.3	.4	.4
7000	-.2	-.2	-.1	-.1	-.1	.2	.3	.3	.4	.4
8000	-.2	-.2	-.2	-.1	-.1	.2				
9000	-.3	-.2	-.2	-.1						
10,000	-.3	-.3	-.2	-.1						
11,000		-.3	-.2	-.1						

(From *Tables of Sound Speed in Sea Water*, SP-58, U.S. Naval Oceanographic Office, Washington, D.C., 1962.)

Table 2.4–4
CORRECTION TO SOUND SPEED, V_o (1449.1 m/sec), FOR CHANGES IN SALINITY (°/₀₀), V_s

S	0.00	0.01	0.02	0.03	0.04	0.05	0.06	0.07	0.08	0.09
0.0	-46.9	-46.8	-46.8	-46.8	-46.8	-46.8	-46.8	-46.8	-46.8	-46.7
0.1	-46.7	-46.7	-46.7	-46.7	-46.7	-46.7	-46.7	-46.6	-46.6	-46.6
0.2	-46.6	-46.6	-46.6	-46.6	-46.5	-46.5	-46.5	-46.5	-46.5	-46.5
0.3	-46.5	-46.5	-46.4	-46.4	-46.4	-46.4	-46.4	-46.4	-46.4	-46.4
0.4	-46.3	-46.3	-46.3	-46.3	-46.3	-46.3	-46.3	-46.3	-46.2	-46.2
0.5	-46.2	-46.2	-46.2	-46.2	-46.2	-46.2	-46.1	-46.1	-46.1	-46.1
0.6	-46.1	-46.1	-46.1	-46.1	-46.0	-46.0	-46.0	-46.0	-46.0	-46.0
0.7	-46.0	-45.9	-45.9	-45.9	-45.9	-45.9	-45.9	-45.9	-45.9	-45.8
0.8	-45.8	-45.8	-45.8	-45.8	-45.8	-45.8	-45.8	-45.7	-45.7	-45.7
0.9	-45.7	-45.7	-45.7	-45.7	-45.7	-45.6	-45.6	-45.6	-45.6	-45.6
1.0	-45.6	-45.6	-45.6	-45.5	-45.5	-45.5	-45.5	-45.5	-45.5	-45.5
1.1	-45.4	-45.4	-45.4	-45.4	-45.4	-45.4	-45.4	-45.4	-45.3	-45.3
1.2	-45.3	-45.3	-45.3	-45.3	-45.3	-45.3	-45.2	-45.2	-45.2	-45.2
1.3	-45.2	-45.2	-45.2	-45.2	-45.1	-45.1	-45.1	-45.1	-45.1	-45.1
1.4	-45.1	-45.0	-45.0	-45.0	-45.0	-45.0	-45.0	-45.0	-45.0	-44.9
1.5	-44.9	-44.9	-44.9	-44.9	-44.9	-44.9	-44.9	-44.8	-44.8	-44.8
1.6	-44.8	-44.8	-44.8	-44.8	-44.8	-44.7	-44.7	-44.7	-44.7	-44.7
1.7	-44.7	-44.7	-44.7	-44.6	-44.6	-44.6	-44.6	-44.6	-44.6	-44.6
1.8	-44.5	-44.5	-44.5	-44.5	-44.5	-44.5	-44.5	-44.5	-44.4	-44.4
1.9	-44.4	-44.4	-44.4	-44.4	-44.4	-44.4	-44.3	-44.3	-44.3	-44.3
2.0	-44.3	-44.3	-44.3	-44.3	-44.2	-44.2	-44.2	-44.2	-44.2	-44.2
2.1	-44.2	-44.1	-44.1	-44.1	-44.1	-44.1	-44.1	-44.1	-44.1	-44.0
2.2	-44.0	-44.0	-44.0	-44.0	-44.0	-44.0	-44.0	-43.9	-43.9	-43.9
2.3	-43.9	-43.9	-43.9	-43.9	-43.9	-43.8	-43.8	-43.8	-43.8	-43.8
2.4	-43.8	-43.8	-43.8	-43.7	-43.7	-43.7	-43.7	-43.7	-43.7	-43.7
2.5	-43.6	-43.6	-43.6	-43.6	-43.6	-43.6	-43.6	-43.6	-43.5	-43.5
2.6	-43.5	-43.5	-43.5	-43.5	-43.5	-43.5	-43.4	-43.4	-43.4	-43.4
2.7	-43.4	-43.4	-43.4	-43.4	-43.3	-43.3	-43.3	-43.3	-43.3	-43.3
2.8	-43.3	-43.2	-43.2	-43.2	-43.2	-43.2	-43.2	-43.2	-43.2	-43.1
2.9	-43.1	-43.1	-43.1	-43.1	-43.1	-43.1	-43.1	-43.0	-43.0	-43.0
3.0	-43.0	-43.0	-43.0	-43.0	-43.0	-42.9	-42.9	-42.9	-42.9	-42.9
3.1	-42.9	-42.9	-42.8	-42.8	-42.8	-42.8	-42.8	-42.8	-42.8	-42.8
3.2	-42.7	-42.7	-42.7	-42.7	-42.7	-42.7	-42.7	-42.7	-42.6	-42.6
3.3	-42.6	-42.6	-42.6	-42.6	-42.6	-42.6	-42.5	-42.5	-42.5	-42.5
3.4	-42.5	-42.5	-42.5	-42.4	-42.4	-42.4	-42.4	-42.4	-42.4	-42.4
3.5	-42.4	-42.3	-42.3	-42.3	-42.3	-42.3	-42.3	-42.3	-42.3	-42.2
3.6	-42.2	-42.2	-42.2	-42.2	-42.2	-42.2	-42.2	-42.1	-42.1	-42.1
3.7	-42.1	-42.1	-42.1	-42.1	-42.0	-42.0	-42.0	-42.0	-42.0	-42.0
3.8	-42.0	-42.0	-41.9	-41.9	-41.9	-41.9	-41.9	-41.9	-41.9	-41.9
3.9	-41.8	-41.8	-41.8	-41.8	-41.8	-41.8	-41.8	-41.8	-41.7	-41.7
4.0	-41.7	-41.7	-41.7	-41.7	-41.7	-41.6	-41.6	-41.6	-41.6	-41.6
4.1	-41.6	-41.6	-41.6	-41.5	-41.5	-41.5	-41.5	-41.5	-41.5	-41.5
4.2	-41.5	-41.4	-41.4	-41.4	-41.4	-41.4	-41.4	-41.4	-41.3	-41.3
4.3	-41.3	-41.3	-41.3	-41.3	-41.3	-41.3	-41.2	-41.2	-41.2	-41.2
4.4	-41.2	-41.2	-41.2	-41.2	-41.1	-41.1	-41.1	-41.1	-41.1	-41.1

Table 2.4–4 (*Continued*)

S	0.00	0.01	0.02	0.03	0.04	0.05	0.06	0.07	0.08	0.09
4.5	-41.1	-41.1	-41.0	-41.0	-41.0	-41.0	-41.0	-41.0	-41.0	-40.9
4.6	-40.9	-40.9	-40.9	-40.9	-40.9	-40.9	-40.9	-40.8	-40.8	-40.8
4.7	-40.8	-40.8	-40.8	-40.8	-40.8	-40.7	-40.7	-40.7	-40.7	-40.7
4.8	-40.7	-40.7	-40.7	-40.6	-40.6	-40.6	-40.6	-40.6	-40.6	-40.6
4.9	-40.5	-40.5	-40.5	-40.5	-40.5	-40.5	-40.5	-40.5	-40.4	-40.4
5.0	-40.4	-40.4	-40.4	-40.4	-40.4	-40.4	-40.3	-40.3	-40.3	-40.3
5.1	-40.3	-40.3	-40.3	-40.2	-40.2	-40.2	-40.2	-40.2	-40.2	-40.2
5.2	-40.2	-40.1	-40.1	-40.1	-40.1	-40.1	-40.1	-40.1	-40.1	-40.0
5.3	-40.0	-40.0	-40.0	-40.0	-40.0	-40.0	-39.9	-39.9	-39.9	-39.9
5.4	-39.9	-39.9	-39.9	-39.9	-39.8	-39.8	-39.8	-39.8	-39.8	-39.8
5.5	-39.8	-39.8	-39.7	-39.7	-39.7	-39.7	-39.7	-39.7	-39.7	-39.7
5.6	-39.6	-39.6	-39.6	-39.6	-39.6	-39.6	-39.6	-39.5	-39.5	-39.5
5.7	-39.5	-39.5	-39.5	-39.5	-39.5	-39.4	-39.4	-39.4	-39.4	-39.4
5.8	-39.4	-39.4	-39.4	-39.3	-39.3	-39.3	-39.3	-39.3	-39.3	-39.3
5.9	-39.2	-39.2	-39.2	-39.2	-39.2	-39.2	-39.2	-39.2	-39.1	-39.1
6.0	-39.1	-39.1	-39.1	-39.1	-39.1	-39.1	-39.0	-39.0	-39.0	-39.0
6.1	-39.0	-39.0	-39.0	-38.9	-38.9	-38.9	-38.9	-38.9	-38.9	-38.9
6.2	-38.9	-38.8	-38.8	-38.8	-38.8	-38.8	-38.8	-38.8	-38.8	-38.7
6.3	-38.7	-38.7	-38.7	-38.7	-38.7	-38.7	-38.7	-38.6	-38.6	-38.6
6.4	-38.6	-38.6	-38.6	-38.6	-38.5	-38.5	-38.5	-38.5	-38.5	-38.5
6.5	-38.5	-38.5	-38.4	-38.4	-38.4	-38.4	-38.4	-38.4	-38.4	-38.4
6.6	-38.3	-38.3	-38.3	-38.3	-38.3	-38.3	-38.3	-38.2	-38.2	-38.2
6.7	-38.2	-38.2	-38.2	-38.2	-38.2	-38.1	-38.1	-38.1	-38.1	-38.1
6.8	-38.1	-38.1	-38.1	-38.0	-38.0	-38.0	-38.0	-38.0	-38.0	-38.0
6.9	-37.9	-37.9	-37.9	-37.9	-37.9	-37.9	-37.9	-37.9	-37.8	-37.8
7.0	-37.8	-37.8	-37.8	-37.8	-37.8	-37.8	-37.7	-37.7	-37.7	-37.7
7.1	-37.7	-37.7	-37.7	-37.6	-37.6	-37.6	-37.6	-37.6	-37.6	-37.6
7.2	-37.6	-37.5	-37.5	-37.5	-37.5	-37.5	-37.5	-37.5	-37.5	-37.4
7.3	-37.4	-37.4	-37.4	-37.4	-37.4	-37.4	-37.3	-37.3	-37.3	-37.3
7.4	-37.3	-37.3	-37.3	-37.3	-37.2	-37.2	-37.2	-37.2	-37.2	-37.2
7.5	-37.2	-37.2	-37.1	-37.1	-37.1	-37.1	-37.1	-37.1	-37.1	-37.0
7.6	-37.0	-37.0	-37.0	-37.0	-37.0	-37.0	-37.0	-36.9	-36.9	-36.9
7.7	-36.9	-36.9	-36.9	-36.9	-36.9	-36.8	-36.8	-36.8	-36.8	-36.8
7.8	-36.8	-36.8	-36.7	-36.7	-36.7	-36.7	-36.7	-36.7	-36.7	-36.7
7.9	-36.6	-36.6	-36.6	-36.6	-36.6	-36.6	-36.6	-36.6	-36.5	-36.5
8.0	-36.5	-36.5	-36.5	-36.5	-36.5	-36.4	-36.4	-36.4	-36.4	-36.4
8.1	-36.4	-36.4	-36.4	-36.3	-36.3	-36.3	-36.3	-36.3	-36.3	-36.3
8.2	-36.3	-36.2	-36.2	-36.2	-36.2	-36.2	-36.2	-36.2	-36.1	-36.1
8.3	-36.1	-36.1	-36.1	-36.1	-36.1	-36.1	-36.0	-36.0	-36.0	-36.0
8.4	-36.0	-36.0	-36.0	-36.0	-35.9	-35.9	-35.9	-35.9	-35.9	-35.9
8.5	-35.9	-35.8	-35.8	-35.8	-35.8	-35.8	-35.8	-35.8	-35.8	-35.7
8.6	-35.7	-35.7	-35.7	-35.7	-35.7	-35.7	-35.6	-35.6	-35.6	-35.6
8.7	-35.6	-35.6	-35.6	-35.6	-35.5	-35.5	-35.5	-35.5	-35.5	-35.5
8.8	-35.5	-35.5	-35.4	-35.4	-35.4	-35.4	-35.4	-35.4	-35.4	-35.3
8.9	-35.3	-35.3	-35.3	-35.3	-35.3	-35.3	-35.3	-35.2	-35.2	-35.2
9.0	-35.2	-35.2	-35.2	-35.2	-35.2	-35.1	-35.1	-35.1	-35.1	-35.1
9.1	-35.1	-35.1	-35.0	-35.0	-35.0	-35.0	-35.0	-35.0	-35.0	-35.0
9.2	-34.9	-34.9	-34.9	-34.9	-34.9	-34.9	-34.9	-34.9	-34.8	-34.8
9.3	-34.8	-34.8	-34.8	-34.8	-34.8	-34.7	-34.7	-34.7	-34.7	-34.7
9.4	-34.7	-34.7	-34.7	-34.6	-34.6	-34.6	-34.6	-34.6	-34.6	-34.6

Table 2.4–4 (*Continued*)

S	0.00	0.01	0.02	0.03	0.04	0.05	0.06	0.07	0.08	0.09
9.5	-34.5	-34.5	-34.5	-34.5	-34.5	-34.5	-34.5	-34.5	-34.4	-34.4
9.6	-34.4	-34.4	-34.4	-34.4	-34.4	-34.4	-34.3	-34.3	-34.3	-34.3
9.7	-34.3	-34.3	-34.3	-34.2	-34.2	-34.2	-34.2	-34.2	-34.2	-34.2
9.8	-34.2	-34.1	-34.1	-34.1	-34.1	-34.1	-34.1	-34.1	-34.0	-34.0
9.9	-34.0	-34.0	-34.0	-34.0	-34.0	-34.0	-33.9	-33.9	-33.9	-33.9
10.0	-33.9	-33.9	-33.9	-33.9	-33.8	-33.8	-33.8	-33.8	-33.8	-33.8
10.1	-33.8	-33.7	-33.7	-33.7	-33.7	-33.7	-33.7	-33.7	-33.7	-33.6
10.2	-33.6	-33.6	-33.6	-33.6	-33.6	-33.6	-33.6	-33.5	-33.5	-33.5
10.3	-33.5	-33.5	-33.5	-33.5	-33.4	-33.4	-33.4	-33.4	-33.4	-33.4
10.4	-33.4	-33.4	-33.3	-33.3	-33.3	-33.3	-33.3	-33.3	-33.3	-33.2
10.5	-33.2	-33.2	-33.2	-33.2	-33.2	-33.2	-33.2	-33.1	-33.1	-33.1
10.6	-33.1	-33.1	-33.1	-33.1	-33.1	-33.0	-33.0	-33.0	-33.0	-33.0
10.7	-33.0	-33.0	-32.9	-32.9	-32.9	-32.9	-32.9	-32.9	-32.9	-32.9
10.8	-32.8	-32.8	-32.8	-32.8	-32.8	-32.8	-32.8	-32.7	-32.7	-32.7
10.9	-32.7	-32.7	-32.7	-32.7	-32.7	-32.6	-32.6	-32.6	-32.6	-32.6
11.0	-32.6	-32.6	-32.6	-32.5	-32.5	-32.5	-32.5	-32.5	-32.5	-32.5
11.1	-32.4	-32.4	-32.4	-32.4	-32.4	-32.4	-32.4	-32.4	-32.3	-32.3
11.2	-32.3	-32.3	-32.3	-32.3	-32.3	-32.2	-32.2	-32.2	-32.2	-32.2
11.3	-32.2	-32.2	-32.2	-32.1	-32.1	-32.1	-32.1	-32.1	-32.1	-32.1
11.4	-32.1	-32.0	-32.0	-32.0	-32.0	-32.0	-32.0	-32.0	-31.9	-31.9
11.5	-31.9	-31.9	-31.9	-31.9	-31.9	-31.9	-31.8	-31.8	-31.8	-31.8
11.6	-31.8	-31.8	-31.8	-31.7	-31.7	-31.7	-31.7	-31.7	-31.7	-31.7
11.7	-31.7	-31.6	-31.6	-31.6	-31.6	-31.6	-31.6	-31.6	-31.5	-31.5
11.8	-31.5	-31.5	-31.5	-31.5	-31.5	-31.5	-31.4	-31.4	-31.4	-31.4
11.9	-31.4	-31.4	-31.4	-31.4	-31.3	-31.3	-31.3	-31.3	-31.3	-31.3
12.0	-31.3	-31.2	-31.2	-31.2	-31.2	-31.2	-31.2	-31.2	-31.2	-31.1
12.1	-31.1	-31.1	-31.1	-31.1	-31.1	-31.1	-31.0	-31.0	-31.0	-31.0
12.2	-31.0	-31.0	-31.0	-31.0	-30.9	-30.9	-30.9	-30.9	-30.9	-30.9
12.3	-30.9	-30.8	-30.8	-30.8	-30.8	-30.8	-30.8	-30.8	-30.8	-30.7
12.4	-30.7	-30.7	-30.7	-30.7	-30.7	-30.7	-30.7	-30.6	-30.6	-30.6
12.5	-30.6	-30.6	-30.6	-30.6	-30.5	-30.5	-30.5	-30.5	-30.5	-30.5
12.6	-30.5	-30.5	-30.4	-30.4	-30.4	-30.4	-30.4	-30.4	-30.4	-30.3
12.7	-30.3	-30.3	-30.3	-30.3	-30.3	-30.3	-30.3	-30.2	-30.2	-30.2
12.8	-30.2	-30.2	-30.2	-30.2	-30.1	-30.1	-30.1	-30.1	-30.1	-30.1
12.9	-30.1	-30.1	-30.0	-30.0	-30.0	-30.0	-30.0	-30.0	-30.0	-30.0
13.0	-29.9	-29.9	-29.9	-29.9	-29.9	-29.9	-29.9	-29.8	-29.8	-29.8
13.1	-29.8	-29.8	-29.8	-29.8	-29.8	-29.7	-29.7	-29.7	-29.7	-29.7
13.2	-29.7	-29.7	-29.6	-29.6	-29.6	-29.6	-29.6	-29.6	-29.6	-29.6
13.3	-29.5	-29.5	-29.5	-29.5	-29.5	-29.5	-29.5	-29.4	-29.4	-29.4
13.4	-29.4	-29.4	-29.4	-29.4	-29.4	-29.3	-29.3	-29.3	-29.3	-29.3
13.5	-29.3	-29.3	-29.2	-29.2	-29.2	-29.2	-29.2	-29.2	-29.2	-29.2
13.6	-29.1	-29.1	-29.1	-29.1	-29.1	-29.1	-29.1	-29.0	-29.0	-29.0
13.7	-29.0	-29.0	-29.0	-29.0	-29.0	-28.9	-28.9	-28.9	-28.9	-28.9
13.8	-28.9	-28.9	-28.9	-28.8	-28.8	-28.8	-28.8	-28.8	-28.8	-28.8
13.9	-28.7	-28.7	-28.7	-28.7	-28.7	-28.7	-28.7	-28.7	-28.6	-28.6

Table 2.4–4 (*Continued*)

S	0.00	0.01	0.02	0.03	0.04	0.05	0.06	0.07	0.08	0.09
14.0	-28.6	-28.6	-28.6	-28.6	-28.6	-28.5	-28.5	-28.5	-28.5	-28.5
14.1	-28.5	-28.5	-28.5	-28.4	-28.4	-28.4	-28.4	-28.4	-28.4	-28.4
14.2	-28.3	-28.3	-28.3	-28.3	-28.3	-28.3	-28.3	-28.3	-28.2	-28.2
14.3	-28.2	-28.2	-28.2	-28.2	-28.2	-28.1	-28.1	-28.1	-28.1	-28.1
14.4	-28.1	-28.1	-28.1	-28.0	-28.0	-28.0	-28.0	-28.0	-28.0	-28.0
14.5	-27.9	-27.9	-27.9	-27.9	-27.9	-27.9	-27.9	-27.9	-27.8	-27.8
14.6	-27.8	-27.8	-27.8	-27.8	-27.8	-27.7	-27.7	-27.7	-27.7	-27.7
14.7	-27.7	-27.7	-27.7	-27.6	-27.6	-27.6	-27.6	-27.6	-27.6	-27.6
14.8	-27.5	-27.5	-27.5	-27.5	-27.5	-27.5	-27.5	-27.5	-27.4	-27.4
14.9	-27.4	-27.4	-27.4	-27.4	-27.4	-27.3	-27.3	-27.3	-27.3	-27.3
15.0	-27.3	-27.3	-27.3	-27.2	-27.2	-27.2	-27.2	-27.2	-27.2	-27.2
15.1	-27.1	-27.1	-27.1	-27.1	-27.1	-27.1	-27.1	-27.1	-27.0	-27.0
15.2	-27.0	-27.0	-27.0	-27.0	-27.0	-27.0	-26.9	-26.9	-26.9	-26.9
15.3	-26.9	-26.9	-26.9	-26.8	-26.8	-26.8	-26.8	-26.8	-26.8	-26.8
15.4	-26.8	-26.7	-26.7	-26.7	-26.7	-26.7	-26.7	-26.7	-26.6	-26.6
15.5	-26.6	-26.6	-26.6	-26.6	-26.6	-26.6	-26.5	-26.5	-26.5	-26.5
15.6	-26.5	-26.5	-26.5	-26.4	-26.4	-26.4	-26.4	-26.4	-26.4	-26.4
15.7	-26.4	-26.3	-26.3	-26.3	-26.3	-26.3	-26.3	-26.3	-26.2	-26.2
15.8	-26.2	-26.2	-26.2	-26.2	-26.2	-26.2	-26.1	-26.1	-26.1	-26.1
15.9	-26.1	-26.1	-26.1	-26.0	-26.0	-26.0	-26.0	-26.0	-26.0	-26.0
16.0	-26.0	-25.9	-25.9	-25.9	-25.9	-25.9	-25.9	-25.9	-25.8	-25.8
16.1	-25.8	-25.8	-25.8	-25.8	-25.8	-25.8	-25.7	-25.7	-25.7	-25.7
16.2	-25.7	-25.7	-25.7	-25.6	-25.6	-25.6	-25.6	-25.6	-25.6	-25.6
16.3	-25.6	-25.5	-25.5	-25.5	-25.5	-25.5	-25.5	-25.5	-25.4	-25.4
16.4	-25.4	-25.4	-25.4	-25.4	-25.4	-25.4	-25.3	-25.3	-25.3	-25.3
16.5	-25.3	-25.3	-25.3	-25.2	-25.2	-25.2	-25.2	-25.2	-25.2	-25.2
16.6	-25.2	-25.1	-25.1	-25.1	-25.1	-25.1	-25.1	-25.1	-25.0	-25.0
16.7	-25.0	-25.0	-25.0	-25.0	-25.0	-24.9	-24.9	-24.9	-24.9	-24.9
16.8	-24.9	-24.9	-24.9	-24.8	-24.8	-24.8	-24.8	-24.8	-24.8	-24.8
16.9	-24.7	-24.7	-24.7	-24.7	-24.7	-24.7	-24.7	-24.7	-24.6	-24.6
17.0	-24.6	-24.6	-24.6	-24.6	-24.6	-24.5	-24.5	-24.5	-24.5	-24.5
17.1	-24.5	-24.5	-24.5	-24.4	-24.4	-24.4	-24.4	-24.4	-24.4	-24.4
17.2	-24.3	-24.3	-24.3	-24.3	-24.3	-24.3	-24.3	-24.3	-24.2	-24.2
17.3	-24.2	-24.2	-24.2	-24.2	-24.2	-24.1	-24.1	-24.1	-24.1	-24.1
17.4	-24.1	-24.1	-24.1	-24.0	-24.0	-24.0	-24.0	-24.0	-24.0	-24.0
17.5	-23.9	-23.9	-23.9	-23.9	-23.9	-23.9	-23.9	-23.9	-23.8	-23.8
17.6	-23.8	-23.8	-23.8	-23.8	-23.8	-23.7	-23.7	-23.7	-23.7	-23.7
17.7	-23.7	-23.7	-23.7	-23.6	-23.6	-23.6	-23.6	-23.6	-23.6	-23.6
17.8	-23.5	-23.5	-23.5	-23.5	-23.5	-23.5	-23.5	-23.5	-23.4	-23.4
17.9	-23.4	-23.4	-23.4	-23.4	-23.4	-23.3	-23.3	-23.3	-23.3	-23.3
18.0	-23.3	-23.3	-23.3	-23.2	-23.2	-23.2	-23.2	-23.2	-23.2	-23.2
18.1	-23.1	-23.1	-23.1	-23.1	-23.1	-23.1	-23.1	-23.0	-23.0	-23.0
18.2	-23.0	-23.0	-23.0	-23.0	-23.0	-22.9	-22.9	-22.9	-22.9	-22.9
18.3	-22.9	-22.9	-22.8	-22.8	-22.8	-22.8	-22.8	-22.8	-22.8	-22.8
18.4	-22.7	-22.7	-22.7	-22.7	-22.7	-22.7	-22.7	-22.6	-22.6	-22.6
18.5	-22.6	-22.6	-22.6	-22.6	-22.6	-22.5	-22.5	-22.5	-22.5	-22.5
18.6	-22.5	-22.5	-22.4	-22.4	-22.4	-22.4	-22.4	-22.4	-22.4	-22.4
18.7	-22.3	-22.3	-22.3	-22.3	-22.3	-22.3	-22.3	-22.2	-22.2	-22.2
18.8	-22.2	-22.2	-22.2	-22.2	-22.1	-22.1	-22.1	-22.1	-22.1	-22.1
18.9	-22.1	-22.1	-22.0	-22.0	-22.0	-22.0	-22.0	-22.0	-22.0	-21.9

Table 2.4–4 (*Continued*)

S	0.00	0.01	0.02	0.03	0.04	0.05	0.06	0.07	0.08	0.09
19.0	-21.9	-21.9	-21.9	-21.9	-21.9	-21.9	-21.9	-21.8	-21.8	-21.8
19.1	-21.8	-21.8	-21.8	-21.8	-21.7	-21.7	-21.7	-21.7	-21.7	-21.7
19.2	-21.7	-21.7	-21.6	-21.6	-21.6	-21.6	-21.6	-21.6	-21.6	-21.5
19.3	-21.5	-21.5	-21.5	-21.5	-21.5	-21.5	-21.5	-21.4	-21.4	-21.4
19.4	-21.4	-21.4	-21.4	-21.4	-21.3	-21.3	-21.3	-21.3	-21.3	-21.3
19.5	-21.3	-21.2	-21.2	-21.2	-21.2	-21.2	-21.2	-21.2	-21.2	-21.1
19.6	-21.1	-21.1	-21.1	-21.1	-21.1	-21.1	-21.0	-21.0	-21.0	-21.0
19.7	-21.0	-21.0	-21.0	-21.0	-20.9	-20.9	-20.9	-20.9	-20.9	-20.9
19.8	-20.9	-20.8	-20.8	-20.8	-20.8	-20.8	-20.8	-20.8	-20.8	-20.7
19.9	-20.7	-20.7	-20.7	-20.7	-20.7	-20.7	-20.6	-20.6	-20.6	-20.6
20.0	-20.6	-20.6	-20.6	-20.5	-20.5	-20.5	-20.5	-20.5	-20.5	-20.5
20.1	-20.5	-20.4	-20.4	-20.4	-20.4	-20.4	-20.4	-20.4	-20.3	-20.3
20.2	-20.3	-20.3	-20.3	-20.3	-20.3	-20.3	-20.2	-20.2	-20.2	-20.2
20.3	-20.2	-20.2	-20.2	-20.1	-20.1	-20.1	-20.1	-20.1	-20.1	-20.1
20.4	-20.0	-20.0	-20.0	-20.0	-20.0	-20.0	-20.0	-20.0	-19.9	-19.9
20.5	-19.9	-19.9	-19.9	-19.9	-19.9	-19.8	-19.8	-19.8	-19.8	-19.8
20.6	-19.8	-19.8	-19.8	-19.7	-19.7	-19.7	-19.7	-19.7	-19.7	-19.7
20.7	-19.6	-19.6	-19.6	-19.6	-19.6	-19.6	-19.6	-19.6	-19.5	-19.5
20.8	-19.5	-19.5	-19.5	-19.5	-19.5	-19.4	-19.4	-19.4	-19.4	-19.4
20.9	-19.4	-19.4	-19.3	-19.3	-19.3	-19.3	-19.3	-19.3	-19.3	-19.3
21.0	-19.2	-19.2	-19.2	-19.2	-19.2	-19.2	-19.2	-19.1	-19.1	-19.1
21.1	-19.1	-19.1	-19.1	-19.1	-19.1	-19.0	-19.0	-19.0	-19.0	-19.0
21.2	-19.0	-19.0	-18.9	-18.9	-18.9	-18.9	-18.9	-18.9	-18.9	-18.8
21.3	-18.8	-18.8	-18.8	-18.8	-18.8	-18.8	-18.8	-18.7	-18.7	-18.7
21.4	-18.7	-18.7	-18.7	-18.7	-18.6	-18.6	-18.6	-18.6	-18.6	-18.6
21.5	-18.6	-18.6	-18.5	-18.5	-18.5	-18.5	-18.5	-18.5	-18.5	-18.4
21.6	-18.4	-18.4	-18.4	-18.4	-18.4	-18.4	-18.3	-18.3	-18.3	-18.3
21.7	-18.3	-18.3	-18.3	-18.3	-18.2	-18.2	-18.2	-18.2	-18.2	-18.2
21.8	-18.2	-18.1	-18.1	-18.1	-18.1	-18.1	-18.1	-18.1	-18.1	-18.0
21.9	-18.0	-18.0	-18.0	-18.0	-18.0	-18.0	-17.9	-17.9	-17.9	-17.9
22.0	-17.9	-17.9	-17.9	-17.8	-17.8	-17.8	-17.8	-17.8	-17.8	-17.8
22.1	-17.8	-17.7	-17.7	-17.7	-17.7	-17.7	-17.7	-17.7	-17.6	-17.6
22.2	-17.6	-17.6	-17.6	-17.6	-17.6	-17.5	-17.5	-17.5	-17.5	-17.5
22.3	-17.5	-17.5	-17.5	-17.4	-17.4	-17.4	-17.4	-17.4	-17.4	-17.4
22.4	-17.3	-17.3	-17.3	-17.3	-17.3	-17.3	-17.3	-17.3	-17.2	-17.2
22.5	-17.2	-17.2	-17.2	-17.2	-17.2	-17.1	-17.1	-17.1	-17.1	-17.1
22.6	-17.1	-17.1	-17.0	-17.0	-17.0	-17.0	-17.0	-17.0	-17.0	-17.0
22.7	-16.9	-16.9	-16.9	-16.9	-16.9	-16.9	-16.9	-16.8	-16.8	-16.8
22.8	-16.8	-16.8	-16.8	-16.8	-16.7	-16.7	-16.7	-16.7	-16.7	-16.7
22.9	-16.7	-16.7	-16.6	-16.6	-16.6	-16.6	-16.6	-16.6	-16.6	-16.5
23.0	-16.5	-16.5	-16.5	-16.5	-16.5	-16.5	-16.5	-16.4	-16.4	-16.4
23.1	-16.4	-16.4	-16.4	-16.4	-16.3	-16.3	-16.3	-16.3	-16.3	-16.3
23.2	-16.3	-16.2	-16.2	-16.2	-16.2	-16.2	-16.2	-16.2	-16.2	-16.1
23.3	-16.1	-16.1	-16.1	-16.1	-16.1	-16.1	-16.0	-16.0	-16.0	-16.0
23.4	-16.0	-16.0	-16.0	-15.9	-15.9	-15.9	-15.9	-15.9	-15.9	-15.9

Table 2.4–4 (*Continued*)

S	0.00	0.01	0.02	0.03	0.04	0.05	0.06	0.07	0.08	0.09
23.5	-15.9	-15.8	-15.8	-15.8	-15.8	-15.8	-15.8	-15.8	-15.7	-15.7
23.6	-15.7	-15.7	-15.7	-15.7	-15.7	-15.6	-15.6	-15.6	-15.6	-15.6
23.7	-15.6	-15.6	-15.6	-15.5	-15.5	-15.5	-15.5	-15.5	-15.5	-15.5
23.8	-15.4	-15.4	-15.4	-15.4	-15.4	-15.4	-15.4	-15.4	-15.3	-15.3
23.9	-15.3	-15.3	-15.3	-15.3	-15.3	-15.2	-15.2	-15.2	-15.2	-15.2
24.0	-15.2	-15.2	-15.1	-15.1	-15.1	-15.1	-15.1	-15.1	-15.1	-15.1
24.1	-15.0	-15.0	-15.0	-15.0	-15.0	-15.0	-15.0	-14.9	-14.9	-14.9
24.2	-14.9	-14.9	-14.9	-14.9	-14.8	-14.8	-14.8	-14.8	-14.8	-14.8
24.3	-14.8	-14.8	-14.7	-14.7	-14.7	-14.7	-14.7	-14.7	-14.7	-14.6
24.4	-14.6	-14.6	-14.6	-14.6	-14.6	-14.6	-14.5	-14.5	-14.5	-14.5
24.5	-14.5	-14.5	-14.5	-14.5	-14.4	-14.4	-14.4	-14.4	-14.4	-14.4
24.6	-14.4	-14.3	-14.3	-14.3	-14.3	-14.3	-14.3	-14.3	-14.2	-14.2
24.7	-14.2	-14.2	-14.2	-14.2	-14.2	-14.2	-14.1	-14.1	-14.1	-14.1
24.8	-14.1	-14.1	-14.1	-14.0	-14.0	-14.0	-14.0	-14.0	-14.0	-14.0
24.9	-13.9	-13.9	-13.9	-13.9	-13.9	-13.9	-13.9	-13.9	-13.8	-13.8
25.0	-13.8	-13.8	-13.8	-13.8	-13.8	-13.7	-13.7	-13.7	-13.7	-13.7
25.1	-13.7	-13.7	-13.6	-13.6	-13.6	-13.6	-13.6	-13.6	-13.6	-13.6
25.2	-13.5	-13.5	-13.5	-13.5	-13.5	-13.5	-13.5	-13.4	-13.4	-13.4
25.3	-13.4	-13.4	-13.4	-13.4	-13.3	-13.3	-13.3	-13.3	-13.3	-13.3
25.4	-13.3	-13.3	-13.2	-13.2	-13.2	-13.2	-13.2	-13.2	-13.2	-13.1
25.5	-13.1	-13.1	-13.1	-13.1	-13.1	-13.1	-13.0	-13.0	-13.0	-13.0
25.6	-13.0	-13.0	-13.0	-13.0	-12.9	-12.9	-12.9	-12.9	-12.9	-12.9
25.7	-12.9	-12.8	-12.8	-12.8	-12.8	-12.8	-12.8	-12.8	-12.7	-12.7
25.8	-12.7	-12.7	-12.7	-12.7	-12.7	-12.6	-12.6	-12.6	-12.6	-12.6
25.9	-12.6	-12.6	-12.6	-12.5	-12.5	-12.5	-12.5	-12.5	-12.5	-12.5
26.0	-12.4	-12.4	-12.4	-12.4	-12.4	-12.4	-12.4	-12.3	-12.3	-12.3
26.1	-12.3	-12.3	-12.3	-12.3	-12.3	-12.2	-12.2	-12.2	-12.2	-12.2
26.2	-12.2	-12.2	-12.1	-12.1	-12.1	-12.1	-12.1	-12.1	-12.1	-12.0
26.3	-12.0	-12.0	-12.0	-12.0	-12.0	-12.0	-12.0	-11.9	-11.9	-11.9
26.4	-11.9	-11.9	-11.9	-11.9	-11.8	-11.8	-11.8	-11.8	-11.8	-11.8
26.5	-11.8	-11.7	-11.7	-11.7	-11.7	-11.7	-11.7	-11.7	-11.7	-11.6
26.6	-11.6	-11.6	-11.6	-11.6	-11.6	-11.6	-11.5	-11.5	-11.5	-11.5
26.7	-11.5	-11.5	-11.5	-11.4	-11.4	-11.4	-11.4	-11.4	-11.4	-11.4
26.8	-11.3	-11.3	-11.3	-11.3	-11.3	-11.3	-11.3	-11.3	-11.2	-11.2
26.9	-11.2	-11.2	-11.2	-11.2	-11.2	-11.1	-11.1	-11.1	-11.1	-11.1
27.0	-11.1	-11.1	-11.0	-11.0	-11.0	-11.0	-11.0	-11.0	-11.0	-11.0
27.1	-10.9	-10.9	-10.9	-10.9	-10.9	-10.9	-10.9	-10.8	-10.8	-10.8
27.2	-10.8	-10.8	-10.8	-10.8	-10.7	-10.7	-10.7	-10.7	-10.7	-10.7
27.3	-10.7	-10.7	-10.6	-10.6	-10.6	-10.6	-10.6	-10.6	-10.6	-10.5
27.4	-10.5	-10.5	-10.5	-10.5	-10.5	-10.5	-10.4	-10.4	-10.4	-10.4
27.5	-10.4	-10.4	-10.4	-10.3	-10.3	-10.3	-10.3	-10.3	-10.3	-10.3
27.6	-10.3	-10.2	-10.2	-10.2	-10.2	-10.2	-10.2	-10.2	-10.1	-10.1
27.7	-10.1	-10.1	-10.1	-10.1	-10.1	-10.0	-10.0	-10.0	-10.0	-10.0
27.8	-10.0	-10.0	-10.0	-9.9	-9.9	-9.9	-9.9	-9.9	-9.9	-9.9
27.9	-9.8	-9.8	-9.8	-9.8	-9.8	-9.8	-9.8	-9.7	-9.7	-9.7
28.0	-9.7	-9.7	-9.7	-9.7	-9.6	-9.6	-9.6	-9.6	-9.6	-9.6
28.1	-9.6	-9.6	-9.5	-9.5	-9.5	-9.5	-9.5	-9.5	-9.5	-9.4
28.2	-9.4	-9.4	-9.4	-9.4	-9.4	-9.4	-9.3	-9.3	-9.3	-9.3
28.3	-9.3	-9.3	-9.3	-9.2	-9.2	-9.2	-9.2	-9.2	-9.2	-9.2
28.4	-9.2	-9.1	-9.1	-9.1	-9.1	-9.1	-9.1	-9.1	-9.0	-9.0

Table 2.4–4 (*Continued*)

S	0.00	0.01	0.02	0.03	0.04	0.05	0.06	0.07	0.08	0.09
28.5	-9.0	-9.0	-9.0	-9.0	-9.0	-8.9	-8.9	-8.9	-8.9	-8.9
28.6	-8.9	-8.9	-8.9	-8.8	-8.8	-8.8	-8.8	-8.8	-8.8	-8.8
28.7	-8.7	-8.7	-8.7	-8.7	-8.7	-8.7	-8.7	-8.6	-8.6	-8.6
28.8	-8.6	-8.6	-8.6	-8.6	-8.5	-8.5	-8.5	-8.5	-8.5	-8.5
28.9	-8.5	-8.5	-8.4	-8.4	-8.4	-8.4	-8.4	-8.4	-8.4	-8.3
29.0	-8.3	-8.3	-8.3	-8.3	-8.3	-8.3	-8.2	-8.2	-8.2	-8.2
29.1	-8.2	-8.2	-8.2	-8.1	-8.1	-8.1	-8.1	-8.1	-8.1	-8.1
29.2	-8.1	-8.0	-8.0	-8.0	-8.0	-8.0	-8.0	-8.0	-7.9	-7.9
29.3	-7.9	-7.9	-7.9	-7.9	-7.9	-7.8	-7.8	-7.8	-7.8	-7.8
29.4	-7.8	-7.8	-7.7	-7.7	-7.7	-7.7	-7.7	-7.7	-7.7	-7.7
29.5	-7.6	-7.6	-7.6	-7.6	-7.6	-7.6	-7.6	-7.5	-7.5	-7.5
29.6	-7.5	-7.5	-7.5	-7.5	-7.4	-7.4	-7.4	-7.4	-7.4	-7.4
29.7	-7.4	-7.3	-7.3	-7.3	-7.3	-7.3	-7.3	-7.3	-7.3	-7.2
29.8	-7.2	-7.2	-7.2	-7.2	-7.2	-7.2	-7.1	-7.1	-7.1	-7.1
29.9	-7.1	-7.1	-7.1	-7.0	-7.0	-7.0	-7.0	-7.0	-7.0	-7.0
30.0	-6.9	-6.9	-6.9	-6.9	-6.9	-6.9	-6.9	-6.9	-6.8	-6.8
30.1	-6.8	-6.8	-6.8	-6.8	-6.8	-6.7	-6.7	-6.7	-6.7	-6.7
30.2	-6.7	-6.7	-6.6	-6.6	-6.6	-6.6	-6.6	-6.6	-6.6	-6.5
30.3	-6.5	-6.5	-6.5	-6.5	-6.5	-6.5	-6.5	-6.4	-6.4	-6.4
30.4	-6.4	-6.4	-6.4	-6.4	-6.3	-6.3	-6.3	-6.3	-6.3	-6.3
30.5	-6.3	-6.2	-6.2	-6.2	-6.2	-6.2	-6.2	-6.2	-6.1	-6.1
30.6	-6.1	-6.1	-6.1	-6.1	-6.1	-6.0	-6.0	-6.0	-6.0	-6.0
30.7	-6.0	-6.0	-6.0	-5.9	-5.9	-5.9	-5.9	-5.9	-5.9	-5.9
30.8	-5.8	-5.8	-5.8	-5.8	-5.8	-5.8	-5.8	-5.7	-5.7	-5.7
30.9	-5.7	-5.7	-5.7	-5.7	-5.6	-5.6	-5.6	-5.6	-5.6	-5.6
31.0	-5.6	-5.6	-5.5	-5.5	-5.5	-5.5	-5.5	-5.5	-5.5	-5.4
31.1	-5.4	-5.4	-5.4	-5.4	-5.4	-5.4	-5.3	-5.3	-5.3	-5.3
31.2	-5.3	-5.3	-5.3	-5.2	-5.2	-5.2	-5.2	-5.2	-5.2	-5.2
31.3	-5.1	-5.1	-5.1	-5.1	-5.1	-5.1	-5.1	-5.1	-5.0	-5.0
31.4	-5.0	-5.0	-5.0	-5.0	-5.0	-4.9	-4.9	-4.9	-4.9	-4.9
31.5	-4.9	-4.9	-4.8	-4.8	-4.8	-4.8	-4.8	-4.8	-4.8	-4.7
31.6	-4.7	-4.7	-4.7	-4.7	-4.7	-4.7	-4.7	-4.6	-4.6	-4.6
31.7	-4.6	-4.6	-4.6	-4.6	-4.5	-4.5	-4.5	-4.5	-4.5	-4.5
31.8	-4.5	-4.4	-4.4	-4.4	-4.4	-4.4	-4.4	-4.4	-4.3	-4.3
31.9	-4.3	-4.3	-4.3	-4.3	-4.3	-4.2	-4.2	-4.2	-4.2	-4.2
32.0	-4.2	-4.2	-4.2	-4.1	-4.1	-4.1	-4.1	-4.1	-4.1	-4.1
32.1	-4.0	-4.0	-4.0	-4.0	-4.0	-4.0	-4.0	-3.9	-3.9	-3.9
32.2	-3.9	-3.9	-3.9	-3.9	-3.8	-3.8	-3.8	-3.8	-3.8	-3.8
32.3	-3.8	-3.7	-3.7	-3.7	-3.7	-3.7	-3.7	-3.7	-3.7	-3.6
32.4	-3.6	-3.6	-3.6	-3.6	-3.6	-3.6	-3.5	-3.5	-3.5	-3.5
32.5	-3.5	-3.5	-3.5	-3.4	-3.4	-3.4	-3.4	-3.4	-3.4	-3.4
32.6	-3.3	-3.3	-3.3	-3.3	-3.3	-3.3	-3.3	-3.2	-3.2	-3.2
32.7	-3.2	-3.2	-3.2	-3.2	-3.2	-3.1	-3.1	-3.1	-3.1	-3.1
32.8	-3.1	-3.1	-3.0	-3.0	-3.0	-3.0	-3.0	-3.0	-3.0	-2.9
32.9	-2.9	-2.9	-2.9	-2.9	-2.9	-2.9	-2.8	-2.8	-2.8	-2.8

Table 2.4–4 (*Continued*)

S	0.00	0.01	0.02	0.03	0.04	0.05	0.06	0.07	0.08	0.09
33.0	-2.8	-2.8	-2.8	-2.7	-2.7	-2.7	-2.7	-2.7	-2.7	-2.7
33.1	-2.7	-2.6	-2.6	-2.6	-2.6	-2.6	-2.6	-2.6	-2.5	-2.5
33.2	-2.5	-2.5	-2.5	-2.5	-2.5	-2.4	-2.4	-2.4	-2.4	-2.4
33.3	-2.4	-2.4	-2.3	-2.3	-2.3	-2.3	-2.3	-2.3	-2.3	-2.2
33.4	-2.2	-2.2	-2.2	-2.2	-2.2	-2.2	-2.1	-2.1	-2.1	-2.1
33.5	-2.1	-2.1	-2.1	-2.1	-2.0	-2.0	-2.0	-2.0	-2.0	-2.0
33.6	-2.0	-1.9	-1.9	-1.9	-1.9	-1.9	-1.9	-1.9	-1.8	-1.8
33.7	-1.8	-1.8	-1.8	-1.8	-1.8	-1.7	-1.7	-1.7	-1.7	-1.7
33.8	-1.7	-1.7	-1.6	-1.6	-1.6	-1.6	-1.6	-1.6	-1.6	-1.5
33.9	-1.5	-1.5	-1.5	-1.5	-1.5	-1.5	-1.5	-1.4	-1.4	-1.4
34.0	-1.4	-1.4	-1.4	-1.4	-1.3	-1.3	-1.3	-1.3	-1.3	-1.3
34.1	-1.3	-1.2	-1.2	-1.2	-1.2	-1.2	-1.2	-1.2	-1.1	-1.1
34.2	-1.1	-1.1	-1.1	-1.1	-1.1	-1.0	-1.0	-1.0	-1.0	-1.0
34.3	-1.0	-1.0	-0.9	-0.9	-0.9	-0.9	-0.9	-0.9	-0.9	-0.9
34.4	-0.8	-0.8	-0.8	-0.8	-0.8	-0.8	-0.8	-0.7	-0.7	-0.7
34.5	-0.7	-0.7	-0.7	-0.7	-0.6	-0.6	-0.6	-0.6	-0.6	-0.6
34.6	-0.6	-0.5	-0.5	-0.5	-0.5	-0.5	-0.5	-0.5	-0.4	-0.4
34.7	-0.4	-0.4	-0.4	-0.4	-0.4	-0.3	-0.3	-0.3	-0.3	-0.3
34.8	-0.3	-0.3	-0.3	-0.2	-0.2	-0.2	-0.2	-0.2	-0.2	-0.2
34.9	-0.1	-0.1	-0.1	-0.1	-0.1	-0.1	-0.1	-0.0	-0.0	-0.0
35.0	0.0	0.0	0.0	0.0	0.1	0.1	0.1	0.1	0.1	0.1
35.1	0.1	0.2	0.2	0.2	0.2	0.2	0.2	0.2	0.3	0.3
35.2	0.3	0.3	0.3	0.3	0.3	0.3	0.4	0.4	0.4	0.4
35.3	0.4	0.4	0.4	0.5	0.5	0.5	0.5	0.5	0.5	0.5
35.4	0.6	0.6	0.6	0.6	0.6	0.6	0.6	0.7	0.7	0.7
35.5	0.7	0.7	0.7	0.7	0.8	0.8	0.8	0.8	0.8	0.8
35.6	0.8	0.9	0.9	0.9	0.9	0.9	0.9	0.9	1.0	1.0
35.7	1.0	1.0	1.0	1.0	1.0	1.0	1.1	1.1	1.1	1.1
35.8	1.1	1.1	1.1	1.2	1.2	1.2	1.2	1.2	1.2	1.2
35.9	1.3	1.3	1.3	1.3	1.3	1.3	1.3	1.4	1.4	1.4
36.0	1.4	1.4	1.4	1.4	1.5	1.5	1.5	1.5	1.5	1.5
36.1	1.5	1.6	1.6	1.6	1.6	1.6	1.6	1.6	1.7	1.7
36.2	1.7	1.7	1.7	1.7	1.7	1.8	1.8	1.8	1.8	1.8
36.3	1.8	1.8	1.8	1.9	1.9	1.9	1.9	1.9	1.9	1.9
36.4	2.0	2.0	2.0	2.0	2.0	2.0	2.0	2.1	2.1	2.1
36.5	2.1	2.1	2.1	2.1	2.2	2.2	2.2	2.2	2.2	2.2
36.6	2.2	2.3	2.3	2.3	2.3	2.3	2.3	2.3	2.4	2.4
36.7	2.4	2.4	2.4	2.4	2.4	2.5	2.5	2.5	2.5	2.5
36.8	2.5	2.5	2.5	2.6	2.6	2.6	2.6	2.6	2.6	2.6
36.9	2.7	2.7	2.7	2.7	2.7	2.7	2.7	2.8	2.8	2.8
37.0	2.8	2.8	2.8	2.8	2.9	2.9	2.9	2.9	2.9	2.9
37.1	2.9	3.0	3.0	3.0	3.0	3.0	3.0	3.0	3.1	3.1
37.2	3.1	3.1	3.1	3.1	3.1	3.2	3.2	3.2	3.2	3.2
37.3	3.2	3.2	3.3	3.3	3.3	3.3	3.3	3.3	3.3	3.4
37.4	3.4	3.4	3.4	3.4	3.4	3.4	3.4	3.5	3.5	3.5
37.5	3.5	3.5	3.5	3.5	3.6	3.6	3.6	3.6	3.6	3.6
37.6	3.6	3.7	3.7	3.7	3.7	3.7	3.7	3.7	3.8	3.8
37.7	3.8	3.8	3.8	3.8	3.8	3.9	3.9	3.9	3.9	3.9
37.8	3.9	3.9	4.0	4.0	4.0	4.0	4.0	4.0	4.0	4.1
37.9	4.1	4.1	4.1	4.1	4.1	4.1	4.2	4.2	4.2	4.2

Table 2.4–4 (*Continued*)

S	0.00	0.01	0.02	0.03	0.04	0.05	0.06	0.07	0.08	0.09
38.0	4.2	4.2	4.2	4.3	4.3	4.3	4.3	4.3	4.3	4.3
38.1	4.4	4.4	4.4	4.4	4.4	4.4	4.4	4.4	4.5	4.5
38.2	4.5	4.5	4.5	4.5	4.5	4.6	4.6	4.6	4.6	4.6
38.3	4.6	4.6	4.7	4.7	4.7	4.7	4.7	4.7	4.7	4.8
38.4	4.8	4.8	4.8	4.8	4.8	4.8	4.9	4.9	4.9	4.9
38.5	4.9	4.9	4.9	5.0	5.0	5.0	5.0	5.0	5.0	5.0
38.6	5.1	5.1	5.1	5.1	5.1	5.1	5.1	5.2	5.2	5.2
38.7	5.2	5.2	5.2	5.2	5.3	5.3	5.3	5.3	5.3	5.3
38.8	5.3	5.4	5.4	5.4	5.4	5.4	5.4	5.4	5.4	5.5
38.9	5.5	5.5	5.5	5.5	5.5	5.5	5.6	5.6	5.6	5.6
39.0	5.6	5.6	5.6	5.7	5.7	5.7	5.7	5.7	5.7	5.7
39.1	5.8	5.8	5.8	5.8	5.8	5.8	5.8	5.9	5.9	5.9
39.2	5.9	5.9	5.9	5.9	6.0	6.0	6.0	6.0	6.0	6.0
39.3	6.0	6.1	6.1	6.1	6.1	6.1	6.1	6.1	6.2	6.2
39.4	6.2	6.2	6.2	6.2	6.2	6.3	6.3	6.3	6.3	6.3
39.5	6.3	6.3	6.4	6.4	6.4	6.4	6.4	6.4	6.4	6.5
39.6	6.5	6.5	6.5	6.5	6.5	6.5	6.6	6.6	6.6	6.6
39.7	6.6	6.6	6.6	6.7	6.7	6.7	6.7	6.7	6.7	6.7
39.8	6.7	6.8	6.8	6.8	6.8	6.8	6.8	6.8	6.9	6.9
39.9	6.9	6.9	6.9	6.9	6.9	7.0	7.0	7.0	7.0	7.0
40.0	7.0	7.0	7.1	7.1	7.1	7.1	7.1	7.1	7.1	7.2
40.1	7.2	7.2	7.2	7.2	7.2	7.2	7.3	7.3	7.3	7.3
40.2	7.3	7.3	7.3	7.4	7.4	7.4	7.4	7.4	7.4	7.4
40.3	7.5	7.5	7.5	7.5	7.5	7.5	7.5	7.6	7.6	7.6
40.4	7.6	7.6	7.6	7.6	7.7	7.7	7.7	7.7	7.7	7.7
40.5	7.7	7.8	7.8	7.8	7.8	7.8	7.8	7.8	7.9	7.9
40.6	7.9	7.9	7.9	7.9	7.9	8.0	8.0	8.0	8.0	8.0
40.7	8.0	8.0	8.1	8.1	8.1	8.1	8.1	8.1	8.1	8.2
40.8	8.2	8.2	8.2	8.2	8.2	8.2	8.3	8.3	8.3	8.3
40.9	8.3	8.3	8.3	8.3	8.4	8.4	8.4	8.4	8.4	8.4
41.0	8.4	8.5	8.5	8.5	8.5	8.5	8.5	8.5	8.6	8.6
41.1	8.6	8.6	8.6	8.6	8.6	8.7	8.7	8.7	8.7	8.7
41.2	8.7	8.7	8.8	8.8	8.8	8.8	8.8	8.8	8.8	8.9
41.3	8.9	8.9	8.9	8.9	8.9	8.9	9.0	9.0	9.0	9.0
41.4	9.0	9.0	9.0	9.1	9.1	9.1	9.1	9.1	9.1	9.1
41.5	9.2	9.2	9.2	9.2	9.2	9.2	9.2	9.3	9.3	9.3
41.6	9.3	9.3	9.3	9.3	9.4	9.4	9.4	9.4	9.4	9.4
41.7	9.4	9.5	9.5	9.5	9.5	9.5	9.5	9.5	9.6	9.6
41.8	9.6	9.6	9.6	9.6	9.6	9.7	9.7	9.7	9.7	9.7
41.9	9.7	9.7	9.8	9.8	9.8	9.8	9.8	9.8	9.8	9.9

(From *Tables of Sound Speed in Sea Water,* SP-58, U.S. Naval Oceanographic Office, Washington, D.C., 1962.)

Table 2.4–5
CORRECTION TO SOUND SPEED, V_0 (1449.1 m/sec), FOR CHANGES IN TEMPERATURE (°C), Y_t

T	0.00	0.01	0.02	0.03	0.04	0.05	0.06	0.07	0.08	0.09
-2.5	-11.7	-11.8	-11.8	-11.8	-11.9	-11.9	-12.0	-12.0	-12.1	-12.1
-2.4	-11.2	-11.3	-11.3	-11.4	-11.4	-11.5	-11.5	-11.6	-11.6	-11.7
-2.3	-10.7	-10.8	-10.8	-10.9	-10.9	-11.0	-11.0	-11.1	-11.1	-11.2
-2.2	-10.3	-10.3	-10.4	-10.4	-10.5	-10.5	-10.6	-10.6	-10.7	-10.7
-2.1	-9.8	-9.8	-9.9	-9.9	-10.0	-10.0	-10.1	-10.1	-10.2	-10.2
-2.0	-9.3	-9.4	-9.4	-9.5	-9.5	-9.6	-9.6	-9.7	-9.7	-9.7
-1.9	-8.8	-8.9	-8.9	-9.0	-9.0	-9.1	-9.1	-9.2	-9.2	-9.3
-1.8	-8.4	-8.4	-8.5	-8.5	-8.6	-8.6	-8.7	-8.7	-8.8	-8.8
-1.7	-7.9	-7.9	-8.0	-8.0	-8.1	-8.1	-8.2	-8.2	-8.3	-8.3
-1.6	-7.4	-7.5	-7.5	-7.6	-7.6	-7.7	-7.7	-7.8	-7.8	-7.9
-1.5	-7.0	-7.0	-7.1	-7.1	-7.1	-7.2	-7.2	-7.3	-7.3	-7.4
-1.4	-6.5	-6.5	-6.6	-6.6	-6.7	-6.7	-6.8	-6.8	-6.9	-6.9
-1.3	-6.0	-6.1	-6.1	-6.2	-6.2	-6.3	-6.3	-6.3	-6.4	-6.4
-1.2	-5.6	-5.6	-5.6	-5.7	-5.7	-5.8	-5.8	-5.9	-5.9	-6.0
-1.1	-5.1	-5.1	-5.2	-5.2	-5.3	-5.3	-5.4	-5.4	-5.5	-5.5
-1.0	-4.6	-4.7	-4.7	-4.8	-4.8	-4.8	-4.9	-4.9	-5.0	-5.0
-0.9	-4.2	-4.2	-4.2	-4.3	-4.3	-4.4	-4.4	-4.5	-4.5	-4.6
-0.8	-3.7	-3.7	-3.8	-3.8	-3.9	-3.9	-4.0	-4.0	-4.1	-4.1
-0.7	-3.2	-3.3	-3.3	-3.4	-3.4	-3.5	-3.5	-3.5	-3.6	-3.6
-0.6	-2.8	-2.8	-2.9	-2.9	-2.9	-3.0	-3.0	-3.1	-3.1	-3.2
-0.5	-2.3	-2.3	-2.4	-2.4	-2.5	-2.5	-2.6	-2.6	-2.7	-2.7
-0.4	-1.8	-1.9	-1.9	-2.0	-2.0	-2.1	-2.1	-2.2	-2.2	-2.3
-0.3	-1.4	-1.4	-1.5	-1.5	-1.6	-1.6	-1.7	-1.7	-1.7	-1.8
-0.2	-0.9	-1.0	-1.0	-1.1	-1.1	-1.1	-1.2	-1.2	-1.3	-1.3
-0.1	-0.5	-0.5	-0.5	-0.6	-0.6	-0.7	-0.7	-0.8	-0.8	-0.9
0.0	0.0	-0.0	-0.1	-0.1	-0.2	-0.2	-0.3	-0.3	-0.4	-0.4
0.0	0.0	0.0	0.1	0.1	0.2	0.2	0.3	0.3	0.4	0.4
0.1	0.5	0.5	0.5	0.6	0.6	0.7	0.7	0.8	0.8	0.9
0.2	0.9	1.0	1.0	1.0	1.1	1.1	1.2	1.2	1.3	1.3
0.3	1.4	1.4	1.5	1.5	1.5	1.6	1.6	1.7	1.7	1.8
0.4	1.8	1.9	1.9	2.0	2.0	2.0	2.1	2.1	2.2	2.2
0.5	2.3	2.3	2.4	2.4	2.5	2.5	2.5	2.6	2.6	2.7
0.6	2.7	2.8	2.8	2.9	2.9	3.0	3.0	3.0	3.1	3.1
0.7	3.2	3.2	3.3	3.3	3.4	3.4	3.4	3.5	3.5	3.6
0.8	3.6	3.7	3.7	3.8	3.8	3.9	3.9	3.9	4.0	4.0
0.9	4.1	4.1	4.2	4.2	4.3	4.3	4.3	4.4	4.4	4.5
1.0	4.5	4.6	4.6	4.7	4.7	4.8	4.8	4.8	4.9	4.9
1.1	5.0	5.0	5.1	5.1	5.2	5.2	5.2	5.3	5.3	5.4
1.2	5.4	5.5	5.5	5.6	5.6	5.6	5.7	5.7	5.8	5.8
1.3	5.9	5.9	6.0	6.0	6.0	6.1	6.1	6.2	6.2	6.3
1.4	6.3	6.4	6.4	6.4	6.5	6.5	6.6	6.6	6.7	6.7
1.5	6.8	6.8	6.8	6.9	6.9	7.0	7.0	7.1	7.1	7.2
1.6	7.2	7.2	7.3	7.3	7.4	7.4	7.5	7.5	7.6	7.6
1.7	7.6	7.7	7.7	7.8	7.8	7.9	7.9	8.0	8.0	8.0
1.8	8.1	8.1	8.2	8.2	8.3	8.3	8.3	8.4	8.4	8.5

Table 2.4–5 (*Continued*)

T	0.00	0.01	0.02	0.03	0.04	0.05	0.06	0.07	0.08	0.09
1.9	8.5	8.6	8.6	8.7	8.7	8.7	8.8	8.8	8.9	8.9
2.0	9.0	9.0	9.1	9.1	9.1	9.2	9.2	9.3	9.3	9.4
2.1	9.4	9.4	9.5	9.5	9.6	9.6	9.7	9.7	9.8	9.8
2.2	9.8	9.9	9.9	10.0	10.0	10.1	10.1	10.1	10.2	10.2
2.3	10.3	10.3	10.4	10.4	10.5	10.5	10.5	10.6	10.6	10.7
2.4	10.7	10.8	10.8	10.8	10.9	10.9	11.0	11.0	11.1	11.1
2.5	11.1	11.2	11.2	11.3	11.3	11.4	11.4	11.5	11.5	11.5
2.6	11.6	11.6	11.7	11.7	11.8	11.8	11.8	11.9	11.9	12.0
2.7	12.0	12.1	12.1	12.1	12.2	12.2	12.3	12.3	12.4	12.4
2.8	12.4	12.5	12.5	12.6	12.6	12.7	12.7	12.7	12.8	12.8
2.9	12.9	12.9	13.0	13.0	13.1	13.1	13.1	13.2	13.2	13.3
3.0	13.3	13.4	13.4	13.4	13.5	13.5	13.6	13.6	13.7	13.7
3.1	13.7	13.8	13.8	13.9	13.9	14.0	14.0	14.0	14.1	14.1
3.2	14.2	14.2	14.3	14.3	14.3	14.4	14.4	14.5	14.5	14.6
3.3	14.6	14.6	14.7	14.7	14.8	14.8	14.9	14.9	14.9	15.0
3.4	15.0	15.1	15.1	15.1	15.2	15.2	15.3	15.3	15.4	15.4
3.5	15.4	15.5	15.5	15.6	15.6	15.7	15.7	15.7	15.8	15.8
3.6	15.9	15.9	16.0	16.0	16.0	16.1	16.1	16.2	16.2	16.3
3.7	16.3	16.3	16.4	16.4	16.5	16.5	16.5	16.6	16.6	16.7
3.8	16.7	16.8	16.8	16.8	16.9	16.9	17.0	17.0	17.1	17.1
3.9	17.1	17.2	17.2	17.3	17.3	17.4	17.4	17.4	17.5	17.5
4.0	17.6	17.6	17.6	17.7	17.7	17.8	17.8	17.9	17.9	17.9
4.1	18.0	18.0	18.1	18.1	18.1	18.2	18.2	18.3	18.3	18.4
4.2	18.4	18.4	18.5	18.5	18.6	18.6	18.7	18.7	18.7	18.8
4.3	18.8	18.9	18.9	18.9	19.0	19.0	19.1	19.1	19.2	19.2
4.4	19.2	19.3	19.3	19.4	19.4	19.4	19.5	19.5	19.6	19.6
4.5	19.7	19.7	19.7	19.8	19.8	19.9	19.9	19.9	20.0	20.0
4.6	20.1	20.1	20.2	20.2	20.2	20.3	20.3	20.4	20.4	20.4
4.7	20.5	20.5	20.6	20.6	20.6	20.7	20.7	20.8	20.8	20.9
4.8	20.9	20.9	21.0	21.0	21.1	21.1	21.1	21.2	21.2	21.3
4.9	21.3	21.3	21.4	21.4	21.5	21.5	21.6	21.6	21.6	21.7
5.0	21.7	21.8	21.8	21.8	21.9	21.9	22.0	22.0	22.0	22.1
5.1	22.1	22.2	22.2	22.3	22.3	22.3	22.4	22.4	22.5	22.5
5.2	22.5	22.6	22.6	22.7	22.7	22.7	22.8	22.8	22.9	22.9
5.3	22.9	23.0	23.0	23.1	23.1	23.2	23.2	23.2	23.3	23.3
5.4	23.4	23.4	23.4	23.5	23.5	23.6	23.6	23.6	23.7	23.7
5.5	23.8	23.8	23.8	23.9	23.9	24.0	24.0	24.0	24.1	24.1
5.6	24.2	24.2	24.3	24.3	24.3	24.4	24.4	24.5	24.5	24.5
5.7	24.6	24.6	24.7	24.7	24.7	24.8	24.8	24.9	24.9	24.9
5.8	25.0	25.0	25.1	25.1	25.1	25.2	25.2	25.3	25.3	25.3
5.9	25.4	25.4	25.5	25.5	25.5	25.6	25.6	25.7	25.7	25.7
6.0	25.8	25.8	25.9	25.9	25.9	26.0	26.0	26.1	26.1	26.1
6.1	26.2	26.2	26.3	26.3	26.3	26.4	26.4	26.5	26.5	26.5
6.2	26.6	26.6	26.7	26.7	26.7	26.8	26.8	26.9	26.9	26.9
6.3	27.0	27.0	27.1	27.1	27.1	27.2	27.2	27.3	27.3	27.3
6.4	27.4	27.4	27.5	27.5	27.5	27.6	27.6	27.7	27.7	27.7
6.5	27.8	27.8	27.9	27.9	27.9	28.0	28.0	28.1	28.1	28.1
6.6	28.2	28.2	28.3	28.3	28.3	28.4	28.4	28.5	28.5	28.5
6.7	28.6	28.6	28.7	28.7	28.7	28.8	28.8	28.8	28.9	28.9
6.8	29.0	29.0	29.0	29.1	29.1	29.2	29.2	29.2	29.3	29.3

Table 2.4–5 (*Continued*)

T	0.00	0.01	0.02	0.03	0.04	0.05	0.06	0.07	0.08	0.09
6.9	29.4	29.4	29.4	29.5	29.5	29.6	29.6	29.6	29.7	29.7
7.0	29.8	29.8	29.8	29.9	29.9	29.9	30.0	30.0	30.1	30.1
7.1	30.1	30.2	30.2	30.3	30.3	30.3	30.4	30.4	30.5	30.5
7.2	30.5	30.6	30.6	30.7	30.7	30.7	30.8	30.8	30.8	30.9
7.3	30.9	31.0	31.0	31.0	31.1	31.1	31.2	31.2	31.2	31.3
7.4	31.3	31.4	31.4	31.4	31.5	31.5	31.5	31.6	31.6	31.7
7.5	31.7	31.7	31.8	31.8	31.9	31.9	31.9	32.0	32.0	32.0
7.6	32.1	32.1	32.2	32.2	32.2	32.3	32.3	32.4	32.4	32.4
7.7	32.5	32.5	32.6	32.6	32.6	32.7	32.7	32.7	32.8	32.8
7.8	32.9	32.9	32.9	33.0	33.0	33.1	33.1	33.1	33.2	33.2
7.9	33.2	33.3	33.3	33.4	33.4	33.4	33.5	33.5	33.5	33.6
8.0	33.6	33.7	33.7	33.7	33.8	33.8	33.9	33.9	33.9	34.0
8.1	34.0	34.0	34.1	34.1	34.2	34.2	34.2	34.3	34.3	34.4
8.2	34.4	34.4	34.5	34.5	34.5	34.6	34.6	34.7	34.7	34.7
8.3	34.8	34.8	34.8	34.9	34.9	35.0	35.0	35.0	35.1	35.1
8.4	35.1	35.2	35.2	35.3	35.3	35.3	35.4	35.4	35.5	35.5
8.5	35.5	35.6	35.6	35.6	35.7	35.7	35.8	35.8	35.8	35.9
8.6	35.9	35.9	36.0	36.0	36.1	36.1	36.1	36.2	36.2	36.2
8.7	36.3	36.3	36.4	36.4	36.4	36.5	36.5	36.5	36.6	36.6
8.8	36.7	36.7	36.7	36.8	36.8	36.8	36.9	36.9	37.0	37.0
8.9	37.0	37.1	37.1	37.1	37.2	37.2	37.3	37.3	37.3	37.4
9.0	37.4	37.4	37.5	37.5	37.6	37.6	37.6	37.7	37.7	37.7
9.1	37.8	37.8	37.9	37.9	37.9	38.0	38.0	38.0	38.1	38.1
9.2	38.1	38.2	38.2	38.3	38.3	38.3	38.4	38.4	38.4	38.5
9.3	38.5	38.6	38.6	38.6	38.7	38.7	38.7	38.8	38.8	38.9
9.4	38.9	38.9	39.0	39.0	39.0	39.1	39.1	39.1	39.2	39.2
9.5	39.3	39.3	39.3	39.4	39.4	39.4	39.5	39.5	39.6	39.6
9.6	39.6	39.7	39.7	39.7	39.8	39.8	39.8	39.9	39.9	40.0
9.7	40.0	40.0	40.1	40.1	40.1	40.2	40.2	40.2	40.3	40.3
9.8	40.4	40.4	40.4	40.5	40.5	40.5	40.6	40.6	40.7	40.7
9.9	40.7	40.8	40.8	40.8	40.9	40.9	40.9	41.0	41.0	41.1
10.0	41.1	41.1	41.2	41.2	41.2	41.3	41.3	41.3	41.4	41.4
10.1	41.5	41.5	41.5	41.6	41.6	41.6	41.7	41.7	41.7	41.8
10.2	41.8	41.8	41.9	41.9	42.0	42.0	42.0	42.1	42.1	42.1
10.3	42.2	42.2	42.2	42.3	42.3	42.4	42.4	42.4	42.5	42.5
10.4	42.5	42.6	42.6	42.6	42.7	42.7	42.7	42.8	42.8	42.9
10.5	42.9	42.9	43.0	43.0	43.0	43.1	43.1	43.1	43.2	43.2
10.6	43.3	43.3	43.3	43.4	43.4	43.4	43.5	43.5	43.5	43.6
10.7	43.6	43.6	43.7	43.7	43.8	43.8	43.8	43.9	43.9	43.9
10.8	44.0	44.0	44.0	44.1	44.1	44.1	44.2	44.2	44.2	44.3
10.9	44.3	44.4	44.4	44.4	44.5	44.5	44.5	44.6	44.6	44.6
11.0	44.7	44.7	44.7	44.8	44.8	44.9	44.9	44.9	45.0	45.0
11.1	45.0	45.1	45.1	45.1	45.2	45.2	45.2	45.3	45.3	45.3
11.2	45.4	45.4	45.5	45.5	45.5	45.6	45.6	45.6	45.7	45.7
11.3	45.7	45.8	45.8	45.8	45.9	45.9	45.9	46.0	46.0	46.0

Table 2.4–5 (*Continued*)

T	0.00	0.01	0.02	0.03	0.04	0.05	0.06	0.07	0.08	0.09
11.4	46.1	46.1	46.2	46.2	46.2	46.3	46.3	46.3	46.4	46.4
11.5	46.4	46.5	46.5	46.5	46.6	46.6	46.6	46.7	46.7	46.7
11.6	46.8	46.8	46.9	46.9	46.9	47.0	47.0	47.0	47.1	47.1
11.7	47.1	47.2	47.2	47.2	47.3	47.3	47.3	47.4	47.4	47.4
11.8	47.5	47.5	47.5	47.6	47.6	47.7	47.7	47.7	47.8	47.8
11.9	47.8	47.9	47.9	47.9	48.0	48.0	48.0	48.1	48.1	48.1
12.0	48.2	48.2	48.2	48.3	48.3	48.3	48.4	48.4	48.4	48.5
12.1	48.5	48.5	48.6	48.6	48.6	48.7	48.7	48.8	48.8	48.8
12.2	48.9	48.9	48.9	49.0	49.0	49.0	49.1	49.1	49.1	49.2
12.3	49.2	49.2	49.3	49.3	49.3	49.4	49.4	49.4	49.5	49.5
12.4	49.5	49.6	49.6	49.6	49.7	49.7	49.7	49.8	49.8	49.8
12.5	49.9	49.9	49.9	50.0	50.0	50.0	50.1	50.1	50.2	50.2
12.6	50.2	50.3	50.3	50.3	50.4	50.4	50.4	50.5	50.5	50.5
12.7	50.6	50.6	50.6	50.7	50.7	50.7	50.8	50.8	50.8	50.9
12.8	50.9	50.9	51.0	51.0	51.0	51.1	51.1	51.1	51.2	51.2
12.9	51.2	51.3	51.3	51.3	51.4	51.4	51.4	51.5	51.5	51.5
13.0	51.6	51.6	51.6	51.7	51.7	51.7	51.8	51.8	51.8	51.9
13.1	51.9	51.9	52.0	52.0	52.0	52.1	52.1	52.1	52.2	52.2
13.2	52.2	52.3	52.3	52.3	52.4	52.4	52.4	52.5	52.5	52.5
13.3	52.6	52.6	52.6	52.7	52.7	52.7	52.8	52.8	52.8	52.9
13.4	52.9	52.9	53.0	53.0	53.0	53.1	53.1	53.1	53.2	53.2
13.5	53.2	53.3	53.3	53.3	53.4	53.4	53.4	53.5	53.5	53.5
13.6	53.6	53.6	53.6	53.7	53.7	53.7	53.8	53.8	53.8	53.9
13.7	53.9	53.9	54.0	54.0	54.0	54.1	54.1	54.1	54.2	54.2
13.8	54.2	54.3	54.3	54.3	54.4	54.4	54.4	54.4	54.5	54.5
13.9	54.5	54.6	54.6	54.6	54.7	54.7	54.7	54.8	54.8	54.8
14.0	54.9	54.9	54.9	55.0	55.0	55.0	55.1	55.1	55.1	55.2
14.1	55.2	55.2	55.3	55.3	55.3	55.4	55.4	55.4	55.5	55.5
14.2	55.5	55.6	55.6	55.6	55.7	55.7	55.7	55.7	55.8	55.8
14.3	55.8	55.9	55.9	55.9	56.0	56.0	56.0	56.1	56.1	56.1
14.4	56.2	56.2	56.2	56.3	56.3	56.3	56.4	56.4	56.4	56.5
14.5	56.5	56.5	56.6	56.6	56.6	56.7	56.7	56.7	56.7	56.8
14.6	56.8	56.8	56.9	56.9	56.9	57.0	57.0	57.0	57.1	57.1
14.7	57.1	57.2	57.2	57.2	57.3	57.3	57.3	57.4	57.4	57.4
14.8	57.5	57.5	57.5	57.5	57.6	57.6	57.6	57.7	57.7	57.7
14.9	57.8	57.8	57.8	57.9	57.9	57.9	58.0	58.0	58.0	58.1
15.0	58.1	58.1	58.2	58.2	58.2	58.2	58.3	58.3	58.3	58.4
15.1	58.4	58.4	58.5	58.5	58.5	58.6	58.6	58.6	58.7	58.7
15.2	58.7	58.8	58.8	58.8	58.8	58.9	58.9	58.9	59.0	59.0
15.3	59.0	59.1	59.1	59.1	59.2	59.2	59.2	59.3	59.3	59.3
15.4	59.3	59.4	59.4	59.4	59.5	59.5	59.5	59.6	59.6	59.6
15.5	59.7	59.7	59.7	59.8	59.8	59.8	59.8	59.9	59.9	59.9
15.6	60.0	60.0	60.0	60.1	60.1	60.1	60.2	60.2	60.2	60.3
15.7	60.3	60.3	60.3	60.4	60.4	60.4	60.5	60.5	60.5	60.6
15.8	60.6	60.6	60.7	60.7	60.7	60.7	60.8	60.8	60.8	60.9
15.9	60.9	60.9	61.0	61.0	61.0	61.1	61.1	61.1	61.1	61.2

Table 2.4–5 (*Continued*)

T	0.00	0.01	0.02	0.03	0.04	0.05	0.06	0.07	0.08	0.09
16.0	61.2	61.2	61.3	61.3	61.3	61.4	61.4	61.4	61.5	61.5
16.1	61.5	61.5	61.6	61.6	61.6	61.7	61.7	61.7	61.8	61.8
16.2	61.8	61.9	61.9	61.9	61.9	62.0	62.0	62.0	62.1	62.1
16.3	62.1	62.2	62.2	62.2	62.3	62.3	62.3	62.3	62.4	62.4
16.4	62.4	62.5	62.5	62.5	62.6	62.6	62.6	62.6	62.7	62.7
16.5	62.7	62.8	62.8	62.8	62.9	62.9	62.9	62.9	63.0	63.0
16.6	63.0	63.1	63.1	63.1	63.2	63.2	63.2	63.3	63.3	63.3
16.7	63.3	63.4	63.4	63.4	63.5	63.5	63.5	63.6	63.6	63.6
16.8	63.6	63.7	63.7	63.7	63.8	63.8	63.8	63.9	63.9	63.9
16.9	63.9	64.0	64.0	64.0	64.1	64.1	64.1	64.2	64.2	64.2
17.0	64.2	64.3	64.3	64.3	64.4	64.4	64.4	64.5	64.5	64.5
17.1	64.5	64.6	64.6	64.6	64.7	64.7	64.7	64.8	64.8	64.8
17.2	64.8	64.9	64.9	64.9	65.0	65.0	65.0	65.0	65.1	65.1
17.3	65.1	65.2	65.2	65.2	65.3	65.3	65.3	65.3	65.4	65.4
17.4	65.4	65.5	65.5	65.5	65.6	65.6	65.6	65.6	65.7	65.7
17.5	65.7	65.8	65.8	65.8	65.8	65.9	65.9	65.9	66.0	66.0
17.6	66.0	66.1	66.1	66.1	66.1	66.2	66.2	66.2	66.3	66.3
17.7	66.3	66.3	66.4	66.4	66.4	66.5	66.5	66.5	66.5	66.6
17.8	66.6	66.6	66.7	66.7	66.7	66.8	66.8	66.8	66.8	66.9
17.9	66.9	66.9	67.0	67.0	67.0	67.0	67.1	67.1	67.1	67.2
18.0	67.2	67.2	67.2	67.3	67.3	67.3	67.4	67.4	67.4	67.4
18.1	67.5	67.5	67.5	67.6	67.6	67.6	67.7	67.7	67.7	67.7
18.2	67.8	67.8	67.8	67.9	67.9	67.9	67.9	68.0	68.0	68.0
18.3	68.1	68.1	68.1	68.1	68.2	68.2	68.2	68.3	68.3	68.3
18.4	68.3	68.4	68.4	68.4	68.5	68.5	68.5	68.5	68.6	68.6
18.5	68.6	68.7	68.7	68.7	68.7	68.8	68.8	68.8	68.9	68.9
18.6	68.9	68.9	69.0	69.0	69.0	69.1	69.1	69.1	69.1	69.2
18.7	69.2	69.2	69.3	69.3	69.3	69.3	69.4	69.4	69.4	69.5
18.8	69.5	69.5	69.5	69.6	69.6	69.6	69.7	69.7	69.7	69.7
18.9	69.8	69.8	69.8	69.9	69.9	69.9	69.9	70.0	70.0	70.0
19.0	70.0	70.1	70.1	70.1	70.2	70.2	70.2	70.2	70.3	70.3
19.1	70.3	70.4	70.4	70.4	70.4	70.5	70.5	70.5	70.6	70.6
19.2	70.6	70.6	70.7	70.7	70.7	70.7	70.8	70.8	70.8	70.9
19.3	70.9	70.9	70.9	71.0	71.0	71.0	71.1	71.1	71.1	71.1
19.4	71.2	71.2	71.2	71.3	71.3	71.3	71.3	71.4	71.4	71.4
19.5	71.4	71.5	71.5	71.5	71.6	71.6	71.6	71.6	71.7	71.7
19.6	71.7	71.8	71.8	71.8	71.8	71.9	71.9	71.9	71.9	72.0
19.7	72.0	72.0	72.1	72.1	72.1	72.1	72.2	72.2	72.2	72.2
19.8	72.3	72.3	72.3	72.4	72.4	72.4	72.4	72.5	72.5	72.5
19.9	72.5	72.6	72.6	72.6	72.7	72.7	72.7	72.7	72.8	72.8
20.0	72.8	72.9	72.9	72.9	72.9	73.0	73.0	73.0	73.0	73.1
20.1	73.1	73.1	73.2	73.2	73.2	73.2	73.3	73.3	73.3	73.3
20.2	73.4	73.4	73.4	73.4	73.5	73.5	73.5	73.6	73.6	73.6
20.3	73.6	73.7	73.7	73.7	73.7	73.8	73.8	73.8	73.9	73.9
20.4	73.9	73.9	74.0	74.0	74.0	74.0	74.1	74.1	74.1	74.2
20.5	74.2	74.2	74.2	74.3	74.3	74.3	74.3	74.4	74.4	74.4

Table 2.4–5 (*Continued*)

T	0.00	0.01	0.02	0.03	0.04	0.05	0.06	0.07	0.08	0.09
20.6	74.4	74.5	74.5	74.5	74.6	74.6	74.6	74.6	74.7	74.7
20.7	74.7	74.7	74.8	74.8	74.8	74.9	74.9	74.9	74.9	75.0
20.8	75.0	75.0	75.0	75.1	75.1	75.1	75.1	75.2	75.2	75.2
20.9	75.3	75.3	75.3	75.3	75.4	75.4	75.4	75.4	75.5	75.5
21.0	75.5	75.5	75.6	75.6	75.6	75.6	75.7	75.7	75.7	75.8
21.1	75.8	75.8	75.8	75.9	75.9	75.9	75.9	76.0	76.0	76.0
21.2	76.0	76.1	76.1	76.1	76.2	76.2	76.2	76.2	76.3	76.3
21.3	76.3	76.3	76.4	76.4	76.4	76.4	76.5	76.5	76.5	76.5
21.4	76.6	76.6	76.6	76.6	76.7	76.7	76.7	76.8	76.8	76.8
21.5	76.8	76.9	76.9	76.9	76.9	77.0	77.0	77.0	77.0	77.1
21.6	77.1	77.1	77.1	77.2	77.2	77.2	77.3	77.3	77.3	77.3
21.7	77.4	77.4	77.4	77.4	77.5	77.5	77.5	77.5	77.6	77.6
21.8	77.6	77.6	77.7	77.7	77.7	77.7	77.8	77.8	77.8	77.8
21.9	77.9	77.9	77.9	77.9	78.0	78.0	78.0	78.1	78.1	78.1
22.0	78.1	78.2	78.2	78.2	78.2	78.3	78.3	78.3	78.3	78.4
22.1	78.4	78.4	78.4	78.5	78.5	78.5	78.5	78.6	78.6	78.6
22.2	78.6	78.7	78.7	78.7	78.7	78.8	78.8	78.8	78.8	78.9
22.3	78.9	78.9	78.9	79.0	79.0	79.0	79.1	79.1	79.1	79.1
22.4	79.2	79.2	79.2	79.2	79.3	79.3	79.3	79.3	79.4	79.4
22.5	79.4	79.4	79.5	79.5	79.5	79.5	79.6	79.6	79.6	79.6
22.6	79.7	79.7	79.7	79.7	79.8	79.8	79.8	79.8	79.9	79.9
22.7	79.9	79.9	80.0	80.0	80.0	80.0	80.1	80.1	80.1	80.1
22.8	80.2	80.2	80.2	80.2	80.3	80.3	80.3	80.3	80.4	80.4
22.9	80.4	80.4	80.5	80.5	80.5	80.5	80.6	80.6	80.6	80.6
23.0	80.7	80.7	80.7	80.7	80.8	80.8	80.8	80.8	80.9	80.9
23.1	80.9	80.9	81.0	81.0	81.0	81.0	81.1	81.1	81.1	81.1
23.2	81.2	81.2	81.2	81.2	81.3	81.3	81.3	81.3	81.4	81.4
23.3	81.4	81.4	81.5	81.5	81.5	81.5	81.6	81.6	81.6	81.6
23.4	81.7	81.7	81.7	81.7	81.8	81.8	81.8	81.8	81.9	81.9
23.5	81.9	81.9	82.0	82.0	82.0	82.0	82.1	82.1	82.1	82.1
23.6	82.2	82.2	82.2	82.2	82.3	82.3	82.3	82.3	82.3	82.4
23.7	82.4	82.4	82.4	82.5	82.5	82.5	82.5	82.6	82.6	82.6
23.8	82.6	82.7	82.7	82.7	82.7	82.8	82.8	82.8	82.8	82.9
23.9	82.9	82.9	82.9	83.0	83.0	83.0	83.0	83.1	83.1	83.1
24.0	83.1	83.2	83.2	83.2	83.2	83.2	83.3	83.3	83.3	83.3
24.1	83.4	83.4	83.4	83.4	83.5	83.5	83.5	83.5	83.6	83.6
24.2	83.6	83.6	83.7	83.7	83.7	83.7	83.8	83.8	83.8	83.8
24.3	83.9	83.9	83.9	83.9	83.9	84.0	84.0	84.0	84.0	84.1
24.4	84.1	84.1	84.1	84.2	84.2	84.2	84.2	84.3	84.3	84.3
24.5	84.3	84.4	84.4	84.4	84.4	84.5	84.5	84.5	84.5	84.5
24.6	84.6	84.6	84.6	84.6	84.7	84.7	84.7	84.7	84.8	84.8
24.7	84.8	84.8	84.9	84.9	84.9	84.9	85.0	85.0	85.0	85.0
24.8	85.0	85.1	85.1	85.1	85.1	85.2	85.2	85.2	85.2	85.3
24.9	85.3	85.3	85.3	85.4	85.4	85.4	85.4	85.4	85.5	85.5
25.0	85.5	85.5	85.6	85.6	85.6	85.6	85.7	85.7	85.7	85.7
25.1	85.8	85.8	85.8	85.8	85.8	85.9	85.9	85.9	85.9	86.0
25.2	86.0	86.0	86.0	86.1	86.1	86.1	86.1	86.2	86.2	86.2
25.3	86.2	86.2	86.3	86.3	86.3	86.3	86.4	86.4	86.4	86.4
25.4	86.5	86.5	86.5	86.5	86.5	86.6	86.6	86.6	86.6	86.7
25.5	86.7	86.7	86.7	86.8	86.8	86.8	86.8	86.9	86.9	86.9

Table 2.4–5 (*Continued*)

T	0.00	0.01	0.02	0.03	0.04	0.05	0.06	0.07	0.08	0.09
25.6	86.9	86.9	87.0	87.0	87.0	87.0	87.1	87.1	87.1	87.1
25.7	87.2	87.2	87.2	87.2	87.2	87.3	87.3	87.3	87.3	87.4
25.8	87.4	87.4	87.4	87.5	87.5	87.5	87.5	87.5	87.6	87.6
25.9	87.6	87.6	87.7	87.7	87.7	87.7	87.8	87.8	87.8	87.8
26.0	87.8	87.9	87.9	87.9	87.9	88.0	88.0	88.0	88.0	88.0
26.1	88.1	88.1	88.1	88.1	88.2	88.2	88.2	88.2	88.3	88.3
26.2	88.3	88.3	88.3	88.4	88.4	88.4	88.4	88.5	88.5	88.5
26.3	88.5	88.5	88.6	88.6	88.6	88.6	88.7	88.7	88.7	88.7
26.4	88.8	88.8	88.8	88.8	88.8	88.9	88.9	88.9	88.9	89.0
26.5	89.0	89.0	89.0	89.0	89.1	89.1	89.1	89.1	89.2	89.2
26.6	89.2	89.2	89.2	89.3	89.3	89.3	89.3	89.4	89.4	89.4
26.7	89.4	89.5	89.5	89.5	89.5	89.5	89.6	89.6	89.6	89.6
26.8	89.7	89.7	89.7	89.7	89.7	89.8	89.8	89.8	89.8	89.9
26.9	89.9	89.9	89.9	89.9	90.0	90.0	90.0	90.0	90.1	90.1
27.0	90.1	90.1	90.1	90.2	90.2	90.2	90.2	90.3	90.3	90.3
27.1	90.3	90.3	90.4	90.4	90.4	90.4	90.5	90.5	90.5	90.5
27.2	90.5	90.6	90.6	90.6	90.6	90.7	90.7	90.7	90.7	90.7
27.3	90.8	90.8	90.8	90.8	90.9	90.9	90.9	90.9	90.9	91.0
27.4	91.0	91.0	91.0	91.1	91.1	91.1	91.1	91.1	91.2	91.2
27.5	91.2	91.2	91.2	91.3	91.3	91.3	91.3	91.4	91.4	91.4
27.6	91.4	91.4	91.5	91.5	91.5	91.5	91.6	91.6	91.6	91.6
27.7	91.6	91.7	91.7	91.7	91.7	91.8	91.8	91.8	91.8	91.8
27.8	91.9	91.9	91.9	91.9	91.9	92.0	92.0	92.0	92.0	92.1
27.9	92.1	92.1	92.1	92.1	92.2	92.2	92.2	92.2	92.3	92.3
28.0	92.3	92.3	92.3	92.4	92.4	92.4	92.4	92.4	92.5	92.5
28.1	92.5	92.5	92.6	92.6	92.6	92.6	92.6	92.7	92.7	92.7
28.2	92.7	92.8	92.8	92.8	92.8	92.8	92.9	92.9	92.9	92.9
28.3	92.9	93.0	93.0	93.0	93.0	93.1	93.1	93.1	93.1	93.1
28.4	93.2	93.2	93.2	93.2	93.2	93.3	93.3	93.3	93.3	93.4
28.5	93.4	93.4	93.4	93.4	93.5	93.5	93.5	93.5	93.5	93.6
28.6	93.6	93.6	93.6	93.7	93.7	93.7	93.7	93.7	93.8	93.8
28.7	93.8	93.8	93.8	93.9	93.9	93.9	93.9	93.9	94.0	94.0
28.8	94.0	94.0	94.1	94.1	94.1	94.1	94.1	94.2	94.2	94.2
28.9	94.2	94.2	94.3	94.3	94.3	94.3	94.4	94.4	94.4	94.4
29.0	94.4	94.5	94.5	94.5	94.5	94.5	94.6	94.6	94.6	94.6
29.1	94.6	94.7	94.7	94.7	94.7	94.8	94.8	94.8	94.8	94.8
29.2	94.9	94.9	94.9	94.9	94.9	95.0	95.0	95.0	95.0	95.0
29.3	95.1	95.1	95.1	95.1	95.1	95.2	95.2	95.2	95.2	95.3
29.4	95.3	95.3	95.3	95.3	95.4	95.4	95.4	95.4	95.4	95.5
29.5	95.5	95.5	95.5	95.5	95.6	95.6	95.6	95.6	95.7	95.7
29.6	95.7	95.7	95.7	95.8	95.8	95.8	95.8	95.8	95.9	95.9
29.7	95.9	95.9	95.9	96.0	96.0	96.0	96.0	96.0	96.1	96.1
29.8	96.1	96.1	96.1	96.2	96.2	96.2	96.2	96.3	96.3	96.3
29.9	96.3	96.3	96.4	96.4	96.4	96.4	96.4	96.5	96.5	96.5
30.0	96.5	96.5	96.6	96.6	96.6	96.6	96.6	96.7	96.7	96.7

Table 2.4–5 (*Continued*)

T	0.00	0.01	0.02	0.03	0.04	0.05	0.06	0.07	0.08	0.09
30.1	96.7	96.7	96.8	96.8	96.8	96.8	96.8	96.9	96.9	96.9
30.2	96.9	97.0	97.0	97.0	97.0	97.0	97.1	97.1	97.1	97.1
30.3	97.1	97.2	97.2	97.2	97.2	97.2	97.3	97.3	97.3	97.3
30.4	97.3	97.4	97.4	97.4	97.4	97.4	97.5	97.5	97.5	97.5
30.5	97.5	97.6	97.6	97.6	97.6	97.6	97.7	97.7	97.7	97.7
30.6	97.7	97.8	97.8	97.8	97.8	97.8	97.9	97.9	97.9	97.9
30.7	97.9	98.0	98.0	98.0	98.0	98.1	98.1	98.1	98.1	98.1
30.8	98.2	98.2	98.2	98.2	98.2	98.3	98.3	98.3	98.3	98.3
30.9	98.4	98.4	98.4	98.4	98.4	98.5	98.5	98.5	98.5	98.5
31.0	98.6	98.6	98.6	98.6	98.6	98.7	98.7	98.7	98.7	98.7
31.1	98.8	98.8	98.8	98.8	98.8	98.9	98.9	98.9	98.9	98.9
31.2	99.0	99.0	99.0	99.0	99.0	99.1	99.1	99.1	99.1	99.1
31.3	99.2	99.2	99.2	99.2	99.2	99.3	99.3	99.3	99.3	99.3
31.4	99.4	99.4	99.4	99.4	99.4	99.5	99.5	99.5	99.5	99.5
31.5	99.6	99.6	99.6	99.6	99.6	99.7	99.7	99.7	99.7	99.7
31.6	99.8	99.8	99.8	99.8	99.8	99.9	99.9	99.9	99.9	99.9
31.7	100.0	100.0	100.0	100.0	100.0	100.1	100.1	100.1	100.1	100.1
31.8	100.2	100.2	100.2	100.2	100.2	100.2	100.3	100.3	100.3	100.3
31.9	100.3	100.4	100.4	100.4	100.4	100.4	100.5	100.5	100.5	100.5
32.0	100.5	100.6	100.6	100.6	100.6	100.6	100.7	100.7	100.7	100.7
32.1	100.7	100.8	100.8	100.8	100.8	100.8	100.9	100.9	100.9	100.9
32.2	100.9	101.0	101.0	101.0	101.0	101.0	101.1	101.1	101.1	101.1
32.3	101.1	101.2	101.2	101.2	101.2	101.2	101.3	101.3	101.3	101.3
32.4	101.3	101.3	101.4	101.4	101.4	101.4	101.4	101.5	101.5	101.5
32.5	101.5	101.5	101.6	101.6	101.6	101.6	101.6	101.7	101.7	101.7
32.6	101.7	101.7	101.8	101.8	101.8	101.8	101.8	101.9	101.9	101.9
32.7	101.9	101.9	102.0	102.0	102.0	102.0	102.0	102.0	102.1	102.1
32.8	102.1	102.1	102.1	102.2	102.2	102.2	102.2	102.2	102.3	102.3
32.9	102.3	102.3	102.3	102.4	102.4	102.4	102.4	102.4	102.5	102.5
33.0	102.5	102.5	102.5	102.6	102.6	102.6	102.6	102.6	102.6	102.7
33.1	102.7	102.7	102.7	102.7	102.8	102.8	102.8	102.8	102.8	102.9
33.2	102.9	102.9	102.9	102.9	103.0	103.0	103.0	103.0	103.0	103.1
33.3	103.1	103.1	103.1	103.1	103.1	103.2	103.2	103.2	103.2	103.2
33.4	103.3	103.3	103.3	103.3	103.3	103.4	103.4	103.4	103.4	103.4
33.5	103.5	103.5	103.5	103.5	103.5	103.5	103.6	103.6	103.6	103.6
33.6	103.6	103.7	103.7	103.7	103.7	103.7	103.8	103.8	103.8	103.8
33.7	103.8	103.9	103.9	103.9	103.9	103.9	104.0	104.0	104.0	104.0
33.8	104.0	104.0	104.1	104.1	104.1	104.1	104.1	104.2	104.2	104.2
33.9	104.2	104.2	104.3	104.3	104.3	104.3	104.3	104.3	104.4	104.4
34.0	104.4	104.4	104.4	104.5	104.5	104.5	104.5	104.5	104.6	104.6
34.1	104.6	104.6	104.6	104.7	104.7	104.7	104.7	104.7	104.7	104.8
34.2	104.8	104.8	104.8	104.8	104.9	104.9	104.9	104.9	104.9	105.0
34.3	105.0	105.0	105.0	105.0	105.0	105.1	105.1	105.1	105.1	105.1
34.4	105.2	105.2	105.2	105.2	105.2	105.3	105.3	105.3	105.3	105.3
34.5	105.4	105.4	105.4	105.4	105.4	105.4	105.5	105.5	105.5	105.5
34.6	105.5	105.6	105.6	105.6	105.6	105.6	105.7	105.7	105.7	105.7
34.7	105.7	105.7	105.8	105.8	105.8	105.8	105.8	105.9	105.9	105.9
34.8	105.9	105.9	106.0	106.0	106.0	106.0	106.0	106.0	106.1	106.1
34.9	106.1	106.1	106.1	106.2	106.2	106.2	106.2	106.2	106.3	106.3

(From *Tables of Sound Speed in Sea Water,* SP-58, U.S. Naval Oceanographic Office, Washington, D.C., 1962.)

Table 2.4–6
CORRECTION TO SOUND SPEED, V_o (1449.1 m/sec), FOR
SIMULTANEOUS CHANGES IN SALINITY, TEMPERATURE, AND PRESSURE, V_{stp}

O METERS
(1.03 kg/cm^2)

‰ \ °C	-4	-2	0	2	4	6	8	10	12	14	16	18	20	22	24	26	28	30	32	34	36
0.0	-1.6	-0.8	-0.0	0.8	1.6	2.4	3.1	3.9	4.7	5.5	6.3	7.1	7.9	8.6	9.4	10.2	11.0	11.8	12.6	13.4	14.1
0.5	-1.6	-0.8	-0.0	0.8	1.5	2.3	3.1	3.9	4.6	5.4	6.2	7.0	7.7	8.5	9.3	10.1	10.8	11.6	12.4	13.2	13.9
1.0	-1.5	-0.8	-0.0	0.8	1.5	2.3	3.1	3.8	4.6	5.3	6.1	6.9	7.6	8.4	9.2	9.9	10.7	11.4	12.2	13.0	13.7
1.5	-1.5	-0.8	-0.0	0.8	1.5	2.3	3.0	3.8	4.5	5.3	6.0	6.8	7.5	8.3	9.0	9.8	10.5	11.3	12.0	12.8	13.5
2.0	-1.5	-0.7	-0.0	0.7	1.5	2.2	3.0	3.7	4.4	5.2	5.9	6.7	7.4	8.1	8.9	9.6	10.4	11.1	11.8	12.6	13.3
2.5	-1.5	-0.7	-0.0	0.7	1.5	2.2	2.9	3.6	4.4	5.1	5.8	6.6	7.3	8.0	8.8	9.5	10.2	10.9	11.7	12.4	13.1
3.0	-1.4	-0.7	-0.0	0.7	1.4	2.2	2.9	3.6	4.3	5.0	5.7	6.5	7.2	7.9	8.6	9.3	10.1	10.8	11.5	12.2	12.9
3.5	-1.4	-0.7	-0.0	0.7	1.4	2.1	2.8	3.5	4.2	5.0	5.7	6.4	7.1	7.8	8.5	9.2	9.9	10.6	11.3	12.0	12.7
4.0	-1.4	-0.7	-0.0	0.7	1.4	2.1	2.8	3.5	4.2	4.9	5.6	6.3	7.0	7.7	8.3	9.0	9.7	10.4	11.1	11.8	12.5
4.5	-1.4	-0.7	-0.0	0.7	1.4	2.1	2.7	3.4	4.1	4.8	5.5	6.2	6.8	7.5	8.2	8.9	9.6	10.3	11.0	11.6	12.3
5.0	-1.4	-0.7	-0.0	0.7	1.3	2.0	2.7	3.4	4.0	4.7	5.4	6.1	6.7	7.4	8.1	8.8	9.4	10.1	10.8	11.4	12.1
5.5	-1.3	-0.7	-0.0	0.7	1.3	2.0	2.6	3.3	4.0	4.6	5.3	6.0	6.6	7.3	7.9	8.6	9.3	9.9	10.6	11.3	11.9
6.0	-1.3	-0.7	-0.0	0.6	1.3	2.0	2.6	3.3	3.9	4.6	5.2	5.9	6.5	7.2	7.8	8.5	9.1	9.8	10.4	11.1	11.7
6.5	-1.3	-0.6	-0.0	0.6	1.3	1.9	2.6	3.2	3.8	4.5	5.1	5.8	6.4	7.0	7.7	8.3	9.0	9.6	10.2	10.9	11.5
7.0	-1.3	-0.6	-0.0	0.6	1.3	1.9	2.5	3.1	3.8	4.4	5.0	5.7	6.3	6.9	7.5	8.2	8.8	9.4	10.1	10.7	11.3
7.5	-1.2	-0.6	-0.0	0.6	1.2	1.9	2.5	3.1	3.7	4.3	4.9	5.6	6.2	6.8	7.4	8.0	8.6	9.3	9.9	10.5	11.1
8.0	-1.2	-0.6	-0.0	0.6	1.2	1.8	2.4	3.0	3.6	4.2	4.8	5.5	6.1	6.7	7.3	7.9	8.5	9.1	9.7	10.3	10.9
8.5	-1.2	-0.6	-0.0	0.6	1.2	1.8	2.4	3.0	3.6	4.2	4.8	5.4	5.9	6.5	7.1	7.7	8.3	8.9	9.5	10.1	10.7
9.0	-1.2	-0.6	-0.0	0.6	1.2	1.8	2.3	2.9	3.5	4.1	4.7	5.3	5.8	6.4	7.0	7.6	8.2	8.8	9.3	9.9	10.5
9.5	-1.1	-0.6	-0.0	0.6	1.1	1.7	2.3	2.9	3.4	4.0	4.6	5.2	5.7	6.3	6.9	7.4	8.0	8.6	9.2	9.7	10.3
10.0	-1.1	-0.6	-0.0	0.6	1.1	1.7	2.2	2.8	3.4	3.9	4.5	5.1	5.6	6.2	6.7	7.3	7.9	8.4	9.0	9.5	10.1
10.5	-1.1	-0.6	-0.0	0.5	1.1	1.6	2.2	2.7	3.3	3.8	4.4	4.9	5.5	6.0	6.6	7.1	7.7	8.2	8.8	9.3	9.9
11.0	-1.1	-0.5	-0.0	0.5	1.1	1.6	2.2	2.7	3.2	3.8	4.3	4.8	5.4	5.9	6.5	7.0	7.5	8.1	8.6	9.2	9.7
11.5	-1.1	-0.5	-0.0	0.5	1.1	1.6	2.1	2.6	3.2	3.7	4.2	4.7	5.3	5.8	6.3	6.9	7.4	7.9	8.4	9.0	9.5
12.0	-1.0	-0.5	-0.0	0.5	1.0	1.5	2.1	2.6	3.1	3.6	4.1	4.6	5.2	5.7	6.2	6.7	7.2	7.7	8.3	8.8	9.3
12.5	-1.0	-0.5	-0.0	0.5	1.0	1.5	2.0	2.5	3.0	3.5	4.0	4.5	5.1	5.6	6.1	6.6	7.1	7.6	8.1	8.6	9.1
13.0	-1.0	-0.5	-0.0	0.5	1.0	1.5	2.0	2.5	3.0	3.5	4.0	4.4	4.9	5.4	5.9	6.4	6.9	7.4	7.9	8.4	8.9
13.5	-1.0	-0.5	-0.0	0.5	1.0	1.4	1.9	2.4	2.9	3.4	3.9	4.3	4.8	5.3	5.8	6.3	6.8	7.2	7.7	8.2	8.7
14.0	-0.9	-0.5	-0.0	0.5	0.9	1.4	1.9	2.4	2.8	3.3	3.8	4.2	4.7	5.2	5.7	6.1	6.6	7.1	7.5	8.0	8.5
14.5	-0.9	-0.5	-0.0	0.5	0.9	1.4	1.8	2.3	2.8	3.2	3.7	4.1	4.6	5.1	5.5	6.0	6.4	6.9	7.4	7.8	8.3
15.0	-0.9	-0.5	-0.0	0.4	0.9	1.3	1.8	2.2	2.7	3.1	3.6	4.0	4.5	4.9	5.4	5.8	6.3	6.7	7.2	7.6	8.1
15.5	-0.9	-0.4	-0.0	0.4	0.9	1.3	1.8	2.2	2.6	3.1	3.5	3.9	4.4	4.8	5.3	5.7	6.1	6.6	7.0	7.4	7.9
16.0	-0.9	-0.4	-0.0	0.4	0.9	1.3	1.7	2.1	2.6	3.0	3.4	3.8	4.3	4.7	5.1	5.5	6.0	6.4	6.8	7.2	7.7
16.5	-0.8	-0.4	-0.0	0.4	0.8	1.2	1.7	2.1	2.5	2.9	3.3	3.7	4.2	4.6	5.0	5.4	5.8	6.2	6.6	7.1	7.5
17.0	-0.8	-0.4	-0.0	0.4	0.8	1.2	1.6	2.0	2.4	2.8	3.2	3.6	4.0	4.4	4.8	5.3	5.7	6.1	6.5	6.9	7.3
17.5	-0.8	-0.4	-0.0	0.4	0.8	1.2	1.6	2.0	2.4	2.7	3.1	3.5	3.9	4.3	4.7	5.1	5.5	5.9	6.3	6.7	7.1
18.0	-0.8	-0.4	-0.0	0.4	0.8	1.1	1.5	1.9	2.3	2.7	3.1	3.4	3.8	4.2	4.6	5.0	5.3	5.7	6.1	6.5	6.9
18.5	-0.7	-0.4	-0.0	0.4	0.7	1.1	1.5	1.9	2.2	2.6	3.0	3.3	3.7	4.1	4.4	4.8	5.2	5.6	5.9	6.3	6.7
19.0	-0.7	-0.4	-0.0	0.4	0.7	1.1	1.4	1.8	2.2	2.5	2.9	3.2	3.6	4.0	4.3	4.7	5.0	5.4	5.7	6.1	6.5
19.5	-0.7	-0.3	-0.0	0.3	0.7	1.0	1.4	1.7	2.1	2.4	2.8	3.1	3.5	3.8	4.2	4.5	4.9	5.2	5.6	5.9	6.3
20.0	-0.7	-0.3	-0.0	0.3	0.7	1.0	1.3	1.7	2.0	2.4	2.7	3.0	3.4	3.7	4.0	4.4	4.7	5.1	5.4	5.7	6.1
20.5	-0.7	-0.3	-0.0	0.3	0.7	1.0	1.3	1.6	2.0	2.3	2.6	2.9	3.3	3.6	3.9	4.2	4.6	4.9	5.2	5.5	5.9
21.0	-0.6	-0.3	-0.0	0.3	0.6	0.9	1.3	1.6	1.9	2.2	2.5	2.8	3.1	3.5	3.8	4.1	4.4	4.7	5.0	5.3	5.7
21.5	-0.6	-0.3	-0.0	0.3	0.6	0.9	1.2	1.5	1.8	2.1	2.4	2.7	3.0	3.3	3.6	3.9	4.2	4.5	4.8	5.2	5.5

Table 2.4–6 (*Continued*)

O METERS
(1.03 kg/cm^2)

‰ \ °C	-4	-2	0	2	4	6	8	10	12	14	16	18	20	22	24	26	28	30	32	34	36
22.0	-0.6	-0.3	-0.0	0.3	0.6	0.9	1.2	1.5	1.8	2.0	2.3	2.6	2.9	3.2	3.5	3.8	4.1	4.4	4.7	5.0	5.3
22.5	-0.6	-0.3	-0.0	0.3	0.6	0.8	1.1	1.4	1.7	2.0	2.2	2.5	2.8	3.1	3.4	3.6	3.9	4.2	4.5	4.8	5.1
23.0	-0.5	-0.3	-0.0	0.3	0.5	0.8	1.1	1.3	1.6	1.9	2.2	2.4	2.7	3.0	3.2	3.5	3.8	4.0	4.3	4.6	4.8
23.5	-0.5	-0.3	-0.0	0.3	0.5	0.8	1.0	1.3	1.5	1.8	2.1	2.3	2.6	2.8	3.1	3.4	3.6	3.9	4.1	4.4	4.6
24.0	-0.5	-0.2	-0.0	0.2	0.5	0.7	1.0	1.2	1.5	1.7	2.0	2.2	2.5	2.7	3.0	3.2	3.5	3.7	4.0	4.2	4.4
24.5	-0.5	-0.2	-0.0	0.2	0.5	0.7	0.9	1.2	1.4	1.6	1.9	2.1	2.4	2.6	2.8	3.1	3.3	3.5	3.8	4.0	4.2
25.0	-0.4	-0.2	-0.0	0.2	0.4	0.7	0.9	1.1	1.3	1.6	1.8	2.0	2.2	2.5	2.7	2.9	3.1	3.4	3.6	3.8	4.0
25.5	-0.4	-0.2	-0.0	0.2	0.4	0.6	0.9	1.1	1.3	1.5	1.7	1.9	2.1	2.3	2.6	2.8	3.0	3.2	3.4	3.6	3.8
26.0	-0.4	-0.2	-0.0	0.2	0.4	0.6	0.8	1.0	1.2	1.4	1.6	1.8	2.0	2.2	2.4	2.6	2.8	3.0	3.2	3.4	3.6
26.5	-0.4	-0.2	-0.0	0.2	0.4	0.6	0.8	1.0	1.1	1.3	1.5	1.7	1.9	2.1	2.3	2.5	2.7	2.9	3.1	3.2	3.4
27.0	-0.4	-0.2	-0.0	0.2	0.4	0.5	0.7	0.9	1.1	1.3	1.4	1.6	1.8	2.0	2.2	2.3	2.5	2.7	2.9	3.1	3.2
27.5	-0.3	-0.2	-0.0	0.2	0.3	0.5	0.7	0.8	1.0	1.2	1.3	1.5	1.7	1.9	2.0	2.2	2.4	2.5	2.7	2.9	3.0
28.0	-0.3	-0.2	-0.0	0.2	0.3	0.5	0.6	0.8	0.9	1.1	1.3	1.4	1.6	1.7	1.9	2.0	2.2	2.4	2.5	2.7	2.8
28.5	-0.3	-0.1	-0.0	0.1	0.3	0.4	0.6	0.7	0.9	1.0	1.2	1.3	1.5	1.6	1.8	1.9	2.0	2.2	2.3	2.5	2.6
29.0	-0.3	-0.1	-0.0	0.1	0.3	0.4	0.5	0.7	0.8	0.9	1.1	1.2	1.3	1.5	1.6	1.8	1.9	2.0	2.2	2.3	2.4
29.5	-0.2	-0.1	-0.0	0.1	0.2	0.4	0.5	0.6	0.7	0.9	1.0	1.1	1.2	1.4	1.5	1.6	1.7	1.9	2.0	2.1	2.2
30.0	-0.2	-0.1	-0.0	0.1	0.2	0.3	0.4	0.6	0.7	0.8	0.9	1.0	1.1	1.2	1.3	1.5	1.6	1.7	1.8	1.9	2.0
30.5	-0.2	-0.1	-0.0	0.1	0.2	0.3	0.4	0.5	0.6	0.7	0.8	0.9	1.0	1.1	1.2	1.3	1.4	1.5	1.6	1.7	1.8
31.0	-0.2	-0.1	-0.0	0.1	0.2	0.3	0.4	0.4	0.5	0.6	0.7	0.8	0.9	1.0	1.1	1.2	1.3	1.3	1.4	1.5	1.6
31.5	-0.2	-0.1	-0.0	0.1	0.2	0.2	0.3	0.4	0.5	0.5	0.6	0.7	0.8	0.9	0.9	1.0	1.1	1.2	1.3	1.3	1.4
32.0	-0.1	-0.1	-0.0	0.1	0.1	0.2	0.3	0.3	0.4	0.5	0.5	0.6	0.7	0.7	0.8	0.9	0.9	1.0	1.1	1.1	1.2
32.5	-0.1	-0.1	-0.0	0.1	0.1	0.2	0.2	0.3	0.3	0.4	0.4	0.5	0.6	0.6	0.7	0.7	0.8	0.8	0.9	1.0	1.0
33.0	-0.1	-0.0	-0.0	0.0	0.1	0.1	0.2	0.2	0.3	0.3	0.4	0.4	0.4	0.5	0.5	0.6	0.6	0.7	0.7	0.8	0.8
33.5	-0.1	-0.0	-0.0	0.0	0.1	0.1	0.1	0.2	0.2	0.2	0.3	0.3	0.3	0.4	0.4	0.4	0.5	0.5	0.5	0.6	0.6
34.0	-0.0	-0.0	-0.0	0.0	0.0	0.1	0.1	0.1	0.1	0.2	0.2	0.2	0.2	0.2	0.3	0.3	0.3	0.3	0.4	0.4	0.4
34.5	-0.0	-0.0	-0.0	0.0	0.0	0.0	0.0	0.1	0.1	0.1	0.1	0.1	0.1	0.1	0.1	0.1	0.2	0.2	0.2	0.2	0.2
35.0	0.0	0.0	0.0	-0.0	-0.0	-0.0	-0.0	-0.0	-0.0	-0.0	-0.0	-0.0	-0.0	0.0	0.0	0.0	0.0	0.0	0.0	0.0	0.0
35.5	0.0	0.0	0.0	-0.0	-0.0	-0.0	-0.0	-0.1	-0.1	-0.1	-0.1	-0.1	-0.1	-0.1	-0.1	-0.1	-0.2	-0.2	-0.2	-0.2	-0.2
36.0	0.0	0.0	0.0	-0.0	-0.0	-0.1	-0.1	-0.1	-0.1	-0.2	-0.2	-0.2	-0.2	-0.2	-0.3	-0.3	-0.3	-0.3	-0.4	-0.4	-0.4
36.5	0.1	0.0	0.0	-0.0	-0.1	-0.1	-0.1	-0.2	-0.2	-0.2	-0.3	-0.3	-0.3	-0.4	-0.4	-0.4	-0.5	-0.5	-0.5	-0.6	-0.6
37.0	0.1	0.0	0.0	-0.0	-0.1	-0.1	-0.2	-0.2	-0.3	-0.3	-0.4	-0.4	-0.4	-0.5	-0.5	-0.6	-0.6	-0.7	-0.7	-0.8	-0.8
37.5	0.1	0.1	0.0	-0.1	-0.1	-0.2	-0.2	-0.3	-0.3	-0.4	-0.4	-0.5	-0.6	-0.6	-0.7	-0.7	-0.8	-0.8	-0.9	-0.9	-1.0
38.0	0.1	0.1	0.0	-0.1	-0.1	-0.2	-0.3	-0.3	-0.4	-0.5	-0.5	-0.6	-0.7	-0.7	-0.8	-0.9	-0.9	-1.0	-1.1	-1.1	-1.2
38.5	0.2	0.1	0.0	-0.1	-0.2	-0.2	-0.3	-0.4	-0.5	-0.6	-0.6	-0.7	-0.8	-0.9	-0.9	-1.0	-1.1	-1.2	-1.3	-1.3	-1.4
39.0	0.2	0.1	0.0	-0.1	-0.2	-0.3	-0.4	-0.5	-0.5	-0.6	-0.7	-0.8	-0.9	-1.0	-1.1	-1.2	-1.3	-1.3	-1.4	-1.5	-1.6
39.5	0.2	0.1	0.0	-0.1	-0.2	-0.3	-0.4	-0.5	-0.6	-0.7	-0.8	-0.9	-1.0	-1.1	-1.2	-1.3	-1.4	-1.5	-1.6	-1.7	-1.8
40.0	0.2	0.1	0.0	-0.1	-0.2	-0.3	-0.5	-0.6	-0.7	-0.8	-0.9	-1.0	-1.1	-1.2	-1.3	-1.5	-1.6	-1.7	-1.8	-1.9	-2.0
40.5	0.2	0.1	0.0	-0.1	-0.2	-0.4	-0.5	-0.6	-0.7	-0.9	-1.0	-1.1	-1.2	-1.4	-1.5	-1.6	-1.7	-1.8	-2.0	-2.1	-2.2
41.0	0.3	0.1	0.0	-0.1	-0.3	-0.4	-0.5	-0.7	-0.8	-0.9	-1.1	-1.2	-1.3	-1.5	-1.6	-1.7	-1.9	-2.0	-2.2	-2.3	-2.4
41.5	0.3	0.1	0.0	-0.1	-0.3	-0.4	-0.6	-0.7	-0.9	-1.0	-1.2	-1.3	-1.5	-1.6	-1.8	-1.9	-2.0	-2.2	-2.3	-2.5	-2.6
42.0	0.3	0.2	0.0	-0.2	-0.3	-0.5	-0.6	-0.8	-0.9	-1.1	-1.3	-1.4	-1.6	-1.7	-1.9	-2.0	-2.2	-2.4	-2.5	-2.7	-2.8

Table 2.4–6 (*Continued*)

500 METERS
(52.47 kg/cm²)

‰ \ °C	−4	−2	0	2	4	6	8	10	12	14	16	18	20	22	24	26	28	30	32	34	36
0.0	−1.7	−0.9	−0.1	0.6	1.4	2.2	3.0	3.7	4.5	5.3	6.1	6.9	7.7	8.5	9.3	10.1	10.9	11.8	12.6	13.4	14.2
0.5	−1.6	−0.9	−0.1	0.6	1.4	2.2	2.9	3.7	4.5	5.2	6.0	6.8	7.6	8.4	9.2	10.0	10.8	11.6	12.4	13.2	14.0
1.0	−1.6	−0.9	−0.1	0.6	1.4	2.1	2.9	3.6	4.4	5.2	5.9	6.7	7.5	8.3	9.0	9.8	10.6	11.4	12.2	13.0	13.8
1.5	−1.6	−0.9	−0.1	0.6	1.3	2.1	2.8	3.6	4.3	5.1	5.8	6.6	7.4	8.1	8.9	9.7	10.5	11.3	12.0	12.8	13.6
2.0	−1.6	−0.8	−0.1	0.6	1.3	2.1	2.8	3.5	4.3	5.0	5.8	6.5	7.3	8.0	8.8	9.5	10.3	11.1	11.9	12.7	13.4
2.5	−1.5	−0.8	−0.1	0.6	1.3	2.0	2.7	3.5	4.2	4.9	5.7	6.4	7.1	7.9	8.6	9.4	10.2	10.9	11.7	12.5	13.2
3.0	−1.5	−0.8	−0.1	0.6	1.3	2.0	2.7	3.4	4.1	4.9	5.6	6.3	7.0	7.8	8.5	9.3	10.0	10.8	11.5	12.3	13.0
3.5	−1.5	−0.8	−0.1	0.6	1.3	2.0	2.7	3.4	4.1	4.8	5.5	6.2	6.9	7.6	8.4	9.1	9.8	10.6	11.3	12.1	12.8
4.0	−1.5	−0.8	−0.1	0.6	1.2	1.9	2.6	3.3	4.0	4.7	5.4	6.1	6.8	7.5	8.2	9.0	9.7	10.4	11.2	11.9	12.6
4.5	−1.4	−0.8	−0.1	0.6	1.2	1.9	2.6	3.3	3.9	4.6	5.3	6.0	6.7	7.4	8.1	8.8	9.5	10.3	11.0	11.7	12.4
5.0	−1.4	−0.8	−0.1	0.5	1.2	1.9	2.5	3.2	3.9	4.5	5.2	5.9	6.6	7.3	8.0	8.7	9.4	10.1	10.8	11.5	12.2
5.5	−1.4	−0.7	−0.1	0.5	1.2	1.8	2.5	3.1	3.8	4.5	5.1	5.8	6.5	7.2	7.8	8.5	9.2	9.9	10.6	11.3	12.0
6.0	−1.4	−0.7	−0.1	0.5	1.2	1.8	2.4	3.1	3.7	4.4	5.0	5.7	6.4	7.0	7.7	8.4	9.1	9.8	10.4	11.1	11.8
6.5	−1.3	−0.7	−0.1	0.5	1.1	1.8	2.4	3.0	3.7	4.3	5.0	5.6	6.3	6.9	7.6	8.2	8.9	9.6	10.3	11.0	11.6
7.0	−1.3	−0.7	−0.1	0.5	1.1	1.7	2.4	3.0	3.6	4.2	4.9	5.5	6.2	6.8	7.4	8.1	8.8	9.4	10.1	10.8	11.4
7.5	−1.3	−0.7	−0.1	0.5	1.1	1.7	2.3	2.9	3.5	4.2	4.8	5.4	6.0	6.7	7.3	8.0	8.6	9.3	9.9	10.6	11.2
8.0	−1.3	−0.7	−0.1	0.5	1.1	1.7	2.3	2.9	3.5	4.1	4.7	5.3	5.9	6.6	7.2	7.8	8.5	9.1	9.7	10.4	11.0
8.5	−1.2	−0.7	−0.1	0.5	1.1	1.6	2.2	2.8	3.4	4.0	4.6	5.2	5.8	6.4	7.0	7.7	8.3	8.9	9.6	10.2	10.8
9.0	−1.2	−0.7	−0.1	0.5	1.0	1.6	2.2	2.8	3.3	3.9	4.5	5.1	5.7	6.3	6.9	7.5	8.1	8.8	9.4	10.0	10.6
9.5	−1.2	−0.6	−0.1	0.5	1.0	1.6	2.1	2.7	3.3	3.9	4.4	5.0	5.6	6.2	6.8	7.4	8.0	8.6	9.2	9.8	10.4
10.0	−1.2	−0.6	−0.1	0.5	1.0	1.5	2.1	2.7	3.2	3.8	4.3	4.9	5.5	6.1	6.7	7.2	7.8	8.4	9.0	9.6	10.2
10.5	−1.1	−0.6	−0.1	0.4	1.0	1.5	2.1	2.6	3.1	3.7	4.3	4.8	5.4	5.9	6.5	7.1	7.7	8.3	8.9	9.4	10.0
11.0	−1.1	−0.6	−0.1	0.4	1.0	1.5	2.0	2.5	3.1	3.6	4.2	4.7	5.3	5.8	6.4	7.0	7.5	8.1	8.7	9.3	9.8
11.5	−1.1	−0.6	−0.1	0.4	0.9	1.4	2.0	2.5	3.0	3.5	4.1	4.6	5.2	5.7	6.3	6.8	7.4	7.9	8.5	9.1	9.6
12.0	−1.1	−0.6	−0.1	0.4	0.9	1.4	1.9	2.4	3.0	3.5	4.0	4.5	5.0	5.6	6.1	6.7	7.2	7.8	8.3	8.9	9.4
12.5	−1.0	−0.6	−0.1	0.4	0.9	1.4	1.9	2.4	2.9	3.4	3.9	4.4	4.9	5.5	6.0	6.5	7.1	7.6	8.1	8.7	9.2
13.0	−1.0	−0.6	−0.1	0.4	0.9	1.4	1.8	2.3	2.8	3.3	3.8	4.3	4.8	5.3	5.9	6.4	6.9	7.4	8.0	8.5	9.0
13.5	−1.0	−0.5	−0.1	0.4	0.9	1.3	1.8	2.3	2.8	3.2	3.7	4.2	4.7	5.2	5.7	6.2	6.7	7.3	7.8	8.3	8.8
14.0	−1.0	−0.5	−0.1	0.4	0.8	1.3	1.8	2.2	2.7	3.2	3.6	4.1	4.6	5.1	5.6	6.1	6.6	7.1	7.6	8.1	8.6
14.5	−0.9	−0.5	−0.1	0.4	0.8	1.3	1.7	2.2	2.6	3.1	3.6	4.0	4.5	5.0	5.5	5.9	6.4	6.9	7.4	7.9	8.4
15.0	−0.9	−0.5	−0.1	0.4	0.8	1.2	1.7	2.1	2.6	3.0	3.5	3.9	4.4	4.9	5.3	5.8	6.3	6.8	7.3	7.7	8.2
15.5	−0.9	−0.5	−0.1	0.3	0.8	1.2	1.6	2.1	2.5	2.9	3.4	3.8	4.3	4.7	5.2	5.7	6.1	6.6	7.1	7.6	8.0
16.0	−0.9	−0.5	−0.1	0.3	0.7	1.2	1.6	2.0	2.4	2.9	3.3	3.7	4.2	4.6	5.1	5.5	6.0	6.4	6.9	7.4	7.8
16.5	−0.9	−0.5	−0.1	0.3	0.7	1.1	1.5	1.9	2.4	2.8	3.2	3.6	4.1	4.5	4.9	5.4	5.8	6.3	6.7	7.2	7.6
17.0	−0.8	−0.4	−0.1	0.3	0.7	1.1	1.5	1.9	2.3	2.7	3.1	3.5	3.9	4.4	4.8	5.2	5.7	6.1	6.5	7.0	7.4
17.5	−0.8	−0.4	−0.1	0.3	0.7	1.1	1.5	1.8	2.2	2.6	3.0	3.4	3.8	4.2	4.7	5.1	5.5	5.9	6.4	6.8	7.2
18.0	−0.8	−0.4	−0.1	0.3	0.7	1.0	1.4	1.8	2.2	2.5	2.9	3.3	3.7	4.1	4.5	4.9	5.3	5.8	6.2	6.6	7.0
18.5	−0.8	−0.4	−0.1	0.3	0.6	1.0	1.4	1.7	2.1	2.5	2.8	3.2	3.6	4.0	4.4	4.8	5.2	5.6	6.0	6.4	6.8
19.0	−0.7	−0.4	−0.1	0.3	0.6	1.0	1.3	1.7	2.0	2.4	2.8	3.1	3.5	3.9	4.3	4.6	5.0	5.4	5.8	6.2	6.6
19.5	−0.7	−0.4	−0.1	0.3	0.6	0.9	1.3	1.6	2.0	2.3	2.7	3.0	3.4	3.8	4.1	4.5	4.9	5.3	5.7	6.0	6.4
20.0	−0.7	−0.4	−0.1	0.3	0.6	0.9	1.2	1.6	1.9	2.2	2.6	2.9	3.3	3.6	4.0	4.4	4.7	5.1	5.5	5.9	6.2
20.5	−0.7	−0.4	−0.1	0.3	0.6	0.9	1.2	1.5	1.8	2.2	2.5	2.8	3.2	3.5	3.9	4.2	4.6	4.9	5.3	5.7	6.0

Table 2.4–6 (*Continued*)

500 METERS
(52.47 kg/cm^2)

‰ \ °C	-4	-2	0	2	4	6	8	10	12	14	16	18	20	22	24	26	28	30	32	34	36
21.0	-0.6	-0.3	-0.1	0.2	0.5	0.8	1.1	1.5	1.8	2.1	2.4	2.7	3.1	3.4	3.7	4.1	4.4	4.8	5.1	5.5	5.8
21.5	-0.6	-0.3	-0.0	0.2	0.5	0.8	1.1	1.4	1.7	2.0	2.3	2.6	2.9	3.3	3.6	3.9	4.3	4.6	4.9	5.3	5.6
22.0	-0.6	-0.3	-0.0	0.2	0.5	0.8	1.1	1.3	1.6	1.9	2.2	2.5	2.8	3.1	3.5	3.8	4.1	4.4	4.8	5.1	5.4
22.5	-0.6	-0.3	-0.0	0.2	0.5	0.7	1.0	1.3	1.6	1.9	2.1	2.4	2.7	3.0	3.3	3.6	4.0	4.3	4.6	4.9	5.2
23.0	-0.5	-0.3	-0.0	0.2	0.5	0.7	1.0	1.2	1.5	1.8	2.1	2.3	2.6	2.9	3.2	3.5	3.8	4.1	4.4	4.7	5.0
23.5	-0.5	-0.3	-0.0	0.2	0.4	0.7	0.9	1.2	1.4	1.7	2.0	2.2	2.5	2.8	3.1	3.4	3.6	3.9	4.2	4.5	4.8
24.0	-0.5	-0.3	-0.0	0.2	0.4	0.7	0.9	1.1	1.4	1.6	1.9	2.1	2.4	2.7	2.9	3.2	3.5	3.8	4.1	4.3	4.6
24.5	-0.5	-0.3	-0.0	0.2	0.4	0.6	0.8	1.1	1.3	1.5	1.8	2.0	2.3	2.5	2.8	3.1	3.3	3.6	3.9	4.2	4.4
25.0	-0.4	-0.2	-0.0	0.2	0.4	0.6	0.8	1.0	1.2	1.5	1.7	1.9	2.2	2.4	2.7	2.9	3.2	3.4	3.7	4.0	4.2
25.5	-0.4	-0.2	-0.0	0.2	0.4	0.6	0.8	1.0	1.2	1.4	1.6	1.8	2.1	2.3	2.5	2.8	3.0	3.3	3.5	3.8	4.0
26.0	-0.4	-0.2	-0.0	0.1	0.3	0.5	0.7	0.9	1.1	1.3	1.5	1.7	2.0	2.2	2.4	2.6	2.9	3.1	3.3	3.6	3.8
26.5	-0.4	-0.2	-0.0	0.1	0.3	0.5	0.7	0.9	1.0	1.2	1.4	1.6	1.8	2.1	2.3	2.5	2.7	2.9	3.2	3.4	3.6
27.0	-0.3	-0.2	-0.0	0.1	0.3	0.5	0.6	0.8	1.0	1.2	1.4	1.5	1.7	1.9	2.1	2.3	2.6	2.8	3.0	3.2	3.4
27.5	-0.3	-0.2	-0.0	0.1	0.3	0.4	0.6	0.8	0.9	1.1	1.3	1.4	1.6	1.8	2.0	2.2	2.4	2.6	2.8	3.0	3.2
28.0	-0.3	-0.2	-0.0	0.1	0.3	0.4	0.5	0.7	0.9	1.0	1.2	1.3	1.5	1.7	1.9	2.1	2.2	2.4	2.6	2.8	3.0
28.5	-0.3	-0.1	-0.0	0.1	0.2	0.4	0.5	0.6	0.8	0.9	1.1	1.2	1.4	1.6	1.7	1.9	2.1	2.3	2.5	2.7	2.8
29.0	-0.2	-0.1	-0.0	0.1	0.2	0.3	0.5	0.6	0.7	0.9	1.0	1.1	1.3	1.4	1.6	1.8	1.9	2.1	2.3	2.5	2.6
29.5	-0.2	-0.1	-0.0	0.1	0.2	0.3	0.4	0.5	0.7	0.8	0.9	1.0	1.2	1.3	1.5	1.6	1.8	1.9	2.1	2.3	2.4
30.0	-0.2	-0.1	-0.0	0.1	0.2	0.3	0.4	0.5	0.6	0.7	0.8	0.9	1.1	1.2	1.3	1.5	1.6	1.8	1.9	2.1	2.2
30.5	-0.2	-0.1	-0.0	0.1	0.2	0.2	0.3	0.4	0.5	0.6	0.7	0.8	1.0	1.1	1.2	1.3	1.5	1.6	1.7	1.9	2.0
31.0	-0.1	-0.1	-0.0	0.1	0.1	0.2	0.3	0.4	0.5	0.6	0.6	0.7	0.9	1.0	1.1	1.2	1.3	1.4	1.6	1.7	1.8
31.5	-0.1	-0.1	-0.0	0.0	0.1	0.2	0.2	0.3	0.4	0.5	0.6	0.6	0.7	0.8	0.9	1.0	1.2	1.3	1.4	1.5	1.6
32.0	-0.1	-0.1	-0.0	0.0	0.1	0.1	0.2	0.3	0.3	0.4	0.5	0.5	0.6	0.7	0.8	0.9	1.0	1.1	1.2	1.3	1.4
32.5	-0.1	-0.0	-0.0	0.0	0.1	0.1	0.2	0.2	0.3	0.3	0.4	0.4	0.5	0.6	0.7	0.8	0.8	0.9	1.0	1.1	1.2
33.0	-0.0	-0.0	-0.0	0.0	0.0	0.1	0.1	0.2	0.2	0.2	0.3	0.4	0.4	0.5	0.5	0.6	0.7	0.8	0.9	1.0	1.0
33.5	-0.0	-0.0	-0.0	0.0	0.0	0.0	0.1	0.1	0.1	0.2	0.2	0.3	0.3	0.4	0.4	0.5	0.5	0.6	0.7	0.8	0.8
34.0	-0.0	-0.0	-0.0	-0.0	0.0	0.0	0.0	0.0	0.1	0.1	0.1	0.2	0.2	0.2	0.3	0.3	0.4	0.4	0.5	0.6	0.6
34.5	0.0	0.0	-0.0	-0.0	-0.0	-0.0	-0.0	-0.0	0.0	0.0	0.0	0.1	0.1	0.1	0.1	0.2	0.2	0.3	0.3	0.4	0.4
35.0	0.0	0.0	0.0	-0.0	-0.0	-0.0	-0.1	-0.1	-0.1	-0.1	-0.1	-0.0	-0.0	-0.0	0.0	0.0	0.1	0.1	0.1	0.2	0.2
35.5	0.1	0.0	0.0	-0.0	-0.1	-0.1	-0.1	-0.1	-0.1	-0.1	-0.1	-0.1	-0.1	-0.1	-0.1	-0.1	-0.1	-0.1	-0.0	0.0	0.0
36.0	0.1	0.0	0.0	-0.0	-0.1	-0.1	-0.1	-0.2	-0.2	-0.2	-0.2	-0.2	-0.3	-0.3	-0.3	-0.3	-0.2	-0.2	-0.2	-0.2	-0.2
36.5	0.1	0.1	0.0	-0.0	-0.1	-0.1	-0.2	-0.2	-0.3	-0.3	-0.3	-0.3	-0.4	-0.4	-0.4	-0.4	-0.4	-0.4	-0.4	-0.4	-0.4
37.0	0.1	0.1	0.0	-0.1	-0.1	-0.2	-0.2	-0.3	-0.3	-0.4	-0.4	-0.4	-0.5	-0.5	-0.5	-0.5	-0.6	-0.6	-0.6	-0.6	-0.6
37.5	0.2	0.1	0.0	-0.1	-0.1	-0.2	-0.3	-0.3	-0.4	-0.4	-0.5	-0.5	-0.6	-0.6	-0.7	-0.7	-0.7	-0.7	-0.7	-0.7	-0.8
38.0	0.2	0.1	0.0	-0.1	-0.2	-0.2	-0.3	-0.4	-0.5	-0.5	-0.6	-0.6	-0.7	-0.7	-0.8	-0.8	-0.9	-0.9	-0.9	-0.9	-1.0
38.5	0.2	0.1	0.0	-0.1	-0.2	-0.3	-0.4	-0.4	-0.5	-0.6	-0.7	-0.7	-0.8	-0.9	-0.9	-1.0	-1.0	-1.1	-1.1	-1.1	-1.2
39.0	0.2	0.1	0.0	-0.1	-0.2	-0.3	-0.4	-0.5	-0.6	-0.7	-0.8	-0.8	-0.9	-1.0	-1.1	-1.1	-1.2	-1.2	-1.3	-1.3	-1.4
39.5	0.3	0.1	0.0	-0.1	-0.2	-0.3	-0.4	-0.6	-0.7	-0.8	-0.8	-0.9	-1.0	-1.1	-1.2	-1.3	-1.3	-1.4	-1.4	-1.5	-1.6
40.0	0.3	0.2	0.0	-0.1	-0.2	-0.4	-0.5	-0.6	-0.7	-0.8	-0.9	-1.0	-1.1	-1.2	-1.3	-1.4	-1.5	-1.6	-1.6	-1.7	-1.8
40.5	0.3	0.2	0.0	-0.1	-0.3	-0.4	-0.5	-0.7	-0.8	-0.9	-1.0	-1.1	-1.2	-1.4	-1.5	-1.5	-1.6	-1.7	-1.8	-1.9	-2.0
41.0	0.3	0.2	0.0	-0.1	-0.3	-0.4	-0.6	-0.7	-0.9	-1.0	-1.1	-1.2	-1.4	-1.5	-1.6	-1.7	-1.8	-1.9	-2.0	-2.1	-2.2
41.5	0.4	0.2	0.0	-0.1	-0.3	-0.5	-0.6	-0.8	-0.9	-1.1	-1.2	-1.3	-1.5	-1.6	-1.7	-1.8	-1.9	-2.1	-2.2	-2.3	-2.4
42.0	0.4	0.2	0.0	-0.2	-0.3	-0.5	-0.7	-0.8	-1.0	-1.1	-1.3	-1.4	-1.6	-1.7	-1.8	-2.0	-2.1	-2.2	-2.3	-2.4	-2.6

Table 2.4–6 (*Continued*)

1000 METERS
(104.09 kg/cm²)

‰ \ °C	-4	-2	0	2	4	6	8	10	12	14	16	18	20	22	24	26	28	30	32	34	36
0.0	-1.7	-1.0	-0.2	0.5	1.3	2.0	2.8	3.6	4.3	5.1	5.9	6.7	7.5	8.4	9.2	10.0	10.9	11.7	12.6	13.5	14.3
0.5	-1.7	-1.0	-0.2	0.5	1.2	2.0	2.7	3.5	4.3	5.1	5.8	6.6	7.4	8.2	9.0	9.9	10.7	11.6	12.4	13.3	14.1
1.0	-1.7	-0.9	-0.2	0.5	1.2	2.0	2.7	3.5	4.2	5.0	5.7	6.5	7.3	8.1	8.9	9.7	10.6	11.4	12.2	13.1	13.9
1.5	-1.6	-0.9	-0.2	0.5	1.2	1.9	2.7	3.4	4.1	4.9	5.7	6.4	7.2	8.0	8.8	9.6	10.4	11.2	12.1	12.9	13.7
2.0	-1.6	-0.9	-0.2	0.5	1.2	1.9	2.6	3.3	4.1	4.8	5.6	6.3	7.1	7.9	8.7	9.4	10.2	11.1	11.9	12.7	13.5
2.5	-1.6	-0.9	-0.2	0.5	1.2	1.9	2.6	3.3	4.0	4.8	5.5	6.2	7.0	7.8	8.5	9.3	10.1	10.9	11.7	12.5	13.3
3.0	-1.5	-0.9	-0.2	0.5	1.2	1.8	2.5	3.2	4.0	4.7	5.4	6.1	6.9	7.6	8.4	9.2	9.9	10.7	11.5	12.3	13.1
3.5	-1.5	-0.9	-0.2	0.5	1.1	1.8	2.5	3.2	3.9	4.6	5.3	6.0	6.8	7.5	8.3	9.0	9.8	10.6	11.3	12.1	13.0
4.0	-1.5	-0.9	-0.2	0.5	1.1	1.8	2.5	3.1	3.8	4.5	5.2	5.9	6.7	7.4	8.1	8.9	9.6	10.4	11.2	12.0	12.8
4.5	-1.5	-0.8	-0.2	0.4	1.1	1.8	2.4	3.1	3.8	4.4	5.1	5.8	6.6	7.3	8.0	8.7	9.5	10.2	11.0	11.8	12.6
5.0	-1.4	-0.8	-0.2	0.4	1.1	1.7	2.4	3.0	3.7	4.4	5.1	5.7	6.4	7.2	7.9	8.6	9.3	10.1	10.8	11.6	12.4
5.5	-1.4	-0.8	-0.2	0.4	1.1	1.7	2.3	3.0	3.6	4.3	5.0	5.6	6.3	7.0	7.7	8.5	9.2	9.9	10.6	11.4	12.2
6.0	-1.4	-0.8	-0.2	0.4	1.0	1.7	2.3	2.9	3.6	4.2	4.9	5.6	6.2	6.9	7.6	8.3	9.0	9.7	10.5	11.2	12.0
6.5	-1.4	-0.8	-0.2	0.4	1.0	1.6	2.2	2.9	3.5	4.1	4.8	5.5	6.1	6.8	7.5	8.2	8.9	9.6	10.3	11.0	11.8
7.0	-1.3	-0.8	-0.2	0.4	1.0	1.6	2.2	2.8	3.4	4.1	4.7	5.4	6.0	6.7	7.3	8.0	8.7	9.4	10.1	10.8	11.6
7.5	-1.3	-0.8	-0.2	0.4	1.0	1.6	2.2	2.8	3.4	4.0	4.6	5.3	5.9	6.6	7.2	7.9	8.6	9.2	9.9	10.6	11.4
8.0	-1.3	-0.7	-0.2	0.4	1.0	1.5	2.1	2.7	3.3	3.9	4.5	5.2	5.8	6.4	7.1	7.7	8.4	9.1	9.8	10.5	11.2
8.5	-1.3	-0.7	-0.2	0.4	0.9	1.5	2.1	2.7	3.3	3.8	4.5	5.1	5.7	6.3	6.9	7.6	8.3	8.9	9.6	10.3	11.0
9.0	-1.2	-0.7	-0.2	0.4	0.9	1.5	2.0	2.6	3.2	3.8	4.4	5.0	5.6	6.2	6.8	7.5	8.1	8.8	9.4	10.1	10.8
9.5	-1.2	-0.7	-0.2	0.4	0.9	1.4	2.0	2.6	3.1	3.7	4.3	4.9	5.5	6.1	6.7	7.3	7.9	8.6	9.2	9.9	10.6
10.0	-1.2	-0.7	-0.2	0.4	0.9	1.4	2.0	2.5	3.1	3.6	4.2	4.8	5.4	6.0	6.6	7.2	7.8	8.4	9.1	9.7	10.4
10.5	-1.2	-0.7	-0.2	0.3	0.9	1.4	1.9	2.5	3.0	3.5	4.1	4.7	5.2	5.8	6.4	7.0	7.6	8.3	8.9	9.5	10.2
11.0	-1.1	-0.7	-0.2	0.3	0.8	1.4	1.9	2.4	2.9	3.5	4.0	4.6	5.1	5.7	6.3	6.9	7.5	8.1	8.7	9.3	10.0
11.5	-1.1	-0.6	-0.2	0.3	0.8	1.3	1.8	2.3	2.9	3.4	3.9	4.5	5.0	5.6	6.2	6.7	7.3	7.9	8.5	9.1	9.8
12.0	-1.1	-0.6	-0.2	0.3	0.8	1.3	1.8	2.3	2.8	3.3	3.8	4.4	4.9	5.5	6.0	6.6	7.2	7.8	8.4	9.0	9.6
12.5	-1.1	-0.6	-0.1	0.3	0.8	1.3	1.7	2.2	2.7	3.2	3.8	4.3	4.8	5.4	5.9	6.5	7.0	7.6	8.2	8.8	9.4
13.0	-1.0	-0.6	-0.1	0.3	0.8	1.2	1.7	2.2	2.7	3.2	3.7	4.2	4.7	5.2	5.8	6.3	6.9	7.4	8.0	8.6	9.2
13.5	-1.0	-0.6	-0.1	0.3	0.7	1.2	1.7	2.1	2.6	3.1	3.6	4.1	4.6	5.1	5.6	6.2	6.7	7.3	7.8	8.4	9.0
14.0	-1.0	-0.6	-0.1	0.3	0.7	1.2	1.6	2.1	2.5	3.0	3.5	4.0	4.5	5.0	5.5	6.0	6.6	7.1	7.7	8.2	8.8
14.5	-1.0	-0.5	-0.1	0.3	0.7	1.1	1.6	2.0	2.5	2.9	3.4	3.9	4.4	4.9	5.4	5.9	6.4	6.9	7.5	8.0	8.6
15.0	-0.9	-0.5	-0.1	0.3	0.7	1.1	1.5	2.0	2.4	2.9	3.3	3.8	4.3	4.8	5.2	5.7	6.3	6.8	7.3	7.8	8.4
15.5	-0.9	-0.5	-0.1	0.3	0.7	1.1	1.5	1.9	2.4	2.8	3.2	3.7	4.2	4.6	5.1	5.6	6.1	6.6	7.1	7.7	8.2
16.0	-0.9	-0.5	-0.1	0.3	0.7	1.1	1.5	1.9	2.3	2.7	3.2	3.6	4.0	4.5	5.0	5.5	5.9	6.4	6.9	7.5	8.0
16.5	-0.9	-0.5	-0.1	0.3	0.6	1.0	1.4	1.8	2.2	2.6	3.1	3.5	3.9	4.4	4.8	5.3	5.8	6.3	6.8	7.3	7.8
17.0	-0.8	-0.5	-0.1	0.2	0.6	1.0	1.4	1.8	2.2	2.6	3.0	3.4	3.8	4.3	4.7	5.2	5.6	6.1	6.6	7.1	7.6
17.5	-0.8	-0.5	-0.1	0.2	0.6	1.0	1.3	1.7	2.1	2.5	2.9	3.3	3.7	4.1	4.6	5.0	5.5	5.9	6.4	6.9	7.4
18.0	-0.8	-0.4	-0.1	0.2	0.6	0.9	1.3	1.7	2.0	2.4	2.8	3.2	3.6	4.0	4.5	4.9	5.3	5.8	6.2	6.7	7.2
18.5	-0.7	-0.4	-0.1	0.2	0.6	0.9	1.2	1.6	2.0	2.3	2.7	3.1	3.5	3.9	4.3	4.7	5.2	5.6	6.1	6.5	7.0
19.0	-0.7	-0.4	-0.1	0.2	0.5	0.9	1.2	1.6	1.9	2.3	2.6	3.0	3.4	3.8	4.2	4.6	5.0	5.5	5.9	6.3	6.8
19.5	-0.7	-0.4	-0.1	0.2	0.5	0.8	1.2	1.5	1.8	2.2	2.5	2.9	3.3	3.7	4.1	4.5	4.9	5.3	5.7	6.2	6.6
20.0	-0.7	-0.4	-0.1	0.2	0.5	0.8	1.1	1.4	1.8	2.1	2.5	2.8	3.2	3.5	3.9	4.3	4.7	5.1	5.5	6.0	6.4
20.5	-0.6	-0.4	-0.1	0.2	0.5	0.8	1.1	1.4	1.7	2.0	2.4	2.7	3.1	3.4	3.8	4.2	4.6	5.0	5.4	5.8	6.2
21.0	-0.6	-0.4	-0.1	0.2	0.5	0.7	1.0	1.3	1.6	2.0	2.3	2.6	3.0	3.3	3.7	4.0	4.4	4.8	5.2	5.6	6.0
21.5	-0.6	-0.3	-0.1	0.2	0.4	0.7	1.0	1.3	1.6	1.9	2.2	2.5	2.9	3.2	3.5	3.9	4.3	4.6	5.0	5.4	5.8

Table 2.4–6 (*Continued*)

1000 METERS
(104.09 kg/cm²)

‰ \ °C	-4	-2	0	2	4	6	8	10	12	14	16	18	20	22	24	26	28	30	32	34	36
22.0	-0.6	-0.3	-0.1	0.2	0.4	0.7	1.0	1.2	1.5	1.8	2.1	2.4	2.7	3.1	3.4	3.7	4.1	4.5	4.8	5.2	5.6
22.5	-0.5	-0.3	-0.1	0.2	0.4	0.7	0.9	1.2	1.5	1.7	2.0	2.3	2.6	2.9	3.3	3.6	3.9	4.3	4.7	5.0	5.4
23.0	-0.5	-0.3	-0.1	0.1	0.4	0.6	0.9	1.1	1.4	1.7	1.9	2.2	2.5	2.8	3.1	3.5	3.8	4.1	4.5	4.8	5.2
23.5	-0.5	-0.3	-0.1	0.1	0.4	0.6	0.8	1.1	1.3	1.6	1.9	2.1	2.4	2.7	3.0	3.3	3.6	4.0	4.3	4.7	5.0
24.0	-0.5	-0.3	-0.1	0.1	0.3	0.6	0.8	1.0	1.3	1.5	1.8	2.0	2.3	2.6	2.9	3.2	3.5	3.8	4.1	4.5	4.8
24.5	-0.4	-0.3	-0.1	0.1	0.3	0.5	0.7	1.0	1.2	1.4	1.7	1.9	2.2	2.5	2.7	3.0	3.3	3.6	4.0	4.3	4.6
25.0	-0.4	-0.2	-0.1	0.1	0.3	0.5	0.7	0.9	1.1	1.4	1.6	1.8	2.1	2.3	2.6	2.9	3.2	3.5	3.8	4.1	4.4
25.5	-0.4	-0.2	-0.1	0.1	0.3	0.5	0.7	0.9	1.1	1.3	1.5	1.7	2.0	2.2	2.5	2.7	3.0	3.3	3.6	3.9	4.2
26.0	-0.4	-0.2	-0.1	0.1	0.3	0.4	0.6	0.8	1.0	1.2	1.4	1.6	1.9	2.1	2.4	2.6	2.9	3.1	3.4	3.7	4.0
26.5	-0.3	-0.2	-0.1	0.1	0.2	0.4	0.6	0.8	0.9	1.1	1.3	1.5	1.8	2.0	2.2	2.5	2.7	3.0	3.3	3.5	3.8
27.0	-0.3	-0.2	-0.1	0.1	0.2	0.4	0.5	0.7	0.9	1.1	1.3	1.4	1.7	1.9	2.1	2.3	2.6	2.8	3.1	3.3	3.6
27.5	-0.3	-0.2	-0.0	0.1	0.2	0.4	0.5	0.7	0.8	1.0	1.2	1.3	1.5	1.7	2.0	2.2	2.4	2.6	2.9	3.2	3.4
28.0	-0.3	-0.2	-0.0	0.1	0.2	0.3	0.5	0.6	0.8	0.9	1.1	1.3	1.4	1.6	1.8	2.0	2.3	2.5	2.7	3.0	3.2
28.5	-0.2	-0.1	-0.0	0.1	0.2	0.3	0.4	0.5	0.7	0.8	1.0	1.2	1.3	1.5	1.7	1.9	2.1	2.3	2.5	2.8	3.0
29.0	-0.2	-0.1	-0.0	0.1	0.2	0.3	0.4	0.5	0.6	0.8	0.9	1.1	1.2	1.4	1.6	1.8	1.9	2.2	2.4	2.6	2.8
29.5	-0.2	-0.1	-0.0	0.0	0.1	0.2	0.3	0.4	0.6	0.7	0.8	1.0	1.1	1.3	1.4	1.6	1.8	2.0	2.2	2.4	2.6
30.0	-0.2	-0.1	-0.0	0.0	0.1	0.2	0.3	0.4	0.5	0.6	0.7	0.9	1.0	1.1	1.3	1.5	1.6	1.8	2.0	2.2	2.4
30.5	-0.1	-0.1	-0.0	0.0	0.1	0.2	0.2	0.3	0.4	0.5	0.6	0.8	0.9	1.0	1.2	1.3	1.5	1.7	1.8	2.0	2.2
31.0	-0.1	-0.1	-0.0	0.0	0.1	0.1	0.2	0.3	0.4	0.5	0.6	0.7	0.8	0.9	1.0	1.2	1.3	1.5	1.7	1.8	2.0
31.5	-0.1	-0.1	-0.0	0.0	0.1	0.1	0.2	0.2	0.3	0.4	0.5	0.6	0.7	0.8	0.9	1.0	1.2	1.3	1.5	1.7	1.8
32.0	-0.1	-0.0	-0.0	0.0	0.0	0.1	0.1	0.2	0.2	0.3	0.4	0.5	0.6	0.7	0.8	0.9	1.0	1.2	1.3	1.5	1.6
32.5	-0.0	-0.0	-0.0	-0.0	0.0	0.0	0.1	0.1	0.2	0.2	0.3	0.4	0.5	0.5	0.6	0.8	0.9	1.0	1.1	1.3	1.4
33.0	-0.0	-0.0	-0.0	-0.0	0.0	0.0	0.0	0.1	0.1	0.2	0.2	0.3	0.3	0.4	0.5	0.6	0.7	0.8	1.0	1.1	1.2
33.5	0.0	0.0	-0.0	-0.0	-0.0	-0.0	-0.0	0.0	0.0	0.1	0.1	0.2	0.2	0.3	0.4	0.5	0.6	0.7	0.8	0.9	1.0
34.0	0.1	0.0	-0.0	-0.0	-0.0	-0.0	-0.0	-0.0	-0.0	0.0	0.0	0.1	0.1	0.2	0.3	0.3	0.4	0.5	0.6	0.7	0.8
34.5	0.1	0.0	-0.0	-0.0	-0.1	-0.1	-0.1	-0.1	-0.1	-0.1	-0.0	-0.0	0.0	0.1	0.1	0.2	0.3	0.3	0.4	0.5	0.6
35.0	0.1	0.0	0.0	-0.0	-0.1	-0.1	-0.1	-0.1	-0.1	-0.1	-0.1	-0.1	-0.1	-0.1	-0.0	0.0	0.1	0.2	0.3	0.3	0.5
35.5	0.1	0.1	0.0	-0.0	-0.1	-0.1	-0.2	-0.2	-0.2	-0.2	-0.2	-0.2	-0.2	-0.2	-0.1	-0.1	-0.0	0.0	0.1	0.2	0.3
36.0	0.2	0.1	0.0	-0.1	-0.1	-0.2	-0.2	-0.2	-0.3	-0.3	-0.3	-0.3	-0.3	-0.3	-0.3	-0.2	-0.2	-0.2	-0.1	-0.0	0.1
36.5	0.2	0.1	0.0	-0.1	-0.1	-0.2	-0.2	-0.3	-0.3	-0.4	-0.4	-0.4	-0.4	-0.4	-0.4	-0.4	-0.4	-0.3	-0.3	-0.2	-0.1
37.0	0.2	0.1	0.0	-0.1	-0.2	-0.2	-0.3	-0.4	-0.4	-0.4	-0.5	-0.5	-0.5	-0.5	-0.5	-0.5	-0.5	-0.5	-0.4	-0.4	-0.3
37.5	0.2	0.1	0.0	-0.1	-0.2	-0.3	-0.3	-0.4	-0.5	-0.5	-0.6	-0.6	-0.6	-0.7	-0.7	-0.7	-0.7	-0.6	-0.6	-0.6	-0.5
38.0	0.3	0.1	0.0	-0.1	-0.2	-0.3	-0.4	-0.5	-0.5	-0.6	-0.7	-0.7	-0.7	-0.8	-0.8	-0.8	-0.8	-0.8	-0.8	-0.8	-0.7
38.5	0.3	0.1	0.0	-0.1	-0.2	-0.3	-0.4	-0.5	-0.6	-0.7	-0.7	-0.8	-0.9	-0.9	-0.9	-1.0	-1.0	-1.0	-1.0	-1.0	-0.9
39.0	0.3	0.2	0.0	-0.1	-0.2	-0.3	-0.5	-0.6	-0.7	-0.7	-0.8	-0.9	-1.0	-1.0	-1.1	-1.1	-1.1	-1.1	-1.2	-1.1	-1.1
39.5	0.3	0.2	0.0	-0.1	-0.2	-0.4	-0.5	-0.6	-0.7	-0.8	-0.9	-1.0	-1.1	-1.1	-1.2	-1.2	-1.3	-1.3	-1.3	-1.3	-1.3
40.0	0.4	0.2	0.0	-0.1	-0.3	-0.4	-0.5	-0.7	-0.8	-0.9	-1.0	-1.1	-1.2	-1.3	-1.3	-1.4	-1.4	-1.5	-1.5	-1.5	-1.5
40.5	0.4	0.2	0.0	-0.1	-0.3	-0.4	-0.6	-0.7	-0.8	-1.0	-1.1	-1.2	-1.3	-1.4	-1.5	-1.5	-1.6	-1.6	-1.7	-1.7	-1.7
41.0	0.4	0.2	0.0	-0.1	-0.3	-0.5	-0.6	-0.8	-0.9	-1.0	-1.2	-1.3	-1.4	-1.5	-1.6	-1.7	-1.7	-1.8	-1.9	-1.9	-1.9
41.5	0.4	0.2	0.0	-0.1	-0.3	-0.5	-0.7	-0.8	-1.0	-1.1	-1.3	-1.4	-1.5	-1.6	-1.7	-1.8	-1.9	-2.0	-2.0	-2.1	-2.1
42.0	0.5	0.3	0.0	-0.2	-0.3	-0.5	-0.7	-0.9	-1.0	-1.2	-1.3	-1.5	-1.6	-1.7	-1.8	-2.0	-2.0	-2.1	-2.2	-2.3	-2.3

Table 2.4–6 (*Continued*)

1500 METERS
(155.81 kg/cm²)

‰ \ °C	−4	−2	0	2	4	6	8	10	12	14	16	18	20	22	24	26
0.0	−1.7	−1.0	−0.3	0.4	1.1	1.9	2.6	3.4	4.2	4.9	5.7	6.5	7.4	8.2	9.0	9.9
0.5	−1.7	−1.0	−0.3	0.4	1.1	1.8	2.6	3.3	4.1	4.9	5.7	6.5	7.3	8.1	8.9	9.8
1.0	−1.7	−1.0	−0.3	0.4	1.1	1.8	2.5	3.3	4.0	4.8	5.6	6.4	7.2	8.0	8.8	9.6
1.5	−1.6	−1.0	−0.3	0.4	1.1	1.8	2.5	3.2	4.0	4.7	5.5	6.3	7.0	7.8	8.7	9.5
2.0	−1.6	−1.0	−0.3	0.4	1.1	1.8	2.5	3.2	3.9	4.6	5.4	6.2	6.9	7.7	8.5	9.3
2.5	−1.6	−0.9	−0.3	0.4	1.0	1.7	2.4	3.1	3.8	4.6	5.3	6.1	6.8	7.6	8.4	9.2
3.0	−1.6	−0.9	−0.3	0.4	1.0	1.7	2.4	3.1	3.8	4.5	5.2	6.0	6.7	7.5	8.3	9.1
3.5	−1.5	−0.9	−0.3	0.4	1.0	1.7	2.3	3.0	3.7	4.4	5.1	5.9	6.6	7.4	8.1	8.9
4.0	−1.5	−0.9	−0.3	0.4	1.0	1.6	2.3	3.0	3.7	4.4	5.1	5.8	6.5	7.2	8.0	8.8
4.5	−1.5	−0.9	−0.3	0.3	1.0	1.6	2.3	2.9	3.6	4.3	5.0	5.7	6.4	7.1	7.9	8.6
5.0	−1.5	−0.9	−0.3	0.3	1.0	1.6	2.2	2.9	3.5	4.2	4.9	5.6	6.3	7.0	7.7	8.5
5.5	−1.4	−0.8	−0.3	0.3	0.9	1.6	2.2	2.8	3.5	4.1	4.8	5.5	6.2	6.9	7.6	8.3
6.0	−1.4	−0.8	−0.3	0.3	0.9	1.5	2.1	2.8	3.4	4.1	4.7	5.4	6.1	6.8	7.5	8.2
6.5	−1.4	−0.8	−0.3	0.3	0.9	1.5	2.1	2.7	3.3	4.0	4.6	5.3	6.0	6.7	7.4	8.1
7.0	−1.3	−0.8	−0.2	0.3	0.9	1.5	2.1	2.7	3.3	3.9	4.5	5.2	5.9	6.5	7.2	7.9
7.5	−1.3	−0.8	−0.2	0.3	0.9	1.4	2.0	2.6	3.2	3.8	4.5	5.1	5.7	6.4	7.1	7.8
8.0	−1.3	−0.8	−0.2	0.3	0.9	1.4	2.0	2.6	3.2	3.8	4.4	5.0	5.6	6.3	7.0	7.6
8.5	−1.3	−0.8	−0.2	0.3	0.8	1.4	1.9	2.5	3.1	3.7	4.3	4.9	5.5	6.2	6.8	7.5
9.0	−1.2	−0.7	−0.2	0.3	0.8	1.4	1.9	2.5	3.0	3.6	4.2	4.8	5.4	6.1	6.7	7.4
9.5	−1.2	−0.7	−0.2	0.3	0.8	1.3	1.9	2.4	3.0	3.5	4.1	4.7	5.3	5.9	6.6	7.2
10.0	−1.2	−0.7	−0.2	0.3	0.8	1.3	1.8	2.4	2.9	3.5	4.0	4.6	5.2	5.8	6.4	7.1
10.5	−1.2	−0.7	−0.2	0.3	0.8	1.3	1.8	2.3	2.8	3.4	3.9	4.5	5.1	5.7	6.3	6.9
11.0	−1.1	−0.7	−0.2	0.3	0.7	1.2	1.7	2.3	2.8	3.3	3.9	4.4	5.0	5.6	6.2	6.8
11.5	−1.1	−0.7	−0.2	0.3	0.7	1.2	1.7	2.2	2.7	3.2	3.8	4.3	4.9	5.5	6.1	6.7
12.0	−1.1	−0.6	−0.2	0.2	0.7	1.2	1.7	2.1	2.7	3.2	3.7	4.2	4.8	5.3	5.9	6.5
12.5	−1.0	−0.6	−0.2	0.2	0.7	1.1	1.6	2.1	2.6	3.1	3.6	4.1	4.7	5.2	5.8	6.4
13.0	−1.0	−0.6	−0.2	0.2	0.7	1.1	1.6	2.0	2.5	3.0	3.5	4.0	4.6	5.1	5.7	6.2
13.5	−1.0	−0.6	−0.2	0.2	0.7	1.1	1.5	2.0	2.5	2.9	3.4	3.9	4.5	5.0	5.5	6.1
14.0	−1.0	−0.6	−0.2	0.2	0.6	1.1	1.5	1.9	2.4	2.9	3.3	3.8	4.3	4.9	5.4	5.9
14.5	−0.9	−0.6	−0.2	0.2	0.6	1.0	1.5	1.9	2.3	2.8	3.3	3.7	4.2	4.7	5.3	5.8
15.0	−0.9	−0.6	−0.2	0.2	0.6	1.0	1.4	1.8	2.3	2.7	3.2	3.6	4.1	4.6	5.1	5.7
15.5	−0.9	−0.5	−0.2	0.2	0.6	1.0	1.4	1.8	2.2	2.6	3.1	3.6	4.0	4.5	5.0	5.5
16.0	−0.9	−0.5	−0.2	0.2	0.6	0.9	1.3	1.7	2.1	2.6	3.0	3.5	3.9	4.4	4.9	5.4
16.5	−0.8	−0.5	−0.2	0.2	0.5	0.9	1.3	1.7	2.1	2.5	2.9	3.4	3.8	4.3	4.7	5.2
17.0	−0.8	−0.5	−0.2	0.2	0.5	0.9	1.3	1.6	2.0	2.4	2.8	3.3	3.7	4.2	4.6	5.1
17.5	−0.8	−0.5	−0.2	0.2	0.5	0.9	1.2	1.6	2.0	2.3	2.8	3.2	3.6	4.0	4.5	5.0
18.0	−0.8	−0.5	−0.2	0.2	0.5	0.8	1.2	1.5	1.9	2.3	2.7	3.1	3.5	3.9	4.4	4.8
18.5	−0.7	−0.4	−0.1	0.2	0.5	0.8	1.1	1.5	1.8	2.2	2.6	3.0	3.4	3.8	4.2	4.7
19.0	−0.7	−0.4	−0.1	0.2	0.5	0.8	1.1	1.4	1.8	2.1	2.5	2.9	3.3	3.7	4.1	4.5
19.5	−0.7	−0.4	−0.1	0.1	0.4	0.7	1.0	1.4	1.7	2.1	2.4	2.8	3.2	3.6	4.0	4.4
20.0	−0.6	−0.4	−0.1	0.1	0.4	0.7	1.0	1.3	1.6	2.0	2.3	2.7	3.1	3.4	3.8	4.2
20.5	−0.6	−0.4	−0.1	0.1	0.4	0.7	1.0	1.3	1.6	1.9	2.2	2.6	2.9	3.3	3.7	4.1
21.0	−0.6	−0.4	−0.1	0.1	0.4	0.6	0.9	1.2	1.5	1.8	2.2	2.5	2.8	3.2	3.6	4.0
21.5	−0.6	−0.3	−0.1	0.1	0.4	0.6	0.9	1.2	1.5	1.8	2.1	2.4	2.7	3.1	3.4	3.8

Table 2.4–6 (*Continued*)

1500 METERS
(155.81 kg/cm^2)

‰ \ °C	-4	-2	0	2	4	6	8	10	12	14	16	18	20	22	24	26
22.0	-0.5	-0.3	-0.1	0.1	0.3	0.6	0.8	1.1	1.4	1.7	2.0	2.3	2.6	3.0	3.3	3.7
22.5	-0.5	-0.3	-0.1	0.1	0.3	0.6	0.8	1.1	1.3	1.6	1.9	2.2	2.5	2.8	3.2	3.5
23.0	-0.5	-0.3	-0.1	0.1	0.3	0.5	0.8	1.0	1.3	1.5	1.8	2.1	2.4	2.7	3.1	3.4
23.5	-0.5	-0.3	-0.1	0.1	0.3	0.5	0.7	1.0	1.2	1.5	1.7	2.0	2.3	2.6	2.9	3.3
24.0	-0.4	-0.3	-0.1	0.1	0.3	0.5	0.7	0.9	1.1	1.4	1.6	1.9	2.2	2.5	2.8	3.1
24.5	-0.4	-0.3	-0.1	0.1	0.3	0.4	0.6	0.9	1.1	1.3	1.6	1.8	2.1	2.4	2.7	3.0
25.0	-0.4	-0.2	-0.1	0.1	0.2	0.4	0.6	0.8	1.0	1.2	1.5	1.7	2.0	2.3	2.5	2.8
25.5	-0.3	-0.2	-0.1	0.1	0.2	0.4	0.6	0.8	1.0	1.2	1.4	1.6	1.9	2.1	2.4	2.7
26.0	-0.3	-0.2	-0.1	0.1	0.2	0.4	0.5	0.7	0.9	1.1	1.3	1.5	1.8	2.0	2.3	2.6
26.5	-0.3	-0.2	-0.1	0.0	0.2	0.3	0.5	0.6	0.8	1.0	1.2	1.4	1.7	1.9	2.1	2.4
27.0	-0.3	-0.2	-0.1	0.0	0.2	0.3	0.4	0.6	0.8	0.9	1.1	1.3	1.5	1.8	2.0	2.3
27.5	-0.2	-0.2	-0.1	0.0	0.1	0.3	0.4	0.5	0.7	0.9	1.0	1.2	1.4	1.7	1.9	2.1
28.0	-0.2	-0.1	-0.1	0.0	0.1	0.2	0.4	0.5	0.6	0.8	1.0	1.1	1.3	1.5	1.8	2.0
28.5	-0.2	-0.1	-0.1	0.0	0.1	0.2	0.3	0.4	0.6	0.7	0.9	1.0	1.2	1.4	1.6	1.8
29.0	-0.2	-0.1	-0.1	0.0	0.1	0.2	0.3	0.4	0.5	0.6	0.8	0.9	1.1	1.3	1.5	1.7
29.5	-0.1	-0.1	-0.0	0.0	0.1	0.2	0.2	0.3	0.4	0.6	0.7	0.8	1.0	1.2	1.4	1.6
30.0	-0.1	-0.1	-0.0	0.0	0.1	0.1	0.2	0.3	0.4	0.5	0.6	0.8	0.9	1.1	1.2	1.4
30.5	-0.1	-0.1	-0.0	-0.0	0.0	0.1	0.2	0.2	0.3	0.4	0.5	0.7	0.8	0.9	1.1	1.3
31.0	-0.1	-0.0	-0.0	-0.0	0.0	0.1	0.1	0.2	0.3	0.3	0.4	0.6	0.7	0.8	1.0	1.1
31.5	-0.0	-0.0	-0.0	-0.0	0.0	0.0	0.1	0.1	0.2	0.3	0.4	0.5	0.6	0.7	0.8	1.0
32.0	0.0	-0.0	-0.0	-0.0	-0.0	0.0	0.0	0.1	0.1	0.2	0.3	0.4	0.5	0.6	0.7	0.9
32.5	0.0	-0.0	-0.0	-0.0	-0.0	-0.0	-0.0	0.0	0.1	0.1	0.2	0.3	0.4	0.5	0.6	0.7
33.0	0.1	0.0	-0.0	-0.0	-0.1	-0.1	-0.0	-0.0	0.0	0.1	0.1	0.2	0.3	0.3	0.5	0.6
33.5	0.1	0.0	-0.0	-0.0	-0.1	-0.1	-0.1	-0.1	-0.1	-0.0	0.0	0.1	0.1	0.2	0.3	0.4
34.0	0.1	0.0	-0.0	-0.1	-0.1	-0.1	-0.1	-0.1	-0.1	-0.1	-0.1	-0.0	0.0	0.1	0.2	0.3
34.5	0.1	0.1	-0.0	-0.1	-0.1	-0.1	-0.2	-0.2	-0.2	-0.2	-0.1	-0.1	-0.1	-0.0	0.1	0.2
35.0	0.2	0.1	0.0	-0.1	-0.1	-0.2	-0.2	-0.2	-0.2	-0.2	-0.2	-0.2	-0.2	-0.1	-0.1	0.0
35.5	0.2	0.1	0.0	-0.1	-0.1	-0.2	-0.2	-0.3	-0.3	-0.3	-0.3	-0.3	-0.3	-0.2	-0.2	-0.1
36.0	0.2	0.1	0.0	-0.1	-0.2	-0.2	-0.3	-0.3	-0.4	-0.4	-0.4	-0.4	-0.4	-0.4	-0.3	-0.3
36.5	0.2	0.1	0.0	-0.1	-0.2	-0.3	-0.3	-0.4	-0.4	-0.5	-0.5	-0.5	-0.5	-0.5	-0.5	-0.4
37.0	0.3	0.1	0.0	-0.1	-0.2	-0.3	-0.4	-0.4	-0.5	-0.5	-0.6	-0.6	-0.6	-0.6	-0.6	-0.6
37.5	0.3	0.2	0.0	-0.1	-0.2	-0.3	-0.4	-0.5	-0.6	-0.6	-0.7	-0.7	-0.7	-0.7	-0.7	-0.7
38.0	0.3	0.2	0.0	-0.1	-0.2	-0.3	-0.4	-0.5	-0.6	-0.7	-0.7	-0.8	-0.8	-0.8	-0.8	-0.8
38.5	0.4	0.2	0.0	-0.1	-0.2	-0.4	-0.5	-0.6	-0.7	-0.8	-0.8	-0.9	-0.9	-1.0	-1.0	-1.0
39.0	0.4	0.2	0.0	-0.1	-0.3	-0.4	-0.5	-0.6	-0.7	-0.8	-0.9	-1.0	-1.0	-1.1	-1.1	-1.1
39.5	0.4	0.2	0.0	-0.1	-0.3	-0.4	-0.6	-0.7	-0.8	-0.9	-1.0	-1.1	-1.1	-1.2	-1.2	-1.3
40.0	0.4	0.2	0.0	-0.1	-0.3	-0.5	-0.6	-0.7	-0.9	-1.0	-1.1	-1.2	-1.3	-1.3	-1.4	-1.4
40.5	0.5	0.2	0.0	-0.1	-0.3	-0.5	-0.7	-0.8	-0.9	-1.1	-1.2	-1.3	-1.4	-1.4	-1.5	-1.5
41.0	0.5	0.3	0.1	-0.1	-0.3	-0.5	-0.7	-0.9	-1.0	-1.1	-1.3	-1.4	-1.5	-1.6	-1.6	-1.7
41.5	0.5	0.3	0.1	-0.2	-0.4	-0.6	-0.7	-0.9	-1.1	-1.2	-1.3	-1.5	-1.6	-1.7	-1.8	-1.8
42.0	0.5	0.3	0.1	-0.2	-0.4	-0.6	-0.8	-1.0	-1.1	-1.3	-1.4	-1.6	-1.7	-1.8	-1.9	-2.0

Table 2.4–6 (*Continued*)

2000 METERS
(207.41 kg/cm^2)

‰ \ °C	−4	−2	0	2	4	6	8	10	12	14	16	18	20	22	24	26
0.0	−1.7	−1.0	−0.4	0.3	1.0	1.7	2.5	3.2	4.0	4.8	5.6	6.4	7.2	8.0	8.9	9.8
0.5	−1.7	−1.0	−0.4	0.3	1.0	1.7	2.4	3.2	3.9	4.7	5.5	6.3	7.1	7.9	8.8	9.6
1.0	−1.7	−1.0	−0.4	0.3	1.0	1.7	2.4	3.1	3.9	4.6	5.4	6.2	7.0	7.8	8.6	9.5
1.5	−1.6	−1.0	−0.3	0.3	1.0	1.7	2.4	3.1	3.8	4.5	5.3	6.1	6.9	7.7	8.5	9.4
2.0	−1.6	−1.0	−0.3	0.3	1.0	1.6	2.3	3.0	3.7	4.5	5.2	6.0	6.8	7.6	8.4	9.2
2.5	−1.6	−1.0	−0.3	0.3	0.9	1.6	2.3	3.0	3.7	4.4	5.1	5.9	6.7	7.4	8.2	9.1
3.0	−1.5	−0.9	−0.3	0.3	0.9	1.6	2.2	2.9	3.6	4.3	5.0	5.8	6.5	7.3	8.1	8.9
3.5	−1.5	−0.9	−0.3	0.3	0.9	1.5	2.2	2.9	3.6	4.2	5.0	5.7	6.4	7.2	8.0	8.8
4.0	−1.5	−0.9	−0.3	0.3	0.9	1.5	2.2	2.8	3.5	4.2	4.9	5.6	6.3	7.1	7.9	8.6
4.5	−1.5	−0.9	−0.3	0.3	0.9	1.5	2.1	2.8	3.4	4.1	4.8	5.5	6.2	7.0	7.7	8.5
5.0	−1.4	−0.9	−0.3	0.3	0.9	1.5	2.1	2.7	3.4	4.0	4.7	5.4	6.1	6.9	7.6	8.4
5.5	−1.4	−0.9	−0.3	0.3	0.8	1.4	2.0	2.7	3.3	4.0	4.6	5.3	6.0	6.7	7.5	8.2
6.0	−1.4	−0.8	−0.3	0.3	0.8	1.4	2.0	2.6	3.2	3.9	4.5	5.2	5.9	6.6	7.3	8.1
6.5	−1.3	−0.8	−0.3	0.2	0.8	1.4	2.0	2.6	3.2	3.8	4.5	5.1	5.8	6.5	7.2	7.9
7.0	−1.3	−0.8	−0.3	0.2	0.8	1.3	1.9	2.5	3.1	3.7	4.4	5.0	5.7	6.4	7.1	7.8
7.5	−1.3	−0.8	−0.3	0.2	0.8	1.3	1.9	2.5	3.1	3.7	4.3	4.9	5.6	6.3	7.0	7.7
8.0	−1.3	−0.8	−0.3	0.2	0.8	1.3	1.8	2.4	3.0	3.6	4.2	4.8	5.5	6.1	6.8	7.5
8.5	−1.2	−0.8	−0.3	0.2	0.7	1.3	1.8	2.4	2.9	3.5	4.1	4.7	5.4	6.0	6.7	7.4
9.0	−1.2	−0.7	−0.3	0.2	0.7	1.2	1.8	2.3	2.9	3.4	4.0	4.6	5.3	5.9	6.6	7.2
9.5	−1.2	−0.7	−0.3	0.2	0.7	1.2	1.7	2.3	2.8	3.4	3.9	4.5	5.2	5.8	6.4	7.1
10.0	−1.2	−0.7	−0.3	0.2	0.7	1.2	1.7	2.2	2.7	3.3	3.9	4.4	5.1	5.7	6.3	7.0
10.5	−1.1	−0.7	−0.3	0.2	0.7	1.1	1.6	2.2	2.7	3.2	3.8	4.4	4.9	5.6	6.2	6.8
11.0	−1.1	−0.7	−0.2	0.2	0.7	1.1	1.6	2.1	2.6	3.1	3.7	4.3	4.8	5.4	6.0	6.7
11.5	−1.1	−0.7	−0.2	0.2	0.6	1.1	1.6	2.1	2.6	3.1	3.6	4.2	4.7	5.3	5.9	6.5
12.0	−1.0	−0.6	−0.2	0.2	0.6	1.1	1.5	2.0	2.5	3.0	3.5	4.1	4.6	5.2	5.8	6.4
12.5	−1.0	−0.6	−0.2	0.2	0.6	1.0	1.5	2.0	2.4	2.9	3.4	4.0	4.5	5.1	5.7	6.3
13.0	−1.0	−0.6	−0.2	0.2	0.6	1.0	1.4	1.9	2.4	2.9	3.4	3.9	4.4	5.0	5.5	6.1
13.5	−1.0	−0.6	−0.2	0.2	0.6	1.0	1.4	1.9	2.3	2.8	3.3	3.8	4.3	4.8	5.4	6.0
14.0	−0.9	−0.6	−0.2	0.2	0.5	0.9	1.4	1.8	2.2	2.7	3.2	3.7	4.2	4.7	5.3	5.8
14.5	−0.9	−0.6	−0.2	0.2	0.5	0.9	1.3	1.7	2.2	2.6	3.1	3.6	4.1	4.6	5.1	5.7
15.0	−0.9	−0.5	−0.2	0.1	0.5	0.9	1.3	1.7	2.1	2.6	3.0	3.5	4.0	4.5	5.0	5.6
15.5	−0.8	−0.5	−0.2	0.1	0.5	0.9	1.2	1.6	2.1	2.5	2.9	3.4	3.9	4.4	4.9	5.4
16.0	−0.8	−0.5	−0.2	0.1	0.5	0.8	1.2	1.6	2.0	2.4	2.8	3.3	3.8	4.3	4.8	5.3
16.5	−0.8	−0.5	−0.2	0.1	0.5	0.8	1.2	1.5	1.9	2.3	2.8	3.2	3.7	4.1	4.6	5.1
17.0	−0.8	−0.5	−0.2	0.1	0.4	0.8	1.1	1.5	1.9	2.3	2.7	3.1	3.6	4.0	4.5	5.0
17.5	−0.7	−0.5	−0.2	0.1	0.4	0.8	1.1	1.4	1.8	2.2	2.6	3.0	3.4	3.9	4.4	4.9
18.0	−0.7	−0.5	−0.2	0.1	0.4	0.7	1.0	1.4	1.7	2.1	2.5	2.9	3.3	3.8	4.2	4.7
18.5	−0.7	−0.4	−0.2	0.1	0.4	0.7	1.0	1.3	1.7	2.0	2.4	2.8	3.2	3.7	4.1	4.6
19.0	−0.7	−0.4	−0.2	0.1	0.4	0.7	1.0	1.3	1.6	2.0	2.3	2.7	3.1	3.5	4.0	4.4
19.5	−0.6	−0.4	−0.2	0.1	0.4	0.6	0.9	1.2	1.6	1.9	2.3	2.6	3.0	3.4	3.8	4.3
20.0	−0.6	−0.4	−0.2	0.1	0.3	0.6	0.9	1.2	1.5	1.8	2.2	2.5	2.9	3.3	3.7	4.2
20.5	−0.6	−0.4	−0.2	0.1	0.3	0.6	0.9	1.1	1.4	1.8	2.1	2.4	2.8	3.2	3.6	4.0
21.0	−0.5	−0.4	−0.1	0.1	0.3	0.6	0.8	1.1	1.4	1.7	2.0	2.3	2.7	3.1	3.5	3.9
21.5	−0.5	−0.3	−0.1	0.1	0.3	0.5	0.8	1.0	1.3	1.6	1.9	2.2	2.6	3.0	3.3	3.7

Table 2.4–6 (*Continued*)

2000 METERS
(207.41 kg/cm²)

‰ \ °C	-4	-2	0	2	4	6	8	10	12	14	16	18	20	22	24	26
22.0	-0.5	-0.3	-0.1	0.1	0.3	0.5	0.7	1.0	1.3	1.5	1.8	2.2	2.5	2.8	3.2	3.6
22.5	-0.5	-0.3	-0.1	0.1	0.3	0.5	0.7	0.9	1.2	1.5	1.8	2.1	2.4	2.7	3.1	3.4
23.0	-0.4	-0.3	-0.1	0.0	0.2	0.4	0.7	0.9	1.1	1.4	1.7	2.0	2.3	2.6	2.9	3.3
23.5	-0.4	-0.3	-0.1	0.0	0.2	0.4	0.6	0.8	1.1	1.3	1.6	1.9	2.2	2.5	2.8	3.2
24.0	-0.4	-0.3	-0.1	0.0	0.2	0.4	0.6	0.8	1.0	1.2	1.5	1.8	2.1	2.4	2.7	3.0
24.5	-0.4	-0.2	-0.1	0.0	0.2	0.4	0.5	0.7	0.9	1.2	1.4	1.7	1.9	2.2	2.6	2.9
25.0	-0.3	-0.2	-0.1	0.0	0.2	0.3	0.5	0.7	0.9	1.1	1.3	1.6	1.8	2.1	2.4	2.7
25.5	-0.3	-0.2	-0.1	0.0	0.1	0.3	0.5	0.6	0.8	1.0	1.2	1.5	1.7	2.0	2.3	2.6
26.0	-0.3	-0.2	-0.1	0.0	0.1	0.3	0.4	0.6	0.8	0.9	1.2	1.4	1.6	1.9	2.2	2.5
26.5	-0.2	-0.2	-0.1	0.0	0.1	0.2	0.4	0.5	0.7	0.9	1.1	1.3	1.5	1.8	2.0	2.3
27.0	-0.2	-0.2	-0.1	0.0	0.1	0.2	0.3	0.5	0.6	0.8	1.0	1.2	1.4	1.7	1.9	2.2
27.5	-0.2	-0.1	-0.1	-0.0	0.1	0.2	0.3	0.4	0.6	0.7	0.9	1.1	1.3	1.5	1.8	2.0
28.0	-0.2	-0.1	-0.1	-0.0	0.1	0.2	0.3	0.4	0.5	0.7	0.8	1.0	1.2	1.4	1.7	1.9
28.5	-0.1	-0.1	-0.1	-0.0	0.0	0.1	0.2	0.3	0.4	0.6	0.7	0.9	1.1	1.3	1.5	1.8
29.0	-0.1	-0.1	-0.1	-0.0	0.0	0.1	0.2	0.3	0.4	0.5	0.7	0.8	1.0	1.2	1.4	1.6
29.5	-0.1	-0.1	-0.1	-0.0	0.0	0.1	0.1	0.2	0.3	0.4	0.6	0.7	0.9	1.1	1.3	1.5
30.0	-0.0	-0.1	-0.1	-0.0	-0.0	0.0	0.1	0.2	0.3	0.4	0.5	0.6	0.8	0.9	1.1	1.3
30.5	-0.0	-0.0	-0.0	-0.0	-0.0	0.0	0.1	0.1	0.2	0.3	0.4	0.5	0.7	0.8	1.0	1.2
31.0	0.0	-0.0	-0.0	-0.0	-0.0	-0.0	0.0	0.1	0.1	0.2	0.3	0.4	0.6	0.7	0.9	1.1
31.5	0.0	-0.0	-0.0	-0.1	-0.1	-0.0	-0.0	0.0	0.1	0.1	0.2	0.3	0.5	0.6	0.7	0.9
32.0	0.1	0.0	-0.0	-0.1	-0.1	-0.1	-0.1	-0.0	0.0	0.1	0.1	0.2	0.3	0.5	0.6	0.8
32.5	0.1	0.0	-0.0	-0.1	-0.1	-0.1	-0.1	-0.1	-0.1	-0.0	0.1	0.1	0.2	0.4	0.5	0.6
33.0	0.1	0.0	-0.0	-0.1	-0.1	-0.1	-0.1	-0.1	-0.1	-0.1	-0.0	0.0	0.1	0.2	0.4	0.5
33.5	0.1	0.1	-0.0	-0.1	-0.1	-0.2	-0.2	-0.2	-0.2	-0.2	-0.1	-0.1	0.0	0.1	0.2	0.4
34.0	0.2	0.1	-0.0	-0.1	-0.1	-0.2	-0.2	-0.2	-0.2	-0.2	-0.2	-0.1	-0.1	-0.0	0.1	0.2
34.5	0.2	0.1	-0.0	-0.1	-0.2	-0.2	-0.3	-0.3	-0.3	-0.3	-0.3	-0.2	-0.2	-0.1	-0.0	0.1
35.0	0.2	0.1	0.0	-0.1	-0.2	-0.2	-0.3	-0.3	-0.4	-0.4	-0.4	-0.3	-0.3	-0.2	-0.2	-0.1
35.5	0.3	0.1	0.0	-0.1	-0.2	-0.3	-0.3	-0.4	-0.4	-0.4	-0.4	-0.4	-0.4	-0.4	-0.3	-0.2
36.0	0.3	0.1	0.0	-0.1	-0.2	-0.3	-0.4	-0.4	-0.5	-0.5	-0.5	-0.5	-0.5	-0.5	-0.4	-0.3
36.5	0.3	0.2	0.0	-0.1	-0.2	-0.3	-0.4	-0.5	-0.5	-0.6	-0.6	-0.6	-0.6	-0.6	-0.5	-0.5
37.0	0.3	0.2	0.0	-0.1	-0.2	-0.4	-0.5	-0.5	-0.6	-0.7	-0.7	-0.7	-0.7	-0.7	-0.7	-0.6
37.5	0.4	0.2	0.0	-0.1	-0.3	-0.4	-0.5	-0.6	-0.7	-0.7	-0.8	-0.8	-0.8	-0.8	-0.8	-0.8
38.0	0.4	0.2	0.0	-0.1	-0.3	-0.4	-0.5	-0.6	-0.7	-0.8	-0.9	-0.9	-0.9	-0.9	-0.9	-0.9
38.5	0.4	0.2	0.0	-0.1	-0.3	-0.4	-0.6	-0.7	-0.8	-0.9	-1.0	-1.0	-1.0	-1.1	-1.1	-1.0
39.0	0.5	0.2	0.0	-0.1	-0.3	-0.5	-0.6	-0.7	-0.9	-1.0	-1.0	-1.1	-1.2	-1.2	-1.2	-1.2
39.5	0.5	0.3	0.0	-0.2	-0.3	-0.5	-0.7	-0.8	-0.9	-1.0	-1.1	-1.2	-1.3	-1.3	-1.3	-1.3
40.0	0.5	0.3	0.1	-0.2	-0.4	-0.5	-0.7	-0.8	-1.0	-1.1	-1.2	-1.3	-1.4	-1.4	-1.5	-1.5
40.5	0.5	0.3	0.1	-0.2	-0.4	-0.6	-0.7	-0.9	-1.0	-1.2	-1.3	-1.4	-1.5	-1.5	-1.6	-1.6
41.0	0.6	0.3	0.1	-0.2	-0.4	-0.6	-0.8	-1.0	-1.1	-1.3	-1.4	-1.5	-1.6	-1.7	-1.7	-1.8
41.5	0.6	0.3	0.1	-0.2	-0.4	-0.6	-0.8	-1.0	-1.2	-1.3	-1.5	-1.6	-1.7	-1.8	-1.8	-1.9
42.0	0.6	0.3	0.1	-0.2	-0.4	-0.6	-0.9	-1.1	-1.2	-1.4	-1.5	-1.7	-1.8	-1.9	-2.0	-2.0

Table 2.4–6 (*Continued*)

2500 METERS (259.42 kg/cm²)

‰ \ °C	−4	−3	−2	−1	0	1	2	3	4	5	6	7	8	9	10	11	12	13	14	15
30.0	0.0	-0.0	-0.0	-0.0	-0.1	-0.1	-0.1	-0.1	-0.1	-0.1	-0.1	-0.0	-0.0	0.0	0.0	0.1	0.1	0.2	0.2	0.3
30.5	0.1	0.0	-0.0	-0.0	-0.1	-0.1	-0.1	-0.1	-0.1	-0.1	-0.1	-0.1	-0.1	-0.0	-0.0	0.0	0.1	0.1	0.1	0.2
31.0	0.1	0.0	0.0	-0.0	-0.0	-0.1	-0.1	-0.1	-0.1	-0.1	-0.1	-0.1	-0.1	-0.1	-0.1	-0.0	-0.0	0.0	0.1	0.1
31.5	0.1	0.1	0.0	-0.0	-0.0	-0.1	-0.1	-0.1	-0.1	-0.1	-0.1	-0.1	-0.1	-0.1	-0.1	-0.1	-0.1	-0.1	-0.0	0.0
32.0	0.1	0.1	0.0	0.0	-0.0	-0.1	-0.1	-0.1	-0.1	-0.2	-0.2	-0.2	-0.2	-0.2	-0.2	-0.2	-0.1	-0.1	-0.1	-0.1
32.5	0.2	0.1	0.1	0.0	-0.0	-0.1	-0.1	-0.1	-0.2	-0.2	-0.2	-0.2	-0.2	-0.2	-0.2	-0.2	-0.2	-0.2	-0.2	-0.1
33.0	0.2	0.1	0.1	0.0	-0.0	-0.1	-0.1	-0.1	-0.2	-0.2	-0.2	-0.2	-0.3	-0.3	-0.3	-0.3	-0.3	-0.3	-0.2	-0.2
33.5	0.2	0.2	0.1	0.0	-0.0	-0.1	-0.1	-0.2	-0.2	-0.2	-0.3	-0.3	-0.3	-0.3	-0.3	-0.3	-0.3	-0.3	-0.3	-0.3
34.0	0.3	0.2	0.1	0.0	-0.0	-0.1	-0.1	-0.2	-0.2	-0.2	-0.3	-0.3	-0.3	-0.4	-0.4	-0.4	-0.4	-0.4	-0.4	-0.4
34.5	0.3	0.2	0.1	0.1	-0.0	-0.1	-0.1	-0.2	-0.2	-0.3	-0.3	-0.3	-0.4	-0.4	-0.4	-0.4	-0.5	-0.5	-0.5	-0.5
35.0	0.3	0.2	0.1	0.1	0.0	-0.1	-0.1	-0.2	-0.2	-0.3	-0.3	-0.4	-0.4	-0.4	-0.5	-0.5	-0.5	-0.5	-0.5	-0.5
35.5	0.3	0.2	0.2	0.1	0.0	-0.1	-0.1	-0.2	-0.3	-0.3	-0.4	-0.4	-0.5	-0.5	-0.5	-0.6	-0.6	-0.6	-0.6	-0.6
36.0	0.4	0.3	0.2	0.1	0.0	-0.1	-0.1	-0.2	-0.3	-0.3	-0.4	-0.4	-0.5	-0.5	-0.6	-0.6	-0.6	-0.7	-0.7	-0.7
36.5	0.4	0.3	0.2	0.1	0.0	-0.1	-0.1	-0.2	-0.3	-0.4	-0.4	-0.5	-0.5	-0.6	-0.6	-0.7	-0.7	-0.7	-0.7	-0.8
37.0	0.4	0.3	0.2	0.1	0.0	-0.1	-0.2	-0.2	-0.3	-0.4	-0.4	-0.5	-0.6	-0.6	-0.7	-0.7	-0.8	-0.8	-0.8	-0.8
37.5	0.4	0.3	0.2	0.1	0.0	-0.1	-0.2	-0.2	-0.3	-0.4	-0.5	-0.5	-0.6	-0.7	-0.7	-0.8	-0.8	-0.9	-0.9	-0.9
38.0	0.5	0.4	0.2	0.1	0.0	-0.1	-0.2	-0.3	-0.3	-0.4	-0.5	-0.6	-0.6	-0.7	-0.8	-0.8	-0.9	-0.9	-1.0	-1.0
38.5	0.5	0.4	0.3	0.1	0.0	-0.1	-0.2	-0.3	-0.4	-0.4	-0.5	-0.6	-0.7	-0.8	-0.8	-0.9	-0.9	-1.0	-1.0	-1.1
39.0	0.5	0.4	0.3	0.2	0.0	-0.1	-0.2	-0.3	-0.4	-0.5	-0.6	-0.6	-0.7	-0.8	-0.9	-0.9	-1.0	-1.1	-1.1	-1.2
39.5	0.6	0.4	0.3	0.2	0.1	-0.1	-0.2	-0.3	-0.4	-0.5	-0.6	-0.7	-0.8	-0.8	-0.9	-1.0	-1.1	-1.1	-1.2	-1.2
40.0	0.6	0.4	0.3	0.2	0.1	-0.1	-0.2	-0.3	-0.4	-0.5	-0.6	-0.7	-0.8	-0.9	-1.0	-1.1	-1.1	-1.2	-1.3	-1.3
40.5	0.6	0.5	0.3	0.2	0.1	-0.1	-0.2	-0.3	-0.4	-0.5	-0.6	-0.7	-0.8	-0.9	-1.0	-1.1	-1.2	-1.3	-1.3	-1.4
41.0	0.6	0.5	0.3	0.2	0.1	-0.1	-0.2	-0.3	-0.4	-0.6	-0.7	-0.8	-0.9	-1.0	-1.1	-1.2	-1.3	-1.3	-1.4	-1.5
41.5	0.7	0.5	0.4	0.2	0.1	-0.1	-0.2	-0.3	-0.5	-0.6	-0.7	-0.8	-0.9	-1.0	-1.1	-1.2	-1.3	-1.4	-1.5	-1.6
42.0	0.7	0.5	0.4	0.2	0.1	-0.1	-0.2	-0.3	-0.5	-0.6	-0.7	-0.8	-1.0	-1.1	-1.2	-1.3	-1.4	-1.5	-1.6	-1.6

3000 METERS (311.51 kg/cm²)

‰ \ °C	−4	−3	−2	−1	0	1	2	3	4	5	6	7	8	9	10	11	12	13	14	15
30.0	0.1	0.1	0.0	-0.0	-0.1	-0.1	-0.1	-0.1	-0.1	-0.2	-0.2	-0.2	-0.1	-0.1	-0.1	-0.1	-0.1	-0.0	0.0	-0.1
30.5	0.1	0.1	0.0	-0.0	-0.1	-0.1	-0.1	-0.1	-0.2	-0.2	-0.2	-0.2	-0.2	-0.2	-0.2	-0.2	-0.1	-0.1	-0.1	-0.1
31.0	0.2	0.1	0.1	0.0	-0.0	-0.1	-0.1	-0.2	-0.2	-0.2	-0.2	-0.2	-0.2	-0.2	-0.2	-0.2	-0.2	-0.2	-0.1	-0.1
31.5	0.2	0.1	0.1	0.0	-0.0	-0.1	-0.1	-0.2	-0.2	-0.2	-0.2	-0.3	-0.3	-0.3	-0.3	-0.3	-0.2	-0.2	-0.2	-0.2
32.0	0.2	0.2	0.1	0.0	-0.0	-0.1	-0.1	-0.2	-0.2	-0.2	-0.3	-0.3	-0.3	-0.3	-0.3	-0.3	-0.3	-0.3	-0.3	-0.2
32.5	0.3	0.2	0.1	0.0	-0.0	-0.1	-0.1	-0.2	-0.2	-0.3	-0.3	-0.3	-0.3	-0.4	-0.4	-0.4	-0.4	-0.4	-0.3	-0.3
33.0	0.3	0.2	0.1	0.0	-0.0	-0.1	-0.1	-0.2	-0.2	-0.3	-0.3	-0.4	-0.4	-0.4	-0.4	-0.4	-0.4	-0.4	-0.4	-0.4
33.5	0.3	0.2	0.1	0.1	-0.0	-0.1	-0.1	-0.2	-0.3	-0.3	-0.4	-0.4	-0.4	-0.4	-0.5	-0.5	-0.5	-0.5	-0.5	-0.5
34.0	0.3	0.2	0.2	0.1	-0.0	-0.1	-0.2	-0.2	-0.3	-0.3	-0.4	-0.4	-0.5	-0.5	-0.5	-0.5	-0.6	-0.6	-0.6	-0.6
34.5	0.4	0.3	0.2	0.1	-0.0	-0.1	-0.2	-0.2	-0.3	-0.4	-0.4	-0.5	-0.5	-0.5	-0.6	-0.6	-0.6	-0.6	-0.6	-0.6

Table 2.4–6 (*Continued*)

3000 METERS
(311.51 kg/cm^2)

‰ \ °C	−4	−3	−2	−1	0	1	2	3	4	5	6	7	8	9	10	11	12	13	14	15
35.0	0.4	0.3	0.2	0.1	0.0	-0.1	-0.2	-0.2	-0.3	-0.4	-0.4	-0.5	-0.5	-0.6	-0.6	-0.7	-0.7	-0.7	-0.7	-0.7
35.5	0.4	0.3	0.2	0.1	0.0	-0.1	-0.2	-0.3	-0.3	-0.4	-0.5	-0.5	-0.6	-0.6	-0.7	-0.7	-0.7	-0.8	-0.8	-0.8
36.0	0.4	0.3	0.2	0.1	0.0	-0.1	-0.2	-0.3	-0.3	-0.4	-0.5	-0.6	-0.6	-0.7	-0.7	-0.8	-0.8	-0.8	-0.9	-0.9
36.5	0.5	0.4	0.2	0.1	0.0	-0.1	-0.2	-0.3	-0.4	-0.4	-0.5	-0.6	-0.7	-0.7	-0.8	-0.8	-0.9	-0.9	-0.9	-1.0
37.0	0.5	0.4	0.3	0.1	0.0	-0.1	-0.2	-0.3	-0.4	-0.5	-0.5	-0.6	-0.7	-0.8	-0.8	-0.9	-0.9	-1.0	-1.0	-1.0
37.5	0.5	0.4	0.3	0.1	0.0	-0.1	-0.2	-0.3	-0.4	-0.5	-0.6	-0.7	-0.7	-0.8	-0.9	-0.9	-1.0	-1.0	-1.1	-1.1
38.0	0.6	0.4	0.3	0.2	0.0	-0.1	-0.2	-0.3	-0.4	-0.5	-0.6	-0.7	-0.8	-0.9	-0.9	-1.0	-1.1	-1.1	-1.1	-1.2
38.5	0.6	0.4	0.3	0.2	0.0	-0.1	-0.2	-0.3	-0.4	-0.5	-0.6	-0.7	-0.8	-0.9	-1.0	-1.0	-1.1	-1.2	-1.2	-1.3
39.0	0.6	0.5	0.3	0.2	0.0	-0.1	-0.2	-0.3	-0.4	-0.6	-0.7	-0.8	-0.9	-0.9	-1.0	-1.1	-1.2	-1.2	-1.3	-1.3
39.5	0.6	0.5	0.3	0.2	0.1	-0.1	-0.2	-0.3	-0.5	-0.6	-0.7	-0.8	-0.9	-1.0	-1.1	-1.2	-1.2	-1.3	-1.4	-1.4
40.0	0.7	0.5	0.4	0.2	0.1	-0.1	-0.2	-0.4	-0.5	-0.6	-0.7	-0.8	-0.9	-1.0	-1.1	-1.2	-1.3	-1.4	-1.4	-1.5
40.5	0.7	0.5	0.4	0.2	0.1	-0.1	-0.2	-0.4	-0.5	-0.6	-0.7	-0.9	-1.0	-1.1	-1.2	-1.3	-1.4	-1.4	-1.5	-1.6
41.0	0.7	0.6	0.4	0.2	0.1	-0.1	-0.2	-0.4	-0.5	-0.6	-0.8	-0.9	-1.0	-1.1	-1.2	-1.3	-1.4	-1.5	-1.6	-1.7
41.5	0.8	0.6	0.4	0.2	0.1	-0.1	-0.2	-0.4	-0.5	-0.7	-0.8	-0.9	-1.0	-1.2	-1.3	-1.4	-1.5	-1.6	-1.7	-1.7
42.0	0.8	0.6	0.4	0.2	0.1	-0.1	-0.2	-0.4	-0.5	-0.7	-0.8	-1.0	-1.1	-1.2	-1.3	-1.4	-1.5	-1.6	-1.7	-1.8

4000 METERS
(415.86 kg/cm^2)

‰ \ °C	−4	−3	−2	−1	0	1	2	3	4	5	6	7	8	9	10	11	12	13	14	15
30.0	0.3	0.2	0.1	0.0	-0.0	-0.1	-0.2	-0.3	-0.3	-0.4	-0.4	-0.4	-0.5	-0.5	-0.5	-0.5	-0.5	-0.5	-0.4	-0.4
30.5	0.3	0.2	0.1	0.0	-0.0	-0.1	-0.2	-0.3	-0.3	-0.4	-0.4	-0.5	-0.5	-0.5	-0.5	-0.5	-0.5	-0.5	-0.5	-0.5
31.0	0.4	0.3	0.2	0.1	-0.0	-0.1	-0.2	-0.3	-0.3	-0.4	-0.5	-0.5	-0.5	-0.6	-0.6	-0.6	-0.6	-0.6	-0.6	-0.6
31.5	0.4	0.3	0.2	0.1	-0.0	-0.1	-0.2	-0.3	-0.4	-0.4	-0.5	-0.5	-0.6	-0.6	-0.6	-0.7	-0.7	-0.7	-0.7	-0.6
32.0	0.4	0.3	0.2	0.1	-0.0	-0.1	-0.2	-0.3	-0.4	-0.4	-0.5	-0.6	-0.6	-0.7	-0.7	-0.7	-0.7	-0.7	-0.7	-0.7
32.5	0.5	0.3	0.2	0.1	-0.0	-0.1	-0.2	-0.3	-0.4	-0.5	-0.5	-0.6	-0.7	-0.7	-0.7	-0.8	-0.8	-0.8	-0.8	-0.8
33.0	0.5	0.3	0.2	0.1	-0.0	-0.1	-0.2	-0.3	-0.4	-0.5	-0.6	-0.6	-0.7	-0.7	-0.8	-0.8	-0.9	-0.9	-0.9	-0.9
33.5	0.5	0.4	0.2	0.1	-0.0	-0.1	-0.2	-0.3	-0.4	-0.5	-0.6	-0.7	-0.7	-0.8	-0.8	-0.9	-0.9	-0.9	-1.0	-1.0
34.0	0.5	0.4	0.3	0.1	-0.0	-0.1	-0.2	-0.4	-0.4	-0.5	-0.6	-0.7	-0.8	-0.8	-0.9	-0.9	-1.0	-1.0	-1.0	-1.0
34.5	0.6	0.4	0.3	0.1	-0.0	-0.1	-0.3	-0.4	-0.5	-0.6	-0.7	-0.7	-0.8	-0.9	-0.9	-1.0	-1.0	-1.1	-1.1	-1.1
35.0	0.6	0.4	0.3	0.1	0.0	-0.1	-0.3	-0.4	-0.5	-0.6	-0.7	-0.8	-0.9	-0.9	-1.0	-1.0	-1.1	-1.1	-1.2	-1.2
35.5	0.6	0.5	0.3	0.1	0.0	-0.1	-0.3	-0.4	-0.5	-0.6	-0.7	-0.8	-0.9	-1.0	-1.0	-1.1	-1.2	-1.2	-1.2	-1.3
36.0	0.6	0.5	0.3	0.2	0.0	-0.1	-0.3	-0.4	-0.5	-0.6	-0.7	-0.8	-0.9	-1.0	-1.1	-1.2	-1.2	-1.3	-1.3	-1.4
36.5	0.7	0.5	0.3	0.2	0.0	-0.1	-0.3	-0.4	-0.5	-0.7	-0.8	-0.9	-1.0	-1.1	-1.1	-1.2	-1.3	-1.3	-1.4	-1.4
37.0	0.7	0.5	0.3	0.2	0.0	-0.1	-0.3	-0.4	-0.6	-0.7	-0.8	-0.9	-1.0	-1.1	-1.2	-1.3	-1.4	-1.4	-1.5	-1.5
37.5	0.7	0.5	0.4	0.2	0.0	-0.1	-0.3	-0.4	-0.6	-0.7	-0.8	-0.9	-1.1	-1.2	-1.2	-1.3	-1.4	-1.5	-1.5	-1.6
38.0	0.8	0.6	0.4	0.2	0.0	-0.1	-0.3	-0.4	-0.6	-0.7	-0.9	-1.0	-1.1	-1.2	-1.3	-1.4	-1.5	-1.6	-1.6	-1.7
38.5	0.8	0.6	0.4	0.2	0.0	-0.1	-0.3	-0.5	-0.6	-0.8	-0.9	-1.0	-1.1	-1.2	-1.3	-1.5	-1.5	-1.6	-1.7	-1.8
39.0	0.8	0.6	0.4	0.2	0.0	-0.1	-0.3	-0.5	-0.6	-0.8	-0.9	-1.0	-1.2	-1.3	-1.4	-1.5	-1.6	-1.7	-1.8	-1.8
39.5	0.8	0.6	0.4	0.2	0.0	-0.1	-0.3	-0.5	-0.6	-0.8	-0.9	-1.1	-1.2	-1.3	-1.5	-1.6	-1.7	-1.8	-1.8	-1.9
40.0	0.9	0.7	0.4	0.2	0.0	-0.1	-0.3	-0.5	-0.7	-0.8	-1.0	-1.1	-1.3	-1.4	-1.5	-1.6	-1.7	-1.8	-1.9	-2.0
40.5	0.9	0.7	0.5	0.3	0.1	-0.1	-0.3	-0.5	-0.7	-0.8	-1.0	-1.2	-1.3	-1.4	-1.6	-1.7	-1.8	-1.9	-2.0	-2.1
41.0	0.9	0.7	0.5	0.3	0.1	-0.1	-0.3	-0.5	-0.7	-0.9	-1.0	-1.2	-1.3	-1.5	-1.6	-1.7	-1.9	-2.0	-2.1	-2.1
41.5	0.9	0.7	0.5	0.3	0.1	-0.1	-0.3	-0.5	-0.7	-0.9	-1.1	-1.2	-1.4	-1.5	-1.7	-1.8	-1.9	-2.0	-2.1	-2.2
42.0	1.0	0.7	0.5	0.3	0.1	-0.1	-0.3	-0.5	-0.7	-0.9	-1.1	-1.3	-1.4	-1.6	-1.7	-1.8	-2.0	-2.1	-2.2	-2.3

Table 2.4–6 (*Continued*)

5000 METERS
(520.58 kg/cm²)

‰ \ °C	-3.5	-3.0	-2.5	-2.0	-1.5	-1.0	-0.5	0.0	0.5	1.0	1.5	2.0	2.5	3.0
32.0	0.6	0.5	0.4	0.3	0.2	0.1	0.1	-0.0	-0.1	-0.2	-0.2	-0.3	-0.4	-0.5
32.5	0.6	0.5	0.4	0.3	0.2	0.2	0.1	-0.0	-0.1	-0.2	-0.3	-0.3	-0.4	-0.5
33.0	0.6	0.5	0.4	0.3	0.3	0.2	0.1	-0.0	-0.1	-0.2	-0.3	-0.3	-0.4	-0.5
33.5	0.7	0.6	0.5	0.4	0.3	0.2	0.1	-0.0	-0.1	-0.2	-0.3	-0.3	-0.4	-0.5
34.0	0.7	0.6	0.5	0.4	0.3	0.2	0.1	-0.0	-0.1	-0.2	-0.3	-0.4	-0.4	-0.5
34.5	0.7	0.6	0.5	0.4	0.3	0.2	0.1	-0.0	-0.1	-0.2	-0.3	-0.4	-0.4	-0.5
35.0	0.7	0.6	0.5	0.4	0.3	0.2	0.1	0.0	-0.1	-0.2	-0.3	-0.4	-0.5	-0.5
35.5	0.8	0.6	0.5	0.4	0.3	0.2	0.1	0.0	-0.1	-0.2	-0.3	-0.4	-0.5	-0.6
36.0	0.8	0.7	0.5	0.4	0.3	0.2	0.1	0.0	-0.1	-0.2	-0.3	-0.4	-0.5	-0.6
36.5	0.8	0.7	0.6	0.4	0.3	0.2	0.1	0.0	-0.1	-0.2	-0.3	-0.4	-0.5	-0.6
37.0	0.8	0.7	0.6	0.5	0.3	0.2	0.1	0.0	-0.1	-0.2	-0.3	-0.4	-0.5	-0.6
37.5	0.8	0.7	0.6	0.5	0.4	0.2	0.1	0.0	-0.1	-0.2	-0.3	-0.4	-0.5	-0.6
38.0	0.9	0.7	0.6	0.5	0.4	0.2	0.1	0.0	-0.1	-0.2	-0.3	-0.4	-0.5	-0.6
38.5	0.9	0.8	0.6	0.5	0.4	0.3	0.1	0.0	-0.1	-0.2	-0.3	-0.4	-0.5	-0.6
39.0	0.9	0.8	0.6	0.5	0.4	0.3	0.1	0.0	-0.1	-0.2	-0.3	-0.4	-0.5	-0.7

‰ \ °C	3.5	4.0	4.5	5.0	5.5	6.0	6.5	7.0	7.5	8.0	8.5	9.0	9.5	10.0	11.0	12.0	13.0	14.0	15.0
32.0	-0.5	-0.6	-0.6	-0.7	-0.8	-0.8	-0.9	-0.9	-1.0	-1.0	-1.0	-1.1	-1.1	-1.1	-1.2	-1.3	-1.3	-1.3	-1.3
32.5	-0.5	-0.6	-0.7	-0.7	-0.8	-0.8	-0.9	-0.9	-1.0	-1.0	-1.1	-1.1	-1.2	-1.2	-1.3	-1.3	-1.4	-1.4	-1.4
33.0	-0.6	-0.6	-0.7	-0.8	-0.8	-0.9	-0.9	-1.0	-1.0	-1.1	-1.1	-1.2	-1.2	-1.3	-1.3	-1.4	-1.4	-1.5	-1.5
33.5	-0.6	-0.6	-0.7	-0.8	-0.8	-0.9	-1.0	-1.0	-1.1	-1.1	-1.2	-1.2	-1.3	-1.3	-1.4	-1.5	-1.5	-1.6	-1.6
34.0	-0.6	-0.7	-0.7	-0.8	-0.9	-0.9	-1.0	-1.1	-1.1	-1.2	-1.2	-1.3	-1.3	-1.4	-1.4	-1.5	-1.6	-1.6	-1.7
34.5	-0.6	-0.7	-0.8	-0.8	-0.9	-1.0	-1.0	-1.1	-1.2	-1.2	-1.3	-1.3	-1.4	-1.4	-1.5	-1.6	-1.7	-1.7	-1.8
35.0	-0.6	-0.7	-0.8	-0.9	-0.9	-1.0	-1.1	-1.1	-1.2	-1.3	-1.3	-1.4	-1.4	-1.5	-1.6	-1.6	-1.7	-1.8	-1.8
35.5	-0.6	-0.7	-0.8	-0.9	-1.0	-1.0	-1.1	-1.2	-1.2	-1.3	-1.4	-1.4	-1.5	-1.5	-1.6	-1.7	-1.8	-1.9	-1.9
36.0	-0.7	-0.7	-0.8	-0.9	-1.0	-1.1	-1.1	-1.2	-1.3	-1.3	-1.4	-1.5	-1.5	-1.6	-1.7	-1.8	-1.9	-1.9	-2.0
36.5	-0.7	-0.8	-0.8	-0.9	-1.0	-1.1	-1.2	-1.2	-1.3	-1.4	-1.4	-1.5	-1.6	-1.6	-1.7	-1.8	-1.9	-2.0	-2.1
37.0	-0.7	-0.8	-0.9	-1.0	-1.0	-1.1	-1.2	-1.3	-1.3	-1.4	-1.5	-1.6	-1.6	-1.7	-1.8	-1.9	-2.0	-2.1	-2.2
37.5	-0.7	-0.8	-0.9	-1.0	-1.1	-1.2	-1.2	-1.3	-1.4	-1.5	-1.5	-1.6	-1.7	-1.7	-1.9	-2.0	-2.1	-2.2	-2.2
38.0	-0.7	-0.8	-0.9	-1.0	-1.1	-1.2	-1.3	-1.3	-1.4	-1.5	-1.6	-1.7	-1.7	-1.8	-1.9	-2.0	-2.1	-2.2	-2.3
38.5	-0.7	-0.8	-0.9	-1.0	-1.1	-1.2	-1.3	-1.4	-1.5	-1.5	-1.6	-1.7	-1.8	-1.8	-2.0	-2.1	-2.2	-2.3	-2.4
39.0	-0.8	-0.9	-1.0	-1.1	-1.2	-1.2	-1.3	-1.4	-1.5	-1.6	-1.7	-1.7	-1.8	-1.9	-2.0	-2.2	-2.3	-2.4	-2.5

Table 2.4–6 (*Continued*)

6000 METERS
(625.75 kg/cm²)

‰ \ °C	-3.5	-3.0	-2.5	-2.0	-1.5	-1.0	-0.5	0.0	0.5	1.0	1.5	2.0	2.5	3.0
32.0	0.9	0.7	0.6	0.5	0.4	0.2	0.1	0.0	-0.1	-0.2	-0.3	-0.4	-0.5	-0.6
32.5	0.9	0.8	0.6	0.5	0.4	0.2	0.1	0.0	-0.1	-0.2	-0.3	-0.4	-0.5	-0.7
33.0	0.9	0.8	0.6	0.5	0.4	0.3	0.1	0.0	-0.1	-0.2	-0.3	-0.5	-0.6	-0.7
33.5	0.9	0.8	0.7	0.5	0.4	0.3	0.1	0.0	-0.1	-0.2	-0.4	-0.5	-0.6	-0.7
34.0	1.0	0.8	0.7	0.5	0.4	0.3	0.1	0.0	-0.1	-0.2	-0.4	-0.5	-0.6	-0.7
34.5	1.0	0.8	0.7	0.5	0.4	0.3	0.1	0.0	-0.1	-0.3	-0.4	-0.5	-0.6	-0.7
35.0	1.0	0.8	0.7	0.5	0.4	0.3	0.1	0.0	-0.1	-0.3	-0.4	-0.5	-0.6	-0.7
35.5	1.0	0.9	0.7	0.6	0.4	0.3	0.1	-0.0	-0.1	-0.3	-0.4	-0.5	-0.6	-0.8
36.0	1.0	0.9	0.7	0.6	0.4	0.3	0.1	-0.0	-0.1	-0.3	-0.4	-0.5	-0.7	-0.8
36.5	1.0	0.9	0.7	0.6	0.4	0.3	0.1	-0.0	-0.1	-0.3	-0.4	-0.5	-0.7	-0.8
37.0	1.1	0.9	0.7	0.6	0.4	0.3	0.1	-0.0	-0.1	-0.3	-0.4	-0.6	-0.7	-0.8
37.5	1.1	0.9	0.8	0.6	0.4	0.3	0.1	-0.0	-0.2	-0.3	-0.4	-0.6	-0.7	-0.8
38.0	1.1	0.9	0.8	0.6	0.5	0.3	0.1	-0.0	-0.2	-0.3	-0.4	-0.6	-0.7	-0.8
38.5	1.1	0.9	0.8	0.6	0.5	0.3	0.1	-0.0	-0.2	-0.3	-0.5	-0.6	-0.7	-0.9
39.0	1.1	1.0	0.8	0.6	0.5	0.3	0.1	-0.0	-0.2	-0.3	-0.5	-0.6	-0.7	-0.9

‰ \ °C	3.5	4.0	4.5	5.0	5.5	6.0	6.5	7.0	7.5	8.0	8.5	9.0	9.5	10.0
32.0	-0.7	-0.8	-0.9	-1.0	-1.1	-1.2	-1.3	-1.3	-1.4	-1.5	-1.5	-1.6	-1.7	-1.7
32.5	-0.8	-0.8	-0.9	-1.0	-1.1	-1.2	-1.3	-1.4	-1.4	-1.5	-1.6	-1.7	-1.7	-1.8
33.0	-0.8	-0.9	-1.0	-1.1	-1.2	-1.2	-1.3	-1.4	-1.5	-1.6	-1.6	-1.7	-1.8	-1.8
33.5	-0.8	-0.9	-1.0	-1.1	-1.2	-1.3	-1.4	-1.4	-1.5	-1.6	-1.7	-1.8	-1.8	-1.9
34.0	-0.8	-0.9	-1.0	-1.1	-1.2	-1.3	-1.4	-1.5	-1.6	-1.7	-1.7	-1.8	-1.9	-2.0
34.5	-0.8	-0.9	-1.0	-1.2	-1.2	-1.3	-1.4	-1.5	-1.6	-1.7	-1.8	-1.9	-1.9	-2.0
35.0	-0.9	-1.0	-1.1	-1.2	-1.3	-1.4	-1.5	-1.6	-1.7	-1.7	-1.8	-1.9	-2.0	-2.1
35.5	-0.9	-1.0	-1.1	-1.2	-1.3	-1.4	-1.5	-1.6	-1.7	-1.8	-1.9	-2.0	-2.0	-2.1
36.0	-0.9	-1.0	-1.1	-1.2	-1.3	-1.5	-1.6	-1.7	-1.7	-1.8	-1.9	-2.0	-2.1	-2.2
36.5	-0.9	-1.0	-1.2	-1.3	-1.4	-1.5	-1.6	-1.7	-1.8	-1.9	-2.0	-2.1	-2.2	-2.2
37.0	-0.9	-1.1	-1.2	-1.3	-1.4	-1.5	-1.6	-1.7	-1.8	-1.9	-2.0	-2.1	-2.2	-2.3
37.5	-1.0	-1.1	-1.2	-1.3	-1.4	-1.6	-1.7	-1.8	-1.9	-2.0	-2.1	-2.2	-2.3	-2.4
38.0	-1.0	-1.1	-1.2	-1.4	-1.5	-1.6	-1.7	-1.8	-1.9	-2.0	-2.1	-2.2	-2.3	-2.4
38.5	-1.0	-1.1	-1.3	-1.4	-1.5	-1.6	-1.7	-1.9	-2.0	-2.1	-2.2	-2.3	-2.4	-2.5
39.0	-1.0	-1.2	-1.3	-1.4	-1.5	-1.7	-1.8	-1.9	-2.0	-2.1	-2.2	-2.3	-2.4	-2.5

Table 2.4–6 (*Continued*)

7000 METERS
(731.39 kg/cm^2)

‰ \ °C	-3.5	-3.0	-2.5	-2.0	-1.5	-1.0	-0.5	0.0	0.5	1.0	1.5	2.0	2.5	3.0
32.0	1.2	1.0	0.9	0.7	0.5	0.4	0.2	0.0	-0.1	-0.3	-0.4	-0.6	-0.7	-0.8
32.5	1.2	1.1	0.9	0.7	0.5	0.4	0.2	0.0	-0.1	-0.3	-0.4	-0.6	-0.7	-0.9
33.0	1.2	1.1	0.9	0.7	0.5	0.4	0.2	0.0	-0.1	-0.3	-0.4	-0.6	-0.7	-0.9
33.5	1.3	1.1	0.9	0.7	0.5	0.4	0.2	0.0	-0.1	-0.3	-0.4	-0.6	-0.8	-0.9
34.0	1.3	1.1	0.9	0.7	0.5	0.4	0.2	0.0	-0.1	-0.3	-0.5	-0.6	-0.8	-0.9
34.5	1.3	1.1	0.9	0.7	0.5	0.4	0.2	0.0	-0.2	-0.3	-0.5	-0.6	-0.8	-0.9
35.0	1.3	1.1	0.9	0.7	0.5	0.4	0.2	0.0	-0.2	-0.3	-0.5	-0.7	-0.8	-1.0
35.5	1.3	1.1	0.9	0.7	0.5	0.4	0.2	0.0	-0.2	-0.3	-0.5	-0.7	-0.8	-1.0
36.0	1.3	1.1	0.9	0.7	0.5	0.4	0.2	-0.0	-0.2	-0.4	-0.5	-0.7	-0.9	-1.0
36.5	1.3	1.1	0.9	0.7	0.5	0.4	0.2	-0.0	-0.2	-0.4	-0.5	-0.7	-0.9	-1.0
37.0	1.3	1.1	0.9	0.7	0.5	0.4	0.2	-0.0	-0.2	-0.4	-0.6	-0.7	-0.9	-1.1
37.5	1.3	1.1	0.9	0.7	0.5	0.4	0.2	-0.0	-0.2	-0.4	-0.6	-0.7	-0.9	-1.1
38.0	1.4	1.2	0.9	0.7	0.5	0.4	0.2	-0.0	-0.2	-0.4	-0.6	-0.8	-0.9	-1.1
38.5	1.4	1.2	1.0	0.8	0.5	0.3	0.2	-0.0	-0.2	-0.4	-0.6	-0.8	-1.0	-1.1
38.5	1.4	1.2	1.0	0.8	0.6	0.3	0.2	-0.0	-0.2	-0.4	-0.6	-0.8	-1.0	-1.1
39.0	1.4	1.2	1.0	0.8	0.6	0.3	0.1	-0.1	-0.2	-0.4	-0.6	-0.8	-1.0	-1.2

‰ \ °C	3.5	4.0	4.5	5.0	5.5	6.0	6.5	7.0	7.5	8.0	8.5	9.0	9.5	10.0
32.0	-1.0	-1.1	-1.2	-1.4	-1.5	-1.6	-1.7	-1.8	-1.9	-2.0	-2.1	-2.2	-2.3	-2.4
32.5	-1.0	-1.1	-1.3	-1.4	-1.5	-1.6	-1.8	-1.9	-2.0	-2.1	-2.2	-2.3	-2.4	-2.5
33.0	-1.0	-1.2	-1.3	-1.4	-1.6	-1.7	-1.8	-1.9	-2.0	-2.2	-2.3	-2.4	-2.5	-2.6
33.5	-1.1	-1.2	-1.3	-1.5	-1.6	-1.7	-1.9	-2.0	-2.1	-2.2	-2.3	-2.4	-2.5	-2.6
34.0	-1.1	-1.2	-1.4	-1.5	-1.6	-1.8	-1.9	-2.0	-2.1	-2.3	-2.4	-2.5	-2.6	-2.7
34.5	-1.1	-1.3	-1.4	-1.5	-1.7	-1.8	-1.9	-2.1	-2.2	-2.3	-2.4	-2.5	-2.6	-2.7
35.0	-1.1	-1.3	-1.4	-1.6	-1.7	-1.8	-2.0	-2.1	-2.2	-2.4	-2.5	-2.6	-2.7	-2.8
35.5	-1.2	-1.3	-1.5	-1.6	-1.8	-1.9	-2.0	-2.2	-2.3	-2.4	-2.5	-2.6	-2.8	-2.9
36.0	-1.2	-1.3	-1.5	-1.6	-1.8	-1.9	-2.1	-2.2	-2.3	-2.5	-2.6	-2.7	-2.8	-2.9
36.5	-1.2	-1.4	-1.5	-1.7	-1.8	-2.0	-2.1	-2.2	-2.4	-2.5	-2.6	-2.8	-2.9	-3.0
37.0	-1.2	-1.4	-1.6	-1.7	-1.9	-2.0	-2.2	-2.3	-2.4	-2.6	-2.7	-2.8	-2.9	-3.1
37.5	-1.3	-1.4	-1.6	-1.7	-1.9	-2.1	-2.2	-2.3	-2.5	-2.6	-2.7	-2.9	-3.0	-3.1
38.0	-1.3	-1.5	-1.6	-1.8	-1.9	-2.1	-2.2	-2.4	-2.5	-2.7	-2.8	-2.9	-3.1	-3.2
38.5	-1.3	-1.5	-1.7	-1.8	-2.0	-2.1	-2.3	-2.4	-2.6	-2.7	-2.9	-3.0	-3.1	-3.2
39.0	-1.3	-1.5	-1.7	-1.9	-2.0	-2.2	-2.3	-2.5	-2.6	-2.8	-2.9	-3.0	-3.2	-3.3

Table 2.4–6 (*Continued*)

8000 METERS
(837.49 kg/cm^2)

‰ \ °C	-3.5	-3.0	-2.5	-2.0	-1.5	-1.0	-0.5	0.0	0.5	1.0	1.5	2.0	2.5	3.0
32.0	1.6	1.4	1.2	0.9	0.7	0.5	0.3	0.1	-0.1	-0.3	-0.5	-0.7	-0.9	-1.1
32.5	1.6	1.4	1.2	0.9	0.7	0.5	0.3	0.1	-0.1	-0.3	-0.5	-0.7	-0.9	-1.1
33.0	1.6	1.4	1.2	0.9	0.7	0.5	0.3	0.1	-0.2	-0.4	-0.6	-0.8	-1.0	-1.2
33.5	1.6	1.4	1.2	0.9	0.7	0.5	0.3	0.0	-0.2	-0.4	-0.6	-0.8	-1.0	-1.2
34.0	1.6	1.4	1.2	0.9	0.7	0.5	0.2	0.0	-0.2	-0.4	-0.6	-0.8	-1.0	-1.2
34.5	1.7	1.4	1.2	0.9	0.7	0.5	0.2	0.0	-0.2	-0.4	-0.6	-0.8	-1.0	-1.2
35.0	1.7	1.4	1.2	0.9	0.7	0.5	0.2	0.0	-0.2	-0.4	-0.7	-0.9	-1.1	-1.3
35.5	1.7	1.4	1.2	0.9	0.7	0.4	0.2	-0.0	-0.2	-0.5	-0.7	-0.9	-1.1	-1.3
36.0	1.7	1.4	1.2	0.9	0.7	0.4	0.2	-0.0	-0.3	-0.5	-0.7	-0.9	-1.1	-1.3
36.5	1.7	1.4	1.2	0.9	0.7	0.4	0.2	-0.0	-0.3	-0.5	-0.7	-0.9	-1.1	-1.3
37.0	1.7	1.4	1.2	0.9	0.7	0.4	0.2	-0.0	-0.3	-0.5	-0.7	-0.9	-1.2	-1.4
37.5	1.7	1.4	1.2	0.9	0.7	0.4	0.2	-0.1	-0.3	-0.5	-0.7	-1.0	-1.2	-1.4
38.0	1.7	1.4	1.2	0.9	0.7	0.4	0.2	-0.1	-0.3	-0.5	-0.8	-1.0	-1.2	-1.4
38.5	1.7	1.4	1.2	0.9	0.7	0.4	0.2	-0.1	-0.3	-0.6	-0.8	-1.0	-1.2	-1.5
39.0	1.7	1.4	1.2	0.9	0.7	0.4	0.1	-0.1	-0.3	-0.6	-0.8	-1.1	-1.3	-1.5

‰ \ °C	3.5	4.0	4.5	5.0	5.5	6.0	6.5	7.0	7.5	8.0	8.5	9.0	9.5	10.0
32.0	-1.3	-1.5	-1.6	-1.8	-2.0	-2.1	-2.3	-2.4	-2.6	-2.7	-2.9	-3.0	-3.1	-3.3
32.5	-1.3	-1.5	-1.7	-1.8	-2.0	-2.2	-2.3	-2.5	-2.6	-2.8	-2.9	-3.1	-3.2	-3.3
33.0	-1.3	-1.5	-1.7	-1.9	-2.1	-2.2	-2.4	-2.5	-2.7	-2.9	-3.0	-3.1	-3.3	-3.4
33.5	-1.4	-1.6	-1.7	-1.9	-2.1	-2.3	-2.4	-2.6	-2.8	-2.9	-3.1	-3.2	-3.3	-3.5
34.0	-1.4	-1.6	-1.8	-2.0	-2.1	-2.3	-2.5	-2.7	-2.8	-3.0	-3.1	-3.3	-3.4	-3.6
34.5	-1.4	-1.6	-1.8	-2.0	-2.2	-2.4	-2.5	-2.7	-2.9	-3.0	-3.2	-3.3	-3.5	-3.6
35.0	-1.5	-1.7	-1.9	-2.0	-2.2	-2.4	-2.6	-2.8	-2.9	-3.1	-3.2	-3.4	-3.5	-3.7
35.5	-1.5	-1.7	-1.9	-2.1	-2.3	-2.5	-2.6	-2.8	-3.0	-3.1	-3.3	-3.5	-3.6	-3.8
36.0	-1.5	-1.7	-1.9	-2.1	-2.3	-2.5	-2.7	-2.9	-3.0	-3.2	-3.4	-3.5	-3.7	-3.8
36.5	-1.6	-1.8	-2.0	-2.2	-2.4	-2.6	-2.7	-2.9	-3.1	-3.3	-3.4	-3.6	-3.7	-3.9
37.0	-1.6	-1.8	-2.0	-2.2	-2.4	-2.6	-2.8	-3.0	-3.1	-3.3	-3.5	-3.7	-3.8	-4.0
37.5	-1.6	-1.8	-2.1	-2.3	-2.5	-2.6	-2.8	-3.0	-3.2	-3.4	-3.5	-3.7	-3.9	-4.0
38.0	-1.7	-1.9	-2.1	-2.3	-2.5	-2.7	-2.9	-3.1	-3.3	-3.4	-3.6	-3.8	-3.9	-4.1
38.5	-1.7	-1.9	-2.1	-2.3	-2.5	-2.7	-2.9	-3.1	-3.3	-3.5	-3.7	-3.8	-4.0	-4.2
39.0	-1.7	-2.0	-2.2	-2.4	-2.6	-2.8	-3.0	-3.2	-3.4	-3.5	-3.7	-3.9	-4.1	-4.2

Table 2.4–6 (*Continued*)

9000 METERS
(943.96 kg/cm^2)

‰ \ °C	-3.5	-3.0	-2.5	-2.0	-1.5	-1.0	-0.5	0.0	0.5	1.0	1.5	2.0	2.5	3.0
32.0	2.1	1.8	1.5	1.2	0.9	0.7	0.4	0.1	-0.1	-0.4	-0.7	-0.9	-1.1	-1.4
32.5	2.1	1.8	1.5	1.2	0.9	0.7	0.4	0.1	-0.2	-0.4	-0.7	-0.9	-1.2	-1.4
33.0	2.1	1.8	1.5	1.2	0.9	0.6	0.4	0.1	-0.2	-0.4	-0.7	-1.0	-1.2	-1.5
33.5	2.1	1.8	1.5	1.2	0.9	0.6	0.3	0.1	-0.2	-0.5	-0.7	-1.0	-1.3	-1.5
34.0	2.1	1.8	1.5	1.2	0.9	0.6	0.3	0.0	-0.2	-0.5	-0.8	-1.0	-1.3	-1.5
34.5	2.1	1.8	1.5	1.2	0.9	0.6	0.3	0.0	-0.3	-0.5	-0.8	-1.1	-1.3	-1.6
35.0	2.1	1.8	1.5	1.2	0.9	0.6	0.3	0.0	-0.3	-0.6	-0.8	-1.1	-1.4	-1.6
35.5	2.1	1.8	1.5	1.2	0.9	0.6	0.3	-0.0	-0.3	-0.6	-0.9	-1.1	-1.4	-1.7
36.0	2.1	1.8	1.5	1.1	0.8	0.5	0.2	-0.0	-0.3	-0.6	-0.9	-1.2	-1.4	-1.7
36.5	2.1	1.8	1.4	1.1	0.8	0.5	0.2	-0.1	-0.4	-0.6	-0.9	-1.2	-1.5	-1.7
37.0	2.1	1.8	1.4	1.1	0.8	0.5	0.2	-0.1	-0.4	-0.7	-0.9	-1.2	-1.5	-1.8
37.5	2.1	1.8	1.4	1.1	0.8	0.5	0.2	-0.1	-0.4	-0.7	-1.0	-1.3	-1.5	-1.8
38.0	2.1	1.7	1.4	1.1	0.8	0.5	0.2	-0.1	-0.4	-0.7	-1.0	-1.3	-1.6	-1.8
38.5	2.1	1.7	1.4	1.1	0.8	0.5	0.2	-0.1	-0.4	-0.7	-1.0	-1.3	-1.6	-1.9
39.0	2.1	1.7	1.4	1.1	0.8	0.4	0.1	-0.2	-0.5	-0.8	-1.1	-1.4	-1.6	-1.9

‰ \ °C	3.5	4.0	4.5	5.0	5.5	6.0	6.5	7.0	7.5	8.0	8.5	9.0	9.5	10.0
32.0	-1.6	-1.9	-2.1	-2.3	-2.5	-2.7	-3.0	-3.2	-3.4	-3.6	-3.7	-3.9	-4.1	-4.3
32.5	-1.7	-1.9	-2.1	-2.4	-2.6	-2.8	-3.0	-3.2	-3.4	-3.6	-3.8	-4.0	-4.2	-4.4
33.0	-1.7	-1.9	-2.2	-2.4	-2.6	-2.9	-3.1	-3.3	-3.5	-3.7	-3.9	-4.1	-4.3	-4.4
33.5	-1.8	-2.0	-2.2	-2.5	-2.7	-2.9	-3.1	-3.3	-3.5	-3.8	-4.0	-4.1	-4.3	-4.5
34.0	-1.8	-2.0	-2.3	-2.5	-2.7	-3.0	-3.2	-3.4	-3.6	-3.8	-4.0	-4.2	-4.4	-4.6
34.5	-1.8	-2.1	-2.3	-2.6	-2.8	-3.0	-3.2	-3.5	-3.7	-3.9	-4.1	-4.3	-4.5	-4.7
35.0	-1.9	-2.1	-2.4	-2.6	-2.8	-3.1	-3.3	-3.5	-3.7	-4.0	-4.2	-4.4	-4.6	-4.7
35.5	-1.9	-2.2	-2.4	-2.7	-2.9	-3.1	-3.4	-3.6	-3.8	-4.0	-4.2	-4.4	-4.6	-4.8
36.0	-2.0	-2.2	-2.5	-2.7	-2.9	-3.2	-3.4	-3.6	-3.9	-4.1	-4.3	-4.5	-4.7	-4.9
36.5	-2.0	-2.3	-2.5	-2.8	-3.0	-3.2	-3.5	-3.7	-3.9	-4.1	-4.4	-4.6	-4.8	-5.0
37.0	-2.0	-2.3	-2.6	-2.8	-3.1	-3.3	-3.5	-3.8	-4.0	-4.2	-4.4	-4.6	-4.9	-5.1
37.5	-2.1	-2.3	-2.6	-2.9	-3.1	-3.3	-3.6	-3.8	-4.1	-4.3	-4.5	-4.7	-4.9	-5.1
38.0	-2.1	-2.4	-2.6	-2.9	-3.2	-3.4	-3.6	-3.9	-4.1	-4.3	-4.6	-4.8	-5.0	-5.2
38.5	-2.2	-2.4	-2.7	-3.0	-3.2	-3.5	-3.7	-3.9	-4.2	-4.4	-4.6	-4.9	-5.1	-5.3
39.0	-2.2	-2.5	-2.7	-3.0	-3.3	-3.5	-3.8	-4.0	-4.2	-4.5	-4.7	-4.9	-5.2	-5.4

Table 2.4–6 (*Continued*)

10,000 METERS (1050.96 kg/cm²)

‰ \ °C	-3.5	-3.0	-2.5	-2.0	-1.5	-1.0	-0.5	0.0	0.5	1.0	1.5	2.0	2.5	3.0
32.0	2.6	2.3	1.9	1.6	1.2	0.9	0.5	0.2	-0.1	-0.5	-0.8	-1.1	-1.4	-1.7
32.5	2.6	2.3	1.9	1.5	1.2	0.8	0.5	0.2	-0.2	-0.5	-0.8	-1.2	-1.5	-1.8
33.0	2.6	2.3	1.9	1.5	1.2	0.8	0.5	0.1	-0.2	-0.5	-0.9	-1.2	-1.5	-1.8
33.5	2.6	2.2	1.9	1.5	1.1	0.8	0.4	0.1	-0.2	-0.6	-0.9	-1.2	-1.6	-1.9
34.0	2.6	2.2	1.9	1.5	1.1	0.8	0.4	0.1	-0.3	-0.6	-1.0	-1.3	-1.6	-1.9
34.5	2.6	2.2	1.8	1.5	1.1	0.7	0.4	0.0	-0.3	-0.7	-1.0	-1.3	-1.6	-2.0
35.0	2.6	2.2	1.8	1.4	1.1	0.7	0.4	0.0	-0.3	-0.7	-1.0	-1.4	-1.7	-2.0
35.5	2.6	2.2	1.8	1.4	1.1	0.7	0.3	-0.0	-0.4	-0.7	-1.1	-1.4	-1.7	-2.1
36.0	2.6	2.2	1.8	1.4	1.0	0.7	0.3	-0.1	-0.4	-0.8	-1.1	-1.5	-1.8	-2.1
36.5	2.5	2.2	1.8	1.4	1.0	0.6	0.3	-0.1	-0.5	-0.8	-1.2	-1.5	-1.8	-2.2
37.0	2.5	2.1	1.8	1.4	1.0	0.6	0.2	-0.1	-0.5	-0.8	-1.2	-1.5	-1.9	-2.2
37.5	2.5	2.1	1.7	1.3	1.0	0.6	0.2	-0.2	-0.5	-0.9	-1.2	-1.6	-1.9	-2.3
38.0	2.5	2.1	1.7	1.3	0.9	0.6	0.2	-0.2	-0.6	-0.9	-1.3	-1.6	-2.0	-2.3
38.5	2.5	2.1	1.7	1.3	0.9	0.5	0.2	-0.2	-0.6	-0.9	-1.3	-1.7	-2.0	-2.4
39.0	2.5	2.1	1.7	1.3	0.9	0.5	0.1	-0.2	-0.6	-1.0	-1.3	-1.7	-2.1	-2.4

‰ \ °C	3.5	4.0	4.5	5.0	5.5	6.0	6.5	7.0	7.5	8.0	8.5	9.0	9.5	10.0
32.0	-2.0	-2.3	-2.6	-2.9	-3.2	-3.5	-3.7	-4.0	-4.3	-4.5	-4.8	-5.0	-5.2	-5.5
32.5	-2.1	-2.4	-2.7	-3.0	-3.2	-3.5	-3.8	-4.1	-4.3	-4.6	-4.8	-5.1	-5.3	-5.6
33.0	-2.1	-2.4	-2.7	-3.0	-3.3	-3.6	-3.9	-4.1	-4.4	-4.7	-4.9	-5.2	-5.4	-5.6
33.5	-2.2	-2.5	-2.8	-3.1	-3.4	-3.7	-3.9	-4.2	-4.5	-4.7	-5.0	-5.2	-5.5	-5.7
34.0	-2.2	-2.5	-2.8	-3.1	-3.4	-3.7	-4.0	-4.3	-4.5	-4.8	-5.1	-5.3	-5.6	-5.8
34.5	-2.3	-2.6	-2.9	-3.2	-3.5	-3.8	-4.1	-4.3	-4.6	-4.9	-5.2	-5.4	-5.7	-5.9
35.0	-2.3	-2.7	-3.0	-3.3	-3.6	-3.9	-4.1	-4.4	-4.7	-5.0	-5.2	-5.5	-5.7	-6.0
35.5	-2.4	-2.7	-3.0	-3.3	-3.6	-3.9	-4.2	-4.5	-4.8	-5.0	-5.3	-5.6	-5.8	-6.1
36.0	-2.4	-2.8	-3.1	-3.4	-3.7	-4.0	-4.3	-4.6	-4.8	-5.1	-5.4	-5.7	-5.9	-6.2
36.5	-2.5	-2.8	-3.1	-3.4	-3.7	-4.0	-4.3	-4.6	-4.9	-5.2	-5.5	-5.7	-6.0	-6.3
37.0	-2.5	-2.9	-3.2	-3.5	-3.8	-4.1	-4.4	-4.7	-5.0	-5.3	-5.5	-5.8	-6.1	-6.3
37.5	-2.6	-2.9	-3.2	-3.6	-3.9	-4.2	-4.5	-4.8	-5.1	-5.3	-5.6	-5.9	-6.2	-6.4
38.0	-2.6	-3.0	-3.3	-3.6	-3.9	-4.2	-4.5	-4.8	-5.1	-5.4	-5.7	-6.0	-6.2	-6.5
38.5	-2.7	-3.0	-3.4	-3.7	-4.0	-4.3	-4.6	-4.9	-5.2	-5.5	-5.8	-6.1	-6.3	-6.6
39.0	-2.7	-3.1	-3.4	-3.7	-4.1	-4.4	-4.7	-5.0	-5.3	-5.6	-5.9	-6.1	-6.4	-6.7

Table 2.4–6 (*Continued*)

11,000 METERS
(1157.22 kg/cm^2)

‰ \ °C	-3.5	-3.0	-2.5	-2.0	-1.5	-1.0	-0.5	0.0	0.5	1.0	1.5	2.0	2.5	3.0
32.0	3.3	2.8	2.4	1.9	1.5	1.1	0.7	0.3	-0.2	-0.6	-1.0	-1.4	-1.7	-2.1
32.5	3.3	2.8	2.4	1.9	1.5	1.1	0.6	0.2	-0.2	-0.6	-1.0	-1.4	-1.8	-2.2
33.0	3.2	2.8	2.3	1.9	1.4	1.0	0.6	0.2	-0.2	-0.7	-1.1	-1.5	-1.9	-2.2
33.5	3.2	2.8	2.3	1.9	1.4	1.0	0.5	0.1	-0.3	-0.7	-1.1	-1.5	-1.9	-2.3
34.0	3.2	2.7	2.3	1.8	1.4	0.9	0.5	0.1	-0.3	-0.8	-1.2	-1.6	-2.0	-2.4
34.5	3.2	2.7	2.2	1.8	1.3	0.9	0.5	0.0	-0.4	-0.8	-1.2	-1.6	-2.0	-2.4
35.0	3.1	2.7	2.2	1.8	1.3	0.9	0.4	0.0	-0.4	-0.8	-1.3	-1.7	-2.1	-2.5
35.5	3.1	2.6	2.2	1.7	1.3	0.8	0.4	-0.0	-0.5	-0.9	-1.3	-1.7	-2.1	-2.5
36.0	3.1	2.6	2.2	1.7	1.2	0.8	0.4	-0.1	-0.5	-0.9	-1.4	-1.8	-2.2	-2.6
36.5	3.1	2.6	2.1	1.7	1.2	0.8	0.3	-0.1	-0.6	-1.0	-1.4	-1.8	-2.2	-2.7
37.0	3.0	2.6	2.1	1.6	1.2	0.7	0.3	-0.2	-0.6	-1.0	-1.5	-1.9	-2.3	-2.7
37.5	3.0	2.5	2.1	1.6	1.1	0.7	0.2	-0.2	-0.7	-1.1	-1.5	-1.9	-2.4	-2.8
38.0	3.0	2.5	2.0	1.6	1.1	0.7	0.2	-0.3	-0.7	-1.1	-1.6	-2.0	-2.4	-2.8
38.5	3.0	2.5	2.0	1.5	1.1	0.6	0.2	-0.3	-0.7	-1.2	-1.6	-2.0	-2.5	-2.9
39.0	3.0	2.5	2.0	1.5	1.0	0.6	0.1	-0.3	-0.8	-1.2	-1.7	-2.1	-2.5	-2.9

‰ \ °C	3.5	4.0	4.5	5.0	5.5	6.0	6.5	7.0	7.5	8.0	8.5	9.0	9.5	10.0
32.0	-2.5	-2.9	-3.2	-3.6	-3.9	-4.3	-4.6	-5.0	-5.3	-5.6	-5.9	-6.2	-6.5	-6.8
32.5	-2.6	-2.9	-3.3	-3.7	-4.0	-4.4	-4.7	-5.0	-5.4	-5.7	-6.0	-6.3	-6.6	-6.9
33.0	-2.6	-3.0	-3.4	-3.7	-4.1	-4.4	-4.8	-5.1	-5.5	-5.8	-6.1	-6.4	-6.7	-7.0
33.5	-2.7	-3.1	-3.4	-3.8	-4.2	-4.5	-4.9	-5.2	-5.5	-5.9	-6.2	-6.5	-6.8	-7.1
34.0	-2.7	-3.1	-3.5	-3.9	-4.2	-4.6	-4.9	-5.3	-5.6	-6.0	-6.3	-6.6	-6.9	-7.2
34.5	-2.8	-3.2	-3.6	-3.9	-4.3	-4.7	-5.0	-5.4	-5.7	-6.0	-6.4	-6.7	-7.0	-7.3
35.0	-2.9	-3.3	-3.6	-4.0	-4.4	-4.7	-5.1	-5.4	-5.8	-6.1	-6.5	-6.8	-7.1	-7.4
35.5	-2.9	-3.3	-3.7	-4.1	-4.4	-4.8	-5.2	-5.5	-5.9	-6.2	-6.5	-6.9	-7.2	-7.5
36.0	-3.0	-3.4	-3.8	-4.1	-4.5	-4.9	-5.3	-5.6	-6.0	-6.3	-6.6	-6.9	-7.3	-7.6
36.5	-3.1	-3.4	-3.8	-4.2	-4.6	-5.0	-5.3	-5.7	-6.0	-6.4	-6.7	-7.0	-7.4	-7.7
37.0	-3.1	-3.5	-3.9	-4.3	-4.7	-5.0	-5.4	-5.8	-6.1	-6.5	-6.8	-7.1	-7.5	-7.8
37.5	-3.2	-3.6	-4.0	-4.4	-4.7	-5.1	-5.5	-5.9	-6.2	-6.6	-6.9	-7.2	-7.6	-7.9
38.0	-3.2	-3.6	-4.0	-4.4	-4.8	-5.2	-5.6	-5.9	-6.3	-6.6	-7.0	-7.3	-7.7	-8.0
38.5	-3.3	-3.7	-4.1	-4.5	-4.9	-5.3	-5.6	-6.0	-6.4	-6.7	-7.1	-7.4	-7.8	-8.1
39.0	-3.4	-3.8	-4.2	-4.6	-5.0	-5.3	-5.7	-6.1	-6.5	-6.8	-7.2	-7.5	-7.9	-8.2

(From *Tables of Sound Speed in Sea Water*, SP-58, U.S. Naval Oceanographic Office, Washington, D.C., 1962.)

Table 2.4–7
SOUND SPEED CONVERSION
Meters/second to Feet/second

m	ft	m	ft	m	ft	m	ft	m	ft	m	ft	m	ft	m	ft
1400	4593.2	1450	4757.2	1500	4921.2	1550	5085.3	1600	5249.3	1650	5413.4	1700	5577.4	1750	5741.5
1401	4596.4	1451	4760.5	1501	4924.5	1551	5088.6	1601	5252.6	1651	5416.7	1701	5580.7	1751	5744.7
1402	4599.7	1452	4763.8	1502	4927.8	1552	5091.9	1602	5255.9	1652	5419.9	1702	5584.0	1752	5748.0
1403	4603.0	1453	4767.1	1503	4931.1	1553	5095.1	1603	5259.2	1653	5423.2	1703	5587.3	1753	5751.3
1404	4606.3	1454	4770.3	1504	4934.4	1554	5098.4	1604	5262.5	1654	5426.5	1704	5590.5	1754	5754.6
1405	4609.6	1455	4773.6	1505	4937.7	1555	5101.7	1605	5265.7	1655	5429.8	1705	5593.8	1755	5757.9
1406	4612.9	1456	4776.9	1506	4940.9	1556	5105.0	1606	5269.0	1656	5433.1	1706	5597.1	1756	5761.1
1407	4616.1	1457	4780.2	1507	4944.2	1557	5108.3	1607	5272.3	1657	5436.3	1707	5600.4	1757	5764.4
1408	4619.4	1458	4783.5	1508	4947.5	1558	5111.5	1608	5275.6	1658	5439.6	1708	5603.7	1758	5767.7
1409	4622.7	1459	4786.7	1509	4950.8	1559	5114.8	1609	5278.9	1659	5442.9	1709	5606.9	1759	5771.0
1410	4626.0	1460	4790.0	1510	4954.1	1560	5118.1	1610	5282.1	1660	5446.2	1710	5610.2	1760	5774.3
1411	4629.3	1461	4793.3	1511	4957.3	1561	5121.4	1611	5285.4	1661	5449.5	1711	5613.5	1761	5777.5
1412	4632.5	1462	4796.6	1512	4960.6	1562	5124.7	1612	5288.7	1662	5452.7	1712	5616.8	1762	5780.8
1413	4635.8	1463	4799.9	1513	4963.9	1563	5127.9	1613	5292.0	1663	5456.0	1713	5620.1	1763	5784.1
1414	4639.1	1464	4803.1	1514	4967.2	1564	5131.2	1614	5295.3	1664	5459.3	1714	5623.3	1764	5787.4
1415	4642.4	1465	4806.4	1515	4970.5	1565	5134.5	1615	5298.5	1665	5462.6	1715	5626.6	1765	5790.7
1416	4645.7	1466	4809.7	1516	4973.7	1566	5137.8	1616	5301.8	1666	5465.9	1716	5629.9	1766	5794.0
1417	4648.9	1467	4813.0	1517	4977.0	1567	5141.1	1617	5305.1	1667	5469.1	1717	5633.2	1767	5797.2
1418	4652.2	1468	4816.3	1518	4980.3	1568	5144.3	1618	5308.4	1668	5472.4	1718	5636.5	1768	5800.5
1419	4655.5	1469	4819.5	1519	4983.6	1569	5147.6	1619	5311.7	1669	5475.7	1719	5639.8	1769	5803.8
1420	4658.8	1470	4822.8	1520	4986.9	1570	5150.9	1620	5314.9	1670	5479.0	1720	5643.0	1770	5807.1
1421	4662.1	1471	4826.1	1521	4990.1	1571	5154.2	1621	5318.2	1671	5482.3	1721	5646.3	1771	5810.4
1422	4665.3	1472	4829.4	1522	4993.4	1572	5157.5	1622	5321.5	1672	5485.6	1722	5649.6	1772	5813.6
1423	4668.6	1473	4832.7	1523	4996.7	1573	5160.8	1623	5324.8	1673	5488.8	1723	5652.9	1773	5816.9
1424	4671.9	1474	4835.9	1524	5000.0	1574	5164.0	1624	5328.1	1674	5492.1	1724	5656.2	1774	5820.2
1425	4675.2	1475	4839.2	1525	5003.3	1575	5167.3	1625	5331.4	1675	5495.4	1725	5659.4	1775	5823.5
1426	4678.5	1476	4842.5	1526	5006.6	1576	5170.6	1626	5334.6	1676	5498.7	1726	5662.7	1776	5826.8
1427	4681.7	1477	4845.8	1527	5009.8	1577	5173.9	1627	5337.9	1677	5502.0	1727	5666.0	1777	5830.0
1428	4685.0	1478	4849.1	1528	5013.1	1578	5177.2	1628	5341.2	1678	5505.2	1728	5669.3	1778	5833.3
1429	4688.3	1479	4852.4	1529	5016.4	1579	5180.4	1629	5344.5	1679	5508.5	1729	5672.6	1779	5836.6
1430	4691.6	1480	4855.6	1530	5019.7	1580	5183.7	1630	5347.8	1680	5511.8	1730	5675.8	1780	5839.9
1431	4694.9	1481	4858.9	1531	5023.0	1581	5187.0	1631	5351.0	1681	5515.1	1731	5679.1	1781	5843.2
1432	4698.2	1482	4862.2	1532	5026.2	1582	5190.3	1632	5354.3	1682	5518.4	1732	5682.4	1782	5846.4
1433	4701.4	1483	4865.5	1533	5029.5	1583	5193.6	1633	5357.6	1683	5521.6	1733	5685.7	1783	5849.7
1434	4704.7	1484	4868.8	1534	5032.8	1584	5196.8	1634	5360.9	1684	5524.9	1734	5689.0	1784	5853.0
1435	4708.0	1485	4872.0	1535	5036.1	1585	5200.1	1635	5364.2	1685	5528.2	1735	5692.2	1785	5856.3
1436	4711.3	1486	4875.3	1536	5039.4	1586	5203.4	1636	5367.4	1686	5531.5	1736	5695.5	1786	5859.6
1437	4714.6	1487	4878.6	1537	5042.6	1587	5206.7	1637	5370.7	1687	5534.8	1737	5698.8	1787	5862.8
1438	4717.8	1488	4881.9	1538	5045.9	1588	5210.0	1638	5374.0	1688	5538.0	1738	5702.1	1788	5866.1
1439	4721.1	1489	4885.2	1539	5049.2	1589	5213.2	1639	5377.3	1689	5541.3	1739	5705.4	1789	5869.4
1440	4724.4	1490	4888.4	1540	5052.5	1590	5216.5	1640	5380.6	1690	5544.6	1740	5708.6	1790	5872.7
1441	4727.7	1491	4891.7	1541	5055.8	1591	5219.8	1641	5383.8	1691	5547.9	1741	5711.9	1791	5876.0
1442	4731.0	1492	4895.0	1542	5059.0	1592	5223.1	1642	5387.1	1692	5551.2	1742	5715.2	1792	5879.3
1443	4734.2	1493	4898.3	1543	5062.3	1593	5226.4	1643	5390.4	1693	5554.5	1743	5718.5	1793	5882.5
1444	4737.5	1494	4901.6	1544	5065.6	1594	5229.6	1644	5393.7	1694	5557.7	1744	5721.8	1794	5885.8
1445	4740.8	1495	4904.8	1545	5068.9	1595	5232.9	1645	5397.0	1695	5561.0	1745	5725.1	1795	5889.1
1446	4744.1	1496	4908.1	1546	5072.2	1596	5236.2	1646	5400.3	1696	5564.3	1746	5728.3	1796	5892.4
1447	4747.4	1497	4911.4	1547	5075.4	1597	5239.5	1647	5403.5	1697	5567.6	1747	5731.6	1797	5895.7
1448	4750.6	1498	4914.7	1548	5078.7	1598	5242.8	1648	5406.8	1698	5570.9	1748	5734.9	1798	5898.9
1449	4753.9	1499	4918.0	1549	5082.0	1599	5246.1	1649	5410.1	1699	5574.1	1749	5738.2	1799	5902.2

(From *Tables of Sound Speed in Sea Water,* SP-58, U.S. Naval Oceanographic Office, Washington, D.C., 1962.)

Figure 2.4–1
SOUND ATTENUATION (ABSORPTION)

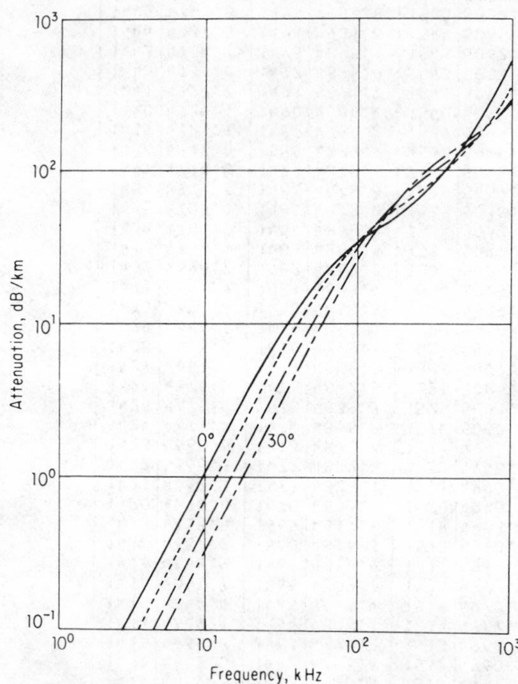

Note: Attenuation coefficients as function of frequency for four temperatures at atmospheric pressure and salinity of 35°/∘∘.

(From Myers, J.J., Holm, C.H., and McAllister, R.F., *Handbook of Ocean and Underwater Engineering,* McGraw-Hill, New York, 1969. With permission.)

Figure 2.4–2
TYPICAL BOTTOM LOSS AS A FUNCTION OF GRAZING ANGLE AND FREQUENCY

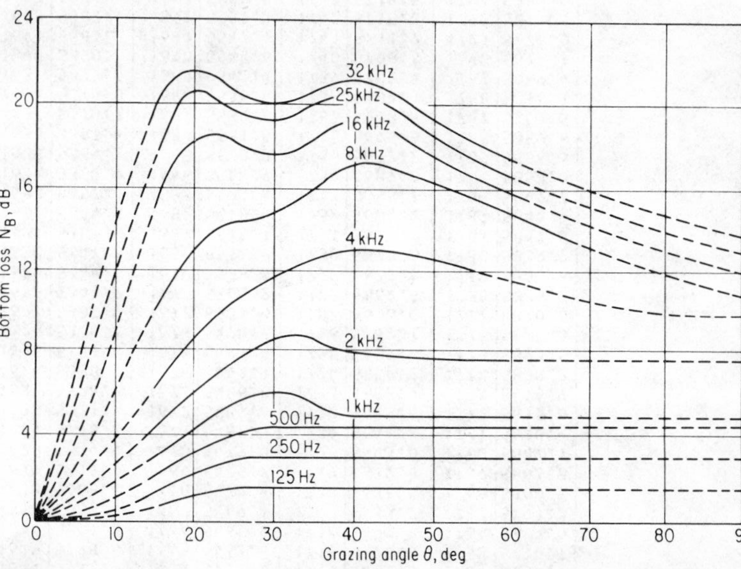

(From Myers, J.J., Holm, C.H., and McAllister, R.F., *Handbook of Ocean and Underwater Engineering,* McGraw-Hill, New York, 1969. With permission.)

Figure 2.4–3

SEA SURFACE LOSS PER BOUNCE (SURFACE CONTACT)

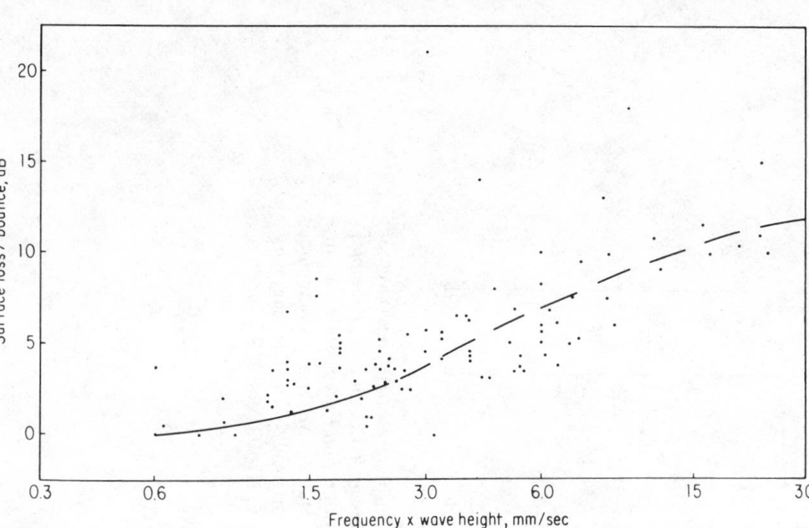

(From Myers, J.J., Holm, C.H., and McAllister, R.F., *Handbook of Ocean and Underwater Engineering*, McGraw-Hill, New York, 1969. With permission.)

Figure 2.4–4

COMPOSITE AMBIENT-SOUND LEVELS

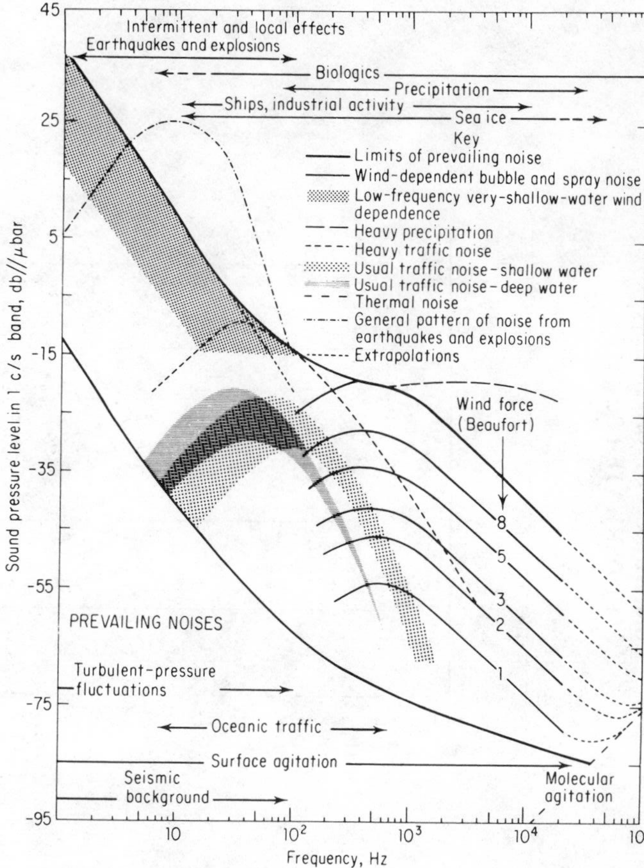

Note: The key identifies component spectra; horizontal arrows show the approximate frequency band of influence of the various sources.

(From Wenz, G.M., Acoustic ambient noise in the ocean, *J. Acoust. Soc. Am.*, 34, 1936, 1962. With permission.)

Figure 2.4–5
COMPARISON OF UNITS FOR UNDERWATER SOUND

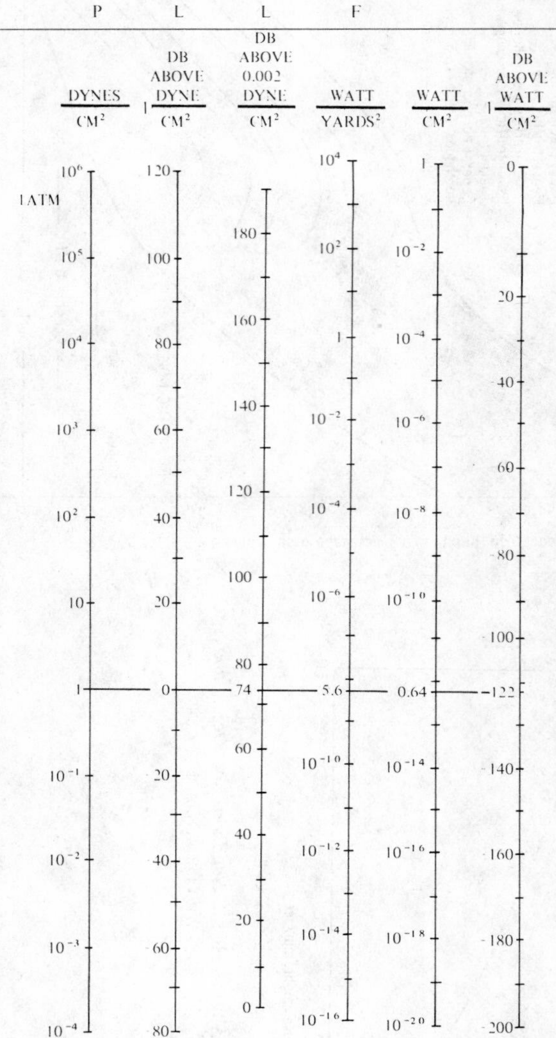

(From U.S. Office of Scientific Research and Development–National Defense Research Committee, *Principles and applications of underwater sound,* Department of the Navy, Headquarters Naval Material Command, Washington, D.C., 1946. Originally issued as summary technical report of Division 6, NDRC, Vol. 7, Washington, D.C., 1946.)

Figure 2.4–6
VOLUME-ATTENUATION COEFFICIENT α AND ATTENUATION LENGTH L IN THE VISIBLE SPECTRUM FOR DISTILLED WATER

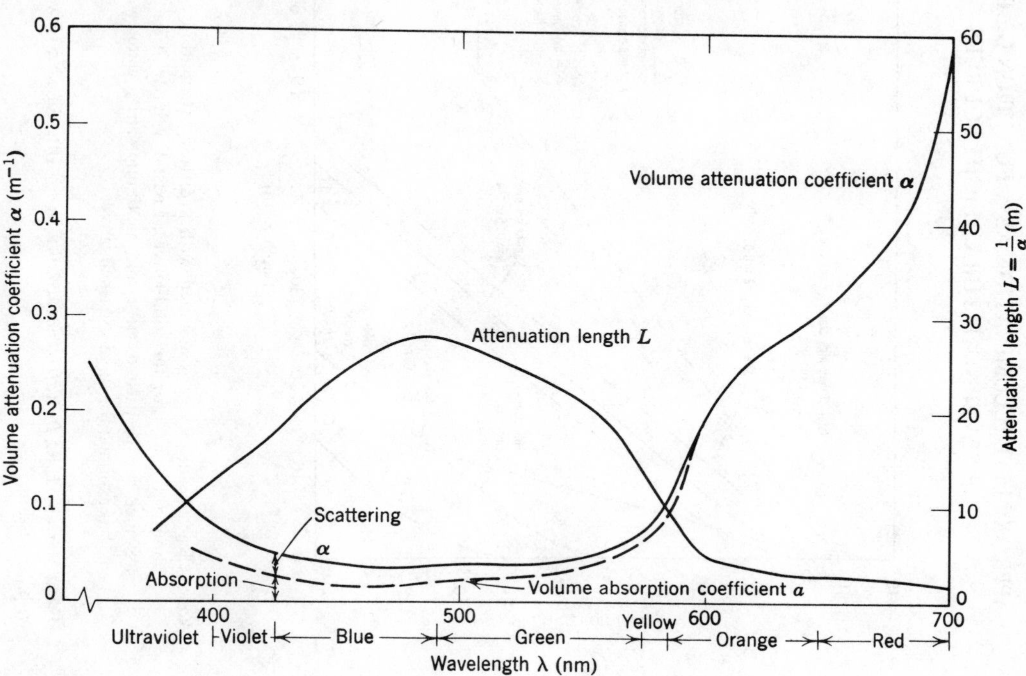

(From Mertens, L.E., *In-Water Photography,* Wiley-Interscience, New York, 1970. With permission. Based on data by Hulburt, E.O., *J. Opt. Soc. Am.,* 35, 1945.)

Figure 2.4–7
VOLUME-ATTENUATION COEFFICIENT

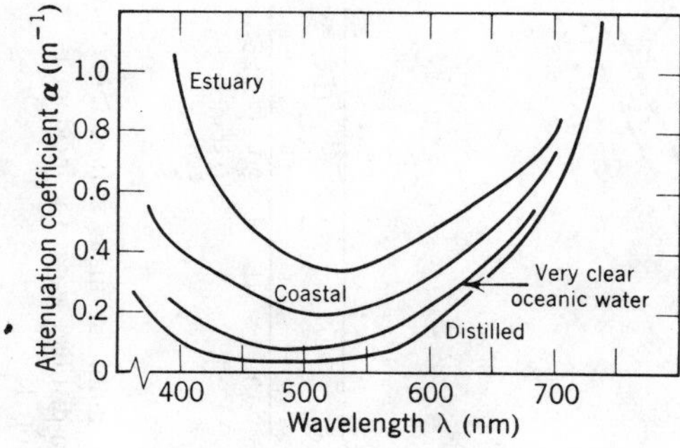

Note: Typical estuary, coastal, and clear oceanic water compared with that of distilled water.

(From Mertens, L.E., *In-Water Photography,* Wiley-Interscience, New York, 1970. With permission.)

Figure 2.4–8
INTENSITY OF ILLUMINATION

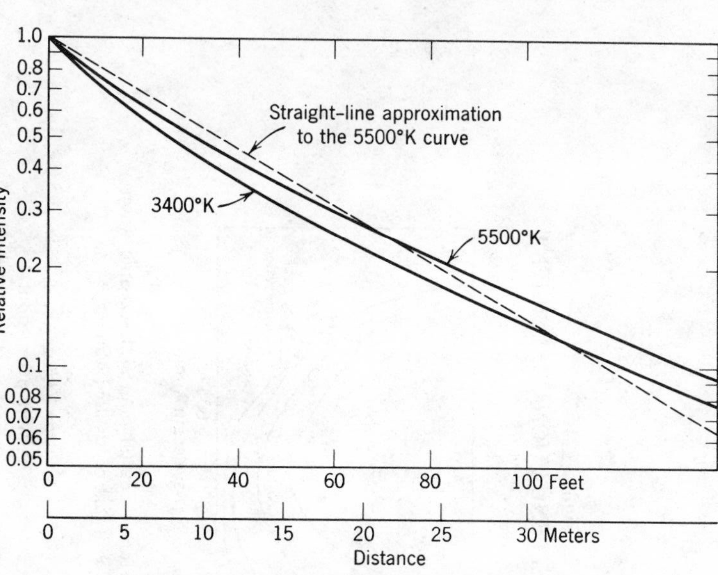

Note: Intensity of illumination as a function of distance along a collimated light beam in distilled water for incident light with a color temperature of 5500 and 3400°K.

(From Mertens, L.E., *In-Water Photography*, Wiley-Interscience, New York, 1970. With permission.)

Figure 2.4–9
APPROXIMATE ILLUMINATION AS A FUNCTION OF DEPTH FOR SEVERAL NATURAL LIGHT SOURCES

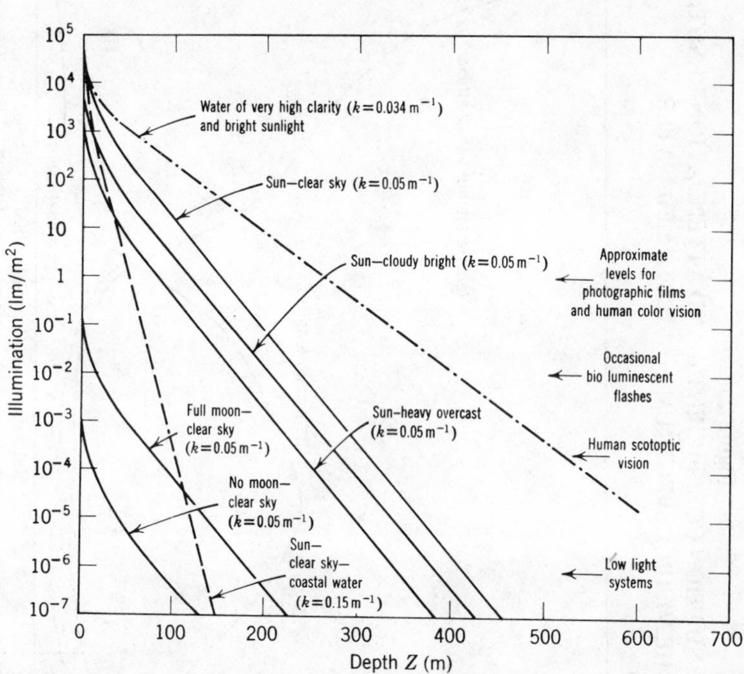

Note: Clear oceanic water is assumed with a diffuse attenuation constant k of about 0.05 m^{-1} for the solid curves. Coastal water with $k = 0.15\ m^{-1}$ is assumed for the dashed curve, and maximum-clarity water with $k = 0.034\ m^{-1}$ is assumed for the dot-dashed curve.

(From Mertens, L.E., *In-Water Photography*, Wiley-Interscience, New York, 1970. With permission.)

ATTENUATION

Attenuation α of a radio wave in sea water, expressed in decibels per meter, is given by

$$\alpha = 8.686\omega\sqrt{\frac{\mu\epsilon}{2}\left[\sqrt{1+\left[\frac{\sigma}{\omega\epsilon}\right]^2}-1\right]}$$

The value of σ relative to ϵ in the squared term accounts for the variation in the slope of the attenuation curve, plotted as a function of frequency in Figure 2.4–11.

Because the polar water molecules rotate at frequencies greater than about 10^{11} kHz, conductivity increases and the propagation number changes so that a propagation "window," a low attenuation band, occurs in the visible light-frequency range (Figure 2.4–11).

(From Myers, J.J., Holm, C.H., and McAllister, R.F., *Handbook of Ocean and Underwater Engineering,* McGraw-Hill, New York, 1969. With permission.)

Figure 2.4–10
VELOCITY OF PROPAGATION IN SEA WATER VS. FREQUENCY,
$\sigma \simeq 4\mu$mhos/m

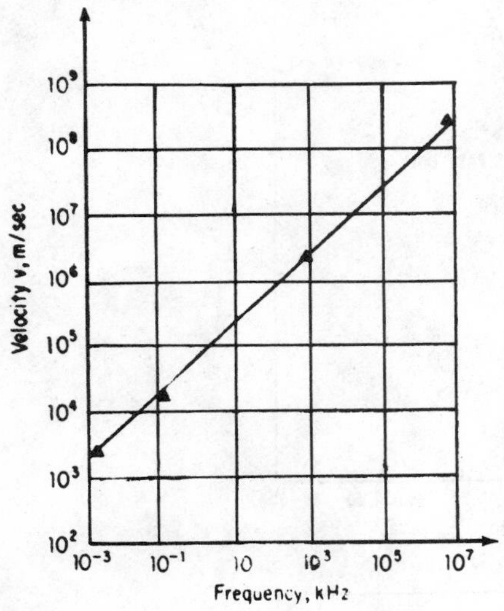

Note: Points marked ▲ are from Hill, M.N., Ed., *The Sea,* Vol. I, Wiley-Interscience, New York, 1962.

(From Myers, J.J., Holm, C.H., and McAllister, R.F., *Handbook of Ocean and Underwater Engineering,* McGraw-Hill, New York, 1969. With permission.)

Figure 2.4–11
ELECTROMAGNETIC WAVE ATTENUATION IN SEA WATER ($\sigma \simeq 4$ mhos/m)

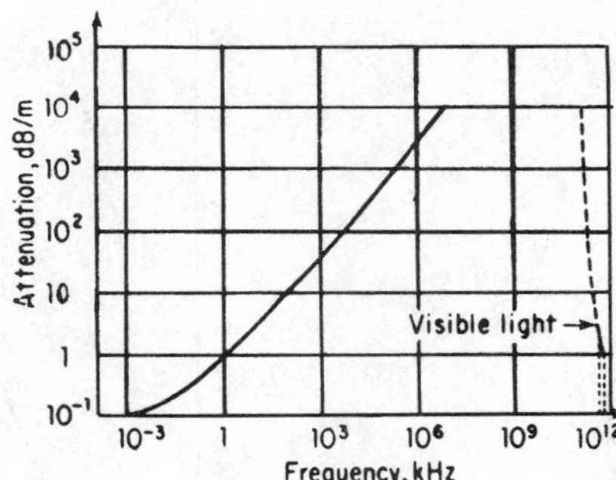

(From Myers, J.J., Holm, C.H., and McAllister, R.F., *Handbook of Ocean and Underwater Engineering,* McGraw-Hill, New York, 1969. With permission.)

Figure 2.4–12
ATTENUATION OF ELECTROMAGNETIC
ENERGY IN SEA WATER

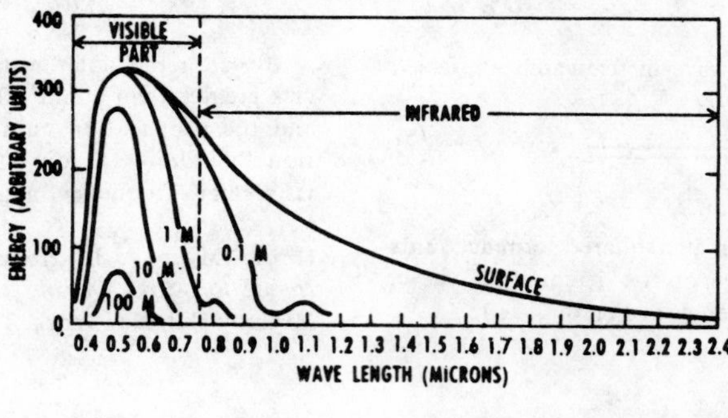

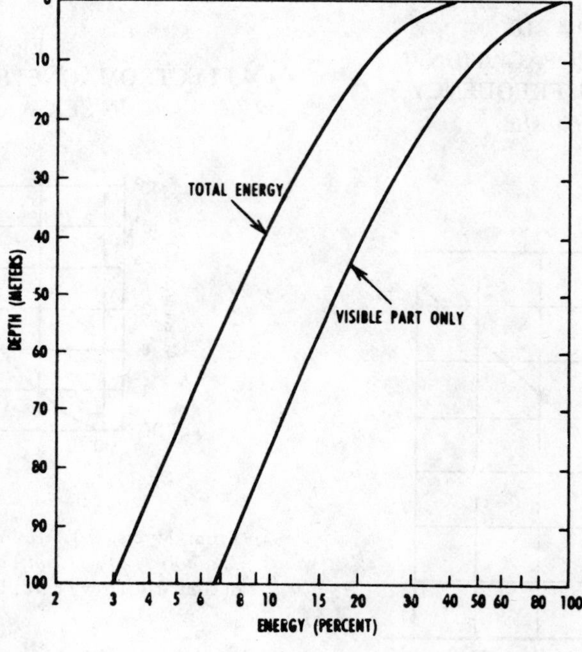

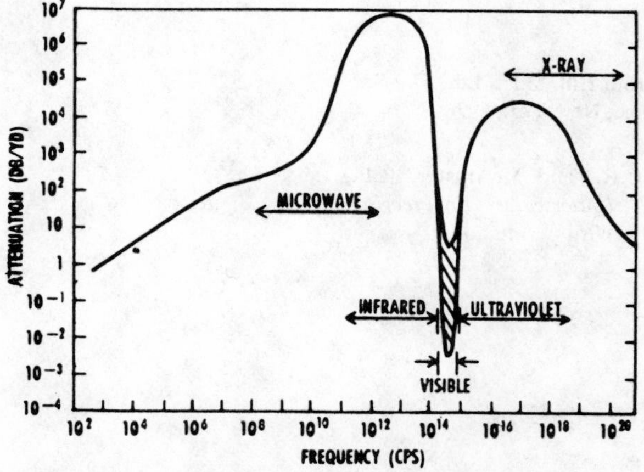

(From Kovit, Bernard, The under-seas environment, *Space/Aeronautics Magazine,* 33, 51, 1960. With permission.)

Section 3

Atmospheric Science

Eric B. Kraus, Ph.D.

3.1 Wind and Dynamic Tables

Table 3.1–1
BEAUFORT WIND SCALE

In 1806 Admiral Sir F. Beaufort devised a scale for recording wind force at sea based on the effect of the wind on a full-rigged man-of-war of that era. In 1838 this scale was adopted by the British Admiralty and with but minor changes had come into general use among mariners for specifying the state of the wind at sea. The International Meteorological Committee (Utrecht, 1874) adopted the Beaufort scale for international use in weather telegraphy, and it now has become the chief scale for specifying the force of the wind and is used in all parts of the world, both on land and on sea.

Since the original Beaufort scale described a state of the atmosphere as manifested by the effects of the wind near the surface, there did not exist originally a set of wind speeds corresponding to the various numbers of the scale. A number of efforts were made to obtain appropriate speed equivalents, but it was found difficult to reach agreement on this matter because the effect of wind variation with height was neglected. The International Meteorological Committee (London, 1921) requested Dr. G. C. Simpson of the British Meteorological Office to investigate the matter, and in 1926 Dr. Simpson proposed a set of speed equivalents that were to apply to anemometers exposed 6 meters above the ground.[1] This scale was adopted by the Committee in Vienna (1926). However, the British Meteorological Office continued to use a scale proposed by Dr. Simpson in 1906[2] and applicable to an anemometer at a height of about 10 meters above the ground, as did the U.S. Weather Bureau. This scale was based on the empirical equation $V=0.836 B^{3/2}$ where V is the wind speed in meters per second and B is the Beaufort force.

In 1946 the International Meteorological Committee meeting in Paris extended the original Beaufort scale to higher values and redefined the speed equivalents to apply to an anemometer at 10 meters above the ground. Up to force 11 these values are consistent with the values for a height of 6 meters adopted in Vienna (1926) and are identical with those proposed by Dr. Simpson in 1906.

Table 3.1–1 gives the speed equivalents of the Paris (1946) resolution and also the "descriptive terms" and "specifications for use on land" from the *Meteorological Observers Handbook* (London, 1939).

[1] Simpson, G.C., The velocity equivalents of the Beaufort scale, Professional Notes No. 44, Air Ministry, Meteorological Office, London, 1926. (See also Anemometers and the Beaufort scale of wind force, *Meteorol. Mag.*, 67, 278, 1933 and Kuhlbrodt, E. *Ann. d. Hydr. & Marit. Meteorol., Zweites Koppen-Heft*, 64, 14, 1936.)

[2] Simpson, G. C., Meteorological Office, Pub. No. 180, London, 1906.

Beaufort Wind Scale

Table A

	Mean wind speeds at 10 m[a]				Limits of wind speed at 10 m[a]			
Force	Knots	m/sec	km/hr	mi/hr	Knots	m/sec	km/hr	mi/hr
0	0	0	0	0	<1	0–0.2	<1	<1
1	2	0.9	3	2	1–3	0.3–1.5	1–5	1–3
2	5	2.4	9	5	4–6	1.6–3.3	6–11	4–7
3	9	4.4	16	10	7–10	3.4–5.4	12–19	8–12
4	13	6.7	24	15	11–16	5.5–7.9	20–28	13–18
5	18	9.3	34	21	17–21	8.0–10.7	29–38	19–24
6	24	12.3	44	28	22–27	10.8–13.8	39–49	25–31
7	30	15.5	55	35	28–33	13.9–17.1	50–61	32–38
8	37	18.9	68	42	34–40	17.2–20.7	62–74	39–46
9	44	22.6	82	50	41–47	20.8–24.4	75–88	47–54
10	52	26.4	96	59	48–55	24.5–28.4	89–102	55–63
11	60	30.5	110	68	56–63	28.5–32.6	103–117	64–72
12	68	34.8	125	78	64–71	32.7–36.9	118–133	73–82
13	76	39.2	141	88	72–80	37.0–41.4	134–149	83–92
14	85	43.8	158	98	81–89	41.5–46.1	150–166	93–103
15	94	48.6	175	109	90–99	46.2–50.9	167–183	104–114
16	104	53.5	193	120	100–108	51.0–56.0	184–201	115–125
17	114	58.6	211	131	109–118	56.1–61.2	202–220	126–136

[a] Resolution 9, International Meteorological Committee, Paris, 1946.

Table 3.1–1 (*Continued*)
BEAUFORT WIND SCALE

Table B

Force	Description of wind[b]	Specifications for use on land[b]
0	Calm	Calm, smoke rises vertically.
1	Light air	Direction of wind shown by smoke drift, but not by wind vanes.
2	Light breeze	Wind felt on face; leaves rustle; ordinary vane moved by wind.
3	Gentle breeze	Leaves and small twigs in constant motion; wind extends light flag.
4	Moderate breeze	Raises dust and loose paper; small branches are moved.
5	Fresh breeze	Small trees in leaf begin to sway; crested wavelets form on inland waters.
6	Strong breeze	Large branches in motion; whistling heard in telegraph wires; umbrellas used with difficulty.
7	Moderate gale	Whole trees in motion; inconvenience felt when walking against wind.
8	Fresh gale	Breaks twigs off trees; generally impedes progress.
9	Strong gale	Slight structural damage occurs (chimney pots and slate removed).
10	Whole gale	Seldom experienced inland; trees uprooted; considerable structural damage occurs.
11	Storm	Very rarely experienced, accompanied by widespread damage.
12 or above	Hurricane	

[b] Meteorological Office, *The Meteorological Observers Handbook,* London, 1939.

(From *Smithsonian Meteorological Tables,* 6th rev. ed., List, R.J., Ed., Smithsonian Institution Press, Washington, D.C., 1971.)

Figure 3.1–1
WORLD MAP OF WIND REGIMES–FEBRUARY

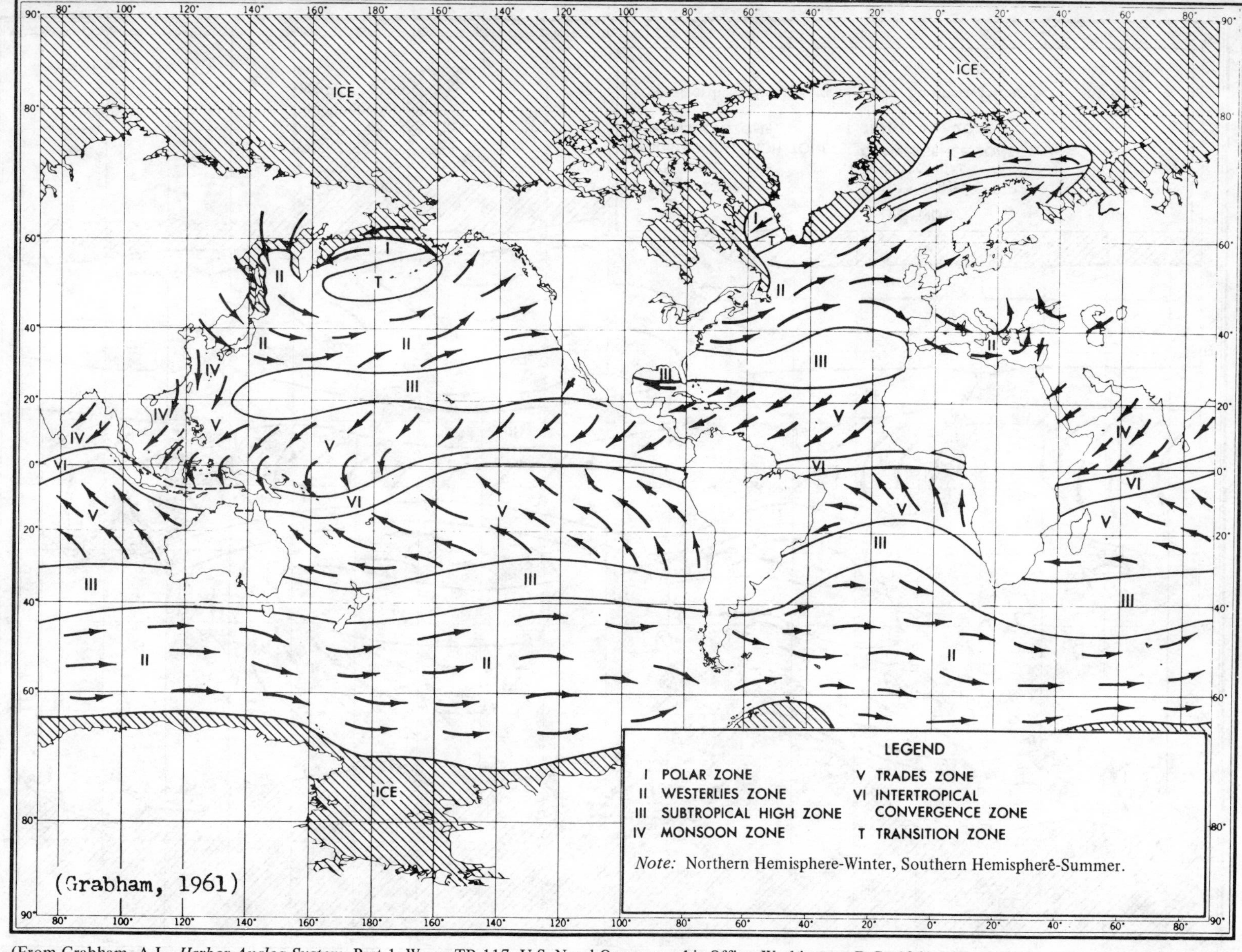

(From Grabham, A.L., *Harbor Analog System*, Part 1, Waves TR-117, U.S. Naval Oceanographic Office, Washington, D.C., 1961.

Figure 3.1–2
WORLD MAP OF WIND REGIMES–AUGUST

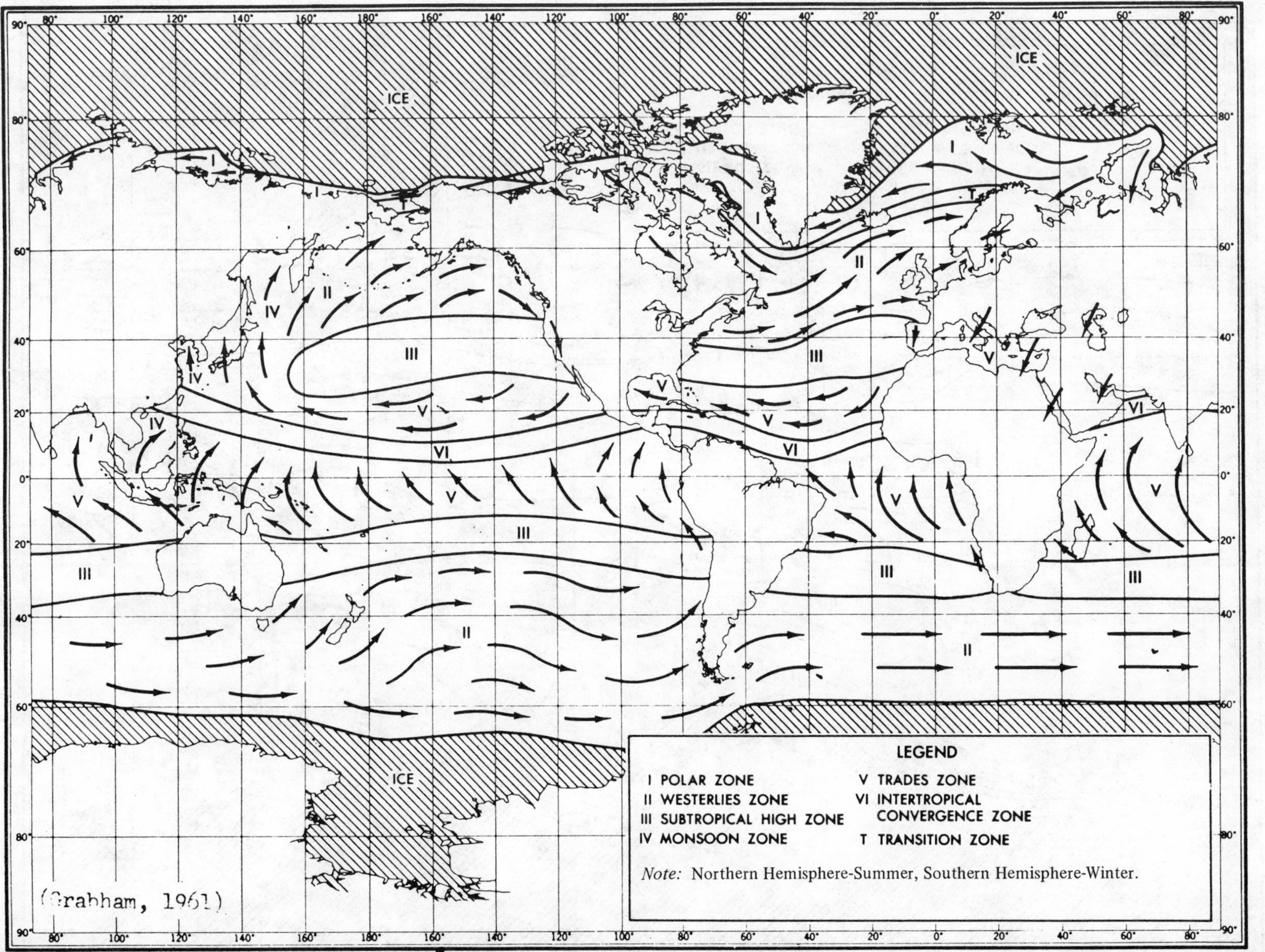

(From Grabham, A.L., *Harbor Analog System*, Part 1, Waves TR-117, U.S. Naval Oceanographic Office, Washington, D.C., 1961.)

Figure 3.1–3

FASTEST MILE OF WIND AT 30 FEET ABOVE GROUND LEVEL WITH RETURN PERIOD OF 2 YEARS

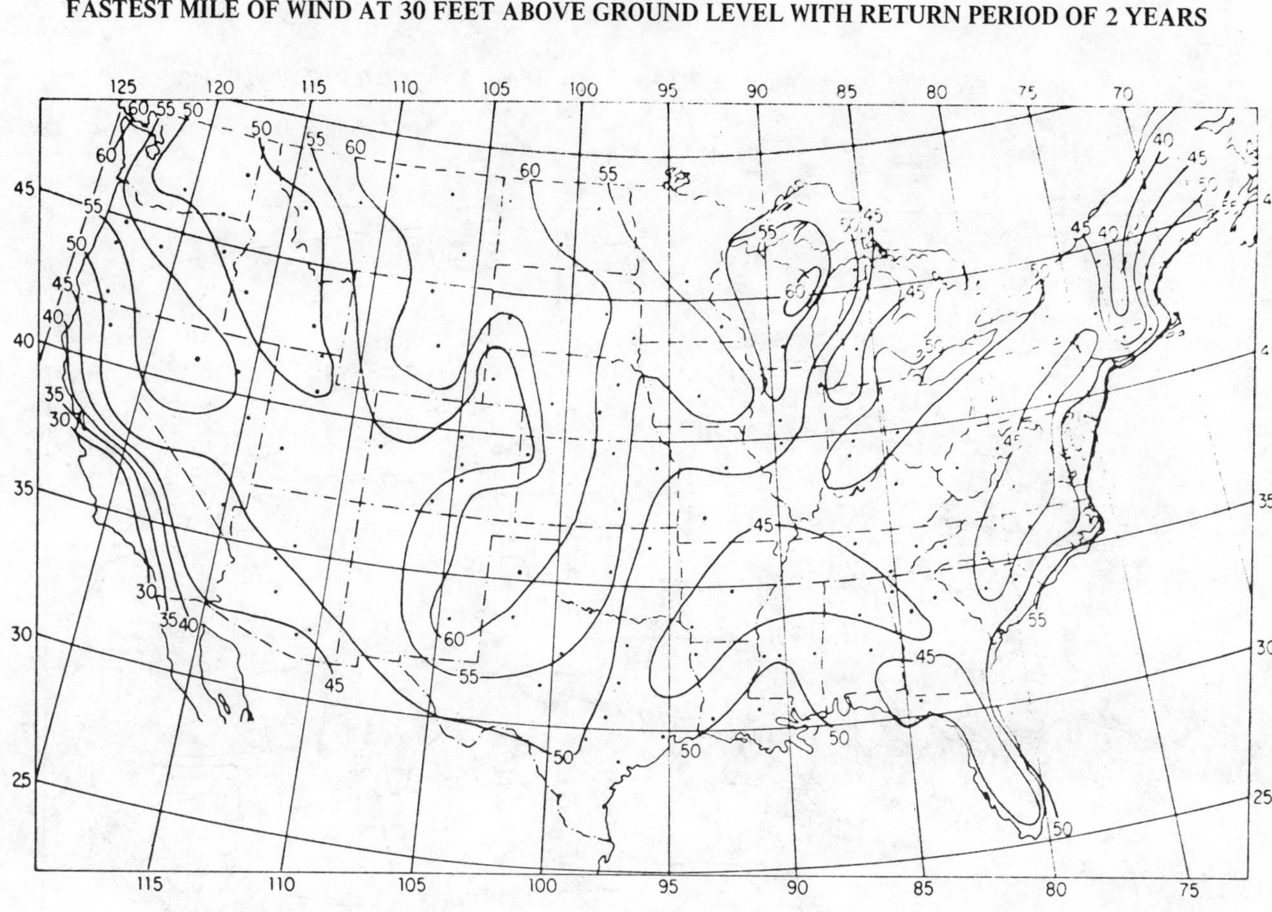

Note: Wind speed is in miles per hour.

(From Myers, J.J., Ed., *Handbook of Ocean and Underwater Engineering,* McGraw-Hill, New York, 1969. With permission.)

Figure 3.1–4
FASTEST MILE OF WIND AT 30 FEET ABOVE GROUND LEVEL WITH RETURN PERIOD OF 50 YEARS

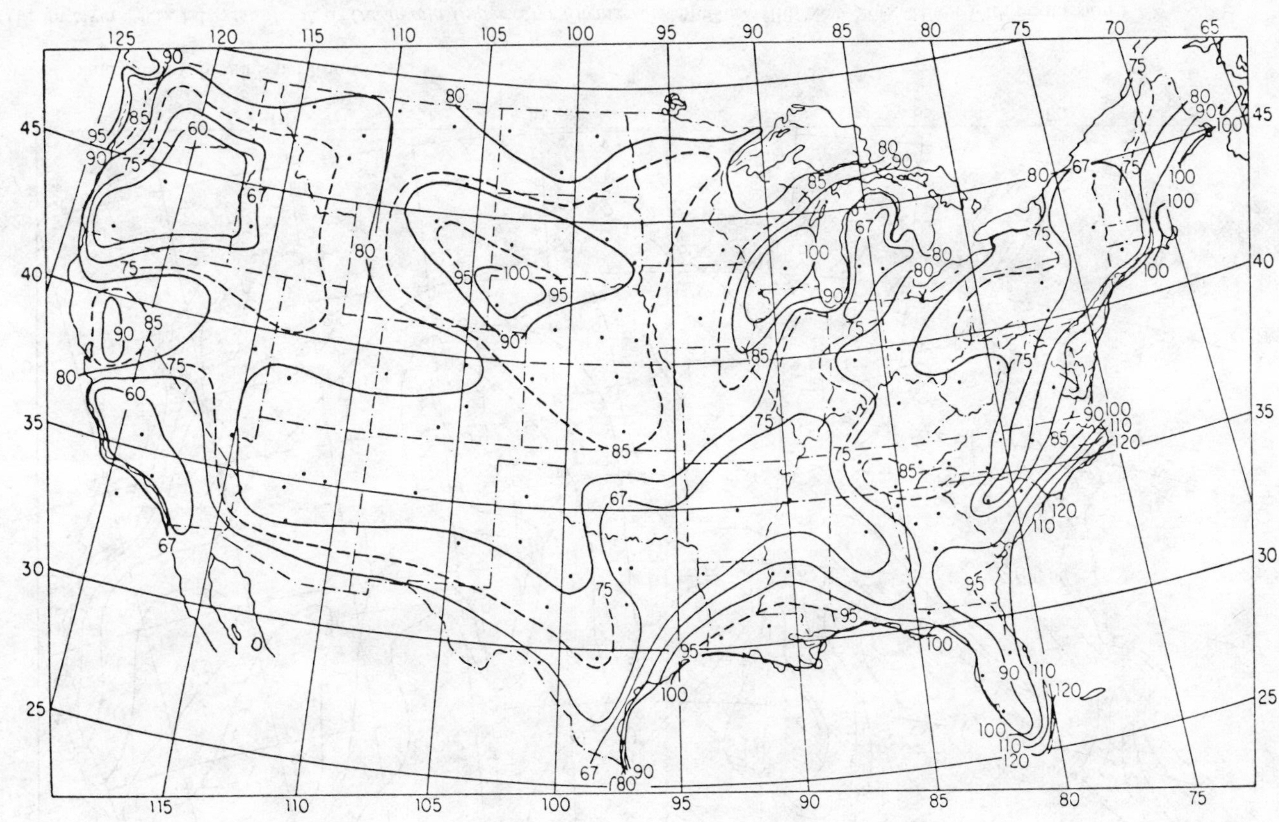

Note: Wind speed is in miles per hour.

(From Myers, J.J., Ed., *Handbook Of Ocean and Underwater Engineering*, McGraw-Hill, New York, 1969. With permission.)

Figure 3.1–5
FASTEST MILE OF WIND AT 30 FEET ABOVE GROUND LEVEL WITH RETURN PERIOD OF 100 YEARS

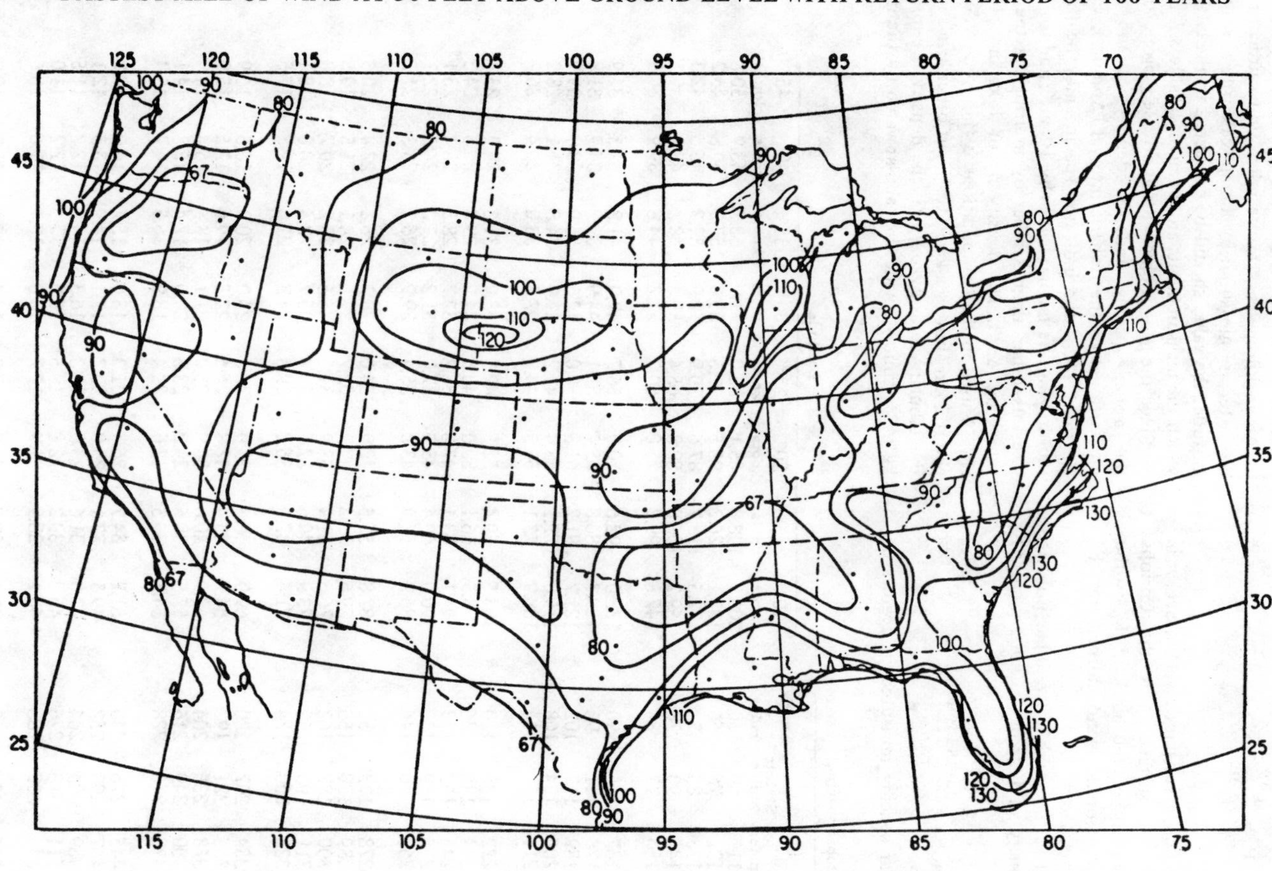

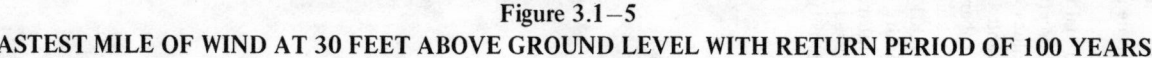

Note: Wind speed is in miles per hour.

(From Myers, J.J., Ed., *Handbook of Ocean and Underwater Engineering,* McGraw-Hill, New York, 1969. With permission.)

Table 3.1–2
GEOSTROPHIC WIND, CONSTANT LEVEL SURFACE

Three Millibar Isobars, Air Density 1 kg m^{-3}

The scalar equation for the geostrophic wind on a constant level surface is

$$V_g = \frac{1}{f\rho}\frac{\partial p}{\partial n}$$

where p is the pressure on a constant level surface, n is distance measured in the surface, f is the Coriolis parameter, ρ is the density of the air, and V_g is the component of the geostrophic wind normal to the direction in which n is measured.

On a constant level surface with a 3 millibar isobaric interval and an air density of 1 kg m^{-3} (0.001 g cm^{-3}) this reduces to

$$V_g(\text{knots}) = \frac{0.0052409}{f\Delta n}$$

where Δn is the isobar spacing measured in degrees of latitude (i.e., one unit of Δn has the length of one degree of latitude at the place for which the isobar spacing is measured). This table gives values of V_g in knots as a function of Δn with auxiliary columns giving equivalents of Δn in kilometers, statute miles, and nautical miles. If the latter are measured by a map scale true at some other latitude, the value should be corrected to the lattitude at which the measurements are taken (see Table 3.3–6).

Since the geostrophic wind is inversely proportional to the isobar spacing and the density ρ, and directly proportional to the isobaric interval (Δpmbar), values of V_g for 1/10 of the indicated spacing may be found by multiplying the tabular values by 10, etc., and for isobaric intervals other than 3 mbar by multiplying the tabular values by $\Delta p/3$. The density ρ_0 of 1 kg m^{-3} (0.001 g cm^{-3}) used in the computations is the average density at about 2 km above sea level; for V_g at other levels multiply the tabular values by ρ_0/ρ (if the density is expressed in kg m^{-3}, simply divide the tabular value by the density).

Isobar spacing				Latitude							
Degrees of Latitude	Kilometers	Statute miles	Nautical miles	10° knots	15° knots	20° knots	25° knots	30° knots	35° knots	40° knots	45° knots
1.0	111	69	60	206.9	138.8	105.1	85.0	71.9	62.7	55.9	50.8
1.1	122	76	66	188.1	126.2	95.5	77.3	65.3	57.0	50.8	46.2
1.2	133	83	72	172.5	115.7	87.6	70.9	59.9	52.2	46.6	42.3
1.3	145	90	78	159.2	106.8	80.8	65.4	55.3	48.2	43.0	39.1
1.4	156	97	84	147.8	99.2	75.0	60.7	51.3	44.8	39.9	36.3
1.5	167	104	90	138.0	92.6	70.0	56.7	47.9	41.8	37.3	33.9
1.6	178	111	96	129.3	86.8	65.7	53.1	44.9	39.2	34.9	31.8
1.7	189	117	102	121.7	81.7	61.8	50.0	42.3	36.9	32.9	29.9
1.8	200	124	108	115.0	77.1	58.4	47.2	39.9	34.8	31.1	28.2
1.9	211	131	114	108.9	73.1	55.3	44.8	37.8	33.0	29.4	26.7
2.0	222	138	120	103.5	69.4	52.5	42.5	35.9	31.3	28.0	25.4
2.1	234	145	126	98.5	66.1	50.0	40.5	34.2	29.8	26.6	24.2
2.2	245	152	132	94.1	63.1	47.8	38.7	32.7	28.5	25.4	23.1
2.3	256	159	138	90.0	60.4	45.7	37.0	31.2	27.2	24.3	22.1
2.4	267	166	144	86.2	57.9	43.8	35.4	29.9	26.1	23.3	21.2
2.5	278	173	150	82.8	55.5	42.0	34.0	28.7	25.1	22.4	20.3
2.6	289	180	156	79.6	53.4	40.4	32.7	27.6	24.1	21.5	19.5
2.7	300	187	162	76.6	51.4	38.9	31.5	26.6	23.2	20.7	18.8
2.8	311	193	168	73.9	49.6	37.5	30.4	25.7	22.4	20.0	18.1
2.9	322	200	174	71.4	47.9	36.2	29.3	24.8	21.6	19.3	17.5
3.0	334	207	180	69.0	46.3	35.0	28.3	24.0	20.9	18.6	16.9
3.2	356	221	192	64.7	43.4	32.8	26.6	22.5	19.6	17.5	15.9
3.4	378	235	204	60.9	40.8	30.9	25.0	21.1	18.4	16.4	14.9
3.6	400	249	216	57.5	38.6	29.2	23.6	20.0	17.4	15.5	14.1
3.8	423	263	228	54.5	36.5	27.6	22.4	18.9	16.5	14.7	13.4
4.0	445	276	240	51.7	34.7	26.3	21.3	18.0	15.7	14.0	12.7
4.2	467	290	252	49.3	33.1	25.0	20.2	17.1	14.9	13.3	12.1
4.4	489	304	264	47.0	31.6	23.9	19.3	16.3	14.2	12.7	11.5
4.6	511	318	276	45.0	30.2	22.8	18.5	15.6	13.6	12.2	11.0
4.8	534	332	288	43.1	28.9	21.9	17.7	15.0	13.1	11.6	10.6
5.0	556	345	300	41.4	27.8	21.0	17.0	14.4	12.5	11.2	10.2
5.5	612	380	330	37.6	25.2	19.1	15.5	13.1	11.4	10.2	9.2
6.0	667	415	360	34.5	23.1	17.5	14.2	12.0	10.4	9.3	8.5
6.5	723	449	390	31.8	21.4	16.2	13.1	11.1	9.6	8.6	7.8
7.0	778	484	420	29.6	19.8	15.0	12.1	10.3	9.0	8.0	7.3
8.0	890	553	480	25.9	17.4	13.1	10.6	9.0	7.8	7.0	6.4
9.0	1001	622	540	23.0	15.4	11.7	9.4	8.0	7.0	6.2	5.6
10.0	1112	691	600	20.7	13.9	10.5	8.5	7.2	6.3	5.6	5.1

Table 3.1–2 (*Continued*)
GEOSTROPHIC WIND, CONSTANT LEVEL SURFACE

Isobar spacing				Latitude							
Degrees of Latitude	Kilometers	Statute miles	Nautical miles	50° knots	55° knots	60° knots	65° knots	70° knots	75° knots	80° knots	85° knots
1.0	111	69	60	46.9	43.9	41.5	39.7	38.2	37.2	36.5	36.1
1.1	122	76	66	42.6	39.9	37.7	36.0	34.8	33.8	33.2	32.8
1.2	133	83	72	39.1	36.6	34.6	33.0	31.9	31.0	30.4	30.1
1.3	145	90	78	36.1	33.7	31.9	30.5	29.4	28.6	28.1	27.7
1.4	156	97	84	33.5	31.3	29.6	28.3	27.3	26.6	26.1	25.8
1.5	167	104	90	31.3	29.2	27.7	26.4	25.5	24.8	24.3	24.0
1.6	178	111	96	29.3	27.4	25.9	24.8	23.9	23.3	22.8	22.5
1.7	189	117	102	27.6	25.8	24.4	23.3	22.5	21.9	21.5	21.2
1.8	200	124	108	26.1	24.4	23.1	22.0	21.2	20.7	20.3	20.0
1.9	211	131	114	24.7	23.1	21.8	20.9	20.1	19.6	19.2	19.0
2.0	222	138	120	23.5	21.9	20.7	19.8	19.1	18.6	18.2	18.0
2.1	234	145	126	22.3	20.9	19.8	18.9	18.2	17.7	17.4	17.2
2.2	245	152	132	21.3	19.9	18.9	18.0	17.4	16.9	16.6	16.4
2.3	256	159	138	20.4	19.1	18.0	17.2	16.6	16.2	15.9	15.7
2.4	267	166	144	19.5	18.3	17.3	16.5	15.9	15.5	15.2	15.0
2.5	278	173	150	18.8	17.5	16.6	15.9	15.3	14.9	14.6	14.4
2.6	289	180	156	18.0	16.9	16.0	15.3	14.7	14.3	14.0	13.9
2.7	300	187	162	17.4	16.2	15.4	14.7	14.2	13.8	13.5	13.4
2.8	311	193	168	16.8	15.7	14.8	14.2	13.7	13.3	13.0	12.9
2.9	322	200	174	16.2	15.1	14.3	13.7	13.2	12.8	12.6	12.4
3.0	334	207	180	15.6	14.6	13.8	13.2	12.7	12.4	12.2	12.0
3.2	356	221	192	14.7	13.7	13.0	12.4	12.0	11.6	11.4	11.3
3.4	378	235	204	13.8	12.9	12.2	11.7	11.2	10.9	10.7	10.6
3.6	400	249	216	13.0	12.2	11.5	11.0	10.6	10.3	10.1	10.0
3.8	423	263	228	12.3	11.5	10.9	10.4	10.1	9.8	9.6	9.5
4.0	445	276	240	11.7	11.0	10.4	9.9	9.6	9.3	9.1	9.0
4.2	467	290	252	11.2	10.4	9.9	9.4	9.1	8.9	8.7	8.6
4.4	489	304	264	10.7	10.0	9.4	9.0	8.7	8.5	8.3	8.2
4.6	511	318	276	10.2	9.5	9.0	8.6	8.3	8.1	7.9	7.8
4.8	534	332	288	9.8	9.1	8.6	8.3	8.0	7.8	7.6	7.5
5.0	556	345	300	9.4	8.8	8.3	7.9	7.6	7.4	7.3	7.2
5.5	612	380	330	8.5	8.0	7.5	7.2	7.0	6.8	6.6	6.6
6.0	667	415	360	7.8	7.3	6.9	6.6	6.4	6.2	6.1	6.0
6.5	723	449	390	7.2	6.7	6.4	6.1	5.9	5.7	5.6	5.5
7.0	778	484	420	6.7	6.3	5.9	5.7	5.5	5.3	5.2	5.2
8.0	890	553	480	5.9	5.5	5.2	5.0	4.8	4.7	4.6	4.5
9.0	1001	622	540	5.2	4.9	4.6	4.4	4.2	4.1	4.1	4.0
10.0	1112	691	600	4.7	4.4	4.1	4.0	3.8	3.7	3.6	3.6

(From *Smithsonian Meteorological Tables,* 6th rev. ed., List, R.J., Ed., Smithsonian Institution, Washington, D.C., 1971.)

Table 3.1–3
CORIOLIS PARAMETER AND LATITUDINAL VARIATION

Latitude	$2\omega \sin \phi$ sec^{-1}	$\beta =$ $(2\omega \cos \phi)/R$ cm^{-1} sec^{-1}	Latitude	$2\omega \sin \phi$ sec^{-1}	$\beta =$ $(2\omega \cos \phi)/R$ cm^{-1} sec^{-1}
0°	0	2.289×10^{-13}	50°	1.1172×10^{-4}	1471×10^{-13}
5	0.1271×10^{-4}	2.280	55	1.1947	1.313
10	0.2533	2.254	60	1.2630	1.145
15	0.3775	2.211	65	1.3218	0.967
20	0.4988	2.151	70	1.3705	0.783
25	0.6164×10^{-4}	2.075×10^{-13}	75	1.4087×10^{-4}	0.593×10^{-13}
30	0.7292	1.982	80	1.4363	0.398
35	0.8365	1.875	85	1.4529	0.199
40	0.9375	1.754	90	1.4584	0
45	1.0313	1.619			

$2\omega \sin \phi$ = Coriolis parameter.
ϕ = latitude.
ω = angular velocity of the earth = 7.292116×10^{-5} rad sec^{-1}.
R = radius of the earth = 6.371229×10^{6} m (mean radius of the International ellipsoid).
β = $(2\omega \cos \phi)/R$ = rate at which the Coriolis parameter increases northward.

Note: $2\omega \cos \phi = 2\omega \sin (90 - \phi)$.

REFERENCE

1. **Rossby, C.-G.,** *J. Mar. Res.*, 2, 38, 1939.

(From *Smithsonian Meteorological Tables,* 6th rev. ed., List, R. J., Ed., Smithsonian Institution, Washington, D.C., 1971.)

Table 3.1–4
ROSSBY'S LONG-WAVE FORMULA

Rossby[1] has shown that in the case of sinusoidal perturbations on a zonal current in an ideal, frictionless, homogeneous, and incompressible atmosphere in horizontal motion, the relation between the velocity of the undisturbed zonal current *U* and the phase velocity of the perturbation *c* is given by:

$$U - c = \frac{\beta L^2}{4\pi^2}$$

where β is the rate of which the Coriolis parameter increases northward (assumed to be constant with latitude for a given zonal current) and *L* is the wave length of the perturbation. *L* is most conveniently measured in terms of degrees of longitude at the latitude in question.[a] Similarly the resulting $\beta L^2/(4\pi^2)$ is measured in terms of degrees of longitude/ 24 hrs; a supplemental column also gives the result in m/sec.

Wave length – degrees of longitude

Latitude	10 °long/24 hr	10 m/sec^{-1}	15 °long/24 hr	15 m/sec^{-1}	20 °long/24 hr	20 m/sec^{-1}	25 °long/24 hr	25 m/sec^{-1}	30 °long/24 hr	30 m/sec^{-1}	35 °long/24 hr	35 m/sec^{-1}
10°	0.5	0.7	1.2	1.5	2.2	2.7	3.4	4.3	4.9	6.2	6.6	8.4
20	0.5	0.6	1.1	1.3	2.0	2.4	3.1	3.7	4.4	5.4	6.0	7.3
30	0.4	0.5	0.9	1.1	1.7	1.9	2.6	2.9	3.8	4.2	5.1	5.7
40	0.3	0.3	0.7	0.7	1.3	1.3	2.0	2.0	3.0	2.9	4.0	4.0
50	0.2	0.2	0.5	0.4	0.9	0.8	1.4	1.2	2.1	1.7	2.8	2.3
60	0.1	0.1	0.3	0.2	0.6	0.4	0.9	0.6	1.3	0.8	1.7	1.1
70	0.1	0.0	0.1	0.1	0.3	0.1	0.4	0.2	0.6	0.3	0.8	0.4
80	0.0	0.0	0.0	0.0	0.1	0.0	0.1	0.0	0.2	0.0	0.2	0.0

Latitude	40 °long/24 hr	40 m/sec^{-1}	45 °long/24 hr	45 m/sec^{-1}	50 °long/24 hr	50 m/sec^{-1}	55 °long/24 hr	55 m/sec^{-1}	60 °long/24 hr	60 m/sec^{-1}	65 °long/24 hr	65 m/sec^{-1}
10°	8.7	11.0	11.0	13.9	13.5	17.2	16.4	20.8	19.5	24.7	22.9	29.0
20	7.9	9.5	10.0	12.1	12.3	14.9	14.9	18.0	17.7	21.5	20.8	25.2
30	6.7	7.5	8.5	9.5	10.5	11.7	12.7	14.1	15.1	16.8	17.7	19.7
40	5.2	5.2	6.6	6.6	8.2	8.1	9.9	9.8	11.8	11.7	13.8	13.7
50	3.7	3.1	4.7	3.9	5.8	4.8	7.0	5.8	8.3	6.9	9.8	8.1
60	2.2	1.4	2.8	1.8	3.5	2.3	4.2	2.7	5.0	3.3	5.9	3.8
70	1.0	0.5	1.3	0.6	1.6	0.7	2.0	0.9	2.4	1.0	2.8	1.2
80	0.3	0.1	0.3	0.1	0.4	0.1	0.5	0.1	0.6	0.1	0.7	0.2

Latitude	70 °long/24 hr	70 m/sec^{-1}	75 °long/24 hr	75 m/sec^{-1}	80 °long/24 hr	80 m/sec^{-1}	85 °long/24 hr	85 m/sec^{-1}	90 °long/24 hr	90 m/sec^{-1}	100 °long/24 hr	100 m/sec^{-1}
10°	26.5	33.6	30.4	38.6	34.6	43.9	39.1	49.6	43.8	55.6	54.1	68.6
20	24.1	29.2	27.7	33.6	31.5	38.2	35.6	43.1	39.9	48.3	49.3	59.7
30	20.5	22.9	23.5	26.3	26.8	39.9	30.2	33.8	33.9	37.9	41.9	46.7
40	16.1	15.9	18.4	18.2	21.0	20.7	23.7	23.4	26.6	26.2	32.8	32.4
50	11.3	9.4	13.0	10.8	14.9	12.3	16.7	13.8	18.7	15.5	23.1	19.2
60	6.9	4.4	7.9	5.1	8.9	5.8	10.1	6.5	11.3	7.3	14.0	9.0
70	3.2	1.4	3.7	1.6	4.2	1.9	4.7	2.1	5.3	2.3	6.6	2.9
80	0.8	0.2	1.0	0.2	1.1	0.2	1.2	0.3	1.4	0.3	1.7	0.4

[a] The length of a degree of longitude at various latitudes is given in table 3.3–4.

Table 3.1–4 (*Continued*)
ROSSBY'S LONG-WAVE FORMULA

	110		120		130		140		160		180	
	°long/24 hr	m/sec^{-1}	°long/24 hr	m/sec^{-1}	°long/24 hr	m/sec^{-1}	°long/24 hr	m/sec^{-1}	°long/24 hr	m/sec^{-1}	°long/24 hr	m/sec^{-1}
10°	65.4	83.0	77.9	98.8	91.4	116.0	106.0	134.5	138.5	175.7	175.3	222.4
20	59.6	72.2	70.9	85.9	83.2	100.8	96.5	116.9	126.1	152.7	159.6	193.3
30	50.7	56.6	60.3	67.3	70.7	79.0	82.0	91.6	107.2	119.6	135.6	151.4
40	39.7	39.2	47.2	46.7	55.4	54.8	64.2	63.5	83.9	83.0	106.2	105.0
50	27.9	23.2	33.2	27.6	39.0	32.4	45.2	37.5	59.1	49.0	74.8	62.1
60	16.9	10.9	20.1	13.0	23.6	15.3	27.4	17.7	35.8	23.1	45.3	29.3
70	7.9	3.5	9.4	4.2	11.1	4.9	12.8	5.7	16.8	7.4	21.2	9.4
80	2.0	0.5	2.4	0.5	2.9	0.6	3.3	0.7	4.3	1.0	5.5	1.2

(From *Smithsonian Meteorological Tables*, 6th rev. ed., List, R. J., Ed., Smithsonian Institution, Washington, D. C., 1971.)

REFERENCE

1. **Rossby, C.-G.,** *J. Mar. Res.*, 2, 38, 1939.

3.2 Radiation

Table 3.2–1
SPECTRAL DISTRIBUTION OF SOLAR RADIATION AT SEA LEVEL

Using Fowle's[1] data for scattering of solar radiation by water vapor and by air, Moon[2] calculated the spectral transmission factors at sea level with 20 mm of precipitable water vapor in the atmosphere. By comparing these with the mean values of observed transmission, he calculated a spectral transmission for dust.[a] He also evaluated the extraterrestrial solar radiation.

By combining the extraterrestrial solar radiation with the scattering by water vapor, air, and dust, and with the absorptions by water vapor and ozone, Moon calculated the solar radiation that reaches sea level for various optical air masses. The data were computed for a pressure of 1 atmosphere on the basis of arbitrary average values of water vapor, dust, and ozone content. These values are

water vapor, 20 mm precipitable water,
dust, 300 particles cm^{-3} near the ground,
ozone, 2.8 mm path length at N. T. P.

The results given here have been adjusted to a solar constant of 1.94 cal cm^{-3} $min.^{-1}$

Wave-length μ	Optical air mass 1	2	3	4	5
	cal cm^{-2} min^{-1}				
0.29–0.40	0.059	0.029	0.015	0.008	0.004
0.40–0.70	.616	.481	.379	.302	.240
0.70–1.1	.454	.393	.343	.301	.266
1.1 –1.5	.140	.103	.084	.071	.060
1.5 –1.9	.075	.066	.060	.056	.052
1.9 –∞	.019	.014	.011	.010	.009
Total	1.363	1.086	0.892	0.748	0.631

[a] This assumes that 20 mm of precipitable water vapor was representative of these observed transmissions, which may not have been the case. Any error so introduced would be small, however.

(From *Smithsonian Meteorological Tables,* 6th rev. ed., List, R. J., Ed., Smithsonian Institution, Washington, D.C., 1971.)

REFERENCES

1. **Fowle, F. E.,** *Smithsonian Misc. Coll.,* 69 (3), 1918.
2. **Moon, P.,** *J. Franklin Inst.,* 5, 583, 1940.

3.2–2
TOTAL SOLAR AND SKY RADIATION

Klein[1] gives equations that permit the evaluation of the total solar and sky radiation Q on a horizontal surface for a cloudless, dust-free atmosphere as a function of the atmospheric transmission obtained from Kimball's chart[2] and the solar zenith distance. Fritz[3] combined Klein's equations and constructed the chart given below. The isopleths give values of Q in cal cm^{-2} min^{-1} as a function of optical air mass m_p (abscissa) and precipitable water vapor w centimeters (ordinate), when the sun is at its mean distance from the earth. To correct for the sun's actual distance from the earth, divide the values by the square of the appropriate radius vector (table 3.3–9). For elevated stations, multiply the values given in the chart by $p/1013$, where p is the barometric pressure in millibars at the place of observation. Dashed lines indicate extrapolated values.

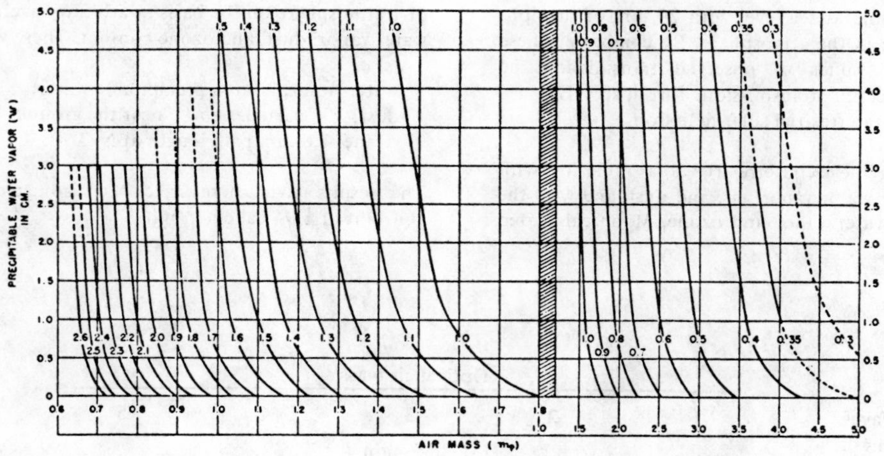

(From *Smithsonian Meteorological Tables,* 6th rev. ed., List, R. J., Ed., Smithsonian Institution, Washington, D.C., 1971.)

REFERENCES

1. **Klein, W. H.,** *J. Meteor.,* 5, 119, 1948.
2. **Kimball, H. H.,** *Month. Weath. Rev.,* 55, 167, 1927; 56, 394, 1928; 58, 43, 1930.
3. **Fritz, S.,** *Heating and Ventilating,* 46, 69, 1949.

Table 3.2–3
SOLAR AND SKY RADIATION

Relation Between the Vertical Component of Direct Solar Radiation and Total Solar and Sky Radiation on a Horizontal Surface

By means of pyrheliometers, Kimball[1] measured the vertical component of direct solar radiation and also the total solar and sky radiation on a horizontal surface for cloudless skies.

	Sun's zenith distance									
	30.0°	48.3°	60.0°	66.5°	70.7°	73.6°	75.7°	77.4°	78.7°	79.8°
Ratio	0.84	0.84	0.80	0.78	0.76	0.72	0.69	0.67	0.65	0.63

(From *Smithsonian Meteorological Tables,* 6th rev. ed., List, R. J., Ed., Smithsonian Institution, Washington, D.C., 1971.)

REFERENCE

1. **Kimball, H. H.,** *Month Weath. Rev.,* 47, 769, 1919. (For variation with height see Klein, W. H., *J. Meteor.,* 5, 119, 1948.)

Table 3.2–4
REFLECTIVITY OF A WATER SURFACE

The reflectivity of a plane water surface for unpolarized light is a function of the angle of incidence of the light and the index of refraction of the water and may be computed from the reflection law of Fresnel

$$R = \frac{1}{2}\left[\frac{\sin^2(i-r)}{\sin^2(i+r)} + \frac{\tan^2(i-r)}{\tan^2(i+r)}\right]$$

where

R = reflectivity,
i = angle of incidence,
r = angle of refraction,

i and r are related to the index of refraction n of the water by $n = \sin i/\sin r$. Although the values given are valid only for a plane undisturbed water surface, Ångström[1] states: ". . . . it is evident that the observed reflection from disturbed water-surfaces only shows small deviations from the values which are to be expected from the Fresnel formula. . . . . Some investigations which I have carried out on artificially disturbed surfaces seem to indicate that the deviation from the Fresnel formula is positive for slight disturbances of the surface, but negative when the amplitude gets large compared with the wave-length of the water waves. The measurements give strong support to the view that in the average case in geophysical discussions we may base computations of the reflection, absorption, and emission power of water-surfaces on the validity of the Fresnel formula."

Values in this table are computed on the assumption that $n = 1.333$, the value of the index of refraction for pure water. The value for sea water is slightly larger, about 1.3398 for sea water of salinity 35°/₀₀, but the difference is negligible.

In considering direct solar radiation, the angle of incidence i = sun's zenith distance.

i	0°	10°	20°	30°	40°	50°	60°	70°	80°	85°	90°
$R(\%)$	2.0	2.0	2.1	2.1	2.5	3.4	6.0	13.4	34.8	58.4	100.0

(From *Smithsonian Meteorological Tables,* 6th rev. ed., List, R. J., Ed., Smithsonian Institution, Washington, D.C., 1971.)

REFERENCE

1. Ångström, A., *Geograf. Ann.*, 7, 323, 1925.

Table 3.2–5
ABSORPTION OF RADIATION BY PURE LIQUID WATER

The decrease in intensity of a parallel beam of radiation of wavelength λ (i.e., of a small wavelength interval in the neighborhood of λ) in the direction of the beam by passing through a slab of pure water of thickness x is expressed by

$$I_\lambda = I_{0\lambda} e^{-k_\lambda x}$$

where $I_{0\lambda}$ is the intensity of the beam entering the slab and $I\lambda$ the intensity after passing through the slab. $k\lambda$ is called the *absorption coefficient.* The term *absorption* refers here to the depletion of energy both by absorption and scattering.

There is disagreement among various investigators as to the values of $k\lambda$ for pure water. The values presented here are those summarized by Dietrich[1]

0.310 to 0.650,[2]
0.700 to 2.650,[3]

Dietrich also indicates the results of other investigators.

The temperature dependence of the absorption produces an increase of about 0.5% in $k\lambda$ for every 1°C rise in temperature in certain portions of the infrared near 0.73 μ, but over a large portion of the spectrum it is much smaller. The values ascribed to Collins have been interpolated by Dietrich for 18°C. He also notes that the effect on the absorption coefficient of the presence of dissolved salts in the concentrations found in sea water has been found to be negligible.

Wave-length	Absorption coefficient	Wave-length	Absorption coefficient	Wave-length	Absorption coefficient	Wave-length	Absorption coefficient
μ	cm^{-1}	μ	cm^{-1}	μ	cm^{-1}	μ	cm^{-1}
0.310	0.0084	0.650	0.0021	1.100	0.203	1.700	7.3
0.320	0.0058			1.1125	0.253	1.725	8.4
0.330	0.00461	0.700	0.0084	1.125	0.359	1.750	10.1
0.340	0.00382	0.7125	0.0128	1.1375	0.572	1.775	12
0.350	0.00333	0.725	0.0166	1.150	0.848		
0.360	0.00281	0.7375	0.0260	1.1625	1.070	1.800	17
0.370	0.00200	0.750	0.0272	1.175	1.198	1.825	27
0.380	0.00148	0.7625	0.0286	1.1875	1.226	1.850	41
0.390	0.00099	0.775	0.0277			1.875	57
		0.7875	0.0262	1.200	1.232		
0.400	0.00072			1.2125	1.232	1.900	73
0.410	0.00050	0.800	0.0240	1.225	1.210	1.925	91
0.420	0.00041	0.8125	0.0238	1.2375	1.173	1.950	106
0.430	0.00030	0.825	0.0271	1.250	1.153	1.975	102
0.440	0.00023	0.8375	0.0365	1.2625	1.133		
0.450	0.00018	0.850	0.0412	1.275	1.168	2.000	85
0.460	0.00015	0.8625	0.0449	1.2875	1.20	2.025	72
0.470	0.00015	0.875	0.0495			2.050	60
0.480	0.00015	0.8875	0.0546	1.300	1.50	2.075	48
0.490	0.00015			1.325	2.18		
		0.900	0.0655	1.350	3.86	2.100	39
0.500	0.00016	0.9125	0.0824	1.375	8.5	2.150	25
0.510	0.00017	0.925	0.111			2.200	21
0.520	0.00019	0.9375	0.182	1.400	16.0	2.250	21
0.530	0.00021	0.950	0.288	1.425	26.9	2.300	24
0.540	0.00024	0.9625	0.406	1.450	28.9	2.350	31
0.550	0.00027	0.975	0.454	1.475	24.5		
0.560	0.00030	0.9875	0.444			2.400	42
0.570	0.00038			1.500	19.4	2.450	60
0.580	0.00055	1.000	0.397	1.525	15.4	2.500	85
0.590	0.00085	1.0125	0.339	1.550	12.0	2.550	100
		1.025	0.275	1.575	9.4	2.600	100
0.600	0.00125	1.0375	0.217			2.650	121
0.610	0.00160	1.050	0.177	1.600	8.0		
0.620	0.00178	1.0625	0.154	1.625	7.5		
0.630	0.00181	1.075	0.153	1.650	7.2		
0.640	0.0020	1.0875	0.174	1.675	7.1		

(From *Smithsonian Meteorological Tables,* 6th rev. ed., List, R. J., Ed., Smithsonian Institution, Washington, D.C., 1971.)

REFERENCES

1. **Dietrich, G.,** *Ann. d. Hydrogr. u. Mar. Meteorol.,* 67, 411, 1939.
2. **Sawyer, W. R.,** *Contr. Canadian Biol. Fish.,* 7, 73, 1931.
3. **Collins, J. R.,** *Phys. Rev.,* 26, 277, 1925.

Table 3.2–6
ABSORPTION OF RADIATION BY SEA WATER

Utterback[1] has made observations of the *extinction coefficient* of typical oceanic waters, defined in the same manner as the absorption coefficient k of ozone as shown in Table 3.2–13. Sverdrup, Johnson, and Fleming[2] have summarized Utterback's observations as follows:

He has made numerous observations in the shallow waters near islands in the inner part of Juan de Fuca Strait and at four stations in the open oceanic waters off the coast of Washington, and these can be considered typical of coastal and oceanic water, respectively. Table 3.2–6 contains the absorption coefficients of pure water at the wavelengths used by Utterback, the minimum, average, and maximum average, and maximum coefficients observed in oceanic water, and the minimum, average, and maximum coefficients observed in coastal water. The minimum and maximum coefficients have all been computed from the four lowest and the four highest values in each group.

Type water	Wavelength[a] – μ						
	0.46	**0.48**	**0.515**	**0.53**	**0.565**	**0.60**	**0.66**
	cm^{-1}	cm^{-1}	cm^{-1}	cm^{-1}	cm^{-1}	cm^{-1}	cm^{-1}
Pure water (from Table 3.2–5)	.00015	.00015	.00018	.00021	.00033	.00125	.00280
Ocean water							
Lowest	.00038	.00026	.00035	.00038	.00074	.00199	
Avg	.00086	.00076	.00078	.00084	.00108	.00272	
Highest	.00160	.00154	.00143	.00140	.00167	.00333	
Coastal water							
Lowest	.00224	.00230	.00192	.00169		.00375	.00477
Avg	.00362	.00334	.00276	.00269		.00437	.00623
Highest	.00510	.00454	.00398	.00348		.00489	.00760

[a] It should be understood that the wavelength actually stands for a spectral band of finite width.

(From *Smithsonian Meteorological Tables,* 6th rev. ed., List, R. J., Ed., Smithsonian Institution, Washington, D.C., 1971.)

REFERENCES

1. **Utterback, C. L.,** *Cons. Perm. Int. Explor. Mer,* Rapp. et Proc.-Verb., 101 (4), 15, 1936.
2. **Sverdrup, H. U., Johnson, M. W., and Fleming, R. H.,** *The Oceans,* Prenctice-Hall, Inc., New York, 1942, p. 84.

Tables 3.2–7 to 3.2–12
HORIZONTAL VISIBILITY

General:

The following tables pertaining to horizontal visibility may be considered to be subdivided into three classes:

1. Tables for converting extinction coefficient[a] (σ) to transmissivity (T), and tables for converting transmissivity to extinction coefficient.

2. Tables giving extinction coefficient as a function of daytime visual range of black objects viewed against the horizon sky. [Angular dimensions of objects are assumed to be in range 0.5° to 5°. Data are presented for two possible values of threshold of luminance contrast, ϵ, viz, $\epsilon = 0.02$ and $\epsilon = 0.05$, corresponding to the respective visual ranges denoted by V_2 and V_5.]

3. Tables applicable to the visual range of point sources of light and permitting computation of any one of the four variable involved if the other three are known (see Equations 11 and 12).

Units:

The kilometer is the unit used here for distance (x, D, and R) and for visual range (V_2 and V_5); the unit of extinction coefficient (σ) is the reciprocal of the kilometer (km^{-1}); the unit of illuminance or flux-density (E) is the lumen kilometer^{-2}; and the unit of luminous intensity (I_0 for a point source) is the candle (candela). The transmissivity, T, is defined as the base of natural logarithms (e) raised to the power ($-\sigma$). T^x and T^D (that is, $e^{-\sigma x}$ and $e^{-\sigma D}$) must be dimensionless, hence the dimension of x and D must be reciprocal to that of σ.

Tables 3.2–7 and 3.2–8–Transmissivity as a Function of Extinction Coefficient, and Extinction Coefficient as a Function of Transmissivity

Assumptions and Computations

Assuming uniform conditions regarding scattering of available light toward the observer along the path of sight and attenuation of light emanating from the object under view by scattering and absorption of luminous flux through the action of the atmospheric aerosol, the capacity of the atmosphere for transmitting such flux may be expressed either in terms of the (generalized) *extinction coefficient*, σ, or of the *transmissivity*, T.

In defining these quantities, we consider a ray of light propagated along the x-axis in an atmosphere having uniform optical properties (homogeneous in composition, density, and concentration of suspensoids). Since the quantities represent the attenuation of luminous flux in the medium, they relate to the ratio of illumination on two imaginary surfaces placed normal to the x-axis and separated by unit distance. Thus let

E = illuminance (luminous flux incident/unit area of surface) at distance x from the chosen origin;

E_0 = illuminance at the origin $x = 0$. (This is generally taken immediately in front of the light source or object being viewed, on the observer's side.)

Then the extinction coefficient and transmissivity are related to these two quantities by the equations:

$$E = E_0 e^{-\sigma x} = E_0 T^x \tag{1}$$

Hence

$$T = e^{-\sigma} \tag{2}$$

$$\sigma = -\log_e T \tag{3}$$

Description

Table 3.2–7 gives values of T as a function of σ, in accord with Equation 2, and Table 3.2–9 gives values of σ as a function of T or of logarithms to the base 10 of T, whichever is most convenient, in accord with Equation 3.

Certain conventions have been adopted to conserve space. In Table 3.2–7, with regard to the range of σ from 0.00 to 10.0, the tabular values are to be appended to the quantities in the indicial column, which immediately follows the column of arguments headed "Extinction Coefficient."

The superscript associated with quantities in the indicial column indicates the total number of ciphers to be placed following the decimal point. If the tabular value is prefixed by an asterisk, the tabular value is to be appended to the quantity in the next lower line of the indicial column.

Examples:

σ	T
0.00	1.0000
0.01	0.9900
4.60	0.01005
4.61	0.009952
6.90	0.001008
7.00	0.0009119

In the lower portion of the second page of Table 3.2–7, giving T as a function of σ in the range from $\sigma = 1$ to 1000 km^{-1}, the value of T is found by multiplying the tabular value by the factor 10 raised to the power shown in parentheses.

[a] This entity is sometimes called the atmospheric attenuation coefficient and has been denoted as β by some authors.[3a, 3b]

Table 3.2–7 (Continued)

Examples:

σ	T
1	3.679×10^{-1}
3	4.979×10^{-2}
40	4.248×10^{-18}

Table 3.2–8 gives values of σ as a function of T or P where $T = 10^P$, ($P = \log_{10} T$).

Examples:

T	σ
2×10^{-4}	8.5172
0.75	0.2877
10^{-240}	552.620
10^{-5}	11.513

Tables 3.2–9 and 3.2–10–Extinction Coefficient as a Function of Visual Range of Black Objects of Standard Angular Dimensions Viewed Against the Horizon Sky in Daytime

Assumptions and Computations

According to Koschmieder[1] and others[2-5] under certain conditions, the apparent luminance (photometric brightness), B_r, of a black object at a distance R from the observer when viewed horizontally against the horizon sky is given by the equation

$$B_r = (1 - e^{-\sigma R}) B_b(A) \quad (4)$$

where

σ = extinction coefficient as previously defined;
$B_b(A)$ = luminance of the horizon background of the black object

The (A) is inserted to indicate that the luminance is a function of the azimuth referred to a vertical through the sun. It will, of course, be understood that the azimuth of the background is the same as that of the object.

Equation 4 is *not* reliable in any azimuth near that of the rising or setting sun.

Duntley[3] has derived a more general relationship that for achromatic objects and backgrounds expresses the fact that the difference of luminance between object and background attenuates exponentially with distance. Equation 5 gives this relationship written in a form representative for a horizontal line of sight in an atmosphere which is homogeneous in its lighting and composition (i.e., scattering, absorption, and attenuation coefficients are constant along the path of sight):

$$\frac{B_r - B_b(A)}{B_0 - B_{b0}(A)} = e^{-\sigma R} \quad (5)$$

where

B_r = apparent luminance of the object at range R;
B_0 = inherent luminance of the object (i.e., at zero range);
$B_b(A)$ = apparent luminance of the background of the object at range R;
$B_{b0}(A)$ = apparent luminance of the background of the object at zero range (i.e., at the location of the object);
R = distance between the object and the point of observation.

The last equation reduces to Equation 4 when one applies the condition for a black object $B_0 = 0$, and when $B_b(A) = B_{b0}(A)$. The latter relation is rigorously valid for a horizon background or for a background at infinity.

Middleton[2,5] has derived theoretical relationships applicable to the visual range of colored objects.

From Equation 4 one obtains

$$\frac{B_r - B_b(A)}{B_b(A)} = -e^{-\sigma R} \quad (6)$$

When the distance R is equal to the visual range of the object, the apparent contrast of luminance represented by the left-hand member of Equation 6 becomes equal to the negative of ϵ, where ϵ = threshold of luminance (brightness) contrast. (The negative sign is indicative of the condition that the object appears darker than the horizon.)

Thus if R becomes V, the visual range of a black object viewed against the horizon sky, the contrast of luminance is expressed by

$$\frac{B_r - B_b(A)}{B_b(A)} = -\epsilon = -e^{\sigma V} \quad (7)$$

From Equation 7

$$V = \frac{1}{\sigma} \log_e \frac{1}{+\epsilon} \quad (8)$$

Although Equation 8 was derived on the assumption that the object is black and is viewed against the horizon sky, the equation is also valid to a close degree of approximation for the case in which an intrinsically dark object is viewed against an intrinsically dark, terrestrial

3.2–7 (*Continued*)

background, *provided* that the background is at a distance at least twice as great as the visual range of the object.

The actual value of the threshold of luminance contrast, ϵ, in practice depends on a number of factors such as angular dimensions of object, degree of confidence of the observer that he has detected the object, and the pattern of luminance in the visual field surrounding the object. The value of ϵ is greater if the observer endeavors to recognize the object rather than merely to detect it with some definite degree of confidence. At low levels of illuminance, the adaptation of the observer's vision to the existing conditions also plays a role in determining ϵ.[6]

The value of ϵ may possibly range from about 0.006 for large objects and almost certain detection to a value of the order of 0.1 for small objects. Koschmieder[1] has used the value 0.02 for ϵ, apparently following Helmholtz, while another value sometimes used is 0.055, although we shall employ 0.05 in round numbers, as well as 0.02.

Let V_2 = visual range as defined by Equation 8 when ϵ = 0.002
and V_5 = visual range as defined by Equation 8 when ϵ = 0.05;

then since $\log_e 1/0.02 = 3.912$ and $\log_e 1/0.05 = 2.996$,

$$V_2 = \frac{3.912}{\sigma} \tag{9}$$

$$V_5 = \frac{2.996}{\sigma} \tag{10}$$

Description

Tables 3.2–9 and 3.2–10 give values of σ as functions of V_2 and V_5 in accord with Equations 9 and 10, respectively.

Note: These investigators used principally 4-ft² black boards as visibility marks at distances between 0.15 and 1.0 km, corresponding to angles subtended at the eye between 0.46° and 0.07°.

Tables 3.2–11 and 3.2–12
Visual Range of Point Sources of Light

Assumptions and Computations

Tables 3.2–11 and 3.2–12 based on Equation 11, below, relate to the visual range of light perceived, as a point source; that is, this equation is valid under the condition that the particles of the atmospheric aerosol are small, namely, of the sizes not exceeding those found in haze or thin fog.

Equation 11 must be used with reservation if the light is not far enough away from the observer to appear as a point source. When fog, cloud, or other light-scattering particles are present in the neighborhood of light sources, the particles will give rise to a diffuse luminance of the atmosphere. In general, this will affect the threshold of illuminance for detection of the lights.[7]

The basic equation, due to Allard, commonly used in regard to the visual range of point sources is

$$E = I_0 D^{-2} e^{-\sigma D} \tag{11}$$

where

D = visual range of point-source light,
I_0 = luminous intensity (candlepower) of light in direction of observer,
σ = atmospheric extinction coefficient,
E = threshold of illuminance (luminous flux incident/unit area just detectable) at the observer's eye, owing to luminous flux emitted by the light.

The appropriate value of E depends greatly on the degree of dark adaptation of the observer. Among the controlling factors are the time history of illuminance to which the observer's eyes have been exposed prior to the observation, the luminance of the horizon sky and background in the direction of observed lights, and the illuminance on a horizontal plane at the point of observation. Presence of other light sources in vicinity of the target light, intermittency of the light, and color of the light also effect the value of E[3].

As a guide regarding choice of the proper value of E, the following data are provided:

E (threshold illuminance) lumens/km²	Condition
1	Twilight, or appreciable light from artificial sources.
2×10^{-1}	Average illuminance on surface and background luminance during night at typical airport.
3×10^{-2} (about $10^{-1.5}$)	Observer's eyes fairly well dark-adapted. No light other than starlight. Foveal threshold against dark background.

To permit evaluation of Equation 11 by means of tables, it is rewritten

$$(\log_e I_0 - \log_e E) = (\sigma D + 2\log_e D) \tag{12}$$

3.2–7 (*Continued*)

Description

Table 3.2–11 gives values of the left-hand member ($\log_e I_0$ – $\log_e E$) as a function of E and I_0, while Table 3.2–12 gives values of the right-hand member, (σD + 2 $\log_e$D), as a function of σ and D.

These tables permit the computation of any one of the four variables as a function of the other three, provided that equation 12 is satisfied.

Examples:

Given: E = 2×10^{-1} lumens/km²
I_0 = 30 candles
D = 5.0 km

To find: σ.
From Table 3.2–11, we find

($\log_e I_0$ – $\log_e E$) = 5.011

Referring to Table 2.1–12, which gives (σD + 2 $\log_e D$), and running along the line for D = 5.0 km., we find by interpolation for σ that the tabular value 5.011 occurs when σ = 0.358, which is the required result.

Given: Assuming ϵ = 0.02, the daytime visual range of a black object viewed against the horizon sky is V_2 = 3.2 km.

To find: σ; then, to find D or a light observed at night for this value of σ under the condition that

E = 1 lumen /km² and I_0 = 100 candles.

From Table 3.2–9, we find σ = 1.222 km^{-1} corresponding to V_2 = 3.2 km.
From Table 3.2–11, ($\log_{eo}$ – $\log_e E$) = 4.605.
Referring to Table 3.2–12, with this tabular value 4.605 = (σD + 2 $\log_e D$) in accord with Equation 12, and σ = 1.222 km^{-1}, we find by double interpolation that D= 2.36 km.

(Prepared by L. P. Harrison, U.S. Weather Bureau. From *Smithsonian Meteorological Tables,* 6th rev. ed., List, R. J., Ed., Smithsonian Institution, Washington, D.C., 1971.)

REFERENCES

1. **Koschmieder, H.,** Theorie der horizonalen Sichtweite, *Beitr. Phys. freien Atmos.,* 12, 33, 1924; 12, 171, 1924.
2. **Middleton, W. E. K.,** *Visibility in meteorology,* 2nd ed., University of Toronto Press, Toronto, 1941.
3. (a) **Duntley, S. Q.,** The reduction of apparent contrast by the atmosphere, *J. Opt. Soc. Am.,* 38, 179, 1948.
   (b) **Duntley, S. Q.,** The visibility of distant objects, *J. Opt. Soc. Am.,* 38, 237, 1948.
4. (a) **Coleman, H. S., Morris, F. J., Rosenberger, H. E., and Walker, M. J.,** A photo-electric method of measuring the atmospheric attenuation of brightness contrast along a horizontal path for the visible region of the spectrum, *J. Opt. Soc. Am.,* 39, 515, 1949.
   (b) **Coleman, H. S. and Rosenberger, H. E.,** A comparison of photographic and photo-electric measurements of atmospheric attenuation of brightness contrast, *J. Opt. Soc. Am.,* 39, 990, 1949.
5. (a) **Middleton, W. E. K.,** On the colors of distant objects, and the visual range of colored objects, *Trans. Roy. Soc. Can., Sect. III,* 29, 127-154, 1935.
   (b) **Middleton, W. E. K.,** The colors of distant objects, *J. Opt. Soc. Am.,* 40, 373, 1950.
6. **Blackwell, H. R.,** Contrast thresholds of the human eye, *J. Opt. Soc. Am.,* 36, 624, 1946.
7. **Douglas, C. A. and Young, L. L.,** Development of a transmissometer for determining visual range, Civil Aeronautics Administration. Technical Development Report No. 47, February, 1945.

Table 3.2–7
TRANSMISSIVITY AS A FUNCTION OF EXTINCTION COEFFICIENT

Table A

$$T = e^{-\sigma}$$

Extinction coefficient σ km.$^{-1}$		.00	.01	.02	.03	.04	.05	.06	.07	.08	.09
0.0	1.	0000	*9900	*9802	*9704	*9608	*9512	*9418	*9324	*9231	*9139
0.1	0.	9048	8958	8869	8781	8694	8607	8521	8437	8353	8270
0.2	0.	8187	8106	8025	7945	7866	7788	7711	7634	7558	7483
0.3	0.	7408	7334	7261	7189	7118	7047	6977	6907	6839	6771
0.4	0.	6703	6636	6570	6505	6440	6376	6313	6250	6188	6126
0.5	0.	6065	6005	5945	5886	5827	5770	5712	5655	5599	5543
0.6	0.	5488	5434	5379	5326	5273	5220	5169	5117	5066	5016
0.7	0.	4966	4916	4868	4819	4771	4724	4677	4630	4584	4538
0.8	0.	4493	4449	4404	4360	4317	4274	4232	4190	4148	4107
0.9	0.	4066	4025	3985	3946	3906	3867	3829	3791	3753	3716
1.0	0.	3679	3642	3606	3570	3535	3499	3465	3430	3396	3362
1.1	0.	3329	3296	3263	3230	3198	3166	3135	3104	3073	3042
1.2	0.	3012	2982	2952	2923	2894	2865	2837	2808	2780	2753
1.3	0.	2725	2698	2671	2645	2618	2592	2567	2541	2516	2491
1.4	0.	2466	2441	2417	2393	2369	2346	2322	2299	2276	2254
1.5	0.	2231	2209	2187	2165	2144	2122	2101	2080	2060	2039
1.6	0.	2019	1999	1979	1959	1940	1920	1901	1882	1864	1845
1.7	0.	1827	1809	1791	1773	1755	1738	1720	1703	1686	1670
1.8	0.	1653	1637	1620	1604	1588	1572	1557	1541	1526	1511
1.9	0.	1496	1481	1466	1451	1437	1423	1409	1395	1381	1367
2.0	0.	1353	1340	1327	1313	1300	1287	1275	1262	1249	1237
2.1	0.	1225	1212	1200	1188	1177	1165	1153	1142	1130	1119
2.2	0.	1108	1097	1086	1075	1065	1054	1044	1033	1023	1013
2.3	0.	1003	*9926	*9827	*9730	*9633	*9537	*9442	*9348	*9255	*9163
2.4	0.0	9072	8982	8892	8804	8716	8629	8544	8458	8374	8291
2.5	0.0	8208	8127	8046	7966	7887	7808	7730	7654	7577	7502
2.6	0.0	7427	7354	7280	7208	7136	7065	6995	6925	6856	6788
2.7	0.0	6721	6654	6588	6522	6457	6393	6329	6266	6204	6142
2.8	0.0	6081	6020	5961	5901	5843	5784	5727	5670	5614	5558
2.9	0.0	5502	5448	5393	5340	5287	5234	5182	5130	5079	5029
3.0	0.0	4979	4929	4880	4832	4784	4736	4689	4642	4596	4550
3.1	0.0	4505	4460	4416	4372	4328	4285	4243	4200	4159	4117
3.2	0.0	4076	4036	3996	3956	3916	3877	3839	3801	3763	3725
3.3	0.0	3688	3652	3615	3579	3544	3508	3474	3439	3405	3371
3.4	0.0	3337	3304	3271	3239	3206	3175	3143	3112	3081	3050
3.5	0.0	3020	2990	2960	2930	2901	2872	2844	2816	2788	2760
3.6	0.0	2732	2705	2678	2652	2625	2599	2573	2548	2522	2497
3.7	0.0	2472	2448	2423	2399	2375	2352	2328	2305	2282	2260
3.8	0.0	2237	2215	2193	2171	2149	2128	2107	2086	2065	2044
3.9	0.0	2024	2004	1984	1964	1945	1926	1906	1887	1869	1850
4.0	0.0	1832	1813	1795	1777	1760	1742	1725	1708	1691	1674
4.1	0.0	1657	1641	1624	1608	1592	1576	1561	1545	1530	1515
4.2	0.0	1500	1485	1470	1455	1441	1426	1412	1398	1384	1370
4.3	0.0	1357	1343	1330	1317	1304	1291	1278	1265	1252	1240
4.4	0.0	1228	1216	1203	1191	1180	1168	1156	1145	1133	1122
4.5	0.0	1111	1100	1089	1078	1067	1057	1046	1036	1026	1015
4.6	0.0	1005	*9952	*9853	*9755	*9658	*9562	*9466	*9372	*9279	*9187
4.7	0.0^2	9095	9005	8915	8826	8739	8652	8566	8480	8396	8312
4.8	0.0^2	8230	8148	8067	7987	7907	7828	7750	7673	7597	7521
4.9	0.0^2	7447	7372	7299	7227	7155	7083	7013	6943	6874	6806
5.0	0.0^2	6738	6671	6605	6539	6474	6409	6346	6282	6220	6158
5.0	0.0^2	6738	6097	5517	4992	4517	4087	3698	3346	3028	2739
6.0	0.0^2	2479	2243	2029	1836	1662	1503	1360	1231	1114	1008
7.0	0.0^3	9119	8251	7466	6755	6113	5531	5005	4528	4097	3707
8.0	0.0^3	3355	3035	2747	2485	2249	2035	1841	1666	1507	1364
9.0	0.0^3	1234	1117	1010	*9142	*8272	*7485	*6773	*6128	*5545	*5017
10.0	0.0^4	4540									

(Prepared by L. P. Harrison, U.S. Weather Bureau. From *Smithsonian Meteorological Tables,* 6th rev. ed., List, R. J., Ed., Smithsonian Institution, Washington, D.C., 1971.)

Table 3.2–7
TRANSMISSIVITY AS A FUNCTION OF EXTINCTION COEFFICIENT

Table B

Extinction coefficient σ km.$^{-1}$		$e^{-\sigma}$	Extinction coefficient σ km.$^{-1}$		$e^{-\sigma}$	Extinction coefficient σ km.$^{-1}$		$e^{-\sigma}$
1	(− 1)	3.679	41	(−18)	1.563	81	(− 36)	6.640
2	(− 1)	1.353	42	(−19)	5.750	82	(− 36)	2.443
3	(− 2)	4.979	43	(−19)	2.115	83	(− 37)	8.986
4	(− 2)	1.832	44	(−20)	7.781	84	(− 37)	3.306
5	(− 3)	6.738	45	(−20)	2.863	85	(− 37)	1.216
6	(− 3)	2.479	46	(−20)	1.053	86	(− 38)	4.474
7	(− 4)	9.119	47	(−21)	3.874	87	(− 38)	1.646
8	(− 4)	3.355	48	(−21)	1.425	88	(− 39)	6.055
9	(− 4)	1.234	49	(−22)	5.243	89	(− 39)	2.227
10	(− 5)	4.540	50	(−22)	1.929	90	(− 40)	8.194
11	(− 5)	1.670	51	(−23)	7.095	91	(− 40)	3.014
12	(− 6)	6.144	52	(−23)	2.610	92	(− 40)	1.109
13	(− 6)	2.260	53	(−24)	9.603	93	(− 41)	4.080
14	(− 7)	8.315	54	(−24)	3.533	94	(− 41)	1.501
15	(− 7)	3.059	55	(−24)	1.300	95	(− 42)	5.521
16	(− 7)	1.125	56	(−25)	4.781	96	(− 42)	2.031
17	(− 8)	4.140	57	(−25)	1.759	97	(− 43)	7.472
18	(− 8)	1.523	58	(−26)	6.470	98	(− 43)	2.749
19	(− 9)	5.603	59	(−26)	2.380	99	(− 43)	1.011
20	(− 9)	2.061	60	(−27)	8.757	100	(− 44)	3.720
21	(−10)	7.583	61	(−27)	3.221			
22	(−10)	2.789	62	(−27)	1.185			
23	(−10)	1.026	63	(−28)	4.360			
24	(−11)	3.775	64	(−28)	1.604			
25	(−11)	1.389	65	(−29)	5.900			
26	(−12)	5.109	66	(−29)	2.171	100	(− 44)	3.720
27	(−12)	1.880	67	(−30)	7.985	200	(− 87)	1.384
28	(−13)	6.914	68	(−30)	2.937	300	(−131)	5.148
29	(−13)	2.544	69	(−30)	1.081	400	(−174)	1.915
30	(−14)	9.358	70	(−31)	3.975	500	(−218)	7.125
31	(−14)	3.442	71	(−31)	1.462	600	(−261)	2.650
32	(−14)	1.266	72	(−32)	5.380	700	(−305)	9.860
33	(−15)	4.659	73	(−32)	1.979	800	(−348)	3.668
34	(−15)	1.714	74	(−33)	7.281	900	(−391)	1.364
35	(−16)	6.305	75	(−33)	2.679	1000	(−435)	5.076
36	(−16)	2.320	76	(−34)	9.854			
37	(−17)	8.533	77	(−34)	3.625			
38	(−17)	3.139	78	(−34)	1.334			
39	(−17)	1.155	79	(−35)	4.906			
40	(−18)	4.248	80	(−35)	1.805			

Note: The numbers in parentheses indicate the power of 10 by which the tabulated values are to be multiplied.

Table 3.2–8
EXTINCTION COEFFICIENT AS A FUNCTION OF TRANSMISSIVITY

$$\sigma = -\log_e T = -\log_e 10^P$$

Transmissivity N / T	1	2	3	4	5	6	7	8	9
	km.$^{-1}$	km.$^{-1}$	km.$^{-1}$	km.$^{-1}$	km.$^{-1}$	km.$^{-1}$	km.$^{-1}$	km.$^{-1}$	km.$^{-1}$
N × 10^{-10}	23.0259	22.3327	21.9272	21.6396	21.4164	21.2341	21.0799	20.9464	20.8286
N × 10^{-9}	20.7233	20.0301	19.6247	19.3370	19.1138	18.9315	18.7774	18.6438	18.5260
N × 10^{-8}	18.4207	17.7275	17.3221	17.0344	16.8112	16.6289	16.4748	16.3412	16.2235
N × 10^{-7}	16.1181	15.4249	15.0195	14.7318	14.5087	14.3263	14.1722	14.0387	13.9209
N × 10^{-6}	13.8155	13.1224	12.7169	12.4292	12.2061	12.0238	11.8696	11.7361	11.6183
N × 10^{-5}	11.5129	10.8198	10.4143	10.1266	9.9035	9.7212	9.5670	9.4335	9.3157
N × 10^{-4}	9.2103	8.5172	8.1117	7.8241	7.6009	7.4186	7.2644	7.1309	7.0131
N × 10^{-3}	6.9078	6.2146	5.8091	5.5215	5.2983	5.1160	4.9618	4.8283	4.7105
N × 10^{-2}	4.6052	3.9120	3.5066	3.2189	2.9957	2.8134	2.6593	2.5257	2.4079
N × 10^{-1}	2.3026	1.6094	1.2040	0.9163	0.6931	0.5108	0.3567	0.2231	0.1054

Transmissivity T	.00	.01	.02	.03	.04	.05	.06	.07	.08	.09
	km.$^{-1}$	km.$^{-1}$	km.$^{-1}$	km.$^{-1}$	km.$^{-1}$	km.$^{-1}$	km.$^{-1}$	km.$^{-1}$	km.$^{-1}$	km.$^{-1}$
0.0	$+\infty$	4.6052	3.9120	3.5066	3.2189	2.9957	2.8134	2.6593	2.5257	2.4079
0.1	2.3026	2.2073	2.1203	2.0402	1.9661	1.8971	1.8326	1.7720	1.7148	1.6607
0.2	1.6094	1 5606	1.5141	1.4697	1.4271	1.3863	1.3471	1.3093	1.2730	1.2379
0.3	1.2040	1.1712	1.1394	1.1087	1.0788	1.0498	1.0217	0.9943	0.9676	0.9416
0.4	0.9163	0.8916	0.8675	0.8440	0.8210	0.7985	0.7765	0.7550	0.7340	0.7133
0.5	0.6931	0.6733	0.6539	0.6349	0.6162	0.5978	0.5798	0.5621	0.5447	0.5276
0.6	0.5108	0.4943	0.4780	0.4620	0.4463	0.4308	0.4155	0.4005	0.3857	0.3711
0.7	0.3567	0.3425	0.3285	0.3147	0.3011	0.2877	0.2744	0.2614	0.2485	0.2357
0.8	0.2231	0.2107	0.1985	0.1863	0.1744	0.1625	0.1508	0.1393	0.1278	0.1165
0.9	0.1054	0.0943	0.0834	0.0726	0.0619	0.0513	0.0408	0.0305	0.0202	0.0101
1.0	0.0000									

P	0	10	20	30	40	50	60	70	80	90
	km.$^{-1}$	km.$^{-1}$	km.$^{-1}$	km.$^{-1}$	km.$^{-1}$	km.$^{-1}$	km.$^{-1}$	km.$^{-1}$	km.$^{-1}$	km.$^{-1}$
−400	921.034	944.060	967.086	990.112						
−300	690.776	713.801	736.827	759.853	782.879	805.905	828.931	851.956	874.982	898.008
−200	460.517	483.543	506.569	529.595	552.620	575.646	598.672	621.698	644.724	667.750
−100	230.259	253.284	276.310	299.336	322.362	345.388	368.414	391.439	414.465	437.491

P	0	1	2	3	4	5	6	7	8	9
	km.$^{-1}$	km.$^{-1}$	km.$^{-1}$	km.$^{-1}$	km.$^{-1}$	km.$^{-1}$	km.$^{-1}$	km.$^{-1}$	km.$^{-1}$	km.$^{-1}$
−100	230.259	232.561	234.864	237.166	239.469	241.771	244.074	246.377	248.679	250.982
− 90	207.233	209.535	211.838	214.140	216.443	218.746	221.048	223.351	225.653	227.956
− 80	184.207	186.509	188.812	191.115	193.417	195.720	198.022	200.325	202.627	204.930
− 70	161.181	163.484	165.786	168.089	170.391	172.694	174.996	177.299	179.602	181.904
− 60	138.155	140.458	142.760	145.063	147.365	149.668	151.971	154.273	156.576	158.878
− 50	115.129	117.432	119.734	122.037	124.340	126.642	128.945	131.247	133.550	135.853
− 40	92.103	94.406	96.709	99.011	101.314	103.616	105.919	108.221	110.524	112.827
− 30	69.078	71.380	73.683	75.985	78.288	80.590	82.893	85.196	87.498	89.801
− 20	46.052	48.354	50.657	52.959	55.262	57.565	59.867	62.170	64.472	66.775
− 10	23.026	25.328	27.631	29.934	32.236	34.539	36.841	39.144	41.447	43.749
− 0	0.000	2.303	4.605	6.908	9.210	11.513	13.816	16.118	18.421	20.723

(Prepared by L. P. Harrison, U.S. Weather Bureau. From *Smithsonian Meteorological Tables*, 6th rev. ed., List, R. J., Ed., Smithsonian Institution, Washington, D.C., 1971.)

Table 3.2–9
EXTINCTION COEFFICIENT AS A FUNCTION OF VISUAL RANGE OF BLACK OBJECTS VIEWED AGAINST HORIZON SKY IN DAYTIME

Where Threshold of Luminance Contrast, ϵ, is 0.02

$$\sigma = \frac{3.912}{V_2}$$

Visual range V_2 km.	0.000 km.$^{-1}$	0.001 km.$^{-1}$	0.002 km.$^{-1}$	0.003 km.$^{-1}$	0.004 km.$^{-1}$	0.005 km.$^{-1}$	0.006 km.$^{-1}$	0.007 km.$^{-1}$	0.008 km.$^{-1}$	0.009 km.$^{-1}$
0.00	.	.	.	.	978.0	782.4	652.0	558.9	489.0	434.7
0.01	391.2	355.6	326.0	300.9	279.4	260.8	244.5	230.1	217.3	205.9
0.02	195.6	186.3	177.8	170.1	163.0	156.5	150.5	144.9	139.7	134.9
0.03	130.4	126.2	122.2	118.5	115.1	111.8	108.7	105.7	102.9	100.3
0.04	97.80	95.41	93.14	90.98	88.91	86.93	85.04	83.23	81.50	79.84
0.05	78.24	76.71	75.23	73.81	72.44	71.13	69.86	68.63	67.45	66.31
0.06	65.20	64.13	63.10	62.10	61.12	60.18	59.27	58.39	57.53	56.70
0.07	55.89	55.10	54.33	53.59	52.86	52.16	51.47	50.81	50.15	49.52
0.08	48.90	48.30	47.71	47.13	46.57	46.02	45.49	44.97	44.45	43.96
0.09	43.47	42.99	42.52	42.06	41.62	41.18	40.75	40.33	39.92	39.52
0.10	39.12	38.73	38.35	37.98	37.62	37.26	36.91	36.56	36.22	35.89
0.11	35.56	35.24	34.93	34.62	34.32	34.02	33.72	33.44	33.15	32.87
0.12	32.60	32.33	32.07	31.80	31.55	31.30	31.05	30.80	30.56	30.33
0.13	30.09	29.86	29.64	29.41	29.19	28.98	28.76	28.55	28.35	28.14
0.14	27.94	27.74	27.55	27.36	27.17	26.98	26.79	26.61	26.43	26.26
0.15	26.08	25.91	25.74	25.57	25.40	25.24	25.08	24.92	24.76	24.60
0.16	24.45	24.30	24.15	24.00	23.85	23.71	23.57	23.43	23.29	23.15
0.17	23.01	22.88	22.74	22.61	22.48	22.35	22.23	22.10	21.98	21.85
0.18	21.73	21.61	21.49	21.38	21.26	21.15	21.03	20.92	20.81	20.70
0.19	20.59	20.48	20.37	20.27	20.16	20.06	19.96	19.86	19.76	19.66
0.20	19.56	19.46	19.37	19.27	19.18	19.08	18.99	18.90	18.81	18.72
0.21	18.63	18.54	18.45	18.37	18.28	18.20	18.11	18.03	17.94	17.86
0.22	17.78	17.70	17.62	17.54	17.46	17.39	17.31	17.23	17.16	17.08
0.23	17.01	16.94	16.86	16.79	16.72	16.65	16.58	16.51	16.44	16.37
0.24	16.30	16.23	16.17	16.10	16.03	15.97	15.90	15.84	15.77	15.71
0.25	15.65	15.59	15.52	15.46	15.40	15.34	15.28	15.22	15.16	15.10
0.26	15.05	14.99	14.93	14.87	14.82	14.76	14.71	14.65	14.60	14.54
0.27	14.49	14.44	14.38	14.33	14.28	14.23	14.17	14.12	14.07	14.02
0.28	13.97	13.92	13.87	13.82	13.77	13.73	13.68	13.63	13.58	13.54
0.29	13.49	13.44	13.40	13.35	13.31	13.26	13.22	13.17	13.13	13.08
0.30	13.04	13.00	12.95	12.91	12.87	12.83	12.78	12.74	12.70	12.66
0.31	12.62	12.58	12.54	12.50	12.46	12.42	12.38	12.34	12.30	12.26
0.32	12.22	12.19	12.15	12.11	12.07	12.04	12.00	11.96	11.93	11.89
0.33	11.85	11.82	11.78	11.75	11.71	11.68	11.64	11.61	11.57	11.54
0.34	11.51	11.47	11.44	11.41	11.37	11.34	11.31	11.27	11.24	11.21
0.35	11.18	11.15	11.11	11.08	11.05	11.02	10.99	10.96	10.93	10.90
0.36	10.87	10.84	10.81	10.78	10.75	10.72	10.69	10.66	10.63	10.60
0.37	10.57	10.54	10.52	10.49	10.46	10.43	10.40	10.38	10.35	10.32
0.38	10.29	10.27	10.24	10.21	10.19	10.16	10.13	10.11	10.08	10.06
0.39	10.03	10.01	9.980	9.954	9.929	9.904	9.879	9.854	9.829	9.805

Visual range V_2 km.	0.00 km.$^{-1}$	0.01 km.$^{-1}$	0.02 km.$^{-1}$	0.03 km.$^{-1}$	0.04 km.$^{-1}$	0.05 km.$^{-1}$	0.06 km.$^{-1}$	0.07 km.$^{-1}$	0.08 km.$^{-1}$	0.09 km.$^{-1}$
0.40	9.780	9.541	9.314	9.098	8.891	8.693	8.504	8.323	8.150	7.984
0.50	7.824	7.671	7.523	7.381	7.244	7.113	6.986	6.863	6.745	6.631
0.60	6.520	6.413	6.310	6.210	6.112	6.018	5.927	5.839	5.753	5.670
0.70	5.589	5.510	5.433	5.359	5.286	5.216	5.147	5.081	5.015	4.952
0.80	4.890	4.830	4.771	4.713	4.657	4.602	4.549	4.497	4.445	4.396
0.90	4.347	4.299	4.252	4.206	4.162	4.118	4.075	4.033	3.992	3.952
1.00	3.912	3.873	3.835	3.798	3.762	3.726	3.691	3.656	3.622	3.589

(Prepared by L. P. Harrison, U.S. Weather Bureau. From *Smithsonian Meteorological Tables*, 6th rev. ed., List, R. J., Ed., Smithsonian Institution, Washington, D.C., 1971.)

Table 3.2–9 (*Continued*)
EXTINCTION COEFFICIENT AS A FUNCTION OF VISUAL RANGE OF BLACK OBJECTS VIEWED AGAINST HORIZON SKY IN DAYTIME

Visual range V_2 km.	.0 km.$^{-1}$	.1 km.$^{-1}$	.2 km.$^{-1}$	.3 km.$^{-1}$	.4 km.$^{-1}$	.5 km.$^{-1}$	.6 km.$^{-1}$	.7 km.$^{-1}$	.8 km.$^{-1}$	.9 km.$^{-1}$
1.10	3.556	3.524	3.493	3.462	3.432	3.402	3.372	3.344	3.315	3.287
1.20	3.260	3.233	3.207	3.180	3.155	3.130	3.105	3.080	3.056	3.033
1.30	3.009	2.986	2.964	2.941	2.919	2.898	2.876	2.855	2.835	2.814
1.40	2.794	2.774	2.755	2.736	2.717	2.698	2.679	2.661	2.643	2.626
1.50	2.608	2.591	2.574	2.557	2.540	2.524	2.508	2.492	2.476	2.460
1.60	2.445	2.430	2.415	2.400	2.385	2.371	2.357	2.343	2.329	2.315
1.70	2.301	2.288	2.274	2.261	2.248	2.235	2.223	2.210	2.198	2.185
1.80	2.173	2.161	2.149	2.138	2.126	2.115	2.103	2.092	2.081	2.070
1.90	2.059	2.048	2.037	2.027	2.016	2.006	1.996	1.986	1.976	1.966
2.00	1.956	1.946	1.937	1.927	1.918	1.908	1.899	1.890	1.881	1.872
2.10	1.863	1.854	1.845	1.837	1.828	1.820	1.811	1.803	1.794	1.786
2.20	1.778	1.770	1.762	1.754	1.746	1.739	1.731	1.723	1.716	1.708
2.30	1.701	1.694	1.686	1.679	1.672	1.665	1.658	1.651	1.644	1.637
2.40	1.630	1.623	1.617	1.610	1.603	1.597	1.590	1.584	1.577	1.571
2.50	1.565	1.559	1.552	1.546	1.540	1.534	1.528	1.522	1.516	1.510
2.60	1.505	1.499	1.493	1.487	1.482	1.476	1.471	1.465	1.460	1.454
2.70	1.449	1.444	1.438	1.433	1.428	1.423	1.417	1.412	1.407	1.402
2.80	1.397	1.392	1.387	1.382	1.377	1.373	1.368	1.363	1.358	1.354
2.90	1.349	1.344	1.340	1.335	1.331	1.326	1.322	1.317	1.313	1.308

Visual range V_2 km.	.0 km.$^{-1}$	.1 km.$^{-1}$	.2 km.$^{-1}$	.3 km.$^{-1}$	.4 km.$^{-1}$	.5 km.$^{-1}$	.6 km.$^{-1}$	.7 km.$^{-1}$	.8 km.$^{-1}$	.9 km.$^{-1}$
3.0	1.304	1.262	1.222	1.185	1.151	1.118	1.087	1.057	1.029	1.003
4.0	0.9780	0.9541	0.9314	0.9098	0.8891	0.8693	0.8504	0.8323	0.8150	0.7984
5.0	0.7824	0.7671	0.7523	0.7381	0.7244	0.7113	0.6986	0.6863	0.6745	0.6631
6.0	0.6520	0.6413	0.6310	0.6210	0.6112	0.6018	0.5927	0.5839	0.5753	0.5670
7.0	0.5589	0.5510	0.5433	0.5359	0.5286	0.5216	0.5147	0.5081	0.5015	0.4952
8.0	0.4890	0.4830	0.4771	0.4713	0.4657	0.4602	0.4549	0.4497	0.4445	0.4396
9.0	0.4347	0.4299	0.4252	0.4206	0.4162	0.4118	0.4075	0.4033	0.3992	0.3952
10.0	0.3912	0.3873	0.3835	0.3798	0.3762	0.3726	0.3691	0.3656	0.3622	0.3589

Visual range V_2 km.	0 km.$^{-1}$	1 km.$^{-1}$	2 km.$^{-1}$	3 km.$^{-1}$	4 km.$^{-1}$	5 km.$^{-1}$	6 km.$^{-1}$	7 km.$^{-1}$	8 km.$^{-1}$	9 km.$^{-1}$
10	.3912	.3556	.3260	.3009	.2794	.2608	.2445	.2301	.2173	.2059
20	.1956	.1863	.1778	.1701	.1630	.1565	.1505	.1449	.1397	.1349
30	.1304	.1262	.1222	.1185	.1151	.1118	.1087	.1057	.1029	.1003
40	.09780	.09541	.09314	.09098	.08891	.08693	.08504	.08323	.08150	.07984
50	.07824	.07671	.07523	.07381	.07244	.07113	.06986	.06863	.06745	.06631
60	.06520	.06413	.06310	.06210	.06112	.06018	.05927	.05839	.05753	.05670
70	.05589	.05510	.05433	.05359	.05286	.05216	.05147	.05081	.05015	.04952
80	.04890	.04830	.04771	.04713	.04657	.04602	.04549	.04497	.04445	.04396
90	.04347	.04299	.04252	.04206	.04162	.04118	.04075	.04033	.03992	.03952
100	.03912	.03873	.03835	.03798	.03762	0.3726	.03691	.03656	.03622	.03589
110	.03556	.03524	.03493	.03462	.03432	.03402	.03372	.03344	.03315	.03287
120	.03260	.03233	.03207	.03180	.03155	.03130	.03105	.03080	.03056	.03033
130	.03009	.02986	.02964	.02941	.02919	.02898	.C2876	.02855	.02835	.02814
140	.02794	.02774	.02755	.02736	.02717	.02698	.02679	.02661	.02643	.02626
150	.02608	.02591	.02574	.02557	.02540	.02524	.02508	.02492	.02476	.02460
160	.02445	.02430	.02415	.02400	.02385	.02371	.02357	.02343	.02329	.02315
170	.02301	.02288	.02274	.02261	.02248	.02235	.02223	.02210	.02198	.02185
180	.02173	.02161	.02149	.02138	.02126	.02115	.02103	.02092	.02081	.02070
190	.02059	.02048	.02037	.02027	.02016	.02006	.01996	.01986	.01976	.01966
200	.01956	.01946	.01937	.01927	.01918	.01908	.01899	.01890	.01881	.01872
210	.01863	.01854	.01845	.01837	.01828	.01820	.01811	.01803	.01794	.01786
220	.01778	.01770	.01762	.01754	.01746	.01739	.01731	.01723	.01716	.01708
230	.01701	.01694	.01686	.01679	.01672	.01665	.01658	.01651	.01644	.01637
240	.01630	.01623	.01617	.01610	.01603	.01597	.01590	.01584	.01577	.01571
250	.01565	.01559	.01552	.01546	.01540	.01534	.01528	.01522	.01516	.01510

Table 3.2–10
EXTINCTION COEFFICIENT AS A FUNCTION OF VISUAL RANGE OF BLACK OBJECTS VIEWED AGAINST HORIZON SKY IN DAYTIME

Where Threshold of Luminance Contrast ϵ, is 0.05

$$\sigma = \frac{2.996}{V_5}$$

Visual range V_5 km.	0.000 km.$^{-1}$	0.001 km.$^{-1}$	0.002 km.$^{-1}$	0.003 km.$^{-1}$	0.004 km.$^{-1}$	0.005 km.$^{-1}$	0.006 km.$^{-1}$	0.007 km.$^{-1}$	0.008 km.$^{-1}$	0.009 km.$^{-1}$
0.00				998.7	749.0	599.2	499.3	428.0	374.5	332.9
0.01	299.6	272.4	249.7	230.5	214.0	199.7	187.3	176.2	166.4	157.7
0.02	149.8	142.7	136.2	130.3	124.8	119.8	115.2	111.0	107.0	103.3
0.03	99.87	96.65	93.63	90.79	88.12	85.60	83.22	80.97	78.84	76.82
0.04	74.90	73.07	71.33	69.67	68.09	66.58	65.13	63.74	62.42	61.14
0.05	59.92	58.75	57.62	56.53	55.48	54.47	53.50	52.56	51.66	50.78
0.06	49.93	49.11	48.32	47.56	46.81	46.09	45.39	44.72	44.06	43.42
0.07	42.80	42.20	41.61	41.04	40.49	39.95	39.42	38.91	38.41	37.92
0.08	37.45	36.99	36.54	36.10	35.67	35.25	34.84	34.44	34.05	33.66
0.09	33.29	32.92	32.57	32.22	31.87	31.54	31.21	30.89	30.57	30.26
0.10	29.96	29.66	29.37	29.09	28.81	28.53	28.26	28.00	27.74	27.49
0.11	27.24	26.99	26.75	26.51	26.28	26.05	25.83	25.61	25.39	25.18
0.12	24.97	24.76	24.56	24.36	24.16	23.97	23.78	23.59	23.41	23.22
0.13	23.05	22.87	22.70	22.53	22.36	22.19	22.03	21.87	21.71	21.55
0.14	21.40	21.25	21.10	20.95	20.81	20.66	20.52	20.38	20.24	20.11
0.15	19.97	19.84	19.71	19.58	19.45	19.33	19.21	19.08	18.96	18.84
0.16	18.73	18.61	18.49	18.38	18.27	18.16	18.05	17.94	17.83	17.73
0.17	17.62	17.52	17.42	17.32	17.22	17.12	17.02	16.93	16.83	16.74
0.18	16.64	16.55	16.46	16.37	16.28	16.19	16.11	16.02	15.94	15.85
0.19	15.77	15.69	15.60	15.52	15.44	15.36	15.29	15.21	15.13	15.06
0.20	14.98	14.91	14.83	14.76	14.69	14.61	14.54	14.47	14.40	14.33
0.21	14.27	14.20	14.13	14.07	14.00	13.93	13.87	13.81	13.74	13.68
0.22	13.62	13.56	13.50	13.43	13.38	13.32	13.26	13.20	13.14	13.08
0.23	13.03	12.97	12.91	12.86	12.80	12.75	12.69	12.64	12.59	12.54
0.24	12.48	12.43	12.38	12.33	12.28	12.23	12.18	12.13	12.08	12.03
0.25	11.98	11.94	11.89	11.84	11.80	11.75	11.70	11.66	11.61	11.57
0.26	11.52	11.48	11.44	11.39	11.35	11.31	11.26	11.22	11.18	11.14
0.27	11.10	11.06	11.01	10.97	10.93	10.89	10.86	10.82	10.78	10.74
0.28	10.70	10.66	10.62	10.59	10.55	10.51	10.48	10.44	10.40	10.37
0.29	10.33	10.30	10.26	10.23	10.19	10.16	10.12	10.09	10.05	10.02
0.30	9.987	9.953	9.921	9.888	9.855	9.823	9.791	9.759	9.727	9.696
0.31	9.665	9.633	9.603	9.572	9.541	9.511	9.481	9.451	9.421	9.392
0.32	9.363	9.333	9.304	9.276	9.247	9.218	9.190	9.162	9.134	9.106
0.33	9.079	9.051	9.024	8.997	8.970	8.943	8.917	8.890	8.864	8.838
0.34	8.812	8.786	8.760	8.735	8.709	8.684	8.659	8.634	8.609	8.585
0.35	8.560	8.536	8.511	8.487	8.463	8.439	8.416	8.392	8.369	8.345
0.36	8.322	8.299	8.276	8.253	8.231	8.208	8.186	8.163	8.141	8.119
0.37	8.097	8.075	8.054	8.032	8.011	7.989	7.968	7.947	7.926	7.905
0.38	7.884	7.864	7.843	7.822	7.802	7.782	7.762	7.742	7.722	7.702
0.39	7.682	7.662	7.643	7.623	7.604	7.585	7.566	7.547	7.528	7.509

Visual range V_5 km.	0.00 km.$^{-1}$	0.01 km.$^{-1}$	0.02 km.$^{-1}$	0.03 km.$^{-1}$	0.04 km.$^{-1}$	0.05 km.$^{-1}$	0.06 km.$^{-1}$	0.07 km.$^{-1}$	0.08 km.$^{-1}$	0.09 km.$^{-1}$
0.40	7.490	7.307	7.133	6.967	6.809	6.658	6.513	6.374	6.242	6.114
0.50	5.992	5.875	5.762	5.653	5.548	5.447	5.350	5.256	5.166	5.078
0.60	4.993	4.911	4.832	4.756	4.681	4.609	4.539	4.472	4.406	4.342
0.70	4.280	4.220	4.161	4.104	4.049	3.995	3.942	3.891	3.841	3.792
0.80	3.745	3.699	3.654	3.610	3.567	3.525	3.484	3.444	3.405	3.366
0.90	3.329	3.292	3.257	3.222	3.187	3.154	3.121	3.089	3.057	3.026

(Prepared by L. P. Harrison, U.S. Weather Bureau. From *Smithsonian Meteorological Tables,* 6th rev. ed., List, R. J., Ed., Smithsonian Institution, Washington, D.C., 1971.)

Table 3.2–10 (*Continued*)
EXTINCTION COEFFICIENT AS A FUNCTION OF VISUAL RANGE OF BLACK OBJECTS VIEWED AGAINST HORIZON SKY IN DAYTIME

Visual range V_s km.	.0 km.$^{-1}$	.1 km.$^{-1}$	.2 km.$^{-1}$	.3 km.$^{-1}$	.4 km.$^{-1}$	.5 km.$^{-1}$	.6 km.$^{-1}$	.7 km.$^{-1}$	.8 km.$^{-1}$	.9 km.$^{-1}$
1.00	2.996	2.966	2.937	2.909	2.881	2.853	2.826	2.800	2.774	2.749
1.10	2.724	2.699	2.675	2.651	2.628	2.605	2.583	2.561	2.539	2.518
1.20	2.497	2.476	2.456	2.436	2.416	2.397	2.378	2.359	2.341	2.322
1.30	2.305	2.287	2.270	2.253	2.236	2.219	2.203	2.187	2.171	2.155
1.40	2.140	2.125	2.110	2.095	2.081	2.066	2.052	2.038	2.024	2.011
1.50	1.997	1.984	1.971	1.958	1.945	1.933	1.921	1.908	1.896	1.884
1.60	1.873	1.861	1.849	1.838	1.827	1.816	1.805	1.794	1.783	1.773
1.70	1.762	1.752	1.742	1.732	1.722	1.712	1.702	1.693	1.683	1.674
1.80	1.664	1.655	1.646	1.637	1.628	1.619	1.611	1.602	1.594	1.585
1.90	1.577	1.569	1.560	1.552	1.544	1.536	1.529	1.521	1.513	1.506
2.00	1.498	1.491	1.483	1.476	1.469	1.461	1.454	1.447	1.440	1.433
2.10	1.427	1.420	1.413	1.407	1.400	1.393	1.387	1.381	1.374	1.368
2.20	1.362	1.356	1.350	1.343	1.338	1.332	1.326	1.320	1.314	1.308
2.30	1.303	1.297	1.291	1.286	1.280	1.275	1.269	1.264	1.259	1.254
2.40	1.248	1.243	1.238	1.233	1.228	1.223	1.218	1.213	1.208	1.203
2.50	1.198	1.194	1.189	1.184	1.180	1.175	1.170	1.166	1.161	1.157
2.60	1.152	1.148	1.144	1.139	1.135	1.131	1.126	1.122	1.118	1.114
2.70	1.110	1.106	1.101	1.097	1.093	1.089	1.086	1.082	1.078	1.074
2.80	1.070	1.066	1.062	1.059	1.055	1.051	1.048	1.044	1.040	1.037
2.90	1.033	1.030	1.026	1.023	1.019	1.016	1.012	1.009	1.005	1.002

Visual range V_s km.	.0 km.$^{-1}$	.1 km.$^{-1}$	.2 km.$^{-1}$	.3 km.$^{-1}$	.4 km.$^{-1}$	.5 km.$^{-1}$	.6 km.$^{-1}$	.7 km.$^{-1}$	.8 km.$^{-1}$	.9 km.$^{-1}$
3.0	.9987	.9665	.9363	.9079	.8812	.8560	.8322	.8097	.7884	.7682
4.0	.7490	.7307	.7133	.6967	.6809	.6658	.6513	.6374	.6242	.6114
5.0	.5992	.5875	.5762	.5653	.5548	.5447	.5350	.5256	.5166	.5078
6.0	.4994	.4911	.4832	.4756	.4681	.4609	.4539	.4472	.4406	.4342
7.0	.4280	.4220	.4161	.4104	.4049	.3995	.3942	.3891	.3841	.3792
8.0	.3745	.3699	.3654	.3610	.3567	.3525	.3484	.3444	.3405	.3366
9.0	.3329	.3292	.3257	.3222	.3187	.3154	.3121	.3089	.3057	.3026
10.0	.2996	.2966	.2937	.2909	.2881	.2853	.2826	.2800	.2774	.2749

Visual range V_s km.	0 km.$^{-1}$	1 km.$^{-1}$	2 km.$^{-1}$	3 km.$^{-1}$	4 km.$^{-1}$	5 km.$^{-1}$	6 km.$^{-1}$	7 km.$^{-1}$	8 km.$^{-1}$	9 km.$^{-1}$
10	.2996	.2724	.2497	.2305	.2140	.1997	.1873	.1762	.1664	.1577
20	.1498	.1427	.1362	.1303	.1248	.1198	.1152	.1110	.1070	.1033
30	.09987	.09665	.09363	.09079	.08812	.08560	.08322	.08097	.07884	.07682
40	.07490	.07307	.07133	.06967	.06809	.06658	.06513	.06374	.06242	.06114
50	.05992	.05875	.05762	.05653	.05548	.05447	.05350	.05256	.05166	.05078
60	.04993	.04911	.04832	.04756	.04681	.04609	.04539	.04472	.04406	.04342
70	.04280	.04220	.04161	.04104	.04049	.03995	.03942	.03891	.03841	.03792
80	.03745	.03699	.03654	.03610	.03567	.03525	.03484	.03444	.03405	.03366
90	.03329	.03292	.03257	.03222	.03187	.03154	.03121	.03089	.03057	.03026
100	.02996	.02966	.02937	.02909	.02881	.02853	.02826	.02800	.02774	.02749
110	.02724	.02699	.02675	.02651	.02628	.02605	.02583	.02561	.02539	.02518
120	.02497	.02476	.02456	.02436	.02416	.02397	.02378	.02359	.02341	.02322
130	.02305	.02287	.02270	.02253	.02236	.02219	.02203	.02187	.02171	.02155
140	.02140	.02125	.02110	.02095	.02081	.02066	.02052	.02038	.02024	.02011
150	.01997	.01984	.01971	.01958	.01945	.01933	.01921	.01908	.01896	.01884
160	.01873	.01861	.01849	.01838	.01827	.01816	.01805	.01794	.01783	.01773
170	.01762	.01752	.01742	.01732	.01722	.01712	.01702	.01693	.01683	.01674
180	.01664	.01655	.01646	.01637	.01628	.01619	.01611	.01602	.01594	.01585
190	.01577	.01569	.01560	.01552	.01544	.01536	.01529	.01521	.01513	.01506
200	.01498	.01491	.01483	.01476	.01469	.01461	.01454	.01447	.01440	.01433
210	.01427	.01420	.01413	.01407	.01400	.01393	.01387	.01381	.01374	.01368
220	.01362	.01356	.01350	.01343	.01338	.01332	.01326	.01320	.01314	.01308
230	.01303	.01297	.01291	.01286	.01280	.01275	.01269	.01264	.01259	.01254
240	.01248	.01243	.01238	.01233	.01228	.01223	.01218	.01213	.01208	.01203
250	.01198	.01194	.01189	.01184	.01180	.01175	.01170	.01166	.01161	.01157

Table 3.2–11
VISUAL RANGE OF POINT SOURCES OF LIGHT

Function ($\log_e I_0$ - $\log_e E$)

Luminous intensity I_0 candles (candela)	Threshold illuminance (flux-density), E, lumens km.$^{-2}$								
	1×10^{-3}	2×10^{-3}	3×10^{-3}	4×10^{-3}	5×10^{-3}	6×10^{-3}	7×10^{-3}	8×10^{-3}	9×10^{-3}
5×10^{-3}	1.609	0.916	0.511	0.223	0.000	−0.182	−0.336	−0.470	−0.588
10^{-2}	2.303	1.609	1.204	0.916	0.693	0.511	0.357	0.223	0.105
5×10^{-2}	3.912	3.219	2.813	2.526	2.303	2.120	1.966	1.833	1.715
10^{-1}	4.605	3.912	3.507	3.219	2.996	2.813	2.659	2.526	2.408
5×10^{-1}	6.215	5.521	5.116	4.828	4.605	4.423	4.269	4.135	4.017
1	6.908	6.215	5.809	5.521	5.298	5.116	4.962	4.828	4.711
2	7.601	6.908	6.502	6.215	5.991	5.809	5.655	5.521	5.404
3	8.006	7.313	6.908	6.620	6.397	6.215	6.060	5.927	5.809
4	8.294	7.601	7.195	6.908	6.685	6.502	6.348	6.215	6.097
5	8.517	7.824	7.419	7.131	6.908	6.725	6.571	6.438	6.320
6	8.700	8.006	7.601	7.313	7.090	6.908	6.754	6.620	6.502
7	8.854	8.161	7.755	7.467	7.244	7.062	6.908	6.774	6.656
8	8.987	8.294	7.889	7.601	7.378	7.195	7.041	6.908	6.790
9	9.105	8.412	8.006	7.719	7.496	7.313	7.159	7.026	6.908
10	9.210	8.517	8.112	7.824	7.601	7.419	7.264	7.131	7.013
15	9.616	8.923	8.517	8.230	8.006	7.824	7.670	7.536	7.419
20	9.903	9.210	8.805	8.517	8.294	8.112	7.958	7.824	7.706
25	10.127	9.433	9.028	8.740	8.517	8.335	8.181	8.047	7.929
30	10.309	9.616	9.210	8.923	8.700	8.517	8.363	8.230	8.112
35	10.463	9.770	9.364	9.077	8.854	8.671	8.517	8.384	8.266
40	10.597	9.903	9.498	9.210	8.987	8.805	8.651	8.517	8.399
45	10.714	10.021	9.616	9.328	9.105	8.923	8.769	8.635	8.517
50	10.820	10.127	9.721	9.433	9.210	9.028	8.874	8.740	8.623
55	10.915	10.222	9.816	9.529	9.306	9.123	8.969	8.836	8.718
60	11.002	10.309	9.903	9.616	9.393	9.210	9.056	8.923	8.805
65	11.082	10.389	9.984	9.696	9.473	9.290	9.136	9.003	8.885
70	11.156	10.463	10.058	9.770	9.547	9.364	9.210	9.077	8.959
75	11.225	10.532	10.127	9.839	9.616	9.433	9.279	9.146	9.028
80	11.290	10.597	10.191	9.903	9.680	9.498	9.344	9.210	9.093
85	11.350	10.657	10.252	9.964	9.741	9.559	9.404	9.271	9.153
90	11.408	10.714	10.309	10.021	9.798	9.616	9.462	9.328	9.210
95	11.462	10.768	10.363	10.075	9.852	9.670	9.516	9.382	9.264
100	11.513	10.820	10.414	10.127	9.903	9.721	9.567	9.433	9.316
200	12.206	11.513	11.107	10.820	10.597	10.414	10.260	10.127	10.009
300	12.612	11.918	11.513	11.225	11.002	10.820	10.666	10.532	10.414
400	12.899	12.206	11.801	11.513	11.290	11.107	10.953	10.820	10.702
500	13.122	12.429	12.024	11.736	11.513	11.331	11.176	11.043	10.925
600	13.305	12.612	12.206	11.918	11.695	11.513	11.359	11.225	11.107
700	13.459	12.766	12.360	12.073	11.849	11.667	11.513	11.379	11.262
800	13.592	12.899	12.494	12.206	11.983	11.801	11.646	11.513	11.395
900	13.710	13.017	12.612	12.324	12.101	11.918	11.764	11.631	11.513
1000	13.816	13.122	12.717	12.429	12.206	12.024	11.870	11.736	11.618
2000	14.509	13.816	13.410	13.122	12.899	12.717	12.563	12.429	12.311
3000	14.914	14.221	13.816	13.528	13.305	13.122	12.968	12.835	12.717
4000	15.202	14.509	14.103	13.816	13.592	13.410	13.256	13.122	13.005
5000	15.425	14.732	14.326	14.039	13.816	13.633	13.479	13.346	13.228
6000	15.607	14.914	14.509	14.221	13.998	13.816	13.661	13.528	13.410
7000	15.761	15.068	14.663	14.375	14.152	13.970	13.816	13.682	13.564
8000	15.895	15.202	14.796	14.509	14.286	14.103	13.949	13.816	13.698
9000	16.013	15.320	14.914	14.626	14.403	14.221	14.067	13.933	13.816
10000	16.118	15.425	15.019	14.732	14.509	14.326	14.172	14.039	13.921

(Prepared by L. P. Harrison, U.S. Weather Bureau. From *Smithsonian Meteorological Tables*, 6th rev. ed., List, R. J., Ed., Smithsonian Institution, Washington, D.C., 1971.)

Table 3.2–11 (*Continued*)
VISUAL RANGE OF POINT SOURCES OF LIGHT

Function ($\log_e I_0$ - $\log_e E$)

Luminous intensity I_0 candles (candela)	Threshold illuminance (flux-density), E, lumens km.$^{-2}$								
	1×10^{-2}	2×10^{-2}	3×10^{-2}	4×10^{-2}	5×10^{-2}	6×10^{-2}	7×10^{-2}	8×10^{-2}	9×10^{-2}
5×10^{-3}	−0.693	−1.386	−1.792	−2.079	−2.303	−2.485	−2.639	−2.773	−2.890
10^{-2}	0.000	−0.693	−1.099	−1.386	−1.609	−1.792	−1.946	−2.079	−2.197
5×10^{-2}	1.609	0.916	0.511	0.223	0.000	−0.182	−0.336	−0.470	−0.588
10^{-1}	2.303	1.609	1.204	0.916	0.693	0.511	0.357	0.223	0.105
5×10^{-1}	3.912	3.219	2.813	2.526	2.303	2.120	1.966	1.833	1.715
1	4.605	3.912	3.507	3.219	2.996	2.813	2.659	2.526	2.408
2	5.298	4.605	4.200	3.912	3.689	3.507	3.352	3.219	3.101
3	5.704	5.011	4.605	4.317	4.094	3.912	3.758	3.624	3.507
4	5.991	5.298	4.893	4.605	4.382	4.200	4.046	3.912	3.794
5	6.215	5.521	5.116	4.828	4.605	4.423	4.269	4.135	4.017
6	6.397	5.704	5.298	5.011	4.787	4.605	4.451	4.317	4.200
7	6.551	5.858	5.452	5.165	4.942	4.759	4.605	4.472	4.354
8	6.685	5.991	5.586	5.298	5.075	4.893	4.739	4.605	4.487
9	6.802	6.109	5.704	5.416	5.193	5.011	4.856	4.723	4.605
10	6.908	6.215	5.809	5.521	5.298	5.116	4.962	4.828	4.711
15	7.313	6.620	6.215	5.927	5.704	5.521	5.367	5.234	5.116
20	7.601	6.908	6.502	6.215	5.991	5.809	5.655	5.521	5.404
25	7.824	7.131	6.725	6.438	6.215	6.032	5.878	5.745	5.627
30	8.006	7.313	6.908	6.620	6.397	6.215	6.060	5.927	5.809
35	8.161	7.467	7.062	6.774	6.551	6.369	6.215	6.081	5.963
40	8.294	7.601	7.195	6.908	6.685	6.502	6.348	6.215	6.097
45	8.412	7.719	7.313	7.026	6.802	6.620	6.466	6.332	6.215
50	8.517	7.824	7.419	7.131	6.908	6.725	6.571	6.438	6.320
55	8.613	7.919	7.514	7.226	7.003	6.821	6.667	6.533	6.415
60	8.700	8.006	7.601	7.313	7.090	6.908	6.754	6.620	6.502
65	8.780	8.086	7.681	7.393	7.170	6.988	6.834	6.700	6.582
70	8.854	8.161	7.755	7.467	7.244	7.062	6.908	6.774	6.656
75	8.923	8.230	7.824	7.536	7.313	7.131	6.977	6.843	6.725
80	8.987	8.294	7.889	7.601	7.378	7.195	7.041	6.908	6.790
85	9.048	8.355	7.949	7.662	7.438	7.256	7.102	6.968	6.851
90	9.105	8.412	8.006	7.719	7.496	7.313	7.159	7.026	6.908
95	9.159	8.466	8.060	7.773	7.550	7.367	7.213	7.080	6.962
100	9.210	8.517	8.112	7.824	7.601	7.419	7.264	7.131	7.013
200	9.903	9.210	8.805	8.517	8.294	8.112	7.958	7.824	7.706
300	10.309	9.616	9.210	8.923	8.700	8.517	8.363	8.230	8.112
400	10.597	9.903	9.498	9.210	8.987	8.805	8.651	8.517	8.399
500	10.820	10.127	9.721	9.433	9.210	9.028	8.874	8.740	8.623
600	11.002	10.309	9.903	9.616	9.393	9.210	9.056	8.923	8.805
700	11.156	10.463	10.058	9.770	9.547	9.364	9.210	9.077	8.959
800	11.290	10.597	10.191	9.903	9.680	9.498	9.344	9.210	9.093
900	11.408	10.714	10.309	10.021	9.798	9.616	9.462	9.328	9.210
1000	11.513	10.820	10.414	10.127	9.903	9.721	9.567	9.433	9.316
2000	12.206	11.513	11.107	10.820	10.597	10.414	10.260	10.127	10.009
3000	12.612	11.918	11.513	11.225	11.002	10.820	10.666	10.532	10.414
4000	12.899	12.206	11.801	11.513	11.290	11.107	10.953	10.820	10.702
5000	13.122	12.429	12.024	11.736	11.513	11.331	11.176	11.043	10.925
6000	13.305	12.612	12.206	11.918	11.695	11.513	11.359	11.225	11.107
7000	13.459	12.766	12.360	12.073	11.849	11.667	11.513	11.379	11.262
8000	13.592	12.899	12.494	12.206	11.983	11.801	11.646	11.513	11.395
9000	13.710	13.017	12.612	12.324	12.101	11.918	11.764	11.631	11.513
10000	13.816	13.122	12.717	12.429	12.206	12.024	11.870	11.736	11.618

Table 3.2–11 (*Continued*)
VISUAL RANGE OF POINT SOURCES OF LIGHT

Function ($\log_e I_0$ - $\log_e E$)

Luminous intensity I_0 candles (candela)	Threshold illuminance (flux-density), E, lumens km.$^{-2}$								
	1×10^{-1}	2×10^{-1}	3×10^{-1}	4×10^{-1}	5×10^{-1}	6×10^{-1}	7×10^{-1}	8×10^{-1}	9×10^{-1}
5×10^{-3}	−2.996	−3.689	−4.094	−4.382	−4.605	−4.787	−4.942	−5.075	−5.193
10^{-2}	−2.303	−2.996	−3.401	−3.689	−3.912	−4.094	−4.248	−4.382	−4.500
5×10^{-2}	−0.693	−1.386	−1.792	−2.079	−2.303	−2.485	−2.639	−2.773	−2.890
10^{-1}	0.000	−0.693	−1.099	−1.386	−1.609	−1.792	−1.946	−2.079	−2.197
5×10^{-1}	1.609	0.916	0.511	0.223	0.000	−0.182	−0.336	−0.470	−0.588
1	2.303	1.609	1.204	0.916	0.693	0.511	0.357	0.223	0.105
2	2.996	2.303	1.897	1.609	1.386	1.204	1.050	0.916	0.799
3	3.401	2.708	2.303	2.015	1.792	1.609	1.455	1.322	1.204
4	3.689	2.996	2.590	2.303	2.079	1.897	1.743	1.609	1.492
5	3.912	3.219	2.813	2.526	2.303	2.120	1.966	1.833	1.715
6	4.094	3.401	2.996	2.708	2.485	2.303	2.148	2.015	1.897
7	4.248	3.555	3.150	2.862	2.639	2.457	2.303	2.169	2.051
8	4.382	3.689	3.283	2.996	2.773	2.590	2.436	2.303	2.185
9	4.500	3.807	3.401	3.114	2.890	2.708	2.554	2.420	2.303
10	4.605	3.912	3.507	3.219	2.996	2.813	2.659	2.526	2.408
15	5.011	4.317	3.912	3.624	3.401	3.219	3.065	2.931	2.813
20	5.298	4.605	4.200	3.912	3.689	3.507	3.352	3.219	3.101
25	5.521	4.828	4.423	4.135	3.912	3.730	3.576	3.442	3.324
30	5.704	5.011	4.605	4.317	4.094	3.912	3.758	3.624	3.507
35	5.858	5.165	4.759	4.472	4.248	4.066	3.912	3.778	3.661
40	5.991	5.298	4.893	4.605	4.382	4.200	4.046	3.912	3.794
45	6.109	5.416	5.011	4.723	4.500	4.317	4.163	4.030	3.912
50	6.215	5.521	5.116	4.828	4.605	4.423	4.269	4.135	4.017
55	6.310	5.617	5.211	4.924	4.700	4.518	4.364	4.230	4.113
60	6.397	5.704	5.298	5.011	4.787	4.605	4.451	4.317	4.200
65	6.477	5.784	5.378	5.091	4.868	4.685	4.531	4.398	4.280
70	6.551	5.858	5.452	5.165	4.942	4.759	4.605	4.472	4.354
75	6.620	5.927	5.521	5.234	5.011	4.828	4.674	4.541	4.423
80	6.685	5.991	5.586	5.298	5.075	4.893	4.739	4.605	4.487
85	6.745	6.052	5.647	5.359	5.136	4.953	4.799	4.666	4.548
90	6.802	6.109	5.704	5.416	5.193	5.011	4.856	4.723	4.605
95	6.856	6.163	5.758	5.470	5.247	5.065	4.911	4.777	4.659
100	6.908	6.215	5.809	5.521	5.298	5.116	4.962	4.828	4.711
200	7.601	6.908	6.502	6.215	5.991	5.809	5.655	5.521	5.404
300	8.006	7.313	6.908	6.620	6.397	6.215	6.060	5.927	5.809
400	8.294	7.601	7.195	6.908	6.685	6.502	6.348	6.215	6.097
500	8.517	7.824	7.419	7.131	6.908	6.725	6.571	6.438	6.320
600	8.700	8.006	7.601	7.313	7.090	6.908	6.754	6.620	6.502
700	8.854	8.161	7.755	7.467	7.244	7.062	6.908	6.774	6.656
800	8.987	8.294	7.889	7.601	7.378	7.195	7.041	6.908	6.790
900	9.105	8.412	8.006	7.719	7.496	7.313	7.159	7.026	6.908
1000	9.210	8.517	8.112	7.824	7.601	7.419	7.264	7.131	7.013
2000	9.903	9.210	8.805	8.517	8.294	8.112	7.958	7.824	7.706
3000	10.309	9.616	9.210	8.923	8.700	8.517	8.363	8.230	8.112
4000	10.597	9.903	9.498	9.210	8.987	8.805	8.651	8.517	8.399
5000	10.820	10.127	9.721	9.433	9.210	9.028	8.874	8.740	8.623
6000	11.002	10.309	9.903	9.616	9.393	9.210	9.056	8.923	8.805
7000	11.156	10.463	10.058	9.770	9.547	9.364	9.210	9.077	8.959
8000	11.290	10.597	10.191	9.903	9.680	9.498	9.344	9.210	9.093
9000	11.408	10.714	10.309	10.021	9.798	9.616	9.462	9.328	9.210
10000	11.513	10.820	10.414	10.127	9.903	9.721	9.567	9.433	9.316

Table 3.2–11 (*Continued*)
VISUAL RANGE OF POINT SOURCES OF LIGHT

Function ($\log_e I_0$ - $\log_e E$)

Luminous intensity I_0 candles (candela)	Threshold illuminance (flux-density), E, lumens km.$^{-2}$								
	1	2	3	4	5	6	7	8	9
5×10^{-3}	−5.298	−5.991	−6.397	−6.685	−6.908	−7.090	−7.244	−7.378	−7.496
10^{-2}	−4.605	−5.298	−5.704	−5.991	−6.215	−6.397	−6.551	−6.685	−6.802
5×10^{-2}	−2.996	−3.689	−4.094	−4.382	−4.605	−4.787	−4.942	−5.075	−5.193
10^{-1}	−2.303	−2.996	−3.401	−3.689	−3.912	−4.094	−4.249	−4.382	−4.500
5×10^{-1}	−0.693	−1.386	−1.792	−2.079	−2.303	−2.485	−2.639	−2.773	−2.890
1	0.000	−0.693	−1.099	−1.386	−1.609	−1.792	−1.946	−2.079	−2.197
2	0.693	0.000	−0.405	−0.693	−0.916	−1.099	−1.253	−1.386	−1.504
3	1.099	0.405	0.000	−0.288	−0.511	−0.693	−0.847	−0.981	−1.099
4	1.386	0.693	0.288	0.000	−0.223	−0.405	−0.560	−0.693	−0.811
5	1.609	0.916	0.511	0.223	0.000	−0.182	−0.336	−0.470	−0.588
6	1.792	1.099	0.693	0.405	0.182	0.000	−0.154	−0.288	−0.405
7	1.946	1.253	0.847	0.560	0.336	0.154	0.000	−0.134	−0.251
8	2.079	1.386	0.981	0.693	0.470	0.288	0.134	0.000	−0.118
9	2.197	1.504	1.099	0.811	0.588	0.405	0.251	0.118	0.000
10	2.303	1.609	1.204	0.916	0.693	0.511	0.357	0.223	0.105
15	2.708	2.015	1.609	1.322	1.099	0.916	0.762	0.629	0.511
20	2.996	2.303	1.897	1.609	1.386	1.204	1.050	0.916	0.799
25	3.219	2.526	2.120	1.833	1.609	1.427	1.273	1.139	1.022
30	3.401	2.708	2.303	2.015	1.792	1.609	1.455	1.322	1.204
35	3.555	2.862	2.457	2.169	1.946	1.764	1.609	1.476	1.358
40	3.689	2.996	2.590	2.303	2.079	1.897	1.743	1.609	1.492
45	3.807	3.114	2.708	2.420	2.197	2.015	1.861	1.727	1.609
50	3.912	3.219	2.813	2.526	2.303	2.120	1.966	1.833	1.715
55	4.007	3.314	2.909	2.621	2.398	2.216	2.061	1.928	1.810
60	4.094	3.401	2.996	2.708	2.485	2.303	2.148	2.015	1.897
65	4.174	3.481	3.076	2.788	2.565	2.383	2.228	2.095	1.977
70	4.249	3.555	3.150	2.862	2.639	2.457	2.303	2.169	2.051
75	4.317	3.624	3.219	2.931	2.708	2.526	2.372	2.238	2.120
80	4.382	3.689	3.283	2.996	2.773	2.590	2.436	2.303	2.185
85	4.443	3.750	3.344	3.056	2.833	2.651	2.497	2.363	2.245
90	4.500	3.807	3.401	3.114	2.890	2.708	2.554	2.420	2.303
95	4.554	3.861	3.455	3.168	2.944	2.762	2.608	2.474	2.357
100	4.605	3.912	3.507	3.219	2.996	2.813	2.659	2.526	2.408
200	5.298	4.605	4.200	3.912	3.689	3.507	3.352	3.219	3.101
300	5.704	5.011	4.605	4.317	4.094	3.912	3.758	3.624	3.507
400	5.991	5.298	4.893	4.605	4.382	4.200	4.046	3.912	3.794
500	6.215	5.521	5.116	4.828	4.605	4.423	4.269	4.135	4.017
600	6.397	5.704	5.298	5.011	4.787	4.594	4.440	4.307	4.189
700	6.551	5.858	5.452	5.165	4.942	4.759	4.605	4.472	4.354
800	6.685	5.991	5.586	5.298	5.075	4.893	4.739	4.605	4.487
900	6.802	6.109	5.704	5.416	5.193	5.011	4.856	4.723	4.605
1000	6.908	6.215	5.809	5.521	5.298	5.116	4.962	4.828	4.711
2000	7.601	6.908	6.502	6.215	5.991	5.809	5.655	5.521	5.404
3000	8.006	7.313	6.908	6.620	6.397	6.215	6.060	5.927	5.809
4000	8.294	7.601	7.195	6.908	6.685	6.502	6.348	6.215	6.097
5000	8.517	7.824	7.419	7.131	6.908	6.725	6.571	6.438	6.320
6000	8.700	8.006	7.601	7.313	7.090	6.908	6.754	6.620	6.502
7000	8.854	8.161	7.755	7.467	7.244	7.062	6.908	6.774	6.656
8000	8.987	8.294	7.889	7.601	7.378	7.195	7.041	6.908	6.790
9000	9.105	8.412	8.006	7.719	7.496	7.313	7.159	7.026	6.908
10000	9.210	8.517	8.112	7.824	7.601	7.419	7.264	7.131	7.013

Table 3.2–11 (*Continued*)
VISUAL RANGE OF POINT SOURCES OF LIGHT

Function ($\log_e I_0 - \log_e E$)

Luminous intensity I_0 candles (candela)	Threshold illuminance (flux-density), E, lumens km.$^{-2}$ 1×10	2×10	3×10	4×10	5×10	6×10	7×10	8×10	9×10
5×10^{-3}	−7.601	−8.294	−8.700	−8.987	−9.210	−9.393	−9.547	−9.680	−9.798
10^{-2}	−6.908	−7.601	−8.006	−8.294	−8.517	−8.700	−8.854	−8.987	−9.105
5×10^{-2}	−5.298	−5.991	−6.397	−6.685	−6.908	−7.090	−7.244	−7.378	−7.496
10^{-1}	−4.605	−5.298	−5.704	−5.991	−6.215	−6.397	−6.551	−6.685	−6.802
5×10^{-1}	−2.996	−3.689	−4.094	−4.382	−4.605	−4.787	−4.942	−5.075	−5.193
1	−2.303	−2.996	−3.401	−3.689	−3.912	−4.094	−4.249	−4.382	−4.500
2	−1.609	−2.303	−2.708	−2.996	−3.219	−3.401	−3.555	−3.689	−3.807
3	−1.204	−1.897	−2.303	−2.590	−2.813	−2.996	−3.150	−3.283	−3.401
4	−0.916	−1.609	−2.015	−2.303	−2.526	−2.708	−2.862	−2.996	−3.114
5	−0.693	−1.386	−1.792	−2.079	−2.303	−2.485	−2.639	−2.773	−2.890
6	−0.511	−1.204	−1.609	−1.897	−2.120	−2.303	−2.457	−2.590	−2.708
7	−0.357	−1.050	−1.455	−1.743	−1.966	−2.148	−2.303	−2.436	−2.554
8	−0.223	−0.916	−1.322	−1.609	−1.833	−2.015	−2.169	−2.303	−2.420
9	−0.105	−0.799	−1.204	−1.492	−1.715	−1.897	−2.051	−2.185	−2.303
10	0.000	−0.693	−1.099	−1.386	−1.609	−1.792	−1.946	−2.079	−2.197
15	0.405	−0.288	−0.693	−0.981	−1.204	−1.386	−1.540	−1.674	−1.792
20	0.693	0.000	−0.405	−0.693	−0.916	−1.099	−1.253	−1.386	−1.504
25	0.916	0.223	−0.182	−0.470	−0.693	−0.875	−1.030	−1.163	−1.281
30	1.099	0.405	0.000	−0.288	−0.511	−0.693	−0.847	−0.981	−1.099
35	1.253	0.560	0.154	−0.134	−0.357	−0.539	−0.693	−0.827	−0.944
40	1.386	0.693	0.288	0.000	−0.223	−0.405	−0.560	−0.693	−0.811
45	1.504	0.811	0.405	0.118	−0.105	−0.288	−0.442	−0.575	−0.693
50	1.609	0.916	0.511	0.223	0.000	−0.182	−0.336	−0.470	−0.588
55	1.705	1.012	0.606	0.318	0.095	−0.087	−0.241	−0.375	−0.492
60	1.792	1.099	0.693	0.405	0.182	0.000	−0.154	−0.288	−0.405
65	1.872	1.179	0.773	0.486	0.262	0.080	−0.074	−0.208	−0.325
70	1.946	1.253	0.847	0.560	0.336	0.154	0.000	−0.134	−0.251
75	2.015	1.322	0.916	0.629	0.405	0.223	0.069	−0.065	−0.182
80	2.079	1.386	0.981	0.693	0.470	0.288	0.134	0.000	−0.118
85	2.140	1.447	1.041	0.754	0.531	0.348	0.194	0.061	−0.057
90	2.197	1.504	1.099	0.811	0.588	0.405	0.251	0.118	0.000
95	2.251	1.558	1.153	0.865	0.642	0.460	0.305	0.172	0.054
100	2.303	1.609	1.204	0.916	0.693	0.511	0.357	0.223	0.105
200	2.996	2.303	1.897	1.609	1.386	1.204	1.050	0.916	0.799
300	3.401	2.708	2.303	2.015	1.792	1.609	1.455	1.322	1.204
400	3.689	2.996	2.590	2.303	2.079	1.897	1.743	1.609	1.492
500	3.912	3.219	2.813	2.526	2.303	2.120	1.966	1.833	1.715
600	4.094	3.401	2.996	2.708	2.485	2.303	2.148	2.015	2.103
700	4.248	3.555	3.150	2.862	2.639	2.457	2.303	2.169	2.051
800	4.382	3.689	3.283	2.996	2.773	2.590	2.436	2.303	2.185
900	4.500	3.807	3.401	3.114	2.890	2.708	2.554	2.420	2.303
1000	4.605	3.912	3.507	3.219	2.996	2.813	2.659	2.526	2.408
2000	5.298	4.605	4.200	3.912	3.689	3.507	3.352	3.219	3.101
3000	5.704	5.011	4.605	4.317	4.094	3.912	3.758	3.624	3.507
4000	5.991	5.298	4.893	4.605	4.382	4.200	4.046	3.912	3.794
5000	6.215	5.521	5.116	4.828	4.605	4.423	4.269	4.135	4.017
6000	6.397	5.704	5.298	5.011	4.787	4.605	4.451	4.317	4.200
7000	6.551	5.858	5.452	5.165	4.942	4.759	4.605	4.472	4.354
8000	6.685	5.991	5.586	5.298	5.075	4.893	4.739	4.605	4.487
9000	6.802	6.109	5.704	5.416	5.193	5.011	4.856	4.723	4.605
10000	6.908	6.215	5.809	5.521	5.298	5.116	4.962	4.828	4.711

Table 3.2–11 (*Continued*)
VISUAL RANGE OF POINT SOURCES OF LIGHT

Function ($\log_e I_0$ - $\log_e E$)

Luminous intensity I_0 candles (candela)	Threshold illuminance (flux-density), E, lumens km.$^{-2}$								
	1×10^{2}	2×10^{2}	3×10^{2}	4×10^{2}	5×10^{2}	6×10^{2}	7×10^{2}	8×10^{2}	9×10^{2}
5×10^{-3}	−9.903	−10.597	−11.002	−11.290	−11.513	−11.695	−11.849	−11.983	−12.101
10^{-2}	−9.210	− 9.903	−10.309	−10.597	−10.820	−11.002	−11.156	−11.290	−11.408
5×10^{-2}	−7.601	− 8.294	− 8.700	− 8.987	− 9.210	− 9.393	− 9.547	− 9.680	− 9.798
10^{-1}	−6.908	− 7.601	− 8.006	− 8.294	− 8.517	− 8.700	− 8.854	− 8.987	− 9.105
5×10^{-1}	−5.298	− 5.991	− 6.397	− 6.685	− 6.908	− 7.090	− 7.244	− 7.378	− 7.496
1	−4.605	− 5.298	− 5.704	− 5.991	− 6.215	− 6.397	− 6.551	− 6.685	− 6.802
2	−3.912	− 4.605	− 5.011	− 5.298	− 5.521	− 5.704	− 5.858	− 5.991	− 6.109
3	−3.507	− 4.200	− 4.605	− 4.893	− 5.116	− 5.298	− 5.452	− 5.586	− 5.704
4	−3.219	− 3.912	− 4.317	− 4.605	− 4.828	− 5.011	− 5.165	− 5.298	− 5.416
5	−2.996	− 3.689	− 4.094	− 4.382	− 4.605	− 4.787	− 4.942	− 5.075	− 5.193
6	−2.813	− 3.507	− 3.912	− 4.200	− 4.423	− 4.605	− 4.759	− 4.893	− 5.011
7	−2.659	− 3.352	− 3.758	− 4.046	− 4.269	− 4.451	− 4.605	− 4.739	− 4.856
8	−2.526	− 3.219	− 3.624	− 3.912	− 4.135	− 4.317	− 4.472	− 4.605	− 4.723
9	−2.408	− 3.101	− 3.507	− 3.794	− 4.017	− 4.200	− 4.354	− 4.487	− 4.605
10	−2.303	− 2.996	− 3.401	− 3.689	− 3.912	− 4.094	− 4.248	− 4.382	− 4.500
15	−1.897	− 2.590	− 2.996	− 3.283	− 3.507	− 3.689	− 3.843	− 3.977	− 4.094
20	−1.609	− 2.303	− 2.708	− 2.996	− 3.219	− 3.401	− 3.555	− 3.689	− 3.807
25	−1.386	− 2.079	− 2.485	− 2.773	− 2.996	− 3.178	− 3.332	− 3.466	− 3.584
30	−1.204	− 1.897	− 2.303	− 2.590	− 2.813	− 2.996	− 3.150	− 3.283	− 3.401
35	−1.050	− 1.743	− 2.148	− 2.436	− 2.659	− 2.842	− 2.996	− 3.129	− 3.247
40	−0.916	− 1.609	− 2.015	− 2.303	− 2.526	− 2.708	− 2.862	− 2.996	− 3.114
45	−0.799	− 1.492	− 1.897	− 2.185	− 2.408	− 2.590	− 2.744	− 2.878	− 2.996
50	−0.693	− 1.386	− 1.792	− 2.079	− 2.303	− 2.485	− 2.639	− 2.773	− 2.890
55	−0.598	− 1.291	− 1.696	− 1.984	− 2.207	− 2.390	− 2.544	− 2.677	− 2.795
60	−0.511	− 1.204	− 1.609	− 1.897	− 2.120	− 2.303	− 2.457	− 2.590	− 2.708
65	−0.431	− 1.124	− 1.529	− 1.817	− 2.040	− 2.223	− 2.377	− 2.510	− 2.628
70	−0.357	− 1.050	− 1.455	− 1.743	− 1.966	− 2.148	− 2.303	− 2.436	− 2.554
75	−0.288	− 0.981	− 1.386	− 1.674	− 1.897	− 2.079	− 2.234	− 2.367	− 2.485
80	−0.223	− 0.916	− 1.322	− 1.609	− 1.833	− 2.015	− 2.169	− 2.303	− 2.420
85	−0.163	− 0.856	− 1.261	− 1.549	− 1.772	− 1.954	− 2.108	− 2.242	− 2.360
90	−0.105	− 0.799	− 1.204	− 1.492	− 1.715	− 1.897	− 2.051	− 2.185	− 2.303
95	−0.051	− 0.744	− 1.150	− 1.438	− 1.661	− 1.843	− 1.997	− 2.131	− 2.249
100	0.000	− 0.693	− 1.099	− 1.386	− 1.609	− 1.792	− 1.946	− 2.079	− 2.197
200	0.693	0.000	− 0.405	− 0.693	− 0.916	− 1.099	− 1.253	− 1.386	− 1.504
300	1.099	0.405	0.000	− 0.288	− 0.511	− 0.693	− 0.847	− 0.981	− 1.099
400	1.386	0.693	0.288	0.000	− 0.223	− 0.405	− 0.560	− 0.693	− 0.811
500	1.609	0.916	0.511	0.223	0.000	− 0.182	− 0.336	− 0.470	− 0.588
600	1.792	1.099	0.693	0.405	0.182	0.000	− 0.154	− 0.288	− 0.405
700	1.946	1.253	0.847	0.560	0.336	0.154	0.000	− 0.134	− 0.251
800	2.079	1.386	0.981	0.693	0.470	0.288	0.134	0.000	− 0.118
900	2.197	1.504	1.099	0.811	0.588	0.405	0.251	0.118	0.000
1000	2.303	1.609	1.204	0.916	0.693	0.511	0.357	0.223	0.105
2000	2.996	2.303	1.897	1.609	1.386	1.204	1.050	0.916	0.799
3000	3.401	2.708	2.303	2.015	1.792	1.609	1.455	1.322	1.204
4000	3.689	2.996	2.590	2.303	2.079	1.897	1.743	1.609	1.492
5000	3.912	3.219	2.813	2.526	2.303	2.120	1.966	1.833	1.715
6000	4.094	3.401	2.996	2.708	2.485	2.303	2.148	2.015	1.897
7000	4.249	3.555	3.150	2.862	2.639	2.457	2.303	2.169	2.051
8000	4.382	3.689	3.283	2.996	2.773	2.590	2.436	2.303	2.185
9000	4.500	3.807	3.401	3.114	2.890	2.708	2.554	2.420	2.303
10000	4.605	3.912	3.507	3.219	2.996	2.813	2.659	2.526	2.408

Table 3.2–11 (*Continued*)
VISUAL RANGE OF POINT SOURCES OF LIGHT

Function ($\log_e I_0$ - $\log_e E$)

Luminous intensity I_0 candles (candela)	Threshold illuminance (flux-density), E, lumens km.$^{-2}$								
	1×10^2	2×10^2	3×10^2	4×10^2	5×10^2	6×10^2	7×10^2	8×10^2	9×10^2
10^4	4.605	3.912	3.507	3.219	2.996	2.813	2.659	2.526	2.408
2×10^4	5.298	4.605	4.200	3.912	3.689	3.507	3.352	3.219	3.101
4×10^4	5.991	5.298	4.893	4.605	4.382	4.200	4.046	3.912	3.794
6×10^4	6.397	5.704	5.298	5.011	4.787	4.605	4.451	4.317	4.200
8×10^4	6.685	5.991	5.586	5.298	5.075	4.893	4.739	4.605	4.487
10^5	6.908	6.215	5.809	5.521	5.298	5.116	4.962	4.828	4.711
5×10^5	8.517	7.824	7.419	7.131	6.908	6.725	6.571	6.438	6.320
10^6	9.210	8.517	8.112	7.824	7.601	7.419	7.264	7.131	7.013
5×10^6	10.820	10.127	9.721	9.433	9.210	9.028	8.874	8.740	8.623
10^7	11.513	10.820	10.414	10.127	9.903	9.721	9.567	9.433	9.316
5×10^7	13.122	12.429	12.024	11.736	11.513	11.331	11.176	11.043	10.925
10^8	13.816	13.122	12.717	12.429	12.206	12.024	11.870	11.736	11.618
5×10^8	15.425	14.732	14.326	14.039	13.816	13.633	13.479	13.346	13.228
10^9	16.118	15.425	15.019	14.732	14.509	14.326	14.172	14.039	13.921
5×10^9	17.728	17.034	16.629	16.341	16.118	15.936	15.782	15.648	15.530

	Threshold illuminance (flux-density), E, lumens km.$^{-2}$								
	1×10	2×10	3×10	4×10	5×10	6×10	7×10	8×10	9×10
10^4	6.908	6.215	5.809	5.521	5.298	5.116	4.962	4.828	4.711
2×10^4	7.601	6.908	6.502	6.215	5.991	5.809	5.655	5.521	5.404
4×10^4	8.294	7.601	7.195	6.908	6.685	6.502	6.348	6.215	6.097
6×10^4	8.700	8.006	7.601	7.313	7.090	6.908	6.754	6.620	6.502
8×10^4	8.987	8.294	7.889	7.601	7.378	7.195	7.041	6.908	6.790
10^5	9.210	8.517	8.112	7.824	7.601	7.419	7.264	7.131	7.013
5×10^5	10.820	10.127	9.721	9.433	9.210	9.028	8.874	8.740	8.623
10^6	11.513	10.820	10.414	10.127	9.903	9.721	9.567	9.433	9.316
5×10^6	13.122	12.429	12.024	11.736	11.513	11.331	11.176	11.043	10.925
10^7	13.816	13.122	12.717	12.429	12.206	12.024	11.870	11.736	11.618
5×10^7	15.425	14.732	14.326	14.039	13.816	13.633	13.479	13.346	13.228
10^8	16.118	15.425	15.019	14.732	14.509	14.326	14.172	14.039	13.921
5×10^8	17.728	17.034	16.629	16.341	16.118	15.936	15.782	15.648	15.530
10^9	18.421	17.728	17.322	17.034	16.811	16.629	16.475	16.341	16.223
5×10^9	20.030	19.337	18.932	18.644	18.421	18.238	18.084	17.951	17.833

	Threshold illuminance (flux-density), E, lumens km.$^{-2}$								
	1	2	3	4	5	6	7	8	9
10^4	9.210	8.517	8.112	7.824	7.601	7.419	7.264	7.131	7.013
2×10^4	9.903	9.210	8.805	8.517	8.294	8.112	7.958	7.824	7.706
4×10^4	10.597	9.903	9.498	9.210	8.987	8.805	8.651	8.517	8.399
6×10^4	11.002	10.309	9.903	9.616	9.393	9.210	9.056	8.923	8.805
8×10^4	11.290	10.597	10.191	9.903	9.680	9.498	9.344	9.210	9.093
10^5	11.513	10.820	10.414	10.127	9.903	9.721	9.567	9.433	9.316
5×10^5	13.122	12.429	12.024	11.736	11.513	11.331	11.176	11.043	10.925
10^6	13.816	13.122	12.717	12.429	12.206	12.024	11.870	11.736	11.618
5×10^6	15.425	14.732	14.326	14.039	13.816	13.633	13.479	13.346	13.228
10^7	16.118	15.425	15.019	14.732	14.509	14.326	14.172	14.039	13.921
5×10^7	17.728	17.034	16.629	16.341	16.118	15.936	15.782	15.648	15.530
10^8	18.421	17.728	17.322	17.034	16.811	16.629	16.475	16.341	16.223
5×10^8	20.030	19.337	18.932	18.644	18.421	18.238	18.084	17.951	17.833
10^9	20.723	20.030	19.625	19.337	19.114	18.932	18.777	18.644	18.526
5×10^9	22.333	21.640	21.234	20.946	20.723	20.541	20.387	20.253	20.135

Table 3.2–11 (*Continued*)
VISUAL RANGE OF POINT SOURCES OF LIGHT

Function ($\log_e I_0 - \log_e E$)

Luminous intensity I_0 candles (candela)	Threshold illuminance (flux-density), E, lumens km.$^{-2}$								
	1×10^{-1}	2×10^{-1}	3×10^{-1}	4×10^{-1}	5×10^{-1}	6×10^{-1}	7×10^{-1}	8×10^{-1}	9×10^{-1}
10^4	11.513	10.820	10.414	10.127	9.903	9.721	9.567	9.433	9.316
2×10^4	12.206	11.513	11.107	10.820	10.597	10.414	10.260	10.127	10.009
4×10^4	12.899	12.206	11.801	11.513	11.290	11.107	10.953	10.820	10.702
6×10^4	13.305	12.612	12.206	11.918	11.695	11.513	11.359	11.225	11.107
8×10^4	13.592	12.899	12.494	12.206	11.983	11.801	11.646	11.513	11.395
10^5	13.816	13.122	12.717	12.429	12.206	12.024	11.870	11.736	11.618
5×10^5	15.425	14.732	14.326	14.039	13.816	13.633	13.479	13.346	13.228
10^6	16.118	15.425	15.019	14.732	14.509	14.326	14.172	14.039	13.921
5×10^6	17.728	17.034	16.629	16.341	16.118	15.936	15.782	15.648	15.530
10^7	18.421	17.728	17.322	17.034	16.811	16.629	16.475	16.341	16.223
5×10^7	20.030	19.337	18.932	18.644	18.421	18.238	18.084	17.951	17.833
10^8	20.723	20.030	19.625	19.337	19.114	18.932	18.777	18.644	18.526
5×10^8	22.333	21.640	21.234	20.946	20.723	20.541	20.387	20.253	20.135
10^9	23.026	22.333	21.927	21.640	21.416	21.234	21.080	20.946	20.829
5×10^9	24.635	23.942	23.537	23.249	23.026	22.844	22.689	22.556	22.438

Luminous intensity I_0 candles (candela)	Threshold illuminance (flux-density), E, lumens km.$^{-2}$								
	1×10^{-2}	2×10^{-2}	3×10^{-2}	4×10^{-2}	5×10^{-2}	6×10^{-2}	7×10^{-2}	8×10^{-2}	9×10^{-2}
10^4	13.816	13.122	12.717	12.429	12.206	12.024	11.870	11.736	11.618
2×10^4	14.509	13.816	13.410	13.122	12.899	12.717	12.563	12.429	12.311
4×10^4	15.202	14.509	14.103	13.816	13.592	13.410	13.256	13.122	13.005
6×10^4	15.607	14.914	14.509	14.221	13.998	13.816	13.661	13.528	13.410
8×10^4	15.895	15.202	14.796	14.509	14.286	14.103	13.949	13.816	13.698
10^5	16.118	15.425	15.019	14.732	14.509	14.326	14.172	14.039	13.921
5×10^5	17.728	17.034	16.629	16.341	16.118	15.936	15.782	15.648	15.530
10^6	18.421	17.728	17.322	17.034	16.811	16.629	16.475	16.341	16.223
5×10^6	20.030	19.337	18.932	18.644	18.421	18.238	18.084	17.951	17.833
10^7	20.723	20.030	19.625	19.337	19.114	18.932	18.777	18.644	18.526
5×10^7	22.333	21.640	21.234	20.946	20.723	20.541	20.387	20.253	20.135
10^8	23.026	22.333	21.927	21.640	21.416	21.234	21.080	20.946	20.829
5×10^8	24.635	23.942	23.537	23.249	23.026	22.844	22.689	22.556	22.438
10^9	25.328	24.635	24.230	23.942	23.719	23.537	23.383	23.249	23.131
5×10^9	26.938	26.245	25.839	25.552	25.328	25.146	24.992	24.858	24.741

Luminous intensity I_0 candles (candela)	Threshold illuminance (flux-density), E, lumens km.$^{-2}$								
	1×10^{-3}	2×10^{-3}	3×10^{-3}	4×10^{-3}	5×10^{-3}	6×10^{-3}	7×10^{-3}	8×10^{-3}	9×10^{-3}
10^4	16.118	15.425	15.019	14.732	14.509	14.326	14.172	14.039	13.921
2×10^4	16.811	16.118	15.713	15.425	15.202	15.019	14.865	14.731	14.614
4×10^4	17.504	16.811	16.406	16.118	15.895	15.713	15.558	15.425	15.307
6×10^4	17.910	17.217	16.811	16.524	16.300	16.118	15.964	15.830	15.713
8×10^4	18.198	17.504	17.099	16.811	16.588	16.406	16.252	16.118	16.000
10^5	18.421	17.728	17.322	17.034	16.811	16.629	16.475	16.341	16.223
5×10^5	20.030	19.337	18.932	18.644	18.421	18.238	18.084	17.951	17.833
10^6	20.723	20.030	19.625	19.337	19.114	18.932	18.777	18.644	18.526
5×10^6	22.333	21.640	21.234	20.946	20.723	20.541	20.387	20.253	20.135
10^7	23.026	22.333	21.927	21.640	21.416	21.234	21.080	20.946	20.829
5×10^7	24.635	23.942	23.537	23.249	23.026	22.844	22.689	22.556	22.438
10^8	25.328	24.635	24.230	23.942	23.719	23.537	23.383	23.249	23.131
5×10^8	26.938	26.245	25.839	25.552	25.328	25.146	24.992	24.858	24.741
10^9	27.631	26.938	26.532	26.245	26.022	25.839	25.685	25.552	25.434
5×10^9	29.240	28.547	28.142	27.854	27.631	27.449	27.295	27.161	27.043

Table 3.2–12
VISUAL RANGE OF POINT SOURCES OF LIGHT

Function $(\sigma D + 2 \log_e D)$

Visual range D km.	Extinction coefficient, σ, km.⁻¹ 0	0.1	0.2	0.3	0.4	0.5	0.6	0.7	0.8	0.9
0.004										
0.005										
0.006										
0.007	−9.924	−9.923	−9.922	−9.922	−9.921	−9.920	−9.920	−9.919	−9.918	−9.917
0.008	−9.657	−9.656	−9.655	−9.654	−9.653	−9.653	−9.652	−9.651	−9.650	−9.649
0.009	−9.421	−9.420	−9.419	−9.418	−9.418	−9.417	−9.416	−9.415	−9.414	−9.413
0.01	−9.210	−9.209	−9.208	−9.207	−9.206	−9.205	−9.204	−9.203	−9.202	−9.201
0.02	−7.824	−7.822	−7.820	−7.818	−7.816	−7.814	−7.812	−7.810	−7.808	−7.806
0.03	−7.013	−7.010	−7.007	−7.004	−7.001	−6.998	−6.995	−6.992	−6.989	−6.986
0.04	−6.438	−6.434	−6.430	−6.426	−6.422	−6.418	−6.414	−6.410	−6.406	−6.402
0.05	−5.991	−5.986	−5.981	−5.976	−5.971	−5.966	−5.961	−5.956	−5.951	−5.946
0.06	−5.627	−5.621	−5.615	−5.609	−5.603	−5.597	−5.591	−5.585	−5.579	−5.573
0.07	−5.319	−5.312	−5.305	−5.298	−5.291	−5.284	−5.277	−5.270	−5.263	−5.256
0.08	−5.051	−5.043	−5.035	−5.027	−5.019	−5.011	−5.003	−4.995	−4.987	−4.979
0.09	−4.816	−4.807	−4.798	−4.789	−4.780	−4.771	−4.762	−4.753	−4.744	−4.735
0.1	−4.605	−4.595	−4.585	−4.575	−4.565	−4.555	−4.545	−4.535	−4.525	−4.515
0.2	−3.219	−3.199	−3.179	−3.159	−3.139	−3.119	−3.099	−3.079	−3.059	−3.039
0.3	−2.408	−2.378	−2.348	−2.318	−2.288	−2.258	−2.228	−2.198	−2.168	−2.138
0.4	−1.833	−1.793	−1.753	−1.713	−1.673	−1.633	−1.593	−1.553	−1.513	−1.473
0.5	−1.386	−1.336	−1.286	−1.236	−1.186	−1.136	−1.086	−1.036	−0.986	−0.936
0.6	−1.022	−0.962	−0.902	−0.842	−0.782	−0.722	−0.662	−0.602	−0.542	−0.482
0.7	−0.713	−0.643	−0.573	−0.503	−0.433	−0.363	−0.293	−0.223	−0.153	−0.083
0.8	−0.446	−0.366	−0.286	−0.206	−0.126	−0.046	0.034	0.114	0.194	0.274
0.9	−0.211	−0.121	−0.031	0.059	0.149	0.239	0.329	0.419	0.509	0.599
1.0	0.000	0.100	0.200	0.300	0.400	0.500	0.600	0.700	0.800	0.900
1.1	0.191	0.301	0.411	0.521	0.631	0.741	0.851	0.961	1.071	1.181
1.2	0.365	0.485	0.605	0.725	0.845	0.965	1.085	1.205	1.325	1.445
1.3	0.525	0.655	0.785	0.915	1.045	1.175	1.305	1.435	1.565	1.695
1.4	0.673	0.813	0.953	1.093	1.233	1.373	1.513	1.653	1.793	1.933
1.5	0.811	0.961	1.111	1.261	1.411	1.561	1.711	1.861	2.011	2.161
1.6	0.940	1.100	1.260	1.420	1.580	1.740	1.900	2.060	2.220	2.380
1.7	1.061	1.231	1.401	1.571	1.741	1.911	2.081	2.251	2.421	2.591
1.8	1.176	1.356	1.536	1.716	1.896	2.076	2.256	2.436	2.616	2.796
1.9	1.284	1.474	1.664	1.854	2.044	2.234	2.424	2.614	2.804	2.994
2.0	1.386	1.586	1.786	1.986	2.186	2.386	2.586	2.786	2.986	3.186
2.1	1.484	1.694	1.904	2.114	2.324	2.534	2.744	2.954	3.164	3.374
2.2	1.577	1.797	2.017	2.237	2.457	2.677	2.897	3.117	3.337	3.557
2.3	1.666	1.896	2.126	2.356	2.586	2.816	3.046	3.276	3.506	3.736
2.4	1.751	1.991	2.231	2.471	2.711	2.951	3.191	3.431	3.671	3.911
2.5	1.833	2.083	2.333	2.583	2.833	3.083	3.333	3.583	3.833	4.083
2.6	1.911	2.171	2.431	2.691	2.951	3.211	3.471	3.731	3.991	4.251
2.7	1.986	2.256	2.526	2.796	3.066	3.336	3.606	3.876	4.146	4.416
2.8	2.059	2.339	2.619	2.899	3.179	3.459	3.739	4.019	4.299	4.579
2.9	2.129	2.419	2.709	2.999	3.289	3.579	3.869	4.159	4.449	4.739
3.0	2.197	2.497	2.797	3.097	3.397	3.697	3.997	4.297	4.597	4.897
3.2	2.326	2.646	2.966	3.286	3.606	3.926	4.246	4.566	4.886	5.206
3.4	2.448	2.788	3.128	3.468	3.808	4.148	4.488	4.828	5.168	5.508
3.6	2.562	2.922	3.282	3.642	4.002	4.362	4.722	5.082	5.442	5.802
3.8	2.670	3.050	3.430	3.810	4.190	4.570	4.950	5.330	5.710	6.090
4.0	2.773	3.173	3.573	3.973	4.373	4.773	5.173	5.573	5.973	6.373

Table 3.2–12 (*Continued*)
VISUAL RANGE OF POINT SOURCES OF LIGHT

Function ($\sigma D + 2 \log_e D$)

Visual range D km.	Extinction coefficient, σ, km.$^{-1}$ 0	0.1	0.2	0.3	0.4	0.5	0.6	0.7	0.8	0.9
4.0	2.773	3.173	3.573	3.973	4.373	4.773	5.173	5.573	5.973	6.373
4.2	2.870	3.290	3.710	4.130	4.550	4.970	5.390	5.810	6.230	6.650
4.4	2.963	3.403	3.843	4.283	4.723	5.163	5.603	6.043	6.483	6.923
4.6	3.052	3.512	3.972	4.432	4.892	5.352	5.812	6.272	6.732	7.192
4.8	3.137	3.617	4.097	4.577	5.057	5.537	6.017	6.497	6.977	7.457
5.0	3.219	3.719	4.219	4.719	5.219	5.719	6.219	6.719	7.219	7.719
5.2	3.297	3.817	4.337	4.857	5.377	5.897	6.417	6.937	7.457	7.977
5.4	3.373	3.913	4.453	4.993	5.533	6.073	6.613	7.153	7.693	8.233
5.6	3.446	4.006	4.566	5.126	5.686	6.246	6.806	7.366	7,926	8.486
5.8	3.516	4.096	4.676	5.256	5.836	6.416	6.996	7.576	8.156	8.736
6.0	3.584	4.184	4.784	5.384	5.984	6.584	7.184	7.784	8.384	8.984
6.2	3.649	4.269	4.889	5.509	6.129	6.749	7.369	7.989	8.609	9.229
6.4	3.713	4.353	4.993	5.633	6.273	6.913	7.553	8.193	8.833	9.473
6.6	3.774	4.434	5.094	5.754	6.414	7.074	7.734	8.394	9.054	9.714
6.8	3.834	4.514	5.194	5.874	6.554	7.234	7.914	8.594	9.274	9.954
7.0	3.892	4.592	5.292	5.992	6.692	7.392	8.092	8.792	9.492	10.192
7.2	3.948	4.668	5.388	6.108	6.828	7.548	8.268	8.988	9.708	10.428
7.4	4.003	4.743	5.483	6.223	6.963	7.703	8.443	9.183	9.923	10.663
7.6	4.056	4.816	5.576	6.336	7.096	7.856	8.616	9.376	10.136	10.896
7.8	4.108	4.888	5.668	6.448	7.228	8.008	8.788	9.568	10.348	11.128
8.0	4.159	4.959	5.759	6.559	7.359	8.159	8.959	9.759	10.559	11.359
8.2	4.208	5.028	5.848	6.668	7.488	8.308	9.128	9.948	10.768	11.588
8.4	4.256	5.096	5.936	6.776	7.616	8.456	9.296	10.136	10.976	11.816
8.6	4.304	5.164	6.024	6.884	7.744	8.604	9.464	10.324	11.184	12.044
8.8	4.350	5.230	6.110	6.990	7.870	8.750	9.630	10.510	11.390	12.270
9.0	4.394	5.294	6.194	7.094	7.994	8.894	9.794	10.694	11.594	12.494
9.2	4.438	5.358	6.278	7.198	8.118	9.038	9.958	10.878	11.798	12.718
9.4	4.481	5.421	6.361	7.301	8.241	9.181	10.121	11.061	12.001	12.941
9.6	4.524	5.484	6.444	7.404	8.364	9.324	10.284	11.244	12.204	13.164
9.8	4.565	5.545	6.525	7.505	8.485	9.465	10.445	11.425	12.405	13.385
10.0	4.605	5.605	6.605	7.605	8.605	9.605	10.605	11.605	12.605	13.605
11.0	4.796	5.896	6.996	8.096	9.196	10.296	11.396	12.496	13.596	14.696
12.0	4.970	6.170	7.370	8.570	9.770	10.970	12.170	13.370	14.570	15.770
13.0	5.130	6.430	7.730	9.030	10.330	11.630	12.930	14.230	15.530	16.830
14.0	5.278	6.678	8.078	9.478	10.878	12.278	13.678	15.078	16.478	17.878
15.0	5.416	6.916	8.416	9.916	11.416	12.916	14.416	15.916	17.416	18.916
16.0	5.545	7.145	8.745	10.345	11.945	13.545	15.145	16.745	18.345	19.945
17.0	5.666	7.366	9.066	10.766	12.466	14.166	15.866	17.566	19.266	20.966
18.0	5.781	7.581	9.381	11.181	12.981	14.781	16.581	18.381	20.181	21.981
19.0	5.889	7.789	9.689	11.589	13.489	15.389	17.289	19.189	21.089	22.989
20.0	5.991	7.991	9.991	11.991	13.991	15.991	17.991	19.991	21.991	23.991
25.0	6.438	8.938	11.438	13.938	16.438	18.938	21.438	23.938	26.438	28.938
30.0	6.802	9.802	12.802	15.802	18.802	21.802	24.802	27.802	30.802	33.802
40.0	7.378	11.378	15.378	19.378	23.378	27.378	31.378	35.378	39.378	43.378
50.0	7.824	12.824	17.824	22.824	27.824	32.824	37.824	42.824		
75.0	8.635	16.135	23.635	31.135	38.635	46.135				
100.0	9.210	19.210	29.210	39.210	49.210					
150.0	10.021	25.021	40.021							
200.0	10.597	30.597	50.597							
250.0	11.043	36.043	61.043							

Table 3.2–12 (*Continued*)
VISUAL RANGE OF POINT SOURCES OF LIGHT

Function ($\sigma D + 2\log_e D$)

Visual range D km.	Extinction coefficient, σ, km.$^{-1}$ 0	1	2	3	4	5	6	7	8	9
0.004										
0.005										
0.006										
0.007	−9.924	−9.917	−9.910	−9.903	−9.896	−9.889	−9.882	−9.875	−9.868	−9.861
0.008	−9.657	−9.649	−9.641	−9.633	−9.625	−9.617	−9.609	−9.601	−9.593	−9.585
0.009	−9.421	−9.412	−9.403	−9.394	−9.385	−9.376	−9.367	−9.358	−9.349	−9.340
0.01	−9.210	−9.200	−9.190	−9.180	−9.170	−9.160	−9.150	−9.140	−9.130	−9.120
0.02	−7.824	−7.804	−7.784	−7.764	−7.744	−7.724	−7.704	−7.684	−7.664	−7.644
0.03	−7.013	−6.983	−6.953	−6.923	−6.893	−6.863	−6.833	−6.803	−6.773	−6.743
0.04	−6.438	−6.398	−6.358	−6.318	−6.278	−6.238	−6.198	−6.158	−6.118	−6.078
0.05	−5.991	−5.941	−5.891	−5.841	−5.791	−5.741	−5.691	−5.641	−5.591	−5.541
0.06	−5.627	−5.567	−5.507	−5.447	−5.387	−5.327	−5.267	−5.207	−5.147	−5.087
0.07	−5.319	−5.249	−5.179	−5.109	−5.039	−4.969	−4.899	−4.829	−4.759	−4.689
0.08	−5.051	−4.971	−4.891	−4.811	−4.731	−4.651	−4.571	−4.491	−4.411	−4.331
0.09	−4.816	−4.726	−4.636	−4.546	−4.456	−4.366	−4.276	−4.186	−4.096	−4.006
0.1	−4.605	−4.505	−4.405	−4.305	−4.205	−4.105	−4.005	−3.905	−3.805	−3.705
0.2	−3.219	−3.019	−2.819	−2.619	−2.419	−2.219	−2.019	−1.819	−1.619	−1.419
0.3	−2.408	−2.108	−1.808	−1.508	−1.208	−0.908	−0.608	−0.308	−0.008	0.292
0.4	−1.833	−1.433	−1.033	−0.633	−0.233	0.167	0.567	0.967	1.367	1.767
0.5	−1.386	−0.886	−0.386	0.114	0.614	1.114	1.614	2.114	2.614	3.114
0.6	−1.022	−0.422	0.178	0.778	1.378	1.978	2.578	3.178	3.778	4.378
0.7	−0.713	−0.013	0.687	1.387	2.087	2.787	3.487	4.187	4.887	5.587
0.8	−0.446	0.354	1.154	1.954	2.754	3.554	4.354	5.154	5.954	6.754
0.9	−0.211	0.689	1.589	2.489	3.389	4.289	5.189	6.089	6.989	7.889
1.0	0.000	1.000	2.000	3.000	4.000	5.000	6.000	7.000	8.000	9.000
1.1	0.191	1.291	2.391	3.491	4.591	5.691	6.791	7.891	8.991	10.091
1.2	0.365	1.565	2.765	3.965	5.165	6.365	7.565	8.765	9.965	11.165
1.3	0.525	1.825	3.125	4.425	5.725	7.025	8.325	9.625	10.925	12.225
1.4	0.673	2.073	3.473	4.873	6.273	7.673	9.073	10.473	11.873	13.273
1.5	0.811	2.311	3.811	5.311	6.811	8.311	9.811	11.311	12.811	14.311
1.6	0.940	2.540	4.140	5.740	7.340	8.940	10.540	12.140	13.740	15.340
1.7	1.061	2.761	4.461	6.161	7.861	9.561	11.261	12.961	14.661	16.361
1.8	1.176	2.976	4.776	6.576	8.376	10.176	11.976	13.776	15.576	17.376
1.9	1.284	3.184	5.084	6.984	8.884	10.784	12.684	14.584	16.484	18.384
2.0	1.386	3.386	5.386	7.386	9.386	11.386	13.386	15.386	17.386	19.386
2.1	1.484	3.584	5.684	7.784	9.884	11.984	14.084	16.184	18.284	20.384
2.2	1.577	3.777	5.977	8.177	10.377	12.577	14.777	16.977	19.177	21.377
2.3	1.666	3.966	6.266	8.566	10.866	13.166	15.466	17.766	20.066	22.366
2.4	1.751	4.151	6.551	8.951	11.351	13.751	16.151	18.551	20.951	23.351
2.5	1.833	4.333	6.833	9.333	11.833	14.333	16.833	19.333	21.833	24.333
2.6	1.911	4.511	7.111	9.711	12.311	14.911	17.511	20.111	22.711	25.311
2.7	1.986	4.686	7.386	10.086	12.786	15.486	18.186	20.886	23.586	26.286
2.8	2.059	4.859	7.659	10.459	13.259	16.059	18.859	21.659	24.459	27.259
2.9	2.129	5.029	7.929	10.829	13.729	16.629	19.529	22.429	25.329	28.229
3.0	2.197	5.197	8.197	11.197	14.197	17.197	20.197	23.197	26.197	29.197
3.2	2.326	5.526	8.726	11.926	15.126	18.326	21.526	24.726	27.926	31.126
3.4	2.448	5.848	9.248	12.648	16.048	19.448	22.848	26.248	29.648	33.048
3.6	2.562	6.162	9.762	13.362	16.962	20.562	24.162	27.762	31.362	34.962
3.8	2.670	6.470	10.270	14.070	17.870	21.670	25.470	29.270	33.070	
4.0	2.773	6.773	10.773	14.773	18.773	22.773	26.773	30.773		

Table 3.2–12 (*Continued*)
VISUAL RANGE OF POINT SOURCES OF LIGHT

Function ($\sigma D + 2\log_e D$)

Visual range D km.	Extinction coefficient, σ, km.⁻¹ 0	1	2	3	4	5	6	7	8	9
4.0	2.773	6.773	10.773	14.773	18.773	22.773	26.773	30.773		
4.2	2.870	7.070	11.270	15.470	19.670	23.870	28.070	32.270		
4.4	2.963	7.363	11.763	16.163	20.563	24.963	29.363	33.763		
4.6	3.052	7.652	12.252	16.852	21.452	26.052	30.652			
4.8	3.137	7.937	12.737	17.537	22.337	27.137	31.937			
5.0	3.219	8.219	13.219	18.219	23.219	28.219	33.219			
5.2	3.297	8.497	13.697	18.897	24.097	29.297	34.497			
5.4	3.373	8.773	14.173	19.573	24.973	30.373				
5.6	3.446	9.046	14.646	20.246	25.846	31.446				
5.8	3.516	9.316	15.116	20.916	26.716	32.516				
6.0	3.584	9.584	15.584	21.584	27.584	33.584				
6.2	3.649	9.849	16.049	22.249	28.449	34.649				
6.4	3.713	10.113	16.513	22.913	29.313	35.713				
6.6	3.774	10.374	16.974	23.574	30.174					
6.8	3.834	10.634	17.434	24.234	31.034					
7.0	3.892	10.892	17.892	24.892	31.892					
7.2	3.948	11.148	18.348	25.548	32.748					
7.4	4.003	11.403	18.803	26.203	33.603					
7.6	4.056	11.656	19.256	26.856	34.456					
7.8	4.108	11.908	19.708	27.508	35.308					
8.0	4.159	12.159	20.159	28.159	36.159					
8.2	4.208	12.408	20.608	28.808	37.008					
8.4	4.256	12.656	21.056	29.456	37.856					
8.6	4.304	12.904	21.504	30.104						
8.8	4.350	13.150	21.950	30.750						
9.0	4.394	13.394	22.394	31.394						
9.2	4.438	13.638	22.838	32.038						
9.4	4.481	13.881	23.281	32.681						
9.6	4.524	14.124	23.724	33.324						
9.8	4.565	14.365	24.165	33.965						
10.0	4.605	14.605	24.605	34.605						
11.0	4.796	15.796	26.796	37.796						
12.0	4.970	16.970	28.970	40.970						
13.0	5.130	18.130	31.130							
14.0	5.278	19.278	33.278							
15.0	5.416	20.416	35.416							
16.0	5.545	21.545	37.545							
17.0	5.666	22.666	39.666							
18.0	5.781	23.781	41.781							
19.0	5.889	24.889	43.889							
20.0	5.991	25.991	45.991							
25.0	6.438	31.438								
30.0	6.802	36.802								
40.0	7.378	47.378								
50.0	7.824	57.824								
75.0	8.635	83.635								
100.0	9.210									
150.0	10.021									
200.0	10.597									
250.0	11.043									

Table 3.2–12 (*Continued*)
VISUAL RANGE OF POINT SOURCES OF LIGHT

Function ($\sigma D + 2 \log_e D$)

Visual range D km.	Extinction coefficient, σ, km.⁻¹ 0	10	15	20	30	40	50	100	500	1000
0.004									−9.043	−7.043
0.005									−8.097	−5.597
0.006						−9.992	−9.932	−9.632	−7.232	−4.232
0.007	−9.924	−9.854	−9.819	−9.784	−9.714	−9.644	−9.574	−9.224	−6.424	−2.924
0.008	−9.657	−9.577	−9.537	−9.497	−9.417	−9.337	−9.257	−8.857	−5.657	−1.657
0.009	−9.421	−9.331	−9.286	−9.241	−9.151	−9.061	−8.971	−8.521	−4.921	−0.421
0.01	−9.210	−9.110	−9.060	−9.010	−8.910	−8.810	−8.710	−8.210	−4.210	0.790
0.02	−7.824	−7.624	−7.524	−7.424	−7.224	−7.024	−6.824	−5.824	2.176	12.176
0.03	−7.013	−6.713	−6.563	−6.413	−6.113	−5.813	−5.513	−4.013	7.987	22.987
0.04	−6.438	−6.038	−5.838	−5.638	−5.238	−4.838	−4.438	−2.438	13.562	33.562
0.05	−5.991	−5.491	−5.241	−4.991	−4.491	−3.991	−3.491	−0.991	19.009	44.009
0.06	−5.627	−5.027	−4.727	−4.427	−3.827	−3.227	−2.627	0.373	24.373	54.373
0.07	−5.319	−4.619	−4.269	−3.919	−3.219	−2.519	−1.819	1.681	29.681	64.681
0.08	−5.051	−4.251	−3.851	−3.451	−2.651	−1.851	−1.051	2.949	34.949	
0.09	−4.816	−3.916	−3.466	−3.016	−2.116	−1.216	−0.316	4.184	40.184	
0.1	−4.605	−3.605	−3.105	−2.605	−1.605	−0.605	0.395	5.395	45.395	
0.2	−3.219	−1.219	−0.219	0.781	2.781	4.781	6.781	16.781	96.781	
0.3	−2.408	0.592	2.092	3.592	6.592	9.592	12.592	27.592		
0.4	−1.833	2.167	4.167	6.167	10.167	14.167	18.167	38.167		
0.5	−1.386	3.614	6.114	8.614	13.614	18.614	23.614	48.614		
0.6	−1.022	4.978	7.978	10.978	16.978	22.978	28.978	58.978		
0.7	−0.713	6.287	9.787	13.287	20.287	27.287	34.287			
0.8	−0.446	7.554	11.554	15.554	23.554	31.554				
0.9	−0.211	8.789	13.289	17.789	26.789	35.789				
1.0	0.000	10.000	15.000	20.000	30.000					
1.1	0.191	11.191	16.691	22.191	33.191					
1.2	0.365	12.365	18.365	24.365	36.365					
1.3	0.525	13.525	20.025	26.525	39.525					
1.4	0.673	14.673	21.673	28.673	42.673					
1.5	0.811	15.811	23.311	30.811						
1.6	0.940	16.940	24.940	32.940						
1.7	1.061	18.061	26.561	35.061						
1.8	1.176	19.176	28.176	37.176						
1.9	1.284	20.284	29.784	39.284						
2.0	1.386	21.386	31.386							
2.1	1.484	22.484	32.984							
2.2	1.577	23.577	34.577							
2.3	1.666	24.666	36.166							
2.4	1.751	25.751	37.751							
2.5	1.833	26.833	39.333							
2.6	1.911	27.911	40.911							
2.7	1.986	28.986	42.486							
2.8	2.059	30.059								
2.9	2.129	31.129								
3.0	2.197	32.197								
3.2	2.326	34.326								
3.4	2.448	36.448								
3.6	2.562	38.562								
3.8	2.670	40.670								
4.0	2.773	42.773								

(From *Smithsonian Meteorological Tables,* 6th rev. ed., List, R. J., Ed., Smithsonian Institution, Washington, D.C., 1971.)

Table 3.2–13
ABSORPTION OF RADIATION BY OZONE

Parts A and B of this table give values of the "decimal" absorption coefficient of ozone, O_3, in the ultraviolet and in the visible bands as determined in the laboratory by Ny and Choong[1] and by Colange,[2] respectively. The average absorption coefficient for narrow wavelength intervals has been taken from curves in the references cited. The pressure dependence is small for these bands.[3,4] Evidence indicates a temperature effect on the absorption coefficients in the ultraviolet bands,[5,6,7] but there is conflicting evidence concerning a possible temperature effect in the visible band.[8,9,10]

The "decimal" absorption coefficient a and the "Naperian" absorption coefficient k are defined by the following expressions

$$I_\lambda = I_{o\lambda} 10^{-ax} = I_{o\lambda} e^{-kx}$$

where $I_{o\lambda}$ is the initial intensity of a parallel beam of radiation of wavelength in the neighborhood of λ and I_λ is the intensity after passing through a layer of ozone x centimeters thick at normal pressure and temperature (0 °C and 760 mm Hg); e is the base of the natural logarithms. Values of a are tabulated, and corresponding values of k may be obtained from the relationship

$$k = a \log_e 10 = 2.3026\, a$$

Part C gives the percentage absorption by ozone under laboratory conditions for a path of ozone 1 centimeter long at 0 °C and 760 mm Hg as given by Sutherland and Callendar.[11] Strong[4] states that the absorption by ozone in the infrared is proportional to the fourth root of the total pressure.

A.—Decimal absorption coefficients of ozone in the ultraviolet.

Wave length	Absorption coefficient	Wave length	Absorption coefficient	Wave length	Absorption coefficient
μ	cm.$^{-1}$	μ	cm.$^{-1}$	μ	cm.$^{-1}$
.210–.220	16.5	.306–.307	2.32	.323–.324	0.192
.220–.230	41.5	.307–.308	2.00	.324–.325	0.189
.230–.240	86	.308–.309	1.83	.325–.326	0.187
.240–.250	126	.309–.310	1.56	.326–.327	0.124
.250–.260	141	.310–.311	1.34	.327–.328	0.133
.260–.270	122	.311–.312	1.17	.328–.329	0.119
.270–.280	71	.312–.313	1.03	.329–.330	0.073
.280–.285	36.1	.313–.314	0.94	.330–.331	0.090
.285–.290	26.0	.314–.315	0.77	.331–.332	0.091
.290–.295	14.9	.315–.316	0.70	.332–.333	0.050
.295–.300	6.4	.316–.317	0.575	.333–.334	0.064
.300–.301	4.58	.317–.318	0.545	.334–.335	0.052
.301–.302	4.02	.318–.319	0.405	.335–.336	0.031
.302–.303	3.55	.319–.320	0.400	.336–.337	0.039
.303–.304	3.18	.320–.321	0.315	.337–.338	0.040
.304–.305	2.85	.321–.322	0.265	.338–.339	0.022
.305–.306	2.56	.322–.323	0.260	.339–.340	0.025

B.—Decimal absorption coefficients of ozone in the visible.

Wave length	Absorption coefficient	Wave length	Absorption coefficient	Wave length	Absorption coefficient
μ	cm.$^{-1}$	μ	cm.$^{-1}$	μ	cm.$^{-1}$
.44–.45	0.002	.51–.52	0.018	.58–.59	0.043
.45–.46	.002	.52–.53	.025	.59–.60	.043
.46–.47	.004	.53–.54	.031	.60–.61	.049
.47–.48	.004	.54–.55	.031	.61–.62	.044
.48–.49	.008	.55–.56	.036	.62–.63	.037
.49–.50	0.012	.56–.57	0.043	.63–.64	0.030
.50–.51	.016	.57–.58	.045		

C.—Percentage absorption of radiation by ozone in the infrared, (for 1 cm. path length at N.T.P.)

Wave length	Absorption
μ	%
4.5– 5.0	75
9.4– 9.8	75
12.5–15.5	17

Table 3.2–13 *(Continued)*
ABSORPTION OF RADIATION BY OZONE

REFERENCES

1. **Ny Tsi-Ze and Choong Shin-Piaw,** *Chin. J. Phys.,* 1, 38, 1933.
2. **Colange, G.,** *J. d. Phys.,* 8, 254, 1927.
3. **Vassy, E.,** Conference on atmospheric ozone held at Oxford, Sept. 9-11, 1936, Royal Meteorological Society, London, 1936, p. 26.
4. **Strong, J.,** *J. Frank. Inst.,* 231, 121, 1941.
5. **Wulf, O. R. and Melvin, E. H.,** *Phys. Rev.,* 38, 330, 1931.
6. **Vassy, E.,** *Ann. Phys.,* 9, 687, 1937.
7. **Gotz, F. W. P.,** *Beitr. Geophys., Ergenbnisse der kosmischen Physik,* 3, 253, 1938.
8. **Humphrey, G. L. and Badger, R. M.,** *J. Chem. Phys.,* 15, 794, 1947.
9. **Vigroux, E.,** *Compte Rend.,* 227, 272, 1948.
10. **Vassy, A. and Vassy, E.,** *J. Chem. Phys.,* 16, 1163, 1948.
11. **Sutherland, G. B. B. M. and Callendar, G. S.,** in *Reports on Progress in Physics,* Vol. IX, The Physical Society, London, 1943.

3.3 Geodetic and Astronomical Tables

Table 3.3–1
GEODETIC AND ASTRONOMICAL CONSTANTS

Table A

Dimensions of the Earth	International ellipsoid of reference[1]	Clarke spheroid of 1866[2]
Semimajor axis = a	6,378,388 m	6,378,206.4 m
Semiminor axis = b	6,356,911.946 m	6,356,583.8 m
Mean radius = $\frac{2a + b}{3}$	6,371,299.315 m	
Radius of sphere of same area	6,371,227.709 m	
Radius of sphere of same volume	6,371,221.266 m	
Length of meridian quadrant	10,002,288.299 m	
Length of equatorial quadrant	10,019,148.4 m	
Area of ellipsoid	510,100,934 km^2	
Volume of ellipsoid	1,083,319.78 x 10^6 km^3	
Flattening = f	1/297	

Table B

Mass of the earth[3]	5.975 x 10^{24} kg
Mean distance earth to sun (astronomical unit)[3]	1.4968 x 10^8 km
Mean linear velocity of the earth in its orbit	29.77 km sec^{-1}
Mean linear velocity of the surface of the earth at the equator	465.1 m/sec^{-1}
Obliquity of the ecliptic	23°27′

Note: The Clarke spheroid of 1866 is the reference spheroid for triangulation in the United States, Canada, and Mexico. The International Ellipsoid of Reference is used in South America and in parts of western Europe. It was adopted in 1924 by the International Union of Geodesy and Geophysics, and its use is recommended by that body wherever practicable. (See *Encyclopedia Britannica*, 1947 ed., article on Geodesy, for data concerning other spheroids.)

REFERENCES

1. U.S. Coast and Geodetic Survey, Spec. Publ. No. 200, Washington, D.C., 1935.
2. U.S. Coast and Geodetic Survey, Spec. Publ. No. 5, Washington, D.C., 1946.
3. **Russell, H. N., Dugan, R. S., and Stewart, J. Q.,** *Astronomy,* Ginn & Co., Boston, 1945.

(From *Smithsonian Meteorological Tables,* 6th rev. ed., List, R. J., Ed., Smithsonian Institution, Washington, D.C., 1971.)

Table 3.3–2
CONVERSION FACTORS

Time

1 mean solar second (sec, s)
 = 1.002738 sidereal seconds
1 mean solar minute (min, m)
 = 60 sec (mean solar)
1 mean solar hour (hr, h)
 = 3,600 sec (mean solar)
 = 60 min (mean solar)
1 mean solar day (da., d)
 = 86,400 sec (mean solar)
 = 1,440 min (mean solar)
 = 24 hr (mean solar)
 = 24 hr, 3 min, 56,555 sec of mean sidereal time
1 tropical (mean solar, ordinary) year (yr)
 = 31.5569×10^6 sec (mean solar)
 = 525,949 min (mean solar)
 = 8,765.81 hr (mean solar)
 = 365.2422 day (mean solar)
 = 366.2422 sidereal days
1 sidereal second
 = 0.997270 sec (mean solar)
1 sidereal day
 = 86,164.1 sec (mean solar)
 = 23 hr, 56 min, 4.091 sec (mean solar)

(From *Smithsonian Meteorological Tables,* 6th rev. ed., List, R. J., Ed., Smithsonian Institution, Washington, D.C., 1971.)

Table 3.3–3
LENGTH OF ONE DEGREE OF THE MERIDIAN

Latitude	International ellipsoid, m	Clarke spheroid of 1866			Latitude	International ellipsoid, m	Clarke spheroid of 1866		
		m	Statute mi	Nautical mi			m	Statute mi	Nautical mi
0–1°	110,575.6	110,567.3	68.703	59.661	45–46	111,145.2	111,140.8	69.060	59.971
1–2	110,575.6	110,568.0	68.704	59.662	46–47	111,164.8	111,160.5	69.072	59.981
2–3	110,577.6	110,569.4	68.705	59.662	47–48	111,184.4	111,180.2	69.084	59.992
3–4	110,579.7	110,571.4	68.706	59.664	48–49	111,203.9	111,199.9	69.096	60.003
4–5	110,582.4	110,574.1	68.707	59.665	49–50	111,223.4	111,219.5	69.108	60.013
5–6	110,585.8	110,577.6	68.710	59.667	50–51	111,242.7	111,239.0	69.121	60.024
6–7	110,589.8	110,581.6	68.712	59.669	51–52	111,261.9	111,258.3	69.133	60.034
7–8	110,594.5	110,586.4	68.715	59.672	52–53	111,281.0	111,277.6	69.145	60.045
8–9	110,599.9	110,591.8	68.718	59.675	53–54	111,299.9	111,296.6	69.156	60.055
9–10	110,605.9	110,597.8	68.722	59.678	54–55	111,318.6	111,315.4	69.168	60.065
10–11	110,612.5	110,604.5	68.726	59.681	55–56	111,337.1	111,334.0	69.180	60.075
11–12	110,619.8	110,611.9	68.731	59.685	56–57	111,355.4	111,352.4	69.191	60.085
12–13	110,627.8	110,619.8	68.736	59.690	57–58	111,373.4	111,370.5	69.202	60.095
13–14	110,636.3	110,628.4	68.741	59.694	58–59	111,391.1	111,388.4	69.213	60.104
14–15	110,645.4	110,637.6	68.747	59.699	59–60	111,408.5	111,405.9	69.224	60.114
15–16	110,655.2	110,647.5	68.753	59.705	60–61	111,425.5	111,423.1	69.235	60.123
16–17	110,665.5	110,657.8	68.759	59.710	61–62	111,422.3	111,439.9	69.246	60.132
17–18	110,676.4	110,668.8	68.766	59.716	62–63	111,458.6	111,456.4	69.256	60.141
18–19	110,687.9	110,680.4	68.773	59.722	63–64	111,474.6	111,472.4	69.266	60.150
19–20	111,699.9	110,692.4	68.781	59.729	64–65	111,490.1	111,488.1	69.275	60.158
20–21	110,712.4	110,705.1	68.789	59.736	65–66	111,505.2	111,503.3	69.285	60.166
21–22	110,725.4	110,718.2	68.797	59.743	66–67	111,519.9	111,518.0	69.294	60.174
22–23	110,739.0	110,731.8	68.805	59.750	67–68	111,534.1	111,532.3	69.303	60.182
23–24	110,753.0	110,746.0	68.814	59.758	68–69	111,547.8	111,546.2	69.311	60.190
24–25	110,767.5	110,760.6	68.823	59.765	69–70	111,561.0	111,559.5	69.320	60.197
25–26	110,782.5	110,775.6	68.833	59.774	70–71	111,573.7	111,572.2	69.328	60.204
26–27	110,797.9	110,791.1	68.842	59.782	71–72	111,585.9	111,584.5	69.335	60.210
27–28	110,813.7	110,807.0	68.852	59.791	72–73	111,597.5	111,596.2	69.343	60.217
28–29	110,829.9	110,823.3	68.862	59.800	73–74	111,608.5	111,607.3	69.349	60.223
29–30	110,846.4	110,840.0	68.873	59.808	74–75	111,619.0	111,617.9	69.356	60.228
30–31	110,863.3	110,857.0	68.883	59.818	75–76	111,628.9	111,627.8	69.362	60.234
31–32	110,880.6	110,874.4	68.894	59.827	76–77	111,638.2	111,637.1	69.368	60.239
32–33	110,898.2	110,892.1	68.905	59.837	77–78	111,646.8	111,645.9	69.373	60.243
33–34	110,916.0	110,910.1	68.916	59.846	78–79	111,654.9	111,653.9	69.378	60.248
34–35	110,934.2	110,928.3	68.928	59.856	79–80	111,662.3	111,661.4	69.383	60.252
35–36	110,952.6	110,946.9	68.939	59.866	80–81	111,699.1	111,668.2	69.387	60.255
36–37	110,971.2	110,965.6	68.851	59.876	81–82	111,675.2	111,674.4	69.391	60.259
37–38	110,990.0	110.984.5	68.962	59.886	82–83	111,680.6	111,679.9	69.395	60.262
38–39	111,009.0	111,003.7	68.974	59.897	83–84	111,685.4	111,684.7	69.398	60.264
39–40	111,028.2	111,023.0	68.986	59.907	84–85	111,689.5	111,688.9	69.400	60.268
40–41	111,047.5	111,042.4	68.998	59.918	85–86	111,693.0	111,692.3	69.402	60.268
41–42	111,066.9	111,061.9	69.011	59.928	86–87	111,695.7	111,695.1	69.404	60.270
42–43	111,086.4	111,081.6	69.023	59.939	87–88	111,697.8	111,697.2	69.405	60.271
43–44	111,105.9	111,101.3	69.035	59.949	88–89	111,699.2	111,698.6	69.406	60.272
44–45	111,125.5	111,121.0	69.047	59.960	89–90	111,699.9	111,699.3	69.407	60.272

(From *Smithsonian Meteorological Tables,* 6th rev. ed., List. R. J., Ed., Smithsonian Institution, Washington, D.C., 1971.)

Table 3.3–4
LENGTH OF ONE DEGREE OF THE PARALLEL

Latitude	International ellipsoid, m	Clarke spheroid of 1866 m	Clarke spheroid of 1866 Statute mi	Clarke spheroid of 1866 Nautical mi	Latitude	International ellipsoid, m	Clarke spheroid of 1866 m	Clarke spheroid of 1866 Statute mi	Clarke spheroid of 1866 Nautical mi
0°	111,324	111,321	69.172	60.068	45	78,850	78,849	48.995	42.546
1	111,307	111,304	69.162	60.059	46	77,467	77,466	48.136	41.801
2	111,257	111,253	69.130	60.031	47	76,060	76,058	47.261	41.041
3	111,172	111,169	69.078	59.986	48	74,629	74,628	46.372	40.268
4	111,055	111,051	69.005	59.922	49	73,175	73,174	45.469	39.484
5	110,903	110,900	68.911	59.840	50	71,699	71,698	44.552	38.688
6	110,718	110,715	68.795	59.741	51	70,201	70,200	43.621	37.880
7	110,500	110,497	68.660	59.622	52	68,681	68,680	42.676	37.060
8	110,248	110,245	68.504	59.487	53	67,140	67,140	41.719	36.229
9	109,962	109,959	68.326	59.333	54	65,579	65,578	40.749	35.386
10	109,644	109,641	68.129	59.161	55	63,997	63,996	39.766	34.532
11	109,292	109,289	67.910	58.971	56	62,396	62,395	38.771	33.668
12	108,907	108,904	67.670	58.764	57	60,775	60,774	37.764	32.794
13	108,489	108,486	67.410	58.538	58	59,136	59,135	36.745	31.909
14	108,038	108,036	67.131	58.295	59	57,478	57,478	35.716	31.015
15	107,555	107,553	66.830	58.034	60	55,803	55,802	34.674	30.110
16	107,039	107,036	66.510	57.756	61	54,110	54,110	33.623	29.197
17	106,490	106,487	66.169	57.459	62	52,401	52,400	32.560	28.275
18	105,909	105,906	65.808	57.146	63	50,675	50,675	31.488	27.344
19	105,296	105,294	65.427	56.816	64	48,934	48,934	30.406	26.404
20	104,651	104,649	65.026	56.468	65	47,178	47,177	29.315	25.456
21	103,975	103,972	64.606	56.102	66	45,407	45,407	28.215	24.501
22	103,266	103,264	64.166	55.720	67	43,622	43,622	27.106	23.538
23	102,527	102,524	63.706	55.321	68	41,824	41,823	25.988	22.567
24	101,756	101,754	63.228	54.905	69	40,012	40,012	24.862	21.590
25	100,954	100,952	62.729	54.473	70	38,189	38,188	23.729	20.606
26	100,122	100,119	62.212	54.024	71	36,353	36,353	22.589	19.616
27	99,259	99,257	61.676	53.558	72	34,506	34,506	21.441	18.619
28	98,366	98,364	61.122	53.076	73	32,648	32,648	20.287	17.617
29	97,443	97,441	60.548	52.578	74	30,781	30,781	19.127	16.609
30	96,490	96,488	59.956	52.064	75	28,904	28,903	17.960	15.596
31	95,508	95,506	59.345	51.534	76	27,017	27,017	16.788	14.578
32	94,497	94,495	58.716	50.989	77	25,123	25,123	15.611	13.556
33	93,457	93,455	58.071	50.428	78	23,220	23,220	14.428	12.529
34	92,389	92,387	57.407	49.851	79	21,311	21,311	13.242	11.499
35	91,292	91,290	56.725	49.259	80	19,395	19,394	12.051	10.465
36	90,168	90,166	56.027	48.653	81	17,472	17,472	10.857	9.428
37	89,016	89,104	55.311	48.031	82	15,545	15,545	9.659	8.388
38	87,836	87,835	54.579	47.395	83	13,612	13,612	8.458	7.345
39	86,630	86,629	53.829	46.744	84	11,675	11,675	7.255	6.300
40	85,398	85,396	53.063	46.079	85	9,735	9,735	6.049	5.253
41	84,139	84,137	52.281	45.399	86	7,792	7,792	4.842	4.205
42	82,855	82,853	51.483	44.706	87	5,846	5,846	3.632	3.154
43	81,545	81,543	50.699	44.000	88	3,898	3,898	2.422	2.103
44	80,210	80,208	49.840	43.280	89	1,949	1,949	1.211	1.052

(From *Smithsonian Meteorological Tables,* 6th rev. ed., List, R. J., Ed., Smithsonian Institution, Washington, D.C., 1971.)

Table 3.3–5
DISTRIBUTION OF WATER AND LAND IN VARIOUS LATITUDE BELTS

	Northern hemisphere				Southern hemisphere			
Latitude	Water 10^6 km²	Land 10^6 km²	Water %	Land %	Water 10^6 km²	Land 10^6 km²	Water %	Land %
90–85°	0.979	–	100.0	–	–	0.978	–	100.0
85–80	2.545	0.384	86.9	13.1	–	2.929	–	100.0
80–75	3.742	1.112	77.1	22.9	0.522	4.332	10.7	89.3
75–70	4.414	2.326	65.5	34.5	2.604	4.136	38.6	61.4
70–65	2.456	6.116	28.7	71.3	6.816	1.756	79.5	20.5
65–60	3.123	7.210	31.2	69.8	10.301	0.032	99.7	0.3
60–55	5.399	6.613	45.0	55.0	12.006	0.006	99.9	0.1
55–50	5.529	8.066	40.7	59.3	13.388	0.207	98.5	1.5
50–45	6.612	8.458	43.8	56.2	14.693	0.377	97.5	2.5
45–40	8.411	8.016	51.2	48.8	15.833	0.594	96.4	3.6
40–35	10.029	7.627	56.8	43.2	16.483	1.173	93.4	6.6
35–30	10.806	7.943	57.7	42.3	15.782	2.967	84.2	15.8
30–25	11.747	7.952	59.6	40.4	15.438	4.261	78.4	21.6
25–20	13.354	7.145	65.2	34.8	15.450	5.049	75.4	24.6
20–15	14.981	6.164	70.8	29.2	16.147	4.998	76.4	23.6
15–10	16.553	5.080	76.5	23.5	17.211	4.422	79.6	20.4
10–5	16.628	5.332	75.7	24.3	16.898	5.062	76.9	23.1
5–0	17.387	4.737	78.6	21.4	16.792	5.332	75.9	24.1
90–0°	154.695	100.281	60.7	39.3	206.364	48.611	80.9	19.1

Note: All oceans and seas 361.059 × 10^6 km² 70.8 percent; all land 148.892 × 10^6 km², 29.2 percent.

(From Kossinna, Erwin, Die Tiefen des Weltmeeres, *Berlin Univ., Inst. f. Meereskunde, Veroff.*, N. F., A Geogr.-naturwiss. Reihe, Heft 9, 1921.)

Table 3.3–6
SCALE VARIATION FOR STANDARD MAP PROJECTIONS

Three map projections are widely used in meteorology: the polar stereographic, the Lambert conformal conic, and the Mercator, each of which is conformal. That is, the shape of any small area on the map is the same as the shape of the corresponding small area of the earth, all angles are preserved (except at the pole on the Lambert and Mercator projections), and the scale is the same in all directions at any point, a function only of the latitude of the point for a given assumed figure of the earth.

$$\Delta m = sk\Delta n$$

where:

Δn = (small) distance on the earth,
Δm = corresponding (small) distance on the map,
s = map scale at standard parallel,
k = scale factor for latitude in question.

Values of k are tabulated below assuming the figure of the earth to be spherical and assuming the figure to be that of the International Ellipsoid of Reference.

	Mercator projection Standard parallel 22½°		Lambert conformal conic projection Standard parallels 30° and 60°		Polar stereographic projection Standard parallel 60°	
Latitude	Sphere k	International ellipsoid k	Sphere k	International ellipsoid k	Sphere k	International ellipsoid k
0°	0.924	0.924	1.283	1.281	1.866	1.860
5	0.927	0.928	1.210	1.208	1.716	1.712
10	0.938	0.938	1.149	1.148	1.590	1.586
15	0.956	0.957	1.099	1.098	1.482	1.480
20	0.983	0.983	1.058	1.058	1.390	1.388
25	1.019	1.019	1.025	1.025	1.312	1.310
30	1.067	1.066	1.000	1.000	1.244	1.243
35	1.128	1.127	0.982	0.982	1.186	1.185
40	1.206	1.205	0.970	0.970	1.136	1.136
45	1.307	1.305	0.966	0.966	1.093	1.093
50	1.437	1.435	0.968	0.969	1.057	1.057
55	1.611	1.608	0.979	0.979	1.026	1.026
60	1.848	1.844	1.000	1.000	1.000	1.000
65	2.186	2.181	1.033	1.033	0.979	0.979
70	2.701	2.694	1.084	1.083	0.962	0.962
75	3.570	3.560	1.162	1.162	0.949	0.949
80	5.320	5.306	1.293	1.292	0.940	0.940
85	10.600	10.570	1.566	1.564	0.935	0.936

REFERENCE

Gregg, W. R. and Tannehill, I. R., *Month. Weath. Rev.,* U.S. Dept. of Commerce, Washington, D.C., 65, 415, 1937.

(From *Smithsonian Meteorological Tables,* 6th rev. ed., List, R. J., Ed., Smithsonian Institution, Washington, D.C., 1971.)

Table 3.3–7
RADIUS OF CURVATURE ON A POLAR STEREOGRAPHIC PROJECTION

In computing gradient wind speeds and in other problems, it is necessary to determine a factor r that depends on curvature of the trajectory. This factor arises in taking account of the horizontal component of the centrifugal force acting on a particle. The problem is twofold: (1) to determine the trajectory of the particle on a map, and (2) to determine the required value of r if the trajectory on the map is known. The first problem is of such nature that it cannot be treated adequately here. (NOTE – In many cases an approximation is made from the curvature of the isobars or streamlines.) The second problem has been solved for the case of a polar stereographic projection, since on this projection a "small circle" on the earth projects as a circle on the map.

Let R be the radius of the earth, r' the true radius of the *small circle* on which the particle is assumed to be traveling at a given instant, and α its angular radius (as seen from the center of the earth). Then $r' = R \sin \alpha$. Since we are concerned with the horizontal component of the centrifugal force, the effective horizontal radius of the curvature required in the gradient wind equation is given by $r = r' \sec \alpha = R \tan \alpha$. If an arc on a map representing the instantaneous trajectory of a particle of air is determined, this arc may be regarded as a portion of a "small circle."

To determine r for a given arc of a trajectory on the map:

1. Complete the circle by extending the arc. (A set of circular templates will prove very useful.)
2. Find the meridian which passes through the center of this circle.
3. Determine the latitudes ϕ_1 and ϕ_2 of the points where this meridian intersects the circle. (Extend the meridian across the pole if necessary.)

4a. If the circle found in Step 1 *does not* contain the pole, find the difference between ϕ_1 and ϕ_2 and enter Part A of the table with this difference as the argument. The corresponding tabular value is the required radius r in statute miles, from the formula $r = R \tan \frac{1}{2} (\phi_1 - \phi_2)$.

4b. If the circle found in Step 1 contains the pole, find the sum $(\phi_1 + \phi_2)$ and enter Part B of the table with this sum as the argument. The corresponding tabular value is the required radius r in statute miles, from the formula $r = R \tan [90° - \frac{1}{2} (\phi_1 + \phi_2)]$.

Table A
Circle not including pole

$\phi_1 - \phi_2$	0 mi	1 mi	2 mi	3 mi	4 mi	5 mi	6 mi	7 mi	8 mi	9 mi
0°	0	35	69	104	138	173	207	242	277	311
10	346	381	416	451	486	521	556	591	627	662
20	698	733	769	805	841	877	914	950	987	1,023
30	1,060	1,097	1,135	1,172	1,210	1,248	1,286	1,324	1,363	1,401
40	1,440	1,479	1,519	1,559	1,599	1,639	1,680	1,721	1,762	1,803
50	1,845	1,887	1,930	1,973	2,016	2,060	2,104	2,148	2,193	2,239
60	2,285	2,331	2,378	2,425	2,473	2,521	2,570	2,619	2,669	2,720
70	2,771	2,822	2,875	2,928	2,982	3,036	3,092	3,148	3,204	3,262
80	3,320	3,380	3,440	3,501	3,563	3,626	3,690	3,755	3,821	3,889
90	3,957									

Table 3.3–7 (*Continued*)
RADIUS OF CURVATURE ON A POLAR STEREOGRAPHIC PROJECTION

Table B

Circle including poles

$\phi_1 + \phi_2$	0 mi	1 mi	2 mi	3 mi	4 mi	5 mi	6 mi	7 mi	8 mi	9 mi
0°		453,433	226,697	151,110	113,313	90,631	75,504	64,697	56,589	50,278
10	45,229	41,093	37,648	34,730	32,227	30,057	28,156	26,477	24,984	23,646
20	22,441	21,350	20,357	19,449	18,616	17,849	17,140	16,482	15,871	15,301
30	14,768	14,269	13,800	13,358	12,943	12,550	12,178	11,826	11,492	11,174
40	10,872	10,583	10,308	10,045	9,794	9,553	9,322	9,100	8,887	8,683
50	8,486	8,296	8,113	7,937	7,766	7,601	7,442	7,288	7,138	6,994
60	6,854	6,718	6,586	6,457	6,332	6,211	6,093	5,978	5,867	5,757
70	5,651	5,547	5,446	5,347	5,251	5,157	5,065	4,975	4,886	4,800
80	4,716	4,633	4,552	4,473	4,395	4,318	4,243	4,170	4,097	4,027
90	3,957	3,889	3,821	3,755	3,690	3,626	3,563	3,501	3,440	3,380
100	3,320	3,262	3,204	3,148	3,092	3,036	2,982	2,928	2,875	2,822
110	2,771	2,720	2,669	2,619	2,570	2,521	2,473	2,425	2,378	2,331
120	2,285	2,239	2,193	2,148	2,104	2,060	2,016	1,973	1,930	1,887
130	1,845	1,803	1,762	1,721	1,680	1,639	1,599	1,559	1,519	1,479
140	1,440	1,401	1,363	1,324	1,286	1,248	1,210	1,172	1,135	1,097
150	1,060	1,023	987	950	914	877	841	805	769	733
160	698	662	627	591	556	521	486	451	416	381
170	346	311	277	242	207	173	138	104	69	35

(From *Smithsonian Meteorological Tables,* 6th rev. ed., List, R. J., Ed., Smithsonian Institution, Washington, D.C., 1971.)

Table 3.3–8
ACCELERATION OF GRAVITY AT SEA LEVEL

$$g\phi = 978.0356\ (1 + 0.0052885 \sin^2 \phi - 0.0000059 \sin^2 2\phi)$$
$$= 980.6160\ (1 - 0.0026373 \cos 2\phi + 0.0000059 \cos^2 2\phi)$$

Latitude	0′ cm sec^{-2}	10′ cm sec^{-2}	20′ cm sec^{-2}	30′ cm sec^{-2}	40′ cm sec^{-2}	50′ cm sec^{-2}
0°	978.036	978.036	978.036	978.036	978.036	978.037
1	978.037	978.038	978.038	978.039	978.040	978.041
2	978.042	978.043	978.044	978.045	978.047	978.048
3	978.050	978.051	978.053	978.055	978.057	978.059
4	978.061	978.063	978.065	978.067	978.070	978.072
5	978.075	978.077	978.080	978.083	978.086	978.089
6	978.092	978.095	987.098	978.102	978.105	978.109
7	978.112	978.116	978.120	978.123	978.127	978.131
8	978.135	978.140	978.144	978.148	978.153	978.157
9	978.162	978.166	978.171	978.176	978.181	978.186
10	978.191	978.106	978.201	978.207	978.212	978.218
11	978.223	978.229	978.234	978.240	978.246	978.252
12	978.258	978.264	978.271	978.277	978.283	978.290
13	978.296	978.303	978.310	978.316	978.323	978.330
14	978.337	978.344	978.351	978.358	978.366	978.373
15	978.381	978.388	978.396	978.403	978.411	978.419
16	978.427	978.435	978.443	978.451	978.459	978.468
17	978.476	978.484	978.493	978.501	978.510	978.519
18	978.528	978.536	978.545	978.554	978.563	978.572
19	978.582	978.591	978.600	978.610	978.619	978.629

Table 3.3–8 (*Continued*)
ACCELERATION OF GRAVITY AT SEA LEVEL

$$g\phi = 978.0356\,(1 + 0.0052885 \sin^2 \phi - 0.0000059 \sin^2 2\phi)$$
$$= 980.6160\,(1 - 0.0026373 \cos 2\phi + 0.0000059 \cos^2 2\phi)$$

Latitude	0′ cm sec^{-2}	10′ cm sec^{-2}	20′ cm sec^{-2}	30′ cm sec^{-2}	40′ cm sec^{-2}	50′ cm sec^{-2}
20	978.638	978.648	978.658	978.667	978.677	978.687
21	978.697	978.707	978.717	978.728	978.738	978.748
22	978.759	978.769	978.780	978.790	978.801	978.812
23	978.822	978.833	978.844	978.855	978.866	978.877
24	978.888	978.899	978.911	978.922	978.933	978.945
25	978.956	978.968	978.979	978.991	979.002	979.014
26	979.026	979.038	979.050	979.062	979.074	979.086
27	979.098	979.110	979.122	979.135	979.147	979.159
28	979.172	979.184	979.197	979.209	979.222	979.234
29	979.247	979.260	979.273	979.286	979.298	979.311
30	979.324	979.337	979.350	979.364	979.377	979.390
31	979.403	979.416	979.430	979.443	979.456	979.470
32	979.483	979.497	979.510	979.524	979.538	979.551
33	979.565	979.579	979.593	979.606	979.620	979.634
34	979.648	979.662	979.676	979.690	979.704	979.718
35	979.732	979.746	979.760	979.775	979.789	979.803
36	979.817	979.832	979.846	979.860	979.875	979.889
37	979.904	979.918	979.933	979.947	979.962	979.976
38	979.991	980.005	980.020	980.035	980.049	980.064
39	980.079	980.093	980.108	980.123	980.138	980.152
40	980.167	980.182	980.197	980.212	980.226	980.241
41	980.256	980.271	980.286	980.301	980.316	980.331
42	980.346	980.361	980.376	980.391	980.406	980.421
43	980.436	980.451	980.466	980.481	980.496	980.511
44	980.526	980.541	980.556	980.571	980.586	980.601
45	980.616	980.631	980.646	980.661	980.676	980.691
46	980.706	980.721	980.736	980.751	980.766	980.781
47	980.796	980.811	980.826	980.841	980.856	980.871
48	980.886	980.901	980.916	980.931	980.946	980.961
49	980.976	980.991	981.006	981.021	981.036	981.050
50	981.065	981.080	981.095	981.110	981.124	981.139
51	981.154	981.169	981.183	981.198	981.213	981.227
52	981.242	981.257	981.271	981.286	981.300	981.315
53	981.329	981.344	981.358	981.373	981.387	981.401
54	981.416	981.430	981.444	981.459	981.473	981.487
55	981.501	981.515	981.529	981.544	981.558	981.572
56	981.586	981.600	981.613	981.627	981.641	981.655
57	981.669	981.683	981.696	981.710	981.724	981.737
58	981.751	981.764	981.778	981.791	981.805	981.818
59	981.831	981.845	981.858	981.871	981.884	981.897
60	981.911	981.924	981.937	981.950	981.962	981.975
61	981.988	982.001	982.014	982.026	982.039	982.051
62	982.064	982.076	982.089	982.101	982.114	982.126
63	982.138	982.150	982.162	982.175	982.187	982.198
64	982.210	982.222	982.234	982.246	982.258	982.269

Table 3.3–8 (*Continued*)
ACCELERATION OF GRAVITY AT SEA LEVEL

$$g\phi = 978.0356\ (1 + 0.0052885\ \sin^2\ \phi - 0.0000059\ \sin^2\ 2\phi)$$
$$= 980.6160\ (1 - 0.0026373\ \cos\ 2\phi + 0.0000059\ \cos^2\ 2\phi)$$

Latitude	0′ cm sec^{-2}	10′ cm sec^{-2}	20′ cm sec^{-2}	30′ cm sec^{-2}	40′ cm sec^{-2}	50′ cm sec^{-2}
65°	982.281	982.292	982.304	982.315	982.327	982.338
66	982.349	982.360	982.371	982.382	982.393	982.404
67	982.415	982.426	982.437	982.448	982.458	982.469
68	982.479	982.490	982.500	982.511	982.521	982.531
69	982.541	982.551	982.561	982.571	982.581	982.591
70	982.601	982.610	982.620	982.629	982.639	982.648
71	982.658	982.667	982.676	982.685	982.694	982.703
72	982.712	982.721	982.730	982.738	982.747	982.756
73	982.764	982.772	982.781	982.789	982.797	982.805
74	982.813	982.821	982.829	982.837	982.845	982.852
75	982.860	982.868	982.875	982.882	982.890	982.897
76	982.904	982.911	982.918	982.925	982.932	982.938
77	982.945	982.952	982.958	982.965	982.971	982.977
78	982.983	982.990	982.996	983.001	983.007	983.013
79	983.019	983.024	983.030	983.035	983.041	983.046
80	983.051	983.056	983.061	983.066	983.071	983.076
81	983.081	983.085	983.090	983.094	983.099	983.103
82	983.107	983.111	983.116	983.119	983.123	983.127
83	983.131	983.134	983.138	983.141	983.145	983.148
84	983.151	983.154	983.157	983.160	983.163	983.166
85	983.168	983.171	983.174	983.176	983.178	983.181
86	983.183	983.185	983.187	983.189	983.190	983.192
87	983.194	983.195	983.197	983.198	983.199	983.201
88	983.202	983.203	983.204	983.204	983.205	983.206
89	983.206	983.207	983.207	983.208	983.208	983.208
90	983.208					

(From *Smithsonian Meteorological Tables,* 6th rev. ed., List, R. J., Ed., Smithsonian Institution, Washington, D.C., 1971.)

Table 3.3–9
EPHEMERIS OF THE SUN

All data are for O^h Greenwich Civil Time in the year 1950. Variations of these data from year to year are negligible for most meteorological purposes; the largest variation occurs through the 4 year, leap year cycle. The year 1950 was selected to represent a mean condition in this cycle.

The *declination* of the sun is its angular distance north (+) or south (–) of the celestial equator.

The *longitude* of the sun is the angular distance of the meridian of sun from the vernal equinox (mean equinox of 1950.0) measured eastward along the ecliptic.

The *equation of time* (apparent – mean) is the correction to be applied to mean solar time in order to obtain apparent (true) solar time.

The *radius vector* of the earth is the distance from the center of the earth to the center of the sun expressed in terms of the length of the semimajor axis of the earth's orbit.

Table 3.3–9 (*Continued*)

Date	Declination °	′	Longitude °	′	Equation of time m	s	Radius vector	Date	Declination °	′	Longitude °	′	Equation of time m	s	Radius vector
Jan. 1	−23	4	280	1	−3	14	0.98324	Feb. 1	−17	19	311	34	−13	34	0.98533
5	22	42	284	5	5	6	.98324	5	16	10	315	37	14	2	.98593
9	22	13	288	10	6	50	.98333	9	14	55	319	40	14	17	.98662
13	21	37	292	14	8	27	.98352	13	13	37	323	43	14	20	.98738
17	20	54	296	19	9	54	.98378	17	12	15	327	46	14	10	.98819
21	20	5	300	23	11	10	.98410	21	10	50	331	48	13	50	.98903
25	19	9	304	27	12	14	.98448	25	9	23	335	49	13	19	.98991
29	18	8	308	31	13	5	.98493								
Mar. 1	−7	53	339	51	−12	38	0.99084	Apr. 1	+4	14	10	42	−4	12	0.99928
5	6	21	343	51	11	48	.99182	5	5	46	14	39	3	1	1.00043
9	4	48	347	51	10	51	.99287	9	7	17	18	35	1	52	1.00160
13	3	14	351	51	9	49	.99396	13	8	46	22	30	−0	47	1.00276
17	1	39	355	50	8	42	.99508	17	10	12	26	25	+0	13	1.00390
21	−0	5	359	49	7	32	.99619	21	11	35	30	20	1	6	1.00500
25	+1	30	3	47	6	20	.99731	25	12	56	34	14	1	53	1.00606
29	3	4	7	44	5	7	.99843	29	14	13	38	7	2	33	1.00708
May 1	+14	50	40	4	+2	50	1.00759	June 1	+21	57	69	56	+2	27	1.01405
5	16	2	43	56	3	17	1.00859	5	22	28	73	46	1	49	1.01465
9	17	9	47	48	3	35	1.00957	9	22	52	77	36	1	6	1.01518
13	18	11	51	40	3	44	1.01051	13	23	10	81	25	+0	18	1.01564
17	19	9	55	32	3	44	1.01138	17	23	22	85	15	−0	33	1.01602
21	20	2	59	23	3	34	1.01218	21	23	27	89	4	1	25	1.01630
25	20	49	63	14	3	16	1.01291	25	23	25	92	53	2	17	1.01649
29	21	30	67	4	2	51	1.01358	29	23	17	96	41	3	7	1.01662
July 1	+23	10	98	36	−3	31	1.01667	Aug. 1	+18	14	128	11	−6	17	1.01494
5	22	52	102	24	4	16	1.01671	5	17	12	132	0	5	59	1.01442
9	22	28	106	13	4	56	1.01669	9	16	6	135	50	5	33	1.01384
13	21	57	110	2	5	30	1.01659	13	14	55	139	41	4	57	1.01318
17	21	21	113	51	5	57	1.01639	17	13	41	143	31	4	12	1.01244
21	20	38	117	40	6	15	1.01610	21	12	23	147	22	3	19	1.01163
25	19	50	121	29	6	24	1.01573	25	11	2	151	14	2	18	1.01076
29	18	57	125	19	6	23	1.01530	29	9	39	155	5	1	10	1.00986
Sept. 1	+8	35	157	59	−0	15	1.00917	Oct. 1	−2	53	187	14	+10	1	1.00114
5	7	7	161	52	+1	2	1.00822	5	4	26	191	11	11	17	1.00001
9	5	37	165	45	2	22	1.00723	9	5	58	195	7	12	27	0.99888
13	4	6	169	38	3	45	1.00619	13	7	29	199	5	13	30	.99774
17	2	34	173	32	5	10	1.00510	17	8	58	203	3	14	25	.99659
21	+1	1	177	26	6	35	1.00397	21	10	25	207	1	15	10	.99544
25	−0	32	181	21	8	0	1.00283	25	11	50	211	0	15	46	.99433
29	2	6	185	16	9	22	1.00170	29	13	12	214	59	16	10	.99326
Nov. 1	−14	11	217	59	+16	21	0.99249	Dec. 1	−21	41	248	13	+11	16	0.98604
5	15	27	222	0	16	23	.99150	5	22	16	252	16	9	43	.98546
9	16	38	226	1	16	12	.99054	9	22	45	256	20	8	1	.98494
13	17	45	230	2	15	47	.98960	13	23	6	260	24	6	12	.98446
17	18	48	234	4	15	10	.98869	17	23	20	264	28	4	17	.98405
21	19	45	238	6	14	18	.98784	21	23	26	268	32	2	19	.98372
25	20	36	242	8	13	15	.98706	25	23	25	272	37	+0	20	.98348
29	21	21	246	11	11	59	.98636	29	23	17	276	41	−1	39	.98334

(From U.S. Naval Observatory, *The American Ephemeris and Nautical Almanac for the Year 1950,* Washington, D.C., 1948.)

Table 3.3–10
SOLAR ALTITUDE AND AZIMUTH

The altitude and azimuth of the sun are given by

$$\sin a = \sin \phi \sin \delta + \cos \phi \cos \delta \cos h \qquad (1)$$

and

$$\sin \alpha = -\cos \delta \sin h / \cos \alpha \qquad (2)$$

where

a = altitude of the sun (angular elevation above the horizon),
ϕ = latitude of the observer,
δ = declination of the sun,
h = hour angle of sun (angular distance from the meridian of the observer),
α = azimuth of the sun (measured eastward from north).

From Equations 1 and 2 it can be seen that the altitude and azimuth of the sun are functions of the latitude of the observer, the time of day (hour angle), and the date (declination).

Table 3.3–11 provides a series of charts, one for each five degrees of latitude (except 5°, 15°, 75°, and 85°) giving the altitude and azimuth of the sun as a function of the true solar time and the declination of the sun in a form originally suggested by Hand.[1] Linear interpolation for intermediate latitudes will give results within the accuracy to which the charts can be read.

On these charts, a point corresponding to the projected position of the sun is determined from the heavy lines corresponding to declination and solar time. To find the solar altitude and azimuth:

1. Select the chart or charts appropriate to the latitude.
2. Find the solar declination δ corresponding to the date in question from table 3.3–10.
3. Determine the *true solar time* as follows:
   a. To the *local standard time* (zone time) add four minutes for each degree of longitude the station is east of the standard meridian or subtract four minutes for each degree west of the standard meridian to get the *local mean solar time*.
   b. To the *local mean solar time* add algebraically the equation of time obtained from table 3.3–11; the sum is the required *true solar time*.
4. Read the required altitude and azimuth at the point determined by the declination and the true solar time. Interpolate linearly between two charts for intermediate latitudes.

It should be emphasized that the solar altitude determined from these charts is the true geometric position of the center of the sun. At low solar elevations terrestrial refraction may considerably alter the apparent position of the sun. Under average atmospheric refraction the sun will appear on the horizon when it actually is about 34′ below the horizon; the effect of refraction decreases rapidly with increasing solar elevation. Since sunset or sunrise is defined as the time when the upper limb of the sun appears on the horizon, and the semidiameter of the sun is 16′, sunset or sunrise occurs under average atmospheric refraction when the sun is 50′ below the horizon. In polar regions especially, unusual atmospheric refraction can make considerable variation in the time of sunset or sunrise.

The 90° N. chart is included for interpolation purposes; the azimuths lose their directional significance at the pole.

To compute solar altitude and azimuth for southern latitudes, change the sign of the solar declination and proceed as above. The resulting azimuths will indicate angular distance from *south* (measured eastward) rather than from north.

(From *Smithsonian Meteorological Tables,* 6th rev. ed., List, R. J., Ed., Smithsonian Institution, Washington, D.C., 1971.)

REFERENCE

1. **Hand, I. F.,** *Heating and Ventilating,* 45, 86, 1948.

Table 3.3–10 (*Continued*)
SOLAR ALTITUDE AND AZIMUTH

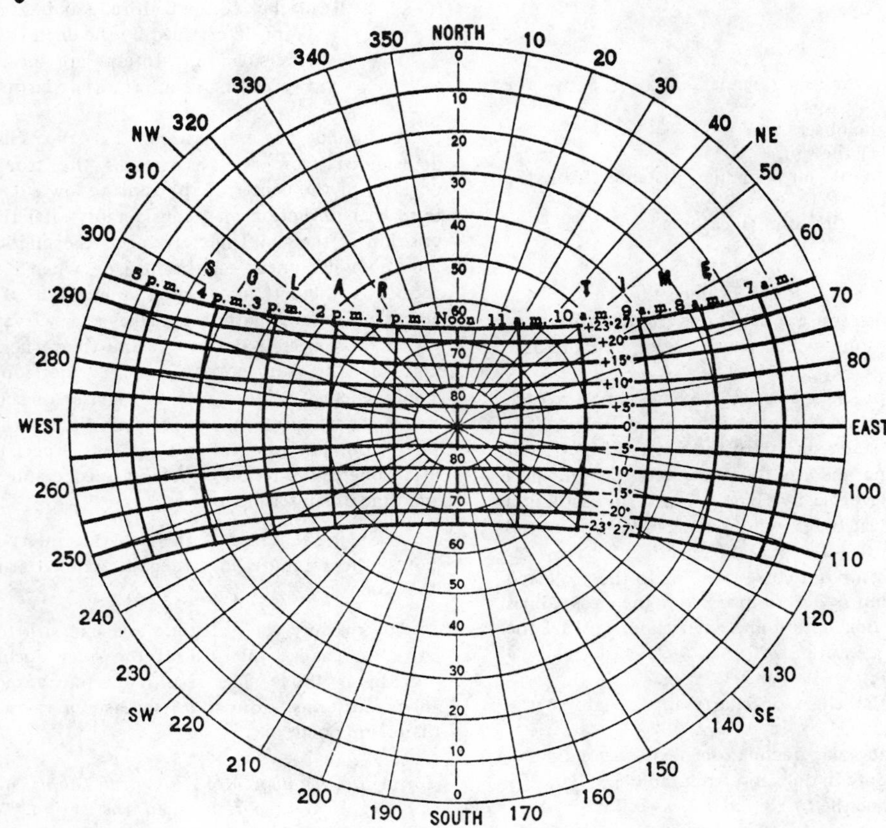

Table 3.3–10 (*Continued*)
SOLAR ALTITUDE AND AZIMUTH

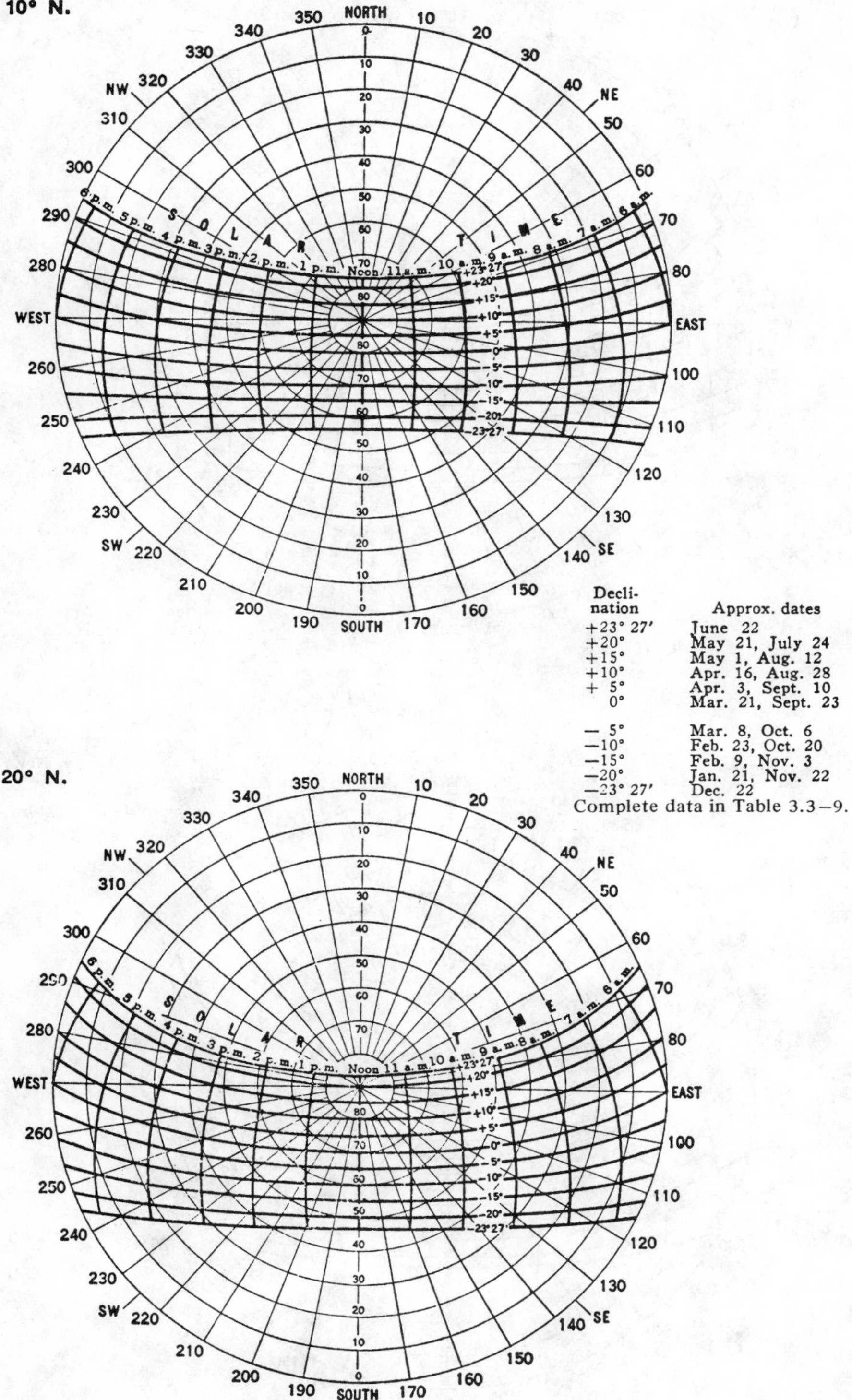

Declination	Approx. dates
+23° 27′	June 22
+20°	May 21, July 24
+15°	May 1, Aug. 12
+10°	Apr. 16, Aug. 28
+ 5°	Apr. 3, Sept. 10
0°	Mar. 21, Sept. 23
− 5°	Mar. 8, Oct. 6
−10°	Feb. 23, Oct. 20
−15°	Feb. 9, Nov. 3
−20°	Jan. 21, Nov. 22
−23° 27′	Dec. 22

Complete data in Table 3.3–9.

Table 3.3–10 (*Continued*)
SOLAR ALTITUDE AND AZIMUTH

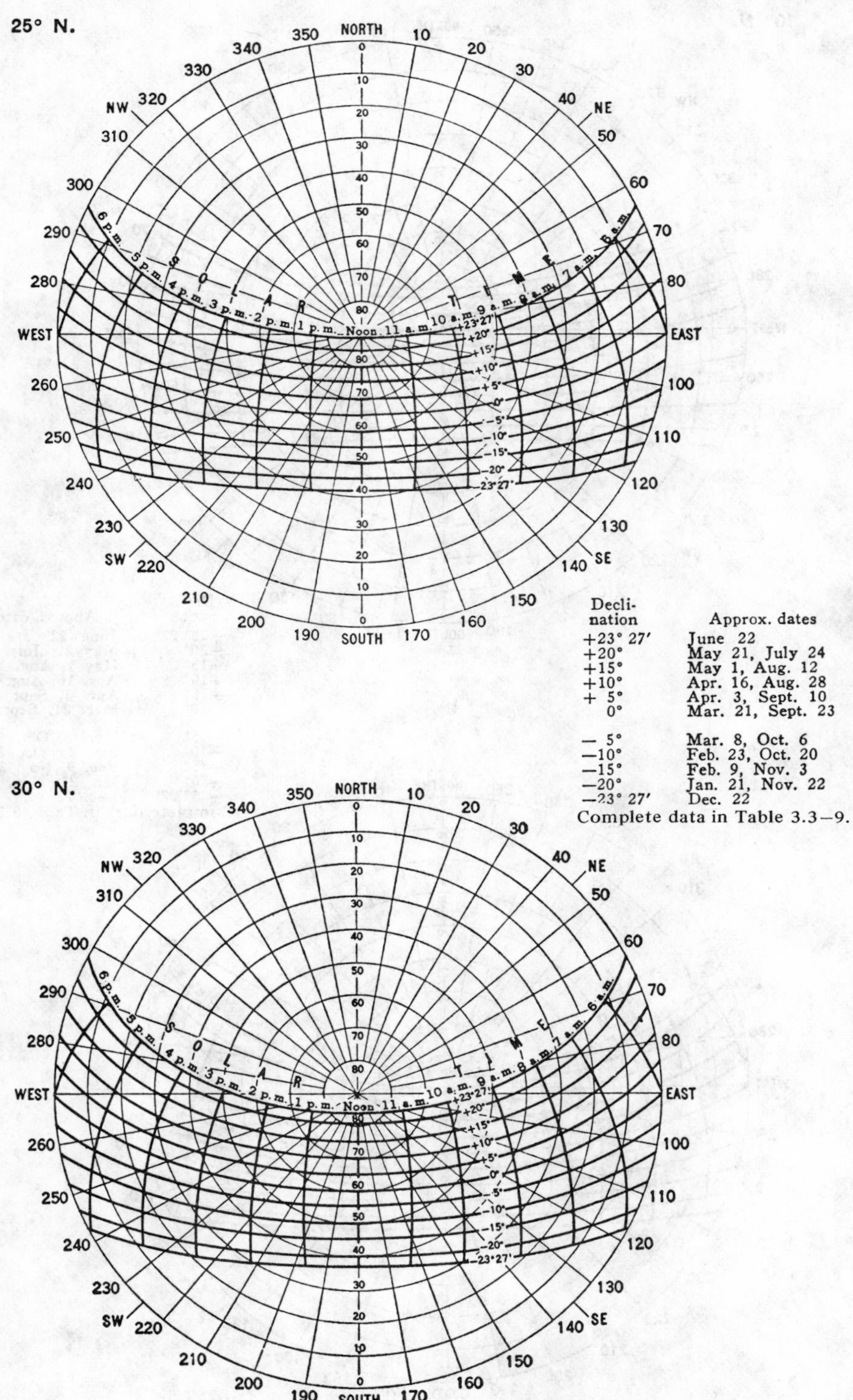

Table 3.3–10 (*Continued*)
SOLAR ALTITUDE AND AZIMUTH

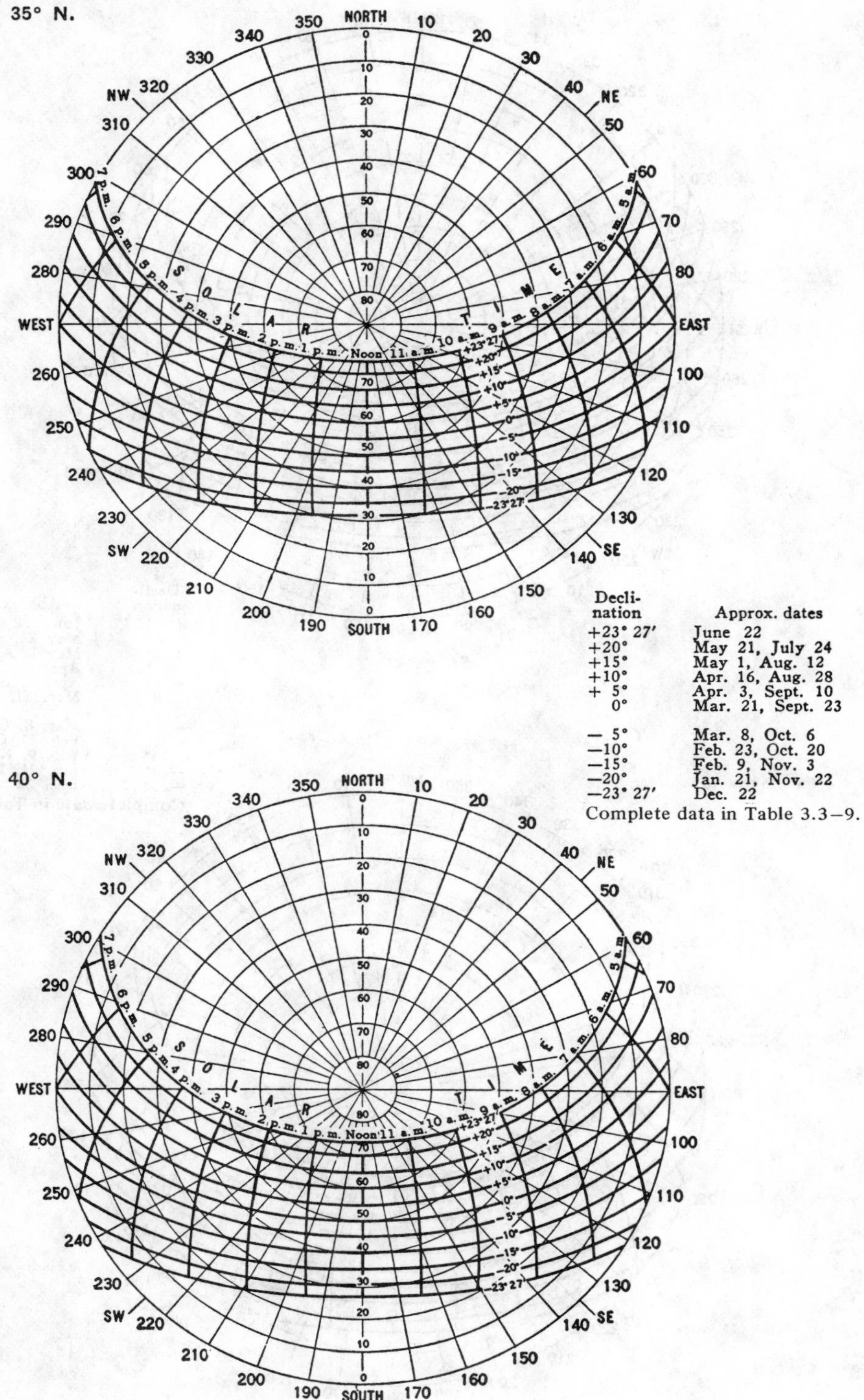

Declination	Approx. dates
+23° 27′	June 22
+20°	May 21, July 24
+15°	May 1, Aug. 12
+10°	Apr. 16, Aug. 28
+ 5°	Apr. 3, Sept. 10
0°	Mar. 21, Sept. 23
— 5°	Mar. 8, Oct. 6
—10°	Feb. 23, Oct. 20
—15°	Feb. 9, Nov. 3
—20°	Jan. 21, Nov. 22
—23° 27′	Dec. 22

Complete data in Table 3.3–9.

Table 3.3–10 (*Continued*)
SOLAR ALTITUDE AND AZIMUTH

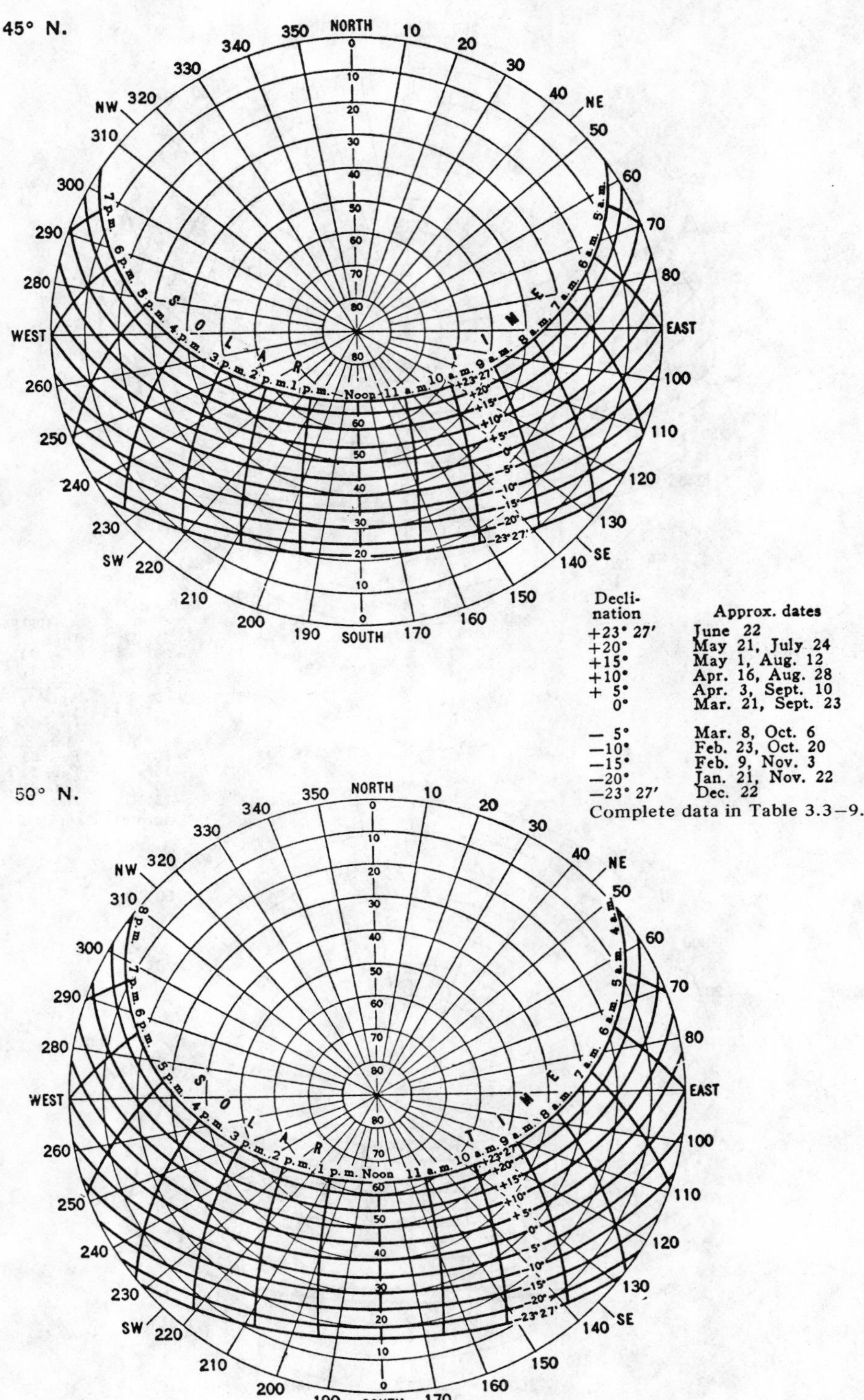

Declination	Approx. dates
+23° 27′	June 22
+20°	May 21, July 24
+15°	May 1, Aug. 12
+10°	Apr. 16, Aug. 28
+ 5°	Apr. 3, Sept. 10
0°	Mar. 21, Sept. 23
— 5°	Mar. 8, Oct. 6
—10°	Feb. 23, Oct. 20
—15°	Feb. 9, Nov. 3
—20°	Jan. 21, Nov. 22
—23° 27′	Dec. 22

Complete data in Table 3.3–9.

Table 3.3–10 (*Continued*)
SOLAR ALTITUDE AND AZIMUTH

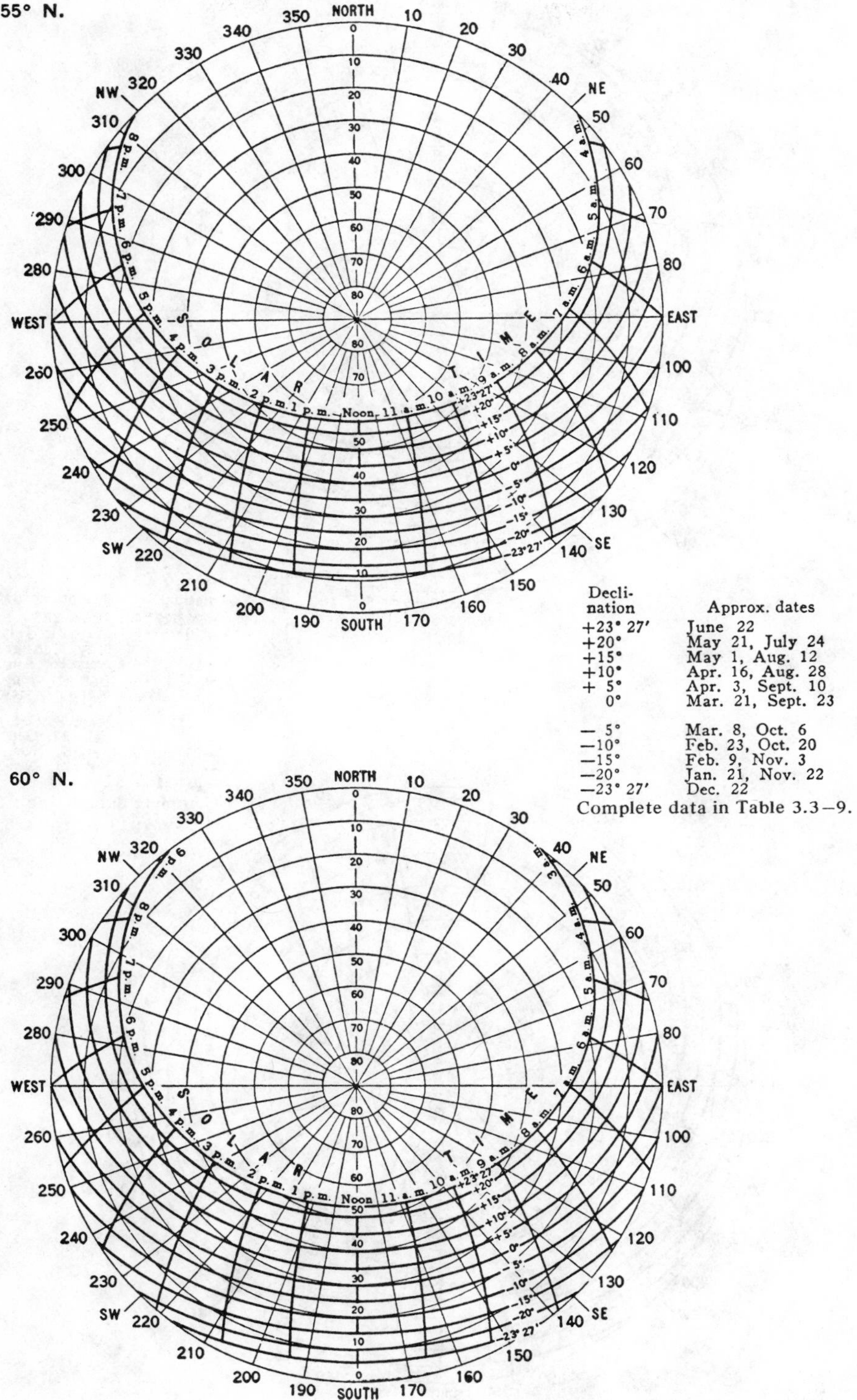

Declination	Approx. dates
+23° 27′	June 22
+20°	May 21, July 24
+15°	May 1, Aug. 12
+10°	Apr. 16, Aug. 28
+ 5°	Apr. 3, Sept. 10
0°	Mar. 21, Sept. 23
— 5°	Mar. 8, Oct. 6
—10°	Feb. 23, Oct. 20
—15°	Feb. 9, Nov. 3
—20°	Jan. 21, Nov. 22
—23° 27′	Dec. 22

Complete data in Table 3.3–9.

Table 3.3–10 (*Continued*)
SOLAR ALTITUDE AND AZIMUTH

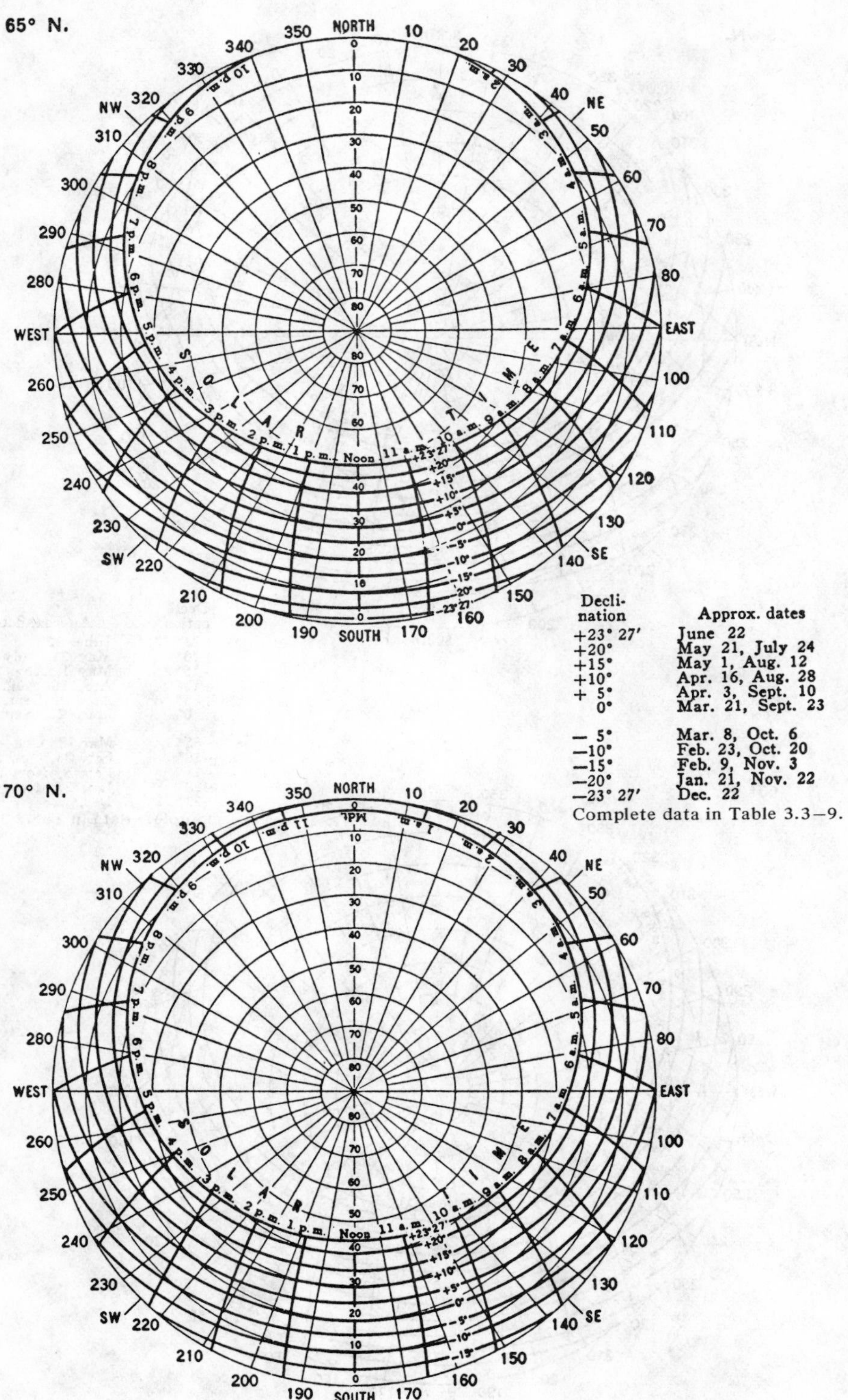

Declination	Approx. dates
+23° 27′	June 22
+20°	May 21, July 24
+15°	May 1, Aug. 12
+10°	Apr. 16, Aug. 28
+ 5°	Apr. 3, Sept. 10
0°	Mar. 21, Sept. 23
— 5°	Mar. 8, Oct. 6
—10°	Feb. 23, Oct. 20
—15°	Feb. 9, Nov. 3
—20°	Jan. 21, Nov. 22
—23° 27′	Dec. 22

Complete data in Table 3.3–9.

Table 3.3–10 (*Continued*)
SOLAR ALTITUDE AND AZIMUTH

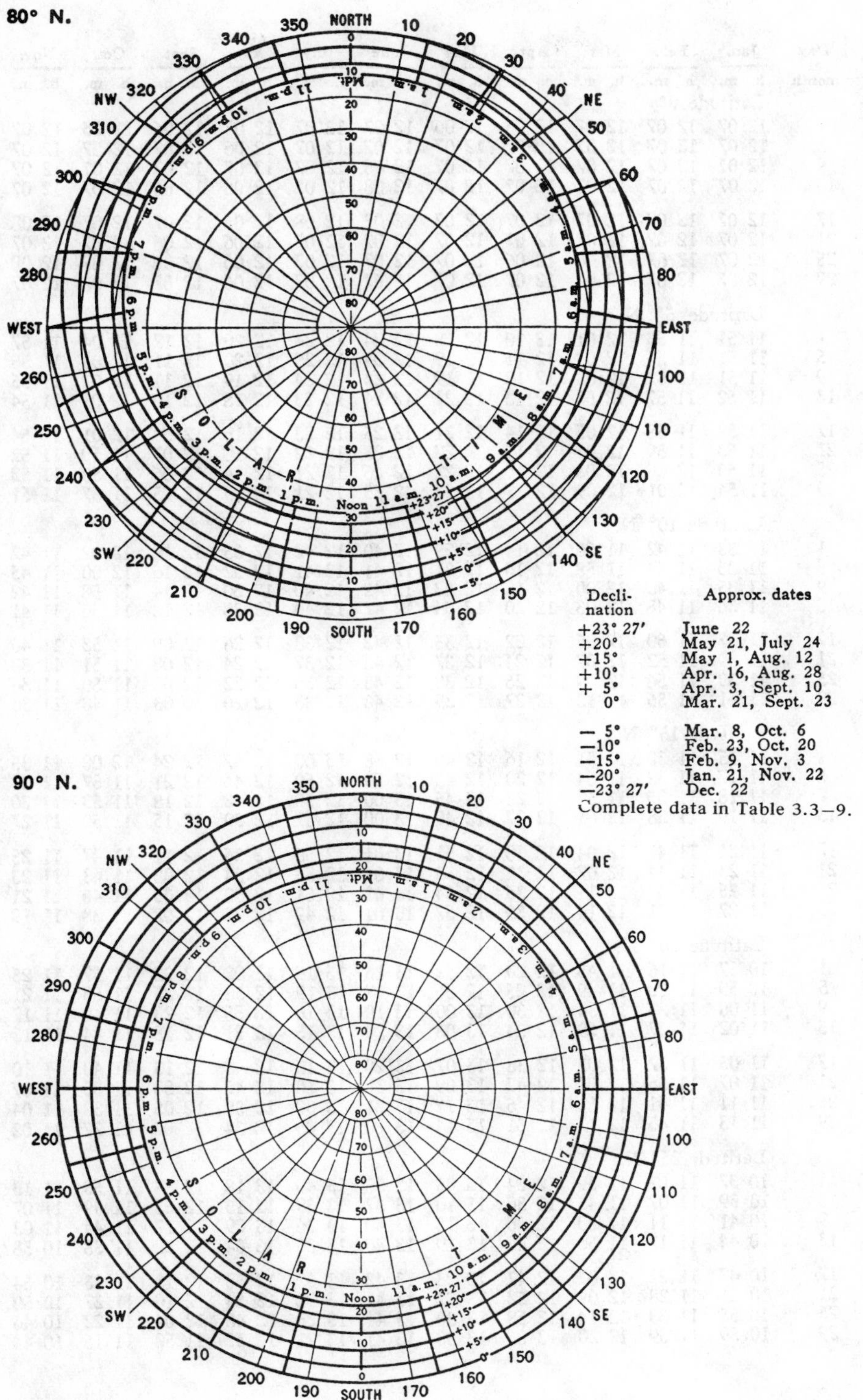

Table 3.3–11
DURATION OF DAYLIGHT

Day of month	Jan.	Feb.	Mar.	Apr.	May	June	July	Aug.	Sept.	Oct.	Nov.	Dec.
	h. m.	h. m.	h. m.	h. m.	h. m.	h. m.	h. m.	h. m.	h. m.	h. m.	h. m.	h. m.
	Latitude 0°											
1	12 07	12 07	12 07	12 06	12 06	12 07	12 07	12 07	12 06	12 06	12 07	12 08
5	12 07	12 07	12 07	12 07	12 07	12 07	12 07	12 06	12 07	12 07	12 07	12 07
9	12 07	12 07	12 07	12 07	12 07	12 08	12 07	12 07	12 07	12 07	12 07	12 07
13	12 07	12 07	12 07	12 07	12 07	12 08	12 07	12 06	12 06	12 07	12 07	12 07
17	12 07	12 07	12 07	12 07	12 07	12 07	12 08	12 06	12 07	12 07	12 08	12 08
21	12 07	12 07	12 07	12 07	12 07	12 07	12 07	12 06	12 06	12 07	12 07	12 07
25	12 07	12 07	12 06	12 06	12 07	12 07	12 07	12 06	12 06	12 07	12 08	12 08
29	12 07	12 07	12 06	12 07	12 07	12 07	12 07	12 06	12 07	12 07	12 07	12 08
	Latitude 5° N.											
1	11 51	11 55	12 01	12 10	12 18	12 24	12 24	12 20	12 12	12 04	11 57	11 52
5	11 51	11 56	12 03	12 11	12 19	12 24	12 25	12 20	12 11	12 03	11 55	11 51
9	11 51	11 57	12 03	12 12	12 19	12 24	12 24	12 19	12 11	12 02	11 55	11 51
13	11 52	11 57	12 05	12 13	12 21	12 24	12 23	12 18	12 10	12 01	11 54	11 50
17	11 52	11 58	12 05	12 14	12 21	12 25	12 23	12 16	12 09	12 01	11 54	11 50
21	11 53	11 59	12 07	12 15	12 22	12 25	12 22	12 16	12 07	11 59	11 52	11 50
25	11 53	12 00	12 08	12 16	12 22	12 25	12 21	12 14	12 06	11 58	11 52	11 50
29	11 54	12 01	12 09	12 17	12 23	12 25	12 21	12 14	12 05	11 57	11 51	11 50
	Latitude 10° N.											
1	11 33	11 42	11 56	12 14	12 29	12 40	12 42	12 33	12 18	12 02	11 47	11 36
5	11 33	11 44	11 58	12 16	12 31	12 41	12 41	12 32	12 16	12 00	11 45	11 35
9	11 35	11 46	12 00	12 18	12 33	12 42	12 40	12 30	12 14	11 58	11 42	11 33
13	11 36	11 48	12 03	12 20	12 34	12 42	12 40	12 28	12 12	11 56	11 41	11 33
17	11 37	11 50	12 05	12 22	12 35	12 42	12 38	12 26	12 09	11 53	11 40	11 32
21	11 39	11 52	12 07	12 24	12 37	12 43	12 37	12 24	12 08	11 51	11 38	11 32
25	11 39	11 54	12 09	12 26	12 38	12 43	12 36	12 22	12 05	11 50	11 36	11 32
29	11 41	11 56	12 12	12 27	12 39	12 43	12 35	12 20	12 03	11 48	11 36	11 33
	Latitude 15° N.											
1	11 15	11 30	11 51	12 16	12 40	12 58	13 00	12 47	12 24	12 00	11 35	11 18
5	11 17	11 32	11 54	12 20	12 43	12 59	12 59	12 44	12 21	11 57	11 33	11 17
9	11 18	11 35	11 57	12 23	12 45	13 00	12 58	12 42	12 18	11 53	11 30	11 16
13	11 19	11 38	12 01	12 27	12 49	13 00	12 57	12 39	12 15	11 50	11 27	11 15
17	11 21	11 41	12 04	12 30	12 51	13 01	12 56	12 36	12 11	11 47	11 25	11 14
21	11 23	11 44	12 07	12 33	12 53	13 01	12 53	12 34	12 08	11 43	11 23	11 14
25	11 25	11 47	12 11	12 36	12 54	13 01	12 51	12 30	12 05	11 40	11 21	11 14
29	11 27	11 51	12 14	12 39	12 57	13 01	12 49	12 27	12 02	11 38	11 19	11 15
	Latitude 20° N.											
1	10 57	11 16	11 45	12 20	12 52	13 16	13 19	13 02	12 32	11 57	11 25	11 00
5	10 59	11 20	11 49	12 25	12 56	13 17	13 19	12 58	12 27	11 53	11 21	10 59
9	11 00	11 23	11 54	12 30	13 00	13 19	13 16	12 55	12 23	11 49	11 17	10 57
13	11 02	11 27	11 59	12 34	13 03	13 20	13 15	12 51	12 18	11 44	11 13	10 56
17	11 05	11 32	12 03	12 38	13 07	13 20	13 12	12 48	12 13	11 40	11 10	10 56
21	11 07	11 36	12 07	12 42	13 09	13 21	13 10	12 42	12 08	11 35	11 07	10 55
25	11 11	11 41	12 12	12 46	13 12	13 21	13 07	12 38	12 05	11 32	11 04	10 56
29	11 13	11 45	12 17	12 51	13 14	13 20	13 05	12 34	12 00	11 27	11 02	10 56
	Latitude 25° N.											
1	10 37	11 02	11 39	12 24	13 05	13 35	13 40	13 18	12 38	11 55	11 13	10 42
5	10 39	11 07	11 45	12 30	13 10	13 37	13 39	13 13	12 33	11 49	11 07	10 39
9	10 41	11 11	11 50	12 36	13 15	13 40	13 36	13 09	12 27	11 44	11 03	10 38
13	10 44	11 17	11 56	12 42	13 19	13 40	13 35	13 04	12 22	11 38	10 58	10 36
17	10 47	11 22	12 02	12 47	13 23	13 42	13 32	12 58	12 15	11 33	10 54	10 36
21	10 51	11 28	12 09	12 52	13 27	13 41	13 28	12 54	12 10	11 27	10 50	10 35
25	10 55	11 33	12 14	12 58	13 30	13 41	13 25	12 48	12 04	11 22	10 46	10 36
29	10 59	11 39	12 20	13 03	13 33	13 41	13 21	12 42	11 58	11 16	10 44	10 36

Table 3.3–11 (*Continued*)
DURATION OF DAYLIGHT

Day of month	Jan.	Feb.	Mar.	Apr.	May	June	July	Aug.	Sept.	Oct.	Nov.	Dec.
	h. m.	h. m.	h. m.	h. m.	h. m.	h. m.	h. m.	h. m.	h. m.	h. m.	h. m.	h. m.
	Latitude 30° N.											
1	10 15	10 46	11 33	12 29	13 20	13 57	14 03	13 34	12 46	11 53	10 59	10 22
5	10 17	10 53	11 40	12 36	13 26	13 59	14 01	13 29	12 39	11 46	10 53	10 19
9	10 21	10 59	11 47	12 43	13 31	14 02	13 58	13 23	12 32	11 38	10 48	10 16
13	10 24	11 05	11 54	12 50	13 37	14 04	13 55	13 17	12 25	11 32	10 42	10 14
17	10 27	11 12	12 02	12 57	13 42	14 04	13 52	13 11	12 18	11 25	10 36	10 14
21	10 33	11 18	12 09	13 04	13 47	14 05	13 48	13 04	12 10	11 17	10 32	10 12
25	10 37	11 25	12 16	13 10	13 50	14 05	13 43	12 58	12 03	11 11	10 28	10 13
29	10 43	11 33	12 24	13 17	13 55	14 03	13 39	12 51	11 56	11 05	10 24	10 14
	Latitude 35° N.											
1	09 51	10 30	11 26	12 34	13 35	14 21	14 29	13 54	12 55	11 50	10 45	10 00
5	09 53	10 37	11 34	12 42	13 43	14 25	14 27	13 47	12 47	11 41	10 37	09 55
9	09 57	10 45	11 44	12 52	13 50	14 27	14 24	13 40	12 38	11 32	10 31	09 52
13	10 02	10 53	11 52	13 00	13 57	14 30	14 19	13 33	12 29	11 24	10 24	09 50
17	10 06	11 01	12 01	13 08	14 03	14 30	14 16	13 25	12 21	11 16	10 18	09 48
21	10 11	11 08	12 09	13 16	14 09	14 31	14 10	13 18	12 12	11 07	10 11	09 48
25	10 17	11 17	12 19	13 24	14 14	14 31	14 05	13 09	12 03	11 00	10 06	09 48
29	10 25	11 26	12 27	13 32	14 19	14 29	13 59	13 01	11 54	10 51	10 01	09 50
	Latitude 40° N.											
1	09 23	10 10	11 18	12 39	13 54	14 49	14 58	14 16	13 05	11 47	10 29	09 33
5	09 27	10 19	11 28	12 50	14 02	14 53	14 55	14 08	12 55	11 36	10 20	09 29
9	09 31	10 28	11 38	13 00	14 11	14 57	14 52	14 00	12 44	11 26	10 11	09 25
13	09 36	10 37	11 50	13 10	14 19	15 00	14 47	13 51	12 34	11 16	10 03	09 22
17	09 42	10 47	12 00	13 20	14 27	15 00	14 42	13 41	12 24	11 06	09 55	09 20
21	09 49	10 58	12 11	13 30	14 34	15 01	14 36	13 32	12 13	10 55	09 48	09 20
25	09 56	11 07	12 21	13 40	14 40	15 01	14 29	13 22	12 03	10 46	09 42	09 20
29	10 03	11 18	12 32	13 49	14 45	14 59	14 22	13 13	11 52	10 37	09 36	09 22
	Latitude 42° N.											
1	09 11	10 02	11 14	12 42	14 02	15 02	15 11	14 26	13 09	11 45	10 22	09 22
5	09 15	10 11	11 26	12 53	14 12	15 07	15 09	14 17	12 58	11 34	10 13	09 17
9	09 19	10 21	11 36	13 04	14 21	15 10	15 04	14 08	12 48	11 24	10 03	09 13
13	09 24	10 31	11 48	13 16	14 29	15 12	14 59	13 59	12 36	11 12	09 54	09 10
17	09 31	10 41	12 00	13 26	14 37	15 14	14 54	13 49	12 25	11 02	09 46	09 08
21	09 39	10 52	12 11	13 37	14 45	15 15	14 48	13 38	12 45	10 51	09 38	09 07
25	09 46	11 03	12 23	13 47	14 52	15 15	14 40	13 28	12 03	10 40	09 30	09 08
29	09 55	11 14	12 34	13 57	14 57	15 13	14 32	13 17	11 52	10 29	09 24	09 09
	Latitude 44° N.											
1	08 58	09 52	11 10	12 45	14 11	15 16	15 26	14 36	13 14	11 45	10 15	09 09
5	09 01	10 03	11 22	12 57	14 21	15 21	15 23	14 27	13 02	11 32	10 04	09 03
9	09 06	10 13	11 34	13 08	14 31	15 24	15 18	14 17	12 50	11 20	09 54	08 59
13	09 12	10 24	11 46	13 20	14 40	15 28	15 13	14 07	12 39	11 08	09 44	08 56
17	09 19	10 35	11 59	13 32	14 49	15 29	15 07	13 56	12 26	10 57	09 35	08 54
21	09 27	10 47	12 11	13 44	14 47	15 29	15 00	13 45	12 14	10 45	09 27	08 53
25	09 35	10 59	12 23	13 55	15 04	15 29	14 52	13 34	12 03	10 34	09 19	08 54
29	09 45	11 10	12 36	14 06	15 11	15 27	14 44	13 23	11 50	10 23	09 12	08 56
	Latitude 46° N.											
1	08 43	09 42	11 06	12 47	14 21	15 30	15 41	14 48	13 19	11 43	10 07	08 56
5	08 47	09 53	11 20	13 00	14 31	15 35	15 38	14 37	13 06	11 30	09 55	08 49
9	08 53	10 05	11 32	13 14	14 42	15 40	15 34	14 27	12 54	11 18	09 44	08 45
13	09 00	10 17	11 46	13 26	14 52	15 42	15 27	14 15	12 41	11 04	09 34	08 42
17	09 07	10 29	11 58	13 38	15 01	15 44	15 21	14 05	12 28	10 52	09 24	08 40
21	09 15	10 42	12 12	13 51	15 10	15 45	15 13	13 53	12 15	10 39	09 15	08 38
25	09 25	10 53	12 25	14 03	15 18	15 45	15 04	13 41	12 02	10 27	09 06	08 39
29	09 35	11 06	12 38	14 14	15 25	15 43	14 56	13 29	11 50	10 15	08 59	08 40

Table 3.3–11 (*Continued*)
DURATION OF DAYLIGHT

Day of month	Jan.	Feb.	Mar.	Apr.	May	June	July	Aug.	Sept.	Oct.	Nov.	Dec.
	h. m.	h. m.	h. m.	h. m.	h. m.	h. m.	h. m.	h. m.	h. m.	h. m.	h. m.	h. m.
Latitude 48° N.												
1	08 27	09 32	11 02	12 51	14 31	15 46	15 59	15 00	13 25	11 41	09 57	08 40
5	08 32	09 43	11 16	13 05	14 42	15 52	15 55	14 49	13 11	11 28	09 45	08 35
9	08 38	09 56	11 30	13 18	14 54	15 57	15 50	14 38	12 57	11 14	09 33	08 29
13	08 44	10 09	11 44	13 32	15 05	16 00	15 43	14 25	12 43	11 00	09 22	08 26
17	08 53	10 21	11 58	13 46	15 15	16 02	15 36	14 13	12 30	10 46	09 12	08 23
21	09 02	10 35	12 12	13 59	15 24	16 03	15 28	14 01	12 16	10 33	09 02	08 22
25	09 12	10 49	12 27	14 11	15 33	16 03	15 18	13 47	12 02	10 20	08 52	08 22
29	09 23	11 02	12 40	14 24	15 41	16 00	15 08	13 35	11 48	10 07	08 44	08 24
Latitude 50° N.												
1	08 10	09 20	10 58	12 55	14 41	16 04	16 18	15 14	13 31	11 39	09 48	08 24
5	08 15	09 33	11 12	13 09	14 54	16 11	16 13	15 03	13 16	11 24	09 35	08 17
9	08 21	09 46	11 28	13 24	15 07	16 16	16 08	14 50	13 01	11 10	09 22	08 12
13	08 30	10 00	11 42	13 38	15 19	16 20	16 01	14 37	12 47	10 56	09 10	08 08
17	08 38	10 15	11 58	13 53	15 30	16 22	15 53	14 23	12 32	10 40	08 58	08 06
21	08 48	10 28	12 13	14 07	15 40	16 23	15 44	14 09	12 17	10 26	08 47	08 04
25	08 59	10 43	12 28	14 21	15 50	16 21	15 34	13 55	12 02	10 12	08 38	08 05
29	09 11	10 58	12 43	14 34	15 59	16 20	15 22	13 41	11 47	09 59	08 29	08 07
Latitude 52° N.												
1	07 51	09 08	10 52	12 57	14 53	16 24	16 39	15 29	13 37	11 38	09 38	08 07
5	07 56	09 21	11 09	13 14	15 08	16 31	16 34	15 16	13 21	11 22	09 23	07 59
9	08 03	09 36	11 25	13 30	15 22	16 37	16 28	15 02	13 05	11 06	09 09	07 53
13	08 12	09 51	11 42	13 46	15 34	16 41	16 21	14 48	12 49	10 50	08 56	07 48
17	08 21	10 05	11 58	14 01	15 46	16 43	16 11	14 33	12 34	10 34	08 43	07 46
21	08 33	10 21	12 14	14 17	15 58	16 44	16 02	14 19	12 17	10 19	08 32	07 44
25	08 45	10 37	12 29	14 31	16 09	16 43	15 50	14 03	12 02	10 04	08 21	07 46
29	08 57	10 52	12 45	14 46	16 18	16 41	15 38	13 48	11 46	09 49	08 12	07 48
Latitude 54° N.												
1	07 29	08 53	10 48	13 02	15 07	16 46	17 03	15 46	13 43	11 36	09 26	07 47
5	07 35	09 09	11 04	13 19	15 23	16 54	16 58	15 31	13 27	11 18	09 11	07 39
9	07 43	09 24	11 22	13 36	15 38	17 01	16 51	15 16	13 10	11 02	08 55	07 32
13	07 52	09 40	11 40	13 53	15 52	17 05	16 43	15 01	12 53	10 44	08 40	07 26
17	08 03	09 57	11 56	14 10	16 05	17 08	16 33	14 45	12 36	10 28	08 27	07 24
21	08 15	10 14	12 14	14 27	16 18	17 09	16 22	14 29	12 19	10 11	08 15	07 22
25	08 28	10 30	12 31	14 43	16 29	17 08	16 10	14 13	12 02	09 55	08 02	07 23
29	08 42	10 48	12 49	15 00	16 39	17 06	15 56	13 56	11 44	09 38	07 52	07 26
Latitude 56° N.												
1	07 05	08 38	10 42	13 07	15 22	17 12	17 31	16 05	13 51	11 34	09 14	07 24
5	07 11	08 53	11 00	13 25	15 39	17 21	17 25	15 49	13 34	11 16	08 56	07 15
9	07 20	09 11	11 19	13 43	15 56	17 28	17 17	15 32	13 15	10 57	08 40	07 07
13	07 30	09 29	11 38	14 02	16 11	17 33	17 08	15 16	12 57	10 38	08 24	07 02
17	07 43	09 47	11 56	14 20	16 26	17 36	16 57	14 59	12 38	10 20	08 09	06 58
21	07 56	10 05	12 15	14 39	16 40	17 37	16 44	14 41	12 19	10 02	07 55	06 57
25	08 10	10 23	12 34	14 56	16 53	17 37	16 31	14 23	12 01	09 44	07 42	06 58
29	08 25	10 42	12 53	15 14	17 04	17 34	16 16	14 05	11 43	09 27	07 30	07 00
Latitude 58° N.												
1	06 36	08 20	10 35	13 11	15 39	17 42	18 03	16 27	14 00	11 31	08 59	06 58
5	06 44	08 37	10 55	13 31	15 57	17 52	17 56	16 09	13 40	11 12	08 41	06 49
9	06 53	08 56	11 15	13 51	16 16	18 01	17 47	15 51	13 21	10 52	08 23	06 39
13	07 06	09 16	11 36	14 11	16 34	18 06	17 37	15 32	13 01	10 32	08 04	06 33
17	07 19	09 35	11 56	14 31	16 50	18 10	17 25	15 13	12 41	10 12	07 48	06 29
21	07 33	09 55	12 16	14 51	17 05	18 11	17 10	14 54	12 21	09 52	07 33	06 27
25	07 49	10 15	12 36	15 11	17 19	18 10	16 55	14 35	12 01	09 33	07 18	06 28
29	08 07	10 35	12 57	15 30	17 33	18 06	16 39	14 15	11 41	09 13	07 05	06 32

Table 3.3–11 (*Continued*)
DURATION OF DAYLIGHT

Day of month	Jan.	Feb.	Mar.	Apr.	May	June	July	Aug.	Sept.	Oct.	Nov.	Dec.
	h. m.	h. m.	h. m.	h. m.	h. m.	h. m.	h. m.	h. m.	h. m.	h. m.	h. m.	h. m.
	Latitude 60° N.											
1	06 03	08 00	10 28	13 17	15 58	18 17	18 43	16 51	14 10	11 28	08 43	06 28
5	06 11	08 19	10 49	13 39	16 19	18 30	18 36	16 32	13 48	11 07	08 23	06 17
9	06 23	08 40	11 11	14 01	16 39	18 39	18 25	16 11	13 27	10 46	08 03	06 06
13	06 36	09 01	11 33	14 23	16 59	18 46	18 12	15 50	13 06	10 24	07 44	05 58
17	06 51	09 23	11 55	14 45	17 18	18 50	17 57	15 30	12 44	10 02	07 24	05 54
21	07 08	09 44	12 18	15 05	17 35	18 53	17 41	15 09	12 23	09 41	07 07	05 52
25	07 26	10 06	12 39	15 27	17 52	18 51	17 24	14 48	12 01	09 20	06 50	05 53
29	07 45	10 28	13 01	15 48	18 08	18 46	17 05	14 26	11 39	08 59	06 35	05 57
	Latitude 61° N.											
1	05 43	07 48	10 24	13 20	16 10	18 39	19 07	17 05	14 16	11 27	08 34	06 11
5	05 53	08 09	10 46	13 43	16 31	18 52	18 58	16 44	13 54	11 05	08 12	05 58
9	06 05	08 31	11 09	14 05	16 53	19 03	18 47	16 23	13 31	10 42	07 51	05 47
13	06 20	08 53	11 32	14 29	17 14	19 10	18 32	16 02	13 08	10 20	07 30	05 39
17	06 35	09 15	11 55	14 51	17 34	19 16	18 16	15 39	12 46	09 58	07 11	05 34
21	06 53	09 38	12 18	15 13	17 53	19 17	17 59	15 17	12 23	09 35	06 53	05 32
25	07 12	10 01	12 40	15 36	18 11	19 15	17 41	14 55	12 01	09 13	06 34	05 33
29	07 33	10 24	13 03	15 59	18 28	19 10	17 21	14 32	11 39	08 51	06 18	05 37
	Latitude 62° N.											
1	05 21	07 36	10 19	13 24	16 21	19 03	19 34	17 21	14 22	11 26	08 24	05 52
5	05 32	07 59	10 43	13 47	16 44	19 16	19 24	16 58	13 58	11 02	08 02	05 37
9	05 45	08 22	11 07	14 11	17 07	19 29	19 11	16 35	13 35	10 39	07 39	05 26
13	06 00	08 44	11 31	14 35	17 29	19 38	18 55	16 12	13 11	10 15	07 18	05 16
17	06 19	09 08	11 54	14 59	17 51	19 44	18 38	15 50	12 48	09 52	06 57	05 11
21	06 38	09 32	12 18	15 22	18 11	19 45	18 19	15 26	12 25	09 28	06 37	05 09
25	06 58	09 56	12 42	15 46	18 32	19 43	17 59	15 03	12 00	09 05	06 17	05 10
29	07 19	10 19	13 06	16 09	18 50	19 38	17 37	14 39	11 37	08 42	06 00	05 15
	Latitude 63° N.											
1	04 56	07 22	10 14	13 27	16 34	19 29	20 06	17 37	14 28	11 24	08 14	05 30
5	05 08	07 47	10 39	13 52	16 58	19 46	19 54	17 14	14 03	11 00	07 50	05 15
9	05 23	08 11	11 05	14 17	17 23	20 00	19 39	16 49	13 39	10 35	07 27	05 02
13	05 40	08 36	11 29	14 41	17 47	20 11	19 21	16 25	13 14	10 11	07 04	04 52
17	05 59	09 00	11 54	15 07	18 11	20 16	19 02	16 00	12 50	09 46	06 41	04 45
21	06 20	09 25	12 19	15 32	18 33	20 19	18 40	15 36	12 25	09 22	06 19	04 42
25	06 42	09 50	12 44	15 56	18 54	20 17	18 18	15 11	12 00	08 57	05 58	04 44
29	07 05	10 14	13 08	16 21	19 15	20 10	17 55	14 46	11 37	08 33	05 40	04 49
	Latitude 64° N.											
1	04 28	07 08	10 10	13 31	16 48	20 01	20 46	17 56	14 34	11 22	08 03	05 06
5	04 41	07 33	10 36	13 57	17 14	20 21	20 31	17 30	14 09	10 57	07 38	04 49
9	04 57	08 00	11 01	14 23	17 41	20 38	20 12	17 04	13 43	10 31	07 13	04 34
13	05 17	08 26	11 27	14 49	18 07	20 51	19 51	16 38	13 18	10 05	06 48	04 22
17	05 39	08 51	11 54	15 15	18 33	20 59	19 30	16 12	12 52	09 40	06 23	04 14
21	06 01	09 17	12 20	15 42	18 57	21 01	19 06	15 46	12 26	09 14	05 59	04 12
25	06 24	09 44	12 46	16 08	19 22	20 59	18 41	15 20	12 00	08 48	05 37	04 14
29	06 49	10 10	13 12	16 35	19 45	20 51	18 15	14 54	11 35	08 22	05 16	04 20
	Latitude 65° N.											
1	03 54	06 52	10 04	13 35	17 03	20 40	21 38	18 17	14 42	11 20	07 51	04 38
5	04 09	07 19	10 32	14 02	17 32	21 05	21 18	17 49	14 15	10 54	07 24	04 17
9	04 29	07 47	10 59	14 30	18 00	21 28	20 55	17 21	13 47	10 27	06 57	04 01
13	04 50	08 14	11 26	14 57	18 29	21 46	20 29	16 53	13 20	10 00	06 30	03 47
17	05 15	08 42	11 53	15 25	18 57	21 58	20 02	16 25	12 54	09 33	06 03	03 38
21	05 39	09 09	12 20	15 52	19 26	22 03	19 34	15 56	12 27	09 06	05 37	03 34
25	06 05	09 37	12 48	16 21	19 53	21 58	19 06	15 30	12 00	08 39	05 13	03 37
29	06 32	10 04	13 14	16 49	20 21	21 47	18 38	15 02	11 34	08 11	04 49	03 44

Table 3.3–11 (*Continued*)
DURATION OF DAYLIGHT

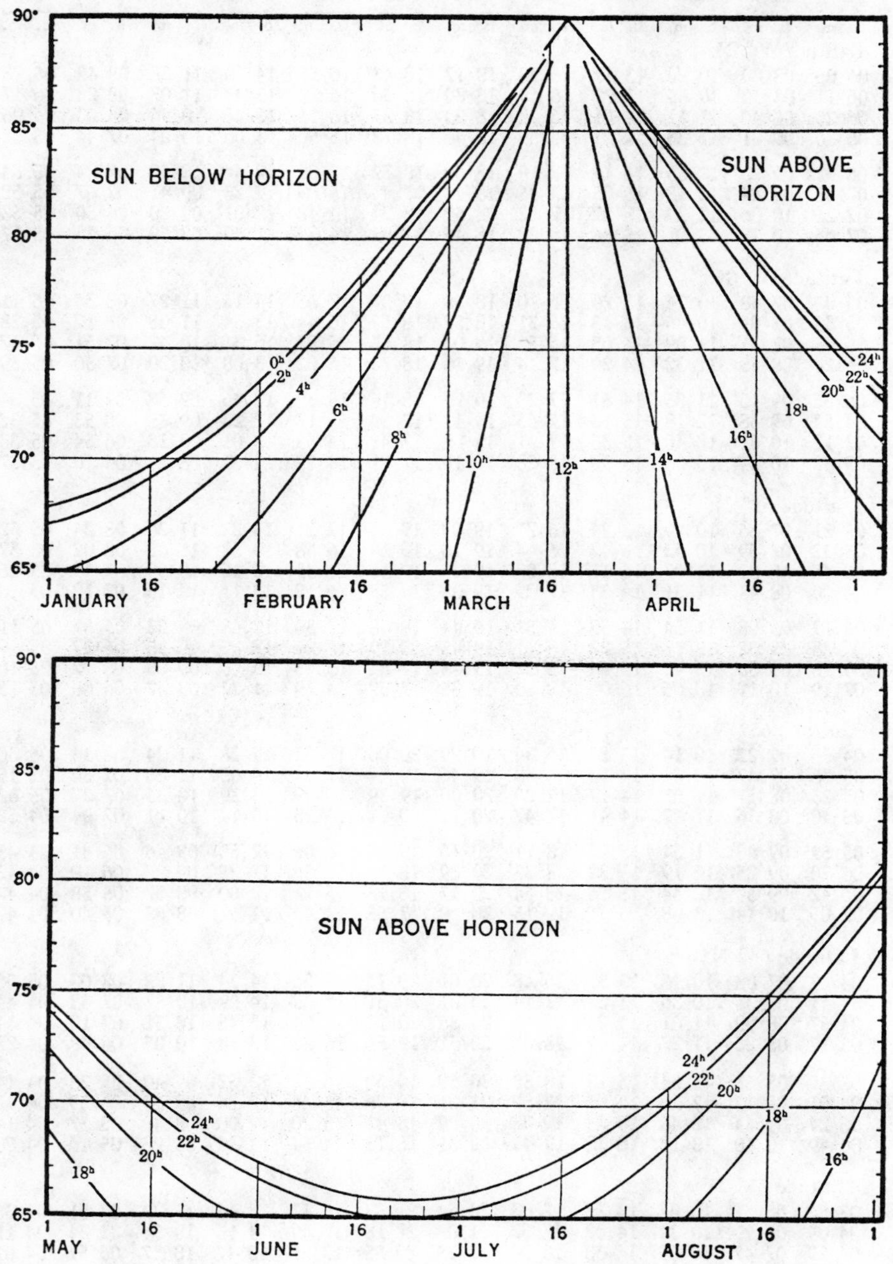

Table 3.3–11 (*Continued*)
DURATION OF DAYLIGHT

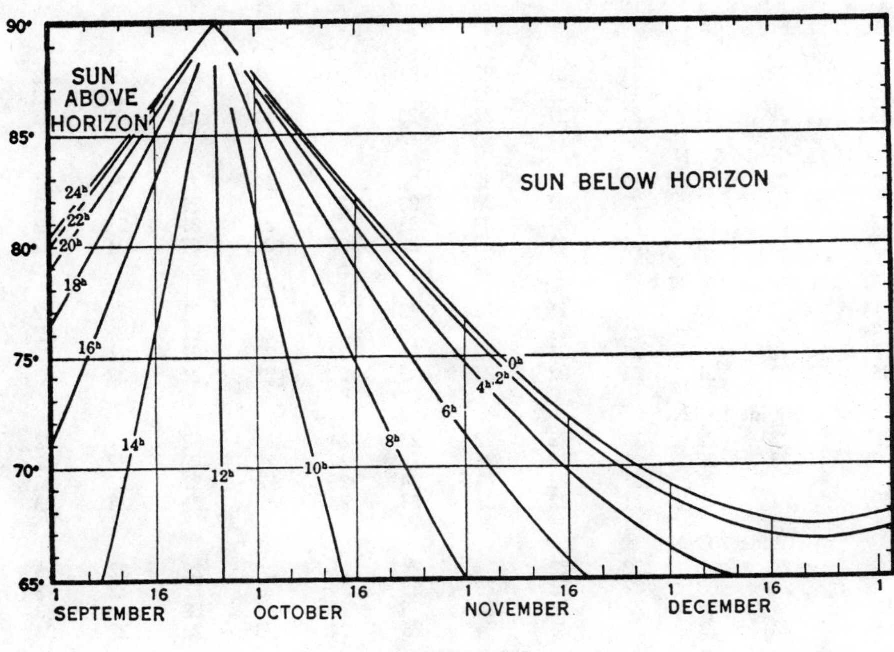

REFERENCES

1. Tables of sunrise and twilight, Supplement to the American ephemeris, 1946, U.S. Naval Observatory, Washington, D.C., 1945.
2. **Kimball, H.,** *Month Weath. Rev.*, 44, 614, 1916.

(From *Smithsonian Meteorological Tables,* 6th rev. ed., List, R. J., Ed., Smithsonian Institution, Washington, D.C., 1971.)

Table 3.3–12
DURATION OF CIVIL TWILIGHT

Day of month	Jan.	Feb.	Mar.	Apr.	May	June	July	Aug.	Sept.	Oct.	Nov.	Dec.
	h. m.	h. m.	h. m.	h. m.	h. m.	h. m.	h. m.	h. m.	h. m.	h. m.	h. m.	h. m.
Latitude 0°												
1	23	22	21	21	22	22	23	22	21	21	21	22
9	22	21	21	21	22	23	22	21	21	21	22	23
17	22	21	21	21	22	23	22	21	21	21	22	23
25	22	21	21	21	22	23	22	21	21	21	22	23
Latitude 5° N.												
1	22	22	21	21	22	22	23	22	21	21	21	22
9	22	21	21	21	22	23	23	22	21	21	22	23
17	22	21	21	21	22	23	22	21	21	21	22	23
25	22	21	21	21	22	23	22	21	21	21	22	23
Latitude 10° N.												
1	23	22	21	21	22	23	23	22	21	21	22	23
9	23	22	21	21	22	23	23	22	21	21	22	23
17	22	21	21	21	22	23	23	22	21	21	22	23
25	22	21	21	22	23	23	22	21	21	22	22	23
Latitude 15° N.												
1	23	22	22	22	22	23	24	23	22	21	22	23
9	23	22	21	22	23	24	24	22	22	22	22	23
17	23	22	21	22	23	24	23	22	21	22	23	23
25	23	22	21	22	23	24	23	22	21	22	23	23
Latitude 20° N.												
1	24	23	22	22	23	24	25	24	22	22	23	24
9	24	23	22	22	23	25	24	23	22	22	23	24
17	24	22	22	23	24	25	24	23	22	22	23	24
25	23	22	22	23	24	25	24	23	22	22	24	24
Latitude 25° N.												
1	25	24	23	23	24	26	26	25	23	23	24	25
9	25	24	23	23	25	26	26	24	23	23	24	25
17	25	23	23	23	25	26	25	24	23	23	24	25
25	24	23	23	24	25	26	25	23	23	23	25	25
Latitude 30° N.												
1	26	25	24	24	25	27	27	26	24	24	25	26
9	26	25	24	24	26	27	27	25	24	24	25	26
17	26	24	24	25	26	28	27	25	24	24	25	26
25	25	24	24	25	27	27	26	25	24	24	26	26
Latitude 35° N.												
1	28	27	25	26	27	29	30	28	26	25	26	28
9	28	26	25	26	28	30	29	27	26	25	27	28
17	27	26	25	26	28	30	29	27	25	26	27	28
25	27	26	25	27	29	30	28	26	25	26	27	28
Latitude 40° N.												
1	30	29	27	27	29	32	33	30	28	27	28	30
9	30	28	27	28	30	33	32	30	27	27	29	30
17	30	28	27	28	31	33	32	29	27	27	29	31
25	29	27	27	29	32	33	31	28	27	28	30	31
Latitude 42° N.												
1	32	30	28	28	31	34	34	32	29	28	29	31
9	31	29	28	29	31	34	34	31	28	28	30	32
17	31	29	28	29	32	34	33	30	28	28	30	32
25	30	28	28	30	33	35	32	29	28	29	31	32

Table 3.3–12 (*Continued*)
DURATION OF CIVIL TWILIGHT

Day of month	Jan.	Feb.	Mar.	Apr.	May	June	July	Aug.	Sept.	Oct.	Nov.	Dec.
	h. m.	h. m.	h. m.	h. m.	h. m.	h. m.	h. m.	h. m.	h. m.	h. m.	h. m.	h. m.
Latitude 44° N.												
1	33	31	29	29	32	35	36	33	30	29	30	32
9	33	30	29	30	33	36	36	32	29	29	31	33
17	32	30	29	30	34	36	35	31	29	29	31	33
25	31	29	29	31	35	36	34	30	29	30	32	33
Latitude 46° N.												
1	34	32	30	30	33	38	38	35	31	30	31	34
9	34	31	30	31	34	38	38	34	30	30	32	34
17	33	31	30	32	36	39	37	32	30	30	33	35
25	33	30	30	33	37	39	36	32	30	31	33	35
Latitude 48° N.												
1	36	33	31	32	35	40	41	36	32	31	33	36
9	36	33	31	32	36	41	40	35	32	31	33	36
17	35	32	31	33	38	41	39	34	31	31	34	36
25	34	31	31	34	39	41	38	33	31	32	35	36
Latitude 50° N.												
1	38	35	33	33	37	43	44	39	34	32	34	37
9	38	34	32	34	38	44	43	37	33	32	35	38
17	37	33	32	35	40	45	42	36	32	33	36	39
25	36	33	33	36	42	45	40	34	32	33	37	39
Latitude 52° N.												
1	41	37	34	34	39	47	48	41	35	34	36	40
9	40	36	34	35	41	48	47	39	34	34	37	40
17	39	35	34	36	43	49	45	38	34	34	38	41
25	38	34	34	38	45	49	43	36	34	35	39	41
Latitude 54° N.												
1	43	39	36	36	42	51	54	44	37	35	38	42
9	43	38	35	37	44	53	52	42	36	35	39	43
17	41	37	35	38	46	55	49	40	36	36	40	44
25	40	36	36	40	49	54	47	38	35	37	41	44
Latitude 56° N.												
1	47	41	38	38	45	58	1 01	48	39	37	40	45
9	46	40	37	39	48	1 01	58	45	38	37	41	47
17	44	39	37	41	51	1 03	55	43	37	38	43	47
25	43	38	38	43	55	1 02	51	41	37	39	44	47
Latitude 58° N.												
1	51	44	40	40	49	1 08	1 13	53	42	39	42	49
9	50	42	39	42	53	1 13	1 08	49	41	39	44	51
17	48	41	39	44	57	1 16	1 03	46	40	40	46	52
25	46	40	40	46	1 03	1 15	57	44	39	41	48	52
Latitude 60° N.												
1	57	48	42	43	54	1 25	1 38	1 00	45	41	45	54
9	55	45	42	45	59	1 36	1 26	54	43	42	47	56
17	52	44	42	47	1 06	1 46	1 15	50	42	42	50	58
25	50	42	42	50	1 15	1 45	1 06	47	41	44	52	58
Latitude 61° N.												
1	1 00	49	43	45	57	1 40	*	1 05	47	43	47	57
9	58	47	43	46	1 03	2 19	1 44	58	45	43	49	1 00
17	55	45	43	49	1 12	*	1 25	53	43	44	52	1 01
25	52	44	43	53	1 25	*	1 13	49	43	45	55	1 01

* Twilight lasts all night.

3.3–12 (*Continued*)
DURATION OF CIVIL TWILIGHT

Day of month	Jan.	Feb.	Mar.	Apr.	May	June	July	Aug.	Sept.	Oct.	Nov.	Dec.
	h. m.	h. m.	h. m.	h. m.	h. m.	h. m.	h. m.	h. m.	h. m.	h. m.	h. m.	h. m.
	Latitude 62° N.											
1	1 04	52	45	46	1 00	*	*	1 10	48	44	49	1 01
9	1 01	49	44	48	1 08	*	*	1 01	46	44	51	1 04
17	58	47	44	51	1 20	*	1 41	55	45	45	54	1 06
25	54	45	45	56	1 40	*	1 21	51	44	47	58	1 06
	Latitude 63° N.											
1	1 09	54	46	48	1 04	*	*	1 17	51	45	51	1 05
9	1 06	51	46	50	1 15	*	*	1 06	48	46	54	1 08
17	1 01	49	46	54	1 32	*	*	59	46	47	57	1 11
25	57	47	47	59	*	*	1 33	54	46	49	1 01	1 11
	Latitude 64° N.											
1	1 15	57	48	50	1 09	*	*	1 27	53	47	53	1 10
9	1 11	53	47	53	1 23	*	*	1 11	50	48	56	1 15
17	1 06	51	47	57	1 53	*	*	1 02	48	49	1 01	1 18
25	1 01	49	48	1 03	*	*	1 56	56	47	51	1 06	1 18
	Latitude 65° N.											
1	1 24	1 00	50	52	1 16	*	*	1 42	55	49	55	1 16
9	1 17	56	49	55	1 36	*	*	1 18	52	49	59	1 22
17	1 11	53	49	1 00	*	*	*	1 07	50	51	1 04	1 27
25	1 04	51	50	1 07	*	*	*	1 00	49	53	1 11	1 27

* Twilight lasts all night.

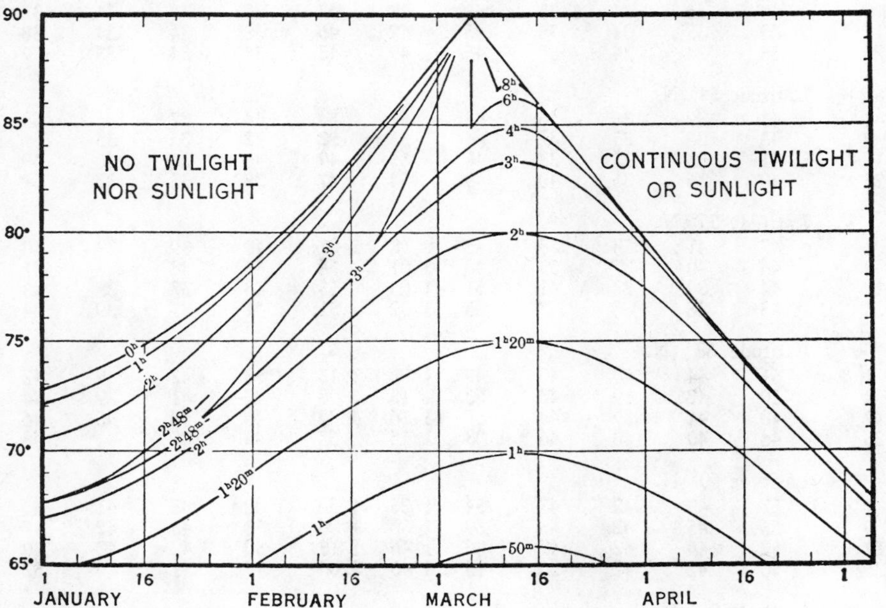

Table 3.3–12 (*Continued*)
DURATION OF CIVIL TWILIGHT

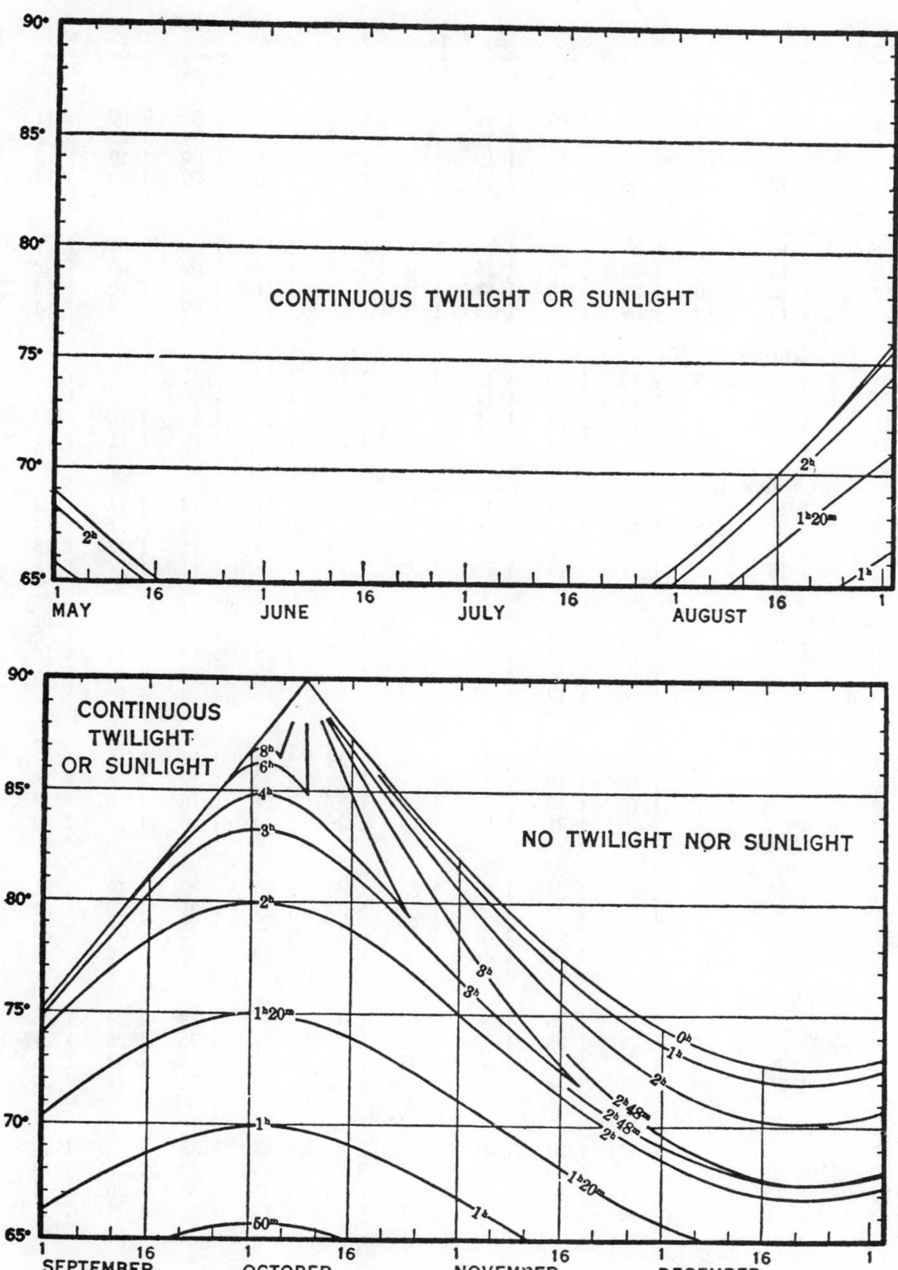

(From *Smithsonian Meteorological Tables,* 6th rev. ed., List, R. J., Ed., Smithsonian Institution, Washington, D.C., 1971.)

Table 3.3–13
DURATION OF ASTRONOMICAL TWILIGHT

Day of month	Jan.	Feb.	Mar.	Apr.	May	June	July	Aug.	Sept.	Oct.	Nov.	Dec.
	h. m.	h. m.	h. m.	h. m.	h. m.	h. m.	h. m.	h. m.	h. m.	h. m.	h. m.	h. m.
	Latitude 0°											
1	1 15	1 12	1 09	1 09	1 11	1 14	1 15	1 12	1 09	1 09	1 11	1 14
9	1 14	1 11	1 09	1 09	1 12	1 15	1 15	1 11	1 09	1 09	1 12	1 15
17	1 14	1 10	1 09	1 10	1 13	1 15	1 14	1 11	1 09	1 10	1 13	1 15
25	1 13	1 10	1 09	1 11	1 14	1 15	1 13	1 10	1 09	1 10	1 14	1 15
	Latitude 5° N.											
1	1 15	1 12	1 09	1 09	1 12	1 15	1 16	1 13	1 10	1 09	1 11	1 14
9	1 14	1 11	1 09	1 10	1 13	1 16	1 15	1 12	1 09	1 09	1 12	1 15
17	1 14	1 10	1 09	1 10	1 14	1 16	1 15	1 11	1 09	1 10	1 13	1 15
25	1 13	1 10	1 09	1 11	1 15	1 16	1 14	1 10	1 09	1 10	1 14	1 15
	Latitude 10° N.											
1	1 15	1 13	1 10	1 10	1 13	1 17	1 18	1 14	1 11	1 10	1 12	1 15
9	1 15	1 12	1 10	1 11	1 14	1 17	1 17	1 13	1 10	1 10	1 13	1 15
17	1 14	1 11	1 10	1 12	1 15	1 18	1 16	1 12	1 10	1 10	1 13	1 15
25	1 13	1 10	1 10	1 12	1 16	1 18	1 15	1 11	1 10	1 11	1 14	1 15
	Latitude 15° N.											
1	1 16	1 14	1 11	1 12	1 15	1 19	1 20	1 17	1 13	1 11	1 13	1 16
9	1 16	1 13	1 11	1 12	1 16	1 20	1 20	1 15	1 12	1 11	1 14	1 16
17	1 15	1 12	1 11	1 13	1 17	1 20	1 19	1 14	1 11	1 12	1 15	1 17
25	1 15	1 12	1 11	1 14	1 19	1 20	1 18	1 13	1 11	1 12	1 15	1 17
	Latitude 20° N.											
1	1 18	1 16	1 13	1 14	1 18	1 23	1 24	1 20	1 15	1 13	1 15	1 18
9	1 18	1 15	1 13	1 15	1 19	1 24	1 23	1 18	1 14	1 13	1 16	1 18
17	1 17	1 14	1 13	1 16	1 21	1 24	1 22	1 17	1 13	1 14	1 16	1 19
25	1 16	1 14	1 14	1 17	1 22	1 24	1 21	1 16	1 13	1 14	1 17	1 19
	Latitude 25° N.											
1	1 21	1 18	1 16	1 17	1 22	1 28	1 29	1 24	1 18	1 16	1 17	1 21
9	1 21	1 18	1 16	1 18	1 24	1 29	1 28	1 22	1 17	1 16	1 18	1 21
17	1 20	1 17	1 16	1 19	1 25	1 29	1 27	1 21	1 16	1 16	1 19	1 22
25	1 19	1 16	1 16	1 21	1 27	1 29	1 25	1 19	1 16	1 17	1 20	1 22
	Latitude 30° N.											
1	1 25	1 22	1 20	1 21	1 27	1 35	1 36	1 30	1 22	1 19	1 21	1 25
9	1 25	1 21	1 19	1 22	1 29	1 36	1 35	1 27	1 21	1 19	1 22	1 25
17	1 24	1 20	1 20	1 24	1 31	1 37	1 33	1 25	1 20	1 20	1 23	1 26
25	1 23	1 20	1 20	1 26	1 33	1 37	1 31	1 24	1 20	1 20	1 24	1 26
	Latitude 35° N.											
1	1 30	1 27	1 24	1 26	1 34	1 44	1 46	1 37	1 28	1 24	1 26	1 30
9	1 30	1 26	1 24	1 28	1 37	1 46	1 45	1 35	1 26	1 24	1 27	1 30
17	1 29	1 25	1 24	1 30	1 40	1 47	1 42	1 32	1 25	1 24	1 28	1 31
25	1 28	1 24	1 25	1 32	1 42	1 47	1 40	1 30	1 24	1 25	1 29	1 31
	Latitude 40° N.											
1	1 37	1 33	1 30	1 33	1 44	1 59	2 02	1 48	1 35	1 30	1 32	1 36
9	1 36	1 32	1 30	1 35	1 48	2 02	2 00	1 44	1 33	1 30	1 33	1 37
17	1 35	1 31	1 31	1 38	1 52	2 03	1 56	1 41	1 32	1 30	1 34	1 38
25	1 34	1 30	1 32	1 41	1 56	2 03	1 52	1 38	1 30	1 31	1 35	1 38
	Latitude 42° N.											
1	1 41	1 36	1 33	1 36	1 49	2 07	2 11	1 54	1 39	1 33	1 34	1 39
9	1 40	1 35	1 33	1 39	1 53	2 11	2 08	1 49	1 36	1 33	1 36	1 40
17	1 39	1 34	1 34	1 42	1 58	2 13	2 03	1 45	1 35	1 33	1 37	1 41
25	1 37	1 33	1 35	1 45	2 03	2 13	1 59	1 42	1 33	1 34	1 38	1 41

Table 3.3–13 (*Continued*)
DURATION OF ASTRONOMICAL TWILIGHT

Day of month	Jan.	Feb.	Mar.	Apr.	May	June	July	Aug.	Sept.	Oct.	Nov.	Dec.
	h. m.	h. m.	h. m.	h. m.	h. m.	h. m.	h. m.	h. m.	h. m.	h. m.	h. m.	h. m.
	Latitude 44° N.											
1	1 44	1 39	1 36	1 40	1 55	2 18	2 23	2 01	1 43	1 36	1 38	1 43
9	1 43	1 38	1 36	1 43	2 00	2 23	2 19	1 56	1 40	1 36	1 39	1 44
17	1 42	1 37	1 37	1 46	2 06	2 25	2 13	1 50	1 38	1 36	1 40	1 45
25	1 41	1 36	1 38	1 51	2 13	2 25	2 07	1 46	1 37	1 37	1 42	1 45
	Latitude 46° N.											
1	1 49	1 43	1 39	1 44	2 01	2 32	2 40	2 10	1 48	1 40	1 41	1 47
9	1 48	1 41	1 40	1 47	2 08	2 39	2 33	2 03	1 44	1 39	1 43	1 48
17	1 46	1 40	1 40	1 52	2 16	2 43	2 25	1 56	1 42	1 39	1 44	1 49
25	1 44	1 40	1 42	1 57	2 25	2 43	2 17	1 51	1 40	1 40	1 46	1 49
	Latitude 48° N.											
1	1 53	1 47	1 43	1 49	2 10	2 54	3 09	2 21	1 53	1 44	1 45	1 52
9	1 52	1 45	1 44	1 53	2 19	3 08	2 56	2 11	1 49	1 43	1 47	1 53
17	1 51	1 44	1 45	1 58	2 29	3 18	2 43	2 04	1 46	1 43	1 49	1 54
25	1 49	1 43	1 46	2 04	2 42	3 17	2 30	1 57	1 44	1 44	1 51	1 54
	Latitude 50° N.											
1	1 59	1 52	1 48	1 54	2 20	*	*	2 35	1 59	1 48	1 50	1 57
9	1 57	1 50	1 48	1 59	2 32	*	*	2 22	1 55	1 47	1 51	1 59
17	1 56	1 48	1 49	2 05	2 49	*	3 13	2 12	1 51	1 48	1 53	2 00
25	1 53	1 48	1 51	2 13	3 12	*	2 49	2 05	1 49	1 48	1 56	2 00
	Latitude 52° N.											
1	2 05	1 57	1 52	2 01	2 34	*	*	2 57	2 07	1 53	1 55	2 03
9	2 04	1 55	1 53	2 06	2 52	*	*	2 37	2 01	1 52	1 57	2 05
17	2 01	1 53	1 54	2 14	3 25	*	*	2 23	1 57	1 52	1 59	2 06
25	1 59	1 52	1 57	2 24	*	*	3 28	2 13	1 54	1 53	2 01	2 06
	Latitude 54° N.											
1	2 13	2 03	1 58	2 08	2 53	*	*	3 49	2 15	1 59	2 00	2 10
9	2 11	2 01	1 59	2 15	3 31	*	*	2 58	2 08	1 58	2 03	2 12
17	2 08	1 59	2 00	2 24	*	*	*	2 37	2 03	1 58	2 05	2 13
25	2 05	1 58	2 04	2 38	*	*	*	2 24	2 00	1 59	2 08	2 14
	Latitude 56° N.											
1	2 21	2 10	2 04	2 17	3 29	*	*	*	2 26	2 05	2 07	2 18
9	2 19	2 07	2 05	2 25	*	*	*	3 43	2 17	2 04	2 09	2 21
17	2 16	2 05	2 07	2 38	*	*	*	2 57	2 11	2 04	2 13	2 22
25	2 12	2 04	2 11	2 59	*	*	*	2 37	2 07	2 05	2 16	2 22
	Latitude 58° N.											
1	2 32	2 18	2 11	2 27	*	*	*	*	2 40	2 12	2 14	2 28
9	2 29	2 14	2 12	2 38	*	*	*	*	2 28	2 11	2 17	2 31
17	2 25	2 12	2 15	2 57	*	*	*	3 34	2 20	2 11	2 21	2 33
25	2 21	2 11	2 20	3 37	*	*	*	2 56	2 15	2 12	2 25	2 33
	Latitude 60° N.											
1	2 44	2 27	2 19	2 40	*	*	*	*	2 58	2 21	2 23	2 40
9	2 41	2 23	2 21	2 56	*	*	*	*	2 41	2 19	2 26	2 44
17	2 36	2 20	2 24	3 28	*	*	*	*	2 30	2 19	2 31	2 46
25	2 31	2 19	2 31	*	*	*	*	3 26	2 24	2 20	2 36	2 46
	Latitude 61° N.											
1	2 52	2 32	2 24	2 47	*	*	*	*	3 10	2 26	2 27	2 46
9	2 48	2 28	2 25	3 07	*	*	*	*	2 49	2 24	2 31	2 51
17	2 42	2 25	2 30	3 59	*	*	*	*	2 37	2 23	2 37	2 54
25	2 37	2 24	2 37	*	*	*	*	3 54	2 29	2 25	2 42	2 54

* Twilight lasts all night.

Table 3.3–13 (*Continued*)
DURATION OF ASTRONOMICAL TWILIGHT

Day of month	Jan.	Feb.	Mar.	Apr.	May	June	July	Aug.	Sept.	Oct.	Nov.	Dec.
	h. m.	h. m.	h. m.	h. m.	h. m.	h. m.	h. m.	h. m.	h. m.	h. m.	h. m.	h. m.
Latitude 62° N.												
1	3 00	2 38	2 29	2 56	*	*	*	*	3 25	2 31	2 33	2 54
9	2 55	2 33	2 31	3 22	*	*	*	*	2 58	2 28	2 37	2 59
17	2 49	2 30	2 35	*	*	*	*	*	2 43	2 28	2 43	3 03
25	2 43	2 29	2 44	*	*	*	*	*	2 35	2 30	2 49	3 03
Latitude 63° N.												
1	3 10	2 44	2 34	3 06	*	*	*	*	3 47	2 37	2 38	3 03
9	3 05	2 39	2 36	3 42	*	*	*	*	3 09	2 34	2 43	3 09
17	2 57	2 35	2 42	*	*	*	*	*	2 51	2 33	2 50	3 13
25	2 50	2 34	2 52	*	*	*	*	*	2 41	2 35	2 57	3 13
Latitude 64° N.												
1	3 22	2 51	2 40	3 19	*	*	*	*	*	2 43	2 44	3 13
9	3 15	2 45	2 42	4 18	*	*	*	*	3 22	2 40	2 50	3 21
17	3 06	2 41	2 49	*	*	*	*	*	3 00	2 39	2 57	3 26
25	2 58	2 40	3 00	*	*	*	*	*	2 48	2 41	3 06	3 26
Latitude 65° N.												
1	3 37	2 59	2 46	3 34	*	*	*	*	*	2 50	2 51	3 25
9	3 27	2 52	2 49	*	*	*	*	*	3 39	2 46	2 58	3 35
17	3 16	2 48	2 56	*	*	*	*	*	3 10	2 45	3 06	3 41
25	3 06	2 46	3 10	*	*	*	*	*	2 56	2 47	3 17	3 42

* Twilight lasts all night.

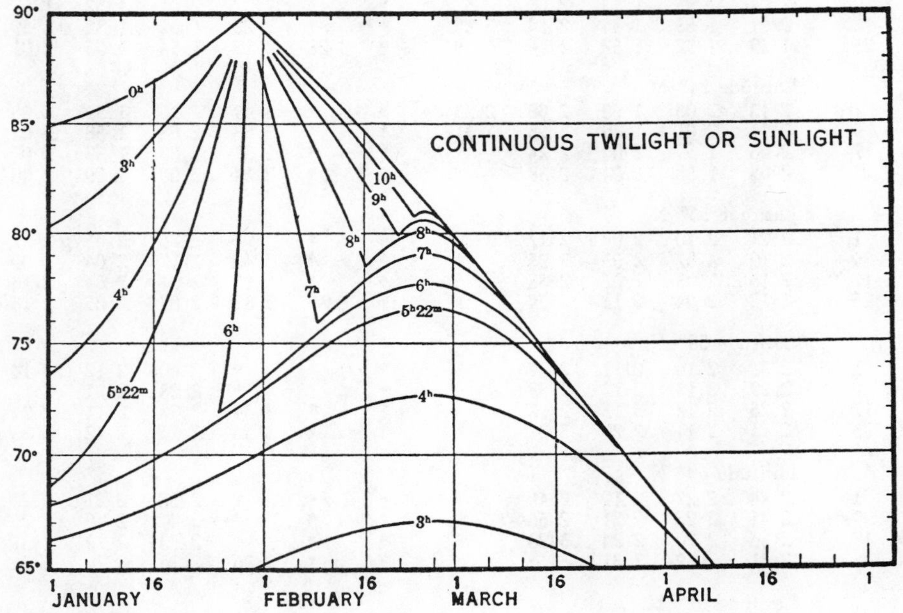

Table 3.3–13 (*Continued*)
DURATION OF ASTRONOMICAL TWILIGHT

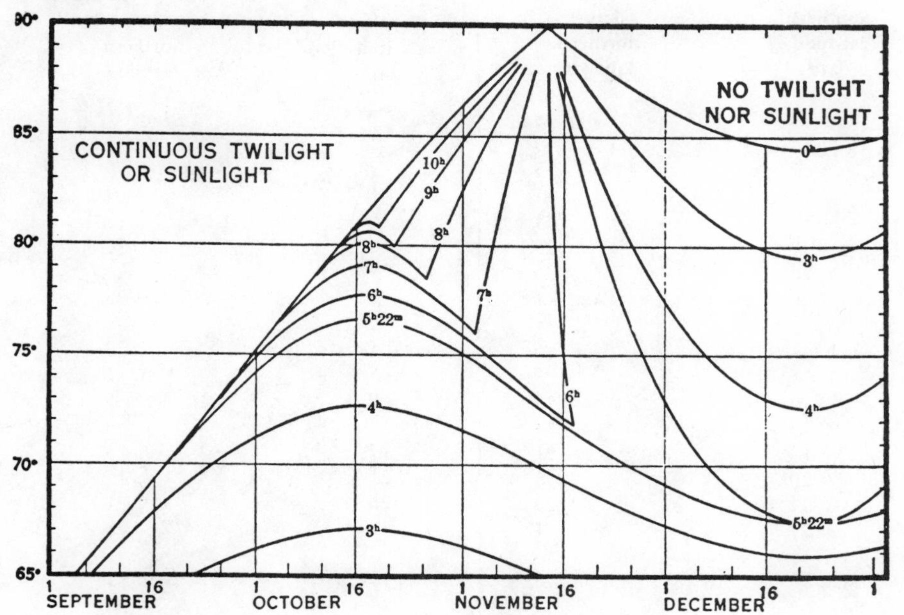

(From *Smithsonian Meteorological Tables,* 6th rev. ed., List, R. J., Ed., Smithsonian Institution, Washington, D.C., 1971.)

Table 3.3–14
DAYLIGHT AND TWILIGHT FOR SOUTHERN LATITUDES

Southern latitude date	Corresponding date– northern latitude
Jan. 3	July 5
7	9
11	13
15	17
18	21
22	25
26	29
29	Aug. 1
Feb. 1	5
5	9
9	13
13	17
17	21
20	25
24	29
27	Sept. 1
Mar. 3	5
7	9
11	13
15	17
19	21
23	25
27	29
29	Oct. 1
Apr. 1	5
5	9
6	9
10	13
14	17
18	21
22	25
26	29
29	Nov. 1
May 3	5
7	9
11	13
15	17
16	17
20	21
24	25
28	29
30	Dec. 1
June 3	5
4	5
8	9
12	13
16	17
20	21
25	25
29	29

Southern latitude date	Corresponding date– northern latitude
July 2	Jan. 1
3	1
7	5
11	9
15	13
20	17
24	21
28	25
Aug. 1	29
5	Feb. 1
9	5
13	9
17	13
21	17
26	21
30	25
Sept. 3	Mar. 1
7	5
11	9
15	13
19	17
23	21
27	25
Oct. 1	29
2	29
5	Apr. 1
9	5
12	9
16	13
20	17
24	21
28	25
Nov. 1	29
3	May 1
7	5
11	9
15	13
18	17
22	21
26	25
30	29
Dec. 3	June 1
6	5
10	9
14	13
18	17
25	25
29	29
31	July 1

(From *Smithsonian Meteorological Tables,* 6th rev. ed., List, R. J., Ed., Smithsonian Institution, Washington, D.C., 1971.)

3.4 Hygrometric Tables

Table 3.4–1
SATURATION VAPOR PRESSURE OVER WATER

Metric units

Temperature	.0	.1	.2	.3	.4	.5	.6	.7	.8	.9
°C.	mb.	mb.	mb.	mb.	mb.	mb.	mb.	mb.	mb.	mb.
−50	0.06356									
−49	0.07124	0.07044	0.06964	0.06885	0.06807	0.06730	0.06654	0.06578	0.06503	0.06429
−48	0.07975	0.07886	0.07797	0.07710	0.07624	0.07538	0.07453	0.07370	0.07287	0.07205
−47	0.08918	0.08819	0.08722	0.08625	0.08530	0.08435	0.08341	0.08248	0.08156	0.08065
−46	0.09961	0.09852	0.09744	0.09637	0.09531	0.09426	0.09322	0.09220	0.09118	0.09017
−45	0.1111	0.1099	0.1087	0.1075	0.1063	0.1052	0.1041	0.1030	0.1018	0.1007
−44	0.1239	0.1226	0.1213	0.1200	0.1187	0.1174	0.1161	0.1149	0.1136	0.1123
−43	0.1379	0.1364	0.1350	0.1335	0.1321	0.1307	0.1293	0.1279	0.1266	0.1252
−42	0.1534	0.1518	0.1502	0.1486	0.1470	0.1455	0.1440	0.1424	0.1409	0.1394
−41	0.1704	0.1686	0.1669	0.1651	0.1634	0.1617	0.1600	0.1583	0.1567	0.1550
−40	0.1891	0.1872	0.1852	0.1833	0.1815	0.1796	0.1777	0.1759	0.1740	0.1722
−39	0.2097	0.2076	0.2054	0.2033	0.2013	0.1992	0.1971	0.1951	0.1931	0.1911
−38	0.2323	0.2299	0.2276	0.2253	0.2230	0.2207	0.2185	0.2162	0.2140	0.2119
−37	0.2571	0.2545	0.2520	0.2494	0.2469	0.2444	0.2419	0.2395	0.2371	0.2347
−36	0.2842	0.2814	0.2786	0.2758	0.2730	0.2703	0.2676	0.2649	0.2623	0.2597
−35	0.3139	0.3108	0.3077	0.3047	0.3017	0.2987	0.2957	0.2928	0.2899	0.2870
−34	0.3463	0.3429	0.3396	0.3362	0.3330	0.3297	0.3265	0.3233	0.3201	0.3170
−33	0.3818	0.3781	0.3745	0.3708	0.3673	0.3637	0.3602	0.3567	0.3532	0.3497
−32	0.4205	0.4165	0.4125	0.4085	0.4046	0.4007	0.3968	0.3930	0.3893	0.3855
−31	0.4628	0.4584	0.4541	0.4497	0.4454	0.4412	0.4370	0.4328	0.4287	0.4246
−30	0.5088	0.5040	0.4993	0.4946	0.4899	0.4853	0.4807	0.4762	0.4717	0.4672
−29	0.5589	0.5537	0.5485	0.5434	0.5383	0.5333	0.5283	0.5234	0.5185	0.5136
−28	0.6134	0.6077	0.6021	0.5966	0.5911	0.5856	0.5802	0.5748	0.5694	0.5642
−27	0.6727	0.6666	0.6605	0.6544	0.6484	0.6425	0.6366	0.6307	0.6249	0.6191
−26	0.7371	0.7304	0.7238	0.7172	0.7107	0.7042	0.6978	0.6914	0.6851	0.6789
−25	0.8070	0.7997	0.7926	0.7854	0.7783	0.7713	0.7643	0.7574	0.7506	0.7438
−24	0.8827	0.8748	0.8671	0.8593	0.8517	0.8441	0.8366	0.8291	0.8217	0.8143
−23	0.9649	0.9564	0.9479	0.9396	0.9313	0.9230	0.9148	0.9067	0.8986	0.8906
−22	1.0538	1.0446	1.0354	1.0264	1.0173	1.0084	0.9995	0.9908	0.9821	0.9734
−21	1.1500	1.1400	1.1301	1.1203	1.1106	1.1009	1.0913	1.0818	1.0724	1.0631
−20	1.2540	1.2432	1.2325	1.2219	1.2114	1.2010	1.1906	1.1804	1.1702	1.1600
−19	1.3664	1.3548	1.3432	1.3318	1.3204	1.3091	1.2979	1.2868	1.2758	1.2648
−18	1.4877	1.4751	1.4627	1.4503	1.4381	1.4259	1.4138	1.4018	1.3899	1.3781
−17	1.6186	1.6051	1.5916	1.5783	1.5650	1.5519	1.5389	1.5259	1.5131	1.5003
−16	1.7597	1.7451	1.7306	1.7163	1.7020	1.6879	1.6738	1.6599	1.6460	1.6323
−15	1.9118	1.8961	1.8805	1.8650	1.8496	1.8343	1.8191	1.8041	1.7892	1.7744
−14	2.0755	2.0586	2.0418	2.0251	2.0085	1.9921	1.9758	1.9596	1.9435	1.9276
−13	2.2515	2.2333	2.2153	2.1973	2.1795	2.1619	2.1444	2.1270	2.1097	2.0925
−12	2.4409	2.4213	2.4019	2.3826	2.3635	2.3445	2.3256	2.3069	2.2883	2.2698
−11	2.6443	2.6233	2.6024	2.5817	2.5612	2.5408	2.5205	2.5004	2.4804	2.4606
−10	2.8627	2.8402	2.8178	2.7956	2.7735	2.7516	2.7298	2.7082	2.6868	2.6655
− 9	3.0971	3.0729	3.0489	3.0250	3.0013	2.9778	2.9544	2.9313	2.9082	2.8854
− 8	3.3484	3.3225	3.2967	3.2711	3.2457	3.2205	3.1955	3.1706	3.1459	3.1214
− 7	3.6177	3.5899	3.5623	3.5349	3.5077	3.4807	3.4539	3.4272	3.4008	3.3745
− 6	3.9061	3.8764	3.8468	3.8175	3.7883	3.7594	3.7307	3.7021	3.6738	3.6456
− 5	4.2148	4.1830	4.1514	4.1200	4.0888	4.0579	4.0271	3.9966	3.9662	3.9361
− 4	4.5451	4.5111	4.4773	4.4437	4.4103	4.3772	4.3443	4.3116	4.2791	4.2468
− 3	4.8981	4.8617	4.8256	4.7897	4.7541	4.7187	4.6835	4.6486	4.6138	4.5794
− 2	5.2753	5.2364	5.1979	5.1595	5.1214	5.0836	5.0460	5.0087	4.9716	4.9347
− 1	5.6780	5.6365	5.5953	5.5544	5.5138	5.4734	5.4333	5.3934	5.3538	5.3144
− 0	6.1078	6.0636	6.0196	5.9759	5.9325	5.8894	5.8466	5.8040	5.7617	5.7197

Table 3.4–1 (*Continued*)
SATURATION VAPOR PRESSURE OVER WATER

Metric units

Temperature	.0	.1	.2	.3	.4	.5	.6	.7	.8	.9
°C.	mb.	mb.	mb.	mb.	mb.	mb.	mb.	mb.	mb.	mb.
0	6.1078	6.1523	6.1971	6.2422	6.2876	6.3333	6.3793	6.4256	6.4721	6.5190
1	6.5662	6.6137	6.6614	6.7095	6.7579	6.8066	6.8556	6.9049	6.9545	7.0044
2	7.0547	7.1053	7.1562	7.2074	7.2590	7.3109	7.3631	7.4157	7.4685	7.5218
3	7.5753	7.6291	7.6833	7.7379	7.7928	7.8480	7.9036	7.9595	8.0158	8.0724
4	8.1294	8.1868	8.2445	8.3026	8.3610	8.4198	8.4789	8.5384	8.5983	8.6586
5	8.7192	8.7802	8.8416	8.9033	8.9655	9.0280	9.0909	9.1542	9.2179	9.2820
6	9.3465	9.4114	9.4766	9.5423	9.6083	9.6748	9.7416	9.8089	9.8765	9.9446
7	10.013	10.082	10.151	10.221	10.291	10.362	10.433	10.505	10.577	10.649
8	10.722	10.795	10.869	10.943	11.017	11.092	11.168	11.243	11.320	11.397
9	11.474	11.552	11.630	11.708	11.787	11.867	11.947	12.027	12.108	12.190
10	12.272	12.355	12.438	12.521	12.606	12.690	12.775	12.860	12.946	13.032
11	13.119	13.207	13.295	13.383	13.472	13.562	13.652	13.742	13.833	13.925
12	14.017	14.110	14.203	14.297	14.391	14.486	14.581	14.678	14.774	14.871
13	14.969	15.067	15.166	15.266	15.365	15.466	15.567	15.669	15.771	15.874
14	15.977	16.081	16.186	16.291	16.397	16.503	16.610	16.718	16.826	16.935
15	17.044	17.154	17.264	17.376	17.487	17.600	17.713	17.827	17.942	18.057
16	18.173	18.290	18.407	18.524	18.643	18.762	18.882	19.002	19.123	19.245
17	19.367	19.490	19.614	19.739	19.864	19.990	20.117	20.244	20.372	20.501
18	20.630	20.760	20.891	21.023	21.155	21.288	21.422	21.556	21.691	21.827
19	21.964	22.101	22.240	22.379	22.518	22.659	22.800	22.942	23.085	23.229
20	23.373	23.518	23.664	23.811	23.959	24.107	24.256	24.406	24.557	24.709
21	24.861	25.014	25.168	25.323	25.479	25.635	25.792	25.950	26.109	26.269
22	26.430	26.592	26.754	26.918	27.082	27.247	27.413	27.580	27.748	27.916
23	28.086	28.256	28.428	28.600	28.773	28.947	29.122	29.298	29.475	29.652
24	29.831	30.011	30.191	30.373	30.555	30.739	30.923	31.109	31.295	31.483
25	31.671	31.860	32.050	32.242	32.434	32.627	32.821	33.016	33.212	33.410
26	33.608	33.807	34.008	34.209	34.411	34.615	34.820	35.025	35.232	35.440
27	35.649	35.859	36.070	36.282	36.495	36.709	36.924	37.140	37.358	37.576
28	37.796	38.017	38.239	38.462	38.686	38.911	39.137	39.365	39.594	39.824
29	40.055	40.287	40.521	40.755	40.991	41.228	41.466	41.705	41.945	42.187
30	42.430	42.674	42.919	43.166	43.414	43.663	43.913	44.165	44.418	44.672
31	44.927	45.184	45.442	45.701	45.961	46.223	46.486	46.750	47.016	47.283
32	47.551	47.820	48.091	48.364	48.637	48.912	49.188	49.466	49.745	50.025
33	50.307	50.590	50.874	51.160	51.447	51.736	52.026	52.317	52.610	52.904
34	53.200	53.497	53.796	54.096	54.397	54.700	55.004	55.310	55.617	55.926
35	56.236	56.548	56.861	57.176	57.492	57.810	58.129	58.450	58.773	59.097
36	59.422	59.749	60.077	60.407	60.739	61.072	61.407	61.743	62.081	62.421
37	62.762	63.105	63.450	63.796	64.144	64.493	64.844	65.196	65.550	65.906
38	66.264	66.623	66.985	67.347	67.712	68.078	68.446	68.815	69.186	69.559
39	69.934	70.310	70.688	71.068	71.450	71.833	72.218	72.605	72.994	73.385
40	73.777	74.171	74.568	74.966	75.365	75.767	76.170	76.575	76.982	77.391
41	77.802	78.215	78.630	79.046	79.465	79.885	80.307	80.731	81.157	81.585
42	82.015	82.447	82.881	83.316	83.754	84.194	84.636	85.079	85.525	85.973
43	86.423	86.875	87.329	87.785	88.243	88.703	89.165	89.629	90.095	90.564
44	91.034	91.507	91.981	92.458	92.937	93.418	93.901	94.386	94.874	95.363
45	95.855	96.349	96.845	97.343	97.844	98.347	98.852	99.359	99.869	100.38
46	100.89	101.41	101.93	102.45	102.97	103.50	104.03	104.56	105.09	105.62
47	106.16	106.70	107.24	107.78	108.33	108.88	109.43	109.98	110.54	111.10
48	111.66	112.22	112.79	113.36	113.93	114.50	115.07	115.65	116.23	116.81
49	117.40	117.99	118.58	119.17	119.77	120.37	120.97	121.57	122.18	122.79
50	123.40	124.01	124.63	125.25	125.87	126.49	127.12	127.75	128.38	129.01

Table 3.4–1 (*Continued*)
SATURATION VAPOR PRESSURE OVER WATER

Temperature	Metric units .0	.1	.2	.3	.4	.5	.6	.7	.8	.9
°C.	mb.	mb.	mb.	mb.	mb.	mb.	mb.	mb.	mb.	mb.
50	123.40	124.01	124.63	125.25	125.87	126.49	127.12	127.75	128.38	129.01
51	129.65	130.29	130.93	131.58	132.23	132.88	133.53	134.19	134.84	135.51
52	136.17	136.84	137.51	138.18	138.86	139.54	140.22	140.91	141.60	142.29
53	142.98	143.68	144.38	145.08	145.78	146.49	147.20	147.91	148.63	149.35
54	150.07	150.80	151.53	152.26	152.99	153.73	154.47	155.21	155.96	156.71
55	157.46	158.22	158.97	159.74	160.50	161.27	162.04	162.82	163.59	164.38
56	165.16	165.95	166.74	167.53	168.33	169.13	169.93	170.74	171.55	172.36
57	173.18	174.00	174.82	175.65	176.48	177.31	178.15	178.99	179.83	180.68
58	181.53	182.38	183.24	184.10	184.96	185.83	186.70	187.58	188.45	189.34
59	190.22	191.11	192.00	192.89	193.79	194.69	195.60	196.51	197.42	198.34
60	199.26	200.18	201.11	202.05	202.98	203.92	204.86	205.81	206.76	207.71
61	208.67	209.63	210.59	211.56	212.53	213.51	214.49	215.48	216.46	217.45
62	218.45	219.45	220.45	221.46	222.47	223.48	224.50	225.52	226.54	227.58
63	228.61	229.65	230.70	231.74	232.79	233.85	234.91	235.97	237.03	238.11
64	239.18	240.26	241.34	242.43	243.52	244.62	245.72	246.82	247.93	249.04
65	250.16	251.28	252.41	253.54	254.67	255.81	256.95	258.10	259.25	260.40
66	261.56	262.73	263.90	265.07	266.25	267.43	268.61	269.80	271.00	272.20
67	273.40	274.61	275.82	277.04	278.26	279.49	280.72	281.96	283.20	284.45
68	285.70	286.96	288.21	289.48	290.75	292.02	293.30	294.58	295.86	297.15
69	298.45	299.75	301.06	302.37	303.69	305.01	306.34	307.67	309.00	310.34
70	311.69	313.04	314.39	315.75	317.12	318.49	319.87	321.25	322.63	324.02
71	325.42	326.82	328.22	329.63	331.05	332.47	333.89	335.33	336.76	338.20
72	339.65	341.10	342.56	344.03	345.50	346.97	348.45	349.93	351.42	352.91
73	354.41	355.91	357.43	358.94	360.46	361.99	363.52	365.06	366.61	368.15
74	369.71	371.27	372.84	374.41	375.99	377.57	379.16	380.75	382.35	383.95
75	385.56	387.18	388.80	390.43	392.06	393.70	395.34	396.99	398.65	400.31
76	401.98	403.65	405.34	407.02	408.71	410.41	412.11	413.82	415.53	417.25
77	418.98	420.71	422.45	424.20	425.95	427.71	429.47	431.24	433.02	434.80
78	436.59	438.38	440.18	441.99	443.80	445.62	447.45	449.28	451.11	452.96
79	454.81	456.67	458.53	460.40	462.28	464.16	466.05	467.94	469.85	471.76
80	473.67	475.59	477.52	479.45	481.39	483.34	485.29	487.25	489.22	491.19
81	493.17	495.16	497.15	499.16	501.17	503.18	505.20	507.23	509.26	511.30
82	513.35	515.41	517.47	519.54	521.62	523.70	525.79	527.89	529.99	532.10
83	534.22	536.35	538.48	540.62	542.77	544.92	547.08	549.25	551.43	553.61
84	555.80	557.99	560.20	562.41	564.62	566.85	569.08	571.32	573.57	575.83
85	578.09	580.36	582.64	584.93	587.22	589.52	591.83	594.14	596.46	598.79
86	601.13	603.48	605.83	608.19	610.56	612.94	615.32	617.72	620.12	622.52
87	624.94	627.36	629.79	632.23	634.68	637.13	639.59	642.07	644.55	647.03
88	649.53	652.03	654.54	657.06	659.59	662.12	664.66	667.22	669.78	672.34
89	674.92	677.50	680.09	682.69	685.30	687.92	690.55	693.18	695.82	698.47
90	701.13	703.80	706.47	709.16	711.85	714.55	717.26	719.98	722.71	725.45
91	728.19	730.94	733.70	736.47	739.25	742.04	744.84	747.64	750.46	753.28
92	756.11	758.95	761.80	764.66	767.52	770.40	773.29	776.18	779.09	782.00
93	784.92	787.85	790.79	793.74	796.69	799.66	802.63	805.62	808.61	811.62
94	814.63	817.65	820.69	823.73	826.78	829.84	832.91	835.99	839.08	842.17
95	845.28	848.40	851.52	854.66	857.80	860.96	864.12	867.30	870.48	873.68
96	876.88	880.09	883.31	886.55	889.79	893.04	896.30	899.57	902.86	906.15
97	909.45	912.76	916.08	919.42	922.76	926.11	929.47	932.84	936.23	939.62
98	943.02	946.43	949.85	953.28	956.73	960.18	963.65	967.12	970.61	974.10
99	977.61	981.13	984.65	988.19	991.74	995.30	998.87	1002.45	1006.04	1009.64
100	1013.25	1016.87	1020.50	1024.14	1027.80	1031.46	1035.13	1038.82	1042.51	1046.22
101	1049.94	1053.67	1057.41	1061.16	1064.93	1068.70	1072.49	1076.28	1080.09	1083.91
102	1087.74									

(From *Smithsonian Meteorological Tables,* 6th rev. ed., List, R. J., Ed., Smithsonian Institution, Washington, D.C., 1971.)

Table 3.4–2
SATURATION VAPOR PRESSURE OVER ICE

Temperature °C.	Metric units									
	.0	.1	.2	.3	.4	.5	.6	.7	.8	.9
Unit:	10^{-5} mb.	10^{-5} mb.	10^{-5} mb.	10^{-5} mb.	10^{-5} mb.	10^{-5} mb.	10^{-5} mb.	10^{-5} mb.	10^{-5} mb.	10^{-5} mb.
–100	1.403									
– 99	1.719	1.685	1.651	1.617	1.585	1.553	1.522	1.491	1.461	1.432
– 98	2.101	2.059	2.019	1.979	1.939	1.901	1.863	1.826	1.790	1.754
– 97	2.561	2.511	2.462	2.414	2.366	2.320	2.274	2.230	2.186	2.143
– 96	3.117	3.057	2.997	2.939	2.882	2.826	2.771	2.717	2.664	2.612
– 95	3.784	3.712	3.640	3.571	3.502	3.435	3.369	3.304	3.240	3.178
– 94	4.584	4.497	4.412	4.329	4.246	4.166	4.087	4.009	3.932	3.858
– 93	5.542	5.438	5.336	5.236	5.138	5.041	4.946	4.853	4.762	4.672
– 92	6.685	6.561	6.439	6.320	6.203	6.088	5.975	5.863	5.754	5.647
– 91	8.049	7.902	7.757	7.615	7.475	7.338	7.203	7.070	6.939	6.811
– 90	9.672	9.497	9.324	9.155	8.988	8.825	8.664	8.506	8.351	8.199
– 89	11.60	11.39	11.19	10.98	10.79	10.59	10.40	10.22	10.03	9.850
– 88	13.88	13.63	13.39	13.15	12.92	12.69	12.46	12.24	12.02	11.81
– 87	16.58	16.29	16.00	15.72	15.45	15.18	14.91	14.65	14.39	14.13
– 86	19.77	19.43	19.09	18.76	18.43	18.11	17.79	17.48	17.18	16.88
– 85	23.53	23.13	22.73	22.34	21.96	21.58	21.21	20.84	20.48	20.12
– 84	27.96	27.48	27.02	26.56	26.10	25.66	25.22	24.79	24.36	23.94
– 83	33.16	32.60	32.05	31.51	30.98	30.45	29.93	29.43	28.93	28.44
– 82	39.25	38.60	37.95	37.32	36.69	36.08	35.48	34.88	34.30	33.72
– 81	46.38	45.62	44.86	44.12	43.40	42.68	41.97	41.28	40.59	39.91
– 80	54.72	53.83	52.95	52.08	51.23	50.39	49.56	48.75	47.95	47.16
– 79	64.44	63.40	62.37	61.36	60.37	59.39	58.43	57.48	56.54	55.62
– 78	75.77	74.56	73.36	72.19	71.03	69.89	68.77	67.66	66.57	65.50
– 77	88.94	87.53	86.14	84.78	83.43	82.11	80.80	79.52	78.25	77.00
– 76	104.2	102.6	101.0	99.41	97.85	96.31	94.79	93.29	91.82	90.37
Unit:	10^{-3} mb.	10^{-3} mb.	10^{-3} mb.	10^{-3} mb.	10^{-3} mb.	10^{-3} mb.	10^{-3} mb.	10^{-3} mb.	10^{-3} mb.	10^{-3} mb.
– 75	1.220	1.201	1.182	1.164	1.146	1.128	1.110	1.093	1.076	1.059
– 74	1.425	1.403	1.382	1.360	1.340	1.319	1.299	1.279	1.259	1.239
– 73	1.662	1.637	1.612	1.587	1.563	1.539	1.515	1.492	1.470	1.447
– 72	1.936	1.907	1.878	1.850	1.822	1.794	1.767	1.740	1.714	1.688
– 71	2.252	2.218	2.185	2.152	2.120	2.088	2.057	2.026	1.995	1.965
– 70	2.615	2.576	2.538	2.501	2.464	2.427	2.391	2.355	2.320	2.286
– 69	3.032	2.988	2.944	2.901	2.858	2.816	2.775	2.734	2.694	2.654
– 68	3.511	3.460	3.410	3.360	3.311	3.263	3.215	3.169	3.122	3.077
– 67	4.060	4.002	3.944	3.887	3.831	3.776	3.721	3.668	3.615	3.562
– 66	4.688	4.621	4.555	4.490	4.426	4.363	4.301	4.239	4.179	4.119
– 65	5.406	5.330	5.255	5.180	5.107	5.035	4.964	4.893	4.824	4.755
– 64	6.225	6.138	6.052	5.968	5.884	5.802	5.721	5.640	5.561	5.483
– 63	7.159	7.060	6.962	6.866	6.771	6.677	6.584	6.493	6.402	6.313
– 62	8.223	8.110	7.999	7.889	7.781	7.674	7.568	7.464	7.361	7.259
– 61	9.432	9.304	9.177	9.053	8.930	8.808	8.688	8.569	8.452	8.337
– 60	10.80	10.66	10.51	10.37	10.24	10.10	9.961	9.826	9.693	9.562
– 59	12.36	12.20	12.03	11.87	11.72	11.56	11.40	11.25	11.10	10.95
– 58	14.13	13.94	13.76	13.58	13.40	13.22	13.04	12.87	12.70	12.53
– 57	16.12	15.91	15.70	15.49	15.29	15.09	14.89	14.70	14.51	14.32
– 56	18.38	18.14	17.91	17.68	17.45	17.22	17.00	16.77	16.55	16.34
– 55	20.92	20.65	20.39	20.12	19.86	19.61	19.36	19.11	18.86	18.62
– 54	23.80	23.50	23.20	22.90	22.61	22.32	22.03	21.75	21.47	21.19
– 53	27.03	26.69	26.35	26.02	25.69	25.37	25.05	24.73	24.42	24.11
– 52	30.67	30.29	29.91	29.53	29.17	28.80	28.44	28.08	27.73	27.38
– 51	34.76	34.33	33.90	33.48	33.06	32.65	32.24	31.84	31.45	31.06
– 50	39.35	38.87	38.39	37.92	37.45	36.99	36.53	36.08	35.64	35.20

Table 3.4–2 (*Continued*)
SATURATION VAPOR PRESSURE OVER ICE

Temperature °C.	Metric units .0	.1	.2	.3	.4	.5	.6	.7	.8	.9
Unit:	mb.	mb.	mb.	mb.	mb.	mb.	mb.	mb.	mb.	mb.
−50	0.03935	0.03887	0.03839	0.03792	0.03745	0.03699	0.03653	0.03608	0.03564	0.03520
−49	0.04449	0.04395	0.04341	0.04289	0.04236	0.04185	0.04134	0.04083	0.04033	0.03984
−48	0.05026	0.04965	0.04905	0.04846	0.04788	0.04730	0.04673	0.04616	0.04560	0.04504
−47	0.05671	0.05603	0.05536	0.05470	0.05405	0.05340	0.05276	0.05212	0.05150	0.05087
−46	0.06393	0.06317	0.06242	0.06168	0.06095	0.06022	0.05950	0.05879	0.05809	0.05740
−45	0.07198	0.07113	0.07030	0.06947	0.06865	0.06784	0.06704	0.06625	0.06547	0.06469
−44	0.08097	0.08003	0.07909	0.07817	0.07725	0.07635	0.07546	0.07457	0.07370	0.07283
−43	0.09098	0.08993	0.08889	0.08786	0.08684	0.08584	0.08484	0.08386	0.08289	0.08192
−42	0.1021	0.1010	0.09981	0.09866	0.09753	0.09641	0.09530	0.09420	0.09312	0.09204
−41	0.1145	0.1132	0.1119	0.1107	0.1094	0.1082	0.1070	0.1057	0.1045	0.1033
−40	0.1283	0.1268	0.1254	0.1240	0.1226	0.1212	0.1198	0.1185	0.1171	0.1158
−39	0.1436	0.1420	0.1404	0.1389	0.1373	0.1358	0.1343	0.1328	0.1313	0.1298
−38	0.1606	0.1588	0.1571	0.1553	0.1536	0.1519	0.1502	0.1485	0.1469	0.1452
−37	0.1794	0.1774	0.1755	0.1736	0.1717	0.1698	0.1679	0.1661	0.1642	0.1624
−36	0.2002	0.1980	0.1959	0.1938	0.1917	0.1896	0.1875	0.1855	0.1834	0.1814
−35	0.2233	0.2209	0.2185	0.2161	0.2138	0.2115	0.2092	0.2069	0.2047	0.2024
−34	0.2488	0.2461	0.2435	0.2409	0.2383	0.2357	0.2332	0.2307	0.2282	0.2257
−33	0.2769	0.2740	0.2711	0.2682	0.2653	0.2625	0.2597	0.2569	0.2542	0.2515
−32	0.3079	0.3047	0.3014	0.2983	0.2951	0.2920	0.2889	0.2859	0.2828	0.2799
−31	0.3421	0.3385	0.3350	0.3315	0.3280	0.3246	0.3212	0.3178	0.3145	0.3112
−30	0.3798	0.3759	0.3720	0.3681	0.3643	0.3605	0.3567	0.3530	0.3494	0.3457
−29	0.4213	0.4170	0.4127	0.4084	0.4042	0.4000	0.3959	0.3918	0.3877	0.3838
−28	0.4669	0.4621	0.4574	0.4527	0.4481	0.4435	0.4390	0.4345	0.4300	0.4256
−27	0.5170	0.5118	0.5066	0.5014	0.4964	0.4913	0.4863	0.4814	0.4765	0.4717
−26	0.5720	0.5663	0.5606	0.5549	0.5493	0.5438	0.5383	0.5329	0.5276	0.5222
−25	0.6323	0.6260	0.6198	0.6136	0.6075	0.6015	0.5955	0.5895	0.5836	0.5778
−24	0.6985	0.6916	0.6848	0.6780	0.6713	0.6646	0.6580	0.6515	0.6450	0.6386
−23	0.7709	0.7634	0.7559	0.7485	0.7412	0.7339	0.7267	0.7195	0.7125	0.7055
−22	0.8502	0.8419	0.8338	0.8257	0.8176	0.8097	0.8018	0.7940	0.7862	0.7785
−21	0.9370	0.9280	0.9190	0.9101	0.9013	0.8926	0.8840	0.8754	0.8669	0.8585
−20	1.032	1.022	1.012	1.002	0.9928	0.9833	0.9739	0.9645	0.9553	0.9461
−19	1.135	1.124	1.114	1.103	1.092	1.082	1.072	1.062	1.052	1.042
−18	1.248	1.236	1.225	1.213	1.201	1.190	1.179	1.168	1.157	1.146
−17	1.371	1.358	1.345	1.333	1.320	1.308	1.296	1.284	1.272	1.260
−16	1.506	1.492	1.478	1.464	1.451	1.437	1.424	1.410	1.397	1.384
−15	1.652	1.637	1.622	1.607	1.592	1.577	1.562	1.548	1.534	1.520
−14	1.811	1.795	1.778	1.762	1.746	1.730	1.714	1.698	1.683	1.667
−13	1.984	1.966	1.948	1.930	1.913	1.895	1.878	1.861	1.844	1.827
−12	2.172	2.153	2.133	2.114	2.095	2.076	2.057	2.039	2.020	2.002
−11	2.376	2.355	2.334	2.313	2.292	2.271	2.251	2.231	2.211	2.191
−10	2.597	2.574	2.551	2.529	2.506	2.484	2.462	2.440	2.419	2.397
− 9	2.837	2.812	2.787	2.763	2.739	2.715	2.691	2.667	2.644	2.620
− 8	3.097	3.070	3.043	3.017	2.991	2.965	2.939	2.913	2.888	2.862
− 7	3.379	3.350	3.321	3.292	3.264	3.236	3.208	3.180	3.152	3.124
− 6	3.685	3.653	3.622	3.591	3.560	3.529	3.499	3.468	3.438	3.409
− 5	4.015	3.981	3.947	3.913	3.879	3.846	3.813	3.781	3.748	3.717
− 4	4.372	4.335	4.298	4.262	4.226	4.190	4.154	4.119	4.084	4.049
− 3	4.757	4.717	4.678	4.638	4.600	4.561	4.523	4.485	4.447	4.409
− 2	5.173	5.130	5.087	5.045	5.003	4.961	4.920	4.878	4.838	4.797
− 1	5.623	5.577	5.530	5.485	5.439	5.394	5.349	5.305	5.260	5.217
− 0	6.107	6.057	6.007	5.958	5.909	5.860	5.812	5.764	5.717	5.670

(From *Smithsonian Meteorological Tables,* 6th rev. ed., List, R. J., Ed., Smithsonian Institution, Washington, D.C. 1971.)

Table 3.4–3
SATURATION VAPOR PRESSURE OVER WATER OF SALINITY 35°/₀₀

The saturation vapor pressure over a plane surface of pure water depends only on the temperature of the water. The salinity decreases the saturation vapor pressure slightly, the empirical relation being

$$e_s = e_w (1 - 0.000537S)$$

where

e_s = saturation vapor pressure over sea water at a given temperature,
e_w = saturation vapor pressure over a plane surface of pure water at the same temperature,
S = salinity in parts per thousand (°/₀₀)

Values of e_s computed for a salinity of 35°/₀₀ are given in the table.

Temp °C	Vapor pressure mbar	Temp °C	Vapor pressure mbar	Temp °C	Vapor pressure mbar	Temp °C	Vapor pressure mbar
−2	5.19	7	9.83	16	17.85	25	31.12
−1	5.57	8	10.52	17	19.02	26	33.01
0	5.99	9	11.26	18	20.26	27	35.02
1	6.44	10	12.05	19	21.57	28	37.13
2	6.92	11	12.88	20	22.96	29	39.33
3	7.43	12	13.76	21	24.42	30	41.68
4	7.98	13	14.70	22	25.96	31	44.13
5	8.56	14	15.69	23	27.59	32	46.71
6	9.17	15	16.74	24	29.30		

(From Sverdrup, H. U., Johnson, M. W., and Fleming, R. H., *The Oceans, Their Physics, Chemistry, and General Biology,* Prentice-Hall, Inc., Englewood Cliffs, New Jersey, © 1942, renewed 1970. With permission.)

Figure 3.4–1
SEA WATER VAPOR PRESSURE

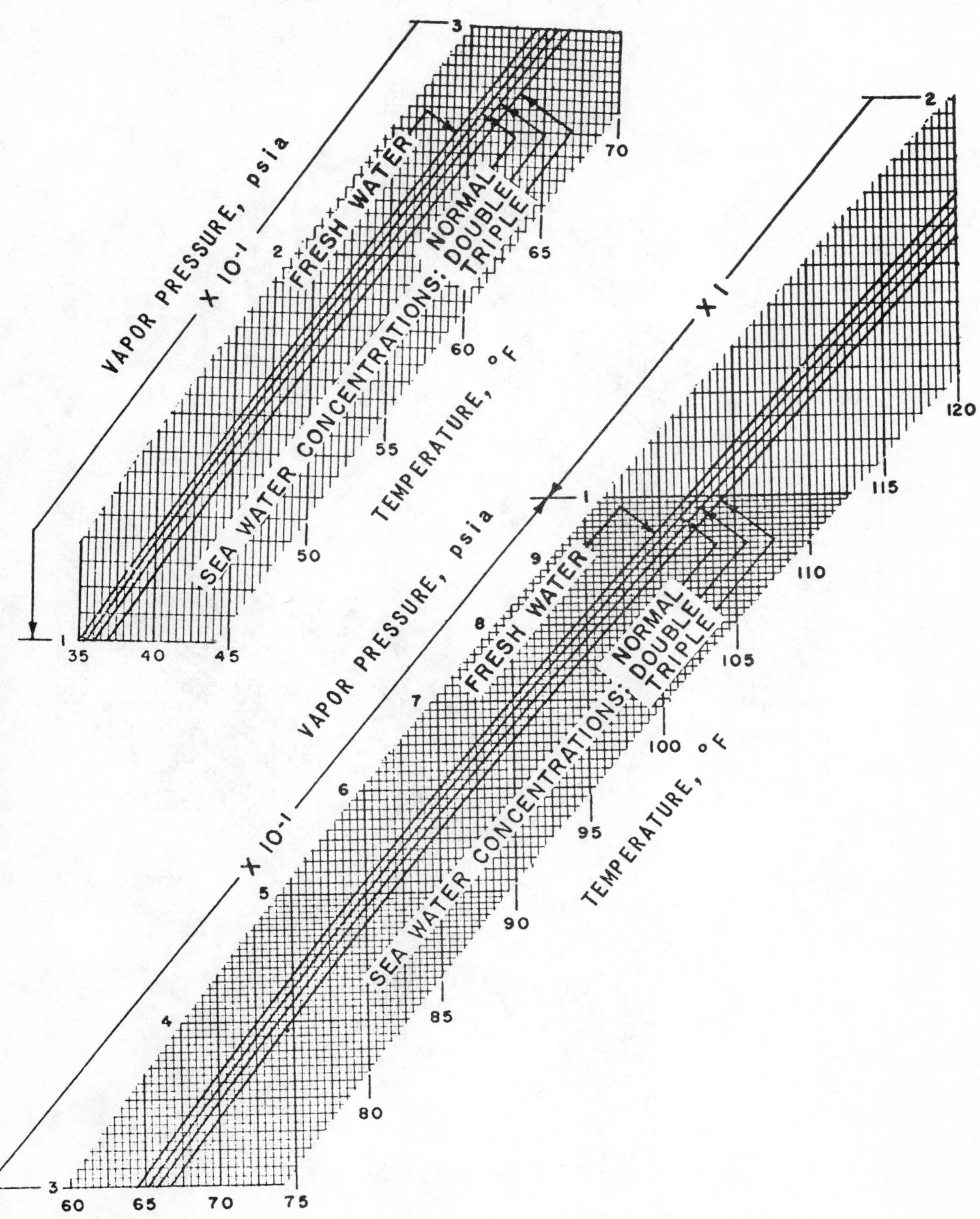

Note: The normal sea water concentration used in this chart has 34.483 g solids/1000 g sea water.

Figure 3.4–1 (*Continued*)
SEA WATER VAPOR PRESSURE

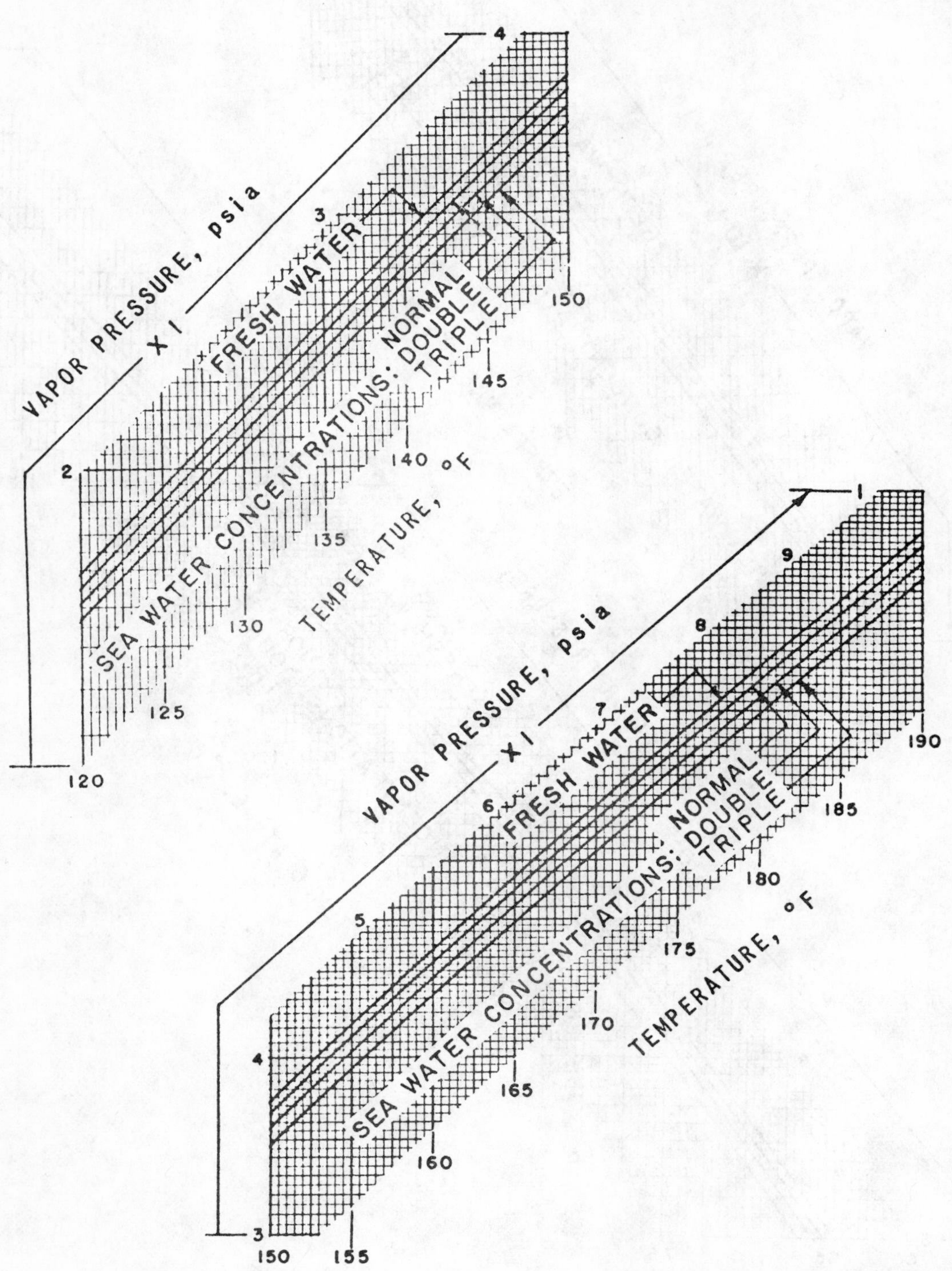

Figure 3.4–1 (*Continued*)
SEA WATER VAPOR PRESSURE

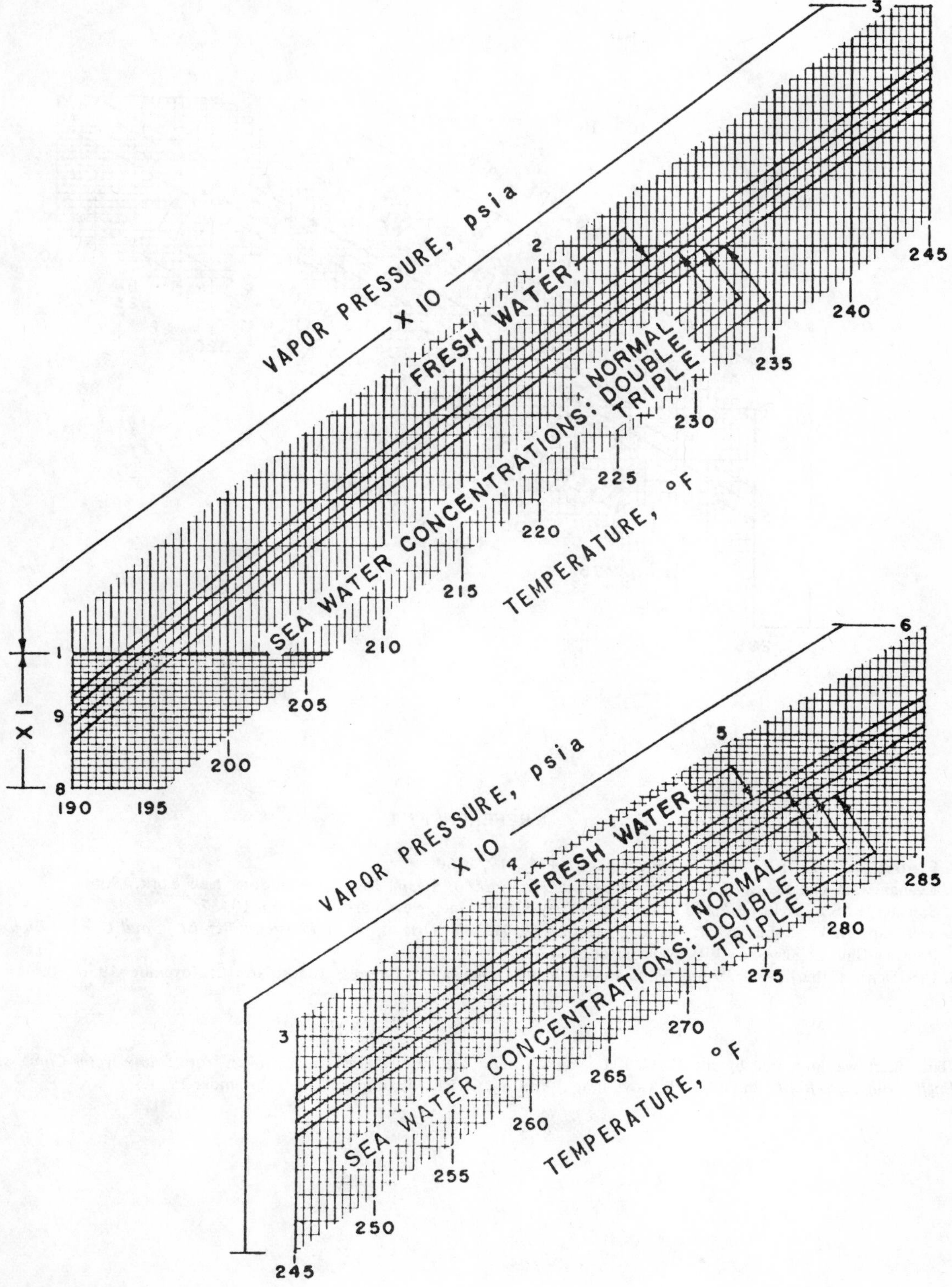

Figure 3.4–1 (*Continued*)
SEA WATER VAPOR PRESSURE

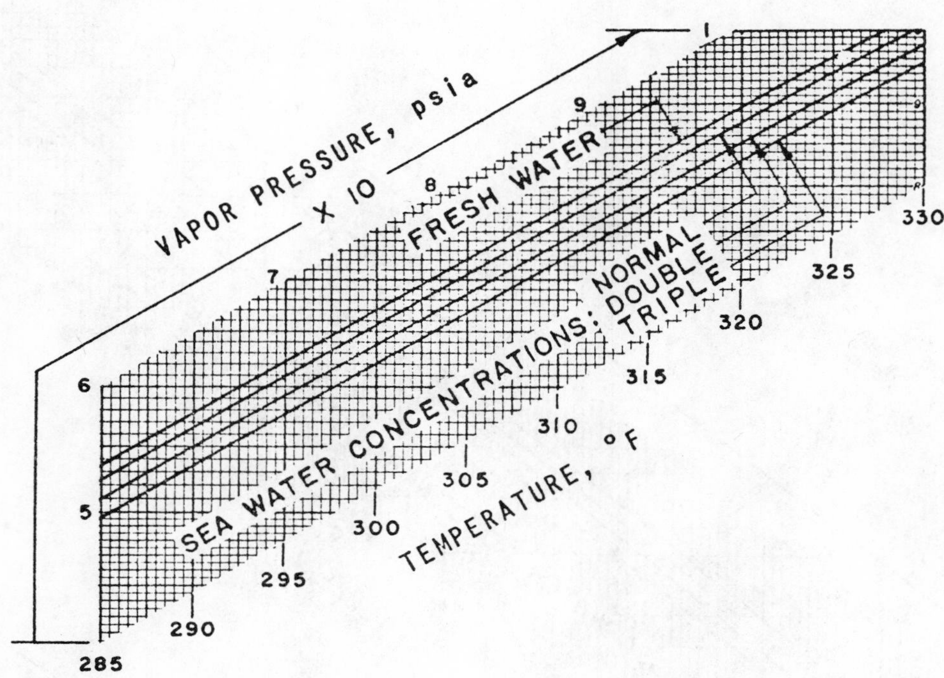

REFERENCES

1. **Frankel, A.,** *Proc. Inst. Mech. Engrs. (London),* 174, 312, 1960.
2. **Keenan, J. H. and Keyes, F. G.,** *Thermodynamic Properties of Steam,* John Wiley & Sons, New York, 1936.
3. **Spiegler, K. S.,** *Salt-Water Purification,* John Wiley & Sons, Inc., New York, 1962, pp. 10, 37.
4. **Sverdrup, H. U., Johnson, M. W., and Fleming, R. H.,** *The Oceans, Their Physics, Chemistry, and General Biology,* Prentice-Hall, Englewood Cliffs, New Jersey, 1942.
5. U.S. Dept. of the Interior, Saline Water Research and Development Progress Report No. 12, November 1956, 70.

(This chart was prepared by the M. W. Kellogg Co. for the Office of Saline Water. Taken from *Saline Water Conversion Engineering Data Book,* 2nd ed., U.S. Government Printing Office, Washington, D.C., November 1971.)

Tables 3.4–4 and 3.4–5
DENSITY OF PURE WATER VAPOR AT SATURATION

The density of pure water vapor (vapor unadmixed with air) at saturation over a plane surface of liquid water, ρ_w, in cgs units is

$$\rho_w = \frac{e_w}{C_v R_w T} \quad (1)$$

where

R_w = gas constant for water vapor, 4.6150 x 10^6 erg g^{-1} °K^{-1}
T = temperature of the vapor, °K
e_w = saturation vapor pressure over water at temperature T
C_v = "compressibility factor" for water vapor.

The factor C_v is introduced into Equation 1 to correct for the deviations of water vapor from ideal gas laws.

For pressures measured in millibars, the density ρ_w in g m^{-3} (1 g m^{-3} = 10^{-6} g cm^{-3}) is

$$\rho_w = 216.68 \frac{e_w(\text{mbar})}{C_v T} \quad (2)$$

In a similar manner, the density of pure water vapor at saturation over a plane surface of ice, ρ_i, is found by substituting e_i, the saturation vapor pressure over ice, for e_w in Equations 1 or 2.

Concentrations of the constitutents of moist air – It is necessary to distinguish between the density of a gas or vapor unadmixed and the concentrations of the constituents of a mixture; this is especially true in dealing with real gases. The vapor concentration d_v and the dry-air concentration d_a are defined as the ratios of the masses of vapor m_v and of dry air m_a, respectively, to the volume V occupied by the mixture

$$d_v = \frac{m_v}{V} \quad (3)$$

$$d_a = \frac{m_a}{V} \quad (4)$$

Since the mixing ratio $r = m_v/m_a$ and the density of moist air $\rho = d_a + d_v$, Equation 3 becomes

$$d_v = \frac{r}{1 + r}\rho \quad (5)$$

On introducing the mixing ratio at saturation over water r_w, where $r = Ur_w$ and U is the relative humidity, Equation 5 becomes

$$d_v = \frac{Ur_w}{1 + Ur_w}\rho \quad (6)$$

(From *Smithsonian Meteorological Tables,* 6th rev. ed., List, R. J., Ed., Smithsonian Institution, Washington, D.C., 1971.)

Table 3.4–4 (*Continued*)
DENSITY OF PURE WATER VAPOR AT SATURATION OVER WATER

Temperature °C.	.0	.1	.2	.3	.4	.5	.6	.7	.8	.9
	g. m.$^{-3}$	g. m.$^{-3}$	g. m.$^{-3}$	g. m.$^{-3}$	g. m.$^{-3}$	g. m.$^{-3}$	g. m.$^{-3}$	g. m.$^{-3}$	g. m.$^{-3}$	g. m.$^{-3}$
−50	0.06171									
−49	0.06886	0.06812	0.06738	0.06664	0.06592	0.06520	0.06449	0.06378	0.06309	0.06240
−48	0.07675	0.07592	0.07510	0.07430	0.07350	0.07270	0.07191	0.07115	0.07038	0.06961
−47	0.08544	0.08453	0.08364	0.08274	0.08187	0.08099	0.08013	0.07927	0.07842	0.07758
−46	0.09501	0.09402	0.09303	0.09205	0.09107	0.09011	0.08915	0.08822	0.08728	0.08635
−45	0.1055	0.1044	0.1033	0.1022	0.1011	0.1001	0.09912	0.09812	0.09702	0.09601
−44	0.1172	0.1160	0.1148	0.1136	0.1124	0.1112	0.1101	0.1090	0.1078	0.1066
−43	0.1298	0.1285	0.1272	0.1258	0.1246	0.1233	0.1220	0.1208	0.1196	0.1183
−42	0.1438	0.1424	0.1409	0.1395	0.1380	0.1367	0.1353	0.1339	0.1325	0.1312
−41	0.1590	0.1574	0.1559	0.1543	0.1528	0.1512	0.1497	0.1482	0.1468	0.1452
−40	0.1757	0.1740	0.1723	0.1706	0.1690	0.1673	0.1656	0.1640	0.1623	0.1606
−39	0.1940	0.1922	0.1902	0.1884	0.1866	0.1847	0.1829	0.1811	0.1793	0.1775
−38	0.2141	0.2119	0.2099	0.2079	0.2058	0.2038	0.2019	0.1998	0.1979	0.1960
−37	0.2359	0.2336	0.2314	0.2291	0.2269	0.2247	0.2225	0.2204	0.2183	0.2162
−36	0.2597	0.2572	0.2548	0.2523	0.2499	0.2475	0.2451	0.2428	0.2405	0.2382
−35	0.2856	0.2829	0.2802	0.2776	0.2750	0.2723	0.2697	0.2672	0.2647	0.2621
−34	0.3138	0.3108	0.3080	0.3050	0.3022	0.2993	0.2966	0.2938	0.2910	0.2883
−33	0.3445	0.3413	0.3382	0.3350	0.3320	0.3289	0.3258	0.3228	0.3198	0.3167
−32	0.3779	0.3744	0.3710	0.3675	0.3642	0.3608	0.3574	0.3542	0.3510	0.3477
−31	0.4141	0.4104	0.4067	0.4029	0.3992	0.3956	0.3920	0.3884	0.3849	0.3814
−30	0.4534	0.4493	0.4453	0.4413	0.4373	0.4334	0.4295	0.4256	0.4218	0.4179
−29	0.4960	0.4916	0.4872	0.4829	0.4785	0.4743	0.4700	0.4659	0.4617	0.4575
−28	0.5422	0.5374	0.5327	0.5280	0.5234	0.5187	0.5141	0.5096	0.5050	0.5006
−27	0.5922	0.5871	0.5820	0.5768	0.5718	0.5668	0.5618	0.5568	0.5519	0.5470
−26	0.6463	0.6407	0.6351	0.6296	0.6242	0.6187	0.6133	0.6079	0.6026	0.5974
−25	0.7047	0.6986	0.6927	0.6867	0.6808	0.6749	0.6691	0.6633	0.6576	0.6519
−24	0.7678	0.7612	0.7548	0.7483	0.7420	0.7357	0.7294	0.7232	0.7170	0.7108
−23	0.8359	0.8289	0.8218	0.8150	0.8081	0.8012	0.7944	0.7877	0.7810	0.7743
−22	0.9093	0.9017	0.8941	0.8867	0.8792	0.8719	0.8645	0.8573	0.8501	0.8429
−21	0.9884	0.9802	0.9720	0.9640	0.9560	0.9481	0.9402	0.9323	0.9246	0.9170
−20	1.074	1.065	1.056	1.047	1.039	1.030	1.022	1.013	1.005	0.9966
−19	1.165	1.156	1.146	1.137	1.128	1.119	1.109	1.100	1.091	1.082
−18	1.264	1.253	1.243	1.233	1.223	1.214	1.204	1.194	1.184	1.175
−17	1.369	1.359	1.348	1.337	1.326	1.316	1.305	1.295	1.284	1.274
−16	1.483	1.471	1.460	1.448	1.437	1.425	1.414	1.403	1.392	1.381
−15	1.605	1.592	1.580	1.568	1.555	1.543	1.531	1.519	1.507	1.495
−14	1.736	1.722	1.709	1.696	1.682	1.669	1.656	1.643	1.630	1.618
−13	1.876	1.861	1.847	1.833	1.819	1.805	1.791	1.777	1.763	1.749
−12	2.026	2.010	1.995	1.980	1.965	1.949	1.934	1.920	1.905	1.890
−11	2.186	2.170	2.153	2.137	2.121	2.105	2.089	2.073	2.057	2.041
−10	2.358	2.340	2.323	2.305	2.288	2.271	2.254	2.237	2.220	2.203
− 9	2.541	2.522	2.504	2.485	2.466	2.448	2.430	2.412	2.394	2.376
− 8	2.737	2.717	2.697	2.677	2.657	2.638	2.618	2.599	2.579	2.560
− 7	2.946	2.925	2.903	2.882	2.861	2.840	2.819	2.798	2.778	2.758
− 6	3.169	3.146	3.123	3.101	3.078	3.056	3.034	3.012	2.990	2.968
− 5	3.407	3.383	3.358	3.334	3.310	3.286	3.263	3.239	3.216	3.193
− 4	3.660	3.634	3.609	3.583	3.557	3.532	3.507	3.481	3.456	3.432
− 3	3.930	3.902	3.875	3.847	3.820	3.793	3.766	3.740	3.713	3.687
− 2	4.217	4.188	4.159	4.129	4.100	4.072	4.043	4.015	3.986	3.958
− 1	4.523	4.491	4.460	4.429	4.398	4.368	4.337	4.307	4.277	4.247
− 0	4.847	4.814	4.781	4.748	4.715	4.683	4.650	4.618	4.586	4.554
0	4.847	4.881	4.915	4.948	4.983	5.017	5.052	5.087	5.122	5.157
1	5.192	5.228	5.264	5.300	5.336	5.373	5.409	5.446	5.483	5.521
2	5.559	5.597	5.635	5.673	5.711	5.750	5.789	5.828	5.868	5.907
3	5.947	5.987	6.028	6.068	6.109	6.150	6.192	6.233	6.275	6.317
4	6.360	6.402	6.445	6.488	6.531	6.575	6.619	6.663	6.707	6.752

Table 3.4–4 (*Continued*)
DENSITY OF PURE WATER VAPOR AT SATURATION OVER WATER

Temperature °C.	.0	.1	.2	.3	.4	.5	.6	.7	.8	.9
	g. m.$^{-3}$	g. m.$^{-3}$	g. m.$^{-3}$	g. m.$^{-3}$	g. m.$^{-3}$	g. m.$^{-3}$	g. m.$^{-3}$	g. m.$^{-3}$	g. m.$^{-3}$	g. m.$^{-3}$
5	6.797	6.842	6.887	6.933	6.979	7.025	7.071	7.118	7.165	7.212
6	7.260	7.307	7.355	7.404	7.452	7.501	7.550	7.600	7.649	7.699
7	7.750	7.801	7.851	7.902	7.954	8.006	8.058	8.110	8.163	8.216
8	8.270	8.324	8.377	8.431	8.485	8.540	8.595	8.650	8.706	8.762
9	8.819	8.875	8.932	8.989	9.046	9.104	9.163	9.221	9.280	9.339
10	9.399	9.459	9.519	9.579	9.641	9.702	9.763	9.825	9.887	9.949
11	10.01	10.08	10.14	10.20	10.27	10.33	10.40	10.46	10.53	10.59
12	10.66	10.73	10.79	10.86	10.93	11.00	11.07	11.14	11.21	11.27
13	11.35	11.42	11.49	11.56	11.63	11.70	11.77	11.85	11.92	11.99
14	12.07	12.14	12.22	12.29	12.37	12.44	12.52	12.60	12.67	12.75
15	12.83	12.91	12.99	13.07	13.14	13.23	13.31	13.39	13.47	13.55
16	13.63	13.72	13.80	13.88	13.97	14.05	14.14	14.22	14.31	14.39
17	14.48	14.57	14.65	14.74	14.83	14.92	15.01	15.10	15.19	15.28
18	15.37	15.46	15.55	15.65	15.74	15.83	15.93	16.02	16.12	16.21
19	16.31	16.41	16.50	16.60	16.70	16.80	16.90	17.00	17.10	17.20
20	17.30	17.40	17.50	17.60	17.71	17.81	17.91	18.02	18.12	18.23
21	18.34	18.44	18.55	18.66	18.77	18.88	18.99	19.10	19.21	19.32
22	19.43	19.54	19.65	19.77	19.88	20.00	20.11	20.23	20.34	20.46
23	20.58	20.70	20.81	20.93	21.05	21.17	21.29	21.42	21.54	21.66
24	21.78	21.91	22.03	22.16	22.28	22.41	22.54	22.66	22.79	22.92
25	23.05	23.18	23.31	23.44	23.58	23.71	23.84	23.97	24.11	24.24
26	24.38	24.52	24.66	24.79	24.93	25.07	25.21	25.35	25.49	25.63
27	25.78	25.92	26.06	26.21	26.35	26.50	26.65	26.79	26.94	27.09
28	27.24	27.39	27.54	27.69	27.85	28.00	28.15	28.31	28.46	28.62
29	28.78	28.93	29.09	29.25	29.41	29.57	29.73	29.89	30.05	30.22
30	30.38	30.55	30.71	30.88	31.05	31.22	31.38	31.55	31.72	31.89
31	32.07	32.24	32.41	32.59	32.76	32.94	33.11	33.29	33.47	33.65
32	33.83	34.01	34.19	34.38	34.56	34.74	34.93	35.11	35.30	35.49
33	35.68	35.87	36.06	36.25	36.44	36.63	36.83	37.02	37.22	37.41
34	37.61	37.81	38.01	38.21	38.41	38.61	38.81	39.01	39.22	39.42
35	39.63	39.84	40.05	40.26	40.47	40.68	40.89	41.10	41.31	41.53
36	41.75	41.96	42.18	42.40	42.62	42.84	43.06	43.28	43.50	43.73
37	43.96	44.18	44.41	44.64	44.87	45.09	45.33	45.56	45.79	46.02
38	46.26	46.50	46.74	46.97	47.21	47.45	47.69	47.94	48.18	48.42
39	48.67	48.92	49.17	49.42	49.66	49.92	50.17	50.42	50.67	50.93
40	51.19	51.45	51.70	51.96	52.22	52.49	52.75	53.01	53.28	53.54
41	53.82	54.09	54.36	54.63	54.90	55.17	55.44	55.72	56.00	56.27
42	56.56	56.84	57.12	57.40	57.68	57.97	58.25	58.54	58.83	59.12
43	59.41	59.70	60.00	60.29	60.59	60.88	61.18	61.48	61.78	62.08
44	62.39	62.70	63.00	63.31	63.62	63.92	64.23	64.55	64.86	65.17
45	65.50	65.81	66.13	66.45	66.77	67.10	67.42	67.74	68.07	68.40
46	68.73	69.06	69.39	69.73	70.06	70.40	70.73	71.07	71.41	71.75
47	72.10	72.45	72.79	73.13	73.49	73.84	74.18	74.53	74.89	75.25
48	75.61	75.96	76.33	76.69	77.05	77.41	77.77	78.14	78.51	78.88
49	79.26	79.63	80.01	80.38	80.76	81.14	81.52	81.90	82.28	82.67
50	83.06	83.45	83.84	84.23	84.62	85.01	85.41	85.81	86.20	86.60
51	87.01	87.41	87.82	88.22	88.63	89.04	89.45	89.86	90.27	90.69
52	91.12	91.54	91.96	92.38	92.80	93.23	93.66	94.09	94.52	94.95
53	95.39	95.83	96.27	96.71	97.14	97.59	98.03	98.47	98.92	99.37
54	99.83	100.3	100.7	101.2	101.7	102.1	102.6	103.0	103.5	104.0
55	104.4	104.9	105.4	105.9	106.3	106.8	107.3	107.8	108.2	108.7
56	109.2	109.7	110.2	110.7	111.2	111.7	112.2	112.7	113.2	113.7
57	114.2	114.7	115.2	115.7	116.2	116.8	117.3	117.8	118.3	118.8
58	119.4	119.9	120.4	121.0	121.5	122.0	122.6	123.1	123.6	124.2
59	124.7	125.3	125.8	126.4	126.9	127.5	128.0	128.6	129.1	129.7
60	130.3									

(From *Smithsonian Meteorological Tables,* 6th rev. ed., List, R. J., Ed., Smithsonian Institution, Washington, D.C., 1971.)

Table 3.4–5
DENSITY OF PURE WATER VAPOR AT SATURATION OVER ICE

Table A

Temperature	Density	Temperature	Density	Temperature	Density	Temperature	Density
°C.	g. m.$^{-3}$	°C.	g. m.$^{-3}$	°C.	g. m.$^{-3}$	°C.	g. m.$^{-3}$
—100	0.00001756	—87	0.0001930	—74	0.001550	—61	0.009633
— 99	.00002139	—86	.0002289	—73	.001799	—60	.01098
— 98	.00002599	—85	.0002710	—72	.002085	—59	.01251
— 97	.00003150	—84	.0003203	—71	.002414	—58	.01423
— 96	.00003812	—83	.0003778	—70	.002789	—57	.01616
— 95	0.00004602	—82	0.0004449	—69	0.003218	—56	0.01834
— 94	.00005544	—81	.0005230	—68	.003708	—55	.02078
— 93	.00006665	—80	.0006138	—67	.004267	—54	..02353
— 92	.00007996	—79	.0007191	—66	.004903	—53	.02660
— 91	.00009574	—78	.0008413	—65	.005627	—52	.03005
— 90	0.0001144	—77	0.0009824	—64	0.006449	—51	0.03390
— 89	.0001365	—76	.001145	—63	.007381	—50	.03821
— 88	.0001624	—75	.001334	—62	.008438		

Table B

Temperature	.0	.1	.2	.3	.4	.5	.6	.7	.8	.9
°C.	g. m.$^{-3}$	g. m.$^{-3}$	g. m.$^{-3}$	g. m.$^{-3}$	g. m.$^{-3}$	g. m.$^{-3}$	g. m.$^{-3}$	g. m.$^{-3}$	g. m.$^{-3}$	g. m.$^{-3}$
— 49	0.04301	0.04250	0.04200	0.04151	0.04102	0.04054	0.04007	0.03959	0.03912	0.03867
— 48	.04837	.04780	.04724	.04670	.04616	.04562	.04509	.04456	.04404	.04352
— 47	.05433	.05371	.05309	.05248	.05188	.05127	.05068	.05009	.04952	.04893
— 46	.06098	.06028	.05959	.05891	.05824	.05757	.05691	.05625	.05561	.05497
— 45	.06836	.06758	.06682	.06606	.06531	.06457	.06383	.06311	.06239	.06168
— 44	0.07656	0.07570	0.07485	0.07401	0.07317	0.07235	0.07154	0.07072	0.06993	0.06914
— 43	.08565	.08470	.08376	.08282	.08190	.08099	.08008	.07919	.07831	.07742
— 42	.09570	.09471	.09364	.09260	.09158	.09057	.08956	.08857	.08759	.08661
— 41	.1069	.1057	.1045	.1035	.1023	.1012	.1001	.09895	.09787	.09679
— 40	.1192	.1179	.1166	.1154	.1141	.1129	.1116	.1105	.1092	.1080
— 39	0.1329	0.1315	0.1300	0.1287	0.1273	0.1259	0.1246	0.1233	0.1219	0.1206
— 38	.1480	.1464	.1449	.1433	.1418	.1403	.1388	.1372	.1358	.1343
— 37	.1646	.1628	.1612	.1595	.1578	.1561	.1544	.1529	.1512	.1496
— 36	.1829	.1810	.1791	.1773	.1754	.1736	.1718	.1700	.1681	.1664
— 35	.2032	.2011	.1990	.1969	.1949	.1928	.1908	.1888	.1869	.1849
— 34	0.2254	0.2231	0.2208	0.2185	0.2163	0.2140	0.2118	0.2096	0.2075	0.2053
— 33	.2498	.2473	.2448	.2423	.2398	.2373	.2349	.2325	.2301	.2278
— 32	.2767	.2739	.2710	.2684	.2656	.2629	.2602	.2576	.2550	.2524
— 31	.3061	.3030	.3000	.2970	.2940	.2911	.2881	.2852	.2824	.2795
— 30	.3385	.3351	.3318	.3284	.3252	.3219	.3187	.3155	.3124	.3092
— 29	0.3739	0.3703	0.3666	0.3629	0.3593	0.3557	0.3522	0.3487	0.3452	0.3419
— 28	.4127	.4086	.4046	.4006	.3967	.3928	.3890	.3852	.3813	.3776
— 27	.4551	.4507	.4463	.4419	.4377	.4334	.4291	.4250	.4208	.4168
— 26	.5015	.4967	.4919	.4871	.4824	.4777	.4731	.4686	.4641	.4595
— 25	.5521	.5469	.5417	.5365	.5313	.5263	.5213	.5162	.5113	.5064
— 24	0.6075	0.6018	0.5961	0.5904	0.5848	0.5792	0.5737	0.5682	0.5628	0.5574
— 23	.6678	.6616	.6553	.6492	.6431	.6370	.6310	.6250	.6192	.6134
— 22	.7336	.7267	.7200	.7133	.7066	.7000	.6935	.6870	.6805	.6741
— 21	.8053	.7979	.7904	.7831	.7758	.7686	.7615	.7544	.7474	.7405
— 20	.8835	.8752	.8670	.8588	.8512	.8434	.8357	.8280	.8204	.8128

Table 3.4–5 (*Continued*)
DENSITY OF PURE WATER VAPOR AT SATURATION OVER ICE

Temperature	.0	.1	.2	.3	.4	.5	.6	.7	.8	.9
°C.	g. m.$^{-3}$	g. m.$^{-3}$	g. m.$^{-3}$	g. m.$^{-3}$	g. m.$^{-3}$	g. m.$^{-3}$	g. m.$^{-3}$	g. m.$^{-3}$	g. m.$^{-3}$	g. m.$^{-3}$
−19	0.9678	0.9588	0.9506	0.9416	0.9326	0.9244	0.9162	0.9081	0.8999	0.8917
−18	1.060	1.050	1.041	1.031	1.022	1.013	1.004	0.9948	0.9858	0.9768
−17	1.160	1.149	1.139	1.129	1.119	1.109	1.099	1.089	1.080	1.070
−16	1.269	1.258	1.247	1.235	1.225	1.213	1.203	1.192	1.181	1.171
−15	1.387	1.375	1.363	1.351	1.339	1.326	1.314	1.303	1.292	1.281
−14	1.515	1.502	1.488	1.475	1.462	1.450	1.437	1.424	1.412	1.399
−13	1.653	1.639	1.624	1.610	1.596	1.582	1.568	1.555	1.541	1.527
−12	1.803	1.787	1.772	1.756	1.741	1.726	1.711	1.697	1.682	1.667
−11	1.964	1.948	1.931	1.914	1.898	1.881	1.865	1.849	1.834	1.818
−10	2.139	2.121	2.103	2.085	2.067	2.050	2.032	2.015	1.998	1.981
− 9	2.328	2.308	2.289	2.270	2.251	2.232	2.213	2.194	2.176	2.157
− 8	2.532	2.511	2.489	2.469	2.449	2.428	2.408	2.388	2.368	2.348
− 7	2.752	2.729	2.707	2.684	2.662	2.640	2.618	2.597	2.575	2.553
− 6	2.990	2.965	2.941	2.917	2.893	2.869	2.845	2.821	2.798	2.775
− 5	3.246	3.219	3.193	3.167	3.140	3.115	3.089	3.064	3.039	3.015
− 4	3.521	3.493	3.464	3.436	3.409	3.381	3.353	3.326	3.299	3.272
− 3	3.817	3.786	3.756	3.726	3.696	3.666	3.637	3.608	3.579	3.550
− 2	4.136	4.103	4.070	4.038	4.006	3.973	3.942	3.910	3.879	3.848
− 1	4.479	4.444	4.408	4.374	4.339	4.304	4.270	4.236	4.202	4.169
− 0	4.847	4.809	4.771	4.734	4.696	4.659	4.623	4.586	4.551	4.515

(From *Smithsonian Meteorological Tables,* 6th rev. ed., List, R. J., Ed., Smithsonian Institution, Washington, D.C., 1971.)

Section 4

Geology

Kurt Bostrom, Ph.D., Cesare Emiliani, Ph.D.

4.1 General Tables

Table 4.1–1
EARTH'S DIMENSIONS

	I.E.R.[a]		I.A.U.[b]
Equatorial radius a_e	6,378.388 km		6,378.160 km
Polar radius a_p	6,356.912 km		6,356.775 km
Flattening factor f	1/297		1/298.25
Radius of sphere of equal volume a_0		6,371 km	
Area of surface		5.101×10^8 km^2	
Volume		1.083×10^{12} km^3	
Mass		5.976×10^{27} g	
Mean density		5.517 g cm^{-3}	
Gravitational constant G		6.670×10^{-8} dynes cm^{-2} g^{-2}	
Normal acceleration of gravity at equator g_e (based on Potsdam standard)		978.0436 cm sec^{-2}	
Mean solar day d		86,400 sec = 24^{hr}	
Sidereal day S		86,164.09 sec = $23^{hr}\ 56^{m}\ 4.09^{sec}$	
Velocity of rotation at equator		465.12 m sec^{-1}	
Mean moment of inertia C_0		8.02×10^{44} g cm^2	

[a] I.E.R. International Ellipsoid of Reference, 1924.
[b] I.A.U. International Astronomical Union, 1966.

(From Wedepohl, K.H., *Handbook of Geochemistry,* Vol. I, Springer-Verlag, Berlin, 1969. With permission.)

REFERENCES

1. *Astronomer's Handbook,* Transactions of the International Astronomical Union, Vol. XIIC, Academic Press, London, 1966.
2. **Gondolatsch, F.,** Mechanical data of planets and satellites, *Landolt-Bornstein,* New series, Group VI: Astronomy, astrophysics and space research, Vol. I, Springer-Verlag, Berlin, 1965.
3. **MacDonald, G. J. F.,** in Geodetic data, *Handbook of Physical Constants,* Clark, S. P., Jr., Ed., Geological Society of America, Memoir 97, 1966.

Table 4.1–2
EARTH'S INTERIOR, MASSES, AND DIMENSIONS OF THE PRINCIPAL SUBDIVISIONS

	Mass,	Mean density,	Surface area,	Radius or thickness,	Volume,	Mean moment of inertia (spherical symmetry),
	10^{25} g	g/cm^3	10^6 km^2	km	10^9 km^3	10^{42} g cm^2
Core	192	11.0	151	3471	1175	90
Mantle	403	4.5			898	705
Below 1000 km	240	5.1	362	1900	474	333
Above 1000 km	163	3.9	505	970–990	424	372
Crust	2.5	2.8	510		8.9	(7)
Continental	2.0	2.75	242[a]	30	7.3	
Oceanic	0.5	2.9	268[a]	6	1.6	
Oceans and marginal seas	0.14	1.03	361[a]	3.8	1.4[a]	(<1)
Whole earth	597.6	5.52	510	6371	1083	802
Atmosphere	0.00051	0.0013[b]	–	8[c]	–	–

[a] See Reference 2.
[b] Surface value.
[c] Scale height of the "homogeneous" atmosphere.

(From Wedepohl, K. H., *Handbook of Geochemistry,* Vol. I, Springer-Verlag, Berlin, 1969. With permission.)

REFERENCES

1. **MacDonald, G. J. F.,** in Geodetic data, *Handbook of Physical Constants,* Clark, S. P., Jr., Ed., Geological Society of America, Memoir 97, 1966.
2. **Poldervaart, A.,** Chemistry of the earth crust, *Geol. Soc. Am. Spec. Pap.,* No. 62, p. 119, 1955.
3. **Schmucker, U.,** in *Handbook of Geochemistry,* Vol. I, Wedepohl, K. H., Ed., Springer-Verlag, Berlin, 1969, chap. 6.

Table 4.1–3
THE SURFACE AREAS OF THE EARTH

	10^6 km^2		10^6 km^2
Continental shield region	105	Land about	
Region of young folded belts	42	29.2% of total	149
Volcanic islands in deep oceanic and suboceanic region	2		
Shelves and continental slopes region	93	Ocean about	
Deep oceanic region	268	70.8% of total	361
		Total surface	510

(From Poldervaart, A., Chemistry of the earth crust, *Geol. Soc. Am. Spec. Pap.*, 62, 119, 1955.)

Table 4.1–4
GEOLOGICAL TIME-SCALES

Era	Period	Epoch	Time since beginning in mil yr				
			Ref 4[a]	Ref. 1[a]	Ref. 2[a]	Ref. 3,7	Ref. 5
Cenozoic	Quaternary	Pleistocene[b]	1	1.5–2	1.5–2	2	
	Tertiary	Pliocence	12	12 ± 1	7	10	
		Miocene	23	26 ± 1	26	27	
		Oligocene	35	37 ± 2	37–38	38	
		Eocene	55	60 ± 2	53–54	55	
		Paleocene	70	67 ± 3	65	65–70	
Mesozoic	Cretaceous		135	137 ± 5	136	130	
	Jurassic		180	195 ± 5	190–195	180	
	Triassic		220	240 ± 10	225	225	
Paleozoic	Permian		270	285 ± 10	280	260	
	Carboniferous		350	340–360	345	340	
	Devonian		400	410 ± 10	395	405	
	Silurian		430	440 ± 15	430–440	435	
	Ordovician		490	500 ± 20	500	480	
	Cambrian		600	570	570	550–570	570
Pre-cambrian	Upper precambrian						1900
	Middle Precambrian						2700
	Lower Precambrian						3500

[a] Used by the I.U.G.S. Commission on Geochronology as base for discussion of a revised geological time-scale.
[b] Subdivisions[6]

Wurmian glaciation 10–70 thousand years
Warthian glaciation 100–120 thousand years
Rissian glaciation 175–210 thousand years
Mindelian glaciation 370–600 thousand years
Gunzian glaciation 750–1,000 thousand years
Begin Calabrian age 1,800 ± 200 thousand years

(From Wedepohl, K. H., *Handbook of Geochemistry,* Vol. I, Springer-Verlag, Berlin, 1969. With permission.)

REFERENCES

1. **Afanassyev, G. D. et al.,** The project of a revised geological time-scale in absolute chronology, Contr. Geol. Sovietiques Congr. geol. inter. 22[e] Sess., India, 287-324, 1964.
2. Holmes' Symposium, Geological Society phanerozoic time-scale, *Q. J. Geol. Soc. Lond.,* 120, 260, 1964.
3. **Krauskopf, K.,** *Introduction to Geochemistry,* McGraw-Hill Book Co., New York, 1967.
4. **Kulp, J. L.,** The geological time-scale, Report of Int. geol. Congr. 21st Sess., Norden, Part III, 18–27, 1960.
5. **Vinogradov, A. P. and Tugarinov, A. I.,** Geochronological scale of the Precambrian, Report Int. geol. Congr. 23rd Sess., Czechoslovakia, 6, 205, 1968.
6. **Zubakov, V. A.,** Geochronology of the continental Pleistocene deposits (based on radiometric data), *Geochem. Int.,* 4, 97, 1967.
7. **Knopf, A.,** private communication.

Table 4.1–5
MEASURES, UNITS, AND CONVERSION FACTORS
Metric and U.S. System

Prefix	Symbol	Meaning	Units
Tera	T	1,000,000,000,000	10^{12}
Giga	G	1,000,000,000	10^{9}
Mega	M	1,000,000	10^{6}
Kilo	k	1,000	10^{3}
Hecto	h	100	10^{2}
Deka	dk	10	10^{1}
Deci	d	0.1	10^{-1}
Centi	c	0.01	10^{-2}
Milli	m	0.001	10^{-3}
Micro	μ	0.000001	10^{-6}
Nano	n	0.000000001	10^{-9}
Pico	p	0.000000000001	10^{-12}

Lengths

Metric system		U.S. system
10^{-8} cm	1 Å	$3.937 \cdot 10^{-9}$ in.
10^{-4} cm	1 μ	$3.937 \cdot 10^{-5}$ in.
	1 cm	0.3937 in.
	2.540 cm	1 in.
	0.3048 m	1 ft
	0.9144 m	1 yd
10^{2} cm	1 m	1.09361 yd
	1.8288 m	1 fath.
10^{5} cm	1 km	0.62137 mi
	1.60935 km	1 mi
	1.852 km	1 int. nautical mi

1 A.U. (astronomical unit) = $1.49598 \cdot 10^{8}$ km

Area

Metric system	U.S. system
1 mm²	0.00155 in.² (sq. in.)
1 cm²	0.155 in.²
6.45163 cm²	1 in.²
0.0929 m²	1 ft²
0.83613 m²	1 yd²
1 m²	10.7639 ft²
1 km²	0.3861 mi²
2.58998 km²	1 mi²

Volume

Metric system	U.S. system
1 mm³	$0.6102 \cdot 10^{-4}$ in.³ (cu. in.)
1 cm³	0.06102 in.³
16.3872 cm³	1 in.³
0.02831 m³	1 ft³
0.76456 m³	1 yd³
1 m³	1.30794 yd³

Liquid measures

Metric system	U.S. system	
1 ml	0.0610 in.³	
0.473 L	28.875 in.³	1 pt
0.946 L	57.749 in.³	1 qt
1 L	61.0 in.³	1.0567 qt
3.7853 L	231 in.³	1 gal

Mass

Metric system	U.S. system
1 g	0.035 oz av (ounce av)
28.349 g	1 oz av
453.59 g	1 lb av (lb av.[a])
1 kg	2.20462 lb av
907.1848 kg	1 ton sh (short ton)
1 t	1.1023 ton sh
1016.047 kg	1 ton 1 (long ton)

[a] 1 lb av = 1 pound avoirdupois is the mass of 27.692 in.³ of water weighed in air at 4°C, 760 mm pressure.

Density

Metric system	U.S. system
1 g/cm³	0.036127 lb/in.³
27.68 g/cm³	1 lb/in.³
0.0160 g/cm³	1 lb/ft³

Table 4.1–5 (Continued)

Energy

	erg	$Joule_{mt}$	$k W_{int}h$	$kcal_l$	Liter-atmos.	BTU
erg	1	0.9997×10^{-7}	2.7769×10^{-14}	2.389×10^{-11}	9.8692×10^{-10}	9.4805×10^{-11}
$Joule_{int}$	1.0002×10^{7}	1	2.7778×10^{-7}	2.390×10^{-4}	9.8722×10^{-3}	9.480×10^{-4}
$kW_{int}h$	3.6011×10^{13}	3.6000×10^{6}	1	8.6041×10^{2}	3.5540×10^{4}	3.413×10^{3}
$kcal_{is}$	4.1853×10^{10}	4.186×10^{3}	1.1622×10^{-3}	1	4.1306×10^{1}	3.9685
Liter-atmos.	1.0133×10^{9}	1.0133×10^{2}	2.8137×10^{-5}	2.421×10^{-2}	1	9.607×10^{-2}
BTU	1.0548×10^{10}	1.0548×10^{3}	2.930×10^{-4}	2.5198×10^{-1}	1.0409×10^{1}	1

Pressure

	bar	Torr	atm.	at	lb/in.^{2}
1 bar (10^6 dynes/cm^2)	1	750	0.98692	1.0197	14.504
1 Torr	0.00133	1	0.00131	0.001359	0.01934
1 atm	1.0133	760	1	1.033	14.696
1 at (l kg/cm^2)	0.98067	735.56	0.96784	1	14.223
1 lb/in.^{2}	0.06895	51.7144	0.068046	0.07031	1

Temperature

Absolute Centigrade or Kelvin (K)	x°K = T°C + 273.18
Degrees Centigrade (°C)	x°C = 5/9 (T°F–32)
	x°C = 5/4 T°R
Degrees Fahrenheit (°F)	x°F = 9/5 T°C + 32
	x°F = 9/4 T°R + 32
Degrees Réaumur (°R)	x°R = 4/9 (T°F–32)
	x°R = 4/5 T°C

Centigrade to Fahrenheit

C	°F	°C	°F	°C	F°
-200	-328	60	140	200	392
-150	-238	70	158	250	482
-100	-148	80	176	300	572
- 50	- 58	90	194	400	752
0	+ 32	100	212	500	932
10	50	110	230	600	1112
20	68	120	248	700	1292
30	86	130	266	800	1472
40	104	140	284	900	1652
50	122	150	302	1000	1832

Time

1 sidereal second	= 0.99727 mean solar second
1 sidereal day	= 86,164 mean solar seconds
1 solar day	= 86,400 mean solar seconds
1 mean solar year	= 365.242 mean solar days = 3.1557×10^{7} mean solar seconds
1 sidereal year	= 365.256 mean solar days = 3.15581×10^{7} mean solar seconds

Table 4.1–5 (Continued)

(From Heydemann, A., in *Handbook of Geochemistry,* Vol. I, Wedepohl, K. H., Ed., Springer-Verlag, Berlin, 1969. With permission.)

REFERENCE

1. **Weast, Robert C., Ed.,** *CRC Handbook of Chemistry and Physics,* 48th ed., Chemical Rubber Co., Cleveland, 1967.

Table 4.1–6
ASTRONOMICAL CONSTANTS

(Reference List of Recommended Constants)

Defining constants

No. ephemeris sec in 1 tropical yr (1900)	s = 31,556,925.9747
Gaussian gravitational constant, defining the A.U.	k = 0.01720209895

Primary constants

Measure of the A.U. in meters	A = 149,600 x 10^6
Velocity of light in m/sec	c = 299,792.5 x 10^3
Equatorial radius for Earth in meters	a_e = 6,378,160
Dynamical form-factor for Earth	J_2 = 0.0010827
Geocentric gravitational constant (units: m^3 s^{-2})	GE = 398,603 x 10^9
Ratio of the masses of the Moon and Earth	μ = 1/81.30
Sidereal mean motion of Moon in radians/sec (1900)	n^* = 2.661699489 x 10^{-6}
General precession in longitude/tropical century (1900)	p = 5,025.″644
Obliquity of the ecliptic (1900)	ϵ = 23°27′08.″26
Constant of nutation (1900)	N = 9.″210

Derived constants

Heliocentric gravitational constant (units: m^3 s^{-2})	GS = 132,718 x 10^{15}
Ratio of masses of Sun and Earth	S/E = 322,958
Ratio of masses of Sun and Earth + Moon	$S/E(1 + \mu)$ = 328,912
Perturbed mean distance of Moon, in meters	$a_☽$ = 384,400 x 10^3

(From Wedepohl, K. H., *Handbook of Geochemistry,* Vol. I, Springer-Verlag, Berlin, 1969. With permission.)

REFERENCE

1. *Astronomer's Handbook,* Transactions of the International Astronomical Union, Vol. XIIC, Academic Press, London, 1966.

Table 4.1–7
SOLAR DIMENSIONS

Radius	6.960×10^{10} cm
Surface area	6.087×10^{22} cm^2
Volume	1.412×10^{33} cm^3
Mass	1.989×10^{33} g
Mean density	1.409 g cm^{-3}
Density at the center	98 g cm^{-3}
Gravitational acceleration at the solar surface	2.740×10^4 cm sec^{-2}
Escape velocity at the surface	6.177×10^7 cm sec^{-1}
Effective temperature	5,785° K
Temperature at the center	13.6×10^6 ° K
Radiation	3.9×10^{33} erg sec^{-1}
Specific surface emission	6.41×10^{10} erg cm^{-2} sec^{-1}
Specific mean energy production	1.96 erg g^{-1} sec^{-1}
Solar constant = extraterrestrial	1.39×10^6 erg cm^{-2} sec^{-1}
energy flux at the mean distance between earth and sun	2.00 cal cm^{-2} min^{-1}

(From Wedepohl, K. H., *Handbook of Geochemistry,* Vol. I, Springer-Verlag, Berlin, 1969. With permission.)

REFERENCE

1. **Waldmeier, M.,** The quiet sun, *Landolt-Bornstein,* New series, Group VI: Astronomy, astrophysics and space research, Vol. I, Springer-Verlag, Berlin, 1965.

Table 4.1–8
DIMENSIONS OF THE PLANETS AND THE MOON

Symbols:

a = semi-major axis of the orbit.
P = sidereal period = true period of the planet's revolution around the Sun (with respect to the fixed star field).
g_{Eq} = total acceleration, including centrifugal acceleration, at equator.
v_e = velocity of escape at equator.
A = Albedo = total reflectivity, wavelength λ_{eff} = 5,500 Å.
T_{max} = max temp for the subsolar point of a slowly rotating planet or satellite (computed from the visual albedo).
T_{av} = avg temp of a rapidly rotating sphere.
Atm. constituents = main atmospheric constituents.

Name	Symbol	a, 10^6 km	P a	Diameter, km	Mass,[a] 10^{26} g	Volume, 10^{10} km^3
Mercury	☿	57.9	0.24085	4,840	3.333	5.958
Venus	♀	108.2	0.61521	12,228	48.70	95.765
Earth	♁	149.6	1.00004	12,742.06	59.76	108.332
Moon	☽	0.384[b]	0.07480[c]	3,476	0.735	2.192
Mars	♂	227.9	1.88089	6,770	6.443	16.250
Jupiter	♃	778	11.86223	140,720	18,993	145,923.204
Saturn	♄	1,427	29.4577	116,820	5,684	83,469.806
Uranus	♅	2,870	84.0153	47,100	867.6	5,481.599
Neptune	♆	4,496	164.7883	44,600	1,029	4,636.610
Pluto	♇	5,881.9 to 5,946.5	247.7	6,000	55.3	10.833

[a] Mass without moons.
[b] Mean distance from Earth.
[c] True period of the Moon's revolution around Earth (with respect to the fixed star field).

Table 4.1–8 (Continued)

Name	ρ g/cm³	g_{Eq}, cm/s²	v_e, km/s	A	T_{max}, °K	$T_{av.}$, °K	Atm. constituents
Mercury	5.62	380	4.29	0.056	625	–	((^{40}Ar))
Venus	5.09	869	10.3	0.76	324	229	CO_2, H_2O
Earth	5.517	978	11.2	0.39	349	246	N_2, O_2
Moon	3.35	162	2.37	0.067	387	274	–
Mars	3.97	372	5.03	0.16	306	216	N_2, CO_2, H_2O
Jupiter	1.30	2301	57.5	0.67	131	93	H_2, CH_4, NH_4
Saturn	0.68	906	33.1	0.69	95	68	H_2, CH_4, NH_3
Uranus	1.58	972	21.6	0.93[d]	67[d]	47[d]	He, H_2, CH_4
Neptune	2.22	1347	24.6	0.84[d]	53[d]	38[d]	He, H_2, CH_4
Pluto	–	–	–	0.14	60	43	Uncertain

[d] Since the albedos of Uranus and Neptune are very low in the red and infrared an effective value A = 0.7 has been adopted for calculating the temperatures.

(From Wedepohl, K. H., *Handbook of Geochemistry*, Vol. I, Springer-Verlag, Berlin, 1969. With permission.)

REFERENCES

1. **Gondolatsch, F.**, Mechanical data of planets and satellites, *Landolt-Bornstein*, New series, Group VI, Astronomy, astrophysics and space research, Vol. I, Springer, Berlin, 1965.
2. **Kuiper, G. P.**, Physics of planets and satellites, *Landolt-Bornstein*, New series, Group VI, Astronomy, astrophysics, and space research, Vol. I, Springer-Verlag Berlin, 1965.

Table 4.1–9

Conversion Tables

Time

1 sidereal sec	= 0.99727 mean solar sec
1 sidereal day	= 86,164 mean solar sec
1 solar day	= 86,400 mean solar sec
1 mean solar year	= 365.242 mean solar days = 3,1557 x 10^7 mean solar sec
1 sidereal year	= 365.256 mean solar days = 3.15581 x 10^7 mean solar sec

(From Wedepohl, K. H., *Handbook of Geochemistry*, Vol. I, Springer Verlag, Berlin, 1969. With permission.)

4.2 Mineralogical Data

TABLES 4.2–1 to 4.2–10
SUMMARY OF THE COMMON MINERALS AND THEIR PROPERTIES

Abbreviations

a	Cryst. a-axis
a_0	Ident. period along a-axis
abs.	Absorption
acic.	Acicular
An.-Eff.	Anisotropic effect (obs. with crossed polarizers on opaque crystals)
b	Cryst. b-axis
b_0	Ident. period along b-axis
Biref.	Birefringence
Birefl.	Bireflection (obs. with one polarizer on opaque crystals)
c	Cryst. c-axis
c_0	Ident. period along c-axis
col.	Columnar
cub.	Cubic
cyc.	Cyclic
diff.	Different
dist.	Distinct
elong.	Elongate
et al.	And others
fib.	Fibrous
hex.	Hexagonal
h. per.	Highly perfect
isom.	Isometric
imp.	Imperfect
κ	Absorption indices
met. lust.	Metallic luster
OP	Optic plane
orhomb.	Orthorhombic
pen. tw.	Penetration twin
per.	Perfect
ps.	Pseudo
poor	Poor
R	Reflectivity
$\bar{R}$	Mean reflectivity
$R_{g,o,r}$	Reflectivity in green, orange, red light
R_α	Reflectivity parallel to n_α vibration direction
rad.	Radiating
tab.	Tabular
tetr.	Tetragonal
trip.	Triplet (twin)
tw.	Twinned after
tw. lam.	Twin lamella

Symbols

Symbol	Meaning
↓	a) Indicates complete solid solution between two or more minerals b) Indicates gradation (contin.) between values, for example, of indices of refraction
$\perp$	Perpendicular
$\parallel$	Parallel
–	To; means minus when indicated with extinction angle
~	Approximately
(–)	Optically negative
(+)	Optically positive

For example:

Symbol	Meaning
$n_\alpha/\perp$ (010)	extinction of n_α against normal to (010)
n_γ/c 15°	extinction of n_γ with respect to c = 15°
$n_\alpha\sim\perp$ (001)	n_α approx. perpend. to (001)
$r>v$	Dispersion of optic angle; 2 V for red greater than blue
$a = b_0$	Morphologic orient. different than lattice. Here a corresp. to b_0
$a = 2\,a_0$	Axial intercepts of morph. orientation and lattice different. Here a corresponds to double the value of a_0

TABLE 4.2–1
ELEMENTS

No.	Name and formula	Crystal class lattice constants	Habit, form	Sp. gr.	Color	Indices of refraction and luster	
1	Platinum Pt	*m3m* a_0 3.9237	(100)(111) (110)	14–19 pure: 21.5	Steel grey	n κ R_{Na}	2.06 Na 4.28 Na 70.1%
2	Copper Cu	*m3m* a_0 3.6153	(111)(100) (110)(210) (311), tw. (111)	8.5–9	Copper-red mostly darkly tar-nished	n κ R_g R_r	0.641 Na 4.09 Na 61% 89% met. lust.
3	Silver Ag	*m3m* a_0 4.0856	(100)(111) (110)(210), tw. (111)	9.6–12 pure: 10.5	Silvery-white, dull, tarnished yellow to black	n κ R_g	0.181 Na 20.3 Na 95.5% met. lust.
4	Gold Au	*m3m* a_0 4.0783	(111)(100) (110) *et al.*, tw. (111)	15.5–19.3 pure: 19.23	Gold to brass-colored	n κ R_{Na}	0.368 Na 7.71 85.1% met. lust.
5	Arsenic As	$\bar{3}m$ a_0 3.768 c_0 10.574	Isom., $(10\bar{1}1)(01\bar{1}2)$ (0001) tw. $(01\bar{1}2)$	5.4–5.9	Light grey, tarnished black	$\bar{R}_g$	61.5% met. lust. dull tarnish
6	Bismuth Bi	$\bar{3}m$ a_0 4.55 c_0 11.85	Isom., $(10\bar{1}1)(0001)$ $(02\bar{2}1)$, tw. $(01\bar{1}2)$	9.7–9.8	Reddish silvery, often multi-colored, tarnished	n κ $\bar{R}_g$	1.78 1.57 67.5%
7	Sulfur α-S	*mmm* a_0 10.44 b_0 12.84_5 c_0 24.37	(111)(113) (011)(001), tw. (101) *et al.*	2.0–2.1	Yellow, waxy-yellow to brown	n_α n_β n_γ	1.960 2.040 2.248 diamond- to greasy-lust.

Note: For list of abbreviations and symbols, see p. 281.

Table 4.2–1 (*Continued*)
SULFIDES, ARSENIDES, ANTIMONIDES

No.	Name and formula	Crystal class lattice constants	Habit, form	Sp. gr.	Color	Indices of refraction and luster	
8	β-Sulfur β-S > 95.6°C	2/*m* a_0 10.92 b_0 10.98 c_0 11.04 β 96°44′	Col.–tab., (001)(110) (011)	1.98	Like α-sulfur	*n*	1.96
9	Graphite (–2H) α-C	6/*mmm* a_0 2.46 c_0 6.708	Tab. (0001), $(11\bar{2}0)$	2.1–2.3 pure: 2.255	Steel grey	*n*	1.93–2.07 met. lust.
10	Diamond β-C ≳ 1200°C	*m*3*m* a_0 3.5668	(111) tw. (111)	3.52	Colorless, in all colors	*n* *n* *n* *n*	2.4478 λ 441 2.4370 λ 480 2.4172 λ 589 2.4109 λ 643

(Compiled by Koritnig, S., in *Introduction to Minerology*, 2nd ed., by Correns, C. W., Springer-Verlag, New York, 1969.)

TABLE 4.2–2
SULFIDES, ARSENIDES, ANTIMONIDES

No.	Name and formula	Crystal glass lattice constants	Habit, form	Sp. gr.	Color	Indices of refraction and luster	
11	Dyscrasite Ag_3Sb	2*mm* a_0 2.99 b_0 5.23 c_0 4.82	Col.–tab. (110)(010) (001)(111) (112)(021) tw. (110)	9.4–10	Silvery, often grey or brown tarnish	$\bar{R}_g$	66% met. lust.

Note: For list of abbreviations and symbols, see p. 281.

Table 4.2–2 (*Continued*)
SULFIDES, ARSENIDES, ANTIMONIDES

No.	Name and formula	Crystal glass lattice constants	Habit, form	Sp. gr.	Color	Indices of refraction and luster	
12	Chalcocite $Cu_2S < 103°C$	*2mm* a_0 11.92 b_0 27.33 c_0 13.44	Tab. (001), (110)(010) (113)(023) tw. (110)(112), ps. hex.	5.7–5.8	Dark lead grey	$\bar{R}_g$	22.5% met. lust.
13	Chalcocite (-H) γ-$Cu_2S > 103°C$	*6/mmm* a_0 3.90 c_0 6.69		5.7–5.8	Dark lead grey		
14	Digenite Cu_9S_5	Cub. a_0 27.85	(111)	5.7–5.8	Dark lead grey, bluish	R_g	24.5%
15	Bornite Cu_5FeS_4	$\bar{4}2m$ ps. cub. a_0 10.94 c_0 21.88	(100)(111), tw. (111) (cub. indic.)	4.9–5.3 o	Iridescent tarnish	$\bar{R}_g$	18.5% met. lust.
16	Acanthite $Ag_2S < 179°C$	*2/m* a_0 4.23 b_0 6.91 c_0 7.87 β 99°35′	Isom., (100) (111)(110) (211) (cub. indic.)	7.3	Dark lead grey, black tarnish	$\bar{R}_g$	37% fresh met. lust.
17	Argentite Ag_2S(179°C–586°C)	*m3m* a_0 4.89	(100)		As above		
18	Pentlandite $(Ni, Fe)_9S_8$ usually Ni:Fe ~ 1:0.9	*m3m* a_0 10.04 to 10.07		4.6–5	Light brown	R_g	51% met. lust.

Table 4.2–2 (*Continued*)
SULFIDES, ARSENIDES, ANTIMONIDES

No.	Name and formula	Crystal glass lattice constants	Habit, form	Sp. gr.	Color	Indices of refraction and luster	
19	Sphalerite α-ZnS (to 20% Fe)	$\bar{4}3m$ a_0 5.43	(110)(311) $(3\bar{1}1)$(100) $(111)(1\bar{1}1)$ *et al.*, tw. (111)(211)	3.9–4.2 pure: 4.06	Brown, yellow, red, green, black	n R_g	2.369 18.5% semimet. lust. to dia- mond lust.
20	Chalcopyrite $CuFeS_2$	$\bar{4}2m$ a_0 5.25 c_0 10.32	$(111)(1\bar{1}\bar{1})$ (201)(101) (001), tw. (100)(111) rare (101)	4.1–4.3	Brass yellow to greenish often iri- descent tarnish	$\bar{R}_g$	42% met. lust.
21	Stannite Cu_2FeSnS_4	$\bar{4}2m$ a_0 5.47 c_0 10.74	Cryst. rare (111)	4.3–4.5	Steel grey (greenish)	$\bar{R}_g$	23% met. lust.
22	Tennantite $Cu_3AsS_{3,25}$ (Cu part. replaced) by Ag, Fe, Zn, Hg)	$\bar{4}3m$ a_0 10.21	Like Tetrahedrite	4.4–5.4	Dark steel grey	R_g	29.5% met. lust.
23	Tetrahedrite $Cu_3SbS_{3,25}$	$\bar{4}3m$ a_0 10.34	(111)(211) $(110)(1\bar{1}1)$ *et al.*, tw. [111]	4.4–5.4	Light steel grey	n R_g	> 2.72 Li 27% met. lust.
24	Germanite $Cu_3(Ge, Fe)S_4$	$\bar{4}3m$ a_0 10.58	Massive	4.29	Violet pink to violet	R_g	22% met. lust.
25	Wurtzite β-ZnS	$6mm$ a_0 3.85 c_0 6.29	Col. *c* to tab. (0001), $(10\bar{1}1)(50\bar{5}2)$	4.0	Light to dark brown	n_ω n_ϵ	2.356 Na 2.378 Na
26	Grennockite β-CdS	$6mm$ a_0 4.15 c_0 6.73	Isom., $(10\bar{1}0)$ $(h0\bar{h}l)(000\bar{1})$	4.82	Yellow to brown- yellow	n_ω n_ϵ	2.506 Na 2.529 Na

Table 4.2–2 (*Continued*)
SULFIDES, ARSENIDES, ANTIMONIDES

No.	Name and formula	Crystal glass lattice constants	Habit, form	Sp. gr.	Color	Indices of refraction and luster	
27	Enargite Cu_3AsS_4	*2mm* a_0 6.47 b_0 7.44 c_0 6.19	Col. *c*, (110) (001)(100) (010), trip. twins (320)	4.4	Steel grey to iron-black, violet-brownish	R_α R_β R_γ	for green: 24.28% 26.16% 28.50% met. lust.
28	Cubanite (Chalmersite) $CuFe_2S_3$	*mmm* a_0 6.46 b_0 11.12 c_0 6.23	Elong. *c*, tw. (110)	4.10	Bronze-yellow	$\overline{R}_g$	41% met. lust.
29	Galena PbS	*m3m* a_0 5.94	(100)(111) (110)(221) (211)(331) *et al.*, tw. (111)	7.2–7.6	Lead grey	n κ R_g	4.3 0.4 43.4%
30	Cinnabar HgS	32 a_0 4.146 c_0 9.497	*a*:*c* 1.1453 isom.–tab., (0001)(10$\overline{1}$1) (20$\overline{2}$1) *et al.*, tw. (0001)	8.1 synth.: 8.176	Red	n_ω n_ϵ	2.913 3.272
31	Pyrrhotite FeS	*6/mmm* a_0 3.45 c_0 5.65 existing also in monoclinic modifications (Fe_7S_8)	Tab. (0001), tw. (10$\overline{1}$2)	4.6	Bronze brown	$\overline{R}_g$	37% met. lust. dull tarnish
32	Niccolite NiAs	*6/mmm* a_0 3.58 c_0 5.11	Flat pyramids, crystals rare	7.3–7.7	Light copper	R_ω R_ϵ	for green: 48.9% 42.8% met. lust. dull tarnish

Table 4.2–2 (*Continued*)
SULFIDES, ARSENIDES, ANTIMONIDES

No.	Name and formula	Crystal glass lattice constants	Habit, form	Sp. gr.	Color	Indices of refraction and luster	
33	Millerite β-NiS	$3m$ a_0 9.62 c_0 3.16	Acic.-fib. *c*, oft. twist. helix	5.3	Brass yellow	$\bar{R}_g$	53% silky met. lust.
34	Covellite CuS	$6/mmm$ a_0 3.80 c_0 16.36	Tab. (0001), $(10\bar{1}0)$	4.68	Bluish- black	n_ω n_ω R_ω R_ϵ	1.00 λ 635 1.97 λ 505 $\epsilon > \omega$ for green: 18.5% 27%
35	Stibnite Sb_2S_3	mmm a_0 11.22 b_0 11.30 c_0 3.84	Col. *c*, tw. (130) rare	4.6–4.7	Lead grey	n_α n_β n_γ x_α x_β x_γ R_g	3.41 4.37 5.12 0.21 0.19 0.12 (values 3.41–0.12: for ~ Na) *c* 44% *b* 30.5%
36	Bismuthinite Bi_2S_3	mmm a_0 11.15 b_0 11.29 c_0 3.98	Radial *c*	6.8–7.2	Lead grey to tin white	 R_α R_β R_γ	for green: 41.46% 48.45% 54.51% met. lust.
37	Pyrite FeS_2	$2/m\bar{3}$ a_0 5.41 to 5.42	Alone and in comb. (100)(210) (111) *et al.*, tw. (110)	5–5.2	Light brass	R_g	54% met. lust.
38	Sperrylite $PtAs_2$	$2/m\bar{3}$ a_0 5.94	(100)(111) (210)	10.6	Tin white	R_g	56.5% met. lust.
39	Cobaltite CoAsS	$2/m\bar{3}$ a_0 5.61	(210)(111) (100)	6.0–6.4	Silvery, reddish to grey	R_g str.	52% str. met. lust.

Table 4.2–2 (*Continued*)
SULFIDES, ARSENIDES, ANTIMONIDES

No.	Name and formula	Crystal glass lattice constants	Habit, form	Sp. gr.	Color	Indices of refraction and luster	
40	Marcasite FeS_2	*mmm* a_0 3.39 b_0 4.45 c_0 5.42	Tab. (001), tw. (110)	4.8–4.9	Light brass yellow to greenish	$\bar{R}_g$	52% met. lust.
41	Safflorite $CoAs_2$	*mmm* a_0 6.35 b_0 4.86 c_0 5.80	Radial *c* tw. (101), trip. (011)	6.9–7.3	Tin white, often dark grey tar-nish	$\bar{R}_g$	58% str. met. lust.
42	Rammelsbergite $NiAs_2$	*mmm* a_0 3.54 b_0 4.79 c_0 5.79	Tw. (101)	7.0–7.3	Tin white, often dark grey tar-nish	$\bar{R}$	yellow ~ 60% str. met. lust.
43	Löllingite $FeAs_2$	*mmm* a_0 2.86 b_0 5.26 c_0 5.93	Acic. *a*, (011)(110)	7.1–7.4	Silvery, grey tarnish	$\bar{R}_g$	57% met. lust.
44	Arsenopyrite FeAsS	2/*m* ps. orthomb. a_0 6.43 b_0 9.53 c_0 5.66 β 90°0′	Col. *a* or *c* and isom., (210) tw. (010) and (100)	5.9–6.2 –	Tin white to light steel grey, often dark tarnish	$\bar{R}_g$	49.0% met. lust.
45	Molybdenite MoS_2	6/*mmm* a_0 3.16 c_0 12.32	Tab. (0001)	4.7–4.8	Lead grey, bluish	*n* R_ω R_ϵ	~ 4.7 for green: 36% 15.5% str. met. lust.

Table 4.2–2 (*Continued*)
SULFIDES, ARSENIDES, ANTIMONIDES

No.	Name and formula	Crystal glass lattice constants	Habit, form	Sp. gr.	Color	Indices of refraction and luster	
46	Skutterudite $CoAs_3$	$2/m\overline{3}$ a_0 8.21 to 8.29	Usu. (100) comb. w. (111)(110)	6.4–6.6	Tin white to light steel grey, dark tarnish	$\overline{R}_g$	60% met. lust.
47	Chloanthite (Ni-Skutterudite) $NiAs_3$	$2/m\overline{3}$ a_0 8.28	Like Skutterudite	6.4–6.6	Tin white to light steel grey, dark tarnish		Met. lust.
48	Proustite Ag_3AsS_3	$3m$ a_0 10.76 c_0 8.66	Like Pyrargyrite, not so faceted	5.57	Scarlet to vermilion, translucent	n_ω n_ϵ $\overline{R}_g$	3.0877 Na 2.7924 Na 28% adamant-diamond lust.
49	Pyrargyrite Ag_3SbS_3	$3m$ a_0 11.06 c_0 8.73	Usu. col. *c* $(11\overline{2}0)(2\overline{1}31)$ $(01\overline{1}2)(11\overline{2}4)$ (3251)(1011) *et al.*, Very faceted, tw. (1120) (1014) *et al.*	5.85	Dark red, dark greyish red, translucent	n_ω n_ϵ $\overline{R}_g$	3.084 Li 2.881 Li 32.5%
50	Stephanite $5\ Ag_2S \cdot Sb_2S_3$	$2mm$ a_0 7.72 b_0 12.34 c_0 8.50	Col.–tab. *c* (001)(010) (111)(021) tw. (110), ps. hex.	6.2–6.4	Lead grey to iron black	$\overline{R}_g$	29% met. lust.

Table 4.2–2 (*Continued*)
SULFIDES, ARSENIDES, ANTIMONIDES

No.	Name and formula	Crystal glass lattice constants	Habit, form	Sp. gr.	Color	Indices of refraction and luster	
51	Bournonite $2PbS \cdot Cu_2S \cdot Sb_2S_3$	2*mm* a_0 8.16 b_0 8.75 c_0 7.81	Tab. (001) ps. tetr. (110)(010) (011)(100) (101)(102) (112) Cycl. tw. (110)	5.8	Steel to lead grey and iron black	$\bar{R}_g$	33.5% fresh: resinous met. lust. usu. dull
52	Jamesonite $4PbS \cdot FeS \cdot 3Sb_2S_3$	2/*m* a_0 15.57 b_0 18.98 c_0 4.03 β 91°48′	Acic.–fib. *b*, (001)(104) (104) tw. (100)	5.7	Lead grey	$\bar{R}_g$	39% met. lust.
53	Realgar As_4S_4	2/*m* a_0 9.29 b_0 13.53 c_0 6.57 β 106°33′	Col. *c*, (110)(210) (001)(011)	3.5–3.6	Red	n_α n_β n_γ	2.46 2.59 } Li 2.61
54	Orpiment As_2S_3	2/*m* a_0 11.49 b_0 9.59 c_0 4.25 β 90°27′	Tab. (010)	3.49	Lemon yellow	n_α n_β n_γ	2.4 2.81 } Li 3.02

(Compiled by Koritnig, S., in *Introduction to Minerology*, 2nd ed., by Correns, C. W., Springer-Verlag, New York, 1969.)

Table 4.2–3
HALIDES

No.	Name and formula	Crystal glass lattice constants	Habit, form	Sp. gr.	Color	Indices of refraction and luster
55	Halite NaCl	$m3m$ a_0 5.6404	(100)	2.1–2.2	Colorless and red, yellow, grey, blue	n 1.5612 λ 431 n 1.5441 λ 589 n 1.5391 λ 686
56	Sylvite KCl	$m3m$ a_0 6.29	(100)	1.9–2	Colorless and colored	n 1.5046 λ 436 n 1.4930 λ 546 n 1.4886 λ 615
57	Cerargyrite AgCl	$m3m$ a_0 5.55	(100), usu. massive in pseudo-morphs	5.5–5.6	Fresh colorless, brown to black tarnish	n 2.096 λ 486 n 2.062 λ 589 n 2.047 λ 656
58	Sal ammoniac α-NH_4Cl	$\bar{4}3m$ a_0 3.87 below 184°C $CsCl_5$ above NaCl lattice	(110) (211)	1.53	Colorless also yellow and brown	n 1.6613 λ 431 n 1.6422 λ 589 n 1.6326 λ 686
59	Fluorite CaF_2	$m3m$ a_0 5.46	(100) (111) (110) (310) (421)	3.1–3.2	Colorless and colored	n 1.43385 (20°C)
60	Cryolite α-Na_3AlF_6 < 550°C	$2/m$ a_0 5.47 b_0 5.62 c_0 7.82 β 90° 11′	(110) (001), tw. (110), (112), (001)	2.95	White and colored	n_α 1.3385 n_β 1.3389 n_γ 1.3396

Note: For list of abbreviations and symbols, see p. 281.

Table 4.2–3 (*Continued*)
HALIDES

No.	Name and formula	Crystal glass lattice constants	Habit, form	Sp. gr.	Color	Indices of refraction and luster	
61	Carnallite $KMgCl_3 \cdot 6H_2O$	*mmm* a_0 9.56 b_0 16.05 c_0 22.56	Ps. hex. cryst. rare (111) (011) (110) (010)	1.60	Colorless and red (by Fe_2O_3)	n_α n_β n_γ	1.466 1.475 1.494
62	Atacamite $Cu_2(OH)_3Cl$	*mmm* a_0 6.02 b_0 9.15 c_0 6.85	Col. *c*, (110) (010) (011) tw. (110)	3.76	Light to dark green	n_α n_β n_γ	1.831 1.861 1.880

(Compiled by Koritnig, S., in *Introduction to Minerology,* 2nd ed., by Correns, C. W., Springer-Verlag, New York, 1969.)

Table 4.2–4
OXIDES, HYDROXIDES

No.	Name and formula	Crystal glass lattice constants	Habit, form	Sp. gr.	Color	Indices of refraction and luster	
63	Ice (I) H_2O	6 *mm* a_0 4.47 c_0 7.33	Tab. (0001)– col. *c*, (0001) $(10\bar{1}0)$	0.9175	Colorless white to light blue	n_ω n_ϵ	1.30907 Na 1.31052 Na
64	Cuprite Cu_2O	*m*3*m* (morph. O) a_0 4.27	(111) (110) (100)	5.8–6.2	Reddish brown to grey	n R_g R_r	2.849 Li 30% 21.5%
65	Zincite ZnO	6*mm* a_0 3.25 c_0 5.19	$(40\bar{4}5)$ $(10\bar{1}1)$ cryst. rare	5.4–5.7	Crimson	n_ω n_ϵ R_g	2.013 2.029 11%

Note: For list of abbreviations and symbols, see p. 281.

Table 4.2–4 (*Continued*)
OXIDES, HYDROXIDES

No.	Name and formula	Crystal glass lattice constants	Habit, form	Sp. gr.	Color	Indices of refraction and luster	
66	Periclase MgO	$m3m$ a_0 4.21	(111) (100)	3.64–3.67	Colorless	n	1.736
67	Tenorite CuO	$2/m$ a_0 4.66 b_0 3.42 c_0 5.12 β 99° 29′	Tab. (100), ps. hex., tw. (100) (011)	6.45	Black	n_β n_β	2.63 Li 3.18 blue
68	Spinel $MgAl_2O_4$ with Fe-content	$m3m$ a_0 8.10	(111), rare (110) (311) (100), tw. (111)	3.5–4.1	Colorless and colored	n	1.72–2.0
69	Magnetite Fe_3O_4	$m3m$ a_0 8.391	(111) (110), rarer (100) (211) (221), tw. (111)	5.2	Black	n R_g	2.42 21% met. lust. dull
70	Chromite $FeCr_2O_4$	$m3m$ a_0 8.361	(111)	4.5–4.8	Black	n	2.1 Li met. lust.
71	Hausmannite $MnMn_2O_4$	$4/mmm$ a_0 5.76 c_0 9.44	(111), tw. (101), oft. cycl.	4.7–4.8	Black	n_ω n_ϵ	2.46 } Li 2.15 } Li greasy met. lust.
72	Chrysoberyl Al_2BeO_4	mmm a_0 5.48 b_0 4.43 c_0 9.41	Tab. (100), (010) (011) (120) (111), tw. (031) usu. trip. ps. hex.	~3.7	Greenish yellow to green	n_α n_β n_γ	1.747 1.748 1.756

Table 4.2–4 (*Continued*)
OXIDES, HYDROXIDES

No.	Name and formula	Crystal glass lattice constants	Habit, form	Sp. gr.	Color	Indices of refraction and luster	
73	Valentinite Sb_2O_3	*mmm* a_0 4.93 b_0 12.48 c_0 5.43	Fib. rad. *c* or *a*, tab. (010), (010) (110) (054) (101) (0.27.4) *et al.*	5.6–5.8	Colorless	n_α n_β n_γ	2.18 2.35 2.35 diamond lust.
74	Senarmontite Sb_2O_3	*m3m* a_0 11.14	(111)	5.2–5.3	Colorless	n	2.087
75	Corundum Al_2O_3	$\bar{3}m$ a_0 4.77 c_0 13.04	Col. *c*, $(11\bar{2}0)$ $(22\bar{4}1)$ (0001)	3.9–4.1	Colorless and colored	n_ω n_ϵ	1.769 1.761
76	Hematite Fe_2O_3	$\bar{3}m$ a_0 5.04 c_0 13.77	Tab. (0001), isom., (2243) (1011), also fib. kidney ore	5.2–5.3	Steel grey to iron black, iridescent lust. or red	n_ω n_ϵ $\bar{R}_g$	3.042 Li 2.7975 Li 26% met. lust.
77	Ilmenite $FeTiO_3$	$\bar{3}$ a_0 5.09 c_0 14.07	Tab. (0001), (1011)	4.5–5.0	Iron black, brownish black	n $\bar{R}_g$	⩾2.72 18%
78	Perovskite $CaTiO_3$	*mmm*[a] a_0 5.37 b_0 7.64 c_0 5.44 ps. cub. a_0 15.26	Ps. cub. (100) with monocl. deform. tw. lam.	4.0	Black to reddish brown	n	2.38
79	Quartz SiO_2 < 573°C	32 a_0 4.9130 c_0 5.4045	Col. *c*, $(10\bar{1}0)$ $(10\bar{1}1)$ $(01\bar{1}1)$ (3031) $(51\bar{6}1)$ $(11\bar{2}1)$ *et al.* tw. [0001] (1120)(1122)	2.65	Colorless, white and different colors	n_ω n_ϵ	1.54425 Na 1.55336 Na glassy lust.

[a] Synthet. $CaTiO_3$

Table 4.2–4 (*Continued*)
OXIDES, HYDROXIDES

No.	Name and formula	Crystal glass lattice constants	Habit, form	Sp. gr.	Color	Indices of refraction and luster	
80	Chalcedony SiO_2	As Quartz	Fib. ⊥ c (fib. c = Quartzine)	2.59–2.61	Colorless, different colors	n n	‖ fiber ~1.532 ⊥ fiber ~1.538
81	Tridymite (low –) SiO_2	$2/m$ or m ps. hex. a_0 18.54 b_0 5.01 c_0 25.79 β 117°40′	Ps. hex. tab. (0001), tw. (1016) and (3034)	2.27	Colorless, white white	n_α n_β n_γ	1.469 1.469+ 1.473 glassy lust.
82	Cristobalite (low –) SiO_2	422 a_0 4.972 c_0 6.921	Ps. cub. (111), tw. (111)	2.32	Colorless	n_ω n_ϵ	1.487 1.484
83	Opal SiO_2 + aq.	Amorph.	—	2.1–2.2	Colorless white, colored	n	1.3–1.45
84	Rutile TiO_2	$4/mmm$ a_0 4.59 c_0 2.96	Col. c, (110) (100) (111); tw. (101) (301)	4.2–4.3	Brownish red to iron black	n_ω n_ϵ $\bar{R}_g$	2.616 Na 2.903 Na 20.5% metallic- diamond lust.
85	Cassiterite SnO_2	$4/mmm$ a_0 4.73 c_0 3.18	Isom. (110) (111) (100) rarer acic. c (110) (321) tw. (101)	6.8–7.1	Brown to black	n_ω n_ϵ $\bar{R}_g$	1.997 2.093 11% diamond lust.
86	Pyrolusite β–$MnO_{2.00-1.89}$	$4/mmm$ a_0 4.39 c_0 2.87	Col. c–isom. (110) (111) (120) (321) (101) usu. fine grained, oft. pseudo-morphic after manganite	Pure: 5.06 usu. 4.9–5.0	Iron grey to black		met. lust.

Table 4.2–4 (*Continued*)
OXIDES, HYDROXIDES

No.	Name and formula	Crystal glass lattice constants	Habit, form	Sp. gr.	Color	Indices of refraction and luster	
87	Cryptomelane $K \leqq_2 Mn_8O_{16}$ ("α-MnO"$_2$)	4/*m* and 2/*m* a_0 9.84 c_0 2.86	Dense globular	4.1–4.9	Black to bluish-black		
88	Psilomelane $(Ba,H_2O)_2Mn_5O_{10}$	2/*m* a_0 9.56 b_0 2.88 c_0 13.85 β 92° 30′	Dense globular	4.4–4.7	Black to bluish-black		
89	Anatase TiO_2	4/*mmm* a_0 3.74 c_0 9.39	(101) (001) (107) (103) *et al.*	3.8–3.9	Yellow to brown and to bluish-black	n_ω n_ϵ	2.5618 2.4986 diamond lust.
90	Brookite TiO_2	*mmm* a_0 9.18 b_0 5.45 c_0 5.15	Tab. (010), elong. *c*	3.9–4.2	Yellow to reddish brown	n_α n_β n_γ	2.583 } 2.586 } Na 2.741 } met. diamond lust.
91	Columbite (Niobite) $(Fe, Mn)Nb_2O_6$ ↓	*mmm* a_0 14.27 b_0 5.74 c_0 5.60	Tab. (010) or col. *a*	5.3 ↓	Brownish black	n_β	2.45 Li
92	Tantalite $(Fe, Mn)Ta_2O_6$ Ta → Nb	*mmm* *a*:*b*:*c* 0.401:1: 0.351	Usu. col. *c*	8.2	Black	n_α n_β n_γ	2.26 2.32 2.43 pitchy to met. lust.
93	Euxenite (Y, Er, Ce, U, Pb, Ca) $(Nb, Ta, Ti)_2(O, OH)_6$	*mmm* a_0 14.57 b_0 5.52 c_0 5.166	Tab. (100) to col. *c*	4.6–5.4	Jet black to olive brown	*n*	~2.1 semi-met. lust.

Table 4.2–4 (*Continued*)
OXIDES, HYDROXIDES

No.	Name and formula	Crystal glass lattice constants	Habit, form	Sp. gr.	Color	Indices of refraction and luster	
94	Samarskite (Yttroniobite, Yttro-columbite) $(Y, Er)_4 [(Nb, Ta)_2 O_7]_3$	*mmm* *a*:*b*:*c* 0.5457:1: 0.5178	Tab. (010)	5.5–6.2	Deep black	n_β	~2.25 semi- met. lust.
95	Uraninite UO_2 (Pitchblende)	*m*3*m* a_0 5.449	(100), (111)	10.3–10.9	Black, brownish		dull pitchy lust.
96	Hydrargillite (Gibbsite) γ-$Al(OH)_3$	2/*m* ps. hex. a_0 8.64 b_0 5.07 c_0 9.72 β 94° 34′	Tab. (001) ps. hex.	2.3–2.4	Colorless, white, greenish	$n_\alpha \sim n_\beta$ n_γ	1.567 1.589
97	Brucite $Mg(OH)_2$	3*m* a_0 3.13 c_0 4.74	Tab. (0001)	2.4	Colorless, white, greenish	n_ω n_ϵ	1.566 1.581
98	Diaspore α-AlOOH	*mmm* a_0 4.41 b_0 9.40 c_0 2.84	Tab. (010)	3.3–3.5	Colorless and different colors	n_α n_β n_γ	1.702 1.722 1.750
99	Goethite α-FeOOH	*mmm* a_0 4.65 b_0 10.02 c_0 3.04	Acic. *c*	4.3	Blackish brown to light yellow	n_α n_β n_γ	2.260 2.394 2.400
100	Manganite γ-MnOOH	2/*m* a_0 8.88 b_0 5.25 c_0 5.71 β 90°	Col. *c*, ps. orhomb. (110) (001) tw. (011)	4.3–4.4	Brownish black	n_α n_β n_γ	2.25 2.25 2.53 imp. met. lust.

Table 4.2–4 (*Continued*)
OXIDES, HYDROXIDES

No.	Name and formula	Crystal glass lattice constants	Habit, form	Sp. gr.	Color	Indices of refraction and luster	
101	Boehmite γ-AlOOH	*mmm* a_o 3.69 b_o 12.2 c_o 2.86	Tab. (001), (110)	3.01	Colorless	n_β	~1.72– 1.64
102	Lepidocrocite · γ-FeOOH	*mmm* a_o 3.88 b_o 12.54 c_o 3.07	Tab. (010)	4.09	Crimson to yellowish red	n_α n_β n_γ	1.94 2.20 Na 2.51 diamond lust.
103	Sassolite $B(OH)_3$	I a_o 7.04 b_o 7.05 c_o 6.58 α 92° 35′ β 101° 10′ γ 119° 50′	Tab. (001), ps. hex.	1.45	White, pale grey	n_α n_β n_γ	1.340 1.456 1.459 glassy to pearly lust.

(Compiled by Koritnig, S., in *Introduction to Minerology,* 2nd ed., by Correns, C. W., Springer-Verlag, New York, 1969.)

Table 4.2–5
NITRATES AND CARBONATES

No.	Name and formula	Crystal glass lattice constants	Habit, form	Sp. gr.	Color	Indices of refraction and luster	
104	Soda niter $NaNO_3$	$\bar{3}m$ a_o 5.07 c_o 16.81	Morph. ind.[a] isom. $(10\bar{1}1)$, tw. $(0\bar{1}12)$	2.27	Colorless or light color	n_ω n_ϵ $n_\epsilon'(10\bar{1}1)$	1.585 1.337 1.467 glassy

Note: For list of abbreviations and symbols, see p. 281.

Table 4.2–5 (*Continued*)
NITRATES AND CARBONATES

No.	Name and formula	Crystal glass lattice constants	Habit, form	Sp. gr.	Color	Indices of refraction and luster
105	Niter KNO_3	*mmm* a_0 5.43 b_0 9.19 c_0 6.46	Fib. *c*	1.9–2.1	Colorless white, grey	n_α 1.335 n_β 1.505 n_γ 1.506 glassy
106	Magnesite $MgCO_3$	$\bar{3}m$ a_0 4.633 c_0 15.016	Morph. ind.[a] isom. $(10\bar{1}1)$	~3.0	Colorless, white to brown, grey	n_ω 1.700 n_ϵ, 1.509 n_ϵ' $(10\bar{1}1)$ 1:599 glassy
107	Siderite $FeCO_3$	$3m$ a_0 4.689 c_0 15.373	Morph. ind.[a] $(10\bar{1}1)$ tw. $(01\bar{1}2)$	3.89	Light yellowish brown	n_ω 1.873 n_ϵ, 1.633 n_ϵ' $(10\bar{1}1)$ 1.747 glassy
108	Smithsonite $ZnCO_3$	$\bar{3}m$ a_0 4.653 c_0 15.025	Morph. ind.[a] $(101\bar{1})$, usu. massive	4.3–4.5	Colorless, mostly colored	n_ω 1.849 n_ϵ, 1.621 n_ϵ' $(10\bar{1}1)$ 1.733 glassy
109	Rhodochrosite $MnCO_3$	$\bar{3}m$ a_0 4.777 c_0 15.664	Morph. ind.[a] $(10\bar{1}1)$, botryoid.	3.3–3.6	Pale to dark red	n_ω 1.814 n_ϵ, 1.596 n_ϵ' $(10\bar{1}1)$ 1.70 glassy
110	Calcite $CaCO_3$	$\bar{3}m$ a_0 4.990 c_0 17.061	Morph. ind.[a] isom. $(10\bar{1}1)$, tab. (0001) and elong *c*, very form- rich. tw. (0001) $(01\bar{1}2)$	2.72	Colorless, white and colored	n_ω 1.6584 Na n_ϵ, 1.4864 Na n_ϵ' $(10\bar{1}1)$ 1.566 glassy
111	Dolomite $CaMg[CO_3]_2$	$\bar{3}$ a_0 4.808 c_0 16.010	Morph. ind.[a] isom. $(10\bar{1}1)$ tw. (0001) $(10\bar{1}1)$	2.85–2.95	Colorless, white and yellowish grey	n_ω 1.6799 Na n_ϵ, 1.5013 Na n_ϵ' $(10\bar{1}1)$ 1.588 glassy

Table 4.2–5 (*Continued*)
NITRATES AND CARBONATES

No.	Name and formula	Crystal glass lattice constants	Habit, form	Sp. gr.	Color	Indices of refraction and luster	
112	Aragonite $CaCO_3$	*mmm* a_0 4.95 b_0 7.96 c_0 5.73	Col.–fib. *c*, (110) (010) (011), tw. (110) ps. hex.	2.95	Colorless, white and different colored	n_α n_β n_γ	1.530 1.682 1.686 glassy
113	Strontianite $SrCO_3$	*mmm* a_0 5.13 b_0 8.42 c_0 6.09	Col.–acic. *c* (110) (011) (021), tw. (110) ps. hex.	3.7	Colorless, white and yellowish	n_α n_β n_γ	1.516 1.664 1.666 glassy
114	Witherite $BaCO_3$	*mmm* a_0 5.26 b_0 8.85 c_0 6.55	Isom.–fib. *c*, (110) (021) (010), tw. (110) ps. hex. (Bipyr.)	~4.28	Colorless, white, grey, yellowish	n_α n_β n_γ	1.529 1.676 1.677 glassy
115	Cerussite $PbCO_3$	*mmm* a_0 5.15 b_0 8.47 c_0 6.11	Isom.–col. *a* or tab. (010), tw. (110) ps. hex.	6.4–6.6	Colorless, white, yellowish, black	n_a n_β n_γ	1.804 2.076 2.078 greasy diamond lust.
116	Azurite $Cu_3[OH|CO_3]_2$	$2/m$ a_0 4.97 b_0 5.84 c_0 10.29 β 92° 24′	Col. *b*–tab. (001), (110)	3.7–3.9	Azur blue	n_α n_β n_γ	1.730 1.758 1.838 glassy
117	Malachite $Cu_2[(OH)_2|CO_3]$	$2/m$ a_0 9.48 b_0 12.03 c_0 3.21 β98° = ½	Col.–fib. *c*, (110) (100) (010) (001), tw. (100)	4.0	Green	n_α n_β n_γ	1.655 1.875 1.909 glassy

Table 4.2–5 (*Continued*)
NITRATES AND CARBONATES

No.	Name and formula	Crystal glass lattice constants	Habit, form	Sp. gr.	Color	Indices of refraction and luster
118	Hydrozincite $Zn_5[(OH)_3|CO_3]_2$	$2/m$ a_0 13.48 b_0 6.32 c_0 5.37 β 95° 30′	Tab. (100) and elong. after *c*, usu. massive	3.2–3.8	Snow white to pale yellow	n_α 1.65 n_β 1.736 n_γ 1.74 variable
119	Soda $Na_2CO_3 \cdot 10\ H_2O$	$2/m$ a_0 12.76 b_0 9.01 c_0 13.47 β 122° 48′	Tab. (010), (110) (011), tw. (001)	1.42–1.47	Colorless, pale grey, yellowish to white	n_α 1.405 n_β 1.425 n_γ 1.440 glassy
120	Hydromagnesite $Mg_5[(OH)|(CO_3)_2]_2$ $4\ H_2O$	Monocl.-ps. orhomb. (222) a_0 18.58 b_0 9.06 c_0 8.42 β 90°	Fib. *c*–tab. (100), elong. *c* tw. (100)	~2.2	White	n_α 1.523 n_β 1.527 n_γ 1.545 pearly lust.

Table 4.2–6
BORATES

No.	Name and formula	Crystal glass lattice constants	Habit, form	Sp. gr.	Color	Indices of refraction and luster
121	Borax $Na_2[B_4O_5(OH)_4] \cdot 8H_2O$	$2/m$ a_0 11.84 b_0 10.63 c_0 12.32 β 106° 35′	Short col. tw. (100) rare	1.7–1.8	Colorless, grey yellowish	n_α 1.447 n_β 1.469 n_γ 1.472 glassy to greasy lust.

Note: For list of abbreviations and symbols, see p. 281.

Table 4.2–6 (*Continued*)
BORATES

No.	Name and formula	Crystal class lattice constants	Habit, form	Sp. gr.	Color	Indices of refraction and luster	
122	Kernite $Na_2[B_4O_4(OH)_2]\cdot 3H_2O$	$2/m$ a_0 15.68 b_0 9.09 c_0 7.02 β 108° 52′	Isom.–col. *c*,, (100) (101) (011) (001)	1.92	Colorless, white	n_α n_β n_γ	1.454 1.472 1.488
123	Boracite $Mg_3[Cl\,B_7O_{13}]$ <265°C	$2mm$ a_0 8.54 b_0 8.54 c_0 12.07	Fib. a. pseu-domorph. after β-B., cycl. tw. (100) of 12 individ.	2.9–3	Colorless, bluish, greenish	n_α n_β n_γ	1.6622 1.6670 1.6730 glassy to diamond lust.
124	Boracite β–$Mg_3[Cl\,B_7O_{13}]$ >265°C	$43m$ a_0 12.10	(100) (110) (111)	2.9–3.0	Colorless, bluish, greenish	n	1.6714

(Compiled by Koritnig, S., in *Introduction to Minerology,* 2nd ed., by Correns, C. W., Springer-Verlag, New York, 1969.)

TABLE 4.2–7
Sulfates, Chromates, Molybdates, Wolframates

No.	Name and formula	Crystal class lattice constants	Habit, form	Sp. gr.	Color	Indices of refraction and luster	
125	*Gluaberite* $CaNa_2[SO_4]_2$	$2/m$ a_0 10.01 b_0 8.21 c_0 8.43 β 11° 11′	Tab. (001) or col. *c*, (100) (111)	2.7–2.8	Colorless, white and light colors	n_α n_β n_γ	1.515 1.532 1.536 glassy to greasy lust.
126	*Anhydrite* $Ca[SO_4]$	$m\,m\,m$ a_0 6.22 b_0 6.97 c_0 6.96	Isom. (100) (010) (001) or col. *b* (101) (010) (011)	2.9–3.0	Colorless, white and light colors	n_α n_β n_γ	1.569 1.575 1.613 glassy lust

Note: For list of abreviations and symbols, see p. 281.

TABLE 4.2–7 *(Continued)*
Sulfates, Chromates, Molybdates, Wolframates

No.	Name and formula	Crystal class lattice constants	Habit, form	Sp. gr.	Color	Indices of refraction and luster	
127	*Celestite* $Sr[SO_4]$	*m m m* a_0 8.38 b_0 5.37 c_0 6.85	Col. *a* tab. (001), (110) (011) (102)	3.9–4.0	Colorless, white, blue *et al.*, colors	n_α n_β n_γ	1.622 1.624 1.631 glassy
128	*Barite* $Ba[SO_4]$	*m m m* a_0 8.87 b_0 5.45 c_0 7.14	Tab. (001), (110) (102), col. *a* (011) (110) (010) *et al.*,	4.48	Colorless, white, colors	n_α n_β n_γ	1.636 1.637 1.648 glassy
129	*Anglesite* $Pb[SO_4]$	*m m m* a_0 8.47 b_0 5.39 c_0 6.94	Isom. (011) (110), tab. (001)	6.3	Colorless white and colors	n_α n_β n_γ	1.877 1.882 1.894 greasy diamond lust.
130	*Brochantite* $Cu_4[(OH)_6|SO_4]$	2/*m* a_0 13.08 b_0 9.85 c_0 6.02 β 103° 22′	Col.–fib. *c*	3.9	Emerald green	n_α n_β n_γ	1.730 1.778 1.803 glassy
131	*Alunite* $KAl_3[(OH)_6|(SO_4)_2]$	3*m* a_0 6.97 c_0 17.38	$(10\bar{1}1)$ ps. cub.	2.6–2.8	Colorless, white reddish, yellowish	n_ω n_ϵ	1.572 1.592
132	*Kieserite* $Mg[SO_4] \cdot H_2O$	2/*m* a_0 6.89 b_0 7.61 c_0 7.63 β 116° 05′	Bipyramid. crystals rare	2.57	Colorless, white, yellowish	n_α n_β n_γ	1.523 1.535 1.586 glassy

TABLE 4.2–7 *(Continued)*
Sulfates, Chromates, Molybdates, Wolframates

No.	Name and formula	Crystal class lattice constants	Habit, form	Sp. gr.	Color	Indices of refraction and luster	
133	*Chalcanthite* $Cu[SO_4] \cdot 5H_2O$	$\bar{1}$ a_0 6.12 b_0 10.69 c_0 5.96 α 97° 35′ β 107° 10′ γ 77° 33′	Broad tab. $(1\bar{1}0)$ (110) $(\bar{1}11)$ (100)	2.2–2.3	Blue	n_α n_β n_γ	1.514 1.5368 1.543 glassy
134	*Melanterite* $Fe[SO_4] \cdot 7H_2O$	$2/m$ a_0 14.11 b_0 6.51 c_0 11.02 β 105° 15′	Short col. to isom. (110) (001), crystals rare	1.9	Green	n_α n_β n_γ	1.471 1.478 1.486 glassy
135	*Epsomite* $Mg[SO_4] \cdot 7H_2O$	222 a_0 11.96 b_0 12.05 c_0 6.88	Fib.–col. *c*, (110) (111)	1.68	Colorless, white	n_α n_β n_γ	1.433 1.455 1.455
136	*Alunogen* $Al_2[SO_4]_3 \cdot 18H_2O$	$\bar{1}$ *a:b:c* 0.8355:1 0.6752 α 89° 58′ β 97° 26′ γ 91° 52′	Tab. (010) or fib. *c*	1.65	White	n_α n_β n_γ	1.475 1.478 1.485 variable
137	*Potasium alum* $KA1[SO_4]_2 \cdot 12H_2O$	$2/m3$ a_0 12.15	(111) (100), tw. (111)	1.76	Colorless	n	1.4562 Na
138	*Astrakanite* (Blödite) $Na_2Mg[SO_4]_2 \cdot 4H_2O$	$2/m$ a_0 11.06 b_0 8.17 c_0 5.50	Col. *c* or tab. (001)	2.23	Colorless, greenish, yellowish	n_α n_β n_γ	1.4826 1.4855 1.4869 glassy lust.

TABLE 4.2–7 (*Continued*)
Sulfates, Chromates, Molybdates, Wolframates

No.	Name and formula	Crystal class lattice constants	Habit, form	Sp. gr.	Color	Indices of refraction and luster
139	*Polyhalite* $K_2Ca_2Mg[SO_4]_4 \cdot 2H_2O$	$\bar{1}$ ps. orhomb. a_0 6.96 b_0 6.97 c_0 8.97$_9$ α 104° 30′ β 101° 30′ γ 113° 54	Elong. *c* or tab. (010), tw. lam. (010) (100)	2.77	Red, white, yellow, grey	n_α 1.547 n_β 1.562 n_γ 1.567 glassy to greasy lust.
140	*Mirabilite* (Glaubersalt) $Na_2[SO_4] \cdot 10H_2O$	2/*m* a_0 11.48 b_0 10.35 c_0 12.82 β 107° 40′	Fib.–col. *b* (001) (100)	1.49	Colorless	n_α 1.394 n_β 1.396 n_γ 1.398
141	*Gypsum* $Ca[SO_4] \cdot 2H_2O$	2/*m* a_0 5.68 b_0 15.18 c_0 6.29 β 113° 50′	Tab. (010) or col. *c*, (010) (110) (111); tw. (100) (101)	2.3–2.4	Colorless, white, yellowish	n_α 1.5205 n_β 1.5526 n_γ 1.5296 glassy lust.
142	*Copiapite* $(Fe^{\cdot\cdot}, Mg)$ $Fe_4^{\cdot\cdot\cdot}[(OH)(SO_4)_3]_2$ $\cdot 20H_2O$	$\bar{1}$ a_0 7.34 b_0 18.19 c_0 7.28 α 93° 50′ β 101° 30′ γ 99° 23′	Tab. (001) ps. orhomb.	2.1	Yellow	n_α 1.531 n_β 1.546 n_γ 1.597
143	*Kainite* $KMg[Cl|SO_4] \cdot 3H_2O$	2/*m* a_0 19.76 b_0 16.26 c_0 9.57 β 94° 56′	Tab. (001) with (111) ($\bar{1}$11) (010)	2.1	White, yellowish, red	n_α 1.495 n_β 1.506 n_γ 1.520

TABLE 4.2–7 (*Continued*)
Sulfates, Chromates, Molybdates, Wolframates

No.	Name and formula	Crystal class lattice constants	Habit, form	Sp. gr.	Color	Indices of refraction and luster
144	*Crocoite* $Pb[CrO_4]$	$2/m$ a_0 7.11 b_0 7.41 c_0 6.81 β 102° 33′	Acic.–col. *c*. (110) (111) ($\bar{4}$01) (301) (120)	5.9–6.0	Orange red	n_α 2.29 n_β 2.36 } Li n_γ 2.66 diamond lust.
145	*Wolframite* $(Mn, Fe)[WO_4]$	$2/m$ a_0 4.79 b_0 5.74 c_0 4.99 β 90° 26′	Tab. (100) or col. to acic. *c*, (100) (110) (210) (001) (102) (011) (111), tw. (100) rare (023)	7.14–7.54	Dark brown to black	n_α 2.26 n_β 2.32 n_γ 2.42 resinous met. lust.
146	*Scheelite* $Ca[WO_4]$	$4/m$ a_0 5.25 c_0 11.40	Isom. (112) (101) (213) (211), tw. (110), (100)	5.9–6.1	Greyish white to yellowish	n_ω 1.9185 n_ϵ 1.9345 greasy diamond lust.
147	*Wulfenite* $Pb[MoO_4]$	4 a_0 5.42 c_0 12.10	Tab. (001) to isom. (101) or (112)	6.7–6.9	Honey to orange yellow	n_ω 2.405 n_ϵ 2.283 diamond lust.

(Compiled by Koritnig, S., in *Introduction to Minerology*, 2nd ed., by Correns, C. W., Springer-Verlag, New York, 1969.)

Table 4.2–8
PHOSPHATES, ARSENATES, VANADATES

No.	Name and formula	Crystal class lattice constants	Habit, form	Sp. gr.	Color	Indices of refraction and luster
148	Triphyline $Li(Fe^{\cdot\cdot},Mn^{\cdot\cdot})[PO_4]$	*mmm* a_0 6.01 b_0 10.36 c_0 4.68	Col. [100]	3.58 (Fe-end-memb.)	Greenish, bluish, grey, blue flecks	n_α 1.694 n_β 1.695 n_γ 1.700 (for Fe:Mn =7:3) greasy
149	Xenotime $Y[PO_4]$	4/*mmm* a_0 6.89 c_0 6.04	Col. *c* to isom., (110) (100) (111) (201)	4.5–5.1	Light brown to reddish brown	n_ω 1.721 n_ϵ 1.816 greasy glassy
150	Monazite $Ce[PO_4]$ Th-bearing	2/*m* a_0 6.79 b_0 7.04 c_0 6.47 β 104° 24′	Tab. (100) to col. *c*, (100) (110) (101) (010), tw. (100)	4.8–5.5	Light yellow to dark reddish brown	n_α 1.796 n_β 1.797 n_γ 1.841 greasy glassy to diamond lust
151	Amblygonite $LiAl[(F, OH)\|PO_4]$	1 a_0 5.19 b_0 7.12 c_0 5.04 α 112° 02′ β 97° 49′ γ 68° 07′	Usu. massive	2.9–3.1	Greenish, violet, white	n_α 1.578–1.607 n_β 1.593–1.614 n_γ 1.598–1.630 glassy, on (001) pearly
152	Lazulite $(Mg, Fe^{\cdot\cdot})Al_2[OH\|PO_4]_2$	2/*m* a_0 7.16 b_0 7.26 c_0 7.24 β 118° 55′	(111), usu. massive	3.1	Sky blue to dark blue	n_α 1.612 n_β 1.634 n_γ 1.643 glassy

Note: For list of abbreviations and symbols, see p. 281.

Table 4.2–8 (*Continued*)
PHOSPHATES, ARSENATES, VANADATES

No.	Name and formula	Crystal class lattice constants	Habit. form	Sp. gr.	Color	Indices of refraction and luster	
153	Descloizite Pb(Zn, Cu)[OH|VO$_4$]	222 a_0 6.06 b_0 9.41 c_0 7.58	Col. *c* or *b* also tab. (100), (110) (111) (100) (021)	5.5–6.2	Brownish red to black	n_α n_β n_γ	2.185 2.265 2.35 diamond lust.
154	*Apatite* Ca$_5$[(F, Cl, OH)|(PO$_4$)$_3$]	6/*m* F-Apatite: a_0 9.39 c_0 6.89 Cl-Apatite: a_0 9.54 c_0 6.86	Col. *c* to broad tab. (0001), $(10\bar{1}0)$ (1011)	3.16–3.22	Colorless and colors	 n_ω n_ϵ n_ω n_ϵ	F-Apatite: 1.6335 1.6316 greasy glassy Cl-Apatite: 1.6684 1.6675
155	*Pyromorphite* Pb$_5$[Cl(PO$_4$)$_3$]	6/*m* a_0 9.97 c_0 7.32	Col. *c*, $(10\bar{1}0)$ (0001)	6.7–7.0	Green, brown, colorless, and other colors	n_ω n_ϵ	2.0596 Na 2.0488 Na greasy diamond lust.
156	*Mimetesite* Pb$_5$[Cl|(AsO$_4$)$_3$]	6/*m* a_0 10.26 c_0 7.44	Col. *c*, (1010), (0001); rare broad tab. (0001);	7.28	Pale yellow to yellowish brown, orange, white, colorless	n_ω n_ϵ	2.147 2.128
157	*Vanadinite* Pb$_5$[Cl|(VO$_4$)$_3$]	6/*m* a_0 10.33 c_0 7.35	Col. *c* or pyramid., $(10\bar{1}0)$ (0001) $(10\bar{1}1)$ $(11\bar{2}1)$	6.8–7.1	Yellow, brown, orange	n_ω n_ϵ	2.4163 Na 2.3503 Na diamond lust.
158	*Scorodite* Fe‴[AsO$_4$]·2H$_2$O	*m m m* a_0 10.28 b_0 10.00 c_0 8.90	(111) (120) (010) (100) (001)	3.1–3.3	Leek green to blackish green	n_α n_β n_γ	1.738–1.784 1.774–1.796 1.797–1.814 glassy

Table 4.2–8 (*Continued*)
PHOSPHATES, ARSENATES, VANADATES

No.	Name and formula	Crystal class lattice constants	Habit, form	Sp. gr.	Color	Indices of refraction and luster
159	*Vivianite* $Fe_3^{\cdot\cdot}[PO_4]_2 \cdot 8H_2O$	$2/m$ a_0 10.08 b_0 13.43 c_0 4.70 β 104° 30′	Col. *c*, also tab. (010), (110) (100) (010) (111), earthy	2.68	Fresh colorless to white, in the air turning to blue	Fresh: n_α 1.580 n_β 1.598 n_γ 1.627 blue, becomes: n_α 1.581 n_β 1.604 n_γ 1.636 glassy
160	*Erythrite* $Co_3[AsO_4]_2 \cdot 8H_2O$	$2/m$ a_0 10.20 b_0 13.37 c_0 4.74 β 105° 01′	Acic. *c*-rare tab. (010), (110) (104) $(10\bar{1})$ (350)	2.95	Pinkish red	n_α 1.629 n_β 1.663 n_γ 1.701 diamond lust.
161	*Annabergite* $Ni_3[AsO_4]_2 \cdot 8H_2O$	$2/m$ a_0 10.14 b_0 13.31 c_0 4.71 β 104° 45′	Fib. *c* or tab. (010), (110) (104) $(10\bar{1})$ (350)	3–3.1	Apple green	n_α 1.622 n_β 1.658 n_γ 1.687
162	*Struvite* $(NH_4)Mg[PO_4] \cdot 6H_2O$	$2mm$ a_0 6.98 b_0 6.10 c_0 11.20	Isom., (101) (011) $(00\bar{1})$, tw. (001)	1.72	Yellow to light brown rarely colorless	n_α 1.495 n_β 1.496 n_γ 1.504
163	*Wavellite* $Al_3[(OH)_3 \mid (PO_4)_2]$ $\cdot 5H_2O$	mmm a_0 9.62 b_0 17.34 c_0 6.99	Rad. fib. *c*, (110) (111)	2.3–2.4	Colorless, grey, yellowish, greenish	n_α 1.525 n_β 1.535 n_γ 1.545 var. glassy

Table 4.2–8 (*Continued*)
PHOSPHATES, ARSENATES, VANADATES

No.	Name and formula	Crystal class lattice constants	Habit, form	Sp. gr.	Color	Indices of refraction and luster	
164	*Turquoise* $CuAl_6[(OH)_2 \mid PO_4]_4$ $\cdot 4H_2O$	$\bar{1}$ a_0 7.48 b_0 9.95 c_0 7.69 α 111° 39′ β 115° 23′ γ 69° 26′	Crystals rare, col.	2.6–2.8	Sky blue to bluish green, apple green	n_α n_β n_γ	1.61 1.62 1.65
165	*Autunite* $Ca[UO_2 \mid PO_4]_2$ $\cdot 12–10H_2O$	$4/m\ m\ m$ a_0 7.00 c_0 20.67	Tab. (001), tw. (110)	3–3.2	Greenish yellow to sulfur yellow	n_α n_β n_γ	1.553 1.575 1.577
166	*Carnotite* $K_2[(UO_2)_2 \mid V_2O_8] \cdot 3H_2O$	$2/m$ a_0 10.47 b_0 8.41 c_0 6.91 β 103° 40′	Tab. (001)	4.5	Yellow, greenish yellow	n_α n_β n_γ	1.750 1.925 1.959

(Compiled by Koritnig, S., in *Introduction to Minerology*, 2nd ed., by Correns, C. W., Springer-Verlag, New York, 1969.)

Table 4.2–9
SILICATES

No.	Name and formula	Crystal class lattice constants	Habit, form	Sp. gr.	Color	Indices of refraction and luster	
Nesosilicates (Inselsilicates)							
167	Phenacite $Be_2[SiO_4]$	$\bar{3}$ a_0 12.45 c_0 8.23	$(10\bar{1}0)$ $(\bar{1}3\bar{2}\bar{2})$ and other forms or col. *c*, $(11\bar{2}0)$ $(10\bar{1}0)$ $(\bar{1}3\bar{2}2)$	3.0	Colorless, pale colored	n_ω n_ϵ	1.654 1.670

Table 4.2–9 (*Continued*)
SILICATES

No.	Name and formula	Crystal class lattice constants	Habit, form	Sp. gr.	Color	Indices of refraction and luster	
168	Willemite $Zn_2[SiO_4]$	$\bar{3}$ a_0 13.96 c_0 9.34	Col. *c*, $(10\bar{1}0)$ $(10\bar{1}1)$ $(30\bar{3}4)$	4.0–4.2	Colorless and different colored, often greenish	n_ω n_ϵ	1.691 1.719
Olivine Group (No. 169–171)							
169	Forsterite (Fo) $Mg_2[SiO_4]$ 0–10 mol. % Fa	*mmm* a_0 6.00 b_0 4.78 c_0 10.28	Isom. (010) (110) (011) (001), tw. (101) rare	3.2 ↓	Yellowish green	n_α n_β n_γ	1.635 1.651 1.670 ↓
170	Olivine (Peridot) $(Mg, Fe)_2[SiO_4]$ 10–30 mol. % Fa	*mmm* a_0 6.01 b_0 4.78 c_0 10.30	Like Forsterite, tw. (101) rare	3.4 ↓	Yellowish green	n_α n_β n_γ	1.647–1.686 1.666–1.707 1.685–1.726 ↓
171	Fayalite (Fa) $Fe_2[SiO_4]$	*mmm* a_0 6.17 b_0 4.81 c_0 10.61	Tw. (101) rare	4.34	Yellowish green to black	n_α n_β n_γ	1.835 1.877 1.886 glassy
172	*Monticellite* $CaMg[SiO_4]$	*m m m* a_0 6.38 b_0 4.83 c_0 11.10	Isom.	3.2	Colorless, white, yellowish	n_α n_β n_γ	1.6505 1.6616 } Na 1.6679
Garnets (No. 173–178)							
173	*Pyrope* $Mg_3Al_2[SiO_4]_3$	*m3m* a_0 11.53	Alone or comb. (110) (211),	~3.5	Crimson	n	~1.70

Table 4.2–9 (*Continued*)
SILICATES

No.	Name and formula	Crystal class lattice constants	Habit, form	Sp. gr.	Color	Indices of refraction and luster	
			rarely (321) (431) (332) (210)	~3.5	Crimson	n	~1.70
174	*Almandine* (Common garnet) $Fe_3^{\cdot\cdot}Al_2[SiO_4]_3$	$m3m$ a_0 11.52	Like pyrope, esp. (211)	~4.2	Red, bluish brown	n	~1.76–1.83
175	*Spessartite* $Mn_3Al_2[SiO_4]_3$	$m3m$ a_0 11.61	Like pyrope	~4.2	Yellow to reddish brown	n	~1.80
176	*Grossularite* $Ca_3Al_2[SiO_4]_3$	$m3m$ a_0 11.85	Like pyrope	~3.5	White, light green, yellowish to orange	n	~1.74
177	*Andradite* $Ca_3Fe_2^{\cdot\cdot\cdot}[SiO_4]_3$	$m3m$ a_0 12.04	(110) with (211)	~3.7	Brown, green, colorless, black	n	~1.89
178	*Melanite* $Ca_3Fe_2^{\cdot\cdot\cdot}[SiO_4]_3$ with Na. Ti for Ca, $Fe^{\cdot\cdot\cdot}$ and Ti for Si (to 25% TiO_2)	$m3m$ a_0 12.05 to 12.16	(110) with (211)	~3.7	Brownish black	n	1.86–2.0
179	*Zircon* $Zr[SiO_4]$	$4/m\,m\,m$ a_0 6.59 c_0 5.94	Col. c, (100) (101) or (110) (101) combined with (211) tw. (112), *et al.*	3.9–4.8	Brown to brownish red and other colors, also colorless	n_ω n_ϵ	1.960 Na 2.01 Na

Table 4.2–9 (*Continued*)
SILICATES

No.	Name and formula	Crystal class lattice constants	Habit, form	Sp. gr.	Color	Indices of refraction and luster	
180	*Euclase* Al[$BeSiO_4$ OH]	$2/m$ a_0 4.63 b_0 14.27 c_0 4.76 β 100° 16′	Col. *c*, very faceted	3.0–3.1	Colorless to light green	n_α n_β n_γ	1.652 1.655 1.671 glassy
181	*Sillimanite* Al[^{6}] Al[^{4}] [O SiO_4][a]	$m\,m\,m$ a_0 7.44 b_0 7.60 c_0 5.75	Fib. *c*, (110) 88°	3.2	Yellowish grey, greyish green, brownish	n_α n_β n_γ	1.657–1.661 1.658–1.670 1.677–1.684
182	*Andalusite* Al[$_6$] Al[$_5$] [O|SiO_4]	$m\,m\,m$ a_0 7.78 b_0 7.92 c_0 5.57	Col. *c*, (110) (001)	3.1–3.2	Greyish to reddish grey	n_α n_β n_γ	1.6290–1.640 1.6328–1.644 1.6390–1.647
183	*Kyanite* Al[$_6$] Al[$_6$] [O|SiO_4]	$\bar{1}$ a_0 7.10 b_0 7.74 c_0 5.57 α 90° 05½′ β 101° 02′ γ 105° 44½′	Col. *c*, (100) (010) (001), tw. (100)	3.6–3.7	Colorless, white, blue or greenish stains	n_α n_β n_γ	1.713 1.722 1.729 var. glassy
184	*Mullite* Al_4 [^{6}] Al[^{4}] [O_3($O_{0.5}$ OH, F)| Si_3AlO_{16}]	Orhomb. a_0 7.50 b_0 7.65 c_0 5.75	Fib. *c*	3.03	White, pale violet	n_α n_β n_γ	1.639 1.641 1.653
185	*Topaz* Al_2 [F_2 |SiO_4]	$m\,m\,m$ a_0 4.65 b_0 8.80 c_0 8.40	Col. *c*-isom., (110) (120) (011) (021) (112) (001)	3.5–3.6	Colorless and pale colors	n_α n_β n_γ	1.607–1.629 1.610–1.630 1.617–1.638 glassy

[a] Contains [$AlSiO_5$]-tetrahedral chains and thus can be included also with inosilicates.

Table 4.2–9 (*Continued*)
SILICATES

No.	Name and formula	Crystal class lattice constants	Habit, form	Sp. gr.	Color	Indices of refraction and luster	
186	*Staurolite* $Fe_2Al_9[O_6(O, OH)_2$ $(SiO_4)_4]$	*m m m* a_0 7.82 b_0 16.52 c_0 5.63	Col. *c*, (110) (001), tw. (032) (232)	3.7–3.8	Reddish to blackish brown	n_α n_β n_γ	1.736–1.747 1.741–1.754 1.746–1.762 glassy
187	*Chloritoid* $(Fe, Mg)_2Al_4$ $[(OH)|O_2(SiO_4)_2]$	2/*m* a_0 9.45 b_0 5.48 c_0 18.16 β 101°30′	Tab. (001) ps. hex.	3.3–3.6	blackish green to black	n_α n_β n_γ	1.714–1.725 1.717–1.728 1.730–1.737
188	*Chondrodite* $Mg_5[(OH, F)_2|(SiO_4)_2]$	2/*m* a_0 7.89 b_0 4.74 c_0 10.29 β 109° 02′	Tab. (010), polysynth. tw. (100)	3.1–3.2	Yellowish to brownish	n_α n_β n_γ	1.601–1.635 1.606–1.645 1.622–1.663
189	*Clinohumite* $Mg_9[(OH, F)_2|(SiO_4)_4]$	2/*m* a_0 13.71 b_0 4.75 c_0 10.29 β 100° 50′	Tw. lam. (100)	~3.2	Brown, yellow, white	n_α n_β n_γ	1.625–1.652 1.638–1.663 1.653 to ~1.67 increases with increasing (FeO + MnO) content
190	*Braunite* $Mn_4^{\cdot\cdot}Mn_3^{\cdot\cdot\cdot}[O_8|SiO_4]$	$\bar{4}2m$ a_0 9.52 c_0 18.68	Isom. (111) (001) (421), tw. (101)	4.7–4.9	Black		greasy met. lust
191	*Sphene* (Titanite) $CaTi[O|SiO_4]$	2/*m* a_0 6.56 b_0 8.72 c_0 7.44 β 119° 43′	Tab. to wedge sh. (111) (100) (001) (102) (110)	3.4–3.6	Yellow to greenish brown, reddish brown	n_α n_β n_γ	1.91–1.88 1.92–1.89 2.04–2.01

Table 4.2–9 (*Continued*)
SILICATES

No.	Name and formula	Crystal class lattice constants	Habit, form	Sp. gr.	Color	Indices of refraction and luster	
192	*Datolite* $CaB[^4][OH\|SiO_4]$	$2/m$ a_0 9.66 b_0 7.64 c_0 4.83 β 90° 09′	Short col. *c* or *a* or broad tab. (100), (100) (110) (011) (102) (111)	2.9–3.0	Colorless, white, greenish, yellowish rarely other colors	n_α n_β n_γ	1.626 1.654 1.670
193	*Gadolinite* $Y_2FeBe_2[O\|SiO_4]_2$ besides Y also other rare earths	$2/m$ a_0 9.89 b_0 7.55 c_0 4.66 β 90° 33½′	Often col. *c*	4–4.7	Pitch black	n_α n_β n_γ n	1.801 1.812 1.824 isotrop.[b] ~1.78
194	*Dumoriente* $(Al, Fe)_7[O_3\|BO_3\|(SiO_4)_3]$	$m\,m\,m$ a_0 11.79 b_0 20.21 c_0 4.70	(110) 56°	3.3–3.4	Dark blue, bluish grey to red	n_α n_β n_γ	1.659–1.678 1.684–1.691 1.686–1.692
Sorosilicates (Group silicates)							
195	*Thortveitite* $Sc_2[Si_2O_7]$ Sc→Y	$2/m$ a_0 6.57 b_0 8.60 c_0 4.75 β 103° 08′	Col. *c* (110), tw. (110)	~3.6	Dark greyish green to black	n_α n_β n_γ	1.756 1.793 1.809
196	*Melilite* $(Ca, Na)_2(Al, Mg)[(Si, Al)_2O_7]$ (solid soln. of *Gehlenite* $Ca_2Al[SiAlO_7]$ and *Akermanite.* $Ca_2Mg[Si_2O_7]$.)	$\bar{4}2m$ a_0 7.74 c_0 5.02	Tab.–short col. *c.* (001) (100) (110) (102)	2.9–3.0	Colorless, yellow, brown, grey	n_ω n_ϵ	1.63–1.66 1.64–1.67 sometimes anom. interf. colors (dark blue), glassy

[b] Metamict.

Table 4.2–9 (*Continued*)
SILICATES

No.	Name and formula	Crystal class lattice constants	Habit, form	Sp. gr.	Color	Indices of refraction and luster	
197	*Lawsonite* $CaAl_2[(OH)_2|Si_2O_7]\cdot$ $\cdot H_2O$	222 a_0 8.90 b_0 5.76 c_0 13.33	Col. *b* or tab. (010), tw. (101)	3.1	Colorless to bluish	n_α n_β n_γ	1.665 1.674 1.684 glassy
198	*Ilvaite* (Lievrite) $CaFe_2^{\cdot\cdot}Fe^{\cdot\cdot\cdot}$ $[OH|O|Si_2O_7]$	*m m m* a_0 8.84 b_0 5.87 c_0 13.10	Col. *c* (110) (120) (010) (111) (101)	4.1	Black	n_α n_β n_γ	~1.88_7 ~1.89 ~1.91 glassy
199	*Hemimorphite* $Zn_4[(OH)_2|Si_2O_7]\cdot H_2O$	2*m m* a_0 10.72 b_0 8.40 c_0 5.12	Tab. (010), (010) (110) (001) (301) $12\bar{1}$), tw. (001)	3.3–3.5	Colorless and pale colors	n_α n_β n_γ	1.614 1.617 1.636 glassy
200	*Clinozoisite* Ca_2Al_3 $[O|OH|SiO_4|Si_2O_7]$	2/*m* a_0 8.94 b_0 5.61 c_0 10.23 β 115°	Col. *b*, (100) (101) (001) (111) (110) (011), tw. (100)	3.35–3.38	Greyish green	n_α n_β n_γ	1.724 1.729 1.734
201	*Epidote* $(Ca_2(Al, Fe^{\cdot\cdot\cdot})Al_2$ $[O|OH|SiO_4|Si_2O_7]$	2/*m* a_0 8.98 b_0 5.64 c_0 10.22 β 115° 24′	Like clinozoisite	3.3–3.5	Dark green to yellowish green, rarely red	n_α n_β n_γ	1.734 1.763 1.780
202	*Allanite* (Orthite) $(Ca, Ce)_2(Fe, Fe^{\cdot\cdot})Al_2$ $[O|OH|SiO_4|Si_2O_7]$	2/*m* a_0 8.98 b_0 5.75 c_0 10.23 β 115° 00′	Tab. (100) to col. *b*, tw. (100)	3–4.2	Pitch black	n_α n_β n_γ	~1.72 ~1.74 ~1.76 var. sometimes isotrop. deer. to n = 1.52, glassy

Table 4.2–9 (*Continued*)
SILICATES

No.	Name and formula	Crystal class lattice constants	Habit, form	Sp. gr.	Color	Indices of refraction and luster	
203	*Zoisite* $Ca_2 Al_3$ $[O|OH|SiO_4|Si_2O_7]$	$m\,m\,m$ a_0 16.24 b_0 5.58 c_0 10.10	Col. *b*, (110) (010) (021)	3.2–3.38	Greenish grey to green	n_α n_β n_γ	1.702 1.703 1.706 var. glassy
204	*Pumpellyite* Ca_2(Mg, Fe, Mn, Al) $(Al, Fe, Ti)_2$ $[(OH, H_2O)_2$ $SiO_4 Si_2O_7]$ (?)	$2/m$ a_0 8.81 b_0 5.94 c_0 19.14 β 97.6°	Tab. (001) or fib., tw. (001)	3.18–3.23	Blue-green, green, brownish	n_α n_β n_γ	1.678–1.703 1.681–1.716 1.688–1.721
205	*Vesuvianite* $Ca_{10}(Mg, Fe)_2 Al_4 [(OH)_4|$ $(SiO_4)_5|(Si_2O_7)_2]$	$4/m\,m\,m$ a_0 15.66 c_0 11.85	Isom. to col. *c*, (100) (110) (100)	3.27–3.45	Brown to diff. shades of green, rarely blue, rose	n_ω n_ϵ	1.705–1.736 1.701–1.732 glassy
Cyclosilicates (Ring/Silicates)							
206	*Benitoite* $BaTi[(Si_3O_9]$	$\overline{6}\,m\,2$ a_0 6.61 c_0 9.73	$(01\overline{1}1)$ $(10\overline{1}1)$ $(10\overline{1}0)$ (0001)	3.7	Pale to sapphire blue	n_ω n_ϵ	1.757 1.804
207	*Axinite* $Ca_2(Mn, Fe)Al_2$ $[OH|BO_3|Si_4O_{12}]$	$\overline{1}$ a_0 7.15 b_0 9.16 c_0 8.96 α 88° 04′ β 81° 36′ γ 77° 42′	Flat. (110) (010) (111) (011) (121) (120) orient. after MILLER	3.3	Clove brown, violet smoky grey, and other colors	n_α n_β n_γ	1.679 1.685 1.689 var. glassy
208	*Beryl* $Al_2Be_3[Si_6O_{18}]$	$6/m\,m\,m$ a_0 9.23 c_0 9.19	Col. *c*, $(10\overline{1}0)$ (0001) $(10\overline{1}1)$ (1121) *et al.*, tw. $(11\overline{2}2)$ rare	2.63–2.80	Colorless and colored	n_ω n_ϵ	1.57–1.602 1.56–1.595 glassy

Table 4.2–9 (*Continued*)
SILICATES

No.	Name and formula	Crystal class lattice constants	Habit, form	Sp. gr.	Color		Indices of refraction and luster
209	*Cordierite* $Mg_2Al_3[AlSi_5O_{18}]$ Mg→Fe	*m m m* a_0 17.13 b_0 9.80 c_0 9.35	Col. *c*, (110) (100) (130) (001), tw. (110) (130) ps. hex.	2.6	Grey to violet to dark blue	n_α n_β n_γ	1.538 1.543 1.545 greasy glassy
210	*Tourmaline* $XY_3Z_6[OH, F)_4|(BO_3)_3|Si_6O_{18}]$ X = Na, Ca, Y = Li, Al, Mg, Fe¨, Mn Z = Al, Mg	3*m* a_0 16.03[c] c_0 7.15[c]	*a*:*c* = 1:0.448 col.-acic. *c*, $(10\bar{1}0)$ $(11\bar{2}0)$ $(10\bar{1}1)$ $(02\bar{2}1)$ $(32\bar{5}1)$ *et al.*,	3–3.25	Colorless and all colors to black often zoned or term. in diff. color	n_ω n_ϵ	1.639–1.692 1.620–1.657 glassy
211	*Dioptase* $Cu_6[Si_6O_{18}]\cdot 6H_2O$	3 a_0 14.61 c_0 7.80	Col. *c*, $(11\bar{2}0)$ $(02\bar{2}1)$ *et al.*, for ex. $(1.15,\bar{1}\bar{6}.7)$, tw. (1011) rare	3.3	Emerald green	n_ω n_ϵ n_ϵ'	~1.644 to 1.658 ~1.697 to 1.709 1.66–1.69 glassy
212	*Chrysocolla* $CuSiO_3\cdot nH_2O$	Amorph. ?	Encrust.	2–2.2	Emerald green to blue	n	~1.46 to 1.635 (?)
213	*Milarite* $KCa_2AlBe_2[Si_{12}O_{39}]\cdot \frac{1}{2}H_2O$	6/*m m m* a_0 10.45 c_0 13.88	$(10\bar{1}1)$ $(10\bar{1}0)$ (0001)	2.6	Colorless to light yellowish green	n_ω n_ϵ	1.532 1.529

[c] For Schorlite.

Table 4.2–9 (*Continued*)
SILICATES

No.	Name and formula	Crystal class lattice constants	Habit, form	Sp. gr.	Color	Indices of refraction and luster	
Inosilicates (Chain or ribbon silicates) Pyroxenes (No. 214–225) Clinopyroxenes (No. 214–222)							
214	*Clinoenstalite* $Mg_2[Si_2O_6]$ (pure)	$2/m$ a_0 9.62 b_0 8.83 c_0 5.19 β 108° 21½′	Col. *c*	3.19	Colorless to yellowish	n_α n_β n_γ	1.651 1.654 1.660
215	*Pigeonite* $(Mg, Fe, Ca)_2[Si_2O_6]$	$2/m$ a_0 9.71 b_0 8.96 c_0 5.25 β 108° 33′	Col. *c*	3.30–3.46	Greenish to black	n_α n_β n_γ	1.69–1.71 1.70–1.71 1.71–1.74
216	*Diopside* $CaMg[Si_2O_6]$ (pure) ↓	$2/m$ a_0 9.73 b_0 8.91 c_0 5.25 β 105° 50′	Col. *c*, (100) (101) (001) (111) *et. al.*	3.27	Green, light green, grey, colorless	n_α n_β n_γ	1.664 1.6715 1.694
217	*Hedenbergite* $CaFe[Si_2O_6]$ (pure)	$2/m$ a_0 9.85 b_0 9.02 c_0 5.26 β 104° 20′	Oft. tab. (010)	3.55	Black to blackish green	n_α n_β n_γ	1.739 1.745 1.757
218	*Augite* approx.: $Ca_{0.81}Mg_{0.75}$ $Fe^{\cdot\cdot}_{0.12}Na_{0.06}$ $(Al, Fe^{\cdot\cdot\cdot}, Ti)_{0.25}$ $[Si_{1.81-1.51}Al_{0.19-0.49}O_6]$	$2/m$ a_0 ≅9.8 b_0 ≅9.0 c_0 ≅5.25 β ≅105°	Short col. *c*, (110) $(\bar{1}00)$ (010) $(\bar{1}11)$ *et al.*, tw. (100) also (101),	3.3–3.5	Leek green to greenish black, brown	n_α n_β n_γ	1.69–1.74 1.70–1.77 1.71–1.78

Table 4.2–9 (*Continued*)
SILICATES

No.	Name and formula	Crystal class lattice constants	Habit, form	Sp. gr.	Color		Indices of refraction and luster
			(001) and (122)				
219	*Spondumene* LiAl[Si_2O_6]	2/*m* a_o 9.52 b_o 8.32 c_o 5.25 β 110° 28′	Col. *c*, (100) (110) (130) (021) (221), tw. (100)	3.1–3.2	Ash grey, yellowish, greenish and other colors	n_α n_β n_γ	1.65–1.668 1.66–1.674 1.676–1.681
220	*Jadeite* NaAl[Si_2O_6] (pure)	2/*m* a_o 9.50 b_o 8.61 c_o 5.24 β 107° 26′	Fib. *c*	3.3–3.5	White to greenish	n_α n_β n_γ	~1.64 ~1.65 ~1.67
221	*Aegirine* (Acmite) NaFe‴[Si_2O_6] (pure)	2/*m* a_o 9.66 b_o 8.79 c_o 5.26 β 107° 20′	Col.-acic. *c*, (110) (661) (221) (310)	3.5–3.7	Green to black, brown to black	n_α n_β n_γ	1.76–1.78 1.80–1.82 1.81–1.83
222	*Aegirinaugite* Formula similar to No. 218, but Fe- and Na-richer	2/*m*	Col. *c*	3.4–3.55	Leek green to greenish black	n_α n_β n_γ	~1.70–1.75 ~1.71–1.78 ~1.73–1.80
Orthopyroxenes (No. 223–225)							
223	*Enstatite* $Mg_2[Si_2O_6]$ 0–12 mol. % Fe-Sil. ↓	*m m m* a_o 18.22 b_o 8.81 c_o 5.21	Short col. *c*, (210) (100) (101) 403)	~3.1 ↓	Grey, yellowish green to dark green	n_α n_β n_γ	1.650 1.653 1.659 (pure end-member) ↓

Table 4.2–9 (*Continued*)
SILICATES

No.	Name and formula	Crystal class lattice constants	Habit, form	Sp. gr.	Color	Indices of refraction and luster
224	*Bronzite* (Mg, Fe) $[Si_2O_6]$ 12–30 mol. % Fe-Sil. ↓	*m m m* a_0 18.20 b_0 8.86 c_0 5.20	Tab. (100)	~3.3 ↓	Brownish green, partly bronze-like iridescence on (100)	n_α 1.671–1.689 n_β 1.676–1.699 n_γ 1.681–1.702 ↓
225	*Hypersthene* (Mg, Fe) $[Si_2O_6]$ 30–50 mol. % Fe-Sil.	*m m m* a_0 18.24 b_0 8.88 c_0 5.21	Tab. (100) or (010) elong. *c*, (100) (010) (210) (211) (111)	~3.5 to 3.8 ↓	Blackish brown, blackish green, partly copper iridescence on (100)	n_α 1.689–1.711 n_β 1.699–1.725 n_γ 1.702–1.727 ↓
Amphiboles (No. 226–232) Ca-Amphiboles (No. 226–228)						
226	*Tremolite* $Ca_2Mg_5[(OH, F)_2Si_8O_{22}]$ *Actinolite* Mg→Fe¨	2/*m* a_0 ≅9.85 b_0 ≅18.1 c_0 ≅5.3 β 104° 50′	Fib.-long col. *c*, (110) (100) tw. (100)	2.9–3.4	Colorless, white, grey, dark green	n_α 1.599–1.688 n_β 1.613–1.697 n_γ 1.624–1.705 glassy
227	*Common mornblende* $(Na,K)_{0.25-1}Ca_{1.5-2}$ $Mg_{1.5-4}Fe_{1-2}(Al, Fe^{\cdots})$ $[(OH)_2Si_{7-6}Al_{1-2}O_{22}]$	2/*m* a_0 9.96 (?) b_0 18.42 c_0 5.37 β 105° 45′	Short col. *c*, (110) (010), tw. (100)	3.0–3.45	Green, bluish green to black	n_α 1.61–1.705 n_β 1.62–1.714 n_γ 1.63–1.730 glassy

Table 4.2–9 (*Continued*)
SILICATES

No.	Name and formula	Crystal class lattice constants	Habit, form	Sp. gr.	Color		Indices of refraction and luster
228	*Oxyhornblende* $Ca_2(Na,K)_{0.5-1.0}$ $(Mg, Fe^{\cdot\cdot})_{3-4}(Fe^{\cdot\cdot\cdot}Al)_{2-1}$ $[(O, OH, F)_2 Si_6 Al_2 O_{22}]$	$2/m$ a_0 9.96 (?) b_0 18.42 c_0 5.37 β 105° 45′	Short col. *c*, (110) (010) (101) (011) (211) tw. (100)	3.2–3.3	Brownish black	n_α n_β n_γ	1.667–1.690 1.672–1.730 1.680–1.72 glassy
Alkali-Amphiboles (No. 299–231)							
229	*Glaucophane* $Na_2 Mg_{1.5-3} Fe^{\cdot\cdot}_{1-1.5}$ $Fe_{0-0.25} Al_{1.75-2}[(OH)_2$ $Si_{7.75-8} Al_{0-0.25} O_{22}]$	$2/m$ a_0 9.74 (?) b_0 18.02 c_0 5.38 β 104° 10′ (?)	Col.–fib. *c*	3–3.15	Bluish grey to blackish blue	n_α n_β n_γ	1.606–1.661 1.622–1.667 1.627–1.670
230	*Riebeckite* $(Na, K)_{2-3} Ca_{0-0.5} Mg_{0-1}$ $Fe^{\cdot\cdot}_{1.5-4} Fe^{\cdot\cdot\cdot}_{0-3}[(OH, O)_2$ $Si_{7.5-8} Al_{0.5-0} O_{22}]$	$2/m$ a_0 9.90 (?) b_0 18.14 c_0 5.32 β 103° 30′ (?)	Col.–fib. *c*	~3.4	Bluish black	n_α n_β n_γ	~1.654–1.701 ~1.662–1.711 ~1.668–1.717
231	*Arfvedsonite* $Na_{2.5} Ca_{0.5}$ $(Fe^{\cdot\cdot}, Mg, Fe^{\cdot\cdot\cdot}, Al)_5$ $[(OH, F)_2 Si_{7.5} Al_{0.5} O_{22}]$	$2/m$ a_0 9.89 (?) b_0 18.35 c_0 5.34 β 104° 15½′ (?)	Crystals rare	~3.45	Bluish black	n_α n_β n_γ	1.674–1.700 1.679–1.709 1.686–1.710
232	*Anthophyllite* $(Mg, Fe)_7[(OH)_2 Si_8 O_{22}]$	*m m m* a_0 18.56 b_0 18.08 c_0 5.28	Fib.–col. *c*	2.9–3.2	Clove brown to yellowish grey	n_α n_β n_γ	1.596–1.64 1.605–1.66 1.615–1.67

Table 4.2–9 (*Continued*)
SILICATES

No.	Name and formula	Crystal class lattice constants	Habit, form	Sp. gr.	Color	Indices of refraction and luster
233	*Wollastonite* (–1T) $Ca_3[Si_3O_9]$ <1126°C	Tricl., ps.-monocline a_0 7.94 b_0 7.32 c_0 7.07 α 90° β 95° 16′ γ 103° 25′	Tab. (100) or (001) elong. *b*, (100) (001) $(\underline{1}01)$ (540) $(\bar{1}11)$ (320), tw. (100)	2.8–2.9	White or pale colors	n_α 1.619 n_β 1.632 n_γ 1.634 glassy
234	Pectolite $Ca_2NaH[Si_3O_9]$	$\bar{1}$ a_0 7.99 b_0 7.04 c_0 7.02 α 90° 31′ β 95° 11′ γ 102° 28′	Fib. *b*, tw. (100)	2.74–2.88	White, colorless	n_α 1.595–1.610 n_β 1.606–1.642 n_γ 1.633–1.643 glassy
235	*Rhodonite* $CaMn_4[Si_5O_{15}]$	$\bar{1}$ a_0 7.79 b_0 12.47 c_0 6.75 α 85° 10′ β 94° 04′ γ 111° 29′	Tab. (010) or col. *b*	3.4–3.68	Light red, black (weathered)	n_α 1.721–1.733 n_β 1.726–1.740 n_γ 1.730–1.744
Phyllosilicates (Layer silicates)						
236	*Apophyllite* $KCa_4[F\|(Si_4O_{10})_2]$ $8H_2O$	$4/m\,m\,m$ a_0 9.00 c_0 15.84	Isom., (100) (111)	2.3–2.4	Colorless, white, reddish, greenish	n_ω 1.535–1.543 n_ϵ 1.537–1.543
237	*Pyrophyllite* $Al_2[(OH)_2\|Si_4O_{10}]$	$2/m$ a_0 5.15 b_0 8.92 c_0 18.59 β 99° 55′	Tab. (001)	2.8	Silvery, yellowish, apple green	n_α 1.552 n_β 1.588 n_γ 1.600

Table 4.2–9 (*Continued*) SILICATES

No.	Name and formula	Crystal class lattice constants	Habit, form	Sp. gr.	Color	Indices of refraction and luster	
238	*Talc* $Mg_3[(OH)_2|Si_4O_{10}]$	$2/m$ a_0 5.27 b_0 9.12 c_0 18.85 β 100° 00′	Tab. (001), ps. hex.	2.7–2.8	Colorless, white to apple green, grey, yellowish and other colors	n_α n_β n_γ	1.539–1.550 1.589–1.594 1.589–1.600
Muscovite series (dioctahedral) (No. 239–243)							
239	*Paragonite* $NaAl_2$ $[(OH, F)_2|AlSi_3O_{10}]$	$2/m$ a_0 5.15 b_0 8.88 c_0 19.28 β~94°	Tab. (001)	2.8–2.9	White to apple green	n_α n_β n_γ	1.564–1.580 ~1.594 to 1.609 1.600–1.609
240	*Muscovite* KAl_2 $[(OH, F)_2|AlSi_3O_{10}]$	$2/m$ a_0 5.19 b_0 9.04 c_0 20.08 β 95° 30′	Tab. (001) ps. hex., rarely $(\underline{1}10)$ (010) $(\underline{1}11)$ *et al.*, tw. (010) with $(0\underline{0}1)$ or $(00\bar{1})$ as comp.-plane	2.78–2.88	Colorless, yellowish, greenish, brownish	n_α n_β n_γ	1.552–1.574 1.582–1.610 1.588–1.616
241	*Glauconite* $(K, Ca, Na)_{<1}(Al, Fe^{\cdot\cdot}, Fe^{\cdot\cdot\cdot}, Mg)_2$ $[(OH)_2Si_{3.65}Al_{0.35}O_{10}]$	$2/m$ (?) a_0 5.25 b_0 9.09 c_0 20.07 β 95° 00′	Scaly grains	2.2–2.8	Green	n_α n_β n_γ	1.590–1.615 1.609–1.643 1.610–1.645

Table 4.2–9 (*Continued*)
SILICATES

No.	Name and formula	Crystal class lattice constants	Habit, form	Sp. gr.	Color	Indices of refraction and luster
242	*Celadonite* (1M) K(Mg, $Fe^{\cdot\cdot}$) (Al, $Fe^{\cdot\cdot\cdot}$) $[(OH)_2 Si_4 O_{10}]$	$2/m$ a_0 5.21 b_0 9.02 c_0 10.27 β 100° 06′	Scaly, radial-col.	2.8	Bluish green	n_α, n_β, n_γ } ~ 1.61 ~ 1.634 to 1.644
243	*Margarite* $CaAl_2 [(OH)_2 \vert Al_2 Si_2 O_{10}]$	$2/m$ a_0 5.13 b_0 8.92 c_0 19.50 β 100° 48′	Tab. (001), ps. hex	3.0–3.1	White, reddish white, pearl grey	n_α 1.632 n_β 1.645 n_γ 1.647
244	*Prehnite* $Ca_2 Al[(OH)_2 AlSl_3 O_{10}]$	$2mm$ a_0 4.63 b_0 5.49 c_0 18.48	$a{:}b{:}c$ 0.842:1: 1.127 tab. (001) or col. c, (110)(010) (031)(111), tw. (100)	2.8–2.95	Colorless, white, yellowish green	n_α 1.615–1.635 n_β 1.624–1.642 n_γ 1.645–1.665 glassy
Biotite series (trioctahedral) (No. 245–248)						
245	*Phlogopite* KMg_3 $[(F,OH)_2 \vert AlSi_3 O_{10}]$ Mg→$Fe^{\cdot\cdot}$	$2/m$ a_0 5.33 b_0 9.23 c_0 20.52 β 100° 12′	Like muscovite	2.75–2.97	Reddish brown, yellowish, greenish, colorless	n_α 1.530–1.590 n_β 1.557–1.637 n_γ 1.558–1.637
246	*Biotite* $K(Mg, Fe, Mn)_3$ $[(OH,F)_2 AlSi_3 O_{10}]$	$2/m$ a_0 5.31 b_0 9.23 c_0 20.36 β 99° 18′	Like muscovite and (112) (101) (132) (221), tw. like muscovite	2.8–3.4	Dark brown and dark green	n_α 1.565–1.625 n_β 1.605–1.696 n_γ 1.605–1.696

Table 4.2–9 (*Continued*)
SILICATES

No.	Name and formula	Crystal class lattice constants	Habit, form	Sp. gr.	Color	Indices of refraction and luster	
247	*Lepidolite* $K(Li, Al)_{2.5-3}$ $[(OH), F)_2 Si_{3-3.5}$ $Al_{1-0.5} O_{10}]$	2/*m* a_0 5.21 b_0 8.97 c_0 20.16 β 100° 48′	Like muscovite, oft. scaly	2.8–2.9	Rose-red, white, grey, greenish	n_α n_β n_γ	1.525–1.548 1.551–1.585 1.554–1.587
248	*Zinnwaldite* $K(Li_{1-1.5} Fe^{\cdot\cdot}_{1-0.5} Al)$ $[(F_{1.5-1} OH_{0.5-1})Si_{3-3.5}$ $Al_{1-0.5} O_{10}]$	2/*m* a_0 5.27 b_0 9.09 c_0 20.14 β 100° 00′	Sim. to muscovite	2.9–3.1	Silvery grey, pale violet, brownish to almost black	n_α n_β n_γ	1.535–1.558 1.570–1.589 1.572–1.590
249	*Stilpnomelane* $(K, Na, Ca)_{0-0.7}$ $(Fe^{\cdot\cdot\cdot}, Fe^{\cdot\cdot}, Mg, Al,$ $Mn)_{2.95-4.1}$ $[(OH)_2 Si_4 O_{10}$ $(O, OH, H_2O)_{1.8-4.25}]$	Morocl. ps. hex. a_0 5.40 b_0 9.42 c_0 12.14[d] β 97° (?)	Platy to rad.	2.6–3.0	Black to greenish black, olive green to brown transparent	n_α n_β n_γ	1.543–1.634 1.576–1.745 1.576–1.745
Montmorillonite series (No. 250–252)							
250	*Beidellite* $\left\{ Al_{2.17}[(OH)_2 Al_{0.83}$ $Si_{3.17}]^{0.32-}Na_{0.32}$ $(H_2O)_4 \right\}$	Monocl. a_0 ~5.23 b_0 ~9.06 c_0 15.8 to 9.2	Tab. (001)		White, reddish, green	n_α n_β n_γ	~1.49 1.52–1.56
251	*Montmorillonite* $\left\{ (Al_{1.67} Mg_{9.33})[(OH)_2$ $Si_4 O_{10}]^{0.33-}Na_{0.33}$ $(H_2O)_4 \right\}$	Monocl. a_0 5.17 b_0 8.94 c_0 15.2 to 9.6 β~90°	Tab. (001)	~2.5 calc. 2.1	White, brownish, greenish	n_α n_β n_γ	~1.488 1.513 1.513

[d] $d(001)$.

Table 4.2–9 (*Continued*) SILICATES

No.	Name and formula	Crystal class lattice constants	Habit, form	Sp. gr.	Color	Indices of refraction and luster
252	*Nontronite* $\{Fe_2^{\cdots}[(OH)_2Al_{0.33}Si_{3.67}O_{10}]^{0.33-}Na_{0.33}(H_2O)_4\}$	Monocl. a_0 ~5.24 b_0 ~9.08 c_0 15.8 to 9.2 β ~90°	Tab. (001) and fib.	2.3–2.5	Olive green to yellowish green and yellowish orange	n_α 1.56–1.62 n_β 1.58–1.65 n_γ 1.58–1.66
253	*Saponite* $\{Mg_3[OH)_2Al_{0.33}Si_{3.67}O_{10}]^{0.33-}Na_{0.33}(H_2O)_4\}$	*m* $d_{(001)}$ 14.8	Fib. (also tab. ?)	~2.3	White yellowish greenish	n_α 1.48–1.53 n_β 1.50–1.58 n_γ 1.51–1.59
254	*Vermiculite* $\{Mg_{2.36}Fe^{\cdots}_{0.48}Al_{0.16}[(OH)_2Al_{1.28}Si_{2.72}O_{10}]^{0.64-}Mg_{0.32}(H_2O)_4\}$	*m* ps. hex. a_0 5.33 b_0 9.18 c_0 28.90 β 97°	Tab. (001)	2.4	Brown, bronze, yellow, green, colorless	n_α 1.525–1.564 n_β 1.545–1.583 n_γ 1.545–1.583
Chlorites (No. 255–259)						
255	*Penninite* $\{Mg, Al)_3[(OH)_2Al_{0.5-0.9}Si_{3.5-3.1}O_{10}]\ Mg_3(OH)_6\}$	2/*m*[e] a_0 5.2–5.3 b_0 9.2–9.3 c_0 28.6 β 96° 50′	Tab. (001), (101) (132)	2.6–2.84 2.84	Bluish green	n_α ~1.560 n_β 1.58–1.60 n_γ ~1.571 Oft. anom. interf. colors, lavend. to ultra blue
256	*Clinochlore* $\{(Mg,Al)_3[(OH)_2AlSi_3O_{10}]Mg_3(OH)_6\}$	2/*m*,[e] similar to penninite	Tab. (001), (112) ($\bar{1}$11) (010)	2.55–2.78	Bluish to blackish green	n_α ~1.57 n_β 1.57–1.59 n_γ ~1.596

[e] Also triclinic (1T, 2T, 3T) modifications known.

Table 4.2–9 (*Continued*)
SILICATES

No.	Name and formula	Crystal class lattice constants	Habit, form	Sp. gr.	Color	Indices of refraction and luster	
257	*Prochlorite* $(Mg, Fe, Al)_3$ $[(OH)_2 Al_{1.2-1.5}$ $Si_{2.8-2.5} O_{10}]$ $Mg_3(OH)_6$	2/*m*[e] a_0 5.36 b_0 9.28 c_0 2.84 β 97° 09′	Freq. vermic.	2.78–2.95	Leek to brownish green blackish green	n_α n_β n_γ	~1.59 1.60–1.65
258	*Chamosite* $(Fe^{\cdot\cdot}, Fe^{\cdot\cdot\cdot})_3$ $[(OH)_2 AlSi_3 O_{10}]$ $(Fe^{\cdot\cdot}, Mg)_3 (O, OH)_6$	2/*m* (?) a_0 5.40 b_0 9.36 c_0 14.03 β 90°	Massive, oolitic	3.2	Blackish green	n_β	~1.64–1.66 anom. interf. color (lavender blue)
259	*Thuringite* $(Fe^{\cdot\cdot}, Fe^{\cdot\cdot\cdot}, Al)_3 [(OH)_2$ $Al_{1.2-2} Si_{2.8-2} O_{10}]$ $Mg, Fe^{\cdot\cdot}, Fe^{\cdot\cdot\cdot})_3$ $(O, OH)_6$	2/*m* a_0 5.39 b_0 9.33 c_0 14.10 β 97° 20′	Tab. (001)	3.2	Olive to dark green	n_α n_β n_γ	1.669 1.682 1.683
260	*Kaolinite* $Al_4 [(OH)_8 \| Si_4 O_{10}]$	T a_0 5.14 b_0 8.93 c_0 7.37 α 91° 48′ β 104° 30′ γ 90°	Tab. (001), (110) (010) ps. hex.	2.6	White yellowish, greenish, bluish	n_α n_β n_γ	1.553–1.563 1.559–1.569 1.560–1.570
261	*Antigorite* (Platy serpentine) $Mg_6 [(OH)_8 \| Si_4 O_{10}]$	2/*m* a_0 43.3 b_0 9.23 c_0 7.27 β 91° 36′	Tab. (001)	2.5–2.6	Light to dark green, yellow to reddish brown, greenish to black	n_α n_β n_γ	1.560 1.570 1.571

[e] Also triclinic (1T, 2T, 3T) modifications known.

Table 4.2–9 (*Continued*)
SILICATES

No.	Name and formula	Crystal class lattice constants	Habit, form	Sp. gr.	Color	Indices of refraction and luster	
262	*Chrysotile* (Fibrous serpentine, Serpentine asbestos) $Mg_6[(OH)_8|Si_4O_{10}]$	$2/m$ a_0 5.34 b_0 9.25 c_0 14.65 β 93° 16′	Fib. a_0 (fib. b_0 = parachrysotile)	2.36–2.50	Oil green to gold	n_α n_β n_γ	1.53–1.549 ~1.54 1.545–1.556
263	*Amesite* $Mg_{3.2}Al_{2.0}Fe^{\cdot\cdot}_{0.8}$ $[(OH)_8|Al_2Si_2O_{10}]$	$6mm$ a_0 5.31 c_0 14.04	Tab. (001)	2.8	Pale bluish green	n_α n_β n_γ	~1.58–1.61 ~1.612
264	*Cronstedtite* $Fe_2^{\cdot\cdot\cdot}Fe_4^{\cdot\cdot}$ $[(OH)_8|Si_2Fe_2^{\cdot\cdot\cdot}O_{10}]$	m a_0 5.49 b_0 9.51 c_0 7.32 β 104° 31′	Elong. to fib. c, also tab. (001), (*hkl*) ps. hex.	3.45	Deep black to deep green	n_β	1.80 glassy
265	*Halloysite* (Endellite) $\left\{\begin{matrix} Al_4[(OH)_8Si_4O_{10}] \\ (H_2O)_4 \end{matrix}\right\}$	m a_0 5.15 b_0 8.9 c_0 10.1 to 9.5 β 100° 12′	Tab. (001)	2.0–2.2 calc. 2.12	White bluish, greenish grey	n	1.490 theoret., usu. to ~1.55 as result of impurities
266	*Metahalloysite* $Al_4[(OH)_8|Si_4O_{10}]$	m a_0 5.15 b_0 8.9 c_0 7.9 to 7.5 β 100° 12′	Tab. (001)	calc. 2.61	White, brownish	n	~1.55
267	*Palygorskite* (Attapulgite $(Mg, Al)_2[OH|Si_4O_{10}]$ $2H_2O+2H_2O$	$2/m$ or orhomb. a_0 5.2 b_0 2·9.0	Fibrous		White grey, yellowish	n_α n_β n_γ	1.511 ~n_γ 1.532–1.540

Table 4.2–9 (*Continued*)
SILICATES

No.	Name and formula	Crystal class lattice constants	Habit, form	Sp. gr.	Color	Indices of refraction and luster	
		c_0 13.4 β 90°–93°					
Tectosilicates (Framework silicates)							
268	*Nepheline* (Na, K)[$AlSiO_4$] Na:K usually ~3:1	6 a_0 10.01 c_0 8.41	Short col. *c*, $(10\bar{1}0)$ (0001) rarely $(10\bar{1}1)$ $(11\bar{2}1)$ $(11\bar{2}0)$	2.6–2.65 pure 2.619	Colorless, white, grey, and other colors	n_ω n_ϵ n_ω n_ϵ	1.536–1.549 1.532–1.544 pure 1.537 1.533 glassy to greasy
269	*Analcime* Na[$AlSi_2O_6$]·H_2O	*m*3*m* a_0 13.71	(211) (100), tw. (001)	2.2–2.3	White, grey, yellowish, flesh colored	n	1.479–1.489 glassy
270	*Leucite*, low- K[$AlSi_2O_6$] <605°C	4/*m* ps. cub. a_0 13.04 c_0 13.85	(211) rare (110), tw. lam. (110) (cub. indic.)	2.5	White to grey	n_α n_β n_γ	1.508 ? 1.509 glassy
Feldspars (No. 271–280) **Alkali Feldspars (No. 271–275)**							
271	*Sanidine* (High-temp. modif.) K[$AlSi_3O_8$] K→Na	2/*m* a_0 8.564 b_0 13.030 c_0 7.175 β 115° 59.6′	Tab. (010); (001) (110) $(\bar{1}01)$, tw. (100)	2.57–2.58	Colorless, yellowish, grey	n_α n_β n_γ	1.5203 1.5248 1.5250

Table 4.2–9 (*Continued*)
SILICATES

No.	Name and formula	Crystal class lattice constants	Habit, form	Sp. gr.	Color	Indices of refraction and luster
272	*Anorthoclase* (K, Na)[$AlSi_3O_8$] solid soln. of Or 70 Ab 30 to Or 20 Ab 80[f]	tricl.[g]	Col. *c*, (110) (201), tw. lattice pattern after albite and pericline laws	2.56–2.62	Colorless, grey	n_α 1.5234 n_β 1.5294 n_γ 1.5305
273	*Orthoclase* (Intermed. state) K[$AlSi_3O_8$] K→Na	$2/m$ a_0 8.5616 b_0 12.996 c_0 7.193 β 116° 0.9′ *et al.*	Broad tab. (010) or col. *a*; (010) (001) (110) (130) ($20\bar{1}$) ($10\bar{1}$)	2.53–2.56	White, yellowish, reddish to red, greenish to green	n_α 1.5168 n_β 1.5202 n_γ 1.5227
274	*Microcline* (Low temp. modif.) K[$AlSi_3O_8$] K→Na	$\bar{1}$ a_0 8.574 b_0 12.981 c_0 7.222 α 90° 41′ β 115° 59′ γ 87° 30′	Like orthoclase, tw. lattice pattern after albite and pericline laws	2.54–2.57	Like orthoclase	n_α 1.5186 n_β 1.5223 n_γ 1.5250
Plagioclases (No. 275–280)[h]						
275	*Albite* (Ab) Na[$AlSi_3O_8$] 0–10 mol. % An ↓	$\bar{1}$ a_0 8.144 b_0 12.787 c_0 7.160 α 94.26° β 116.58° γ 86.67°	Tab. (010) lath shaped *c* col. *b*, (010) (001) (110) ($1\bar{1}0$) (100) ($10\bar{1}$) ($20\bar{1}$) ($0\bar{2}1$) (021)	2.605 ↓	Colorless, white, grey greenish	n_α 1.5286 n_β 1.5326 n_γ 1.5388 ↓

[f] Usually with higher An-content as orthoclase, but rarely more than 20-25 mol % An.
[g] Structurally undefined phase (paramorph after high temp. mod.).
[h] All values for lattice constants and opt. properties apply to low temperature modification.

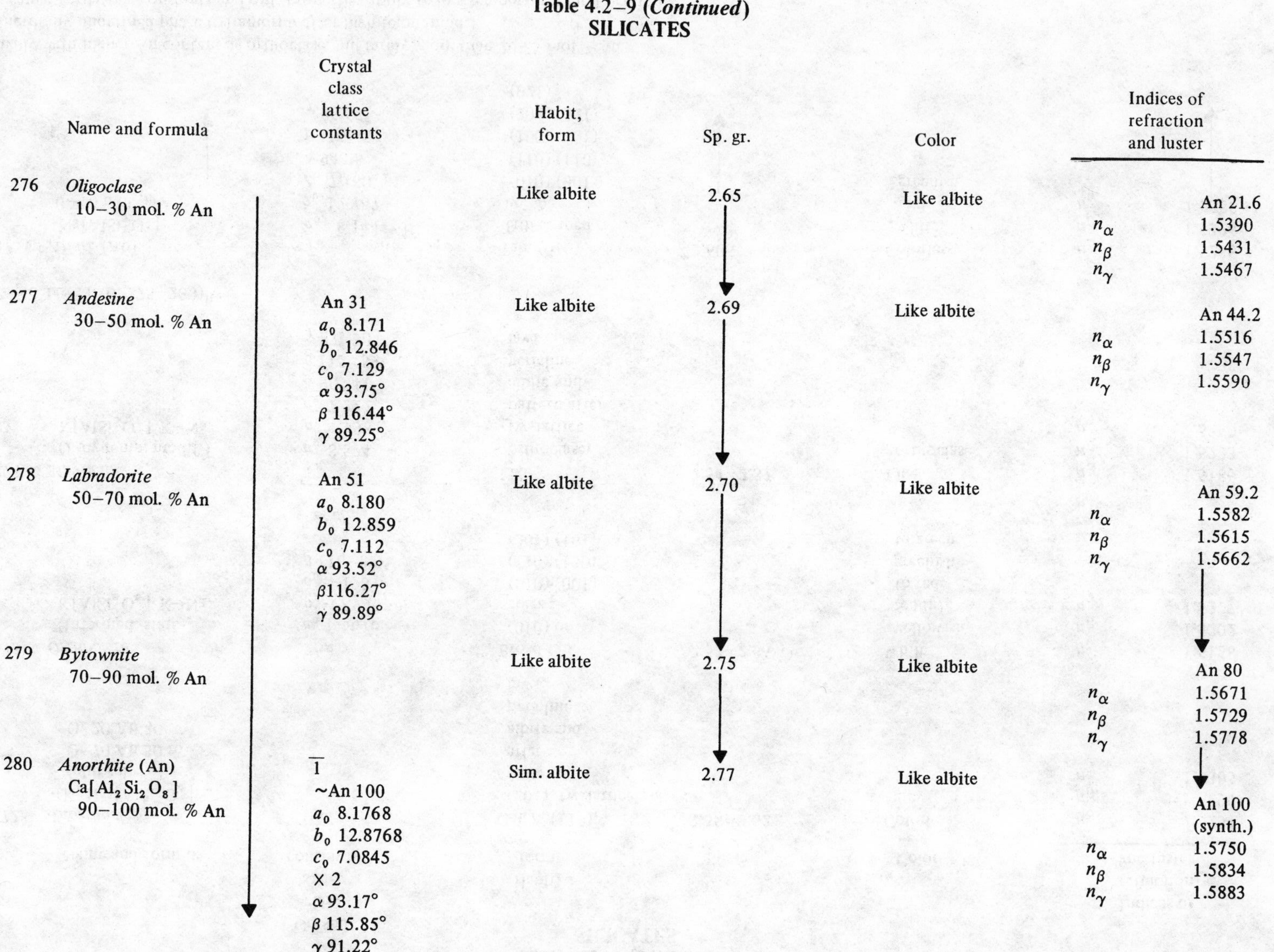

Table 4.2–9 (*Continued*)
SILICATES

No.	Name and formula	Crystal class lattice constants	Habit, form	Sp. gr.	Color	Indices of refraction and luster
276	*Oligoclase* 10–30 mol. % An		Like albite	2.65	Like albite	An 21.6 n_α 1.5390 n_β 1.5431 n_γ 1.5467
277	*Andesine* 30–50 mol. % An	An 31 a_0 8.171 b_0 12.846 c_0 7.129 α 93.75° β 116.44° γ 89.25°	Like albite	2.69	Like albite	An 44.2 n_α 1.5516 n_β 1.5547 n_γ 1.5590
278	*Labradorite* 50–70 mol. % An	An 51 a_0 8.180 b_0 12.859 c_0 7.112 α 93.52° β116.27° γ 89.89°	Like albite	2.70	Like albite	An 59.2 n_α 1.5582 n_β 1.5615 n_γ 1.5662
279	*Bytownite* 70–90 mol. % An		Like albite	2.75	Like albite	An 80 n_α 1.5671 n_β 1.5729 n_γ 1.5778
280	*Anorthite* (An) $Ca[Al_2Si_2O_8]$ 90–100 mol. % An	$\overline{1}$ ~An 100 a_0 8.1768 b_0 12.8768 c_0 7.0845 × 2 α 93.17° β 115.85° γ 91.22°	Sim. albite	2.77	Like albite	An 100 (synth.) n_α 1.5750 n_β 1.5834 n_γ 1.5883

Table 4.2–9 (*Continued*)
SILICATES

No.	Name and formula	Crystal class lattice constants	Habit, form	Sp. gr.	Color	Indices of refraction and luster	
281	*Cancrinite* $(Na_2, Ca)_4$ $[CO_3 \| (H_2O)_{0-3} \|$ $(AlSiO_4)_6]$ $CO_3 \rightarrow SO_4$	6 a_0 12.63–12.78 c_0 5.11–5.19	Col.-acic.*c*, (1010) (0001) $(10\bar{1}1)$, tw. lam. rare	2.4–2.5	Colorless, yellowish, pink, light blue	n_ω n_ϵ	1.515–1.524 1.491–1.502
Sodalite group (No. 282–285)							
282	*Sodalite* $Na_8[Cl_2 \| (AlSiO_4)_6]$ ↓	$\bar{4}3m$ a_0 8.83–8.91	(110), less frequent (100) (211) (210) (111), tw. (111)	2.3 ↓	Colorless, white, grey, blue, rarely green, red	n	~1.483–1.487
283	*Nosean* $Na_8[SO_4 \| (AlSiO_4)_6]$	$\bar{4}3m$ a_0 8.98–9.15	Like sodalite	2.3–2.4 ↓	Like sodalite	n	~1.495
284	*Hauynite* $(Na, Ca)_{8-4}$ $[(SO_4)_{2-1} \| (AlSiO_4)_6]$	$\bar{4}3m$ a_0 9.12	Like sodalite	2.5	Like sodalite	n	~1.502
285	*Lazurite* (Lapis lazuli) $(Na, Ca)_8$ $[(SO_4, S, Cl)_2 \| (AlSiO_4)_6]$	$\bar{4}3m$ a_0 9.08	Crystals rare, (110)	2.38–2.45	Dark blue also greenish	n	~1.50
Scapolites (No. 286–289)							
286	*Marialite* (Ma) 0–20% Me $Na_8[(Cl_2, SO_4, CO_3)$ $(AlSi_3O_8)_6]$ ↓	$4/m$ a_0 12.075 c_0 7.516 ↓	$a = a_0\sqrt{2}$ c/a 0.4425, col. *c*, (110) (100) (111) (101), rarely (311) (210)	2.50 ↓	Colorless, white, grey greenish, also red and blue	n_ω n_ϵ ↓	1.539 1.537

Table 4.2–9 (*Continued*)
SILICATES

No.	Name and formula	Crystal class lattice constants	Habit, form	Sp. gr.	Color	Indices of refraction and luster	
287	*Dipyre* 20–50% Me	↓	Like Ma	↓	Like Ma	↓	
288	*Mizzonite* 50–80% Me	↓	Like Ma	↓	Like Ma	↓	
289	*Meionite* (Me) 80–100% Me $Ca_8[(Cl_2, SO_4, CO_3)_2$ (?) $(Al_2Si_2O_8)_6]$	$4/m$ a_0 12.13 c_0 7.69	Like Ma c/a 0.4393	2.78	Like Ma	n_ω n_ϵ	1.596 1.557 glassy
Zeolites (No. 290–299)							
290	*Natrolite* $Na_2[Al_2Si_3O_{10}]\cdot 2H_2O$	$2\,m\,m$ a_0 18.35 b_0 18.70 c_0 6.61	Acic. c, ps. tetr., (110) (111)	2.2–2.4	Colorless, white, grey, yellowish, reddish	n_α n_β n_γ	1.480 1.482 1.493
291	*Mesolite* $Na_2Ca_2[Al_2Si_3O_{10}]_3\cdot$ $8H_2O$	2 a_0 3·18.9 b_0 6.55 c_0 18.48 β 90° 00′	Acic.–fib. b, ps. orhomb.	2.2–2.4	Like natrolite	n_α n_β n_γ	~1.504 ~1.505 ~1.505
292	*Thomsonite* $NaCa_2[Al_2(Al, Si)$ $Si_2O_{10}]_2\cdot 5H_2O$	$m\,m\,m$ ps. tetr. a_0 13.07 b_0 13.09 c_0 13.25	Col.–fib. c, (110) (011), tw. (110)	2.3–2.4	White, grey, yellow, red	n_α n_β n_γ	1.511–1.530 1.513–1.532 1.518–1.545 glassy
293	*Scolecite* $Ca[Al_2Si_3O_{10}]\cdot 3H_2O$	m (?) a_0 18.48 b_0 18.94 c_0 6.54 β 90° 45′	Ps. orhomb., tw. (100)	2.2–2.4	Like natrolite	n_α n_β n_γ	1.507–1.513 1.516–1.520 1.517–1.521

Table 4.2–9 (*Continued*)
SILICATES

No.	Name and formula	Crystal class lattice constants	Habit, form	Sp. gr.	Color	Indices of refraction and luster
294	*Laumontite* $Ca[AlSi_2O_6]_2 \cdot 4\ H_2O$	2 or *m* a_0 14.90 b_0 13.17 c_0 7.55 β 111° 30′	Col. *c*, (110) tw. (100)	2.25–2.35	White, colorless, yellowish, reddish	n_α 1.505–1.513 n_β 1.515–1.524 n_γ 1.517–1.525
295	*Heulandite* $Ca[Al_2Si_7O_{18}] \cdot 6\ H_2O$	2/*m* a_0 17.71 b_0 17.84 c_0 7.46 β 116° 20′	Tab. (010), elong. *c*; tw. lam. (001)	2.2	Colorless, white, grey, brownish, brick red	n_α 1.498–1.496 n_β 1.499–1.497 n_γ 1.505–1.501 glassy on (010) pearly
296	*Stilbite* $Ca[Al_2Si_7O_{18}] \cdot 7\ H_2O$	2/*m* a_0 13.63 b_0 18.17 c_0 11.31 β 129° 10′	Tab. (010) elong. *a*; (110) (010) (001), almost always cruciform tw. (001)	2.1–2.2	Colorless, white, grey, brownish, rarely red	n_α 1.494–1.500 n_β 1.498–1.504 n_γ 1.500–1.508 glassy
297	*Phillipsite* $KCa[Al_3Si_5O_{16}] \cdot 6\ H_2O$	2/*m* a_0 10.02 b_0 14.28 c_0 8.64 β 125° 40′	Tab. (101) elong. *a* or acic. *c*, (110) (010) (001) almost always tw. (001) and (021), partly ps. cub.	2.2	Colorless, white, yellowish, grey	n_α ~1.48–(?) n_β =1.48–1.57 n_γ ~1.503–(?)

Table 4.2–9 (*Continued*)
SILICATES

No.	Name and formula	Crystal glass lattice constants	Habit, form	Sp. gr.	Color	Indices of refraction and luster	
298	*Harmotome* $Ba[Al_2Si_6O_{16}]\cdot 6H_2O$	$2/m$ a_0 9.82 b_0 14.13 c_0 8.68 β 124° 50′	Cruciform tw. (001) and (021)	2.44–2.5	White and light colors	n_α n_β n_γ	1.503 1.505 1.508
299	*Chabasite* (Ca, Na_2) $[Al_2Si_4O_{12}]\cdot 6H_2O$	$3m$ a_0 13.78 c_0 14.97	Isom. ps. cub., $(10\bar{1}1)$ $(01\bar{1}2)$ $(02\bar{2}1)$, tw. (0001)	2.1	Colorless, white, reddish brown	n_ω n_ϵ	~1.48

Table 4.2–10
ORGANIC COMPOUNDS

No.	Name and formula	Crystal class lattice constants	Habit, form	Sp. gr.	Color	Indices of refraction and luster	
300	Whewellite $Ca[C_2O_4]\cdot H_2O$	$2/m$ a_0 6.29 b_0 14.59 c_0 9.97_5 β 107° 18′	Short col. *c*, tw. (101)	2.23	Colorless to translucent	n_α n_β n_γ	1.491 1.555 1.650 pearly, glassy

Table 4.3–1
AVERAGE CHEMICAL ANALYSES OF CERTAIN TYPES OF PLUTONIC IGNEOUS ROCKS

	Granite	Syenite	Granodiorite	Quartz diorite	Diorite	Gabbro	Olivine diabase	Diabase	Dunite	Lherzolite (peridotite)	Plateau basalt
Number of analyses averaged	546	50	40	55	70	41	12	90	10	13	43
SiO_2	70.18	60.19	65.01	61.59	56.77	48.24	48.54	50.48	40.49	43.95	48.80
TiO_2	0.39	0.67	0.57	0.66	0.84	0.97	1.31	1.45	0.02	0.10	2.19
Al_2O_3	14.47	16.28	15.94	16.21	16.67	17.88	15.24	15.34	0.86	4.82	13.98
Fe_2O_3	1.57	2.74	1.74	2.54	3.16	3.16	3.06	3.84	2.84	2.20	3.59
FeO	1.78	3.28	2.65	3.77	4.40	5.95	8.88	7.78	5.54	6.34	9.78
MnO	0.12	0.14	0.07	0.10	0.13	0.13	0.21	0.20	0.16	0.19	0.17
MgO	0.88	2.49	1.91	2.80	4.17	7.51	8.08	5.79	46.32	36.81	6.70
CaO	1.99	4.30	4.42	5.38	6.74	10.99	9.38	8.94	0.70	3.57	9.38
Na_2O	3.48	3.98	3.70	3.37	3.39	2.55	2.69	3.07	0.10	0.63	2.59
K_2O	4.11	4.49	2.75	2.10	2.12	0.89	0.98	0.97	0.04	0.21	0.69
H_2O[a]	0.84	1.16	1.04	1.22	1.36	1.45	1.35	1.89	2.88	1.08	1.80
P_2O_5	0.19	0.28	0.20	0.26	0.25	0.28	0.28	0.25	0.05	0.10	0.33

Note: Totals reduced to 100.00.

[a] Since most of the analysts neglected the effect of the adsorption of water by their specimens when pulverized, the proportion given for this oxide is in general somewhat too high. On the whole, about three fourths of the total water indicated was driven off at temperatures no higher than 105°C.

(Compiled by R. A. Daly in Clark, S. P., Jr., *Handbook of Physical Constants,* Geological Society of America, Memoir 97, 1966. With permission.)

Figure 4.3–1
GENERALIZED MINERALOGICAL CONSTITUTIONS OF IGNEOUS ROCKS

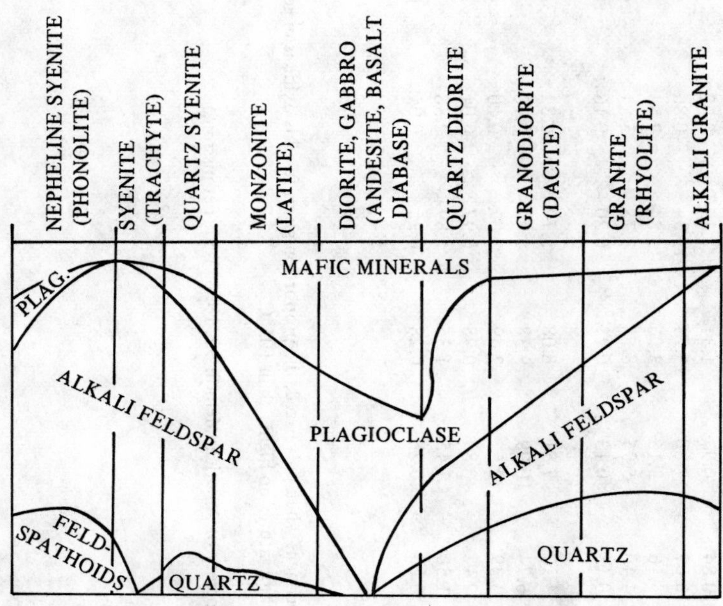

(From Clark, S. P., Jr., *Handbook of Physical Constants,* Geological Society of America, Memoir 97, 1966. With permission.)

REFERENCE

Tyrrell, G. W., *The Principles of Petrology,* 2nd ed., Dutton, New York, 1929.

TABLE 4.3–2
COMPILATIONS OF ABUNDANCES

Atomic no.	Element	Suess–Urey[5]	Cameron[6]	Clayton–Fowler[7]	Chondrites[8]	Sun[9]	B stars[9]
1	H	4.00×10^{10}	3.2×10^{10}	–	–	3.2×10^{10}	3.6×10^{10}
2	He	3.08×10^{9}	2.6×10^{9}	–	–	–	5.7×10^{9}
3	Li	100	38	–	38	0.29	–
4	Be	20	7	–	0.64(1)	7.2	–
5	B	24	6	–	–	–	–
6	C	3.5×10^{6}	1.66×10^{7}	–	–	1.66×10^{7}	7.1×10^{6}
7	N	6.6×10^{6}	3.0×10^{6}	–	–	3.0×10^{6}	5.4×10^{6}
8	O	2.15×10^{7}	2.9×10^{7}	–	–	2.9×10^{7}	2.1×10^{7}
9	F	1,600	$\sim 10^{3}$	–	–	–	1.2×10^{5}
10	Ne	8.6×10^{6}	2.9×10^{6}	–	–	–	1.9×10^{7}
11	Na	4.38×10^{4}	4.18×10^{4}	–	–	6.3×10^{4}	–
12	Mg	9.12×10^{5}	1.046×10^{6}	–	–	7.9×10^{5}	3.1×10^{6}
13	Al	9.48×10^{4}	8.93×10^{4}	–	–	5.0×10^{4}	5.8×10^{4}
14	Si	1.00×10^{6}	1.00×10^{6}	–	–	1.00×10^{6}	1.00×10^{6}
15	P	1.00×10^{4}	9,320	–	–	6,900	1.08×10^{4}
16	S	3.75×10^{5}	6.0×10^{5}	–	–	6.3×10^{5}	1.08×10^{6}
17	Cl	8,850	1,836	–	–	–	5.8×10^{4}
18	Ar	1.5×10^{5}	2.4×10^{5}	–	–	–	2.9×10^{5}
19	K	3,160	2,970	–	3,290	1,580	–
20	Ca	4.90×10^{4}	7.28×10^{4}	–	4.5×10^{4}	4.5×10^{4}	–
21	Sc	28	29	–	32	21	–
22	Ti	2,440	3,140	–	2,090	1,510	–
23	V	220	590	–	–	158	–
24	Cr	7,800	1.20×10^{4}	–	6,400	5,000	–
25	Mn	6,850	6,320	–	7,200	2,500	–
26	Fe	6.00×10^{5}	8.50×10^{4}	–	–	1.17×10^{5}	–
27	Co	1,800	750	–	1,190	1,380	–
28	Ni	2.74×10^{4}	1.5×10^{4}	–	2.48×10^{4}	2.6×10^{4}	–
29	Cu	212	39	316	186	3,500	–
30	Zn	486	202	360	–	800	–

Table 4.3–2 (*Continued*)

Atomic no.	Element	Suess–Urey[5]	Cameron[6]	Clayton–Fowler[7]	Chondrites[8]	Sun[9]	B stars[9]
31	Ga	11.4	9.05	32	–	7.2	–
32	Ge	50.5	134	49.1	18.7	62	–
33	As	4.0	4.4	2.18	–	–	–
34	Se	67.6	18.8	30.9	18.8	–	–
35	Br	13.4 ,	3.95	6.9	–	–	–
36	Kr	51.3	20	17.9	–	–	–
37	Rb	6.5	5.0	4.24	4.6–5.8	9.5	–
38	Sr	18.9	21	17.55	–	13.5	–
39	Y	8.9	3.6	11.35	–	5.6	–
40	Zr	54.5	23	39.8	–	54	–
41	Nb	1.00	0.81	3.5	–	2.8	–
42	Mo	2.42	2.42	2.77	–	2.5	–
44	Ru	1.49	1.58	0.83	1.3(2)	0.93	–
45	Rh	0.214	0.26	0.13	0.27	0.19	–
46	Pd	0.675	1.00	0.601	–	0.51	–
47	Ag	0.26	0.26	0.166	0.131	0.044	–
48	Cd	0.89	0.89	0.804	–	0.91	–
49	In	0.11	0.11	0.071	0.0013	0.46	–
50	Sn	1.33	1.33	1.88	–	1.10	–
51	Sb	0.246	0.15	0.091	–	2.8	–
52	Te	4.67	3.00	1.86	0.5–2(3)	–	–
53	I	0.80	0.46	0.21	0.02–0.3(3)	–	–
54	Xe	4.0	3.15	2.61	–	–	–
55	Cs	0.456	0.25	0.13	0.10–0.14	–	–
56	Ba	3.66	4.0	3.68	3.96–6.44	4.0	–
57	La	2.00	0.38	0.70	0.40	–	–
58	Ce	2.26	1.08	1.17	0.62	–	–
59	Pr	0.40	0.16	0.176	0.15	–	–
60	Nd	1.44	0.69	0.777	0.74	–	–
62	Sm	0.664	0.24	0.595	0.25	–	–
63	Eu	0.187	0.083	0.149	0.078–0.097	–	–
64	Gd	0.684	0.33	0.410	0.36	–	–
65	Tb	0.0956	0.054	0.083	0.056	–	–
66	Dy	0.556	0.33	0.449	0.39	–	–

Table 4.3–2 (*Continued*)

Atomic no.	Element	Suess–Urey[5]	Cameron[6]	Clayton–Fowler[7]	Chondrites[8]	Sun[9]	B stars[9]
67	Ho	0.118	0.076	0.084	0.078	–	–
68	Er	0.316	0.21	0.359	0.21	–	–
69	Tm	0.0318	0.032	0.060	0.039	–	–
70	Yb	0.220	0.18	0.387	0.19	1.07	–
71	Lu	0.050	0.031	0.035	0.036	–	–
72	Hf	0.438	0.16	0.236	–	–	–
73	Ta	0.065	0.021	0.030	0.017–0.019	–	–
74	W	0.49	0.11	0.184	0.11	–	–
75	Re	0.135	0.054	0.052	–	–	–
76	Os	1.00	0.73	0.511	0.73(2)	–	–
77	Ir	0.821	0.500	0.39	0.38	–	–
78	Pt	1.625	1.157	0.80	–	–	–
79	Au	0.145	0.13	0.13	0.13	–	–
80	Hg	0.284	0.27	0.62	0.04–8.4	–	–
81	Tl	0.108	0.11	0.74	$(3.8–10) \times 10^{-4}$	–	–
82	Pb	0.47	2.2	6.5	0.05–0.28	2.5(4)	–
83	Bi	0.144	0.14	0.92	0.0016	–	–
90	Th	–	0.069	–	0.026	–	–
92	U	–	0.042	–	$(7.2–7.9) \times 10^{-3}$	–	–

(From Clark, S. P., Jr., *Handbook of Physical Constants,* Geological Society of America, Memoir 97, 1966. With permission.)

REFERENCES

1. **Sill, C. W. and Willis, C. P.,** *Geochim. Cosmochim. Acta,* 26, 1209, 1962.
2. **Bate, G. L. and Huizenga, J. R.,** *Geochim. Cosmochim. Acta,* 27, 345, 1963.
3. **Goles, G. C. and Anders, E.,** *J. Geophys. Res.,* 66, 3075, 1961.
4. **Helliwell, T. M.,** *Astrophys. J.,* 133, 566, 1961.
5. **Suess, H. E. and Urey, H. C.,** *Rev. Modern Phys.,* 28, 53, 1956.
6. **Cameron, A. G. W.,** *Astrophys. J.,* 129, 676, 1959; unpublished notes, 1963.
7. **Clayton, D. D. et al.,** *Ann. Phys. (NY),* 12, 331, 1961.
8. **Ehmann, W. D.,** *J. Chem. Educ.,* 38, 53, 1961.
9. **Aller, L. H.,** *The Abundance of the Elements,* Interscience, New York, 1961.

Table 4.3–3
ISOTOPIC ABUNDANCES AND ATOMIC WEIGHTS

Atomic no.	Symbol	Mass no.	Abundance, %	1961 atomic wt
1	H	1	99.99	1.00797
		2	0.01	
2	He	3	$10^{-4}-10^{-5}$	4.0026
		4	100	
3	Li	6	7.4	6.939
		7	92.6	
4	Be	9	100	9.0133
5	B	10	~19	10.811
		11	~81	
6	C	12	98.9	12.01115
		13	1.1	
7	N	14	99.6	14.0067
		15	0.4	
8	O	16	99.8	15.9994
		17	0.04	
		18	0.2	
9	F	19	100	18.9984
10	Ne	20	90.9	20.183
		21	0.3	
		22	8.8	
11	Na	23	100	22.9898
12	Mg	24	78.8	24.312
		25	10.2	
		26	11.1	
13	Al	27	100	26.9815
14	Si	28	92.2	28.086
		29	4.7	
		30	3.1	
15	P	31	100	30.9738
16	S	32	95.0	32.064
		33	0.8	
		34	4.2	
		36	0.02	
17	Cl	35	75.5	35.453
		37	24.5	
18	A	36	0.3	39.948
		38	0.06	
		40	99.6	
19	K	39	93.1	39.102
		40	0.01	
		41	6.9	
20	Ca	40	97.0	40.08
		42	0.6	
		43	0.1	
		44	2.1	
		46	0.003	
		48	0.2	
21	Sc	45	100	44.956
22	Ti	46	8.0	47.90
		47	7.7	
		48	73.5	
		49	5.5	
		50	5.3	
23	V	50	0.2	50.942
		51	99.8	

Table 4.3–3 (*Continued*)
ISOTOPIC ABUNDANCES AND ATOMIC WEIGHTS

Atomic no.	Symbol	Mass no.	Abundance, %	1961 atomic wt.
24	Cr	50	4.3	51.996
		52	83.8	
		53	9.6	
		54	2.4	
25	Mn	55	100	54.9381
26	Fe	54	5.8	55.847
		56	91.7	
		57	2.2	
		58	0.3	
27	Co	59	100	58.9332
28	Ni	58	67.8	58.71
		60	26.2	
		61	1.2	
		62	3.7	
		64	1.2	
29	Cu	63	69.1	63.54
		65	30.9	
30	Zn	64	48.9	65.37
		66	27.8	
		67	4.1	
		68	18.6	
		70	0.6	
31	Ga	69	60.5	69.72
		71	39.5	
32	Ge	70	20.6	72.59
		72	27.4	
		73	7.7	
		74	36.7	
		76	7.7	
33	As	75	100	74.9216
34	Se	74	0.9	78.96
		76	9.0	
		77	7.6	
		78	23.5	
		80	49.8	
		82	9.2	
35	Br	79	50.6	79.909
		81	49.4	
36	Kr	78	0.4	83.80
		80	2.3	
		82	11.6	
		83	11.5	
		84	56.9	
		86	17.4	
37	Rb	85	72.2	85.47
		87	27.8	
38	Sr	84	0.5	87.62
		86	9.9	
		87	7.0	
		88	82.6	
39	Y	89	100	88.905
40	Zr	90	51.5	91.22
		91	11.2	
		92	17.1	
		94	17.4	
		96	2.8	
41	Nb	93	100	92.906

Table 4.3–3 (*Continued*)
ISOTOPIC ABUNDANCES AND ATOMIC WEIGHTS

Atomic no.	Symbol	Mass no.	Abundance, %	1961 atomic wt
42	Mo	92	15.9	95.94
		94	9.1	
		95	15.7	
		96	16.5	
		97	9.5	
		98	23.7	
		100	9.6	
44	Ru	96	5.6	101.07
		98	1.9	
		99	12.8	
		100	12.7	
		101	17.0	
		102	31.5	
		104	18.5	
45	Rh	103	100	102.905
46	Pd	102	1.0	106.4
		104	11.0	
		105	22.2	
		106	27.3	
		108	26.7	
		110	11.8	
47	Ag	107	51.4	107.870
		109	48.6	
48	Cd	106	1.2	112.40
		108	0.9	
		110	12.4	
		111	12.7	
		112	24.1	
		113	12.3	
		114	28.9	
		116	7.6	
49	In	113	4.3	114.82
		115	95.7	
50	Sn	112	1.0	118.69
		114	0.6	
		115	0.3	
		116	14.2	
		117	7.6	
		118	24.0	
		119	8.6	
		120	33.0	
		122	4.7	
		124	6.0	
51	Sb	121	57.3	121.75
		123	42.7	
52	Te	120	0.1	127.60
		122	2.5	
		123	0.9	
		124	4.6	
		125	7.0	
		126	18.7	
		128	31.8	
		130	34.5	
53	I	127	100	126.9044

Table 4.3–3 (*Continued*)
ISOTOPIC ABUNDANCES AND ATOMIC WEIGHTS

Atomic no.	Symbol	Mass no.	Abundance, %	1961 atomic wt
54	Xe	124	0.1	131.30
		126	0.1	
		128	1.9	
		129	26.4	
		130	4.1	
		131	21.2	
		132	26.9	
		134	10.4	
		136	8.9	
55	Cs	133	100	132.905
56	Ba	130	0.1	137.34
		132	0.2	
		134	2.6	
		135	6.7	
		136	8.1	
		137	11.9	
		138	70.4	
57	La	138	0.1	138.91
		139	99.9	
58	Ce	136	0.2	140.12
		138	0.2	
		140	88.5	
		142	11.1	
59	Pr	141	100	140.907
60	Nd	142	27.2	144.24
		143	12.2	
		144	23.8	
		145	8.3	
		146	17.2	
		148	5.7	
		150	5.6	
62	Sm	144	3.1	150.35
		147	15.1	
		148	11.3	
		149	13.8	
		150	7.5	
		152	26.6	
		154	22.5	
63	En	151	47.8	151.96
		153	52.2	
64	Gd	152	0.2	157.25
		154	2.2	
		155	15.1	
		156	20.6	
		157	15.7	
		158	24.5	
		160	21.6	
65	Tb	159	100	158.924
66	Dy	156	0.1	162.50
		158	0.1	
		160	2.3	
		161	19.0	
		162	25.5	
		163	24.9	
		164	28.1	
67	Ho	165	100	164.930

Table 4.3–3 (*Continued*)
ISOTOPIC ABUNDANCES AND ATOMIC WEIGHTS

Atomic no.	Symbol	Mass no.	Abundance, %	1961 atomic wt
68	Er	162	0.1	167.26
		164	1.6	
		166	33.4	
		167	22.9	
		168	27.1	
		170	14.9	
69	Tm	169	100	168.934
70	Yb	169	0.1	173.04
		170	3.1	
		171	14.4	
		172	21.9	
		173	16.2	
		174	31.6	
		176	12.6	
71	Lu	175	97.4	174.97
		176	2.6	
72	Hf	174	0.2	178.49
		176	5.2	
		177	18.5	
		178	27.1	
		179	13.8	
		180	35.2	
73	Ta	180	0.01	180.948
		181	100	
74	W	180	0.1	183.85
		182	26.4	
		183	14.4	
		184	30.6	
		186	28.4	
75	Re	185	37.1	186.2
		187	62.9	
76	Os	184	0.02	190.2
		186	1.6	
		187	1.6	
		188	13.3	
		189	16.1	
		190	26.4	
		192	41.0	
77	Ir	191	38.5	192.2
		193	61.5	
78	Pt	190	0.01	195.09
		192	0.8	
		194	32.9	
		195	33.8	
		196	25.2	
		198	7.2	
79	Au	197	100	196.967
80	Hg	196	0.1	200.59
		198	10.0	
		199	16.8	
		200	23.1	
		201	13.2	
		202	29.8	
		204	6.9	
81	Ti	203	29.5	204.37
		205	70.5	

Table 4.3–3 (*Continued*)
ISOTOPIC ABUNDANCES AND ATOMIC WEIGHTS

Atomic no.	Symbol	Mass no.	Abundance, %	1961 atomic wt
82	Pb	204	1.4	207.19
		206	25.2	
		207	21.5	
		208	52.0	
83	Bi	209	100	208.980
90	Th	232	100	232.038
92	U	234	~0.006	238.03
		235	0.72	
		238	99.28	

(From Clark, S. P., Jr., *Handbook of Physical Constants,* Geological Society of America, Memoir 97, 1966. With permission.)

Table 4.3–4
AVERAGES OF GRANITIC ROCKS

	Alkali granites (48)	Alkali rhyolites (21)	Granites (72)	Rhyolites (22)	Quartz monzonites (121)	Quartz latites (58)	Grano-diorites (137)	Rhyodacites (115)	Quartz diorites (58)	Dacites (50)
SiO_2	73.86	74.57	72.08	73.66	69.15	70.15	66.88	66.27	66.15	63.58
TiO_2	0.20	0.17	0.37	0.22	0.56	0.42	0.57	0.66	0.62	0.64
Al_2O_3	13.75	12.58	13.86	13.45	14.63	14.41	15.66	15.39	15.56	16.67
Fe_2O_3	0.78	1.30	0.86	1.25	1.22	1.68	1.33	2.14	1.36	2.24
FeO	1.13	1.02	1.67	0.75	2.27	1.55	2.59	2.23	3.42	3.00
MnO	0.05	0.05	0.06	0.03	0.06	0.06	0.07	0.07	0.08	0.11
MgO	0.26	0.11	0.52	0.32	0.99	0.63	1.57	1.57	1.94	2.12
CaO	0.72	0.61	1.33	1.13	2.45	2.15	3.56	3.68	4.65	5.53
Na_2O	3.51[a]	4.13	3.08	2.99	3.35	3.65	3.84	4.13	3.90	3.98
K_2O	5.13[a]	4.73	5.46	5.35	4.58	4.50	3.07	3.01	1.42	1.40
H_2O^+	0.47	0.66	0.53	0.78	0.54	0.68	0.65	0.68	0.69	0.56
P_2O_5	0.14	0.07	0.18	0.07	0.20	0.12	0.21	0.17	0.21	0.17
qz[b]	32.2	31.1	29.2	33.2	24.8	26.1	21.9	20.8	24.1	19.6
or	30.0	27.8	32.2	31.7	27.2	26.7	18.3	17.8	8.3	8.3
ab	29.3	35.1	26.2	25.1	28.3	30.9	32.5	35.1	33.0	34.1
an	2.8	2.0	5.6	5.0	11.1	9.5	16.4	14.5	20.8	23.3
c	1.4	–	0.8	0.9	–	–	–	–	–	–
$CaSiO_3$	–	0.1	–	–	–	0.2	–	1.3	0.3	1.3
$MgSiO_3$	0.6	0.3	1.3	0.8	2.5	1.6	3.9	3.9	4.9	5.3
$FeSiO_3$	1.1	0.6	1.7	–	2.2	0.8	2.9	1.3	4.1	2.8
ac	–	–	–	–	–	–	–	–	–	–
mt	1.2	1.9	1.4	1.9	1.9	2.5	1.9	3.0	2.1	3.3
il	0.5	0.3	0.8	0.5	1.1	0.8	1.1	1.4	1.2	1.2
ap	0.3	0.2	0.4	0.2	0.5	0.3	0.5	0.3	0.5	0.3

Note: Effusive rocks include obsidians; number of analyses used for average in parentheses.

a Pegmatites mainly differ in averages by their higher potassium and slightly lower sodium contents (~6.3% K_2O).

b The following abbreviations are used for normative minerals: qz = quartz; or = K-feldspar; ab = albite; an = anorthite; c = corundum; lc = leucite; ne = nepheline; ac = acmite; mt = magnetite; il = ilmenite; ap = apatite; cc = calcite.

(From Wedepohl, K. H., Ed., *Handbook of Geochemistry,* Vol. I, Springer-Verlag, Berlin, 1969.

REFERENCE

Nockolds, S. R., Average chemical compositions of some igneous rocks, *Bull. Geol. Soc. Am.,* 65, 1007, 1954.

Table 4.3–5
AVERAGES OF INTERMEDIATE ROCKS

	Alkali syenites (25)	Alkali trachytes (15)	Syenites (18)	Trachytes (24)	Monzonites (46)	Latites (42)	Monzo-diorites (56)	Latite andesites (38)	Diorites (50)	Andesites (49)
SiO_2	61.86	61.95	59.41	58.31	55.36	54.02	54.66	56.00	51.86	54.20
TiO_2	0.58	0.73	0.83	0.66	1.12	1.18	1.09	1.29	1.50	1.31
Al_2O_3	16.91	18.03	17.12	18.05	16.58	17.22	16.98	16.81	16.40	17.17
Fe_2O_3	2.32	2.33	2.19	2.54	2.57	3.83	3.26	3.74	2.73	3.48
FeO	2.63	1.51	2.83	2.02	4.58	3.98	5.38	4.36	6.97	5.49
MnO	0.11	0.13	0.08	0.14	0.13	0.12	0.14	0.13	0.18	0.15
MgO	0.96	0.63	2.02	2.07	3.67	3.87	3.95	3.39	6.12	4.36
CaO	2.54	1.89	4.06	4.25	6.76	6.76	6.99	6.87	8.40	7.92
Na_2O	5.46	6.55	3.92	3.85	3.51	3.32	3.76	3.56	3.36	3.67
K_2O	5.91	5.53	6.53	7.38	4.68	4.43	2.76	2.60	1.33	1.11
H_2O^+	0.53	0.54	0.63	0.53	0.60	0.78	0.60	0.92	0.80	0.86
P_2O_5	0.19	0.18	0.38	0.20	0.44	0.49	0.43	0.33	0.35	0.28
qz[a]	1.7	–	2.0	–	–	0.5	2.0	7.2	0.3	5.7
or	35.0	32.8	38.4	43.9	27.8	26.1	16.7	15.6	7.8	6.7
ab	46.1	54.0	33.0	28.8	29.3	27.8	31.9	29.9	28.3	30.9
an	4.2	3.3	10.0	9.7	15.8	19.2	21.1	22.2	25.8	27.2
ne	–	0.6	–	2.0	–	–	–	–	–	–
$CaSiO_3$	3.0	2.1	3.0	4.2	6.3	4.5	4.5	4.1	5.6	4.2
$MgSiO_3$	2.4	1.6	5.0	3.2	8.0	9.7	9.9	8.5	15.3	10.9
$FeSiO_3$	2.1	–	2.1	0.5	4.1	2.4	5.4	3.0	8.5	5.3
Mg_2SiO_4	–	–	–	1.4	0.8	–	–	–	–	–
Fe_2SiO_4	–	–	–	0.2	0.4	–	–	–	–	–
mt	3.3	3.3	3.3	3.7	3.7	5.6	4.9	5.3	3.9	5.1
il	1.2	1.4	1.5	1.2	2.1	2.3	2.1	2.4	2.9	2.4
ap	0.5	0.4	1.0	0.5	1.0	1.2	1.0	0.8	0.8	0.7

Note: Number of analyses in parentheses.

[a] The following abbreviations are used for normative minerals: qz = quartz; or = K-feldspar; ab = albite; an = anorthite; c = corundum; lc = leucite; ne = nepheline; ac = acmite; mt = magnetite; il = ilmenite; ap = apatite; cc = calcite.

(From Wedepohl, K. H., Ed., *Handbook of Geochemistry,* Vol. I, Springer-Verlag, Berlin, 1969. With permission.)

REFERENCE

Nockolds, S. R., Average chemical compositions of some igneous rocks, *Bull. Geol. Soc. Am.,* 65, 1007, 1954.

Table 4.3–6
AVERAGES OF GABBROIC-BASALTIC ROCKS

	Gabbros (160)	Tholeiitic basalts (137)	Alkali olivine basalts (96)
SiO_2	48.36	50.83	45.78[a]
TiO_2	1.32	2.03	2.63
Al_2O_3	16.81	14.07	14.64
Fe_2O_3	2.55	2.88	3.16
FeO	7.92	9.00	8.73
MnO	0.18	0.18	0.20
MgO	8.06	6.34	9.39[a]
CaO	11.07	10.42	10.74
Na_2O	2.26	2.23	2.63[a]
K_2O	0.56	0.82	0.95[a]
H_2O^+	0.64	0.91	0.76
P_2O_5	0.24	0.23	0.39
qz[b]	–	3.5	–
or	3.3	5.0	6.1
ab	18.9	18.9	18.3
an	34.2	25.9	24.7
ne	–	–	2.3
$CaSiO_3$	8.0	10.3	10.8
$MgSiO_3$	14.0	15.8	7.1
$FeSiO_3$	7.4	11.2	2.9
Mg_2SiO_4	4.3	–	11.5
Fe_2SiO_4	2.5	–	5.0
mt	3.7	4.2	4.6
il	2.4	3.8	5.0
ap	0.6	0.5	1.0

Note: Number of analyses used for averages in parentheses.

[a] The mean of literature data from Turner, Verhoogen is higher in SiO_2 (48.4), Na_2O (3.2), K_2O (1.3), mainly compensated by lower MgO.

[b] The following abbreviations are used for normative minerals: qz = quartz; or = K-feldspar; ab = albite; an = anorthite; c = corundum; lc = leucite; ne = nepheline; ac = acmite; mt = magnetite; il = ilmenite; ap = apatite; cc = calcite.

(From Wedepohl, K. H., Ed., *Handbook of Geochemistry*, Vol. I, Springer-Verlag, Berlin, 1969. With permission.)

REFERENCES

1. **Nockolds, S. R.**, Average chemical compositions of some igneous rocks, *Bull. Geol. Soc. Am.*, 65, 1007, 1954.
2. **Turner, F. J. and Verhoogen, J.**, *Igneous and Metamorphic Petrology*, 2nd ed., McGraw-Hill, New York, 1960.

Table 4.3–7
AVERAGES OF PERIDOTITIC AND ANORTHOSITIC ROCKS

	Peridotite (23)	Anorthosite (9)	Normative minerals[a]	Peridotite (23)	Anorthosite (9)
SiO_2	43.54	54.54	qz	–	1.4
TiO_2	0.81	0.52	or	1.7	6.7
Al_2O_3	3.99	25.72	ab	4.7	39.3
Fe_2O_3	2.51	0.83	an	7.5	45.9
FeO	9.84	1.46	ne	–	–
MnO	0.21	0.02	$CaSiO_3$	3.9	0.3
MgO	34.02	0.83	$MgSiO_3$	14.8	2.1
CaO	3.46	9.62	$FeSiO_3$	2.6	1.2
Na_2O	0.56	4.66	Mg_2SiO_4	49.1	–
K_2O	0.25	1.06	Fe_2SiO_4	9.6	–
H_2O^+	0.76	0.63	mt	3.7	1.2
P_2O_5	0.05	0.11	il	1.5	0.9
			ap	0.1	0.3

Note: Number of analyses used for averages in parentheses.

[a] The following abbreviations are used for normative minerals: qz = quartz; or = K-feldspar; ab = albite; an = anorthite; c = corundum; lc = leucite; ne = nepheline; ac = acmite; mt = magnetite; il = ilmenite; ap = apatite; cc = calcite.

(From Wedepohl, K. H., Ed., *Handbook of Geochemistry,* Vol. I, Springer-Verlag, Berlin, 1969. With permission.)

REFERENCE

Nockolds, S. R., Average chemical compositions of some igneous rocks, *Bull. Geol. Soc. Am.,* 65, 1007, 1954.

Table 4.3–8
AVERAGES OF ALKALIC ROCKS

	Nepheline syenites (80)	Phonolites (47)	Essexites (15)	Nepheline tephrites (8)	Leucite tephrites (31)	Ijolites (11)	Olivine nephelinites (21)	Olivine leucitites (11)	Olivine melilitites (10)
SiO_2	55.38	56.90	46.88	44.82	47.05	42.58	40.29	43.64	37.08
TiO_2	0.66	0.59	2.81	2.65	1.54	1.41	2.90	2.54	3.31
Al_2O_3	21.30	20.17	17.07	15.42	16.05	18.46	11.32	10.82	8.08
Fe_2O_3	2.42	2.26	3.62	4.28	3.49	4.01	4.87	5.11	5.12
FeO	2.00	1.85	5.94	6.61	5.78	4.19	7.69	5.89	7.23
MnO	0.19	0.19	0.16	0.16	0.17	0.20	0.22	0.15	0.18
MgO	0.57	0.58	4.85	7.27	6.20	3.22	13.28	13.86	16.19
CaO	1.98	1.88	9.49	10.32	10.80	11.38	12.99	10.66	16.30
Na_2O	8.84	8.72	5.09	5.30	2.35	9.55	3.14	2.16	2.30
K_2O	5.34	5.42	2.64	1.26	5.38	2.55	1.44	4.09	1.36
H_2O^+	0.96	0.96	0.97	1.56	0.60	0.55	1.08	0.72	1.89
P_2O_5	0.19	0.17	0.48	0.35	0.59	1.52	0.78	0.63	0.96
CO_2	0.17	–	–	–	–	0.38	–	–	–
Cl	–	0.23	–	–	–	–	–	–	–
SO_3	–	0.13	–	–	–	–	–	–	–
or[a]	31.1	31.7	15.6	7.8	22.2	10.0	–	6.9	–
ab	32.0	36.2	14.7	12.6	–	–	–	–	–
an	2.8	1.7	16.1	14.5	17.5	–	12.8	6.1	7.5
lc	–	–	–	–	7.4	3.9	6.5	13.8	6.5
ne	23.3	18.7	15.3	17.3	10.8	43.7	14.2	9.9	10.5
Ca_2SiO_4	–	–	–	–	–	–	1.6	–	12.8
$CaSiO_3$	2.1	2.9	11.6	14.3	13.6	18.5	17.2	17.8	10.7
$MgSiO_3$	1.2	1.4	8.2	10.4	9.3	8.0	13.1	14.5	8.6
$FeSiO_3$	0.8	0.9	2.4	2.5	3.2	2.4	2.2	1.1	0.8
Mg_2SiO_4	0.1	–	2.8	5.5	4.3	–	14.1	14.1	22.3

Table 4.3–8 (*Continued*)
AVERAGES OF ALKALIC ROCKS

	Nepheline syenites (80)	Phonolites (47)	Essexites (15)	Nepheline tephrites (8)	Leucite tephrites (31)	Ijolites (11)	Olivine nephelinites (21)	Olivine leucitites (11)	Olivine melitites (10)
Fe_2SiO_4	0.1	–	0.8	1.5	1.7	–	2.7	1.2	2.5
mt	3.5	3.3	5.3	6.3	5.1	5.8	7.2	7.4	7.4
il	1.4	1.2	5.3	5.0	2.9	2.7	5.5	4.9	6.2
ap	0.4	0.3	1.2	0.8	1.3	3.6	1.8	1.5	2.3
cc	0.4	–	–	–	–	0.9	–	–	–

Note: Number of analyses used for averages in parentheses.

[a] The following abbreviations are used for normative minerals: qz = quartz; or = K-feldspar; ab = albite; an = anorthite; c = corundum; lc = leucite; ne = nepheline; ac = acmite; mt = magnetite; il = ilmenite; ap = apatite; cc = calcite.

(From Wedepohl, K. H., Ed., *Handbook of Geochemistry,* Vol. I, Springer-Verlag, Berlin, 1969. With permission.)

REFERENCE

Nockolds, S. R., Average chemical compositions of some igneous rocks, *Bull. Geol. Soc. Am.,* 65, 1007, 1954.

Table 4.3–9
AVERAGE CHEMICAL COMPOSITION OF SELECTED SEDIMENTARY ROCKS

	Sandstones[1] (253), %	Sandstones,[b,2] from platforms (3700), %	Greywackes[3] (61[c]), %	Shales,[1,4–6] mainly from geosynelines (277), %	Shales,[2] from platforms (6800), %
SiO_2	78.7	70.0	66.7	58.9	50.7
TiO_2	0.25	0.58	0.6	0.78	0.78
Al_2O_3	4.8	8.2	13.5	16.7	15.1
Fe_2O_3	1.1	2.5[a]	1.6	2.8	4.4[a]
FeO	0.3	1.5[a]	3.5	3.7	2.1[a]
MnO	0.03[a]	0.06[a]	0.1	0.09	0.08
MgO	1.2	1.9	2.1	2.6	3.3
CaO	5.5	4.3	2.5	2.2	7.2
Na_2O	0.45	0.58	2.9	1.6	0.8
K_2O	1.3	2.1	2.0	3.6	3.5
H_2O^+	1.3	3.0	2.4	5.0	5.0
P_2O_5	0.08	0.10[a]	0.2	0.16	0.10[a]
C/CO_2	n.d./5.0	0.26[a]/3.9	0.1/1.2	0.6[a]/1.3	0.67[a]/6.1
S/SO_3	n.d./0.07	n.d./0.7	0.1/0.3	0.24[a]/n.d.	n.d./0.6

Note: Number of samples used for average in parentheses.

[a] Data are from literature compilations different from those referred to at head of the column.
[b] Psammitic rocks in general.
[c] Similar to an average of 70 greywackes from the Harz mountains (Germany), the type locality.

	Tillites[4] (68), %	Limestones[7] (93) %	Carbonate rocks,[2] from platforms (1500–8300), %	Cherts[8] (10), %	Pelagic clays[d,9] (430)
SiO_2	58.9	6.9	8.2	89.9	54.9
TiO_2	0.79	0.05	n.d.	0.2	0.78
Al_2O_3	15.9	1.7	2.2	3.7	16.6
Fe_2O_3	3.3	0.98	1.0[a]	2.3	7.7
FeO	3.7	1.3	0.68[a]	n.d.	7.7
MnO	0.10	0.08	0.07[a]	0.1	(2.0)
MgO	3.3	0.97	7.7	0.5	3.4
CaO	3.2	47.6	40.5	0.3	0.72
Na_2O	2.1	0.08	n.d.	0.7	1.3
K_2O	3.9	0.57	n.d.	0.7	2.7
H_2O^+	3.0	0.84	n.d.	1.2	(9.2)
P_2O_5	0.21	0.16	0.07[a]	0.9	0.72
C/CO_2	n.d./0.6	38.3	0.23[a]/35.5	(0.3)/n.d.	Computed carbonate free
S/SO_3	0.08/0.09	0.11/0.02	n.d./3.1	n.d.	n.d.

Note: Number of samples used for average in parentheses.

[a] Data are from literature compilations different from those referred to at head of the column.
[d] Weighted average for the three oceans, sea salt free samples (35 samples of sea salt containing Pacific clays, reported by Goldberg and Arrhinius,[10] contain about 6–7% NaCl. This is a high value compared with 3–4% NaCl in Atlantic clays, analyzed by Behne[1]).

Table 4.3–9 (Continued)
AVERAGE CHEMICAL COMPOSITION OF SELECTED SEDIMENTARY ROCKS

(From Wedepohl, K. H., Ed., *Handbook of Geochemistry,* Vol. I, Springer-Verlag, Berlin, 1969. With permission.)

REFERENCES

1. **Clarke, F. W.,** Data of geochemistry, 5th ed., *U.S. Geol. Survey Bull.,* 770, 1924.
2. **Vinogradov, A. P. and Ronov, A. B.,** Composition of the sedimentary rocks of the Russian platform in relation to the history of its tectonic movements, *Geochemistry (U.S.S.R.)* (Engl. transl.), 6, 533, 1956.
3. **Pettijohn, F. J.,** Chemical composition of sandstones – excluding carbonate and volcanic sands, in Data of geochemistry, Fleischer, M., Ed., U.S. Geol. Survey, Profess. papers 440-S, 1963.
4. **Goldschmidt, V. M.,** Grundlagen der quantitativen Geochemie, *Fortschr. Mineral. Krist. Petrogr.,* 17, 112, 1933.
5. **Minami, E.,** Selen-Gehalte von europäischen und japanischen Tonschiefern, *Nachr. Ges. Wiss. Göttingen, Math.-physik.,* Kl. 4, 1, 143, 1935.
6. **Shaw, D. M.,** Geochemistry of pelitic rocks. III. Major elements and general geochemistry, *Bull. Geol. Soc. Am.,* 67, 919, 1956.
7. **Wedepohl, K. H.,** unpublished data.
8. **Cressman, E. R.,** Nondetrital siliceous sediments, in Data of geochemistry, Fleischer, M., Ed., U.S. Geol. Survey, Profess. papers 440-T, 1962.
9. **Landergren, S.,** On the geochemistry of deep-sea sediments, Repts. Swed. Deep-Sea Exped. 10, Spec. Inv. 5, 59, 1964.
10. **Goldberg, E. D. and Arrhenius, G. O. S.,** Chemistry of Pacific pelagic sediments, *Geochim. Cosmochim. Acta,* 13, 153, 1958.
11. **Behne, W.,** Untersuchungen zur Geochemie des Chlor und Brom., *Geochim. Cosmochim. Acta,* 3, 186, 1953.

Table 4.3–10
AVERAGE MINERAL COMPOSITION OF SELECTED SEDIMENTARY ROCK TYPES IN PERCENT

	Sandstones[1]	Greywackes[1]	Shales[a,2]	Limestones[b,c]
Quartz	82	37	20	
Plagioclase / Potassium feldspar	5	28	10–15	
Muscovite (M)/illite (I)	8 (M)		45–55 (I)	14
Chlorite (C)		29 (C)		
Kaolinite			14	
Calcite / Dolomite	3	3	3	
Calcite				84
Dolomite				2
Accessories	2	3	1	

Note: The important mineral of a group is in parentheses.

[a] Data on the clay minerals are mainly averages of Weaver's[3] 70,000 x-ray analyses of American shales, which are comparable with the author's averages of European Paleozoic and Mesozoic shales. The quartz content is only from European shales, which contain on the average more plagioclase than K-feldspar. The average sodium of shales from table 4.3–9, 1.2% Na_2O, indicates about 10% albite beside 0.25 soluble NaCl. The figure for illite includes expanded clay minerals.

[b] By computing the mineral constituents from the analysis of 345 limestones, which Clarke[4] has published (7.5% silicates, 36% dolomite), one realizes that a large number of dolomites have been included in the composite of American limestones. The average carbonate rocks from the Russian platform (table 4.3–9, Reference 2) contain about 12% silicates and 35% dolomite. It seems to be reasonable to assume that between a quarter and a third of all carbonate rocks consist of dolomites.

[c] Computed from table 4.3–9.

(From Wedepohl, K. H., Ed., *Handbook of Geochemistry,* Vol. I, Springer-Verlag, Berlin, 1969. With permission.)

REFERENCES

1. **Huckenholz, H.G.,** A contribution to the classification of sandstones, *Geol. Fören. i Stockholm Förh.,* 85, 156, 1963a.
2. **Wedepohl, K. H.,** unpublished data, 1957.
3. **Weaver, C. E.,** Potassium, illite and the ocean, *Geochim. Cosmochim. Acta,* 31, 2181, 1967.
4. **Clarke, F. W.,** Data of geochemistry, 5th ed., *U.S. Geol. Survey Bull.,* 770, 1924.

Table 4.3–11
THE DISSOLVED LOAD OF STREAMS

	x 10^{15} l/yr[1]	Dissolved solids,[1] ppm	10^{15} g/yr[1]	x 10^{15} l/yr[2]	Dissolved solids, ppm, including organic[2]	10^{15} g/yr[2]
North America	4.55	142	0.646	6.43	89	0.572
Europe	2.50	182	0.455	3.00	101	0.303
Asia	11.05	142	1.570	12.25	111	1.360
Africa	5.90	121	0.715	6.05	96	0.581
Australia	0.32	59	0.019	0.61	176	0.107
South America	8.01	69	0.552	8.10	71	0.575
Total	32.33	120	3.957	36.45	88	3.498

(From Wedepohl, K. H., Ed., *Handbook of Geochemistry,* Vol. I, Springer-Verlag, Berlin, 1969. With permission.)

Table 4.3–12
SEDIMENT LOAD OF STREAMS IN VARIOUS REGIONS OF THE U.S.

Drainage region	Drainage area x 10^3 km^2	Runoff x 10^{15} l/yr	Avg concentration suspended load, mg/l	Avg concentration dissolved load, mg/l	Avg annual suspended load, 10^{15} g/yr	Avg annual dissolved load, 10^{15} g/yr
Colorado	637	0.021	13,930	760		
Pacific Slopes, Calif.	303	0.072	970	167		
Western Gulf	829	0.049	1,880	770		
Mississippi	3,240	0.555	604	248		
S. Atlantic and eastern Gulf	735	0.291	131	171		
N. Atlantic	383	0.188	156	128		
Columbia	679	0.309	106	138		
Total	6,807	1.485	602	214	0.894	0.318

(From Judson, S. and Ritter, D. F., Rates of regional denundation in the United States, *J. Geophys. Res.*, 49, 3395, 1964.)

Table 4.3–13
AVERAGE COMPOSITION OF STREAMS

	ppm
HCO_3^-	58.4
$SO_4^=$	11.2
Cl^-	7.8
NO_3^-	1.0
Ca^{++}	15.0
Mg^{++}	4.1
Na^+	6.3
K^+	2.3
(Fe)	(0.67)
SiO_2	13.1
Total	120

(From Livingstone, D., Chemical composition of rivers and lakes, U.S. Geol. Surv. Profess. paper 440-G, 1963.)

Table 4.3–14
THE TRACE ELEMENT COMPOSITION OF STREAMS

	ppb = μg/l	Approximate estimate, ppb	Region	Ref.
Lithium	3.3	3	North America	1
Boron	13	10	USSR	2
Fluorine	88	100	USSR	2
	150		Japan	3
Aluminum	360	400	Japan	3
Phosphorus	19	20	Columbia R.	4
Scandium	0.004	0.004	Columbia R.	4
Titanium	2.7	3	Maine (US) lakes and streams	5
Vanadium	0.9	0.9	Japan	6
Chromium	1.4	1	US streams, Rhone, Amazon	7
	0.3		Maine (US) lakes and streams	5
Manganese	12	7	USSR,	2
	4.0		Maine (US) lakes and streams,	5
	4.8		Columbia R.	4
Cobalt	0.19	0.2	US streams, Rhone, Amazon	7
Nickel	0.3	0.3	Maine (US) lakes and streams	5
Copper	0.9	7	Japan,	3
	10		USSR,	
	12		Maine (US) lakes and streams	5
	4.4		Columbia R.	4
Zinc	5.0	20	Japan,	3
	45		USSR,	
	16		Columbia R.	4
Gallium	0.089	0.09	Saale and Elbe (Germany)	8
Germanium				
Arsenic	1.7	2	Japan,	3
	1.6		Columbia R.	4
Selenium	0.20	0.2	US streams, Rhone, Amazon	7
Bromine	19	20	USSR	2
Rubidium	1.1	1	US streams, Rhone, Amazon	7
Strontium	46	50	Eastern US	9
Yttrium		0.7		estimate[a]
Zirconium				
Niobium				
Molybdenum	0.6	1	Japan	3
	1.8		US streams, Amazon	7
Ruthenium				
Rhodium				
Palladium				
Silver	0.39	0.3	US streams, Rhone, Amazon	7

[a] Estimate based on prorating rare-earth values in streams using La concentration in streams and the relative proportions of rare-earths found in the oceans.

Table 4.3–14 (*Continued*)
THE TRACE ELEMENT COMPOSITION OF STREAMS

	ppb = μg/l	Approximate estimate, ppb	Region	Ref.
Cadmium				
Indium				
Tin				
Antimony	1.1	1	US streams, Rhone, Amazon	7
Tellerium				
Iodine	7.1	7	USSR	2
Cesium	0.020	0.02	US streams, Rhone, Amazon	7
Barium	11	10	Eastern US	9
Lanthanum	0.2	0.2	Sweden	10
		0.19	Columbia R.	4
Cerium		0.06		estimate[a]
Praseodymium		0.03		estimate[a]
Neodymium		0.2		estimate[a]
Samarium		0.03		estimate[a]
Europium		0.007		estimate[a]
Gadolinium		0.04		estimate[a]
Terbium		0.008		estimate[a]
Dysprosium		0.05		estimate[a]
Holmium		0.01		estimate[a]
Erbium		0.05		estimate[a]
Thulium		0.009		estimate[a]
Ytterbium		0.05		estimate[a]
Lutetium		0.008		estimate[a]
Hafnium				
Tantalum				
Tungsten	0.03	0.03	Sweden	10
Rhenium				
Osmium				
Iridium				
Platinum				
Gold	0.002	0.002	Sweden	10
Mercury	0.074	0.07	Saale and Elbe (Germany)	11
Thallium	?			
Lead	3.9	3	Saale and Elbe (Germany)	11
	2.3		Maine (US) lakes and streams	5
Bismuth	?			
Thorium	0.096	0.1	Amazon	12
Uranium	0.06	0.04	Sweden	10
	0.043		Amazon	12
	0.026		North America	13

[a] Estimate based on prorating rare-earth values in streams using La concentration in streams and the relative proportions of rare-earths found in the oceans.

(From Turekian, K. K., in *Handbook of Geochemistry,* Vol. I, Wedepohl, K. H., Ed., Springer-Verlag, Berlin, 1969. With permission.)

Table 4.3–14 (*Continued*)

REFERENCES

1. **Durum, W. H. and Haffty, J.,** Occurrence of minor elements in water, *U.S. Geol. Surv. Circ.,* 445, 1960.
2. **Konovalov, G. S.,** The transport of microelements by the most important rivers of the U.S.S.R., *Dokl. Akad. Nauk. USSR,* 129, (4) 912, 1959. (Translated into English by M. Fleischer, U.S. Geol. Surv.)
3. **Sugawara, K.,** personal communication, 1967.
4. **Silker, W. B.,** Variations in elemental concentrations in the Columbia River, *Limnol. Oceanogn.,* 9, 540, 1964.
5. **Turekian, K. K. and Kleinkopf, M. D.,** Estimates of the average abundance of Cu, Mn, Pb, Ti, Ni, and Cr in surface waters of Maine, *Bull. Geol. Soc. Am.,* 67, 1129, 1956.
6. **Sugawara, K., Naito, H., and Yamada, S.,** Geochemistry of vanadium in natural waters, *J. Earth Sci. Nagoya Univ.,* 4, 44, 1956.
7. **Kharkar, D. P., Turekian, K. K., and Bertine, K. K.,** Stream supply of dissolved silver, molybdenum, antimony, selenium, chromium, cobalt, rubidium and cesium to the oceans, *Geochim. Cosmochim. Acta,* 32, 285, 1968.
8. **Heide, F. and Kodderitzsch, H.,** Der Galliumgehalt des Saale- und Elbewassers, *Naturwissenschaften,* 51, 104, 1964.
9. **Turekian, K. K.,** Trace elements in sea water and other natural waters, Annual report AEC Contract AT (30-1)-2912, Publ. Yale-2912-12, 1966.
10. **Landström, O. and Wenner, C. G.,** Neutron-activation analysis of natural water applied to hydrogeology, *Aktiebolaget Atomenergi (Sweden),* AE-204, 1965.
11. **Heide, F., Lerz, H., and Bohm, G.,** Gehalt des Saalewassers an Blei und Quecksilber, *Naturwissenschaften,* 44, 441, 1957.
12. **Moore, W. S.,** Amazon and Mississippi River concentrations of uranium, thorium, and radium isotopes, *Earth Planet. Sci. Lett.,* 2, 231, 1967.
13. **Rona, E. L. and Urry, W. D.,** Radioactivity of ocean sediments. VIII. Radium and uranium content of ocean and river waters, *Am. J. Sci.,* 250, 241, 1952.

Table 4.3–15
COMPOSITION OF CLEAN DRY AIR NEAR SEA LEVEL

Component	Content, % by vol	Mol wt
Nitrogen	78.084	28.0134
Oxygen	20.9476	31.9988
Argon	0.934	39.948
Carbon dioxide	0.0314	44.00995
Neon	0.001818	20.183
Helium	0.000524	4.0026
Krypton	0.000114	83.80
Xenon	0.0000087	131.30
Hydrogen	0.00005	2.01594
Methane	0.0002	16.04303
Nitrous oxide	0.00005	44.0128
Ozone		47.9982
Summer	0–0.000007	
Winter	0–0.000002	
Sulfur dioxide	0–0.0001	64.0628
Nitrogen dioxide	0–0.000002	46.0055
Ammonia	0–trace	17.03061
Carbon monoxide	0–trace	28.01055
Iodine	0–0.000001	253.8088

(From Wedepohl, K. H., Ed., *Handbook of Geochemistry*, Vol. I, Springer-Verlag, Berlin, 1969. With permission.)

Table 4.3–16
AVERAGE CHEMICAL COMPOSITION OF PRECIPITATION AND RIVER WATER IN JAPAN

	Precipitation, ppm	River water, ppm	River water relative to precipitation normalized to Cl ratio = 1
Na	1.1	5.1	1
K	0.26	1.0	0.8
Mg	0.36	2.4	0.7
Ca	0.94	6.3	1.4
Sr	0.011	0.057	1.1
Cl	1.1	5.2	1
I	0.0018	0.0022	0.3
F	0.08	0.15	0.4
S	1.5	3.5	0.5
Si	0.83	8.1	0.5
Fe	0.23	0.48	0.4
Al	0.11	0.36	0.7
P	0.014		
Mo	0.00006	0.0006	2.1
V	0.0014	0.0010	0.2
Cu	0.0008	0.0014	0.4
Zn	0.0042	0.0050	0.2
As	0.0016	0.0017	0.2

(From Sugawara, K., personal communication, in Wedepohl, K. H., Ed., *Handbook of Geochemistry,* Vol. I, Springer-Verlag, Berlin, 1969. With permission.)

4.4 Physical and Geophysical Data

Table 4.4–1
AVERAGE DENSITIES OF HOLOCRYSTALLINE IGNEOUS ROCKS

Rock	No. samples	Mean density	Range of density
Granite	155	2.667	2.516–2.809
Granodiorite	11	2.716	2.668–2.785
Syenite	24	2.757	2.630–2.899
Quartz diorite	21	2.806	2.680–2.960
Diorite	13	2.839	2.721–2.960
Norite	11	2.984	2.720–3.020
Gabbro, including olivine gabbro	27	2.976	2.850–3.120
Diabase, fresh	40	2.965	2.804–3.110
Peridotite, fresh	3	3.234	3.152–3.276
Dunite[1]	15	3.277	3.204–3.314
Pyroxenite	8	3.231	3.10 –3.318
Anorthosite	12	2.734	2.640–2.920

(Compiled by R. A. Daly in *Handbook of Physical Constants,* Clark, S. P., Jr., Ed., Geological Society of America, Memoir 97, 1966. With permission.)

REFERENCE

1. **Birch, F.,** *J. Geophys. Res.,* 65, 1083, 1960.

Table 4.4–2
AVERAGE DENSITIES OF NATURAL GLASSES

Glass	No. determinations	Range of density	Mean density	Ref.
Rhyolite obsidian	15	2.330–2.413	2.370	2
Trachyte obsidian	3	2.435–2.467	2.450	2
Pitchstone	4	2.321–2.37	2.338	1
Andesite glass	3	2.40–2.573	2.474	1
Leucite tephrite glass	2	2.52–2.58	2.55	1
Basalt glass	11	2.704–2.851	2.772	2

(Compiled by R. A. Daly in *Handbook of Physical Constants,* Clark, S. P., Jr., Ed., Geological Society of America, Memoir 97, 1966. With permission.)

REFERENCES

1. **George, W. O.,** *J. Geol.,* 32, 353, 1924.
2. **Tilley,** *Min. Mag.,* 19, 275, 1922.

Table 4.4–3
DENSITY OF CRYSTALLINE ROCK AND CORRESPONDING GLASS

Artificially Prepared

	Density		Difference % rock density	Ref.
	Rock	Glass		
Granite, Shap Fells	2.656	2.446	7.90	3
Granite, Peterhead	2.630	2.376	9.66	3
Syenite, Plauen'scher Grund	2.724	2.560	6.02	3
Tonalite, New Zealand	2.765	2.575	6.87	3
Diorite, Guernsey	2.833	2.680	5.40	3
Diorite, Markfield	2.880	2.710	5.90	3
Gabbro, Carrock Fell	2.940	2.791	5.07	3
Olivine dolerite, Clee Hills	2.889	2.775	3.95	3
Dolerite, Rowley Rag	2.800	2.640	5.71	3
Dolerite, Whin Sill	2.925	2.800	4.27	3
Diabase, Palisades	2.975	2.761	7.19	1
Diabase, Vinal Haven	2.96	2.76	6.8	2
Eclogite	3.415	2.746 (?)	19.6	4

(Compiled by R. A. Daly in *Handbook of Physical Constants,* Clark, S. P., Jr., Ed., Geological Society of America, Memoir 97, 1966. With permission.)

REFERENCES

1. **Day, A. L. et al.,** *Am. J. Sci.,* 37, 1, 1914.
2. **Dane, E. B.,** unpublished.
3. **Douglas,** *Geol. Soc. Lond., Quart. J.,* 63, 145, 1907.
4. **Joly and Poole,** *Philos. Mag.,* 3, 1242, 1927.

Table 4.4–4
COEFFICIENTS OF VOLUME EXPANSION

$\alpha_V = \frac{1}{V}\left(\frac{dV}{dT}\right)$ of Selected Silicates at Atmospheric Pressure

Compositions, where stated, are in mole percent. The coefficients were derived by analytically differentiating polynomial functions fitted to the volume-temperature data by the method of least squares. Most sets of measurements commence at room temperature giving poor control of the derived functions at 20°C, compared to the control at higher temperatures, and leading to an uncertain estimate of α_V at 20°C. The values enclosed in parentheses were derived by extrapolating from temperatures where adequate control on the functions could be established. Less credence should be given the values at 20°C than those at 400°C or 800°C.

Compound	$\alpha_V \times 10^6$ °C^{-1}			
	20°C	400°C	800°C	Ref.
Akermanite	(26)	30	33	11
Andalusite	16	29	43	19
Coesite	8	11	14	18
Cordierite (synthesized at 1420°C)	(14)	18	22	11
Feldspars				
Adularia $Or_{88.3}Ab_{9.3}An_{2.4}$	14	20	24	3
Microcline $Or_{83.5}Ab_{16.5}$	(7)	17	23	15
Plagioclase $Ab_{99}An_1$	18	27	33	6
Plagioclase $Ab_{77}An_{23}$	12	19	24	6
Plagioclase $Ab_{56}An_{44}$	13	17	20	6
Plagioclase Ab_5An_{95}	12	12	20	6

Table 4.4–4 (*Continued*)

Compound	$\alpha_V \times 10^6$ °C^{-1} 20°C	400°C	800°C	Ref.
Garnets				
Almandine	15	25	30	17
Andradite	21	25	29	17
Grossularite	18	23	28	17
Pyrope	19	26	30	17
Spessartite	15	28	34	17
Gehlenite	(23)	25	26	11
Hornblende	23	28	33	8
Kyanite	11	28	30	19
Merwinite	(29)	38	42	11
Mullite	9.5	15	17	1
Nepheline				
$Ne_{78}Ks_{22}$	(31)	53	72	16
$Ne_{59}Ks_{41}$	(66)	51	49	16
Olivine				
Fa_{100}	(27)	30	31	12
$Fa_{80}Fo_{20}$	(26)	32	34	13
$Fa_{41}Fo_{59}$	(27)	32	35	13
$Fa_{15}Fo_{85}$	(25)	32	39	13
$Fa_{10.1}Fo_{89.9}$	(23)	31	39	10
Fo_{100}	24	38	44	18
Monticellite	(32)	36	39	11
Fe-Monticellite	(25)	32	38	12
Pseudo-wollastonite	(30)	32	36	11
Pyroxenes				
Augite	18	25	32	9
Clinoenstatite	(25)	29	33	11
Diopside	24	28	32	7
Jadeite	(20)	29	(38)	20
Quartz	34	69	–3	2, 4, 14
Sillimanite	10	18	26	19
Topaz	14	20	25	5
Zircon	9.3	13.7	17.7	1

(From Clark, S. P., Jr., *Handbook of Physical Constants,* Geological Society of America, Memoir 97, 1966. With permission.)

REFERENCES

1. **Austin, J. B.,** *J. Am. Ceram. Soc.,* 14, 795, 1931.
2. **Jay, A. H.,** *Proc. R. Soc.,* A142, 237, 1933.
3. **Kozu and Saiki,** *Sci. Rep.,* Tohoku Univ. Ser. 3(2), 203, 1925.
4. **Kozu and Takane,** *Sci. Rep.,* Tohoku Univ. Ser. 3(3), 392, 1929.
5. **Kozu and Ueda,** *Sci. Rep.,* Tohoku Univ. Ser. 3(3), 161, 1929.
6. **Kozu and Ueda,** *Proc. Imp. Acad. Jap.,* 9, 262, 1933.
7. **Kozu and Ueda,** *Proc. Imp. Acad. Jap.,* 9, 317, 1933.
8. **Kozu and Ueda,** *Proc. Imp. Acad. Jap.,* 10, 25, 1934.
9. **Kozu and Ueda,** *Proc. Imp. Acad. Jap.,* 10, 87, 1934.
10. **Kozu, Ueda, and Tsurmuri,** *Proc. Imp. Acad. Jap.,* 10, 83, 1934.
11. **Rigby, G. R. and Green, A. T.,** *Trans. Br. Ceram. Soc.,* 41, 123, 1941.
12. **Rigby, G. R., Lovell, G. H. B., and Green, A. T.,** *Trans. Br. Ceram. Soc.,* 44, 37, 1945.
13. **Rigby, G. R., Lovell, G. H. B., and Green, A. T.,** *Trans. Br. Ceram. Soc.,* 45, 237, 1946.
14. **Rosenholtz, J. L. and Smith, D. T.,** *Am. Min.,* 26, 103, 1941.
15. **Rosenholtz, J. L. and Smith, D. T.,** *Am. Min.,* 27, 344, 1942.
16. **Sahama, T. G.,** *J. Petrology,* 3, 65, 1962.
17. **Skinner, B. J.,** *Am. Min.,* 41, 428, 1956.
18. **Skinner, B. J.,** U.S. Geol. Survey, Prof. Paper 450D, 109, 1962.
19. **Skinner, B. J., Clark, S. P., and Appleman, D. E.,** *Am. J. Sci.,* 259, 651, 1961.
20. **Yoder, H. S. and Weir, C. E.,** *Am. J. Sci.,* 249, 683, 1951.

Table 4.4–5
DENSITY AT HIGH TEMPERATURE

Liquid and Crystalline States

	Temp °C	Density		Density difference,[b] %	Volumetric thermal expansion of liquid	Ref.
		Crystal	Liquid			
Rocks						
Diabase	1200	–	2.614	–	44×10^{-6}	1
Diabase, Palisades	1200	2.89	2.603	9.9	160?	5
Diabase, Vinal Haven	1250	2.88	2.64	8.6	38	4, 9
Diabase, Olonetze	1200	–	2.79	–	279	14
Basalt, Transcaucasia	1250	–	2.63	–	82	14
Diorite	1250	–	2.60	–	140	14
Minerals						
Akermanite (synthetic)	1458 (m.p.)[a]	–	2.724	4.4	56	4, 12
Diopside (synthetic)	1391 (m.p.)	3.14	2.671	14.9	64	4, 10
Plagioclase ($Ab_{30}An_{70}$)	1480	2.63	2.519	4.2	56	4, 9
Other materials						
Copper	1083 (m.p.)	8.29	7.96	3.9	143	3
Iron, pure	1535 (m.p.)	7.30	7.25	1.?	144	2, 13
LiF	870 (m.p.)	2.027	1.789	11.8	147	6, 8
NaCl	804 (m.p.)	1.904	1.549	18.6	367	6, 7
$NaNO_3$	308 (m.p.)	2.122	1.909	10.1	363	8, 11
KCl	776 (m.p.)	1.766	1.524	13.6	402	6, 8
KBr	730 (m.p.)	2.473	2.122	14.2	391	6, 8
K_2SiO_3	1050	–	2.24	–	205	14

[a] m.p. = melting point.
[b] Density difference = difference in density between crystal and liquid at indicated temperature, %.

(From Clark, S. P., Jr., *Handbook of Physical Constants,* Geological Society of America, Memoir 97, 1966. With permission.)

REFERENCES

1. **Barus,** *U.S. Geol. Sur. Bull.,* 103, 1891.
2. **Benedicks, Ericsson, and Ericsson,** *Arch. Eisenhuttenwesen,* 3, 473, 1929.
3. **Bornenian and Sauerwald,** *Z. Metallkunde,* 14, 145, 1922.
4. **Dane, E. B.,** *Am. J. Sci.,* 239, 809, 1941.
5. **Day, A. L. et al.,** *Am. J. Sci.,* 37, 1, 1914.
6. **Eucken and Damnohl,** *Z. Electrochemie,* 40, 814, 1934.
7. **Hanlein,** *Glastech. Ber.,* 10, 126, 1932.
8. **Jaeger,** *Z. Anorgan. Chemie,* 101, 1, 1917.
9. **Kozu and Ueda,** *Proc. Imp. Acad. Jap.,* 9, 262, 1933.
10. **Kozu and Ueda,** *Proc. Imp. Acad. Jap.,* 9, 317, 1933.
11. **Kracek, F. C.,** *J. Am. Chem. Soc.,* 53, 2609, 1931.
12. **Rigby, G. R. and Green, A. T.,** *Trans. Br. Ceram. Soc.,* 41, 123, 1941.
13. **Schmidt,** *Ergeb. de Rontgenkunde,* Leipzig, 1933.
14. **Wolarowitsch and Leontjewa,** *Z. Anorgan. Chemie,* 225, 327, 1935.

Table 4.4–6
THERMAL EXPANSION OF ROCKS

Temperature Interval, 20–100°C

Rock type	No. determinations	Avg linear expansion coefficient $\frac{1}{L}\frac{\Delta L}{\Delta T}$
Granites and rhyolites	21	8 ± 3 x 10^{-6}
Andesites and diorites	4	7 ± 2
Basalts, gabbros, and diabases	10	5.4 ± 1
Sandstones	10	10 ± 2
Quartzites	2	11
Limestones	20	8 ± 4
Marbles	9	7 ± 2
Slates	3	9 ± 1

Note: The limits include nearly all the determined values.

(From Clark, S. P., Jr., *Handbook of Physical Constants,* Geological Society of America, Memoir 97, 1966. With permission.)

REFERENCES

1. **Wheeler,** *Trans. R. Soc. Canada,* 3, 19, 1910.
2. **Souder and Hidnert,** *U.S. Bur. Stands. Sci. Paper 352,* 1919.
3. **Griffith,** *Iowa Eng. Exp. Sta. Bull.,* 131, 1937.

Table 4.4–7
WAVE VELOCITIES IN IGNEOUS ROCKS

Small Pressures and Depths and Normal Temperatures

These velocity data, listed according to position in the main sequence of igneous rocks, are primarily for correlation with near-surface rocks. Both laboratory and field measurements are included. It is apparent that seismic velocity alone cannot distinguish between rocks over the wide range of composition from syenite to diorite. Much of the scatter in values at small depths and low pressures can be ascribed to the disturbing effect of porosity. The reader should be wary of the data because they fall in a range where the pressure effect is large. Although a gross relationship between velocity and composition is indicated, the well-known systematic correlation becomes pronounced only when porosities are reduced. Reliable comparisons between seismic (field) and ultrasonic (laboratory) measurements show fairly good consistency between the two methods.

Material	Velocities in km/sec[a] V_P	V_S	Remarks[b]	Ref.
Nephelite syenite, Arkansas	5.53	–	*f*	1
Labradorite trachyte	5.41	3.05	*l*; pressure 200 bars	2
Granite				
Barriefield, Ont.	5.64	2.87	*l*; 20 bars	3
Quincy, Mass.	5.0	–	*f*	1
Quincy, Mass.	5.88	2.94	*l*; 90 bars	3
Westerly, R.I.	5.0	–	*f*	1
Westerly, R.I.	5.76	3.23	*l*	4

[a] 1 km/sec = 3280.8 ft/sec.
[b] *f* = field determination; *l* = laboratory determination.

Table 4.4–7 (*Continued*)

Velocities in km/sec[a]

Material	V_P	V_S	Remarks[b]	Ref.
Rockport, Mass.	5.1	–	*f*	1
Arbuckle Mts., Okla.	5.46	–	*f*	5
Yosemite, Calif.	5.2	–	*f*	6
Bear Mtn., Tex.	5.52	3.04	*l*; 35 bars	7
Japan	5.12	3.03	*l*; 18 granites	8
Ronne, Denmark	4.8	–	*f*	9
New South Wales	5.6	–	*f*	10
US and Canada	5.22	–	*l*; 9 rocks	11
Leningrad, USSR	5.40–5.60	–	*f*; V_P/V_S: 1.69–1.75	12
Ukraine, USSR	5.55–6.00	–	*f*; V_P/V_S: 1.6–1.8	12
Quartz monzonite				
Westerly, R.I.	5.26	2.89	*l*; 35 bars	7
Granodiorite				
Lakeside, Calif.	4.88	3.16	*l*	13
New South Wales	4.6	–	*f*	10
Weston, Mass.	4.78	3.10	*l*	14
Diorite				
Salem, Mass.	5.78	3.06	*l*; 35 bars	7
Andesite				
Colorado	5.23	2.73	*l*; 35 bars	7
Gabbro diorite	5.4	–	–	15
Hornblende gabbro	6.60	3.56	*l*; 200 bars	2
Gabbro				
Escondido, Calif.	6.69	3.47	*l*; 200 bars	2
Duluth, Minn.	6.45	3.42	*l*; 200 bars	2
Johannisburg, E. Prussia	6.5	–	*f*; depth 1200 m	16
Diabase				
E. Siberia	5.8–6.6	–	*f*; V_P/V_S: 1.8–2.3	12
Basalt				
Germany	6.4	3.2	*l*	17
Germany	5.6	–	*f*	18
Germany	5.06	2.72	*f*; depth 710 m	19
Colorado	5.41	3.21	*l*; 200 bars	2
Gabbro-diabase-anorthosite	6.26	–	*l*; 6 rocks 18 samples	11
Norite				
Elizabethtown, NY	6.18	3.24	*l*; 35 bars	7
Sudbury, Ont.	6.22	3.49	*f*	20
Eclogite				
Fichtel Mtn., Germany	8.0	4.3	*l*	17
Anorthosite				
Adirondack Mts., NY	6.63	–	*f*	21
Dunite				
Jackson City, N.C.	7.40	3.79	*l*; 200 bars	2
Twin Sisters, Wash.	8.60	4.37	*l*; 70 bars	3

[a] 1 km/sec = 3280.8 ft/sec.
[b] *f* = field determination; *l* = laboratory determination.

(From Clark, S. P., Jr., *Handbook of Physical Constants,* Geological Society of America, Memoir 97, 1966. With permission.)

Table 4.4–7 (*Continued*)
WAVE VELOCITIES IN IGNEOUS ROCKS

REFERENCES

1. **Leet, L. D. and Ewing, M.,** *Trans. Am. Geophys. Union,* 12, 61, 1931; *Physics,* 2, 160, 1932.
2. **Hughes, D. S. and Maurette, C.,** *Geophysics,* 22, 23, 1957.
3. **Hughes, D. S. and Cross, J. H.,** *Geophysics,* 16, 577, 1951.
4. **Knopoff, L.,** *Trans. Am. Geophys. Union,* 35, 969, 1954.
5. **Weatherby, B. B., Born, W. T., and Harding, R. L.,** *Am. Assoc. Petroleum Geologists Bull.,* 18, 106, 1934.
6. **Gutenberg, B.,** *Beitr. z. angew Geophysik,* 6, 125, 1937.
7. **Hughes, D. S. and Jones, H. J.,** *Geol. Soc. Am. Bull.,* 61, 843, 1950; *Trans. Am. Geophys. Union,* 32, 173, 1951.
8. **Kubotera,** *J. Phys. Earth,* 2, 33, 1954.
9. **Brockamp,** *Z. f. Geophys.,* 11, 39, 1935.
10. **Edge and Laby,** *Principles and Practices of Geophysical Prospecting,* Cambridge University Press, 1931.
11. **Birch, F.,** *Contributions in Geophysics,* Pergamon Press, London, 1957, p. 158.
12. **Molotova, Y. I. and Vassil'ev, L. V.,** *Bull. (Izvest.) Acad. Sci. USSR,* Geoph. Ser. (Eng. ed.), 8, 731, 1960.
13. **Press,** unpublished.
14. **Birch, F. and Bancroft, D.,** *J. Geol.,* 46, 59, 1938; 48, 152, 1940.
15. **Thoenen, J. R. and Windes, S. L.,** *U.S. Bur. Mines Rept. Inv.,* Progress report, 1, R.I. 3353, 1937.
16. **Reich, H.,** *Geol. Jahrb.,* 64, 243, 1950.
17. **Baule and Muller,** in *Encyclopedia of Physics,* Vol. 47, Flugge, S., Ed., Springer-Verlag, Berlin, 1956.
18. **Brockamp and Wolcken,** *Z. f. Geophys.,* 5, 163, 1929.
19. **Meisser and Martin,** *Z. f. Geophys.,* 3, 106, 1927.
20. **Leet, L. D.,** *Trans. Am. Geophys. Union,* 14, 288, 1933; *Physics,* 4, 375, 1933.
21. **Katz, S.,** *Seismol. Soc. Am. Bull.,* 45, 303, 1955.

Table 4.4–8
COMPRESSIONAL WAVE VELOCITIES IN ROCKS AS A FUNCTION OF PRESSURE

Rock	Density, g/cm³	*P* (bars) = 10	V_P in km/sec					
			500	1000	2000	4000	6000	10,000
Serpentinite (chrysotile), Thetford, Que.	2.601	5.6	–	5.67	5.73	5.80	5.87	6.00
Serpentinite (antigorite), Ludlow, Vt.	2.614	4.7	6.33	6.46	6.59	6.70	6.75	6.82
Granite, "G-1," Westerly, R.I.	2.619	4.1	5.63	5.84	5.97	6.10	6.16	6.23
Granite								
Quincy, Mass.	2.621	5.1	6.04	6.11	6.20	6.30	6.37	6.45
Rockport, Mass.	2.624	5.0	5.96	6.18	6.29	6.39	6.43	6.51
Stone Mtn., Ga.	2.625	3.7	5.42	5.94	6.16	6.27	6.33	6.40
Chelmsford, Mass.	2.626	4.2	5.64	5.91	6.09	6.22	6.28	6.35
Gneiss, Pelham, Mass.	2.643	⊥3.4[a]	5.67	5.91	6.06	6.18	6.27	6.31
Quartz monzonite, Porterville, Calif.	2.644	5.1	–	5.95	6.07	6.22	6.28	6.37
Quartzite, Montana	2.647	5.6	–	6.11	6.15	6.22	6.26	6.35

[a] The symbol ⊥ indicates propagation normal to foliation or schistosity.

Table 4.4–8 (*Continued*)
COMPRESSIONAL WAVE VELOCITIES IN ROCKS
AS A FUNCTION OF PRESSURE

Rock	Density, g/cm³	P (bars) = 10	V_P in km/sec					
			500	1000	2000	4000	6000	10,000
Granite,								
Hyderabad, India	2.654	5.4	6.26	6.31	6.38	6.44	6.49	6.56
Barre, Vt.	2.655	5.1	5.86	6.06	6.15	6.25	6.32	6.39
Sandstone,								
(Catskill), N.Y.	2.659	3.9	5.0	5.27	5.44	5.63	5.75	(5.85)
Pyrophyllite ("Lava")	2.662	3.5	–	4.73	5.02	5.38	5.58	5.89
Granite,								
Sacred Heart, Minn.	2.662	5.9	–	6.24	6.28	6.34	6.38	6.45
Barriefield, Ont.	2.672	5.7	6.21	6.29	6.35	6.42	6.46	6.51
Gneiss,								
Hell Gate, N.Y.	2.675	⊥5.1[a]	6.06	6.13	6.23	6.33	6.37	6.50
Granite,								
Hyderabad, India (A)	2.676	5.7	–	6.42	6.46	6.51	6.55	6.61
"Granite,"								
Englehart, Ont.	2.679	6.1	6.28	6.33	6.37	6.43	6.48	6.57
Graywacke,								
New Zealand	2.679	5.4	5.63	5.76	5.87	5.98	6.04	6.13
"Granite,"								
Latchford, Ont.	2.683	5.7	6.13	6.19	6.25	6.30	6.34	6.41
Albitite,								
Sylmar, Pa.	2.687	6.40	–	6.62	6.65	6.68	6.72	6.76
Granodiorite,								
Butte, Mont. (mean)	2.705	4.4	–	6.27	6.35	6.43	6.48	6.56
Graywacke,								
Quebec	2.705	5.4	–	5.92	6.04	6.14	6.20	6.28
Serpentinite,								
Calif.	2.710	5.8	–	6.02	6.08	6.15	6.21	6.31
Slate,								
(Cambridge), Medford, Mass.	2.734	5.49	–	5.79	5.91	6.02	6.10	6.22
"Charnockite,"								
Pallavaram, India	2.740	6.15	–	6.24	6.30	6.36	6.40	6.46
Granodiorite, gneiss								
(Bethlehem), N.H.	2.758	⊥4.4	–	5.95	6.07	6.16	6.21	6.30
Tonalite,								
Val Verde, Calif.	2.763	5.1	–	6.33	6.43	6.49	6.54	6.60
Anorthosite,								
Tahawus, NY	2.768	6.73	–	6.86	6.90	6.94	6.97	7.02
Stillwater Complex, Mont.	2.770	6.5	–	6.97	7.01	7.05	7.07	7.10
Augite syenite,								
Ontario	2.780	5.7	–	6.58	6.63	6.70	6.73	6.79
Mica schist,								
Woodsville, Vt.	2.797	5.7	⊥	6.43	6.48	6.53	6.57	6.64
Serpentinite,								
Ludlow, Vt.	2.798	6.4	–	6.51	6.57	6.67	6.74	6.84
Quartz diorite,								
San Luis Rey quadrangle, Calif.	2.798	5.1	–	6.43	6.52	6.60	6.64	6.71
Anorthosite,								
Bushveld Complex	2.807	5.7	6.92	6.98	7.05	7.13	7.16	7.21
Chlorite schist,								
Chester Quarry, Vt.	2.841	4.8	–	6.75	6.82	6.92	6.98	7.07
Quartz diorite,								
Dedham, Mass.	2.906	5.5	–	6.46	6.53	6.60	6.65	6.71

[a] The symbol ⊥ indicates propagation normal to foliation or schistosity.

Table 4.4–8 (*Continued*)
COMPRESSIONAL WAVE VELOCITIES IN ROCKS AS A FUNCTION OF PRESSURE

Rock	Density, g/cm³	P (bars) = 10	V_P in km/sec 500	1000	2000	4000	6000	10,000
Talc schist, Chester, Vt.	2.914	4.9	–	6.30	6.50	6.71	6.82	6.97
Gabbro, Mellen, Wis.	2.931	6.8	7.04	7.07	7.09	7.13	7.16	7.21
Diabase (Nippissing), Cobalt, Ont.	2.964	6.55	–	6.64	6.67	6.71	6.75	6.82
Diabase, "W-1," Centreville, Va.	2.976	6.14	–	6.70	6.76	6.82	6.86	6.93
Diabase, Holyoke, Mass.	2.977	6.25	6.40	6.43	6.47	6.52	6.56	6.63
Norite, Pretoria, Transvaal	2.978	6.6	7.02	7.07	7.11	7.16	7.20	7.28
Dunite (altered), Webster, N.C.	2.980	6.0	–	6.37	6.46	6.55	6.64	6.79
Diabase (Keweenawan), Sudbury, Ont.	3.003	6.4	6.67	6.72	6.76	6.81	6.84	6.91
Diabase, Frederick, Md.	3.012	6.76	–	6.77	6.80	6.84	6.88	6.92
Gabbro, French Creek, Pa.	3.054	5.8	6.74	6.93	7.02	7.11	7.17	7.23
Amphibolite, Madison Co., Mont.	3.120	6.89	–	7.17	7.21	7.27	7.31	7.35
Jadeite, Japan	3.180	7.6	–	8.21	8.22	8.23	8.24	8.28
Actinolite schist, Chester, Vt.	3.194	6.61	–	7.20	7.32	7.41	7.47	7.54
Dunite, Webster, N.C.	3.244	7.0	–	7.54	7.59	7.65	7.69	7.78
Pyroxenite, Sonoma Co., Calif.	3.247	6.8	–	7.73	7.79	7.88	7.93	8.01
Dunite, Mt. Dun, New Zealand	3.258	7.5	7.69	7.75	7.80	7.86	7.92	8.00
Dunite, Balsam Gap, N.C.	3.267	7.0	7.82	7.89	8.01	8.13	8.19	8.28
Bronzitite, Stillwater Complex, Mont.	3.279	7.42	–	7.62	7.65	7.72	7.75	7.83
Bushveld Complex	3.288	–	7.40	7.49	7.60	7.75	7.85	8.02
Dunite, Addie, N.C.	3.304	7.70	–	7.99	8.05	8.14	8.20	8.28
Twin Sisters Peaks, Wash.	3.312	7.7	8.11	8.19	8.27	8.32	8.35	8.42
"Eclogite," Tanganyika	3.328	6.64	7.30	7.38	7.46	7.57	7.62	7.71
Jadeite, Burma	3.331	8.45	–	8.67	8.69	8.72	8.75	8.78
Eclogite, Kimberley, South Africa	3.338	6.6	7.49	7.56	7.65	7.79	7.85	7.92
Harzburgite, Bushveld Complex	3.369	6.9	7.74	7.78	7.81	7.85	7.90	7.95
Eclogite, Kimberley, South Africa	3.376	7.17	7.65	7.68	7.73	7.79	7.82	7.87
Sunnmore, Norway	3.376	5.2	–	7.13	7.30	7.46	7.54	7.69
Healdsburg, Calif.	3.441	7.31	–	7.69	7.81	7.89	7.94	8.01

Table 4.4–8 (*Continued*)
COMPRESSIONAL WAVE VELOCITIES IN ROCKS AS A FUNCTION OF PRESSURE

Rock	Density, g/cm³	*P* (bars) = 10	V_P in km/sec 500	1000	2000	4000	6000	10,000
Garnet (grossularite), Conn.	3.561	6.3	–	8.41	8.55	8.72	8.83	8.99
Dunite, Mooihoek Mine, Transvaal	3.744	6.7	7.13	7.16	7.21	7.27	7.30	7.36
Garnet (almandite-pyrope)	3.950	5.9	–	7.81	7.91	7.99	8.01	8.07
Microcline, Labrador	2.571	–	6.84	6.95	7.01	7.06	7.09	7.15
Serpentine, Middlefield, Mass.	2.789	–	6.71	6.74	6.79	6.84	6.90	6.97
Magnesite	2.802	–	7.06	7.11	7.19	7.27	7.33	7.45
Dolomite, Williamstown, Mass.	2.845	–	6.77	6.93	7.06	7.17	7.23	7.36
Wollastonite	2.873	–	–	7.21	7.42	7.56	7.64	7.71
Monticellite, Crestmore, Calif.	3.014	–	7.22	7.27	7.31	7.36	7.40	7.50
Idocrase, Crestmore, Calif.	3.144	–	6.10	6.54	6.95	7.27	7.40	7.54
Sillimanite, Williamstown, S. Australia	3.187	–	9.51	9.55	9.60	9.65	9.68	9.73

(From Clark, S. P., Jr., *Handbook of Physical Constants,* Geological Society of America, Memoir 97, 1966. With permission.)

REFERENCES

1. **Birch, F.,** *J. Geophys. Res.,* 65, 1083, 1960; 66, 2199, 1961.
2. **Simmons, G.,** *J. Geophys. Res.,* 69, 1117, 1964.

Table 4.4–9
SHEAR WAVE VELOCITIES IN ROCKS AS A FUNCTION OF PRESSURE

Rock	Density, g/cm³	P(bars) = 1	V_S in km/sec 500	1000	2000	4000	6000	10,000
Serpentinite (chrysotile), Thetford, Que.	2.602	2.71	2.79	2.81	2.82	2.85	2.87	2.90
Albitite, Sylmar, Pa.	2.615	3.43	3.54	3.57	3.61	3.65	3.68	3.73
Granite, Westerly, R.I.	2.635	2.77	3.27	3.36	3.44	3.51	3.54	3.58
Rockport, Mass.	2.638	3.07	3.47	3.54	3.61	3.68	3.71	3.77
Stone Mtn., Ga.	2.639	2.43	3.36	3.53	3.66	3.74	3.76	3.80
Quartz monzonite, Porterville, Calif.	2.652	3.16	3.55	3.63	3.71	3.78	3.81	3.86
Granite, Barre, Vt.	2.665	2.79	3.35	3.48	3.52	3.64	3.67	3.70
Serpentinite, Calif.	2.718	3.12	3.17	3.18	3.20	3.23	3.24	3.28
Anorthosite, Stillwater Complex, Mont.	2.750	3.56	3.65	3.69	3.72	3.76	3.77	3.81
Serpentinite, Ludlow, Vt.	2.806	3.61	3.69	3.70	3.73	3.77	3.80	3.83
Magnesite	2.848	4.05	4.08	4.11	4.14	4.19	4.23	4.29
Gabbro, San Marcos, Calif.	2.874	3.59	3.70	3.73	3.76	3.79	3.82	3.84
Quartz diorite, Dedham, Mass.	2.928	3.39	3.65	3.69	3.74	3.78	3.81	3.84
Monticellite, Crestmore, Calif.	2.975	3.85	3.90	3.94	3.97	4.00	4.02	4.06
Diabase, "W-1," Centreville, Va.	2.984	3.49	3.64	3.68	3.72	3.75	3.77	3.80
Norite, Pretoria, Transvaal	2.984	3.56	3.81	3.84	3.86	3.89	3.90	3.94
Diabase, Frederick, Md.	3.017	3.71	3.75	3.77	3.79	3.81	3.82	3.85
Idocrase, Crestmore, Calif.	3.140	3.13	3.63	3.80	3.96	4.12	4.19	4.28
Amphibolite, Montana	3.070	3.90	4.13	4.18	4.21	4.25	4.27	4.30
Sillimanite, Williamstown, S. Australia	3.187	4.93	5.04	5.06	5.08	5.11	5.13	5.15
Jadeite, Japan	3.203	4.65	4.71	4.72	4.75	4.78	4.79	4.82
Dunite, Webster, N.C.	3.264	4.01	4.25	4.28	4.30	4.33	4.36	4.40
Dunite, Mt. Dun, New Zealand	3.270	4.17	4.34	4.37	4.41	4.45	4.48	4.54
Bronzitite, Stillwater Complex, Montana	3.287	4.48	4.54	4.56	4.58	4.62	4.63	4.66
Dunite, Twin Sisters, Wash.	3.326	4.60	4.67	4.69	4.72	4.77	4.79	4.83
Hornblende-garnet granulite, Sonoma Co., Calif.	3.360	3.83	4.15	4.22	4.27	4.33	4.35	4.38
Eclogite, Healdsburg, Calif.	3.444	4.26	4.39	4.43	4.48	4.53	4.55	4.58
Eclogite 1552, Norway	3.577	4.07	4.36	4.41	4.47	4.52	4.55	4.60
Eclogite 1553, Norway	3.578	3.70	4.38	4.46	4.52	4.58	4.61	4.66
Dunite, Mooihoek Mine, Transvaal	3.760	3.68	3.76	3.77	3.80	3.83	3.86	3.90

Table 4.4–9 (*Continued*)

(From Clark, S. P., Jr., *Handbook of Physical Constants,* Geological Society of America, Memoir 97, 1966. With permission.)

REFERENCE

1. **Simmons, G.,** *J. Geophys. Res.,* 69, 1123, 1964.

Table 4.4–10
GUTENBERG'S VELOCITIES

Depth, km	Mantle Velocity, km/sec V_P	V_S	Core r/r_c [b]	Core Velocity, km/sec
60	8.15	4.6	1.00	8.04
100	8.0	4.4	0.90	8.44
150	7.85	4.35	0.80	8.90
200	8.05	4.4	0.70	9.31
300	8.5	4.6	0.60	9.63
400	9.0	4.95	0.50	9.88
500	9.6	5.3	0.40	10.08
600	10.1	5.6	0.38	10.11
700	10.5	5.9	0.374	10.11
800	10.9	6.15	0.37	10.17
900	11.3[a]	6.3[a]	0.36	10.48
1000	11.4	6.35	0.35	10.76
1200	11.8	6.5	0.34	10.93
1400	12.05	6.6	0.33	11.04
1600	12.3	6.75	0.32	11.09
1800	12.55	6.85	0.31	11.12
2000	12.8	6.95	0.30	11.13
2200	13.0	7.0	0.25	11.15
2400	13.2	7.1	0.20	11.17
2600	13.45	7.2	0.15	11.17
2800	13.7	7.25	0.10	11.16
2900	13.7	7.2	0.05	11.15
2920	13.65	7.2	0.00	11.15

[a] Discontinuity in slope.
[b] r_c = 3451 km.

(From Clark, S. P., Jr., *Handbook of Physical Constants,* Geological Society of America, Memoir 97, 1966. With permission.)

Table 4.4–11
CONDUCTIVITY OF ROCKS

Rock type and locality	No. determi-nations	Conductivity (10^{-3} cal/cm sec °C) Mean	Range	Ref.
Granite and quartz monzonite				
Adams Tunnel, Colo.	59	7.89	6.7–8.6	2
Granite				
Loetschberg Tunnel, Switzerland	12	7.77	6.2–9.0	8
Granodiorite				
Steamboat Springs, Nev.	5	6.64	6.2–6.9	4
Grass Valley, Calif.	14	7.61	7.0–8.3	9
Quartz-feldspar porphyry				
Jacoba Bore, Orange Free State, S. Africa (25°C)	5	8.0	7.6–8.6	5
Syenite and syenite porphyry				
Kirkland Lake, Ont.	37	7.66	6.3–9.5	12
Altered Rhyolite				
Timmins, Ont.	6	8.23	7.4–8.8	12
Norite				
Sudbury, Ont.	5	6.42	5.5–7.3	12
Serpentinized peridotite				
Thetford Mines, Quebec	5	6.34	5.7–7.0	12
Agglomerate				
Roodepoort Bore, Transvaal, S. Africa	5	7.4	7.1–8.0	14
Karoo dolerite				
Kestell Bore, Orange Free State (35°C)	9	4.8	4.0–5.5	14
Ventersdorp lava				
Jacoba Bore, Orange Free State (25°C)	9	7.4	6.3–8.6	5
Ventersdorp lava				
Roodepoort Bore, Transvaal	15	7.2	6.4–8.0	14
Portage Lake lava				
Calumet, Mich.				
Dense flows	27	5.01	4.1–6.6	3
Amygdaloidal tops	10	6.4	5.5–9.0	3
Porphyrite and diabase				
Grass Valley, Calif.	21	7.14	6.2–8.2	9
Quartz diorite gneiss				
Adams Tunnel, Colo.	17	7.75	6.6–8.5	2
Injection gneiss and schist				
Adams Tunnel, Colo.	41	7.74	4.0–11.0	2
Gneiss				
Gotthard Tunnel, Switzerland	15	6.68	5.1–8.0	8
Gneiss				
Simplon Tunnel, Switzerland				
Perpendicular	22	6.34	4.6–7.7	8
Parallel	8	8.90	6.0–11.4	8
Schistes Lustrees				
Simplon Tunnel, Switzerland				
Perpendicular	8	5.74	4.1–6.8	8
Parallel	7	7.50	6.8–8.9	8

Note: The measurements were made at a temperature of about 20°C unless otherwise noted. The values are the means of groups of measurements. Only cases in which there are five or more measurements from a single lithologic unit are included (σ = standard deviation).

Table 4.4–11 (*Continued*)
CONDUCTIVITY OF ROCKS

Rock type and locality	No. determinations	Conductivity (10^{-3} cal/cm sec °C) Mean	Range	Ref.
Gneiss				
Chester, Vt.				
Perpendicular	9	6.24	4.9–8.7	10
Parallel	9	8.33	6.1–10.4	10
Amphibolite				
Homestake Mine Lead, S.D.	6	6.92	6.1–9.1	4
Calcareous mica phyllite				
Homestake Mine				
Perpendicular	7	7.89	6.5–9.0	4
Parallel	9	11.83	9.5–14.0	4
Quartzite				
Homestake Mine	6	16.05	14.2–17.6	4
Witwatersrand quartzite				
Gerhardminnebron Bore, Transvaal (25°C)	17	14.3	8.7–19.2	5
	21	14.5	10.4–18.9	14
Witwatersrand quartzite				
Roodepoort Bore, Transvaal	7	10.1	7.4–12.7	14
Dolomite and anhydrite				
Loetschberg Tunnel, Switzerland	7	11.93	8.9–13.9	8
Limestone				
Toronto, Canada	6	6.12	4.7–7.1	12
Dolomite				
Borehole HB15, Transvaal	8	13.2	$\sigma = 1.0$	7
Dolomite				
Gerhardminnebron Bore Transvaal (25°C)	7	11.0	9.6–12.0	5
Karoo sandstone				
Kestell Bore, Orange Free State (35°C)	7	4.7	3.5–7.7	14
Karoo shale				
Kestell Bore, Orange Free State (35°C)	6	5.7	4.7–6.9	14
Asmari limestone				
Masjid-i-Sulaiman, Iran	21	5.2	$\sigma = .9$	11
Argillaceous limestone				
Resolute Bay, N.W.T.	5	7.3	6.6–8.0	13
Fars marl, shale, etc.				
Masjid-i-Sulaiman, Iran	5	4.9	$\sigma = .3$	11
Shale				
Berry No. 1 Well, Kern Co., Calif.				
1000–5290 feet	14	3.55	2.8–4.2	1
5290–8780 feet	17	4.20	3.2–5.6	1
Copper Harbor Conglomerate				
Calumet, Mich.	31	4.98	2.2–7.9	3
Jacobsville sandstone				
Calumet, Mich.	8	6.78	5.1–10.2	3
Permian marl				
Yorkshire, England	5	5.22	4.2–6.6	6
Carboniferous sandstone				
Nottinghamshire	6	6.62	6.0–7.7	6
Carboniferous shale				
England	11	3.26	3.0–4.3	6
Millstone grit				
Nottinghamshire	8	8.85	7.7–11.0	6
Triassic marl				
Yorkshire	5	3.52	2.2–5.3	6

Table 4.4–11 (*Continued*)

(From Clark, S. P., Jr., *Handbook of Physical Constants,* Geological Society of America, Memoir 97, 1966. With permission.)

REFERENCES

1. **Benfield, A. E.,** *Am. J. Sci.,* 245, 1, 1947.
2. **Birch, F.,** *Geol. Soc. Am. Bull.,* 61, 567, 1950.
3. **Birch, F.,** *Am. J. Sci.,* 252, 1, 1954.
4. **Birch, F.,** unpublished.
5. **Bullard, E.,** *Proc. R. Soc. (London),* A173, 474, 1939.
6. **Bullard, E. L. and Niblett, G. B.,** *Mon. Not. R. Astr. Soc., Geophys. Suppl.,* 6, 222, 1951.
7. **Carte, A. F.,** *Proc. Phys. Soc. (London),* B67, 664, 1954.
8. **Clark, S. P. and Niblett, G. B.,** *Mon. Not. R. Astr. Soc., Geophys. Suppl.,* 7, 176, 1956.
9. **Clark, S. P.,** *Trans. Am. Geophys. Union,* 38, 239, 1957.
10. **Clark, S. P.,** unpublished.
11. **Coster, H. D.,** *Mont. Not. R. Astr. Soc., Geophys. Suppl.,* 5, 131, 1947.
12. **Misener, A. D., Thompson, L. G. D., and Uffen, R. J.,** *Trans. Am. Geophys. Union,* 32, 729, 1951.
13. **Misener, A. D.,** *Trans. Am. Geophys. Union,* 36, 1055, 1955.
14. **Mossop, S. C. and Gafner, G.,** *J. Chem. Met., Min. Soc., S. Afr.,* 52, 61, 1951.

Table 4.4–12
EFFECT OF TEMPERATURE ON THE CONDUCTIVITY OF ROCKS

Rock type and locality	Temp °C	Conductivity 10^{-3} cal/cm sec °C	Density, gm/cm³	Ref.
Granite				
Barre, Vt.	0	6.66	2.65	1
	50	6.25		
	100	5.90		
	200	5.50		
Westerly, R.I.	0	5.80	2.64	1
	50	5.60		
	100	5.42		
	200	5.12		
Rockport, Mass.	0	8.4	2.61	1
	50	7.8		
	100	7.2		
	200	6.5		
	300	5.9		
Granite gneiss				
Pelham, Mass.	–	–	2.64	
Parallel to foliation	0	7.42	–	1
	100	6.58		
Perpendicular to foliation	0	5.17	–	1
	100	4.82		
Quartz monzonite				
California	0	7.56	2.64	1
	50	6.98		
	100	6.55		
	200	5.91		
Tonalite				
California	0	6.42	2.74	1
	100	5.90		
	200	5.52		
Syenite				
Ontario	50	5.25	2.80	1
	100	5.08		
	200	4.99		
Albitite				
Pennsylvania	0	4.85	2.61	1
	100	4.80		
	200	4.70		
	300	4.55		
Bronzitite				
Montana	0	11.0	3.26	1
	100	9.3		
	200	8.7		
Dunite				
North Carolina (mean of 3 samples)	0	12.4	3.26	1
	50	10.5		
	100	9.4		
	200	8.1		
Marble				
Proctor, Vt.	–	–	2.69	1
Parallel to bedding	0	7.36		
	100	6.0		
	200	5.2		

Table 4.4–12 (*Continued*)
EFFECT OF TEMPERATURE ON THE CONDUCTIVITY OF ROCKS

Rock type and locality	Temp °C	Conductivity, 10^{-3} cal/cm sec °C	Density, gm/cm³	Ref.
Perpendicular to bedding	0	7.2		
	100	5.7		
	200	5.1		
Limestone				
	20	5.7	–	5
	350	3.2		
	0	5.4	–	4
	100	4.9		
Solenhofen, Bavaria	30	5.24	2.61	2
	75	4.52		
	0	7.2	2.61	1
	100	5.5		
	200	4.8		
Carbonaceous (Pa.)	–	–	2.69	1
Parallel to bedding	0	8.2		
	100	7.0		
	200	6.5		
Perpendicular to bedding	0	6.1		
	100	5.4		
Dolomite	0	11.9	2.83	1
Pennsylvania	50	10.3		
	100	9.3		
	200	7.95		
Anorthosite	0	4.43	2.74	1
Transvaal	100	4.54		
(Bytownite)	200	4.69		
Quebec	0	4.13	2.70	1
(Labradorite)	100	4.20		
	200	4.34		
	300	4.50		
Montana	0	4.02	2.74	1
(Bytownite)	100	4.10		
	200	4.27		
Diabase				
Maryland	0	5.62	3.01	1
	100	5.35		
	200	5.37		
Maine	0	5.23	2.96	1
	100	5.10		
	200	5.03		
	300	4.99		
Massachusetts	0	5.04	2.96	1
	100	5.01		
	200	5.01		
	300	5.03		
	400	5.06		
Diabasic basalt	30	4.04	–	2
	75	4.14		
Gabbro				
Pennsylvania	0	5.55	3.03	1
	100	5.25		
	200	5.13		

Table 4.4–12 (*Continued*)
EFFECT OF TEMPERATURE ON THE CONDUCTIVITY OF ROCKS

Rock type and locality	Temp °C	Conductivity, 10^{-3} cal/cm sec °C	Density, gm/cm³	Ref.
Wisconsin	0	4.75	2.87	1
	100	4.75		
	200	4.76		
	300	4.78		
	400	4.81		
Bronzitite				
Transvaal	0	11.1	3.29	1
	50	9.2		
	100	8.5		
	200	7.8		
	300	7.3		
Quartzite	0	14.9	–	4
	100	12.5		
Quartzitic sandstone	–	–	2.64	1
Parallel to bedding	0	13.6		
	100	10.6		
	200	9.0		
Perpendicular to bedding	0	13.1		
	100	10.3		
	200	8.7		
Slate				
	0	5.2	–	4
	100	4.7		
Pennsylvania	0	4.6	2.76	1
Perpendicular to bedding	100	4.2		
	200	4.1		
Pyrophyllite				
Transvaal				
Parallel to bedding[a]	0	11.9	–	3
	100	10.0		
	200	8.5		
	300	7.5		
	400	6.7		

[a] Values read from curve; conductivity perpendicular to the bedding is about half as large as parallel to the bedding.

(From Clark, S. P., Jr., *Handbook of Physical Constants,* Geological Society of America, Memoir 97, 1966. With permission.)

REFERENCES

1. **Birch, F. and Clark, F.,** *Am. J. Sci.,* 238, 529, 1940; 238, 613, 1940.
2. **Bridgman, P. W.,** *Am. J. Sci.,* 7, 81, 1924.
3. **Carte, A. E.,** *Br. J. App. Phys.,* 6, 326, 1955.
4. **Ensor, C. R.,** *Proc. Phys. Soc. (London),* 43, 590, 1931.
5. **Poole,** *Phil. Mag.,* 24, 45, 1912; 27, 58, 1914.

Table 4.4–13
CONDUCTIVITY OF DEEP-SEA SEDIMENTS

Sediment type	Water content, % wet wt	Density, gm/cm³	Conductivity, 10^{-3} cal/cm sec °C	Ref.
Red clay	52	1.43	1.93	3
	54	1.39	1.93	
	56.5	1.38	1.93	
	50	1.47	2.17	
	50	1.47	2.20	
	42.5	1.58	2.37	
	43.5	1.57	2.43	
	52.5	1.41	1.91	
	52	1.40	1.96	
	69.5	1.20	1.68	
	61.8	1.27	1.73	
Mud	55	1.32	1.91	
	52.5	1.36	1.90	
	56.5	1.31	1.88	
	51.5	1.37	1.94	
	46	1.47	2.06	
Globigerina ooze and glacial clay	41.3	1.58	2.31	1
	39.8	1.62	2.40	
	44.7	1.52	2.24	
	43.8	1.56	2.23	
	40.5	1.55	2.52	
	37.5	1.61	2.60	
	31.5	1.83	2.72	
	50.0	1.44	2.04	
	47.0	1.50	2.19	
	43.1	1.55	2.27	
	20.2	2.14	3.24	
	38.2	1.59	2.54	
	43.7	1.46	2.27	
	40.3	1.56	2.44	
	32.2	1.72	2.68	
Globigerina ooze	37.8	1.54	2.33	2
	43.8	1.47	2.07	
	43.4	1.47	2.22	
	36.9	1.55	2.55	
	38.5	1.54	2.52	
Dark mud	46.8	1.43	2.08	
	45.7	1.45	2.17	
	44.4	1.47	2.24	
	44.6	1.47	2.24	
	42.6	1.49	2.24	
	38.0	1.57	2.39	
	37.8	1.57	2.30	
	38.9	1.56	2.44	

Note: These measurements show a close correspondence between conductivity and water content and little dependence on type of sediment.[4]

(From Clark, S. P., Jr., *Handbook of Physical Constants,* Geological Society of America, Memoir 97, 1966. With permission.)

REFERENCES

1. **Bullard, E.,** *Proc. R. Soc. (Lond.),* A 222, 408, 1954.
2. **Bullard, E.,** unpublished.
3. **Butler, D. W.,** unpublished.
4. **Ratcliffe, E. H.,** *J. Geophys. Res.,* 65, 1535, 1960.

Table 4.4–14
HEAT FLOW IN THE ATLANTIC OCEAN

Including Black Sea, Caribbean Sea, and Mediterranean Sea

SYMBOLS

Lat = Station latitude in degrees and minutes
Long = Station longitude in degrees and minutes
Elev. = Station elevation on land in meters
Depth = Station depth at sea in meters
∇T = Temperature gradient in 10^{-3} °C/cm
K = Thermal conductivity in 10^{-3} cal/cm sec °C
Q = Heat flow in 10^{-6} cal/cm² sec

No. = Number of heat-flow values averaged together
Ref. = Reference number
Yr = Year of publication
() = Heat-flow value derived from estimated conductivity
* = Heat-flow value obtained when penetration of the temperature gradient probe is partial
? = Heat-flow value questionable

Station	Lat	Long	Depth	∇T	K	Q	No.	Ref.	Yr
Black Sea	–	–	2269	.48	4.0	1.9?	7	1	61
CH21-1	29°51′N	54°36′W	5610	.50	2.08	1.04	1	2	64
CH21-4	28°56′N	46°44′W	4370	.30	2.24	.67	1	2	64
CH21-5	28°47′N	44°55′W	3940	.51	2.22	1.13	1	2	64
CH21-10	29°04′N	43°12′W	3080	.4	1.96	<.8	1	2	64
CH21-12	28°51′N	42°49′W	3520	.38	2.11	.81	1	2	64
CH21-13	29°02′N	41°10′W	4060	.2	1.94	.4	1	2	64
CH19-C	20°13′N	66°35′W	5810	.56	2.27	1.28	1	2	64
CH19-7-1	20°14′N	66°35′W	5770	.75	2.05	1.54	1	2	64
A-282-3	23°20′N	70°02′W	5480	.54	2.09	1.12	1	3	63
A-282-5	23°28′N	72°18′W	5300	.66	1.77	1.17	1	3	63
A-282-6	25°14′N	73°16′W	5310	.53	2.03	1.08	1	3	63
A-282-7	26°59′N	72°13′W	5150	.58	1.86	1.09	1	3	63
A-282-9	25°18′N	69°01′W	5580	.55	2.11	1.17	1	3	63
A-282-10	23°37′N	67°54′W	5650	.53	2.00	1.06	1	3	63
A-282-11	21°47′N	68°51′W	5560	.61	2.10	1.27	1	3	63
A-282-12	20°22′N	67°23′W	5410	.87	2.01	1.76	1	3	63
A-282-13	21°54′N	66°37′W	5640	.61	1.94	1.19	1	3	63
A-282-14	23°40′N	65°37′W	5800	.59	1.92	1.13	1	3	63
A-282-15	25°29′N	64°34′W	5680	.57	1.92	1.09	1	3	63
A-282-17	25°26′N	66°40′W	5580	.64	1.90	1.22	1	3	63
A-282-18	27°05′N	67°56′W	5200	.57	1.88	1.07	1	3	63
A-282-20	28°44′N	69°05′W	5330	.58	2.06	1.18	1	3	63
A-282-21	28°51′N	66°50′W	5240	.62	1.93	1.19	1	3	63
A-282-22	28°54′N	64°39′W	4900	.61	1.80	1.11	1	3	63
A-282-23	30°27′N	67°58′W	5230	.55	1.91	1.05	1	3	63
AII-1-1	32°02′N	74°09′W	4870	.40	2.05	.81	1	3	63
AII-1-3	30°56′N	74°36′W	3430	.47	1.99	.94	1	3	63
AII-1-5	29°10′N	76°22′W	4990	.46	2.51	1.17	1	3	63
C-36-1	21°08′N	65°02′W	5696	.53	1.82	.96	1	4	64
C-36-3	19°24′N	61°30′W	5468	.73	1.89	~1.37	1	4	64
C-36-5	16°45′N	57°38′W	5853	.12	2.28	>.27	1	4	64
C-36-6	16°47′N	57°49′W	5853	.15	2.0	>.3	1	4	64
C-36-7	16°34′N	57°52′W	4330	.54	1.96	1.06	1	4	64
C-36-8	16°35′N	57°54′W	4330	.54	1.93	1.05	1	4	64

Table 4.4–14 (*Continued*)

Station	Lat	Long	Depth	∇*T*	*K*	*Q*	No.	Ref.	Yr
C-36-9	16°57′N	58°24′W	5890	.22	2.01	>.44	1	4	64
C-36-10	16°18′N	58°37′W	5599	.60	1.86	1.11	1	4	64
ATS296-4	39°32′N	65°50′W	4330	.47	2.29	>1.08	1	4	64
ATS296-6	39°33′N	66°17′W	4325	.56	2.37	>1.33	1	4	64
ATS296-7	39°47′N	65°16′W	4467	.48	2.22	1.07	1	4	64
ATS296-8	39°26′N	65°09′W	4757	.54	2.10	1.14	1	4	64
ATS296-9	39°46′N	66°28′W	3922	.56	2.11	<1.18	1	4	64
C-39-1	20°00′N	59°11′W	5811	.47	1.96	.92	1	4	64
C-39-2	25°18′N	55°44′W	5932	.72	1.93	~1.39	1	4	64
C-39-3	24°04′N	55°14′W	5984	.33	1.82	.60	1	4	64
C-39-5	28°30′N	57°59′W	5800	.48	1.98	.95	1	4	64
C-39-6	29°56′N	60°33′W	5715	.72	1.84	1.33	1	4	64
C-39-7	29°47′N	62°12′W	4865	.66	1.81	1.19	1	4	64
B-D-6	39°36′N	12°13′W	3020	.46	2.30	1.06*	1	5	61
B-D-7	35°59′N	9°59′W	4534	.37	2.31	.87	1	5	61
B-D-8	35°58′N	4°34′W	1251	.57	2.13	1.22	1	5	61
B-D-9	45°28′N	5°47′W	4592	.33	2.26	.75	1	5	61
B-D-10	46°32′N	13°04′W	4413	.50	2.17	1.09	1	5	61
B-D-11	46°30′N	22°58′W	4084	.57	2.25	1.29	1	5	61
B-D-12	46°37′N	27°18′W	4109	3.15	2.07	6.52*	1	5	61
B-D-13	36°20′N	21°00′W	4844	.54	2.12	1.14	1	5	61
B-D-14	35°36′N	19°02′W	5375	.67	2.01	1.34*	1	5	61
B-D-15	35°34′N	18°56′W	5380	.46	2.01	.93*	1	5	61
B-D-16	36°39′N	17°21′W	5146	.53	2.13	1.14	1	5	61
B-D-17	44°55′N	10°45′W	4844	.64	2.18	1.39	1	5	61
B-D-18	40°59′N	15°09′W	5305	.49	2.32	1.14*	1	5	61
B-D-19	42°18′N	11°53′W	3063	.36	2.18	.78	1	5	61
B-D-20	41°27′N	14°40′W	5260	.55	2.18	1.21*	1	5	61
B-D-21	43°42′N	12°39′W	5030	.51	2.29	1.16	1	5	61
CHAIN-1	35°35′N	61°08′W	4590	.62	1.92	1.20	1	6	61
CHAIN-2	35°35′N	61°15′W	4680	.68	1.92	1.31	1	6	61
CHAIN-3	51°18′N	29°35′W	3260	3.7	1.7	>6.2	1	6	61
CHAIN-4	53°53′N	24°05′W	3350	.73	2.10	1.54	1	6	61
V-15-3	00°59′S	38°10′W	4137	.66	2.31	1.52	1	7	62
V-15-4	00°12′N	39°54′W	4111	.48	2.23	1.07	1	7	62
V-15-5	02°30′N	40°55′W	4285	.63	2.19	1.38	1	7	62
V-15-6	05°04′N	41°01′W	4544	.83	2.23	1.85	1	7	62
V-15-7	06°59′N	41°04′W	4636	.90	2.25	2.03	1	7	62
V-15-8	10°45′N	41°21′W	5002	1.51	2.23	3.37	1	7	62
V-15-10	14°14′N	57°06′W	5002	.73	2.19	1.60	1	7	62
V-15-12	17°21′N	65°11′W	4169	.52	2.23	1.16	1	7	62
V-15-13	20°49′N	66°25′W	5227	.68	2.23	1.52	1	7	62
V-15-14	23°14′N	66°36′W	5605	.61	2.23	1.36	1	7	62
V-15-16	21°34′N	67°06′W	5115	.75	2.23	1.67	1	7	62
V-15-19	19°50′N	65°53′W	7934	.52	2.23	1.16	1	7	62
V-15-23	32°35′N	74°24′W	4521	.46	2.23	1.03	1	7	62
V-15-24	32°47′N	74°49′W	4462	.47	2.22	1.04	1	7	62
LSDA-55	33°45′S	15°00′E	4170	.77	2.45	1.88	1	8	64
LSDA-56	33°15′S	11°59′E	4630	.43	2.37	(1.01)	1	8	64
LSDA-57	32°30′S	09°01′E	5040	.40	2.01	.8*	1	8	64

Table 4.4–14 (*Continued*)

Station	Lat	Long	Depth	∇T	K	Q	No.	Ref.	Yr
LSDA-58B	32°00′S	06°06′E	5210	.55	2.01	(1.1)*	1	8	64
LSDA-59	31°37′S	02°47′E	4215	.04	2.18	(.09)	1	8	64
LSDA-60	31°21′S	01°58′E	4190	1.00	2.18	2.17	1	8	64
LSDA-61	30°52′S	00°56′W	3810	.41	2.18	(.90)	1	8	64
LSDA-63	30°16′S	04°21′W	4890	.46	2.15	.99	1	8	64
LSDA-64	30°06′S	05°45′W	4340	.34	2.19	(.74)	1	8	64
LSDA-65	29°43′S	07°16′W	4150	.22	2.23	.48	1	8	64
LSDA-66	29°48′S	08°24′W	4155	.12	2.23	(.27)	1	8	64
LSDA-67	29°51′S	09°25′W	3940	.21	2.32	.48	1	8	64
LSDA-68	29°49′S	10°18′W	3735	.51	2.28	(1.16)	1	8	64
LSDA-69	29°51′S	11°07′W	3690	.50	2.28	(1.15)	1	8	64
LSDA-70	29°55′S	11°54′W	3400	.18	2.28	(.41)	1	8	64
LSDA-71	29°51′S	12°46′W	3200	.50	2.24	1.12	1	8	64
LSDA-72B	29°45′S	14°11′W	3385	.48	2.24	(1.08)	1	8	64
LSDA-73	29°50′S	14°51′W	3735	.15	2.24	(.34)	1	8	64
LSDA-74	29°50′S	15°33′W	3405	.32	2.24	(.72)	1	8	64
LSDA-75	27°22′S	12°34′W	3520	.99	2.27	(2.24)	1	8	64
LSDA-76	27°27′S	10°56′W	3580	.59	2.27	1.34	1	8	64
LSDA-77	26°47′S	13°54′W	2480	.78	2.27	(1.7)*	1	8	64
LSDA-78	25°58′S	14°51′W	3785	.44	2.27	(1.0)*	1	8	64
LSDA-79	24°03′S	15°32′W	4100	.05	2.18	.10	1	8	64
LSDA-80	23°47′S	14°27′W	4000	.41	2.18	(.9)	1	8	64
LSDA-81	23°42′S	12°12′W	3580	.51	2.18	(1.12)	1	8	64
LSDA-82	22°43′S	13°07′W	3605	3.44	2.27	(7.8)*	1	8	64
LSDA-83	21°21′S	11°35′W	2515	3.58	2.27	8.14	1	8	64
LSDA-85	21°15′S	10°39′W	3535	.45	2.18	(.97)	1	8	64
LSDA-86	20°10′S	11°30′W	2925	3.35	2.18	(7.3)*	1	8	64
LSDA-87	19°53′S	12°26′W	2710	1.73	2.18	(3.78)	1	8	64
LSDA-88	19°44′S	12°55′W	3500	.48	2.18	1.04	1	8	64
LSDA-89	18°58′S	12°49′W	3125	.51	2.18	(1.11)	1	8	64
LSDA-90	18°58′S	12°00′W	2510	2.14	2.27	(4.85)	1	8	64
LSDA-91	18°32′S	10°15′W	3395	.21	2.15	.45	1	8	64
LSDA-92	18°08′S	11°15′W	3305	.34	2.18	(.75)	1	8	64
LSDA-93	17°39′S	12°22′W	3440	.74	2.18	(1.61)	1	8	64
LSDA-94	17°15′S	13°20′W	3340	.22	2.18	(.47)	1	8	64
LSDA-95	16°46′S	14°30′W	3455	.62	2.18	(1.35)	1	8	64
LSDA-96	16°15′S	15°45′W	3435	.20	2.18	(.43)	1	8	64
LSDA-97	15°48′S	16°50′W	3820	1.07	2.18	(2.33)	1	8	64
LSDA-98	15°23′S	17°54′W	4390	.23	2.18	(.51)	1	8	64
LSDA-99	14°55′S	19°22′W	4230	.19	2.24	.43	1	8	64
LSDA-100	10°00′S	15°26′W	3595	.13	2.23	.29	1	8	64
LSDA-101	09°11′S	13°20′W	2690	.04	2.16	.08	1	8	64
LSDA-102	09°03′S	10°29′W	3550	.18	2.23	(.40)	1	8	64
LSDA-103	06°43′S	13°27′W	3245	.12	2.18	(.26)	1	8	64
LSDA-104	05°41′S	11°12′W	2905	1.18	2.18	2.58	1	8	64
LSDA-105	04°57′S	09°28′W	3500	.53	2.18	(1.15)	1	8	64
LSDA-106	00°56′S	10°37′W	4040	.50	2.12	(1.07)	1	8	64
LSDA-107	00°28′S	10°51′W	4350	.42	2.12	(.89)	1	8	64
LSDA-108	00°03′N	11°02′W	4125	.68	2.12	1.45	1	8	64
LSDA-109	00°26′N	11°14′W	4215	.85	2.12	(1.80)	1	8	64

Table 4.4–14 (*Continued*)

Station	Lat	Long	Depth	∇*T*	*K*	*Q*	No.	Ref.	Yr
LSDA-110	00°52′N	11°28′W	4950	.07	2.12	(.15)	1	8	64
LSDA-111	02°38′N	12°12′W	4735	.76	1.81	1.37	1	8	64
LSDA-112	05°01′N	12°45′W	4390	.82	1.91	1.56	1	8	64
LSDA-113	07°24′N	17°08′W	4800	.71	1.95	1.39	1	8	64
LSDA-114	06°47′N	19°18′W	4360	.46	2.09	.96	1	8	64
LSDA-115	06°21′N	20°49′W	3590	.58	2.12	(1.22)	1	8	64
LSDA-116	05°07′N	25°15′W	4360	.92	2.16	1.99	1	8	64
LSDA-117	03°21′N	30°52′W	2590	.16	2.34	.37	1	8	64
LSDA-118	03°18′N	31°00′W	2820	1.16	2.31	(2.68)	1	8	64
LSDA-119	03°15′N	31°35′W	2415	1.00	2.31	(2.3)*	1	8	64
LSDA-120	03°57′N	34°04′W	3340	.82	2.28	1.87	1	8	64
LSDA-121	05°42′N	32°51′W	2955	2.23	2.28	(5.08)	1	8	64
LSDA-122	05°59′N	32°28′W	3300	2.26	2.31	(5.22)	1	8	64
LSDA-124	08°26′N	34°23′W	4790	.76	2.04	1.56	1	8	64
LSDA-125	09°39′N	37°40′W	4045	.11	2.16	(.23)	1	8	64
LSDA-126	09°34′N	39°32′W	3340	.57	2.28	(1.31)	1	8	64
LSDA-127	09°41′N	40°49′W	2315	.74	2.28	(1.7)*	1	8	64
LSDA-128	09°45′N	41°18′W	3295	.74	2.28	(1.70)	1	8	64
LSDA-130	11°35′N	44°03′W	2755	1.05	2.28	(2.4)*	1	8	64
LSDA-131	11°34′N	44°48′W	3830	.40	2.12	.84	1	8	64
LSDA-132	11°34′N	45°33′W	4105	1.11	2.08	(2.30)	1	8	64
LSDA-133	12°17′N	46°13′W	4515	.22	2.08	(.46)	1	8	64
LSDA-134	14°59′N	58°19′W	3535	.32	2.22	.72	1	8	64
LSDA-135	15°04′N	59°58′W	4480	.32	2.20	.71	1	8	64
LSDA-136	15°04′N	60°30′W	2335	.93	2.15	2.0*	1	8	64
LSDA-137	15°02′N	62°15′W	2720	.93	2.15	(2.0)	1	8	64
LSDA-139	15°00′N	63°50′W	2082	.66	2.06	1.36	2	8	64
ZEP-4	13°36′N	71°59′W	4232	.72	2.0	1.4	1	9	64
ZEP-5	13°43′N	68°38′W	5042	.58	1.9	1.1	1	9	64
ZEP-8	14°22′N	62°19′W	2877	.70	1.9	1.3*	1	9	64
ZEP-9	16°24′N	57°39′W	4647	.39	1.8	.7?	1	9	64
ZEP-11	19°10′N	52°03′W	5344	.81	1.7	1.4	1	9	64
ZEP-12	20°12′N	49°01′W	4632	.30	1.5	.5	1	9	64
ZEP-13	21°06′N	46°30′W	3912	.16	1.9	.3	1	9	64
ZEP-14	21°04′N	44°57′W	3255	.84	2.1	1.8	1	9	64
ZEP-15	21°56′N	45°46′W	3372	3.24	2.0	6.5	1	9	64
ZEP-16	23°06′N	45°39′W	3983	1.48	2.0	3.0	1	9	64
ZEP-17	23°34′N	44°14′W	4960	.81	2.0	1.6	1	9	64
ZEP-18	23°57′N	44°59′W	3493	1.34	2.1	2.8*	1	9	64
ZEP-19	23°36′N	42°28′W	4113	.23	2.1	.5*	1	9	64
ZEP-20	24°16′N	39°06′W	5439	.19	1.9	.4	1	9	64
ZEP-22	25°05′N	34°13′W	5602	.36	1.9	.7	1	9	64
ZEP-23	26°14′N	26°27′W	5210	.59	2.0	1.2	1	9	64
ZEP-25	26°57′N	19°58′W	4298	.46	2.1	1.0	1	9	64
ZEP-26	31°12′N	11°50′W	3210	.50	2.2	1.1*	1	9	64
ZEP-27	33°35′N	9°43′W	4340	.45	2.2	1.0	1	9	64
ZEP-32	40°37′N	5°50′E	2720	.56	2.2	1.2?	1	9	64
D 4775	29°02′N	25°27′W	5342	–	–	1.39	1	10	63
D 4777	28°60′N	25°26′W	5344	–	–	1.20	1	10	63
D 4778	29°03′N	25°33′W	5342	–	–	1.13	1	10	63

Table 4.4–14 (*Continued*)

Station	Lat	Long	Depth	∇T	K	Q	No.	Ref.	Yr
D 4784	29°04′N	25°27′W	5339	–	–	1.21	1	10	63
D 4788	29°05′N	25°15′W	5299	–	–	1.29	1	10	63
D 4809	28°51′N	25°27′W	4871	–	–	1.11	1	10	63
D 4813	28°50′N	25°24′W	4862	–	–	1.05	1	10	63
D 4817	29°34′N	25°18′W	5400	–	–	1.03	1	10	63
D 4821	29°35′N	25°23′W	5297	–	–	1.23	1	10	63
D 4822	29°08′N	24°19′W	5281	–	–	1.33	1	10	63
D 4528	45°19′N	11°27′W	4143	–	–	1.13	1	11	63
D 4531	45°19′N	11°28′W	4125	–	–	1.00	1	11	63
C19-6-17	31°54′N	64°44′W	4262	–	–	.97	1	11	63
CH21-8	29°04′N	44°11′W	–	–	–	+?	1	11	63
CH21-14	34°00′N	15°51′W	3810	–	–	.57	1	11	63
CH21-16	34°06′N	14°24′W	4315	–	–	.94	1	11	63
CH21-18	39°31′N	05°26′E	2826	–	–	>.87	1	11	63
CH21-19	42°14′N	07°09′E	2731	–	–	2.5	1	11	63
D 4790	27°10′N	21°06′W	4702	–	–	1.06	1	11	63
D 4794	27°10′N	21°00′W	4682	–	–	~1.2	1	11	63
D 4795	27°13′N	21°05′W	4707	–	–	.92	1	11	63
D 4805	29°35′N	23°52′W	5240	–	–	1.13	1	11	63
D 4824	43°06′N	19°50′W	5959	–	–	1.30	1	11	63
V18-151	19°51′N	84°56′W	4564	.7	2.0	(1.4)	1	12	64
V18-153	26°35′N	88°49′W	2582	.22	2.3	.5	1	12	64
V18-155	26°28′N	68°25′W	5284	.55	2.0	1.1	1	12	64
V18-158	38°45′N	67°33′W	4184	.55	1.8	1.0	1	12	64
V18-159	39°11′N	65°26′W	4730	.55	2.0	(1.1)	1	12	64
V19-1	34°50′N	70°15′W	4716	.42	1.9	(.8)	1	12	64
V19-2	32°36′N	71°19′W	5392	.63	1.9	(1.2)	1	12	64
V19-3	28°20′N	68°06′W	5261	.68	1.9	1.3	1	12	64
V19-4	27°28′N	68°27′W	2858	.47	1.9	.9	1	12	64
V19-5	24°16′N	67°11′W	5562	.63	1.9	(1.2)	1	12	64
V19-6	16°06′N	66°29′W	4520	.6	2.0	1.2	1	12	64
C7-2	13°06′N	63°09′W	1060	.55	2.0	(1.1)	1	12	64
C7-3	12°34′N	66°18′W	4529	.4	2.0	(.8)	1	12	64
C7-4	13°59′N	71°43′W	3948	.75	2.0	(1.5)	1	12	64
C7-5	12°04′N	74°54′W	3611	.5	2.0	(1.0)	1	12	64
C7-6	14°11′N	76°32′W	4087	.6	2.0	(1.2)	1	12	64
C7-9	14°50′N	73°50′W	3460	.5	2.0	(1.0)	1	12	64
C7-10	15°23′N	73°17′W	3324	.75	2.0	(1.5)	1	12	64
C7-11	16°08′N	72°48′W	2893	.55	2.0	(1.1)	1	12	64
C7-12	14°36′N	70°57′W	3525	.5	2.0	(1.0)	1	12	64
Bullard 1	49°46′N	12°30′W	2032	.426	2.59	1.10	1	13	54
Bullard 2	49°58′N	18°33′W	4017	.548	2.58	1.42	1	13	54
Bullard 3	49°09′N	17°38′W	4532	.237	2.43	.58	1	13	54
Bullard 4	48°14′N	16°58′W	4670	.254	2.28	.58	1	13	54
Bullard 5	48°52′N	15°00′W	4710	.455	2.64	1.20	1	13	54

Table 4.4–14 (*Continued*)

REFERENCES

1. **Sisoev,** *Okeanologiya,* 1, 886, 1961.
2. **Lister, C. R. B. and Reitzel, J. S.,** *J. Geophys. Res.,* 69, 2151, 1964.
3. **Reitzel, J.,** *J. Geophys. Res.,* 68, 5191, 1963.
4. **Birch, F. S.,** M.Sc. thesis, University of Wisconsin, Madison, 1964.
5. **Bullard, E.,** *Geophys. J.,* 4, 282, 1961.
6. **Reitzel, J.,** *J. Geophys. Res.,* 66, 2267, 1961.
7. **Gerard, R. et al.,** *J. Geophys. Res.,* 67, 785, 1962.
8. **Vacquier, V. and Von Herzen, R. P.,** *J. Geophys. Res.,* 69, 1093, 1964.
9. **Nason, R. D. and Lee, W. H. K.,** *J. Geophys. Res.,* 69, 4875, 1964.
10. **Lister, C. R. B.,** *J. Geophys. Res.,* 68, 5569, 1963.
11. **Lister, C. R. B.,** *Geophys. J.,* 7, 571, 1963.
12. **Langseth, M. G. and Grim, P. J.,** *J. Geophys. Res.,* 69, 4916, 1964.
13. **Bullard, E.,** *Proc. R. Soc. Lond.,* 222A, 408, 1954.

Table 4.4-15
HEAT FLOW IN THE INDIAN OCEAN

Including Andaman Sea, Gulf of Aden, and Red Sea

Station	Lat	Long	Depth	∇T	K	Q	No.	Ref.	Yr
MSN-12	9°14′S	127°30′E	3300	.81	2.09	1.69	1	1	65
MSN-15	7°46′S	121°14′E	4840	.84	2.02	1.7	1	1	65
MSN-16	11°58′S	115°26′E	5010	.63	1.77	1.12	1	1	65
MSN-17	12°48′S	115°24′E	5400	.64	1.65	1.05	1	1	65
MSN-18	10°11′S	115°19′E	4330	.24	1.63	.39	1	1	65
MSN-20	13°19′S	109°34′E	4630	.80	1.85	1.48	1	1	65
MSN-21	11°39′S	109°35′E	4605	1.00	1.87	1.87	1	1	65
MSN-23	8°49′S	109°36′E	3300	.26	1.88	.48	1	1	65
MSN-24	12°21′S	101°25′E	4745	.78	1.99	1.56	1	1	65
MSN-28	16°59′S	93°29′E	5230	.61	1.63	1.0	1	1	65
MSN-29	18°14′S	86°42′E	4455	.89	1.83	1.63	1	1	65
MSN-30	15°51′S	81°10′E	5000	1.01	1.71	1.73	1	1	65
MSN-32	14°05′S	72°15′E	5200	.77	1.55	1.20	1	1	65
MSN-33	14°56′S	70°13′E	4460	.07	2.06	.14	1	1	65
MSN-34	16°25′S	66°01′E	3660	1.40	1.99	2.78	1	1	65
MSN-35	16°58′S	64°46′E	4055	1.10	1.99	(2.19)	1	1	65
MSN-36	17°48′S	62°40′E	3740	.15	2.26	.34	1	1	65
MSN-38	26°22′S	74°08′E	4130	2.48	1.98	4.91	1	1	65
MSN-40	33°20′S	72°37′E	4220	.42	2.19	.91	1	1	65
MSN-41	37°44′S	71°47′E	4260	.66	2.08	1.38	1	1	65
MSN-42	42°09′S	70°37′E	4200	.80	2.08	1.67	1	1	65
MSN-43	39°50′S	75°03′E	3780	–	2.0	–?	1	1	65
MSN-44	38°26′S	79°34′E	3410	.25	2.0	(.5)	1	1	65
MSN-45	37°50′S	85°22′E	3600	.35	2.0	(.7)	1	1	65
MSN-46	37°18′S	90°42′E	3855	.65	2.0	(1.3)	1	1	65
MSN-47	36°19′S	98°41′E	4375	.39	1.93	.76	1	1	65
MSN-48	39°18′S	119°52′E	4895	.58	1.78	1.04	1	1	65
MSN-49	49°31′S	132°14′E	3500	.72	1.8	(1.3)	1	1	65
Z-1	12°27′N	47°07′E	1820	2.95	2.03	5.98	1	1	65
Z-2	12°57′N	48°16′E	2205	1.88	1.92	(3.62)	1	1	65

Note: See list of symbols in Table 4.4–14.

Table 4.4–15 (*Continued*)

Station	Lat	Long	Depth	∇*T*	*K*	*Q*	No.	Ref.	Yr
Z-3	13°17′N	49°15′E	2425	1.78	1.81	3.22	1	1	65
Z-4	12°54′N	49°38′E	2200	1.29	1.92	(2.47)	1	1	65
Z-5	12°25′N	50°33′E	2420	1.53	2.02	3.09	1	1	65
Z-6	9°08′N	54°42′E	3705	.79	2.11	1.66	1	1	65
Z-7	9°09′N	57°30′E	3265	.68	2.01	(1.37)	1	1	65
Z-8	9°16′N	59°00′E	3200	.91	1.91	1.74	1	1	65
Z-9	9°34′N	59°52′E	3895	.84	2.01	(1.68)	1	1	65
Z-10	9°32′N	61°24′E	4580	.45	2.10	.95	1	1	65
Z-11	9°34′N	63°06′E	4505	.10	2.25	(.23)*	1	1	65
Z-12	9°40′N	66°19′E	4450	.35	2.30	.8*	1	1	65
Z-13	9°48′N	69°15′E	4550	.69	2.17	1.49	1	1	65
Z-14	9°50′N	71°50′E	2370	.58	2.21	1.29	1	1	65
Z-15	9°56′N	73°08′E	1925	.81	2.09	1.70	1	1	65
Z-16	9°59′N	74°50′E	2285	.82	1.92	1.57	1	1	65
LSDA-1	8°13′N	70°39′E	4145	.71	2.03	1.44	1	1	65
LSDA-2	3°57′N	70°49′E	4130	.84	1.91	1.6*	1	1	65
LSDA-3	0°05′S	71°50′E	4200	.51	2.15	1.1*	1	1	65
LSDA-4	2°40′S	73°16′E	2980	.79	2.28	1.8*	1	1	65
LSDA-5	5°21′S	75°08′E	5220	.92	1.64	1.51	1	1	65
LSDA-6	5°23′S	72°47′E	2530	.84	2.28	1.92	1	1	65
LSDA-7	5°40′S	70°17′E	3935	.30	1.88	.57	1	1	65
LSDA-8	5°52′S	66°36′E	4370	.16	1.90	(.30)	1	1	65
LSDA-9	5°34′S	63°42′E	4210	.87	1.91	1.67	1	1	65
LSDA-10	5°26′S	59°14′E	3980	1.19	1.97	2.35*	2	1	65
LSDA-11	5°30′S	57°56′E	2525	.61	2.02	1.23	1	1	65
LSDA-12	9°56′S	57°07′E	4045	.76	2.03	(1.55)	2	1	65
LSDA-13	10°21′S	58°31′E	3575	.46	2.02	.92	1	1	65
LSDA-14	10°34′S	59°51′E	2315	.71	2.04	1.44	1	1	65
LSDA-15	13°42′S	59°42′E	3900	.50	2.00	1.00	1	1	65
LSDA-16	17°20′S	57°42′E	4145	.60	2.21	1.32	1	1	65
LSDA-17	22°01′S	57°34′E	4750	.51	1.77	.90	1	1	65
LSDA-18	24°34′S	57°26′E	5000	.77	1.57	1.21	1	1	65
LSDA-19	26°53′S	58°12′E	5540	.58	1.58	.91	1	1	65
LSDA-20	29°53′S	61°52′E	4620	.41	1.70	.7	1	1	65
LSDA-21B	31°25′S	61°56′E	4420	.24	1.73	.42	1	1	65
LSDA-22	32°55′S	62°25′E	4745	.43	1.59	.68	1	1	65
LSDA-23B	39°44′S	63°56′E	4810	1.70	2.18	(3.7)*	1	1	65
LSDA-24	44°36′S	70°57′E	3580	.79	1.89	1.49	1	1	65
LSDA-25	35°47′S	73°37′E	4380	.20	1.93	.38	1	1	65
LSDA-26	36°52′S	76°22′E	3925	.94	2.17	2.03	1	1	65
LSDA-30	31°28′S	114°24′E	3740	.52	2.04	1.05	2	1	65
LSDA-32	29°42′S	111°30′E	5340	.82	2.18	(1.79)	1	1	65
LSDA-33	25°03′S	104°12′E	5100	.71	1.63	1.15	1	1	65
LSDA-34	16°25′S	89°19′E	5625	.85	1.64	1.39	1	1	65
LSDA-35	13°48′S	90°50′E	5200	.82	1.59	1.30	1	1	65
LSDA-36	13°09′S	93°13′E	5230	1.83	1.64	3.0*	1	1	65
LSDA-37	14°56′S	108°09′E	5580	.68	1.70	1.15	1	1	65
LSDA-38	13°46′S	115°32′E	5680	.69	1.65	1.14	1	1	65
LSDA-39	13°31′S	118°29′E	5680	.57	1.64	.93	1	1	65
LSDA-50	30°08′S	37°47′E	4990	.51	1.97	1.00	1	1	65

Table 4.4–15 (*Continued*)

Station	Lat	Long	Depth	∇T	K	Q	No.	Ref.	Yr
LSDA-51	31°04′S	36°40′E	4535	.98	2.26	(2.22)	1	1	65
LSDA-52	31°39′S	35°57′E	2545	.34	2.40	.82	1	1	65
LSDA-53	32°14′S	34°16′E	2660	.63	2.30	(1.45)	1	1	65
LSDA-54	32°22′S	32°47′E	3560	.02	2.12	.04	1	1	65
LSDH-1	9°07′N	72°59′E	2135	.77	2.08	1.61	1	1	65
LSDH-2	9°03′N	73°10′E	2110	.57	2.08	1.18	1	1	65
LSDH-3	7°24′N	70°40′E	4110	.66	2.19	1.44*	1	1	65
LSDH-4	5°22′S	74°17′E	4780	1.15	1.64	1.88	1	1	65
LSDH-5	5°40′S	69°40′E	3815	.00	2.00	.00	1	1	65
LSDH-6	5°53′S	65°57′E	4260	.61	1.90	1.16	1	1	65
LSDH-7	5°31′S	63°04′E	4255	1.16	1.94	(2.26)	1	1	65
LSDH-8	5°28′S	60°02′E	4100	.78	1.97	(1.54)	1	1	65
LSDH-9	5°26′S	59°29′E	3952	1.96	2.02	3.95*	2	1	65
LSDH-11	4°10′S	57°15′E	3765	.94	2.03	1.9*	1	1	65
LSDH-13	9°49′S	56°28′E	3885	.13	2.03	.27	1	1	65
LSDH-14	10°05′S	57°53′E	3935	.64	2.02	(1.29)	1	1	65
LSDH-15	10°30′S	59°23′E	2858	.66	1.94	1.28	2	1	65
LSDH-18	31°14′S	62°58′E	5062	.14	1.60	.22	2	1	65
LSDH-20	33°16′S	61°43′E	4695	1.13	1.56	1.77	1	1	65
LSDH-21	39°54′S	67°53′E	4065	.00	2.18	.00	1	1	65
LSDH-22	40°47′S	72°46′E	4000	.17	2.30	.40	1	1	65
LSDH-23	40°58′S	75°08′E	4030	.25	2.16	.54	1	1	65
LSDH-24	40°19′S	76°32′E	3020	.94	2.25	2.12	1	1	65
LSDH-25	36°05′S	75°59′E	3290	.80	2.17	(1.74)	1	1	65
LSDH-26	37°21′S	76°35′E	3380	.44	2.10	.92	1	1	65
LSDH-27	32°58′S	96°02′E	4030	.01	2.1	(.01)	1	1	65
LSDH-28	32°06′S	100°20′E	2450	1.22	2.37	2.9*	1	1	65
LSDH-29	32°45′S	102°45′E	4760	.54	1.71	.93	1	1	65
LSDH-30	32°59′S	103°33′E	5130	.75	1.70	1.27	1	1	65
LSDH-32	33°01′S	111°11′E	4390	2.34	2.26	(5.3)*	1	1	65
LSDH-33	32°17′S	113°58′E	4190	.44	2.26	.99	1	1	65
LSDH-34	29°16′S	110°42′E	5550	.92	2.18	2.0*	1	1	65
LSDH-35	25°40′S	105°22′E	4830	.69	1.63	(1.13)	1	1	65
LSDH-36	24°33′S	103°39′E	5400	.64	1.63	(1.04)	1	1	65
LSDH-37	20°11′S	96°22′E	4910	.66	1.59	1.05	1	1	65
LSDH-38	14°12′S	89°50′E	5315	.66	1.63	1.07	1	1	65
LSDH-39	13°39′S	91°31′E	5150	.93	1.59	(1.48)	1	1	65
LSDH-40	13°23′S	92°32′E	5200	1.85	1.73	3.20	1	1	65
LSDH-43	14°06′S	101°22′E	5110	1.11	1.63	1.81	1	1	65
LSDH-44	14°56′S	107°16′E	5805	.79	1.74	1.37	1	1	65
LSDH-45	14°58′S	109°12′E	5630	.65	1.74	(1.13)	1	1	65
LSDH-46	14°13′S	114°54′E	5670	.63	1.62	1.02	1	1	65
LSDH-47	13°09′S	116°29′E	5670	.69	1.60	1.11	1	1	65
LSDH-48	13°41′S	117°23′E	5715	.58	1.62	(.94)	1	1	65
V18-54	36°55′S	23°24′E	5064	.63	2.42	1.53	1	1	65
V18-55	38°59′S	29°56′E	4202	.62	2.52	1.57	1	1	65
V18-58	31°12′S	48°05′E	4395	.74	2.23	1.65	1	1	65
V18-59	26°42′S	50°28′E	5266	1.08	1.68	1.81	1	1	65
V18-60	23°59′S	51°11′E	4928	.87	1.92	1.67	1	1	65
V18-61	21°26′S	51°37′E	4959	.73	1.99	1.46	1	1	65

Table 4.4–15 (*Continued*)

Station	Lat	Long	Depth	∇T	K	Q	No.	Ref.	Yr
V18-63	20°35′S	63°32′E	3296	.16	2.67	.43	1	1	65
V18-67	25°29′S	85°09′E	4559	.96	2.74	>2.64	1	1	65
V18-69	25°47′S	93°43′E	4435	.74	1.75	1.30	1	1	65
V18-70	25°46′S	95°58′E	4937	.75	1.81	1.35	1	1	65
V18-71	25°41′S	99°04′E	5365	.68	1.76	1.20	1	1	65
V18-72	25°41′S	101°56′E	4720	.85	1.82	1.54	1	1	65
V18-73	27°59′S	108°40′E	5148	.63	2.00	1.26	1	1	65
V18-74	36°07′S	118°47′E	4590	.47	2.19	1.02	1	1	65
V18-76	37°27′S	133°40′E	5570	.52	2.22	>1.15	1	1	65
V19-54	7°43′S	103°15′E	6411	.96	2.03	1.95	1	1	65
V19-55	7°16′S	102°02′E	5663	.91	1.89	1.72	1	1	65
V19-57	14°31′S	101°21′E	5363	.71	1.69	1.20	1	1	65
V19-58	16°20′S	100°33′E	5906	.60	1.86	1.12	1	1	65
V19-59	18°11′S	99°24′E	5754	.70	1.81	1.26	1	1	65
V19-60	19°02′S	97°15′E	5500	.89	1.91	1.70	1	1	65
V19-61	20°56′S	91°12′E	4840	.83	1.87	1.55	1	1	65
V19-64	18°23′S	82°08′E	5224	.85	1.63	1.38	1	1	65
V19-65	16°11′S	82°06′E	5380	.37	1.77	.66	1	1	65
V19-66	14°11′S	82°08′E	4798	.74	1.84	1.36	1	1	65
V19-67	12°44′S	82°01′E	–	1.20	1.68	~2.02	1	1	65
V19-68	10°13′S	81°37′E	5107	.97	1.63	1.58	1	1	65
V19-69	7°54′S	81°25′E	5229	.58	1.76	1.02	1	1	65
V19-70	7°04′S	80°46′E	5045	.77	1.79	1.38	1	1	65
V19-72	7°07′N	76°33′E	1770	.49	2.22	1.09	1	1	65
V19-73	7°35′N	74°13′E	2769	.80	2.15	1.72	1	1	65
V19-74	8°07′N	73°15′E	2186	.71	2.32	1.65	1	1	65
V19-75	8°09′N	70°38′E	4128	.76	2.36	1.80	1	1	65
V19-76	8°09′N	69°15′E	4650	.90	2.11	1.90	1	1	65
V19-78	8°07′N	62°47′E	4325	.49	2.32	1.13	1	1	65
V19-79	7°26′N	61°04′E	3605	1.19	2.50	2.98	1	1	65
V19-80	6°42′N	59°20′E	2857	.28	2.30	.64	1	1	65
V19-82	7°04′N	60°55′E	2680	.61	2.02	1.23	1	1	65
V19-83	6°52′N	60°42′E	3356	.25	2.41	.61	1	1	65
V19-84	6°37′N	59°48′E	2923	.91	2.33	2.12	1	1	65
V19-85	6°10′N	57°10′E	4128	.50	2.31	1.16	1	1	65
V19-87	4°43′N	52°05′E	5111	.54	1.96	1.05	1	1	65
V19-88	2°29′N	51°28′E	5095	.63	1.78	1.12	1	1	65
V19-89	0°29′S	53°41′E	4857	.93	1.92	1.78	1	1	65
V19-90	2°40′S	54°45′E	4186	.74	2.30	1.71	1	1	65
V19-91	3°34′S	51°51′E	5056	.88	1.89	(1.66)	1	1	65
V19-92	3°24′S	48°46′E	4987	.58	1.99	~1.15	1	1	65
V19-93	3°11′S	45°49′E	4607	.61	1.90	1.15	1	1	65
V19-94	3°43′S	43°52′E	4089	.56	2.32	1.30	1	1	65
V19-95	4°13′S	41°33′E	2722	.52	2.44	1.27	1	1	65
V19-96	5°20′S	40°26′E	1863	.74	2.34	1.72	1	1	65
V19-97	6°59′S	41°11′E	3369	.62	2.39	1.48	1	1	65
V19-98	9°28′S	43°19′E	3643	.69	2.18	1.50	1	1	65
V19-100	13°08′S	44°09′E	3548	.65	2.10	1.37	1	1	65
V19-101	14°53′S	42°51′E	3250	.58	2.30	1.33	1	1	65
V19-102	16°56′S	41°06′E	2548	.29	2.51	.72	1	1	65

Table 4.4–15 (*Continued*)

Station	Lat	Long	Depth	∇T	K	Q	No.	Ref.	Yr
V19-103	17°54′S	39°30′E	2314	.50	2.23	1.12	1	1	65
V19-106	22°57′S	42°10′E	3175	.64	2.18	1.40	1	1	65
V19-107	22°58′S	41°22′E	3885	–	–	–?	1	1	65
V19-108	23°11′S	39°58′E	3345	.70	2.19	1.54	1	1	65
V19-109	23°22′S	38°51′E	3087	.61	2.36	1.44	1	1	65
V19-110	23°31′S	37°51′E	2903	.80	1.99	1.60	1	1	65
V19-111	25°20′S	36°47′E	2203	.56	2.34	1.32	1	1	65
V19-112	31°42′S	38°10′E	5018	.59	2.03	1.20	1	1	65
V19-114	34°24′S	31°25′E	4124	.67	2.23	~1.50	1	1	65
V19-115	35°30′S	29°57′E	4565	.53	2.49	1.32	1	1	65
V19-116	35°55′S	27°45′E	4656	.63	2.67	1.68	1	1	65
AND-1	10°01′N	93°45′E	4206	3.1	1.70	5.27	1	2	64
AND-2	11°01′N	93°42′E	2562	1.3	1.83	2.38	1	2	64
AND-3	11°56′N	93°22′E	1390	.5	1.79	.90	1	2	64
AND-4	12°44′N	93°58′E	2151	1.1	1.76	1.94	1	2	64
DIS 5116	5°35′N	61°57′E	3560	.663	2.02	1.34	1	3	65
DIS 5122	5°35′N	61°56′E	3560	.642	2.01	1.29	1	3	65
DIS 5125	2°45′N	60°15′E	4806	.265	1.70	.45	1	3	65
DIS 5135	2°55′N	59°53′E	4697	.412	1.77	.73	1	3	65
DIS 5139	1°54′N	56°10′E	4812	.728	1.73	1.26	1	3	65
DIS 5144	1°41′S	42°13′E	2255	.700	2.00	1.40	1	3	65
DIS 5149	2°24′S	43°24′E	3552	.643	1.96	1.26	1	3	65
DIS 5152	2°32′S	44°56′E	4160	.618	1.86	1.15	1	3	65
DIS 5155	2°48′S	47°03′E	4812	.610	1.77	1.08	1	3	65
DIS 5160	3°30′S	49°40′E	5042	.723	1.77	1.28	1	3	65
DIS 5165	3°33′S	51°29′E	5100	.418	1.70	.71	1	3	65
DIS 5171	2°10′S	57°25′E	4402	.221	2.26	.50?	1	3	65
DIS 5177	2°12′S	57°20′E	4402	.519	2.12	1.10	1	3	65
DIS 5180	6°39′S	54°16′E	3824	.748	2.06	1.54	1	3	65
DIS 5190	2°51′S	47°00′E	4800	.659	1.82	1.20	1	3	65
DIS 5194	2°34′S	44°53′E	4180	.597	1.91	1.14	1	3	65
DIS 5201	1°42′S	42°15′E	2046	.613	2.04	1.25	1	3	65
DIS 5204	3°31′S	48°23′E	4940	.761	1.80	1.37	1	3	65
DIS 5207	3°34′S	50°29′E	5082	.710	1.83	1.30	1	3	65
DIS 5215	2°25′S	54°45′E	4360	.750	2.00	(1.50)	1	3	65
DIS 5226	11°07′N	54°03′E	4028	.745	2.09	1.55	1	3	65
DIS 5227	11°39′N	47°50′E	1900	1.80	2.14	3.85	1	3	65
DIS 5229	12°29′N	47°02′E	2197	2.69	2.29	6.15	1	3	65
DIS 5230	12°56′N	46°36′E	1600	1.50	2.16	3.25	1	3	65
DIS 5231	15°58′N	41°31′E	1735	1.81	2.31	4.18	1	3	65
DIS 5232	18°24′N	39°47′E	1480	.404	2.62	1.06	1	3	65
DIS 5234	20°27′N	37°55′E	0870	–	2.75	+?	1	3	65

(From Clark, S. P., Jr., *Handbook of Physical Constants,* Geological Society of America, Memoir 97, 1966. With permission.)

REFERENCES

1. **Von Herzen, R. P. and Langseth, M. G.**, in *Physics and Chemistry of the Earth,* Vol. 6, Ahrens, L. H., Ed., Pergamon Press, New York, 1965.
2. **Burns,** *J. Geophys. Res.*, 69, 4918, 1964.
3. **Sclater, J.**, private communication, 1964.

Table 4.4–16
HEAT FLOW IN THE PACIFIC OCEAN

Including Japan Sea, Bering Sea, and Gulf of California

Station	Lat	Long	Depth	∇T	K	Q	No.	Ref.	Yr.
Eniwetok	11°30′N	162°15′E	0	.18	5.	0.9	1	3	56
E1	38°09′N	142°58′E	1710	.130	2.10	.27	1	4	62
E2	37°59′N	143°58′E	7345	.542	2.11	1.14	1	4	62
E6	38°12′N	147°55′E	5631	1.05	1.95	2.05	1	4	62
F20	33°39′N	161°39′E	5605	.681	2.00	(1.36)	1	5	64
F23	34°23′N	142°15′E	7490	.630	2.21	1.39	1	5	64
F24	34°04′N	142°56′E	5110	.598	2.07	1.24*	1	5	64
F25	33°53′N	145°26′E	5770	.549	1.81	.99*	1	5	64
Akko 7	39°22′N	150°03′E	5480	1.74	1.90	3.30*	1	5	64
Akko 8	39°30′N	143°28′E	2800	.546	2.16	~1.18	1	5	64
MYJ 1	34°32′N	139°46′E	1710	.574	2.54	1.46*	1	5	64
Akko 11	29°53′N	137°56′E	3960	.397	2.06	.82	1	5	64
Akko 12	32°35′N	138°06′E	3970	1.20	2.42	2.88*	1	5	64
G1	40°02′N	142°31′E	810	.702	1.75	1.26*?	1	5	64
G12	43°26′N	148°15′E	5175	.407	1.53	.62	1	5	64
G202	40°28′N	142°59′E	1550	.464	2.16	1.00*?	1	5	64
G*2	39°42′N	145°25′E	5315	.610	1.82	1.11	1	5	64
G*5	40°24′N	145°40′E	5215	.344	1.67	.58	1	5	64
G*10	41°52′N	145°09′E	4435	.356	1.80	.64*	1	5	64
G*11	41°02′N	146°00′E	5495	.568	2.44	1.38	1	5	64
Akko M1	38°11′N	133°45′E	0970	1.08	1.98	2.13?	1	6	65
Akko M2	40°47′N	132°04′E	3080	.35	1.78	.63	1	6	65
Akko M3	40°48′N	134°24′E	3400	1.30	1.79	2.33	1	6	65
Akko M4	38°01′N	135°57′E	2550	1.39	1.75	2.44	1	6	65
Akko M5	40°13′N	136°52′E	2525	.80	1.70	1.40	1	6	65
Akko M6	40°59′N	137°24′E	3422	.96	2.08	1.98	1	6	65
Akko M7	40°23′N	139°11′E	2670	1.18	1.95	2.02	1	6	65
Akko M8	39°29′N	137°59′E	2508	.72	1.81	1.30	1	6	65
EN 1	39°00′N	139°10′E	0720	.83	1.67	1.4?	1	6	65
EN 2	38°32′N	139°10′E	0320	.26	1.82	.5?	1	6	65
H 11	39°50′N	153°52′E	5560	.50	1.74	.88	1	6	65
H 12	40°05′N	152°01′E	5475	.51	1.68	.86	1	6	65
H 14A	40°02′N	146°02′E	5150	.59	1.59	.94*	1	6	65
Makko 1	37°21′N	134°07′E	2440	1.45	1.83	2.66	1	6	65
Makko 2	39°10′N	133°02′E	2720	1.18	1.57	1.84	1	6	65
Saiko 3	40°01′N	132°29′E	3330	1.36	1.65	2.24	1	6	65
Saiko 4	41°01′N	131°54′E	3470	1.34	1.59	2.13	1	6	65
Saiko 5	41°20′N	132°48′E	3600	1.21	1.56	1.89*	1	6	65
Makko 3	41°34′N	133°35′E	3650	1.29	1.56	2.08	1	6	65
Makko 4	39°55′N	134°50′E	1450	1.09	1.65	1.80?	1	6	65
Makko 5	38°58′N	135°25′E	3180	1.23	1.69	2.08	1	6	65
Makko 6	38°02′N	135°57′E	2740	1.35	1.65	2.23	1	6	65
Makko 7	38°13′N	137°52′E	1970	1.25	1.80	2.25?	1	6	65
Makko 8	39°13′N	132°25′E	2340	1.06	1.96	2.07	1	6	65
Makko 9	40°08′N	136°44′E	2650	1.47	1.78	2.62	1	6	65

Note: See list of symbols in Table 4.4–14.

Table 4.4–16 (*Continued*)

Station	Lat	Long	Depth	∇*T*	*K*	*Q*	No.	Ref.	Yr
Makko 10	41°03′N	136°06′E	3450	1.25	1.55	1.95	1	6	65
Makko 11	42°00′N	138°10′E	3670	1.33	1.88	2.51	1	6	65
Makko 12	41°59′N	139°23′E	1480	1.41	1.92	2.70?	1	6	65
Makko 13	43°32′N	140°20′E	0700	1.15	1.62	1.87?	1	6	65
Makko 14	43°59′N	139°20′E	1710	1.22	1.80	2.19?	1	6	65
Makko 15	44°31′N	138°26′E	2430	1.13	1.72	1.94	1	6	65
Makko 16	44°59′N	137°29′E	1630	1.34	1.73	2.32?	1	6	65
Makko 17	45°00′N	138°36′E	2150	.45	1.80	.79*	1	6	65
Makko 18	45°02′N	139°37′E	0885	1.00	1.92	1.92?	1	6	65
Makko 19	45°05′N	140°44′E	0330	1.31	2.04	2.66*?	1	6	65
Tokko-1	31°58′N	140°29′E	–	1.58	2.10	<3.2*	1	6	65
Tokko-3	33°44′N	139°34′E	–	1.54	1.60	2.46*	1	6	65
Tokko-4	33°55′N	139°14′E	–	1.12	1.60	1.79	1	6	65
Men-2A	33°45′N	119°31′W	1900	.72	2.00	1.43	1	7	64
Men-3	33°58′N	122°34′W	4200	.30	1.89	.57	1	7	64
Men-4	34°02′N	125°15′W	4640	.60	1.81	1.08	1	7	64
Men-5	36°04′N	125°04′W	4450	.50	1.87	.94	1	7	64
Men-6	38°25′N	126°09′W	4230	1.70	2.03	3.45	1	7	64
Men-7	39°47′N	126°21′W	4140	.96	2.04	1.96	1	7	64
Men-8	40°33′N	126°31′W	3150	1.89	2.06	3.9*	1	7	64
Men-9	40°56′N	126°31′W	3120	2.35	1.96	4.60	1	7	64
Men-10	41°30′N	126°32′W	2960	3.06	1.89	5.79	1	7	64
Men-11	40°36′N	127°25′W	3280	2.84	1.96	5.56	1	7	64
Men-12	40°07′N	128°10′W	4510	.98	1.92	1.88	1	7	64
Men-13	40°40′N	129°13′W	3220	2.01	2.05	4.12	1	7	64
Men-14	40°00′N	131°00′W	4520	.60	1.90	1.14	1	7	64
Men-15	42°02′N	133°07′W	3870	.40	1.87	.75	1	7	64
Men-16	40°25′N	133°06′W	4070	.36	2.00	.72	1	7	64
Men-17	39°30′N	133°05′W	4750	.17	2.07	.35	1	7	64
Men-18	41°06′N	135°32′W	4060	.48	2.08	1.00	1	7	64
Men-19	41°07′N	151°22′W	5100	.91	2.03	1.84	1	7	64
Men-20	39°21′N	149°56′W	5500	.19	2.04	.39	1	7	64
Men-21	40°38′N	149°01′W	4840	.91	2.07	1.88	1	7	64
Men-22	40°47′N	146°00′W	4720	.50	2.11	1.05	1	7	64
Men-23	40°41′N	142°52′W	4730	.61	1.96	1.19	1	7	64
Men-24	40°44′N	139°22′W	4520	.91	2.06	1.88	1	7	64
Men-26	38°40′N	142°36′W	5290	.63	2.02	1.27	1	7	64
Men-27	39°05′N	139°26′W	5290	.87	2.05	1.78	1	7	64
Men-28	38°02′N	137°58′W	5380	.86	1.97	1.69	1	7	64
Men-29	39°33′N	135°59′W	5140	.49	2.00	(.98)	1	7	64
Men-30	38°00′N	134°00′W	4810	.85	2.02	1.72	1	7	64
Men-31	39°32′N	133°05′W	4740	.05	2.07	.10	1	7	64
Men-33	39°30′N	131°47′W	4510	.23	2.02	.46	1	7	64
Men-34	40°44′N	131°45′W	3640	.49	1.95	.95	1	7	64
Men-36	39°36′N	129°31′W	4540	.59	1.90	(1.12)	1	7	64
Men-37	38°01′N	128°46′W	4750	.83	2.03	(1.68)	1	7	64
Men-38	32°36′N	118°06′W	2010	.99	1.97	1.96	1	7	64
Men-39	32°32′N	117°31′W	1240	1.1	1.83	2.03	1	7	64
GU-1	32°32′N	117°31′W	1230	1.41	1.83	(2.58)	1	7	64
GU-2	32°29′N	118°03′W	1890	1.47	1.89	2.78	1	7	64

Table 4.4–16 (*Continued*)

Station	Lat	Long	Depth	∇T	K	Q	No.	Ref.	Yr
GU-3	32°14′N	118°27′W	1630	.95	1.88	1.78	1	7	64
GU-4	32°03′N	118°50′W	1480	.95	1.99	1.89	1	7	64
GU-5	31°50′N	119°06′W	1690	1.15	1.88	2.16	1	7	64
GU-6	31°37′N	119°35′W	3720	.44	1.93	.84	1	7	64
GU-7	31°26′N	120°04′W	3970	.89	1.87	1.66	1	7	64
GU-8	31°14′N	120°32′W	3840	.87	1.88	1.64	1	7	64
GU-9B	31°01′N	120°55′W	3970	1.30	1.98	2.58	1	7	64
GU-10	30°48′N	121°31′W	4100	1.20	2.02	2.42	1	7	64
GU-11	29°03′N	121°04′W	4160	.15	2.10	.31	1	7	64
GU-12	29°09′N	120°35′W	3910	.83	1.97	1.64	1	7	64
GU-13	29°16′N	120°04′W	3830	2.30	1.93	4.43	1	7	64
GU-14	29°22′N	119°35′W	3710	1.20	1.99	2.39	1	7	64
GU-15B	29°35′N	118°56′W	3800	.81	2.02	1.64	1	7	64
GU-16	29°37′N	118°27′W	3570	.19	2.06	.39	1	7	64
GU-17	29°33′N	117°59′W	3580	1.29	2.02	2.61	1	7	64
GU-18	28°59′N	117°28′W	3542	1.48	1.94	2.87	6	7	64
GU-19	28°52′N	117°26′W	3550	2.11	1.94	(4.09)	1	7	64
GU-20	28°58′N	117°21′W	3550	.92	1.94	(1.79)	1	7	64
GU-21	29°06′N	117°28′W	3620	.97	1.94	(1.89)	1	7	64
GU-22	29°54′N	117°36′W	2840	1.12	2.08	2.34	1	7	64
SB-1	31°16′N	117°45′W	1930	1.06	2.12	2.25	1	7	64
SB-2	31°15′N	117°46′W	1950	1.58	2.12	3.35	1	7	64
SB-3	30°54′N	117°53′W	2050	.92	2.03	1.87	1	7	64
SB-4	30°53′N	117°53′W	2040	.98	2.03	1.99	1	7	64
SB-5	30°18′N	117°31′W	3250	1.42	2.04	2.90	1	7	64
SB-6A	29°18′N	117°29′W	3950	1.58	2.03	3.20	1	7	64
SB-8	28°57′N	117°31′W	3480	1.14	2.07	2.37	1	7	64
SB-9	29°09′N	116°43′W	4060	1.29	2.08	2.69	1	7	64
SB-10	29°08′N	116°42′W	4070	1.33	2.08	2.77	1	7	64
SB-11	30°30′N	116°30′W	2840	1.50	2.04	3.07	1	7	64
SB-12	30°31′N	116°33′W	2840	1.39	2.04	2.84	1	7	64
H-1	31°27′N	120°59′W	3835	.53	1.89	1.01	1	7	64
H-2	29°41′N	121°36′W	4000	.96	1.95	(1.88)	1	7	64
T-1	32°35′N	117°31′W	1225	1.12	1.83	(2.05)	1	7	64
T-2	32°33′N	117°31′W	1220	1.08	1.83	(1.98)	1	7	64
EHF-1	31°11′N	119°16′W	3690	.63	2.04	1.28	1	7	64
Mohole	28°59′N	117°30′W	3570	1.38	2.04	2.81	1	8	64
V-1	27°08′N	111°38′W	1840	1.58	1.77	2.80	1	9	63
V-2	27°17′N	111°22′W	1870	1.78	1.65	2.94	1	9	63
V-3	27°38′N	111°44′W	1775	2.55	1.64	4.19	1	9	63
V-4	26°46′N	111°04′W	1750	1.68	1.75	2.95	1	9	63
V-5	24°09′N	108°55′W	3020	2.13	1.99	4.24	1	9	63
V-6	22°58′N	108°04′W	2900	.34	1.81	.62	1	9	63
V-7	21°59′N	107°41′W	3055	2.96	1.86	5.51	1	9	63
V-8	21°00′N	107°04′W	3300	2.11	1.89	3.98	1	9	63
V-9	20°55′N	106°25′W	4450	1.07	2.00	2.14	1	9	63
V-10	20°10′N	107°43′W	3290	.71	1.76	1.25	1	9	63
V-11	19°45′N	108°28′W	2600	.79	1.82	1.43	1	9	63
V-12	20°48′N	109°34′W	2910	1.33	1.81	2.40	1	9	63
V-13	22°33′N	109°29′W	2860	2.96	2.08	6.15	1	9	63

Table 4.4–16 (*Continued*)

Station	Lat	Long	Depth	∇T	K	Q	No.	Ref.	Yr
D-1	1°23′S	131°31′W	4450	.06	2.29	.14	1	10	59
D-2	14°59′S	136°01′W	4510	.35	1.86	~.65	1	10	59
D-3	21°40′S	147°41′W	4760	.56	1.74	.97	1	10	59
D-4	40°37′S	132°52′W	5120	.61	1.80	1.1	1	10	59
D-5	42°16′S	125°50′W	4620	.08	1.71	.14	1	10	59
D-6	46°44′S	123°18′W	4140	.35	2.09	.73	1	10	59
D-7	44°27′S	110°44′W	3180	.92	2.24	2.06	1	10	59
D-8	43°43′S	107°33′W	3180	1.34	2.28	3.06	1	10	59
D-9	43°44′S	104°25′W	3850	1.03	2.03	2.09	1	10	59
D-10	42°44′S	96°03′W	4580	1.48	1.55	2.30	1	10	59
D-11	41°06′S	86°38′W	3310	.51	2.0	1.0	1	10	59
D-12	23°23′S	72°10′W	4110	.49	1.82	>.89	1	10	59
D-13	23°28′S	72°58′W	3750	.41	1.96	.80	1	10	59
D-14	21°33′S	79°09′W	4550	.89	1.82	1.62	1	10	59
D-15	20°49′S	81°08′W	2340	.35	2.26	.79	1	10	59
D-16	20°48′S	81°09′W	2400	.68	2.26	1.54	1	10	59
D-17	13°35′S	79°09′W	4440	.79	1.84	1.46	1	10	59
D-18	12°49′S	77°53′W	2260	1.35	2.02	2.72	1	10	59
D-19	12°54′S	78°06′W	3700	.56	1.91	1.07	1	10	59
D-20	12°38′S	78°38′W	5950	.08	2.09	.17	1	10	59
D-21	12°59′S	78°21′W	5900	.08	1.94	.17	1	10	59
D-22	18°26′S	78°16′W	4220	.14	1.86	.26	1	10	59
D-23	18°20′S	79°21′W	3090	.46	2.14	.98	1	10	59
D-24	19°01′S	81°29′W	4230	.55	1.86	1.02	1	10	59
D-25	27°04′S	88°53′W	3880	1.04	2.04	2.12	1	10	59
D-26	28°00′S	96°20′W	3200	.10	2.25	.23	1	10	59
D-27	27°55′S	106°57′W	2910	2.10	2.16	4.54	1	10	59
D-28	23°15′S	117°48′W	3500	.92	1.90	~1.76	1	10	59
D-29	14°44′S	112°06′W	3060	3.45	2.22	7.66	1	10	59
D-30	13°30′S	108°31′W	3580	.43	2.34	1.01	1	10	59
D-31	11°39′S	109°48′W	3280	3.61	2.24	8.09	1	10	59
D-32	9°55′S	110°39′W	2840	3.90	2.04	7.95	1	10	59
D-33	5°56′S	112°29′W	4040	.44	2.00	.87	1	10	59
D-34	3°40′S	114°13′W	4330	.94	1.82	1.71	1	10	59
D-35	1°28′N	116°04′W	3810	.28	1.97	.56	1	10	59
D-36	4°06′N	115°41′W	4200	.20	2.13	.43	1	10	59
LFG-1	33°13′N	118°36′W	1300	1.00	1.8	1.8	1	11	62
LFG-2	36°40′N	123°03′W	3320	1.1	2.0	2.2	1	11	62
LFG-3	36°39′N	123°16′W	3470	1.10	2.1	2.3	1	11	62
LFG-5	36°34′N	123°41′W	3770	1.10	2.1	(2.3)	1	11	62
LFG-7	44°17′N	138°36′W	4220	.45	2.2	1.0	1	11	62
LFG-8	48°20′N	157°22′W	5220	.25	2.0	.5	1	11	62
LFG-11	52°33′N	175°09′W	3240	.59	1.7	1.0	1	11	62
LFG-12	54°17′N	176°15′W	3740	.60	1.5	.9	1	11	62
LFG-13	55°41′N	177°40′W	4160	.81	1.6	1.3	1	11	62
LFG-14A	56°05′N	176°10′W	3690	.69	1.6	1.1	1	11	62
LFG-14B	56°13′N	176°18′W	3670	.62	1.6	1.0	1	11	62
LFG-16	53°23′N	163°20′W	4230	.21	1.9	.4	1	11	62
LFG-17	54°08′N	156°52′W	5680	1.42	1.9	(2.7)	1	11	62
LFG-19	57°11′N	149°38′W	2950	.55	2.0	1.1	1	11	62

Table 4.4–16 (*Continued*)

Station	Lat	Long	Depth	∇*T*	*K*	*Q*	No.	Ref.	Yr
LFG-20	57°34′N	147°37′W	4880	.50	2.4	(1.2)	1	11	62
LFG-22	59°05′N	145°05′W	4220	.92	2.4	2.2	1	11	62
LFG-24	59°07′N	144°20′W	4000	.56	2.7	1.5	1	11	62
LFG-25	59°09′N	143°39′W	3920	.74	2.3	1.7	1	11	62
LFG-27	59°14′N	142°50′W	2670	.62	2.1	1.3	1	11	62
LFG-28	58°11′N	139°31′W	2910	.68	2.2	1.5	1	11	62
LFG-29	57°42′N	140°08′W	3310	.72	1.8	1.3	1	11	62
LFG-30	56°58′N	139°12′W	3340	.92	2.4	2.2	1	11	62
LFG-35	54°27′N	134°41′W	2560	1.86	2.2	(4.1)	1	11	62
LFG-37	54°13′N	135°27′W	2900	1.35	2.0	2.7	1	11	62
LFG-38	54°07′N	135°51′W	2740	1.22	1.8	2.2	1	11	62
LFG-39	53°07′N	133°27′W	2900	.94	1.7	1.6	1	11	62
LFG-40	53°15′N	133°30′W	2910	.61	1.8	1.1	1	11	62
LFG-41	50°04′N	132°25′W	3100	.30	2.3	.7	1	11	62
LFG-42	48°19′N	131°38′W	3050	.52	2.3	1.2	1	11	62
LFG-43	46°15′N	131°59′W	3290	.36	2.2	.8	1	11	62
LFG-44	43°51′N	130°55′W	3320	1.45	2.2	3.2	1	11	62
LFG-45	42°19′N	130°39′W	3430	.24	2.1	.5	1	11	62
LFG-46	40°36′N	130°26′W	3760	.05	2.0	.1?	1	11	62
LFG-47	40°35′N	129°22′W	3240	1.71	2.1	3.6	1	11	62
LFG-48	38°35′N	127°45′W	4630	.30	2.0	.6	1	11	62
LFG-50	36°19′N	125°56′W	4620	1.11	1.8	2.0	1	11	62
MSN-2	23°15′N	130°46′W	4930	.11	2.04	.22	1	12	63
MSN-3	20°02′N	135°11′W	5180	.75	2.08	1.56	1	12	63
MSN-64	10°34′S	151°05′W	5070	.73	1.62	1.18	1	12	63
MSN-65	8°17′S	151°36′W	5190	.87	1.65	1.44	1	12	63
MSN-66	5°55′S	149°39′W	5160	.47	1.59	.75	1	12	63
MSN-67	4°22′S	149°29′W	4600	.44	1.69	.74	1	12	63
MSN-68	5°20′N	146°13′W	5090	.64	1.62	1.03	1	12	63
MSN-69	7°02′N	145°38′W	5100	.91	1.66	1.51	1	12	63
MSN-70	8°07′N	145°24′W	5000	.80	1.67	1.34	1	12	63
MSN-71	9°06′N	145°18′W	5300	.79	1.77	1.40	1	12	63
MSN-72	10°59′N	142°37′W	4890	2.77	1.61	(4.46)	1	12	63
MSN-73	11°03′N	142°28′W	5000	.66	1.61	1.06	1	12	63
MSN-74	13°04′N	138°59′W	5000	.41	1.58	.64	1	12	63
MSN-75	15°11′N	136°52′W	4990	.70	1.83	1.28	1	12	63
MSN-76	24°18′N	126°30′W	4750	.43	2.10	.90	1	12	63
MSN-77	29°07′N	121°03′W	4080	.10	2.00	.19	1	12	63
MSN-78	31°01′N	119°04′W	3620	1.43	1.91	2.73	1	12	63
RIS-1	28°02′N	117°12′W	3900	1.22	2.07	2.52	1	12	63
RIS-2	26°11′N	117°18′W	4000	.91	2.14	1.95	1	12	63
RIS-3	24°12′N	117°23′W	3935	.62	2.02	1.26	1	12	63
RIS-4	22°13′N	117°21′W	3890	1.29	2.08	2.69	1	12	63
RIS-5	20°18′N	117°27′W	4010	.33	1.83	.60	1	12	63
RIS-6	18°46′N	117°14′W	4090	1.20	1.80	2.16	1	12	63
RIS-8	14°26′N	117°12′W	4110	1.60	1.76	2.82	1	12	63
RIS-9	12°54′N	117°24′W	4230	.24	1.69	.41	1	12	63
RIS-10	11°28′N	117°38′W	4310	.52	1.90	.99	1	12	63
RIS-11	9°43′N	117°32′W	4230	.33	1.63	.54	1	12	63
RIS-12	8°06′N	117°51′W	3880	.59	1.95	1.15	1	12	63

Table 4.4–16 (*Continued*)

Station	Lat	Long	Depth	∇T	K	Q	No.	Ref.	Yr
RIS-13	6°45′N	117°51′W	4000	.41	1.87	.76	1	12	63
RIS-14	5°20′N	117°52′W	4355	.38	1.88	.71	1	12	63
RIS-15	3°54′N	118°08′W	4110	.35	1.99	.69	1	12	63
RIS-16	4°03′N	117°01′W	4160	.46	1.99	(.91)	1	12	63
RIS-17	4°03′N	115°53′W	4120	.78	2.13	(1.66)	1	12	63
RIS-18	4°03′N	115°36′W	4170	.19	2.13	(.40)	1	12	63
RIS-19	4°13′N	114°58′W	4210	.34	2.06	(.70)	1	12	63
RIS-20	4°25′N	113°41′W	3980	.30	1.98	.60	1	12	63
RIS-21	4°34′N	112°31′W	3950	.54	1.98	(1.07)	1	12	63
RIS-22	4°44′N	111°33′W	4060	.65	1.87	1.21	1	12	63
RIS-24B	5°04′N	109°11′W	3980	1.25	2.06	2.57	1	12	63
RIS-25	5°13′N	107°59′W	3760	.98	2.04	(1.99)	1	12	63
RIS-26	5°14′N	106°33′W	3820	1.15	2.02	2.32	1	12	63
RIS-27	5°24′N	105°41′W	3645	.79	1.95	(1.55)	1	12	63
RIS-28	5°37′N	104°27′W	3570	.86	1.87	1.61	1	12	63
RIS-29	5°43′N	103°29′W	3305	2.26	1.76	(3.98)	1	12	63
RIS-30	5°37′N	104°03′W	3400	.87	1.87	(1.63)	1	12	63
RIS-31	5°34′N	103°08′W	3300	.90	1.76	1.58	1	12	63
RIS-32B	5°41′N	102°36′W	3130	2.76	1.76	(4.86)	1	12	63
RIS-33	5°39′N	102°06′W	3175	4.24	1.75	7.42	1	12	63
RIS-34B	5°42′N	101°43′W	3440	.36	1.84	(.67)	1	12	63
RIS-35	5°36′N	101°09′W	3250	.92	1.93	1.78	1	12	63
RIS-36	5°41′N	100°50′W	3405	.64	1.94	(1.25)	1	12	63
RIS-37	5°44′N	101°56′W	3285	.69	1.75	(1.20)	1	12	63
RIS-38	5°43′N	99°55′W	3420	.58	1.94	1.12	1	12	63
RIS-39	6°05′N	98°47′W	3470	.54	1.74	(.94)	1	12	63
RIS-40	6°41′N	97°25′W	3520	.21	1.74	.37	1	12	63
RIS-41	6°58′N	96°06′W	3785	.05	1.67	(.08)	1	12	63
RIS-42	6°57′N	94°58′W	3740	.73	1.60	1.17	1	12	63
RIS-43	5°05′N	93°56′W	3540	.66	1.72	(1.13)	1	12	63
RIS-44	4°07′N	92°09′W	3150	.28	1.95	.55	1	12	63
RIS-45	3°16′N	90°42′W	2360	.44	2.00	(.87)	1	12	63
RIS-46	2°17′N	89°28′W	2160	.24	2.09	.51	1	12	63
RIS-47B	1°13′N	88°32′W	2480	2.79	1.89	5.27	1	12	63
RIS-48B	0°15′N	86°23′W	2760	2.52	1.85	(4.66)	1	12	63
RIS-49	0°09′S	85°58′W	2750	.36	1.81	.65	1	12	63
RIS-50	1°41′S	85°33′W	2440	3.11	1.91	(5.94)	1	12	63
RIS-51	1°45′S	85°31′W	2385	1.00	1.98	(1.98)	1	12	63
RIS-52	2°44′S	85°29′W	3220	1.53	1.98	3.03	1	12	63
RIS-53	3°52′S	84°50′W	3395	1.22	1.98	(2.42)	1	12	63
RIS-54	9°07′S	81°33′W	4700	.50	1.75	.87	1	12	63
RIS-55	8°51′S	80°53′W	6280	.46	2.00	(.91)	1	12	63
RIS-56	8°47′S	80°35′W	2975	.54	2.00	(1.07)	1	12	63
RIS-57	12°34′S	78°35′W	5940	.12	2.09	(.26)	1	12	63
RIS-58	12°46′S	80°00′W	4630	.64	1.79	(1.14)	1	12	63
RIS-59	12°59′S	81°32′W	4800	1.21	1.68	2.04	1	12	63
RIS-60	13°04′S	82°58′W	4990	1.51	1.70	(2.56)	1	12	63
RIS-61	13°11′S	84°25′W	4740	.86	1.72	1.48	1	12	63
RIS-62B	13°24′S	86°15′W	4500	.21	1.69	(.36)	1	12	63
RIS-63	13°32′S	87°26′W	4240	.29	1.66	.48	1	12	63

Table 4.4–16 (*Continued*)

Station	Lat	Long	Depth	∇T	K	Q	No.	Ref.	Yr
RIS-64	13°33′S	89°05′W	4080	.58	1.80	(1.05)	1	12	63
RIS-65	13°43′S	90°30′W	3900	.08	1.93	.15	1	12	63
RIS-66	13°40′S	92°00′W	3830	.78	2.01	(1.57)	1	12	63
RIS-67	13°35′S	93°28′W	3880	1.55	2.08	3.22	1	12	63
RIS-68	13°37′S	94°58′W	3720	1.00	2.08	(2.08)	1	12	63
RIS-69	13°37′S	96°44′W	4150	1.10	1.86	2.04	1	12	63
RIS-70	13°32′S	97°48′W	3740	.62	2.05	1.28	1	12	63
RIS-71	13°26′S	99°11′W	3950	.87	1.91	(1.66)	1	12	63
RIS-72	13°23′S	100°30′W	4210	.22	1.77	.39	1	12	63
RIS-73	13°16′S	101°24′W	4300	1.74	1.80	(3.14)	1	12	63
RIS-74B	13°18′S	102°18′W	4430	.79	2.22	1.75	1	12	63
RIS-75	13°11′S	103°30′W	4170	.78	2.10	(1.63)	1	12	63
RIS-76	13°03′S	104°41′W	3720	.40	1.98	.79	1	12	63
RIS-77	12°59′S	105°31′W	3910	.64	2.13	(1.37)	1	12	63
RIS-78	12°54′S	106°29′W	3720	1.33	2.27	3.02	1	12	63
RIS-79	12°50′S	107°31′W	3710	.41	2.22	(.92)	1	12	63
RIS-80	12°48′S	107°59′W	3550	.50	2.16	1.09	1	12	63
RIS-81	12°43′S	108°32′W	3550	.98	2.17	(2.13)	1	12	63
RIS-82	12°44′S	109°02′W	3415	.91	2.17	(1.97)	1	12	63
RIS-83	12°40′S	109°30′W	3405	1.06	2.17	(2.31)	1	12	63
RIS-84	12°39′S	110°01′W	3255	1.34	2.18	2.93	1	12	63
RIS-85	12°35′S	110°29′W	3180	2.17	2.18	(4.74)	1	12	63
RIS-86	12°35′S	110°15′W	3165	1.36	2.18	(2.96)	1	12	63
RIS-87	12°33′S	110°47′W	3010	1.20	1.82	(2.18)	1	12	63
RIS-88B	12°33′S	111°13′W	3105	1.52	1.82	2.76	1	12	63
RIS-89	12°32′S	111°29′W	3030	1.64	1.88	(3.08)	1	12	63
RIS-90	12°33′S	112°01′W	3075	3.27	1.94	(6.35)	1	12	63
RIS-91	12°32′S	112°16′W	3175	1.75	2.00	(3.50)	1	12	63
RIS-92	12°30′S	112°37′W	3170	.98	2.05	2.00	1	12	63
RIS-93	12°26′S	113°05′W	3230	1.43	2.05	(2.94)	1	12	63
RIS-94	12°25′S	113°31′W	3325	.87	2.05	(1.79)	1	12	63
RIS-95	13°02′S	113°17′W	3240	2.10	1.90	(4.00)	1	12	63
RIS-96	13°36′S	112°42′W	3025	1.85	1.75	3.24	1	12	63
RIS-97	14°02′S	112°20′W	2960	1.48	1.75	(2.59)	1	12	63
RIS-98	14°47′S	112°32′W	3020	.60	2.22	(1.34)	1	12	63
RIS-99	14°47′S	112°54′W	3065	.92	2.09	(1.93)	1	12	63
RIS-100	14°41′S	113°30′W	3010	3.62	1.96	7.10	1	12	63
RIS-101	14°40′S	113°45′W	3170	4.10	1.96	(8.04)	1	12	63
RIS-102	14°38′S	114°02′W	2975	2.38	1.95	(4.65)	1	12	63
RIS-103	14°15′S	113°11′W	3045	3.14	1.85	(5.80)	1	12	63
RIS-104	14°15′S	113°33′W	3020	2.07	1.95	(4.03)	1	12	63
RIS-105	14°15′S	113°50′W	3045	.43	1.94	.84	1	12	63
RIS-106	14°15′S	114°09′W	3015	1.69	1.94	(3.27)	1	12	63
RIS-107	14°17′S	114°32′W	3120	.96	1.94	(1.87)	1	12	63
RIS-108	14°17′S	114°59′W	3210	.57	2.04	(1.17)	1	12	63
RIS-109	14°18′S	115°37′W	3440	.45	2.14	.97	1	12	63
RIS-110	14°15′S	116°23′W	3280	.79	2.17	(1.72)	1	12	63
RIS-111	14°14′S	117°35′W	3440	.45	2.20	1.00	1	12	63
RIS-112	13°59′S	118°33′W	3380	.32	2.19	(.70)	1	12	63
RIS-113	14°00′S	119°39′W	3270	.06	2.19	.13	1	12	63

Table 4.4–16 (*Continued*)

Station	Lat	Long	Depth	∇*T*	*K*	*Q*	No.	Ref.	Yr
RIS-114B	14°04′S	120°16′W	3600	.69	2.13	(1.48)	1	12	63
RIS-115	14°03′S	121°17′W	3680	.31	2.13	(.67)	1	12	63
RIS-116	14°01′S	122°28′W	3935	.03	2.07	.07	1	12	63
RIS-117	14°07′S	123°47′W	3860	.67	2.07	(1.39)	1	12	63
RIS-118	13°33′S	121°48′W	3640	.75	2.13	(1.60)	1	12	63
RIS-119	13°33′S	121°50′W	3665	.12	2.13	(.25)	1	12	63
RIS-120	13°52′S	125°20′W	3680	.47	2.20	1.04	1	12	63
RIS-121	14°02′S	127°07′W	3930	.09	2.05	(.18)	1	12	63
RIS-122	14°02′S	128°25′W	3995	.54	1.90	1.02	1	12	63
RIS-123	14°02′S	129°48′W	4120	1.49	1.74	(2.60)	1	12	63
RIS-124	14°03′S	130°18′W	4090	.47	1.74	(.82)	1	12	63
RIS-125	14°03′S	131°44′W	4010	.30	1.58	.48	1	12	63
RIS-127	14°02′S	133°45′W	4290	.50	1.57	(.79)	1	12	63
RIS-128	14°02′S	134°55′W	4220	.75	1.56	1.17	1	12	63
RIS-129	14°03′S	136°34′W	4290	.36	1.56	(.57)	1	12	63
RIS-130	14°09′S	138°06′W	4040	1.10	1.55	1.70	1	12	63
RIS-131	14°03′S	139°35′W	3925	.86	1.94	1.67	1	12	63
RIS-132	14°55′S	141°34′W	2610	.84	2.15	(1.8)	1	12	63
RIS-133	15°15′S	142°26′W	3725	.52	2.15	1.12	1	12	63
RIS-134	16°30′S	145°07′W	1440	.79	2.14	~1.70	1	12	63
RIS-135	16°52′S	145°49′W	2750	.66	2.05	1.35	1	12	63
RIS-136	17°05′S	147°13′W	4190	.12	1.72	.21	1	12	63
RIS-137	16°46′S	148°52′W	4200	.09	1.75	(.16)	1	12	63
RIS-138	16°34′S	148°30′W	4250	.65	1.75	1.13	1	12	63
RIS-140	14°43′S	145°40′W	2770	.54	2.20	1.20	1	12	63
RIS-141	13°37′S	145°03′W	4390	.17	1.72	.29	1	12	63
RIS-142	13°03′S	144°03′W	4960	.58	2.24	1.29	1	12	63
RIS-143	12°46′S	143°34′W	4480	.64	1.71	(1.10)	1	12	63
RIS-144	11°58′S	142°27′W	4520	.73	1.62	1.19	1	12	63
RIS-145	11°05′S	140°57′W	4270	.22	2.11	(.46)	1	12	63
RIS-146	10°30′S	139°59′W	4140	.18	2.11	.37	1	12	63
RIS-147	8°38′S	138°18′W	4080	.83	2.01	1.67	1	12	63
RIS-148	7°27′S	137°11′W	4400	.43	1.82	~.78	1	12	63
RIS-149	6°23′S	136°11′W	4350	.80	1.64	1.31	1	12	63
RIS-151	4°06′S	133°59′W	4445	.63	1.95	1.22	1	12	63
RIS-152	2°46′S	132°58′W	4350	.82	1.98	(1.63)	1	12	63
RIS-153	1°40′S	131°52′W	4345	.31	2.01	.63	1	12	63
RIS-154	1°21′S	131°31′W	4510	.11	2.01	(.23)	1	12	63
RIS-155	1°25′S	131°04′W	4480	.37	2.01	(.74)	1	12	63
RIS-156	1°27′S	130°34′W	4580	.20	2.01	(.40)	1	12	63
RIS-157	0°47′S	131°42′W	4425	.39	2.01	(.78)	1	12	63
RIS-158	0°18′N	132°00′W	4410	.41	1.96	(.80)	1	12	63
RIS-159	2°04′N	132°32′W	4305	.22	1.91	.42	1	12	63
RIS-160	3°36′N	133°00′W	4375	.00	2.00	(.01)?	1	12	63
RIS-161	3°58′N	133°09′W	4375	.10	2.00	(.19)	1	12	63
RIS-162	5°38′N	133°26′W	4390	.21	2.08	.44	1	12	63
RIS-163	7°14′N	133°47′W	4410	.82	2.08	(1.7)	1	12	63
RIS-164	9°03′N	133°40′W	4980	1.08	1.67	1.80	1	12	63
RIS-165	10°57′N	133°56′W	4910	.85	1.67	(1.42)	1	12	63
RIS-166	12°56′N	133°36′W	4810	.64	1.67	(1.07)	1	12	63

Table 4.4–16 (*Continued*)

Station	Lat	Long	Depth	∇*T*	*K*	*Q*	No.	Ref.	Yr
RIS-167	14°58′N	133°42′W	4775	.74	1.82	1.34	1	12	63
RIS-169	18°15′N	133°06′W	5190	1.05	1.91	2.00	1	12	63
RIS-170	19°59′N	133°03′W	5060	.64	1.91	(1.23)	1	12	63
RIS-172	23°30′N	132°43′W	4880	.61	2.02	(1.23)	1	12	63
RIS-173	25°19′N	132°37′W	4530	.38	2.13	.80	1	12	63
RIS-174	27°15′N	132°28′W	4815	.49	2.10	(1.02)	1	12	63
RIS-175	28°26′N	135°54′W	4740	.77	2.07	1.59	1	12	63
RIS-176	28°29′N	134°35′W	4660	.36	2.00	(.71)	1	12	63
RIS-177	28°18′N	133°21′W	4385	.74	1.92	1.43	1	12	63
RIS-178	27°54′N	132°37′W	3700	.51	1.92	(.98)	1	12	63
RIS-180	28°10′N	131°04′W	4550	1.10	1.96	(2.16)	1	12	63
RIS-181	28°17′N	129°36′W	4740	.52	2.00	1.05	1	12	63
RIS-182	28°21′N	127°59′W	4660	.97	1.98	(1.92)	1	12	63
RIS-183	28°27′N	126°37′W	4500	.88	1.96	1.73	1	12	63
RIS-184	28°35′N	125°00′W	4445	1.13	1.96	(2.22)	1	12	63
RIS-185	28°47′N	123°37′W	4370	.94	1.77	1.66	1	12	63
RIS-186	28°56′N	122°27′W	4220	1.10	1.96	(2.16)	1	12	63
RIS-187	29°33′N	121°44′W	4005	1.15	2.05	(2.36)	1	12	63
MP-21	20°48′N	159°42′W	4500	.65	1.79	1.16	1	13	58
MP-32	18°18′N	173°23′W	3900	.35	2.05	.72	1	13	58
MP-35-2	19°28′N	174°35′W	4900	.62	2.07	1.29	1	13	58
MP-36	16°45′N	176°24′W	5040	.66	1.80	1.19	1	13	58
MP-38	19°02′N	177°19′W	4750	.69	1.57	1.09	1	13	58
STN-1	32°35′N	122°30′W	4000	.67	1.90	(1.27)	1	13	58
CAP-2B	0°40′N	169°17′E	4310	.76	2.48	1.88	1	13	58
CAP-5B	9°04′S	174°51′E	5000	.72	1.87	1.35	1	13	58
CAP-9B	18°59′S	177°36′E	2700	.63	2.40	1.51	1	13	58
CAP-10B	21°56′S	178°33′E	3900	1.25	2.07	2.58	1	13	58
CAP-31B	17°28′S	158°40′W	4880	.86	1.83	1.58	1	13	58
CAP-33B	12°48′S	143°33′W	4300	.21	1.71	.36	1	13	58
CAP-40B	14°45′S	112°11′W	3020	2.15	2.44	5.25	1	13	58
CAP-48B	5°52′N	123°55′W	4100	.73	2.26	1.65	1	13	58
CAP-50B	14°59′N	124°12′W	4350	1.24	1.96	2.43	1	13	58
ACA-B5-1	13°08′N	91°57′W	6170	.24	1.92	.47	1	13	58
ACA-B6	11°55′N	91°37′W	3600	.46	1.67	.76	1	13	58
ACA-B8	9°49′N	93°02′W	3730	.14	1.76	.25	1	13	58
ACA-B9	12°14′N	98°44′W	3500	.40	1.72	.69	1	13	58
ACA-B11	10°52′N	105°04′W	3300	1.83	1.95	>3.57	1	13	58
ACA-B11B	10°54′N	104°25′W	2950	1.40	1.95	(2.73)	1	13	58
ACA-B13	12°12′N	111°04′W	3600	.48	1.95	(.93)	1	13	58
ACA-B13A	20°44′N	115°42′W	3910	.59	2.02	1.19	1	13	58
GUA-P6	25°01′N	123°04′W	4300	.48	2.30	1.11	1	13	58
GUA-P7	24°54′N	123°05′W	4200	.49	2.30	1.13	1	13	58
V18-100	09°42′S	136°28′W	4329	.96	1.72	1.65	1	1	65
V18-101	08°00′S	133°50′W	4696	1.24	1.56	1.93	1	1	65
V18-102	07°20′S	133°03′W	4477	.99	1.52	1.50	1	1	65
V18-105	05°19′S	130°22′W	4661	.57	1.65	.94	1	1	65
V18-107	03°37′S	127°41′W	4564	.23	1.66	.38	1	1	65
V18-108	02°51′S	126°12′W	4612	.36	1.78	.59	1	1	65
V18-109	01°06′S	124°37′W	4550	.28	2.16	.60	1	1	65

Table 4.4–16 (*Continued*)

Station	Lat	Long	Depth	∇T	K	Q	No.	Ref.	Yr
V18-110	01°14′S	122°55′W	4389	.48	2.33	1.12	1	1	65
V18-111	01°03′N	120°46′W	4371	.36	2.31	.83	1	1	65
V18-112	02°12′N	119°40′W	4332	1.52	2.30	(3.50)	1	1	65
V18-113	03°10′N	118°28′W	4217	.71	2.13	1.51	1	1	65
V18-114	04°14′N	117°00′W	4161	.42	2.19	.82	1	1	65
V18-116	06°23′N	113°32′W	4104	.15	1.85	.28	1	1	65
V18-118	08°01′N	109°18′W	4065	1.92	1.67	3.21	1	1	65
V18-119	08°46′N	107°09′W	3488	1.74	1.83	3.18	1	1	65
V18-122	10°16′N	103°05′W	3190	1.91	1.55	2.96	1	1	65
V18-125	11°54′N	100°44′W	3360	1.22	1.65	2.01	1	1	65
V18-126	12°38′N	99°27′W	3426	1.78	1.64	2.62	1	1	65
V18-127	12°54′N	98°52′W	3342	.96	1.80	(1.73)	1	1	65
V18-128	12°49′N	97°47′W	3720	.42	1.72	.46	1	1	65
V18-129	13°09′N	97°07′W	3590	.64	1.80	(1.15)	1	1	65
V18-130	13°19′N	96°51′W	2757	5.78	1.85	10.?	1	1	65
V18-131	14°31′N	96°18′W	3890	1.55	1.91	2.96	1	1	65
V18-134	12°47′N	96°17′W	3987	.76	1.82	1.38	1	1	65
V18-135	08°49′N	97°16′W	3793	.66	1.61	1.06	1	1	65
V18-140	06°37′N	88°24′W	3247	1.91	1.60	3.06	1	1	65
V18-141	06°44′N	86°30′W	2892	.56	1.82	1.02	1	1	65
V18-142	06°04′N	85°43′W	1819	1.53	1.97	3.01	1	1	65
V18-143	05°42′N	85°16′W	1840	1.41	2.15	3.03	1	1	65
V18-144	05°18′N	84°45′W	3005	1.40	1.78	2.50	1	1	65
V18-145	05°34′N	83°24′W	3064	1.95	1.76	3.43	1	1	65
V18-146	06°06′N	82°05′W	3031	1.91	1.80	(3.44)	1	1	65
V18-148	06°42′N	80°42′W	3424	1.70	1.80	(3.06)	1	1	65
V19-8	07°04′N	78°59′W	3345	1.63	1.69	2.75	1	1	65
V19-9	04°56′N	78°16′W	3819	2.83	2.16	6.11	1	1	65
V19-10	03°12′N	80°08′W	1711	.91	2.08	1.89	1	1	65
V19-11	02°28′N	81°42′W	2398	1.12	1.79	2.00	1	1	65
V19-14	02°22′S	84°39′W	2724	.07	1.78	.12	1	1	65
V19-15	03°35′S	83°56′W	3153	1.17	1.67	1.95	1	1	65
V19-19	11°59′S	81°31′W	4749	1.21	1.53	1.85	1	1	65
V19-23	13°13′S	92°53′W	3647	.83	2.19	1.82	1	1	65
V19-26	16°21′S	104°48′W	4199	.78	2.42	1.8	1	1	65
V19-27	17°01′S	108°52′W	3624	.76	2.49	1.9	1	1	65
V19-28	17°01′S	110°23′W	3449	.71	2.1	(1.5)	1	1	65
V19-29	17°00′S	110°51′W	3438	.58	2.23	1.3	1	1	65
V19-30	17°00′S	111°12′W	3537	.44	2.06	.9	1	1	65
V19-31	17°01′S	111°33′W	3320	.57	2.1	(1.2)	1	1	65
V19-32	17°02′S	111°53′W	3256	.67	2.1	(1.4)	1	1	65
V19-33	17°02′S	112°12′W	3184	1.57	2.1	(3.3)	1	1	65
V19-34	17°01′S	112°34′W	2981	1.10	2.1	(2.3)	1	1	65
V19-35	17°01′S	112°55′W	3175	.81	2.1	(1.7)	1	1	65
V19-36	17°01′S	113°31′W	3056	.86	2.1	(1.8)	1	1	65
V19-37	17°02′S	113°54′W	2830	1.67	2.1	(3.5)	1	1	65
V19-38	17°00′S	114°11′W	3177	.76	2.1	(1.6)	1	1	65
V19-39	17°00′S	114°32′W	3139	1.00	2.1	(2.1)	1	1	65
V19-40	17°00′S	114°53′W	3157	.76	2.1	(1.6)	1	1	65
V19-41	16°58′S	115°12′W	3270	.24	2.1	(.5)	1	1	65

Table 4.4–16 (*Continued*)

Station	Lat	Long	Depth	∇T	K	Q	No.	Ref.	Yr
V19-42	16°58′S	115°33′W	3300	3.38	2.1	(7.1)	1	1	65
V19-43	16°58′S	115°56′W	3336	1.00	2.1	(2.1)	1	1	65
V19-44	16°57′S	116°18′W	3407	.71	2.1	(1.4)	1	1	65
V19-45	16°58′S	116°48′W	3374	1.05	2.1	(2.2)	1	1	65
V19-46	16°59′S	117°53′W	3422	.76	2.1	(1.6)	1	1	65
V19-48	16°39′S	124°23′W	3760	.43	2.1	(.9)	1	1	65
H-4	28°14′N	127°38′W	4580	.710	2.07	1.47	1	2	64
H-5	24°46′N	134°30′W	4530	.632	1.97	1.25	2	2	64
H-7	23°03′N	137°55′W	5295	.935	2.00	(1.87)	1	2	64
H-8	23°00′N	143°58′W	4850	1.32	2.10	2.78	1	2	64
H-9	22°58′N	148°24′W	5470	.726	1.90	(1.38)	1	2	64
H-10	23°00′N	150°38′W	5580	.763	1.86	1.42	1	2	64
H-11	22°59′N	152°59′W	5060	.860	1.86	1.6*	1	2	64
H-12	22°29′N	154°26′W	4390	.758	1.98	(1.5)*	1	2	64
H-15	19°08′N	157°20′W	4610	1.04	1.68	1.74*	1	2	64
H-17	23°36′N	156°07′W	4260	.695	1.87	1.30	1	2	64
H-18	21°56′N	154°48′W	4660	.353	2.01	.71	1	2	64
H-19	23°07′N	156°07′W	4260	.742	1.90	1.41	1	2	64
LSDH-68	20°15′N	154°13′W	5480	.527	1.67	.88*	1	2	64
LSDH-69	19°59′N	151°09′W	5305	.773	1.85	1.43	1	2	64
LSDH-70	20°06′N	145°16′W	5410	.774	1.90	1.47	1	2	64
LSDH-71	21°26′N	140°23′W	5200	.672	2.04	1.37	1	2	64
LSDH-72	22°12′N	138°57′W	5100	.721	2.08	1.50	2	2	64
LSDH-73	23°10′N	130°58′W	4870	.659	2.07	1.36	2	2	64
LSDH-74	27°30′N	125°47′W	4483	.441	2.02	.89	2	2	64

(From Clark, S. P., Jr., *Handbook of Physical Constants,* Geological Society of America, Memoir 97, 1966. With permission.)

REFERENCES

1. **Langseth, M. G. et al.,** *J. Geophys. Res.,* 70, 367, 1965.
2. **Rhea, K. et al.,** *Mar. Geol.,* 1, 220, 1964.
3. **Birch, F.,** *Geol. Soc. Am. Bull.,* 67, 941, 1956.
4. **Uyeda, S. et al.,** *J. Geophys. Res.,* 67, 1186, 1962.
5. **Uyeda, S. and Horai, K.,** *J. Geophys. Res.,* 69, 2121, 1964.
6. **Yasui, M. et al.,** personal communication, 1964.
7. **Von Herzen, R. P.,** *Mar. Geol.,* 1, 225, 1964.
8. **Von Herzen, R. P. and Maxwell, A. E.,** *J. Geophys. Res.,* 69, 741, 1964.
9. **Von Herzen, R. P.,** *Science,* 140, 1207, 1963.
10. **Von Herzen, R. P.,** *Nature,* 183, 882, 1959.
11. **Foster, T. D.,** *J. Geophys. Res.,* 67, 2991, 1962.
12. **Von Herzen, R. P. and Uyeda, S.,** *J. Geophys. Res.,* 68, 4219, 1963.
13. **Maxwell, A. E.,** Ph.D. thesis, University of California, 1958.

Table 4.4–17
HEAT FLOW IN THE ARCTIC OCEAN

Station	Lat.	Long.	Depth	∇T	K	Q	No.	Ref.	Yr
FL-1	82°30′N	156°26′W	3747	0.683	2.13	1.45	1	1	65
FL-2	82°12′N	156°24′W	3742	0.674	2.07	1.40	1	1	65
FL-3	82°31′N	156°54′W	3741	0.672	2.20	1.48	1	1	65
FL-6	82°42′N	158°04′W	3740	0.625	2.11	1.32	1	1	65
FL-8	82°39′N	157°28′W	3742	0.665	2.19	1.46	1	1	65
FL-9	82°46′N	156°51′W	3743	0.634	2.16	1.37	1	1	65
FL-10	82°57′N	155°54′W	3507	0.496	2.72	1.35	1	1	65
FL-11	83°00′N	156°07′W	3520	0.547	2.60	1.42	1	1	65
FL-12	83°06′N	156°01′W	3473	0.552	2.67	1.47	1	1	65
FL-13	83°08′N	156°47′W	3577	0.540	2.60	1.40	1	1	65
FL-14	83°08′N	157°18′W	3216	0.394	2.76	1.09	1	1	65
FL-15	82°60′N	158°16′W	3137	0.295	2.63	0.78	1	1	65
FL-16	83°01′N	159°03′W	2247	0.338	2.68	0.91	1	1	65
FL-17	82°60′N	159°02′W	2215	0.296	2.61	0.77	1	1	65
FL-19	83°03′N	162°52′W	3417	0.440	2.43	1.07	1	1	65
FL-21	83°01′N	163°37′W	3494	0.478	2.66	1.27	1	1	65
FL-22	82°53′N	163°17′W	3750	0.666	2.14	1.43	1	1	65
FL-23	82°39′N	162°49′W	3748	0.676	2.18	1.47	1	1	65
FL-24	82°22′N	162°07′W	3743	0.570	2.52	1.44	1	1	65
FL-25	82°26′N	160°40′W	3760	0.631	2.10	1.32	1	1	65

Note: See list of symbols in Table 4.4–14.

(From Clark, S. P., Jr., *Handbook of Physical Constants,* Geological Society of America, Memoir 97, 1966. With permission.)

REFERENCE

1. **Lachenbruch, A. H. and Marshall, B. V.,** *Trans. Am. Geophys. Union,* 45, 123, 1964.

Table 4.4–18
MAXIMUM OBSERVED TEMPERATURES OF BASALTIC LAVAS

Locality and rock type	Temp, °C	Remarks	Ref.
Halemaumau, 1912, basalt, Lava lake	1210	Optical pyrometer; 25-degree correction for emissivity included; measured in daylight.	1
Halemaumau, 1917, basalt, Lava lake	1120–1170	Seger cones in iron pipe 3.8 cm in internal diam. Immersed for 8 min to depths from 8–13 m in Lava lake. Correction of 200° for failure of cones to attain temperature of lava included.	2
Nyamuragira, 1938, Leucite basalt, fountains	1095	Optical pyrometer; 25-degree correction for emissivity included; measured in daylight.	3
Paricutin, 1944, basalt	1200–1250	Optical pyrometer; measured in daylight; no correction for emissivity.	4
	1110	Thermocouple in porcelain tube, 10 cm into lava; 3 mi from source of flow.	
Mauna Loa, 1950, basalt		Optical pyrometer; 25-degree correction for emissivity included; measured at night.	5
dome fountain	1085–1105		
throat of spatter cone	1115–1135		
Mihara, 1950, basalt, fountain	1240	Optical pyrometer; 30-degree correction for emissivity included; measured in daylight.	6
Mihara, 1951, basalt, flow	1125	Platinum/platinum-rhodium thermocouple, hot junction unprotected.	7
Kilauea, 1952, basalt, fountains	1145	Glowing-filament optical pyrometer; 25-degree correction for emissivity included; measured at night.	8
Kilauea, 1955, basalt, fountains	1110	Glowing-filament optical pyrometer; 25-degree correction for emissivity included. Extrapolated from distance of 200–300 ft to correct for atmospheric absorption; measured at night.	9
Nyiragongo, 1956, Nephelinite fountain in Lava lake	980	Optical pyrometer; 20-degree correction for emissivity included; measured at night.	10
Capelinhos, Azores, 1957, basalt, fountains	1005	Optical pyrometer; 20-degree correction for emissivity included; measured at night.	11

(From Clark, S. P., Jr., *Handbook of Physical Constants,* Geological Society of America, Memoir 97, 1966. With permission.)

REFERENCES

1. **Day, A. L. and Sheperd, E. S.,** *Geol. Soc. Am. Bull.,* 24, 601, 1913.
2. **Jagger,** *J. Wash. Acad. Sci.,* 7, 398, 1917.
3. **Verhoogen,** *Explor. du Parc National Albert, Fasc.,* 1, 134, 1948.
4. **Zies, E. G.,** *Trans. Am. Geophys. Union,* 27, 178, 1946.
5. **Finch, R. H. and Macdonald, G. A.,** *U.S. Geol. Survey Bull.,* 996-B, 1953, 75.
6. **Tsuya, N. et al.,** *Bull. Earthquake Res. Inst.,* 32, 59, 1954.
7. **Minakami,** *Bull. Earthquake Res. Inst.,* 29, 491, 1951.
8. **Macdonald, G. A.,** *U.S. Geol. Survey Bull.,* 1021-B, 1955, 87.
9. **Macdonald, G. A. and Eaton,** *Volcano Lett.,* 529, 6, 1955 and Macdonald, G. A., private comm.
10. **Sahama, G.,** *Explor. du Parc National Albert, Fasc.,* 2, 15, 1958.
11. **Mulford, S. F.,** *Cranbrook Inst. Sci. News Lett.,* 28, 17, 1958.

Table 4.4–19
MAGNETIC PROPERTIES OF FERRIMAGNETIC MINERALS AND THREE FERROMAGNETIC METALS

Mineral	Curie or Néel point θ°C	Curie or Néel point θ°K	Saturation magnetization emu/g	Coercive force oe.	Thermoremanent magnetization: Intensity emu/cm³	Thermoremanent magnetization: External field in oe.	Ref.
Magnetite	578	851	92–93 (24°C)	20	–	–	4
Fe_3O_4			98.2 (0°K)				
Ulvöspinel	–273	0	–	–	–	–	4
Fe_2TiO_4	–152	121	–	–	–	–	1
Hematite	675	948	0.5 (24°C)	7,600	–	–	4
Fe_2O_3				(natural)			
	670	943	–	360	0.34	2.0	6
				(synthetic)			
	670	943	0.39 (24°C)	430	–	–	5
				(synthetic)			
Ilmenite	–205	68	–	–	–	–	2
$FeTiO_3$							
Hem_{40}-Ilm_{60}	230	503	20 (24°C)	117	–1.94	2.0	6
				(synthetic)	(self-reversing)		
Maghemite	675	948	83.5 (24°C)	–	–	–	4
Fe_2O_3							
Pyrrhotite	300–325	573–598	62 (24°C)	15–20	–	–	4
$Fe_{1-x}S$			–	–	0.04–0.23	0.5	6
Iron	770	1043	21,500	1.8	–	–	3
Nickel	358	631	6100	0.7	–	–	3
Bar	–	–	–	–	3.0	0.5	6
Powder	–	–	–	–	3.8	2.0	6
Cobalt	1120	1393	17,900	10	–	–	3

(From Clark, S. P., Jr., *Handbook of Physical Constants,* Geological Society of America, Memoir 97, 1966. With permission.)

REFERENCES

1. **Akimoto, S. et al.,** *J. Geomag. Geoelect.,* 9, 165, 1957.
2. **Bizette and Tsai,** *Compt. Rend.,* 242, 2124, 1956.
3. **Bozorth, R. M.,** *Ferromagnetism,* Van Nostrand, New York, 1951.
4. **Nagata, T.,** *Rock Magnetism,* Maruzen and Co., Tokyo, 1953.
5. **Nagata, T. and Akimoto, S.,** *Geofisica pura e appl.,* 34, 36, 1966.
6. **Uyeda, S.,** *Jap. J. Geophys.,* 2, 1, 1958.

Table 4.4–20
RANGE OF MAGNETIC SUSCEPTIBILITY IN MAJOR ROCK TYPES

Susceptibility in cgs emu per cm^3

Rock type	No. samples	Percentage of samples with susceptibility: Less than 10^{-4}	Between 10^{-4} and 10^{-3}	Between 10^{-3} and 4×10^{-3}	Greater than 4×10^{-3}
Mafic effusive rocks	97	5	29	47	19
Mafic plutonic rocks	53	24	27	28	21
Granites and allied rocks	74	60	23	16	1
Gneisses, schists, slates	45	71	22	7	0
Sedimentary rocks	48	73	19	4	4

(From Clark, S. P., Jr., *Handbook of Physical Constants,* Geological Society of America, Memoir 97, 1966. With permission.)

4.5 General Physico-chemical and Physical Data

Table 4.5–1
DENSITY OF ELEMENTS

Element	Temp, °C	Density, g/cm³	lb/ft³	Observer
Aluminum, hard drawn	20	2.699	168.5	Edwards, 1925
Liquid	659	2.382	148.7	Moorman, 1921
Antimony				
Vacuo-distilled	20	6.618	413.1	Kahlbaum, 1902
Compressed	20	6.691	417.7	Kahlbaum, 1902
Amorphous	–	6.22	388.3	Herard
Argon, liquid	–183	1.3845	86.4	Baly-Donnan
	–189	1.4233	88.9	Baly-Donnan
Arsenic				
Metallic	15	5.73	357.7	Lashchenko, 1922
Amorphous, brown–black	–	3.70	231.0	Guenther
Yellow	18	2.0	124.9	Erdmann and Reppert, 1908
Barium	–	3.78	236.0	Guntz
	25	3.5	218.5	Biltz and Huttig, 1920
Bismuth				
Electrolytic	–	9.747	608.5	Classen, 1890
	20	9.80	611.8	Johnston and Adams, 1912
Vacuo-distilled	20	9.781	610.6	Kahlbaum, 1902
Liquid	271	10.00	624.3	Vincentini-Omodei
	271	10.24	639.25	Plüss, 1915
Solid	271	9.67	603.7	Vincentini-Omodei
Boron				
Crystal	–	3.33	158.3	Wigand
Amorphous	–	2.34	152.9	Moissan
Bromine, liquid	–	3.12	194.8	Richards-Stull
Cadmium				
Cast	20	8.648	539.9	Egerton and Lee, 1923
Wrought	–	8.67	541.2	
Vacuo-distilled	20	8.648	539.9	Kahlbaum, 1902
Solid	318	8.37	522.5	Vincentini-Omodei
Liquid	318	7.99	498.8	Vincentini-Omodei
	349	7.94	495.7	Arpi, 1914
Cesium	20	1.873	116.9	Richards-Brink
Calcium	–	1.54	96.1	Brink
Carbon				
Crystal	–	3.52	219.7	Wigand
Graphite	–	2.25	140.5	Wigand
Cerium				
Electrolytic	–	6.79	423.9	Muthmann-Weiss
Pure	–	6.9	430.7	Muthmann-Weiss
Chlorine, liquid	–33.6	1.507	94.1	Drugman-Ramsay
Chromium	–	6.52–73	407.0–420.1	
Pure	20	6.92	432.0	Moissan
	28	7.20	449.5	Brenner, 1948
Cobalt	21	8.71	543.7	Tilden
	–	8.9	555.6	Kalmus and Harper, 1915

Note: The density is given in g/cm³ and lb/ft³ at the temperature stated. Where no temperature is given ordinary atmospheric temperature is understood.

Table 4.5–1 (*Continued*)
DENSITY OF ELEMENTS

Element	Temp, °C	Density, g/cm³	lb/ ft³	Observer
Columbium	15	8.4	524.4	Muthmann-Weiss
Copper				
Cast	–	8.30–95	518.1–558.7	
Annealed	20	8.89	555.0	Dellinger, 1911
Wrought	–	8.85–95	552.5–558.7	
Hard-drawn	20	8.89	555.0	Dellinger, 1911
Vacuo-distilled	20	8.9326	557.6	Kahlbaum, 1902
Compressed	20	8.9376	558.0	Kahlbaum, 1902
Liquid	–	8.217	513.0	Roberts-Wrightson
Erbium	–	4.77(?)	298.0	St. Meyer
Fluorine, liquid	–200	1.14	71.2	Moissan-Dewar
Gallium	25	5.903	369.1	Bur. Stand., 1934
Germanium	20	5.46	340.9	Winkler
Glucinum (beryllium)	20	1.84	114.9	Fichter and Jablczynski, 1913
Gold				
Cast	–	19.3	1204.8	
Cold rolled	20	19.296	1204.6	Rose, 1912
Wrought	–	19.33	1206.7	
Drawn annealed	20	19.26	1202.3	Kahlbaum and Sturm, 1905
Vacuo-distilled	20	18.88	1178.6	Kahlbaum, 1902
Compressed	20	19.27	1203.0	Kahlbaum, 1902
Helium, liquid	–269	0.15	9.4	Onnes
Hydrogen, liquid	–252	0.07	4.4	Dewar, 1904
Indium	–	7.28	454.5	Richards
Iodine	20	4.94	308.4	Richards-Stull
Iridium	17	22.42	1399.6	Deville-Debray
Iron, pure	–	7.85–88	490.1–491.9	
Electrolytic, rolled	20	7.90	493.2	Tritton and Hanson, 1924
Gray cast	–	7.03–13	438.9–445.1	
White cast	–	7.58–73	473.2–482.6	
Wrought	–	7.80–90	486.9–493.2	
Liquid	–	6.88	429.5	Roberts-Austen
Steel	–	7.60–80	474.4–486.9	
Krypton, liquid	–146	2.16	134.8	Ramsay-Travers
Lanthanum	–	6.15	383.9	Muthmann-Weiss
Lead				
Vacuo-distilled	20	11.342	708.0	Kahlbaum, 1902
Compressed	20	11.347	708.4	Kahlbaum, 1902
Solid	325	11.005	687.0	Vincentini-Omodei
Liquid	325	10.645	664.5	Vincentini-Omodei
	400	10.597	661.5	Day, Sosman, 1914
	850	10.078	629.1	Day, Sosman, 1914
Lithium	20	0.534	33.3	Richards-Brink, 1907
Magnesium	–	1.741	108.7	Voigt
Manganese	–	7.42	463.2	Prelinger
Mercury				
Liquid	0	13.596	848.8	Regnault, Volkmann
	20	13.546	845.6	
	–38.8	13.690	854.6	Vincentini-Omodei

Table 4.5–1 (*Continued*)
DENSITY OF ELEMENTS

Element	Temp, °C	Density, g/cm³	lb/ft³	Observer
Solid	−38.8	14.193	886.0	Vincentini-Omodei
	−188	14.383	897.9	Dewar, 1902
Molybdenum	–	9.01	562.5	Moissan
	–	10.2	636.8	Fink, 1910
Neodymium	–	6.96	434.5	Muthmann-Weiss
Nickel	–	8.60–90	536.9–555.6	
Nitrogen, liquid	−195	0.81	50.6	Baly-Donnan, 1902
	−205	0.854	53.3	Baly-Donnan, 1902
Osmium	–	22.5	1404.6	Deville-Debray
Oxygen, liquid	−184	1.14	71.2	
Palladium	–	12.16	759.1	Richards-Stull
Phosphorus				
White	–	1.83	114.2	
Red	–	2.20	137.3	
Metallic	15	2.34	146.1	Hittorf
Platinum	20	21.37	1334.1	Richards-Stull
Potassium	20	0.87	54.3	Richards-Brink, 1907
Solid	62.1	0.851	53.1	Vincentini-Omodei
Liquid	62.1	0.83	51.8	Vincentini-Omodei
Praesodymium	–	6.475	404.2	Muthmann-Weiss
Rhodium	–	12.44	776.6	Holborn-Henning
Rubidium	20	1.532	95.6	Richards-Brink, 1907
Ruthenium	0	12.06	752.9	Toby
Samarium	–	7.7–8	480.7–486.9	Muthmann-Weiss
Selenium	–	4.3–8	268.4–299.6	
Silicon				
Crystal	20	2.42	151.1	Richards-Stull-Brink
Amorphous	15	2.35	146.7	Vigoroux
Silver				
Cast	–	10.42–53	650.5–657.4	
Wrought	–	10.6	661.7	
Vacuo-distilled	20	10.492	655.0	Kahlbaum, 1902
Compressed	20	10.503	655.7	Kahlbaum, 1902
Liquid	–	9.51	593.7	Wrightson
Sodium	20	0.9712	60.6	Richards-Brink, 1907
Solid	97.6	0.9519	59.4	Vincentini-Omodei
Liquid	97.6	0.9287	58.0	Vincentini-Omodei
Solid	−188	1.0066	62.8	Dewar
Strontinum	–	2.50–58	156.1–161.1	Matthiessen
Sulfur	–	2.0–1	124.9–131.1	
Liquid	–	1.811	112.1	Vincentini-Omodei
Tantalum	–	16.6	1036.3	
Tellurium				
Crystal	–	6.25	390.2	
Amorphous	20	6.02	375.8	Beljankin
Thallium	–	11.86	740.4	Richards-Stull
Thorium	–	11.3–11.7	705.4–730.4	Rentschler, Marden, 1925

Table 4.5–1 (*Continued*)
DENSITY OF ELEMENTS

Element	Temp, °C	Density, g/cm³	lb/ ft³	Observer
Tin				
White cast	–	7.29	455.1	Matthiessen
Wrought	–	7.30	455.7	
Crystallized	–	6.97–7.18	435.1–448.2	
Solid	226	7.184	448.5	Vincentini-Omodei
Liquid	226	6.99	436.4	Vincentini-Omodei
Gray	–	5.8	362.1	
Titanium	18	4.5	280.9	Mixter
Tungsten	–	18.6–19.1	1161.1–1192.4	
Uranium	13	18.7	1167.4	Zimmermann
Vanadium	–	5.69	355.3	Ruff-Martin
	20	5.96	372.1	Hull, 1922
Xenon, liquid	-109	3.52	219.7	Ramsay-Travers
Yttrium	–	3.80	237.2	St. Meyer
Zinc				
Cast	–	7.04–16	439.5–447.0	
Wrought	–	7.19	448.9	
Vacuo-distilled	20	6.92	432.0	Kahlbaum, 1902
Compressed	20	7.13	445.1	Kahlbaum, 1902
Liquid	–	6.48	404.5	Roberts-Wrightson
Zirconium	–	6.44	402.0	

(From Hodgman, Charles D., Ed., *Handbook of Chemistry and Physics*, 36th ed., Chemical Rubber Co., Cleveland, 1954. With permission.)

Table 4.5–2
DENSITY OF ALLOYS

Alloy	Composition	g/cm³	lb/ft³
Aluminum and copper	10 Al, 90 Cu	7.69	480.06
	5 Al, 95 Cu	8.37	522.51
	3 Al, 97 Cu	8.69	542.49
Aluminum and zinc	91 Al, 9 Zn	2.80	174.80
Bell metal	78 Cu, 22 Sn	8.70	543.11
Bismuth, lead and tin	53 Bi, 40 Pb, 7 Sn	10.56	659.23
Brass			
Yellow	70 Cu, 30 Zn cast	8.44	526.88
	rolled	8.56	534.38
	drawn	8.70	543.11
Red	90 Cu, 10 Zn	8.60	536.87
White	50 Cu, 50 Zn	8.20	511.01
Bronze	90 Cu, 10 Sn(gun metal)	8.78	548.11
	85 Cu, 15 Sn	8.89	554.98
	80 Cu, 20 Sn	8.74	545.61
	75 Cu, 25 Sn	8.83	551.23

Note: The density is given in g/cm³ at ordinary atmospheric temperatures.

Table 4.5–2 (*Continued*)
DENSITY OF ALLOYS

Alloy	Composition	g/cm³	lb/ft³
Cadmium and tin	32 Cd, 68 Sn	7.70	480.69
Constantan	60 Cu, 40 Ni	8.88	554.35
German silver	26.3 Cu, 36.6 Zn, 36.8 Ni	8.30	518.14
	52 Cu, 26 Zn, 22 Ni	8.45	527.51
	59 Cu, 30 Zn, 11 Ni	8.34	520.64
	63 Cu, 30 Zn, 6 Ni	8.30	518.14
Gold and copper	98 Au, 2 Cu	18.84	1176.12
	96 Au, 4 Cu	18.36	1146.16
	94 Au, 6 Cu	17.95	1120.56
	92 Au, 8 Cu	17.52	1093.72
	90 Au, 10 Cu	17.16	1071.25
	88 Au, 12 Cu	16.81	1049.40
	86 Au, 14 Cu	16.47	1028.17
Invar	63.8 Fe, 36 Ni, 0.2 C	8.00	499.42
Lead and tin	87.5 Pb, 12.5 Sn	10.60	661.73
	84 Pb, 16 Sn	10.33	644.87
	77.8 Pb, 22.2 Sn	10.05	627.39
	63.7 Pb, 36.3 Sn	9.43	588.69
	46.7 Pb, 53.3 Sn	8.73	544.99
	30.5 Pb, 69.5 Sn	8.24	514.40
Magnalium	90 Al, 10 Mg	2.50	156.07
	70 Al, 30 Mg	2.00	124.85
Manganese bronze	95 Cu, 5 Mn	8.80	549.36
Manganin	84 Cu, 12 Mn, 4 Ni	8.50	530.63
Monel metal	71 Ni, 27 Cu, 2 Fe	8.90	555.60
Nickelin	–	8.77	547.48
Phosphor bronze	79.7 Cu, 10 Sn, 9.5 Sb, 0.8 P	8.80	549.36
Plantinum and iridium	90 Pt, 10 Ir	21.62	1349.67
	85 Pt, 15 Ir	21.62	1349.67
	66.67 Pt, 33.33 Ir	21.87	1365.28
	5 Pt, 95 Ir	22.38	1397.12
Speculum metal	67 Cu, 33 Sn	8.60	536.87
Steel	99 Fe, 1 C	7.83	488.80
Manganese	86 Fe, 13 Mn, 1 C	7.81	487.55
Wood's metal	50 Bi, 25 Pb, 12.5 Cd, 12.5 Sn	9.70	659.23

(From Hodgman, Charles D., Ed., *Handbook of Chemistry and Physics,* 36th ed., Chemical Rubber Co., Cleveland, 1954. With permission.)

Table 4.5–3
DENSITY OF VARIOUS SOLIDS

Substance	g/cm³	lb/ft³	Substance	g/cm³	lb/ft³
Agate	2.5–2.7	156–168	Flint	2.63	164
Alabaster			Fluorite	3.18	198
Carbonate	2.69–2.78	168–173	Galena	7.3–7.6	460–470
Sulfate	2.26–2.32	141–145	Gamboge	1.2	75
Albite	2.62–2.65	163–165	Garnet	3.15–4.3	197–268
Amber	1.06–1.11	66–69	Gas carbon	1.88	117
Amphiboles	2.9–3.2	180–200	Gelatin	1.27	79
			Glass		
Anorthite	2.74–2.76	171–175	Common	2.4–2.8	150–175
Asbestos	2.0–2.8	125–175	Flint	2.9–5.9	180–370
Asbestos slate	1.8	112	Glue	1.27	79
Asphalt	1.1–1.5	69–94	Granite	2.64–2.76	165–172
Basalt	2.4–3.1	150–190			
			Graphite	2.30–2.72	144–170
Beeswax	0.96–0.97	60–61	Gum arabic	1.3–1.4	81–87
Beryl	2.69–2.7	168–169	Gypsum	2.31–2.33	144–145
Biotite	2.7–3.1	170–190	Hematite	4.9–5.3	306–330
Bone	1.7–2.0	106–125	Hornblende	3.0	187
Brick	1.4–2.2	87–137			
			Ice	0.917	57.2
Butter	0.86–0.87	53–54	Ivory	1.83–1.92	114–120
Calamine	4.1–4.5	255–280	Leather, dry	0.86	54
Calcspar	2.6–2.8	162–175	Lime, slaked	1.3–1.4	81–87
Camphor	0.99	62	Limestone	2.68–2.76	167–171
Caoutchouc	0.92–0.99	57–62			
			Linoleum	1.18	74
Cardboard	0.69	43	Magnetite	4.9–5.2	306–324
Celluloid	1.4	87	Malachite	3.7–4.1	231–256
Cement, set	2.7–3.0	170–190	Marble	2.6–2.84	160–177
Chalk	1.9–2.8	118–175	Meerschaum	0.99–1.28	62–80
Charcoal					
Oak	0.57	35	Mica	2.6–3.2	165–200
Pine	0.28–0.44	18–28	Muscovite	2.76–3.00	172–187
			Ochre	3.5	218
Cinnabar	8.12	507	Opal	2.2	137
Clay	1.8–2.6	112–162	Paper	0.7–1.15	44–72
Coal					
Anthracite	1.4–1.8	87–112	Paraffin	0.87–0.91	54–57
Bituminous	1.2–1.5	75–94	Peat blocks	0.84	52
Cocoa butter	0.89–0.91	56–57	Pitch	1.07	67
Coke	1.0–1.7	62–105	Porcelain	2.3–2.5	143–156
			Porphyry	2.6–2.9	162–181
Copal	1.04–1.14	65–71	Pressed wool pulp		
Cork	0.22–0.26	14–16	board	0.19	12
Cork linoleum	0.54	34	Pyrite	4.95–5.1	309–318
Corundum	3.9–4.0	245–250	Quartz	2.65	165
Diamond	3.01–3.52	188–220	Resin	1.07	67
			Rock salt	2.18	136
Dolomite	2.84	177			
Ebonite	1.15	72	Rubber, hard	1.19	74
Emery	4.0	250	Rubber		
Epidote	3.25–3.50	203–218	Soft commercial	1.1	69
Feldspar	2.55–2.75	159–172	Pure gum	0.91–0.93	57–58

Note: The approximate density of various solids at ordinary atmospheric temperature. In the case of substances with voids, such as paper or leather, the bulk density is indicated rather than the density of the solid portion.

Table 4.5–3 (*Continued*)
DENSITY OF VARIOUS SOLIDS

Substance	g/cm³	lb/ft³	Substance	g/cm³	lb/ft³
Sandstone	2.14–2.36	134–147	Dogwood	0.76	47
Serpentine	2.50–2.65	156–165	Ebony	1.11–1.33	69–83
Silica			Elm	0.54–0.60	34–37
Fused transparent	2.21	138	Hickory	0.60–0.93	37–58
Translucent	2.07	129	Holly	0.76	47
Slag	2.0–3.9	125–240	Juniper	0.56	35
Slate	2.6–3.3	162–205	Larch	0.50–0.56	31–35
Soapstone	2.6–2.8	162–175	Lignum vitae	1.17–1.33	73–83
Spermaceti	0.95	59	Locust	0.67–0.71	42–44
Starch	1.53	95	Logwood	0.91	57
Sugar	1.59	99	Mahogany		
Talc	2.7–2.8	168–174	Honduras	0.66	41
Tallow			Spanish	0.85	53
Beef	0.94	59	Maple	0.62–0.75	39–47
Mutton	0.94	59	Oak	0.60–0.90	37–56
Tar	1.02	66	Pear	0.61–0.73	38–45
Topaz	3.5–3.6	219–223	Pine		
Tourmaline	3.0–3.2	190–200	Pitch	0.83–0.85	52–53
Wax, sealing	1.8	112	White	0.35–0.50	22–31
Wood (seasoned):			Yellow	0.37–0.60	23–37
Alder	0.42–0.68	26–42	Plum	0.66–0.78	41–49
Apple	0.66–0.84	41–52	Poplar	0.35–0.5	22–31
Ash	0.65–0.85	40–53	Satinwood	0.95	59
Balsa	0.11–0.14	7–9	Spruce	0.48–0.70	30–44
Bamboo	0.31–0.40	19–25	Sycamore	0.40–0.60	24–37
Basswood	0.32–0.59	20–37	Teak		
Beech	0.70–0.90	43–56	Indian	0.66–0.88	41–55
Birch	0.51–0.77	32–48	African	0.98	61
Blue gum	1.00	62	Walnut	0.64–0.70	40–43
Box	0.95–1.16	59–72	Water gum	1.00	62
Butternut	0.38	24	Willow	0.40–0.60	24–37
Cedar	0.49–0.57	30–35			
Cherry	0.70–0.90	43–56			

(From Hodgman, Charles D., Ed., *Handbook of Chemistry and Physics,* 36th ed., Chemical Rubber Co., Cleveland, 1954. With permission.)

REFERENCE

Forsythe, W. E., Ed., *Smithsonian Physical Tables,* Smithsonian Institution, Washington, D.C., 1954.

Table 4.5–4
DENSITY OF VARIOUS LIQUIDS

Liquid	g/cm³	lb/ft³	Temp, °C
Acetone	0.792	49.4	20
Alcohol			
Ethyl	0.791	49.4	20
Methyl	0.810	50.5	0
Benzene	0.899	56.1	0
Carbolic acid	0.950–0.965	59.2–60.2	15
Carbon disulfide	1.293	80.7	0
Carbon tetrachloride	1.595	99.6	20
Chloroform	1.489	93.0	20
Ether	0.736	45.9	0
Gasoline	0.66–0.69	41.0–43.0	–
Glycerin	1.260	78.6	0
Kerosene	0.82	51.2	–
Mercury	13.6	849.0	–
Milk	1.028–1.035	64.2–64.6	–
Naphtha			
Petroleum ether	0.665	41.5	15
Wood	0.848–0.810	52.9–50.5	0
Oils			
Castor	0.969	60.5	15
Cocoanut	0.925	57.7	15
Cotton seed	0.926	57.8	16
Creosote	1.040–1.100	64.9–68.6	15
Linseed, boiled	0.942	58.8	15
Olive	0.918	57.3	15
Sea-water	1.025	63.99	15
Turpentine (spirits)	0.87	54.3	–
Water	1.00	62.43	4

(From Hodgman, Charles D., Ed., *Handbook of Chemistry and Physics,* 36th ed., Chemical Rubber Co., Cleveland, 1954. With permission.)

REFERENCE

Forsythe, W. E., Ed., *Smithsonian Physical Tables,* Smithsonian Institution, Washington, D.C., 1954.

Table 4.5–5
DENSITY OF ALCOHOL

Density of Ethyl Alcohol in g/cm^3
Computed from Mendeleev's Formula

Temp, °C	0	1	2	3	4
0	.80625	.80541	.80457	.80374	.80290
10	.79788	.79704	.79620	.79535	.79451
20	.78945	.78860	.78775	.78691	.78606
30	.78097	.78012	.77927	.77841	.77756

Temp, °C	5	6	7	8	9
0	.80207	.80123	.80039	.79956	.79872
10	.79367	.79283	.79198	.79114	.79029
20	.78522	.78437	.78352	.78267	.78182
30	.77671	.77585	.77500	.77414	.77329

(From Hodgman, Charles D., Ed., *Handbook of Chemistry and Physics,* 36th ed., Chemical Rubber Co., Cleveland, 1954. With permission.)

Table 4.5–6
DENSITY AND VOLUME OF MERCURY

Temp, °C	Mass, g/ml	Vol of 1 g, ml	Temp, °C	Mass, g/ml	Vol in 1 g, ml
–10	13.6202	0.0734205	15	13.5585	0.0737546
–9	13.6177	0.0734338	16	13.5561	0.0737680
–8	13.6152	0.0734472	17	13.5536	0.0737813
–7	13.6128	0.0734606	18	13.5512	0.0737947
–6	13.6103	0.0734739	19	13.5487	0.0738081
–5	13.6078	0.0734873	20	13.5462	0.0738215
–4	13.6053	0.0735006	21	13.5438	0.0738348
–3	13.6029	0.0735140	22	13.5413	0.0738482
–2	13.6004	0.0735273	23	13.5389	0.0738616
–1	13.5979	0.0735407	24	13.5364	0.0738750
0	13.5955	0.0735540	25	13.5340	0.0738883
1	13.5930	0.0735674	26	13.5315	0.0739017
2	13.5906	0.0735808	27	13.5291	0.0739151
3	13.5881	0.0735941	28	13.5266	0.0739285
4	13.5856	0.0736075	29	13.5242	0.0739419
5	13.5832	0.0736209	30°	13.5217	0.0739552
6	13.5807	0.0736342	31	13.5193	0.0739686
7	13.5782	0.0736476	32	13.5168	0.0739820
8	13.5758	0.0736610	33	13.5144	0.0739953
9	13.5733	0.0736744	34	13.5119	0.0740087
10	13.5708	0.0736877	35	13.5095	0.0740221
11	13.5684	0.0737011	36	13.5070	0.0740354
12	13.5659	0.0737145	37	13.5046	0.0740488
13	13.5634	0.0737278	38	13.5021	0.0740622
14	13.5610	0.0737412	39	13.4997	0.0740756

Note: Based on the density of mercury at 0°C by Thiesen and Scheel, 1898.

Table 4.5–6 (*Continued*)
DENSITY AND VOLUME OF MERCURY

Temp, °C	Mass, g/ml	Vol. of 1 g, ml	Temp, °C	Mass, g/ml	Vol. in 1 g, ml
40	13.4973	0.0740891	210	13.0913	0.0763865
50	13.4729	0.0742229	220	13.0678	0.0765239
60	13.4486	0.0743569	230	13.0443	0.0766616
70	13.4244	0.0744910			
80	13.4003	0.0746252	240	13.0209	0.0767996
			250	12.9975	0.0769381
90	13.3762	0.0747594	260	12.9741	0.0770769
100	13.3522	0.0748939	270	12.9507	0.0772161
110	13.3283	0.0750285	280	12.9273	0.0773558
120	13.3044	0.0751633			
130	13.2805	0.0752982			
			290	12.9039	0.0774958
140	13.2567	0.0754334	300	12.8806	0.0776364
150	13.2330	0.0755688	310	12.8572	0.0777774
160	13.2093	0.0757044	320	12.8339	0.0779189
170	13.1856	0.0758402	330	12.8105	0.0780609
180	13.1620	0.0759764			
			340	12.7872	0.0782033
190	13.1384	0.0761128	350	12.7638	0.0783464
200	13.1148	0.0762495	360	12.7405	0.0784900

(From Hodgman, Charles D., Ed., *Handbook of Chemistry and Physics,* 36th ed., Chemical Rubber Co., Cleveland, 1954. With permission.)

REFERENCE

Forsythe, W. E., Ed., *Smithsonian Physical Tables,* Smithsonian Institution, Washington, D.C., 1954.

Table 4.5–7
DENSITY OF SATURATED VAPORS

At the Temperature of Normal Ebullition

Vapor	Temp, °C	Density
Acetic acid	118.5	0.00315
Benzene	80.2	0.00275
Chloroform	61.2	0.00443
Ether	34.6	0.00311
Ethyl alcohol	78.3	0.00164
Methyl alcohol	64.7	0.00121
Water	100.0	0.000596

(From Hodgman, Charles D., Ed., *Handbook of Chemistry and Physics,* 36th ed., Chemical Rubber Co., Cleveland, 1954. With permission.)

Table 4.5–8
DENSITY OF GASES IN LIQUID AND SOLID FORM

Gas	Liquid		Solid		Observer
	Temp, °C	D, g/cm³	Temp, °C	D, g/cm³	
Acetylene	−23.5	0.52	–	–	Mathias, 1909
	+30.3	0.40	–	–	–
Air (20.9% oxygen)	−147	0.92	–	–	–
Ammonia	−10.7	0.65	–	–	Andreeff, 1859
	+16.3	0.61	–	–	Andreeff, 1859
Argon	−187*	1.41	−233	1.65	Baly and Donnan, 1902
Carbon dioxide	−60	1.19	−79	1.53	Behn, 1910
	+20	0.77	–	–	Amagat
Carbon monoxide	−109*	0.79	–	–	–
	−68	0.86	–	–	Baly and Donnan
Chlorine	−33.6*	1.56	–	1.9	Knietsch, 1890
Chlorine	+20	1.41	–	–	Knietsch, 1890
Ethane	−88	0.546	–	–	–
Ethylene	−102	0.566	–	–	–
Ethylene	−21	0.41	–	–	Cailletet and Mathias, 1886
Ethylene	+10	0.21	–	–	–
Fluorine	−187*	1.11	–	1.3	–
Helium	−269*	0.122	–	–	Kamerling-Onnes and Perrier, 1910
Hydrogen	−253*	0.07	−260	0.076	Dewar, 1904
Hydrogen chloride	−85.8	1.194	–	–	–
Hydrogen fluoride	+13.6	0.988	–	–	–
Hydrogen phosphide (phosphine)	−90	0.746	–	–	–
Hydrogen sulfide	−61	0.86	–	–	–
Krypton	−146	2.6	–	2.(?)	–
Methane	−164	0.415	–	–	–
Methyl chloride	+18	0.920	–	–	–
Neon	−245.9*	1.204	–	1.0	–
Nitrogen	−196*	0.804	−253	1.03	Dewar, 1904
Nitrous oxide	−20	1.0	–	–	Cailletet and Mathias
Nitrous oxide	+17	0.80	–	–	Villard, 1897
Oxygen	−123	0.89	–	–	Cailletet and Hautefeuille, 1881
	−182.7*	1.14	−253	−1.41	Kamerling-Onnes and Perrier, 1910
	−205	1.25	–	–	Baly and Donnan
Ozone, O_3	−183	1.71	–	–	–
Sulfur dioxide	−10*	1.46	–	–	Pierre
	+20	1.38	–	–	Cailletet and Mathias
Xenon	−109.1*	3.06	–	2.7(?)	–

Note: Temperatures marked * are the temperatures of normal ebullition.

(From Hodgman, Charles D., Ed., *Handbook of Chemistry and Physics,* 36th ed., Chemical Rubber Co., Cleveland, 1954. With permission.)

Table 4.5–9
HEAT CONDUCTIVITY
Table A
Metals

Substance	Temp, °C	Conductivity	Observer
Aluminum	−160	0.514	Lees, 1908
	18	0.480	Jaeger and Diesselhorst, 1900
	18	0.504	Lees, 1908
	100	0.492	Jaeger and Diesselhorst, 1900
	100	0.49	Angell, 1911
	200	0.55	Angell, 1911
	300	0.64	Angell, 1911
	400	0.76	Angell, 1911
	600	1.01	Angell, 1911
Antimony	0	0.0442	Lorenz, 1881
	100	0.040	Lorenz, 1881
	0–30	0.042	Berget, 1890
Bismuth	−186	0.025	Macchia, 1907
	0	0.0177	Lorenz
	18	0.0194	Jaeger and Diesselhorst, 1900
	100	0.0161	Jaeger and Diesselhorst, 1900
Brass			
70Cu + 30Zn	−160	0.181	Lees, 1908
70Cu + 30Zn	17	0.260	Lees, 1908
Yellow	0	0.204	Lorenz
Red	0	0.246	Lorenz
Bronze, aluminum (90Cu, 10Al)	–	0.18	Van Aubel
Cadmium	−160	0.239	Lees, 1908
	0	0.220	Lorenz
	18	0.222	Jaeger and Diesselhorst, 1900
	100	0.216	Jaeger and Diesselhorst, 1900
Constantan	18	0.054	Jaeger and Diesselhorst, 1900
(60Cu, 40Ni)	100	0.064	Jaeger and Diesselhorst, 1900
Copper, pure	−160	1.097	Lees, 1908
	13	1.00	Angström, 1863
	18	0.918	Jaeger and Diesselhorst, 1900
Copper, pure	100	0.908	Jaeger and Diesselhorst, 1900
	100–197	1.043	Hering, 1910
	100–268	0.969	Hering, 1910
	100–370	0.931	Hering, 1910
	100–541	0.902	Hering, 1910
	100–837	0.858	Hering, 1910

Note: Giving the quantity of heat in calories, which is transmitted per sec through a plate one cm thick across an area of one cm² when the temperature difference is one degree C.

Table 4.5–9 (*Continued*)
HEAT CONDUCTIVITY

Substance	Temp, °C	Conductivity	Observer
German silver	0	0.070	Lorenz, 1881
	100	0.089	Lorenz, 1881
52Cu, 26Zn, 22Ni	–	0.10	Glage, 1905
Gold	17	0.705	Barratt, 1914
	18	0.700	Jaeger and Diesselhorst, 1900
	100	0.703	Jaeger and Diesselhorst, 1900
Iridium	17	0.141	Barratt, 1914
Iron			
Pure	18	0.161	Jaeger and Diesselhorst
	100	0.151	Jaeger and Diesselhorst
	100–727	0.202	Hering, 1910
	100–1245	0.191	Hering, 1910
Wrought	−160	0.152	Lees, 1908
	18	0.144	Jaeger and Diesselhorst
	100	0.143	Jaeger and Diesselhorst
Cast	18	0.109	Jaeger and Diesselhorst
	100	0.108	Jaeger and Diesselhorst
	54	0.114	Callendar
	102	0.111	Callendar
Steel	−160	0.113	Lees, 1908
	18	0.115	Lees, 1908
	18	0.108	Jaeger and Diesselhorst
	100	0.107	Jaeger and Diesselhorst
Lead	−160	0.092	Lees, 1908
	18	0.083	Jaeger and Diesselhorst
	100	0.082	Jaeger and Diesselhorst
Magnesium	0–100	0.376	Lorenz, 1881
Manganin	18	0.0519	Jaeger and Diesselhorst
84Cu, 4Ni, 12Mn	100	0.06310	Jaeger and Diesselhorst
	−160	0.035	Lees, 1908
Mercury	0	0.0148	H. F. Weber, 1880
	50	0.0189	H. F. Weber, 1880
	17	0.0197	R. Weber, 1902
Molybdenum	17	0.346	Barratt, 1914
Nickel	−160	0.129	Lees, 1908
	18	0.142	Jaeger and Diesselhorst, 1900
	100	0.138	Jaeger and Diesselhorst, 1900
	300	0.126	Angell, 1911
	600	0.088	Angell, 1911
	800	0.068	Angell, 1911
	1200	0.058	Angell, 1911
Palladium	18	0.1683	Jaeger and Diesselhorst, 1900
	100	0.182	

Table 4.5–9 (*Continued*)
HEAT CONDUCTIVITY

Substance	Temp, °C	Conductivity	Observer
Platinum	18	0.1664	Jaeger and Diesselhorst, 1900
	100	0.1733	Jaeger and Diesselhorst, 1900
Platinum-iridium 10% Ir	17	0.074	Barratt, 1914
Platinum-rhodium 10% Rh	17	0.072	Barratt, 1914
Platinoid	18	0.060	Lees, 1908
Rhodium	17	0.210	Barratt, 1914
Silver, pure	−160	0.998	Lees, 1908
	18	0.974	Lees, 1908
	18	1.006	Jaeger and Diesselhorst, 1900
	100	0.992	Jaeger and Diesselhorst, 1900
Tin	−160	0.192	Lees, 1908
	0	0.1528	Lorenz, 1881
	18	0.155	Jaeger and Diesselhorst, 1900
	100	0.145	Jaeger and Diesselhorst, 1900
	100	0.1423	Lorenz, 1881
Tantalum	17	0.130	Barratt, 1914
Tungsten	17	0.476	Barratt, 1914
	18	0.35	Coolidge
Wood's alloy	–	0.0319	H. F. Weber
Zinc	−160	0.278	Lees, 1908
	18	0.2653	Jaeger and Diesselhorst
	100	0.2619	Jaeger and Diesselhorst

Table 4.5–9 (*Continued*)
HEAT CONDUCTIVITY
Table B
Various Solids

Substance	Conductivity	Observer
Asbestos fiber, 500°C	0.00019	Randolph, 1912
Paper	0.0006	–
	0.0004	Lees-Chorlton, 1896
Basalt	0.0052	Hecht, 1903
Brick, common red	0.0015	Herschel-Lebour and Dunn, 1879
Blotting paper	0.00015	Lees-Chorlton, 1896
Carbon	0.01	
Carborundum	0.0005	Lorenz
Brick, 150°–1200°	0.032–0.027	Wologdine
Cardboard	0.0005	–
Cement, Portland	0.00071	Lees-Chorlton, 1896
Chalk	0.0020	Herschel-Lebour and Dunn, 1879
Concrete		
Cinder	0.00081	–
Stone	0.0022	Norton
Cork	0.00072	G. Forbes, 1875
	0.00013	Lees, 1892–8
Cotton wool	0.000043	G. Forbes
Felted	0.000033	G. Forbes
Diatomic earth	0.00013	Hutton-Blard
Earth's crust, avg	0.004	–
Ebonite	0.00042	Lees
	0.00014	Barratt, 1914
Eiderdown, d = .109	0.000046	Peclet, 1878
Felt	0.000087	–
Fiber, red	0.0011	Barratt, 1914
Fire brick	0.00028	Hutton-Blard
	0.0011	Barratt, 1914
Flannel	0.00023	
Gas carbon		
20°	0.0085	Barratt, 1914
100°	0.0095	Barratt, 1914
Glass		
Crown (window)	0.0025	Lees, 1892–8
Flint	0.002	Lees, 1892–8
Jena	0.001–0.002	Lees, 1892–8
Soda		
20°	0.0017	Barratt, 1914
100°	0.0018	Barratt, 1914
Granite		
100°	0.0045–0.0060	Poole, 1912
500°	0.0040	Poole, 1912
Graphite	0.012	–
Graphite brick, 300°–700°	0.24	Wologdine, 1909
Gutta percha	0.00048	Péclet, 1878
Gypsum	0.0031	R. Weber, 1878

Note: Approximate values at ordinary temperatures.

Table 4.5–9 (*Continued*)
HEAT CONDUCTIVITY

Substance	Conductivity	Observer
Haircloth, felt	0.000042	G. Forbes
Ice	0.005	–
	0.0039	–
	0.0022	Forbes, 1875
Infusorial earth		
100°	0.00034	Skinner
300°	0.00040	Skinner
Pressed bricks, 100°	0.00030	Skinner
Lamp black, 100	0.00007	Randolph, 1912
Leather		
Cowhide	0.00042	Lees-Chorlton, 1896
Chamois	0.00015	Lees-Chorlton, 1896
Lime	0.00029	Hutton-Blard
Linen	0.00021	Lees-Chorlton, 1896
Magnesia, MgO	0.00016–0.00045	Hutton-Blard
Brick, 50°–1130°	0.0027–0.0072	Wologdine, 1909
Magnesium carbonate		
100°	0.00023	Skinner
300°	0.00025	Skinner
Marble	0.0071	Lees, 1892–8
Mica, perpendicular to cleavage plane	0.0018	Lees
Paper	0.0003	Lees
Paraffin	0.0006	Lees
0°	0.00023	R. Weber, 1878
Plaster of Paris	0.00070	Lees-Chorlton, 1896
Porcelain	0.0025	Lees, 1892–8
165°–1055°	0.0039–0.0047	Wologdine, 1909
Quartz		
Parallel to axis	0.030	Lees, 1892–8
Perpendicular to axis	0.016	Lees, 1892–8
Rubber, para	0.00045	Lees, 1892–8
Sand, dry	0.00093	Herschel-Lebour and Dunn, 1879
Sandstone	0.0055	Herschel-Lebour and Dunn, 1879
Sawdust	0.00012	G. Forbes, 1875
Silica, fused		
20°	0.00237	Barratt, 1914
100°	0.00255	Barratt, 1914
Silica brick, 100°–1000°C	0.002–0.003	Wologdine, 1909
Silk	0.000095	Lees-Chorlton, 1896
Slate	0.004700	Lees, 1892–8
Snow, compact	0.00051	Hjeltström
Soil, dry	0.00033	Lees-Chorlton, 1896
Wax, bees'	0.00009	G. Forbes
Wood		
Fir ‖ to axis	0.00030	–
Perpendicular to axis	0.00009	–

Table 4.5–9 (*Continued*)
HEAT CONDUCTIVITY

Substance	Conductivity	Observer
Liquids		
Acetic acid	0.00047	H. F. Weber
Amyl alcohol	0.000328	H. F. Weber
Aniline, 12°	0.00041	—
Benzole, 5°	0.000333	H. F. Weber
Carbon disulphide, 9°–15°	0.000343	H. F. Weber
Chloroform, 9°–15°	0.000288	H. F. Weber
Ether, 9°–15°	0.000303	H. F. Weber
Ethyl alcohol	0.000423	H. F. Weber
Glycerine, 9°–15°	0.000637	Graetz
Methyl alcohol	0.000495	H. F. Weber
Oils		
Olive	0.000395	Wachsmuth
Castor	0.000425	Wachsmuth
Petroleum, 13°	0.000355	Graetz
Turpentine	0.000325	Graetz
Vaseline, 25°	0.00044	Lees
Water		
0°	0.00139	Martin, Lang 1933
4°	0.00138	Weber
15°	0.00144	Martin, Lang 1933
20°	0.00143	Milner, Chattock
Gases		
Air, 0°	0.0000568	Winklemann
Argon, 0°	0.0000389	Schwarze
Ammonia gas, 0°	0.0000458	Winklemann
Carbon dioxide		
0°	0.0000307	Winklemann
Monoxide	0.0000499	Winklemann
Ethylene	0.0000395	Winklemann
Helium, 0°	0.000339	Schwarze
Hydrogen		
0°	0.000327	Winklemann
100°	0.000369	Graetz
Methane, 7°–8°	0.0000647	Winklemann
Nitric oxide, NO, 8°	0.0000460	Winklemann
Nitrogen, 7°–8°	0.0000524	Winklemann
Nitrous oxide, N_2O	0.0000350	Winklemann
Oxygen, 7°–8°	0.0000563	Winklemann

(From Hodgman, Charles D., Ed., *Handbook of Chemistry and Physics*, 36th ed., Chemical Rubber Co., Cleveland, 1954, 2247. With permission.)

Table 4.5–10
THERMAL CONDUCTIVITY OF MATERIALS

Soft Flexible Materials in Sheet Form

		D[a]	K[b]
Dry zero	Kapok between burlap or paper	1.0	0.24
		2.0	0.25
Cabot's® quilt	Eel grass between kraft paper	3.4	0.25
		4.6	0.26
Hair felt	Felted cattle hair	11.0	0.26
		13.0	0.26
Balsam wool	Chemically treated wood fiber	2.2	0.27
Hairinsul®	75% hair 25% jute	6.3	0.27
	50% hair 50% jute	6.1	0.26
Linofelt	Flax fibers between paper	4.9	0.28
Thermofelt	Jute and asbestos fibers, felted	10.0	0.37
	Hair and asbestos fibers, felted	7.8	0.28

Loose Materials

		D[a]	K[b]
Rock wool	Fibrous material made from rock,	6.0	0.26
	also made in sheet form, felted, and	10.0	0.27
	confined with wire netting	14.0	0.28
		18.0	0.29
Glass wool	Pyrex glass, curled	4.0	0.29
		10.0	0.29
Sil-O-Cel®	Powdered diatomaceous earth	10.6	0.31
Regranulated	Fine particles	9.4	0.30
cork	about 3/16 in. particles	8.1	0.31
Thermofill®	Gypsum in powdered form	26.	0.52
		34.	0.60
Sawdust	Various	12.0	0.41
	Redwood	10.9	0.42
Shavings	Various, from planer	8.8	0.41
Charcoal	From maple, beech and birch,		
	coarse	13.2	0.36
	6 mesh	15.2	0.37
	20 mesh	19.2	0.39

Semiflexible Materials in Sheet Form

		D[a]	K[b]
Flaxlinum	Flax fiber	13.0	0.31
Fibrofelt	Flax and rye fiber	13.6	0.32

Semirigid Materials in Board Form

		D[a]	K[b]
Corkboard	No added binder; very low density.	5.4	0.25
Corkboard	No added binder; low density.	7.0	0.27
Corkboard	No added binder; medium density.	10.6	0.30
Corkboard	No added binder; high density.	14.0	0.34
Eureka	Corkboard with asphaltic binder.	14.5	0.32
Rock cork	Rock wool block with binder, also called "Tucork."	14.5	0.326
Lith	Board containing rock wool, flax and straw pulp.	14.3	0.40

[a] D= Density in lb/ft³.

[b] K= Thermal conductivity in B.T.U./hr, ft², and temp gradient of 1 ° F/in. thickness. The lower the conductivity, the greater the insulating values.

[c] From various commercial laboratories and the work of O. R. Sweeney at Iowa State College.

4.5–10 (*Continued*)
THERMAL CONDUCTIVITY OF MATERIALS

Stiff Fibrous Materials in Sheet Form

		D[a]	K[b]
Insulite®	Wood pulp	16.2	0.34
		16.9	0.34
Celotex®	Sugar cane fiber	13.2	0.34
		14.8	0.34
Masonite®[c]		K = 0.33	
Insoboard®[c]		0.33	
Maizewood[c]		0.33–0.39	
Cornstalk pith board[c]		0.24–0.30	
Maftex[c]		0.34	

Cellular Gypsum

	D[a]	K[b]
Insulex or Pyrocell®	8	0.35
	12	0.44
	18	0.59
	24	0.77
	30	1.00

Woods (Across Grain)

	D[a]	K[b]
Balsa	7.3	0.33
	8.8	0.38
	20	0.58
Cypress	29	0.67
White pine	32	0.78
Mahogany	34	0.90
Virginia pine	34	0.98
Oak	38	1.02
Maple	44	1.10

Miscellaneous Building Materials

	K		K[b]
Cinder concrete	2–3	Limestone	4–9
Building gypsum	about 3	Concrete	6–9
Plaster	2–5	Sandstone	8–16
Building brick	3–6	Marble	14–20
Glass	5–6	Granite	13–28

[a] D= Density in lb/ft^3.
[b] K= Thermal conductivity in B.T.U./hr, ft^2, and temp gradient of 1 ° F/in. thickness. The lower the conductivity, the greater the insulating values.
[c] From various commercial laboratories and the work of O. R. Sweeney at Iowa State College.

(From Weast, Robert C., Ed., *CRC Handbook of Chemistry and Physics*, 50th ed., Chemical Rubber Co., Cleveland, 1969. With permission.)

Table 4.5–11
VELOCITY OF SOUND
Solids

Substance	Density g/cm³	V_l[a] m/sec	Vs[b] m/sec	Vext[c] m/sec
Metals:				
Aluminum, rolled	2.7	6,420	3,040	5,000
Beryllium	1.87	12,890	8,880	12,870
Brass (70 Cu, 30 Zn)	8.6	4,700	2,110	3,480
Copper, annealed	8.93	4,760	2,325	3,810
Copper, rolled	8.93	5,010	2,270	3,750
Duralumin 17S	2.79	6,320	3,130	5,150
Gold, hard drawn	19.7	3,240	1,200	2,030
Iron, electrolytic	7.9	5,950	3,240	5,120
Iron, Armco	7.85	5,960	3,240	5,200
Lead, annealed	11.4	2,160	700	1,190
Lead, rolled	11.4	1,960	690	1,210
Magnesium, drawn, annealed	1.74	5,770	3,050	4,940
Molybdenum	10.1	6,250	3,350	5,400
Monel metal	8.90	5,350	2,720	4,400
Nickel (unmagnetized)	8.85	5,480	2,990	4,800
Nickel	8.9	6,040	3,000	4,900
Platinum	21.4	3,260	1,730	2,800
Silver	10.4	3,650	1,610	2,680
Steel, mild	7.85	5,960	3,235	5,200
Steel, 347 Stainless	7.9	5,790	3,100	5,000
Steel (1% C)	7.84	5,940	3,220	5,180
Steel (1% C, hardened)	7.84	5,854	3,150	5,070
Tin, rolled	7.3	3,320	1,670	2,730
Titanium	4.5	6,070	3,125	5,080
Tungsten, annealed	19.3	5,220	2,890	4,620
Tungsten, drawn	19.3	5,410	2,640	4,320
Tungsten carbide	13.8	6,655	3,980	6,220
Zinc, rolled	7.1	4,210	2,440	3,850
Various:				
Fused silica	2.2	5,968	3,764	5,760
Glass, pyrex	2.32	5,640	3,280	5,170
Glass, heavy silicate flint	3.88	3,980	2,380	3,720
Glass, light borate crown	2.24	5,100	2,840	4,540
Lucite	1.18	2,680	1,100	1,840
Nylon 6-6	1.11	2,620	1,070	1,800
Polyethylene	0.90	1,950	540	920
Polystyrene	1.06	2,350	1,120	2,240
Rubber, butyl	1.07	1,830		
Rubber, gum	0.95	1,550		
Rubber, neoprene	1.33	1,600		
Brick	1.8			3,650
Clay rock	2.2			3,480
Cork	0.25			500
Marble	2.6			3,810

[a] Vl = Velocity of plane longitudinal wave in bulk material.
[b] Vs = Velocity of plane transverse (shear) wave.
[c] Vext = Velocity of longitudinal wave (extensional wave) in thin rods.

Table 4.5–11 (*Continued*)
VELOCITY OF SOUND

Solids

Substance	Density g/cm³	V_l[a] m/sec	Vs[b] m/sec	Vext[c] m/sec
Paraffin	0.9			1,300
Tallow				390
Woods:				
Ash, along the fiber				4,670
Ash, across the rings				1,390
Ash, along the rings				1,260
Beech, along the fiber				3,340
Elm, along the fiber				4,120
Maple, along the fiber				4,110
Oak, along the fiber				3,850

[a] **Vl = Velocity of plane longitudinal wave in bulk material.**
[b] **Vs = Velocity of plane transverse (shear) wave.**
[c] **Vext = Velocity of longitudinal wave (extensional wave) in thin rods.**

Liquids

Substance	Formula	Density, g/cm³	Velocity, 25°C m/sec	$-\Delta v/\Delta t$ m/sec °C
Acetone	C_3H_6O	0.79	1,174	4.5
Benzene	C_6H_6	0.870	1,295	4.65
Carbon disulphide	CS_2	1.26	1,149	–
Carbon tetrachloride	CCl_4	1.595	926	2.7
Castor oil	$C_{11}H_{10}O_{10}$	0.969	1,477	3.6
Chloroform	$CHCl_3$	1.49	987	3.4
Ethanol	C_2H_6O	0.79	1,207	4.0
Ethanol amide	C_2H_7NO	1.018	1,724	3.4
Ethyl ether	$C_4H_{10}O$	0.713	985	4.87
Ethylene glycol	$C_2H_6O_2$	1.113	1,658	2.1
Glycerol	$C_3H_8O_3$	1.26	1,904	2.2
Kerosene	–	0.81	1,324	3.6
Mercury	Hg	13.5	1,450	–
Methanol	CH_4O	0.791	1,103	3.2
Nitrobenzene	$C_6H_5NO_2$	1.20	1,463	3.6
Turpentine	–	0.88	1,255	–
Water (distilled)	H_2O	0.998	1,498	–2.4
Water (sea)	–	1.025	1,531	–2.4
Xylene hexafluoride	$C_5H_4F_6$	1.37	879	–

Table 4.5–11 (*Continued*)
VELOCITY OF SOUND

Gases and Vapors

Substance	Formula	Density, g/l	Velocity, m/sec	Δv/Δt m/sec °C
Gases (0° C)				
Air, dry		1.293	331.45	0.59
Ammonia	NH_3	0.771	415	
Argon	A	1.783	308	0.56
Carbon monoxide	CO	1.25	338	0.6
Carbon dioxide	CO_2	1.977	259	0.4
Chlorine	Cl_2	3.214	206	
Deuterium	D_2		890	1.6
Ethane (10° C)	C_2H_6	1.356	308	
Ethylene	C_2H_4	1.260	317	
Helium	He	0.178	965	0.8
Hydrogen	H_2	0.0899	1,284	2.2
Hydrogen bromide	HBr	3.50	200	
Hydrogen chloride	HCl	1.639	296	
Hydrogen iodide	HI	5.66	157	
Hydrogen sulfide	H_2S	1.539	289	
Illuminating (coal gas)			453	
Methane	CH_4	0.7168	430	
Neon	Ne	0.900	435	0.8
Nitric oxide (10° C)	NO	1.34	324	
Nitrogen	N_2	1.251	334	0.6
Nitrous oxide	N_2O	1.977	263	0.5
Oxygen	O_2	1.429	316	0.56
Sulfur dioxide	SO_2	2.927	213	0.47
Vapors (97.1° C)				
Acetone	C_3H_6O		239	0.32
Benzene	C_6H_6		202	0.3
Carbon tetrachloride	CCl_4		145	
Chloroform	$CHCl_3$		171	0.24
Ethanol	C_2H_6O		269	0.4
Ethyl ether	$C_4H_{10}O$		206	0.3
Methanol	CH_4O		335	0.46
Water vapor (134° C)	H_2O		494	

(Compiled by G. E. Becker, Bell Telephone Laboratories. From Weast, Robert C., Ed., *CRC Handbook of Chemistry and Physics*, 50th ed., Chemical Rubber Co., Cleveland, 1969. With permission.)

REFERENCES

1. *American Institute of Physics Handbook,* McGraw-Hill, New York, 1957.
2. **Forsythe, W. E., Ed.,** *Smithsonian Physical Tables,* Smithsonian Institution, Washington, D.C., 1954.
3. **Mason, W. P.,** *Physical Acoustics and the Properties of Solids,* Academic Press, New York, 1958.
4. **Chalmers, B. and Quarell, A. G.,** *Physical Examination of Metals,* St. Martin's, New York, 1961.
5. **Mason, W. P.,** *Piezoelectric Crystals and Their Application to Ultrasonics,* Van Nostrand, New York, 1950.
6. **Bergmann,** *Der Ultraschall,* Hirzel, Stuttgart, 1954.

Table 4.5–12
SOUND VELOCITY IN WATER ABOVE 212°F

Temp, °F	Velocity, m/sec	Velocity, ft/sec
186.8	1552	5092
200	1548	5079
210	1544	5066
220	1538	5046
230	1532	5026
240	1524	5000
250	1516	4974
260	1507	4944
270	1497	4911
280	1487	4879
290	1476	4843
300	1465	4806
310	1453	4767
320	1440	4724
330	1426	4678
340	1412	4633
350	1398	4587
360	1383	4537
370	1368	4488
380	1353	4439
390	1337	4386
400	1320	4331
410	1302	4272
420	1283	4209
430	1264	4147
440	1244	4081
450	1220	4010
460	1200	3940
470	1180	3880

(From Weast, Robert C., Ed., *CRC Handbook of Chemistry and Physics,* 50th ed., Chemical Rubber Co., Cleveland, 1969. With permission.)

Table 4.5–13
PROPERTIES OF METALS AS CONDUCTORS

Metal	Resistivity μohm-cm, 20°C	Temp coefficient, 20°C	Specific gravity	Tensile strength, lb/in.	Melting point °C
Advance.® See *Constantan.*					
Aluminum	2.824	0.0039	2.70	30,000	659
Antimony	41.7	0.0036	6.6	–	630
Arsenic	33.3	0.0042	5.73	–	–
Bismuth	120	0.004	9.8	–	271
Brass	7	0.002	8.6	70,000	900
Cadmium	7.6	0.0038	8.6	–	321
Calido.® See *Nichrome.*					
Climax	87	0.0007	8.1	150,000	1250
Cobalt	9.8	0.0033	8.71	–	1480
Constantan	49	0.00001	8.9	120,000	1190
Copper					
Annealed	1.7241	0.00393	8.89	30,000	1083
Hard drawn	1.771	0.00382	8.89	60,000	–
Eureka. See *Constantan.*					
Excello	92	0.00016	8.9	95,000	1500
Gas carbon	5000	–.0005	–	–	3500
German silver, 18% Ni	33	0.0004	8.4	150,000	1100
Gold	2.44	0.0034	19.3	20,000	1063
Ideal. See *Constantan.*					
Iron, 99.98% pure	10	0.005	7.8	–	1530
Lead	22	0.0039	11.4	3,000	327
Magnesium	4.6	0.004	1.74	33,000	651
Manganin	44	0.00001	8.4	150,000	910
Mercury	95.783	0.00089	13.546	0	–38.9
Molybdenum, drawn	5.7	0.004	9.0	–	2500
Monel metal	42	0.0020	8.9	160,000	1300
Nichrome®	100	0.0004	8.2	150,000	1500
Nickel	7.8	0.006	8.9	120,000	1452
Palladium	11	0.0033	12.2	39,000	1550
Phosphor bronze	7.8	0.0018	8.9	25,000	750
Platinum	10	0.003	21.4	50,000	1755
Silver	1.59	0.0038	10.5	42,000	960
Steel, E. B. B.	10.4	0.005	7.7	53,000	1510
Steel, B. B.	11.9	0.004	7.7	58,000	1510
Steel, Siemens-Martin	18	0.003	7.7	100,000	1510
Steel, manganese	70	0.001	7.5	230,000	1260
Tantalum	15.5	0.0031	16.6	–	2850
Therlo®	47	0.00001	8.2	–	–
Tin	11.5	0.0042	7.3	4,000	232
Tungsten, drawn	5.6	0.0045	19	500,000	3400
Zinc	5.8	0.0037	7.1	10,000	419

(From Weast, Robert C., Ed., *CRC Handbook of Chemistry and Physics,* 50th ed., Chemical Rubber Co., Cleveland, 1969. With permission.)

Table 4.5–14
MAGNETIC PROPERTIES OF TRANSFORMER STEELS

Ordinary Transformer Steel

B (gauss)	H (oersted)	Permeability = B/H
2,000	0.60	3,340
4,000	0.87	4,600
6,000	1.10	5,450
8,000	1.48	5,400
10,000	2.28	4,380
12,000	3.85	3,120
14,000	10.9	1,280
16,000	43.0	372
18,000	149	121

High Silicon Transformer Steel

B	H	Permeability
2,000	0.50	4,000
4,000	0.70	5,720
6,000	0.90	6,670
8,000	1.28	6,250
10,000	1.99	5,020
12,000	3.60	3,340
14,000	9.80	1,430
16,000	47.4	338
18,000	165	109

(From Weast, Robert C., Ed., *CRC Handbook of Chemistry and Physics,* 50th ed., Chemical Rubber Co., Cleveland, 1969. With permission.)

Table 4.5–15
SATURATION CONSTANTS FOR MAGNETIC SUBSTANCES

Substance	For saturation: Field intensity	For saturation: Induced magnetization
Cobalt	9,000	1,300
Iron		
Wrought	2,000	1,700
Cast	4,000	1,200
Manganese steel	7,000	200
Nickel		
Hard	8,000	400
Annealed	7,000	515
Vicker's steel	15,000	1,600

(From Weast, Robert C., Ed., *CRC Handbook of Chemistry and Physics,* 50th ed., Chemical Rubber Co., Cleveland, 1969. With permission.)

Table 4.5–16
INITIAL PERMEABILITY OF HIGH PURITY IRON

For Various Temperatures

Temp, °C	Permeability, gauss/oersted
0	920
200	1,040
400	1,440
600	2,550
700	3,900
770	12,580

(Compiled by L. Alberts and B.J. Shepstone. From Weast, Robert C., Ed., *CRC Handbook of Chemistry and Physics,* 50th ed., Chemical Rubber Co., Cleveland, 1969. With permission.)

Table 4.5–17
MAGNETIC MATERIALS

High-permeability Materials

Material	Form	Approximate percent composition: Fe	Ni	Co	Mo	Other	Typical heat treatment, °C	Permeability at $B = 20$ gausses	Max permeability	Saturation flux density B gausses	Hysteresis[c] loss, W_h ergs/cm^3	Coercive[c] force H_c oersteds	Resistivity μohm-cm	Density, g/cm^3
Cold rolled steel	Sheet	98.5	–	–	–	–	950 Anneal	180	2,000	21,000	–	1.8	10	7.88
Iron	Sheet	99.91	–	–	–	–	950 Anneal	200	5,000	21,500	5,000	1.0	10	7.88
Purified iron	Sheet	99.95	–	–	–	–	1480 H_2 + 880	5,000	180,000	21,500	300	0.05	10	7.88
4% Silicon-iron	Sheet	96	–	–	–	4 Si	800 Anneal	500	7,000	19,700	3,500	0.5	60	7.65
Grain oriented[a]	Sheet	97	–	–	–	3 Si	800 Anneal	1,500	30,000	20,000	–	0.15	47	7.67
45 Permalloy®	Sheet	54.7	45	–	–	0.3 Mn	1050 Anneal	2,500	25,000	16,000	1,200	0.3	45	8.17
45 Permalloy®[b]	Sheet	54.7	45	–	–	0.3 Mn	1200 H_2 Anneal	4,000	50,000	16,000	–	0.07	45	8.17
Hipernik®	Sheet	50	50	–	–	–	1200 H_2 Anneal	4,500	70,000	16,000	220	0.05	50	8.25
Monimax	Sheet	–	–	–	–	–	1125 H_2 Anneal	2,000	35,000	15,000	–	0.1	80	8.27
Sinimax	Sheet	–	–	–	–	–	1125 H_2 Anneal	3,000	35,000	11,000	–	–	90	–
78 Permalloy®	Sheet	21.2	78.5	–	–	0.3 Mn	1050 + 600 Q[d]	8,000	100,000	10,700	200	0.05	16	8.60
4–79 Permalloy®	Sheet	16.7	79	–	4	0.3 Mn	1100 + Q	20,000	100,000	8,700	200	0.05	55	8.72
Mu metal	Sheet	18	75	–	–	2 Cr, 5 Cu	1175 H_2	20,000	100,000	6,500	–	0.05	62	8.58
Supermalloy	Sheet	15.7	79	–	5	0.3 Mn	1300 H_2 + Q	100,000	800,000	8,000	–	0.002	60	8.77
Permendur	Sheet	49.7	–	50	–	0.3 Mn	800 Anneal	800	5,000	24,500	12,000	2.0	7	8.3
2V Permendur	Sheet	49	–	49	–	2 V	800 Anneal	800	4,500	24,000	6,000	2.0	26	8.2
Hiperco®	Sheet	64	–	34	–	Cr	850 Anneal	650	10,000	24,200	–	1.0	25	8.0
2–81 Permalloy®	Insulated powder	17	81	–	2	–	650 Anneal	125	130	8,000	–	<1.0	10^6	7.8
Carbonyl iron	Insulated powder	99.9	–	–	–	–	–	55	132	–	–	–	–	7.86
Ferroxcube® III	Sintered powder	$MnFe_2O_4 + ZnFe_2O_4$					–	1,000	1,500	2,500	–	.1	10^8	5.0

[a] Properties in direction of rolling.
[b] Similar properties for Nicaloi, 4750 alloy, Carpenter 49, Armco 48.
[c] At saturation.
[d] Q, quench or controlled cooling.

Table 4.5–17 (*Continued*)
MAGNETIC MATERIALS

Permanent Magnet Alloys

Material	Percent composition (remainder Fe)	Heat treatment[f] temp, °C	Magnetizing force H_{max} oersteds	Coercive force H_c oersteds	Residual induction B_r gausses	Energy product BH_{max} × 10^{-6}	Method of fabrication[g]	Mechanical properties[h]	Wt, lb/in.³
Carbon steel	1 Mn, 0.9 C	Q 800	300	50	10,000	0.20	HR, M, P	H, S	.280
Tungsten steel	5 W, 0.3 Mn, 0.7 C	Q 850	300	70	10,300	0.32	HR, M, P	H, S	.292
Chromium steel	3.5 Cr, 0.9 C, 0.3 Mn	Q 830	300	65	9,700	0.30	HR, M, P	H, S	.280
17% Cobalt steel	17 Co, 0.75 C, 2.5 Cr, 8 W	–	1,000	150	9,500	0.65	HR, M, P	H, S	–
36% Cobalt steel	36 Co, 0.7 C, 4 Cr, 5 W	Q 950	1,000	240	9,500	0.97	HR, M, P	H, S	.296
Remalloy or Comol	17 Mo, 12 Co	Q 1200, B 700	1,000	250	10,500	1.1	HR, M, P	H	.295
Alnico I	12 Al, 20 Ni, 5 Co	A 1200, B 700	2,000	440	7,200	1.4	C, G	H, B	.249
Alnico II	10 Al, 17 Ni, 2.5 Co, 6 Cu	A 1200, B 600	2,000	550	7,200	1.6	C, G	H, B	.256
Alnico II (sintered)	10 Al, 17 Ni, 2.5 Co, 6 Cu	A 1300	2,000	520	6,900	1.4	Sn, G	H	.249
Alnico IV	12 Al, 28 Ni, 5 Co	Q 1200, B 650	3,000	700	5,500	1.3	Sn, C, G	H	.253
Alnico V	8 Al, 14 Ni, 24 Co, 3 Cu	AF 1300, B 600	2,000	550	12,500	4.5	C, G	H, B	.264
Alnico VI	8 Al, 15 Ni, 24 Co, 3 Cu, 1 Ti	–	3,000	750	10,000	3.5	C, G	H, B	.268
Alnico XII	6 Al, 18 Ni, 35 Co, 8 Ti	–	3,000	950	5,800	1.5	C, G	H, B	.26
Vicalloy I	52 Co, 10 V	B 600	1,000	300	8,800	1.0	C, CR, M, P	D	.295
Vicalloy II (wire)	52 Co, 14 V	CW + B 600	2,000	510	10,000	3.5	C, CR, M, P	D	.292
Cunife (wire)	60 Cu, 20 Ni	CW + B 600	2,400	550	5,400	1.5	C, CR, M, P	D, M	.311
Cunico	50 Cu, 21 Ni, 29 Co	–	3,200	660	3,400	0.80	C, CR, M, P	D, M	.300
Vectolite	30 Fe_2O_3, 44 Fe_3O_4, 26 C_2O_3	–	3,000	1,000	1,600	0.60	Sn, G	W	.113
Silmanal	86.8 Ag, 8.8 Mn, 4.4 Al	–	20,000	6,000[e]	550	0.075	C, CR, M, P	D, M	.325
Platinum-cobalt	77 Pt, 23 Co	Q 1200, B 650	15,000	3,600	5,900	6.5	C, CR, M	D	–
Hyflux®	Fine powder	–	2,000	390	6,600	0.97	–	–	.176

[e] Value given is intrinsic H_c.
[f] Q – quenched in oil or water; A – air cooled; B – baked; F – cooled in magnetic field; CW – cold worked.
[g] HR – hot rolled or forged; CR – cold rolled or drawn; M – machined; G – must be ground; P – punched; C – cast; Sn – sintered.
[h] H – hard; B – brittle; S – strong; D – ductile; M – malleable; W – weak.

(From Weast, Robert C., Ed., *CRC Handbook of Chemistry and Physics*, 50th ed., Chemical Rubber Co., 1969. With permission.)

Table 4.5–18
MAGNETIC SUSCEPTIBILITY OF THE ELEMENTS AND INORGANIC COMPOUNDS

Substance	Formula	Temp, °K	Susceptibility, 10^{-6} cgs
Aluminum (s)	Al	ord.	+16.5
Aluminum (*l*)	Al	–	+12.0
Fluoride	AlF_3	302	−13.4
Oxide	Al_2O_3	ord.	−37.0
Sulfate	$Al_2(SO_4)_3$	ord.	−93.0
Sulfate	$Al_2(SO_4)_3 \cdot 18H_2O$	ord.	−323.0
Ammonia (g)	NH_3	ord.	−18.0
Ammonia (aq)	NH_3	ord.	−17.0
Ammonium			
Acetate	$NH_4C_2H_3O_2$	ord.	−41.1
Bromide	NH_4Br	ord.	−47.0
Carbonate	$(NH_4)_2CO_3$	ord.	−42.50
Chlorate	NH_4ClO_3	ord.	−42.1
Chloride	NH_4Cl	ord.	−36.7
Fluoride	NH_4F	ord.	−23.0
Hydroxide (aq)	NH_4OH	ord.	−31.5
Iodate	NH_4IO_3	ord.	−62.3
Iodide	NH_4I	ord.	−66.0
Nitrate	NH_4NO_3	ord.	−33.6
Sulfate	$(NH_4)_2SO_4$	ord.	−67.0
Thiocyanate	NH_4SCN	ord.	−48.1
Americium (s)	Am	300	+1000.0
Antimony (s)	Sb	293	−99.0
Antimony (*l*)	Sb	–	−2.5
Bromide	$SbBr_3$	ord.	−115.0
Chloride, tri	$SbCl_3$	ord.	−86.7
Chloride, penta	$SbCl_5$	ord.	−120.0
Fluoride	SbF_3	ord.	−46.0
Iodide	SbI_3	ord.	−147.0
Oxide	Sb_2O_3	ord.	−69.4
Sulfide	Sb_2S_3	ord.	−86.0
Argon (g)	A	ord.	−19.6
Arsenic (α)	As	293	−5.5
Arsenic (β)	As	293	−23.7
Arsenic (γ)	As	293	−23.0
Bromide	$AsBr_3$	ord.	−106.0
Chloride	$AsCl_3$	ord.	−79.9
Iodide	AsI_3	ord.	−142.0
Sulfide	As_2S_3	ord.	−70.0
Arsenious acid	H_3AsO_3	ord.	−51.2

Note: This table lists the magnetic susceptibilities of one g formula wt of a number of paramagnetic and diamagnetic inorganic compounds as well as the magnetic susceptibilities of the elements. In each instance the magnetic moment is expressed in cgs units.

Table 4.5–18 (*Continued*)
MAGNETIC SUSCEPTIBILITY OF THE ELEMENTS AND INORGANIC COMPOUNDS

Substance	Formula	Temp. °K.	Susceptibility 10^{-6} cgs
Barium	Ba	ord.	+20.6
Acetate	$Ba(C_2H_3O_2)_2 \cdot H_2O$	ord.	−100.1
Bromate	$Ba(BrO_3)_2$	ord.	−105.8
Bromide	$BaBr_2$	ord.	−92.0
Brothide	$BaBr_2 \cdot 2H_2O$	ord.	−119.0
Carbonate	$Ba(CO_3)$	ord.	−58.9
Chlorate	$Ba(ClO_3)_2$	ord.	−87.5
Chloride	$BaCl_2$	ord.	−72.6
Chloride	$BaCl_2 \cdot 2H_2O$	ord.	−100.0
Fluoride	BaF_2	ord.	−51.0
Hydroxide	$Ba(OH)_2$	ord.	−53.2
Hydroxide	$Ba(OH)_2 \cdot 8H_2O$	ord.	−157.0
Iodate	$Ba(IO_3)_2$	ord.	−122.5
Iodide	BaI_2	ord.	−124.0
Iodide	$BaI_2 \cdot 2H_2O$	ord.	−163.0
Nitrate	$Ba(NO_3)_2$	ord.	−66.5
Oxide	BaO	ord.	−29.1
Oxide	BaO_2	ord.	−40.6
Sulfate	$BaSO_4$	ord.	−71.3
Beryllium (s)	Be	ord.	−9.0
Chloride	$BeCl_2$	ord.	−26.5
Hydroxide	$Be(OH)_2$	ord.	−23.1
Nitrate (aq)	$Be(NO_3)_2$	298	−41.0
Oxide	BeO	ord.	−11.9
Sulfate	$BeSO_4$	ord.	−37.0
Bismuth (s)	Bi	ord.	−280.1
Bismuth (*l*)	Bi	–	−10.5
Bromide	$BiBr_3$	ord.	−147.0
Chloride	$BiCl_3$	ord.	−26.5
Chromate	$Bi_2(CrO_4)_3$	ord.	+154.0
Fluoride	BiF_3	303	−61.0
Hydroxide	$Bi(OH)_3$	ord.	−65.8
Iodide	BiI_3	ord.	−200.5
Nitrate	$Bi(NO_3)_3$	ord.	−91.0
Nitrate	$Bi(NO_3)_3 \cdot 5H_2O$	ord.	−159.0
Oxide	BiO	ord.	−110.0
Oxide	Bi_2O_3	ord.	−83.0
Phosphate	$BiPO_4$	ord.	−77.0
Sulfate	$Bi_2(SO_4)_3$	ord.	−199.0
Sulfide	Bi_2S_3	ord.	−123.0
Boric acid	H_3BO_3	ord.	−34.1
Boron (s)	B	ord.	−6.7
Chloride	BCl_3	ord.	−59.9
Oxide	B_2O_3	ord.	−39.0
Bromine (*l*)	Br_2	–	−56.4
Bromine (g)	Br_2	–	−73.5
Fluoride	BrF_3	ord.	−33.9
Fluoride	BrF_5	ord.	−45.1
Cadmium (s)	Cd	ord.	−19.8

Table 4.5–18 (*Continued*)
MAGNETIC SUSCEPTIBILITY OF THE ELEMENTS AND INORGANIC COMPOUNDS

Substance	Formula	Temp. °K.	Susceptibility 10^{-6} cgs
Cadmium (*l*)	Cd	–	−18.0
Acetate	$Cd(C_2H_3O_2)_2$	ord.	−83.7
Bromide	$CdBr_2$	ord.	−87.3
Bromide	$CdBr_2 \cdot 4H_2O$	ord.	−140.0
Carbonate	$CdCO_3$	ord.	−46.7
Chloride	$CdCl_2$	ord.	−68.7
Chloride	$CdCl_2 \cdot 2H_2O$	ord.	−99.0
Chromate	$CdCrO_4$	ord.	−16.8
Cyanide	$Cd(CN)_2$	ord.	−54.0
Fluoride	CdF_2	ord.	−40.6
Hydroxide	$Cd(OH)_2$	ord.	−41.0
Iodate	$Cd(IO_3)_2$	ord.	−108.4
Iodide	CdI_2	ord.	−117.2
Nitrate	$Cd(NO_3)_2$	ord.	−55.1
Nitrate	$Cd(NO_3)_2 \cdot 4H_2O$	ord.	−140.0
Oxide	CdO	ord.	−30.0
Phosphate	$Cd_3(PO_4)_2$	ord.	−159.0
Sulfate	$CdSO_4$	ord.	−59.2
Sulfide	CdS	ord.	−50.0
Calcium (s)	Ca	–	+40.0
Acetate	$Ca(C_2H_3O_2)_2$	ord.	−70.5
Bromate	$Ca(BrO_3)_2$	ord.	−84.9
Bromide	$CaBr_2$	ord.	−73.8
Bromide	$CaBr_2 \cdot 3H_2O$	ord.	−115.0
Carbonate	$CaCO_3$	ord.	−38.2
Chloride	$CaCl_2$	ord.	−54.7
Fluoride	CaF_2	ord.	−28.0
Hydroxide	$Ca(OH)_2$	ord.	−22.0
Iodate	$Ca(IO_3)_2$	ord.	−101.4
Iodide	CaI_2	ord.	−109.0
Nitrate (aq)	$Ca(NO_3)_2$	ord.	−45.9
Oxide	CaO	ord.	−15.0
Oxide	CaO_2	ord.	−23.8
Sulfate	$CaSO_4$	ord.	−49.7
Sulfate	$CaSO_4 \cdot 2H_2O$	ord.	−74.0
Carbon (dia)	C	ord.	−5.9
Carbon (graph)	C	ord.	−6.0
Dioxide	CO_2	ord.	−21.0
Monoxide	CO	ord.	−9.8
Cerium (α)	Ce	80.5	+5160.0
Cerium (β)	Ce	293	+2450.0
Cerium (β)	Ce	80.5	+6230.0
Cerium (γ)	Ce	287.9	+2420.0
Cerium (γ)	Ce	125.6	+4640.0
Cerium (γ)	Ce	80.5	+5200.0
Chloride	$CeCl_3$	287	+2490.0
Fluoride	CeF_3	293	+2190.0
Nitrate	$Ce(NO_3)_3 \cdot 5H_2O$	292	+2310.0
Oxide	CeO_2	293	+26.0
Sulfate	$CeSO_4$	ord.	+37.0
Sulfate	$Ce_2(SO_4)_3 \cdot 5H_2O$	293	+4540.0
Sulfate	$Ce(SO_4)_2 \cdot 4H_2O$	293	−97.0
Sulfide	CeS	ord.	+2110.0
Sulfide	Ce_2S_3	292	+5080.0

Table 4.5–18 (*Continued*)
MAGNETIC SUSCEPTIBILITY OF THE ELEMENTS AND INORGANIC COMPOUNDS

Substance	Formula	Temp. °K.	Susceptibility 10^{-6} cgs
Cesium (s)	Cs	ord.	+29.0
Cesium (*l*)	Cs	–	+26.5
Bromate	$CsBrO_3$	ord.	–75.1
Bromide	CsBr	ord.	–67.2
Carbonate	Cs_2CO_3	ord.	–103.6
Chlorate	$CsClO_3$	ord.	–65.0
Chloride	CsCl	ord.	–86.7
Fluoride	CsF	ord.	–44.5
Iodate	$CsIO_3$	ord.	–83.1
Iodide	CsI	ord.	–82.6
Oxide	CsO_2	293	+1534.0
Oxide	CsO_2	90	+4504.0
Sulfate	Cs_2SO_4	ord.	–116.0
Sulfide	Cs_2S	ord.	–104.0
Chlorine (*l*)	Cl_2	ord.	–40.5
Fluoride, tri	ClF_3	ord.	–26.5
Chromium	Cr	273	+180.0
Chromium	Cr	1713	+224.0
Acetate	$Cr(C_2H_3O_2)_3$	293	+5104.0
Chloride	$CrCl_2$	293	+7230.0
Chloride	$CrCl_3$	293	+6890.0
Fluoride	CrF_3	293	+4370.0
Oxide	Cr_2O_3	300	+1960.0
Oxide	CrO_3	ord.	+40.0
Sulfate	$Cr_2(SO_4)_3$	293	+11,800.0
Sulfate	$Cr_2(SO_4)_3 \cdot 8H_2O$	290	+12,700.0
Sulfate	$Cr_2(SO_4)_3 \cdot 10H_2O$	290	+12,600.0
Sulfate	$Cr_2(SO_4)_3 \cdot 14H_2O$	290	+12,160.0
Sulfate	$CrSO_4 \cdot 6H_2O$	293	+9690.0
Sulfide	CrS	ord.	+2390.0
Cobalt	Co	–	ferro
Acetate	$Co(C_2H_3O_2)_2$	293	+11,000.0
Bromide	$CoBr_2$	293	+13,000.0
Chloride	$CoCl_2$	293	+12,660.0
Chloride	$CoCl_2 \cdot 6H_2O$	293	+9710.0
Cyanide	$Co(CN)_2$	303	+3825.0
Fluoride	CoF_2	293	+9490.0
Fluoride	CoF_3	293	+1900.0
Iodide	CoI_2	293	+10,760.0
Oxide	CoO	260	+4900.0
Oxide	Co_2O_3	ord.	+4560.0
Oxide	Co_3O_4	ord.	+7380.0
Phosphate	$Co_3(PO_4)_2$	291	+28,110.0
Sulfate	$CoSO_4$	293	+10,000.0
Sulfate	$Co_2(SO_4)_3$	297	+1000.0
Sulfide	CoS	688	+251.0
Sulfide	CoS	293	+225.0
Thiocyanate	$Co(SCN)_2$	303	+11,090.0
Copper (s)	Cu	296	–5.46

Table 4.5–18 (*Continued*)
MAGNETIC SUSCEPTIBILITY OF THE ELEMENTS AND INORGANIC COMPOUNDS

Substance	Formula	Temp. °K.	Susceptibility 10^{-6} cgs
Copper (*l*)	Cu	–	−6.16
Bromide	CuBr	ord.	−49.0
Bromide	$CuBr_2$	341.6	+653.3
Bromide	$CuBr_2$	292.7	+685.5
Bromide	$CuBr_2$	189	+736.9
Bromide	$CuBr_2$	90	+658.7
Chloride	CuCl	ord.	−40.0
Chloride	$CuCl_2$	373.3	+1030.0
Chloride	$CuCl_2$	289	+1080.0
Chloride	$CuCl_2$	170	+1815.0
Chloride	$CuCl_2$	69.25	+2370.0
Chloride	$CuCl_2 \cdot 2H_2O$	293	+1420.0
Cyanide	CuCN	ord.	−24.0
Fluoride	CuF_2	293	+1050.0
Fluoride	CuF_2	90	+1420.0
Fluoride	$CuF_2 \cdot 2H_2O$	293	+1600.0
Hydroxide	$Cu(OH)_2$	292	+1170.0
Iodide	CuI	ord.	−63.0
Nitrate	$Cu(NO_3)_2 \cdot 3H_2O$	293	+1570.0
Nitrate	$Cu(NO_3)_2 \cdot 6H_2O$	293	+1625.0
Oxide	Cu_2O	293	−20.0
Oxide	CuO	780	+259.6
Oxide	CuO	561	+267.3
Oxide	CuO	397	+256.9
Oxide	CuO	289.6	+238.9
Oxide	CuO	120	+156.2
Phosphide	Cu_3P	ord.	−33.0
Phosphide	CuP_2	ord.	−35.0
Sulfate	$CuSO_4$	293	+1330.0
Sulfate	$CuSO_4 \cdot H_2O$	293	+1520.0
Sulfate	$CuSO_4 \cdot 3H_2O$	ord.	+1480.0
Sulfate	$CuSO_4 \cdot 5H_2O$	293	+1460.0
Sulfide	CuS	293	−2.0
Thiocyanate	CuSCN	ord.	−48.0
Dysprosium	Dy	293.2	103,500.0
Oxide	Dy_2O_3	287.2	+89,600.0
Sulfate	$Dy_2(SO_4)_3$	293	+91,400.0
Sulfate	$Dy_2(SO_4)_3 \cdot 8H_2O$	291.2	+92,760.0
Sulfide	Dy_2S_3	292	+95,200.0
Erbium	Er	291	+44,300.0
Oxide	Er_2O_3	286	+73,920.0
Sulfate	$Er_2(SO_4)_3 \cdot 8H_2O$	293	+74,600.0
Sulfide	Er_2S_3	292	+77,200.0
Europium	Eu	293	+34,000.0
Bromide	$EuBr_2$	292	+26,800.0
Chloride	$EuCl_2$	292	+26,500.0
Fluoride	EuF_2	292	+23,750.0
Iodide	EuI_2	292	+26,000.0
Oxide	Eu_2O_3	298	+10,100.0
Sulfate	$EuSO_4$	293	+25,730.0
Sulfate	$Eu_2(SO_4)_3$	293	+10,400.0
Sulfate	$Eu_2(SO_4)_3 \cdot 8H_2O$	293	+9,540.0
Sulfide	EuS	293	+23,800.0
Sulfide	EuS	195	+35,400.0

Table 4.5–18 (*Continued*)
MAGNETIC SUSCEPTIBILITY OF THE ELEMENTS AND INORGANIC COMPOUNDS

Substance	Formula	Temp. °K.	Susceptibility 10^{-6} cgs
Gadolinium	Gd	300.6	+755,000.0
Chloride	$GdCl_3$	293	+27,930.0
Oxide	Gd_2O_3	293	+53,200.0
Sulfate	$Gd_2(SO_4)_3$	285.5	+54,200.0
Sulfate	$Gd_2(SO_4)_3 \cdot 8H_2O$	293	+53,280.0
Sulfide	Gd_2S_3	292	+55,500.0
Gallium (s)	Ga	80	−24.4
Gallium (s)	Ga	290	−21.6
Gallium (*l*)	Ga	313	+2.5
Chloride	$GaCl_3$	ord.	−63.0
Iodide	GaI_3	ord.	−149.0
Oxide	Ga_2O	ord.	−34.0
Sulfide	Ga_2S	ord.	−36.0
Sulfide	GaS	ord.	−23.0
Sulfide	Ga_2S_3	ord.	−80.0
Germanium	Ge	293	−76.84
Chloride	$GeCl_4$	ord.	−72.0
Fluoride	GeF_4	ord.	−50.0
Iodide	GeI_4	ord.	−174.0
Oxide	GeO	ord.	−28.8
Oxide	GeO_2	ord.	−34.3
Sulfide	GeS	ord.	−40.9
Sulfide	GeS_2	ord.	−53.3
Gold (s)	Au	296	−28.0
Gold (*l*)	Au	–	−34.0
Bromide	AuBr	ord.	−61.0
Chloride	AuCl	ord.	−67.0
Chloride	$AuCl_3$	ord.	−112.0
Fluoride	AuF_3	ord.	+74.0
Iodide	AuI	ord.	−91.0
Phosphide	AuP_3	ord.	−107.0
Hafnium (s)	Hf	298	+75.0
Hafnium (s)	Hf	1673	+104.0
Oxide	HfO_2	ord.	−23.0
Helium (g)	He	ord.	−1.88
Holmium	Ho	–	–
Oxide	Ho_2O_3	293	+88,100.0
Sulfate	$Ho_2(SO_4)_3$	293	+91,700.0
Sulfate	$Ho_2(SO_4)_3 \cdot 8H_2O$	293	+91,600.0
Hydrogen (g)	H_2	–	−3.98
Bromide (*l*)	HBr	273	–
Bromide (aq)	HBr	ord.	–
Chloride (*l*)	HCl	273	−22.6
Chloride (aq)	HCl	300	−22.0
Fluoride (*l*)	HF	287	−8.6
Fluoride (aq)	HF	ord.	−9.3
Iodide (*l*)	HI	281	−47.7
Iodide (*l*)	HI	233	−48.3
Iodide (s)	HI	195	−47.3

Table 4.5–18 (*Continued*)
MAGNETIC SUSCEPTIBILITY OF THE ELEMENTS AND INORGANIC COMPOUNDS

Substance	Formula	Temp. °K.	Susceptibility 10^{-6} cgs
Iodide (aq)	HI	ord.	−50.2
Oxide, See Water			
Peroxide	H_2O_2	ord.	−17.7
Sulfide	H_2S	ord.	−25.5
Indium	In	ord.	−64.0
Bromide	$InBr_3$	ord.	−107.0
Chloride	InCl	ord.	−30.0
Chloride	$InCl_2$	ord.	−56.0
Chloride	$InCl_3$	ord.	−86.0
Fluoride	InF_2	ord.	−61.0
Oxide	In_2O	ord.	−47.0
Oxide	In_2O_3	ord.	−56.0
Sulfide	In_2S	ord.	−50.0
Sulfide	InS	ord.	−28.0
Sulfide	In_2S_3	ord.	−98.0
Iodic acid	HIO_3	ord.	−48.0
Metaper	HIO_4	ord.	−56.5
Orthoparaper	H_5IO_6	ord.	−71.4
Iodine (s)	I_2	ord.	−88.7
Iodine (atomic)	I	1303	+869.0
Iodine (atomic	I	1400	+1120.0
Chloride	ICl	ord.	−54.6
Chloride	ICl_3	ord.	−90.2
Fluoride	IF_5	ord.	−58.1
Oxide	I_2O_5	ord.	−79.4
Iridium	Ir	298	+25.6
Iridium	Ir	698	+32.1
Chloride	$IrCl_3$	ord.	−14.4
Oxide	IrO_2	298	+224.0
Iron	Fe	–	ferro
Bromide	$FeBr_2$	ord.	+13,600.0
Carbonate	$FeCO_3$	293	+11,300.0
Chloride	$FeCl_2$	293	+14,750.0
Chloride	$FeCl_2 \cdot 4H_2O$	293	+12,900.0
Chloride	$FeCl_3$	293	+13,450.0
Chloride	$FeCl_3$	398	+9,980.0
Chloride	$FeCl_3 \cdot 6H_2O$	290	+15,250.0
Fluoride	FeF_2	293	+9,500.0
Fluoride	FeF_3	305	+13,760.0
Fluoride	$FeF_3 \cdot 3H_2O$	293	+7870.0
Iodide	FeI_2	ord.	+13,600.0
Nitrate	$Fe(NO_3)_3 \cdot 9H_2O$	293	+15,200.0
Oxide	FeO	293	+7200.0
Oxide	Fe_2O_3	1033	+3586.0
Phosphate	$FePO_4$	ord.	+11,500.0
Sulfate	$FeSO_4$	293	+10,200.0
Sulfate	$FeSO_4 \cdot H_2O$	290	+10,500.0
Sulfate	$FeSO_4 \cdot 7H_2O$	293	+11,200.0
Sulfide	FeS	293	+1074.0

Table 4.5–18 (*Continued*)
MAGNETIC SUSCEPTIBILITY OF THE ELEMENTS AND INORGANIC COMPOUNDS

Substance	Formula	Temp. °K.	Susceptibility 10^{-6} cgs
Krypton	Kr	–	–28.8
Lanthanum	La	ord.	+118.0
Oxide	La_2O_3	ord.	–78.0
Sulfate	$La_2(SO_4)_3 \cdot 9H_2O$	293	–262.0
Sulfide	La_2S_3	292	–37.0
Sulfide	La_2S_4	293	–100.0
Lead (s)	Pb	289	–23.0
Lead (*l*)	Pb	330	–15.5
Acetate	$Pb(C_2H_3O_2)_2$	ord.	–89.1
Bromide	$PbBr_2$	ord.	–90.6
Carbonate	$PbCo_3$	ord.	–61.2
Chloride	$PbCl_2$	ord.	–73.8
Chromate	$PbCrO_4$	ord.	–18.0
Fluoride	PbF_2	ord.	–58.1
Iodate	$Pb(IO_3)_2$	ord.	–131.0
Iodide	PbI_2	ord.	–126.5
Nitrate	$Pb(NO_3)_2$	ord.	–74.0
Oxide	PbO	ord.	–42.0
Phosphate	$Pb_3(PO_4)_2$	ord.	–182.0
Sulfate	$PbSO_4$	ord.	–69.7
Sulfide	PbS	ord.	–84.0
Thiocyanate	$Pb(CNS)_2$	ord.	–82.0
Lithium	Li	ord.	+14.2
Acetate	$LiC_2H_3O_2$	ord.	–34.0
Bromate	$LiBrO_3$	ord.	–39.0
Bromide	LiBr	ord.	–34.7
Carbonate	Li_2CO_3	ord.	–27.0
Chlorate (aq)	$LiClO_3$	ord.	–28.8
Chloride	LiCl	ord.	–24.3
Fluoride	LiF	ord.	–10.1
Hydride	LiH	ord.	–4.6
Hydroxide	LiOH	ord.	–12.3
Iodate	$LiIO_3$	ord.	–47.0
Iodide	LiI	ord.	–50.0
Nitrate	$LiNO_3 \cdot 3H_2O$	ord.	–62.0
Sulfate	Li_2SO_4	ord.	–40.0
Lutetium	Lu	ord.	>0.0
Magnesium	Mg	ord.	+13.1
Acetate	$Mg(C_2H_3O_2)_2 \cdot 4H_2O$	ord.	–116.0
Bromide	$MgBr_2$	ord.	–72.0
Carbonate	$MgCO_3$	ord.	–32.4
Carbonate	$MgCO_3 \cdot 3H_2O$	ord.	–72.7
Chloride	$MgCl_2$	ord.	–47.4
Fluoride	MgF_2	ord.	–22.7
Hydroxide	$Mg(OH)_2$	288	–22.1
Iodide	MgI_2	ord.	–111.0
Oxide	MgO	ord.	–10.2
Phosphate	$Mg_3(PO_4)_2 \cdot 4H_2O$	ord.	–167.0
Sulfate	$MgSO_4$	294	–50.0
Sulfate	$MgSO_4 \cdot H_2O$	ord.	–61.0
Sulfate	$MgSO_4 \cdot 5H_2O$	ord.	–109.0
Sulfate	$MgSO_4 \cdot 7H_2O$	ord.	–135.7

Table 4.5–18 (*Continued*)
MAGNETIC SUSCEPTIBILITY OF THE ELEMENTS AND INORGANIC COMPOUNDS

Substance	Formula	Temp. °K.	Susceptibility 10^{-6} cgs
Manganese (α)	Mn	293	+529.0
Manganese (β)	Mn	293	+483.0
Acetate	$Mn(C_2H_3O_2)_2$	293	+13,650.0
Bromide	$MnBr_2$	294	+13,900.0
Carbonate	$MnCO_3$	293	+11,400.0
Chloride	$MnCl_2$	293	+14,350.0
Chloride	$MnCl_2 \cdot 4H_2O$	293	+14,600.0
Fluoride	MnF_2	290	+10,700.0
Fluoride	MnF_3	293	+10,500.0
Hydroxide	$MN(OH)_2$	293	+13,500.0
Iodide	MnI_2	293	+14,400.0
Oxide	MnO	293	+4850.0
Oxide	Mn_2O_3	293	+14,100.0
Oxide	MnO_2	293	+2280.0
Oxide	Mn_3O_4	298	+12,400.0
Sulfate	$MnSO_4$	293	+13,660.0
Sulfate	$MnSO_4 \cdot H_2O$	293	+14,200.0
Sulfate	$MnSO_4 \cdot 4H_2O$	293	+14,600.0
Sulfate	$MnSO_4 \cdot 5H_2O$	293	+14,700.0
Sulfide (α)	MnS	293	+5630.0
Sulfide (β)	MnS	293	+3850.0
Mercury (s)	Hg	–	–24.1
Mercury (*l*)	Hg	293	–33.44
Mercury (g)	Hg	–	–78.3
Acetate	$HgC_2H_3O_2$	ord.	–70.5
Acetate	$Hg(C_2H_3O_2)_2$	ord.	–100.0
Bromate	$HgBrO_3$	ord.	–57.7
Bromide	HgBr	ord.	–57.2
Bromide	$HgBr_2$	ord.	–94.2
Chloride	HgCl	ord.	–52.0
Chloride	$HgCl_2$	ord.	–82.0
Chromate	Hg_2CrO_4	ord.	–63.0
Chromate	$HgCrO_4$	ord.	–12.5
Cyanide	$Hg(CN)_2$	ord.	–67.0
Fluoride	HgF	ord.	–53.0
Fluoride	HgF_2	302	–62.0
Hydroxide	$Hg_2(OH)_2$	ord.	–100.0
Iodate	$HgIO_3$	ord.	–92.0
Iodide	HgI	ord.	–83.0
Iodide	HgI_2	ord.	–128.6
Nitrate	$HgNO_3$	ord.	–55.9
Nitrate	$Hg(NO_3)_2$	ord.	–74.0
Oxide	Hg_2O	ord.	–76.3
Oxide	HgO	ord.	–44.0
Sulfate	Hg_2SO_4	ord.	–123.0
Sulfate	$HgSO_4$	ord	–78.1
Sulfide	HgS	ord.	–55.4
Thiocyanate	$Hg(SCN)_2$	ord.	–96.5
Molybdenum	Mo	298	+89.0
Molybdenum	Mo	63.8	+108.0
Molybdenum	Mo	20.4	+149.2
Bromide	$MoBr_3$	293	+525.0
Bromide	$MoBr_4$	293	+520.0
Bromide	Mo_3Br_6	290.5	–46.0

Table 4.5–18 (*Continued*)
MAGNETIC SUSCEPTIBILITY OF THE ELEMENTS AND INORGANIC COMPOUNDS

Substance	Formula	Temp. °K.	Susceptibility 10^{-6} cgs
Chloride	$MoCl_3$	290	+43.0
Chloride	$MoCl_4$	291	+1750.0
Chloride	$MoCl_5$	289	+990.0
Fluoride	MoF_6	ord.	−26.0
Oxide	Mo_2O_3	ord.	−42.0
Oxide	MoO_2	289	+41.0
Oxide	MoO_3	292.5	+3.0
Oxide	Mo_3O_8	ord.	+42.0
Sulfide	MoS_3	289	−63.0
Neodymium	Nd	287.7	5628.0
Fluoride	NdF_3	293	+4980.0
Nitrate	$Nd(NO_3)_3$	293	+5020.0
Oxide	Nd_2O_3	292.0	+10,200.0
Sulfate	$Nd_2(SO_4)_3$	293	+9990.0
Sulfide	Nd_2S_3	292	+5550.0
Neon	Ne	ord.	−6.74
Nickel	Ni	–	ferro
Acetate	$Ni(C_2H_3O_2)_2$	293	+4690.0
Bromide	$NiBr_2$	293	+5600.0
Chloride	$NiCl_2$	293	+6145.0
Chloride	$NiCl_2 \cdot 6H_2O$	293	+4240.0
Fluoride	NiF_2	293	+2410.0
Hydroxide	$Ni(OH)_2$	ord.	+4500.0
Iodide	NiI_2	293	+3875.0
Nitrate	$Ni(NO_3)_2 \cdot 6H_2O$	293.5	+4300.0
Oxide	NiO	293	+660.0
Sulfate	$NiSO_4$	293	+4005.0
Sulfide	NiS	293	+190.0
Sulfide	Ni_3S_2	ord.	+1030.0
Niobium	Nb	298	+195.0
Oxide	Nb_2O_5	ord.	−10.0
Nitric acid	HNO_3	ord.	−19.9
Nitrogen	N_2	ord.	−12.0
Oxide	N_2O	285	−18.9
Oxide (g)	NO	293	+1461.0
Oxide (g)	NO	203.8	+1895.0
Oxide (g)	NO	146.9	+2324.0
Oxide (*l*)	NO	117.64	+114.2
Oxide (s)	NO	90	+19.8
Oxide	N_2O_3	291	−16.0
Oxide	NO_2	408	+150.0
Oxide	N_2O_4	303.6	−22.1
Oxide	N_2O_4	295.1	−23.0
Oxide	N_2O_4	257	−25.4
Oxide (aq)	N_2O_5	289	−35.6
Osmium	Os	298	+9.9
Chloride	$OsCl_2$	ord.	+41.3

Table 4.5–18 (*Continued*)
MAGNETIC SUSCEPTIBILITY OF THE ELEMENTS AND INORGANIC COMPOUNDS

Substance	Formula	Temp. °K.	Susceptibility 10^{-6} cgs
Oxygen (g)	O_2	293	+3449.0
Oxygen (*l*)	O_2	90.1	+7699.0
Oxygen (*l*)	O_2	70.8	+8685.0
Oxygen (s, γ)	O_2	54.3	+10,200.0
Oxygen (s, β)	O_2	–	–
Oxygen (s, α)	O_2	23.7	+1760.0
Ozone (*l*)	O_3	–	+6.7
Palladium	Pd	288	+567.4
Chloride	$PdCl_2$	291.3	–38.0
Fluoride	PdF_3	293	+1760.0
Hydride	PdH	ord.	+1077.0
Hydride	Pd_4H	ord.	+2353.0
Phosphoric acid (aq)	H_3PO_4	ord.	–43.8
Phosphorous acid (aq)	H_3PO_3	ord.	–42.5
Phosphorous (red)	P	–	–20.8
Phosphorous (black)	P	–	–26.6
Chloride	PCl_3	ord.	–63.4
Platinum	Pt	290.3	+201.9
Chloride	$PtCl_2$	298	–54.0
Chloride	$PtCl_3$	ord.	–66.7
Chloride	$PtCl_4$	ord.	–93.0
Fluoride	PtF_4	293	+455.0
Oxide	Pt_2O_3	ord.	–37.70
Plutonium	Pu	293	+610.0
Fluoride	PuF_4	301	+1760.0
Fluoride	PuF_6	295	+173.0
Oxide	PuO_2	300	+730.0
Potassium	K	ord.	+20.8
Acetate (aq)	$KC_2H_3O_2$	28	–45.0
Bromate	$KBrO_3$	ord.	–52.6
Bromide	KBr	ord.	–49.1
Carbonate	K_2CO_3	ord.	–59.0
Chlorate	$KClO_3$	ord.	–42.8
Chloride	KCl	ord.	–39.0
Chromate	K_2CrO_4	ord.	–3.9
Chromate	$K_2Cr_2O_7$	293	+29.4
Cyanide	KCN	ord.	–37.0
Ferricyanide	$K_3Fe(CN)_6$	297	+2290.0
Ferrocyanide	$K_4Fe(CN)_6$	ord.	–130.0
Ferrocyanide	$K_4Fe(CN)_6 \cdot 3H_2O$	ord.	–172.3
Fluoride	KF	ord.	–23.6
Hydroxide (aq)	KOH	ord.	–22.0
Iodate	KIO_3	ord.	–63.1
Iodide	KI	ord.	–63.8
Nitrate	KNO_3	ord.	–33.7
Nitrite	KNO_2	ord.	–23.3
Oxide	KO_2	293	+3230.0
Oxide	KO_3	ord.	+1185.0
Permanganate	$KMnO_4$	ord.	+20.0
Sulfate	K_2SO_4	ord.	–67.0

Table 4.5–18 (*Continued*)
MAGNETIC SUSCEPTIBILITY OF THE ELEMENTS AND INORGANIC COMPOUNDS

Substance	Formula	Temp. °K.	Susceptibility 10^{-6} cgs
Sulfate	$KHSO_4$	ord.	−49.8
Sulfide	K_2S	ord.	−60.0
Sulfide	K_2S_2	ord.	−71.0
Sulfide	K_2S_3	ord.	−80.0
Sulfide	K_2S_4	ord.	−89.0
Sulfide	K_2S_5	ord.	−98.0
Sulfite	K_2SO_3	ord.	−64.0
Thiocyanate	KSCN	ord.	−48.0
Praseodymium	Pr	293	+5010.0
Chloride	$PrCl_3$	307.1	+44.5
Oxide	PrO_2	293	+1930.0
Oxide	Pr_2O_3	827	+4000.0
Oxide	Pr_2O_3	294.5	+8994.0
Sulfate	$Pr_2(SO_4)_3$	291	+9660.0
Sulfate	$Pr_2(SO_4)_3 \cdot 8H_2O$	289	+9880.0
Sulfide	Pr_2S_3	292	+10,770.0
Rhenium	Re	293	+67.6
Chloride	$ReCl_5$	293	+1225.0
Oxide	ReO_2	ord.	+44.0
Oxide	$ReO_2 \cdot 2H_2O$	295	+74.0
Oxide	ReO_3	ord.	+16.0
Oxide	Re_2O_7	ord.	−16.0
Sulfide	ReS_2	ord.	+38.0
Rhodium	Rh	298	+111.0
Rhodium	Rh	723	+123.0
Chloride	$RhCl_3$	298	−7.5
Fluoride	RhF_4	293	+500.0
Oxide	Rh_2O_3	298	+104.0
Sulfate	$Rh_2(SO_4)_3 \cdot 6H_2O$	298	+104.0
Sulfate	$Rh_2(SO_4)_3 \cdot 14H_2O$	298	+149.0
Rubidium	Rb	303	+17.0
Bromide	RbBr	ord.	−56.4
Carbonate	Rb_2CO_3	ord.	−75.4
Chloride	RbCl	ord.	−46.0
Fluoride	RbF	ord.	−31.9
Iodide	RbI	ord.	−72.2
Nitrate	$RbNO_3$	ord.	−41.0
Oxide	RbO_2	293	+1527.0
Sulfate	Rb_2SO_4	ord.	−88.4
Sulfide	Rb_2S	ord.	−80.0
Sulfide	Rb_2S_2	ord.	−90.0
Ruthenium	Ru	298	+43.2
Ruthenium	Ru	723	+50.2
Chloride	$RuCl_3$	290.9	+1998.0
Oxide	RuO_2	298	+162.0
Samarium	Sm	291	+1860.0
Samarium	Sm	195	+2230.0
Bromide	$SmBr_2$	293	+5337.0
Bromide	$SmBr_3$	293	+972.0
Oxide	Sm_2O_3	292	+1988.0

Table 4.5–18 (*Continued*)
MAGNETIC SUSCEPTIBILITY OF THE ELEMENTS AND INORGANIC COMPOUNDS

Substance	Formula	Temp. °K.	Susceptibility 10^{-6} cgs
Oxide	Sm_2O_3	170	+1960.0
Oxide	Sm_2O_3	85	+2282.0
Sulfate	$Sm_2(SO_4)_3 \cdot 8H_2O$	293	+1710.0
Sulfide	Sm_2S_3	292	+3300.0
Scandium	Sc	292	+315.0
Selenic acid	H_2SeO_4	ord.	−51.2
Selenious acid	H_2SeO_3	ord.	−45.4
Selenium (s)	Se	ord.	−25.0
Selenium (*l*)	Se	900	−24.0
Bromide	Se_2Br_2	ord.	−113.0
Chloride	Se_2Cl_2	ord.	−94.8
Fluoride	SeF_6	ord.	−51.0
Oxide	SeO_2	ord.	−27.2
Silicon	Si	ord.	−3.9
Bromide	$SiBr_4$	ord.	−128.6
Carbide	SiC	ord.	−12.8
Chloride	$SiCl_4$	ord.	−88.3
Hydroxide	$Si(OH)_4$	ord.	−42.6
Oxide	SiO_2	ord.	−29.6
Silver (s)	Ag	296	−19.5
Silver (*l*)	Ag	–	−24.0
Acetate	$AgC_2H_3O_2$	ord.	−60.4
Bromide	AgBr	283	−59.7
Carbonate	Ag_2CO_3	ord.	−80.90
Chloride	AgCl	ord.	−49.0
Chromate	Ag_2CrO_4	ord.	−40.0
Cyanide	AgCN	ord.	−43.2
Fluoride	AgF	ord.	−36.5
Iodide	AgI	ord.	−80.0
Nitrate	$AgNO_3$	ord.	−45.7
Nitrite	$AgNO_2$	ord.	−42.0
Oxide	Ag_2O	ord.	−134.0
Oxide	AgO	287	−19.6
Permanganate	$AgMnO_4$	300	−63.0
Phosphate	Ag_3PO_4	ord.	−120.0
Sulfate	Ag_2SO_4	ord.	−92.90
Thiocyanate	AgSCN	ord.	−61.8
Sodium	Na	ord.	+16.0
Acetate	$NaC_2H_3O_2$	ord.	−37.6
Borate, tetra	$Na_2B_4O_7$	ord.	−85.0
Bromate	$NaBrO_3$	ord.	−44.2
Bromide	NaBr	ord.	−41.0
Carbonate	Na_2CO_3	ord.	−41.0
Chlorate	$NaClO_3$	ord.	−34.7
Chloride	NaCl	ord.	−30.3
Chromate, di	$Na_2Cr_2O_7$	ord.	+55.0
Fluoride	NaF	ord.	−16.4
Hydroxide (aq)	NaOH	300	−16.0
Iodate	$NaIO_3$	ord.	−53.0
Iodide	NaI	ord.	−57.0

Table 4.5–18 (*Continued*)
MAGNETIC SUSCEPTIBILITY OF THE ELEMENTS AND INORGANIC COMPOUNDS

Substance	Formula	Temp. °K.	Susceptibility 10^{-6} cgs
Nitrate	$NaNO_3$	ord.	–25.6
Nitrite	$NaNO_2$	ord.	–14.5
Oxide	Na_2O	ord.	–19.8
Oxide	Na_2O_2	ord.	–28.10
Phosphate, meta	$NaPO_3$	ord.	–42.5
Phosphate	Na_2HPO_4	ord.	–56.6
Sulfate	Na_2SO_4	ord.	–52.0
Sulfate	$Na_2SO_4 \cdot 10H_2O$	ord.	–184.0
Sulfide	Na_2S	ord.	–39.0
Sulfide	Na_2S_2	ord.	–53.0
Sulfide	Na_2S_3	ord.	–68.0
Sulfide	Na_2S_4	ord.	–84.0
Sulfide	Na_2S_5	ord.	–99.0
Strontium	Sr	ord.	+92.0
Acetate	$Sr(C_2H_3O_2)_2$	ord.	–79.0
Bromate	$Sr(BrO_3)_2$	ord.	–93.5
Bromide	$SrBr_2$	ord.	–86.6
Bromide	$SrBr_2 \cdot 6H_2O$	ord.	–160.0
Carbonate	$SrCO_3$	ord.	–47.0
Chlorate	$Sr(ClO_3)_2$	ord.	–73.0
Chloride	$SrCl_2$	ord.	–63.0
Chloride	$SrCl_2 \cdot 6H_2O$	ord.	–145.0
Chromate	$SrCrO_4$	ord.	–5.1
Fluoride	SrF_2	ord.	–37.2
Hydroxide	$Sr(OH)_2$	ord.	–40.0
Hydroxide	$Sr(OH)_2 \cdot 8H_2O$	ord.	–136.0
Iodate	$Sr(IO_3)_2$	ord.	–108.0
Iodide	SrI_2	ord.	–112.0
Nitrate	$Sr(NO_3)_2$	ord.	–57.2
Nitrate	$Sr(NO_3)_2 \cdot 4H_2O$	ord.	–106.0
Oxide	SrO	ord.	–35.0
Oxide	SrO_2	ord.	–32.3
Sulfate	$SrSO_4$	ord.	–57.9
Sulfur (α)	S	ord.	–15.5
Sulfur (β)	S	ord.	–14.9
Sulfur (l)	S	–	–15.4
Sulfur (g)	S	828	+700.0
Sulfur (g)	S	1023	+464.0
Chloride	S_2Cl_2	ord.	–62.2
Chloride	SCl_2	ord.	–49.4
Chloride	SCl_3	ord.	–49.4
Fluoride	SF_6	ord.	–44.0
Iodide	SI	ord.	–52.7
Oxide (l)	SO_2	ord.	–18.2
Sulfuric acid	H_2SO_4	ord.	–39.8
Tantalum	Ta	293	+154.0
Tantalum	Ta	2143	+124.0
Chloride	$TaCl_5$	304	+140.0
Fluoride	TaF_3	293	+795.0
Oxide	Ta_2O_5	ord.	–32.0

Table 4.5–18 (*Continued*)
MAGNETIC SUSCEPTIBILITY OF THE ELEMENTS AND INORGANIC COMPOUNDS

Substance	Formula	Temp. °K.	Susceptibility 10^{-6} cgs
Technetium	Tc	402	250.0
Technetium	Tc	298	270.0
Technetium	Tc	78	290.0
Oxide	$TcO_2 \cdot 2H_2O$	300	+244.0
Oxide	Tc_2O_7	298	−40.0
Tellurium (s)	Te	ord.	−39.5
Tellurium (*l*)	Te	–	−6.4
Bromide	$TeBr_2$	ord.	−106.0
Chloride	$TeCl_2$	ord.	−94.0
Fluoride	TeF_6	ord.	−66.0
Terbium	Tb	273	+146,000.00
Oxide	Tb_2O_3	288.1	+78,340.0
Sulfate	$Tb_2(SO_4)_3$	293	+78,200.0
Sulfate	$Tb_2(SO_4)_3 \cdot 8H_2O$	293	+76,500.0
Thallium (α)	Tl	ord.	−50.9
Thallium (β)	Tl	>508	−32.3
Thallium (*l*)	Tl	573	−26.8
Acetate	$TlC_2H_3O_2$	ord.	−69.0
Bromate	$TlBrO_3$	ord.	−75.9
Bromide	TlBr	ord.	−63.9
Carbonate	Tl_2CO_3	ord.	−101.6
Chlorate	$TlClO_3$	ord.	−65.5
Chloride	TlCl	ord.	−57.8
Chromate	Tl_2CrO_4	ord.	−39.3
Cyanide	TlCN	ord.	−49.0
Fluoride	TlF	ord.	−44.4
Iodate	$TlIO_3$	ord.	−86.8
Iodide	TlI	ord.	−82.2
Nitrate	$TlNO_3$	ord.	−56.5
Nitrite	$TlNO_2$	ord.	−50.8
Oxide	Tl_2O_3	ord.	+76.0
Phosphate	Tl_3PO_4	ord.	−145.2
Sulfate	Tl_2SO_4	ord.	−112.6
Sulfide	Tl_2S	ord.	−88.8
Thiocyanate	TlCNS	ord.	−66.7
Thorium	Th	293	+132.0
Thorium	Th	90	+153.0
Chloride	$ThCl_4 \cdot 8H_2O$	305.2	−180.0
Nitrate	$Th(NO_3)_4$	ord.	−108.0
Oxide	ThO_2	ord.	−16.0
Thulium	Tm	291	+25,500.0
Oxide	Tm_2O_3	296.5	+51,444.0
Tin, white	Sn	ord.	+3.1
Tin, gray	Sn	280	−37.0
Tin, gray	Sn	100	−31.7
Tin (*l*)	Sn	–	−4.5
Bromide	$SnBr_4$	ord.	−149.0
Chloride	$SnCl_2$	ord.	−69.0
Chloride	$SnCl_2 \cdot 2H_2O$	ord.	−91.4

Table 4.5–18 (*Continued*)
MAGNETIC SUSCEPTIBILITY OF THE ELEMENTS AND INORGANIC COMPOUNDS

Substance	Formula	Temp. °K.	Susceptibility 10^{-6} cgs
Chloride (*l*)	$SnCl_4$	ord.	–115.0
Hydroxide	$Sn(OH)_4$	ord.	–60.0
Oxide	SnO	ord.	–19.0
Oxide	SnO_2	ord.	–41.0
Titanium	Ti	293	+153.0
Titanium	Ti	90	+150.0
Bromide	$TiBr_2$	288	+640.0
Bromide	$TiBr_3$	441	+520.0
Bromide	$TiBr_3$	291	+660.0
Bromide	$TiBr_3$	195	+680.0
Bromide	$TiBr_3$	90	+220.0
Carbide	TiC	ord.	+8.0
Chloride	$TiCl_2$	288	+570.0
Chloride	$TiCl_3$	685	+705.0
Chloride	$TiCl_3$	373	+1030.0
Chloride	$TiCl_3$	292	+1110.0
Chloride	$TiCl_3$	212	+690.0
Chloride	$TiCl_3$	90	+220.0
Chloride	$TiCl_4$	ord.	–54.0
Fluoride	TiF_3	293	+1300.0
Iodide	TiI_2	288	+1790.0
Iodide	TiI_3	434	+221.0
Iodide	TiI_3	292	+160.0
Iodide	TiI_3	195	+159.0
Iodide	TiI_3	90	+167.0
Oxide	Ti_2O_3	382	+152.0
Oxide	Ti_2O_3	298	+125.6
Oxide	TiO_3	248	+132.4
Oxide	TiO_2	ord.	+5.9
Sulfide	TiS	ord.	+432.0
Tungsten	W	298	+59.0
Bromide	WBr_5	293	+250.0
Carbide	WC	ord.	+10.0
Chloride	WCl_2	293	–25.0
Chloride	WCl_5	293	+387.0
Chloride	WCl_6	ord.	–71.0
Fluoride	WF_6	ord.	–40.0
Oxide	WO_2	ord.	+57.0
Oxide	WO_3	ord.	–15.8
Sulfide	WS_2	303	+5850.0
Tungstic acid, ortho	H_2WO_4	ord.	–28.0
Uranium (α)	U	78	+395.0
Uranium (α)	U	298	+409.0
Uranium (α)	U	623	+440.0
Uranium (β)	U	–	–
Uranium (γ)	U	1393	+514.0
Bromide	UBr_3	294	+4740.0
Bromide	UBr_4	293	+3530.0
Chloride	UCl_3	300	+3460.0
Chloride	UCl_4	294	+3680.0
Fluoride	UF_4	300	+3530.0
Fluoride	UF_6	ord.	+43.0

Table 4.5–18 (*Continued*)
MAGNETIC SUSCEPTIBILITY OF THE ELEMENTS AND INORGANIC COMPOUNDS

Substance	Formula	Temp. °K.	Susceptibility 10^{-6} cgs
Hydrides	UH_3	462	+2821.0
Hydrides	UH_3	391	+3568.0
Hydrides	UH_3	295	+6244.0
Hydrides	UH_3	255	+9306.0
Iodide	UI_3	293	+4460.0
Oxide	UO	293	+1600.0
Oxide	UO_2	293	+2360.0
Oxide	UO_3	ord.	+128.0
Sulfate	$U(SO_4)_2$	ord.	+31.0
Sulfide (α)	US_2	290.5	+3137.0
Sulfide (β)	US_2	290.5	+3470.0
Sulfide	U_2S_3	ord.	+5206.0
Sulfide	U_3S_5	ord.	+11,220.0
Vanadium	V	298	+255.0
Bromide	VBr_2	293	+3230.0
Bromide	VBr_2	195	+3760.0
Bromide	VBr_2	90	+4470.0
Bromide	VBr_3	293	+2890.0
Bromide	VBr_3	195	+4110.0
Bromide	VBr_3	90	+8540.0
Chloride	VCl_2	293	+2410.0
Chloride	VCl_3	293	+3030.0
Chloride	VCl_4	293	+1130.0
Chloride	VCl_4	195	+1700.0
Chloride	VCl_4	90	+4360.0
Fluoride	VF_3	293	+2730.0
Oxide	VO_2	290	+270.0
Oxide	V_2O_3	293	+1976.0
Oxide	V_2O_5	ord.	+128.0
Sulfide	VS	ord.	+600.0
Sulfide	V_2S_3	293	+1560.0
Water (g)	H_2O	>373	−13.1
Water (*l*)	H_2O	373	−13.09
Water (*l*)	H_2O	293	−12.97
Water (*l*)	H_2O	273	−12.93
Water (s)	H_2O	273	−12.65
Water (s)	H_2O	223	−12.31
Water (*l*)	DHO	302	−12.97
Water (*l*)	D_2O	293	−12.76
Water (*l*)	D_2O	276.8	−12.66
Water (s)	D_2O	276.8	−12.54
Water (s)	D_2O	213	−12.41
Xenon	Xe	ord.	−43.9
Ytterbium	Yb	292	+249.0
Ytterbium	Yb	90	+639.0
Sulfide	Yb_2S_3	292	+18,300.0
Yttrium	Y	292	+2.15
Yttrium	Y	90	+2.43
Oxide	Y_2O_3	293	+44.4
Sulfide	Y_2S_3	ord.	+100.0

Table 4.5–18 (*Continued*)
MAGNETIC SUSCEPTIBILITY OF THE ELEMENTS AND INORGANIC COMPOUNDS

Substance	Formula	Temp. °K.	Susceptibility 10^{-6} cgs
Zinc (s)	Zn	ord.	−11.4
Zinc (*l*)	Zn	—	−7.8
Acetate	$Zn(C_2H_3O_2)_2 \cdot 2H_2O$	ord.	−101.0
Carbonate	$ZnCO_3$	ord.	−34.0
Chloride	$ZnCl_2$	296	−65.0
Cyanide	$Zn(CN)_2$	ord.	−46.0
Fluoride	ZnF_2	299.6	−38.2
Hydroxide	$Zn(OH)_2$	ord.	−67.0
Iodide	ZnI_2	ord.	−98.0
Nitrate (aq)	$Zn(NO_3)_2$	ord.	−63.0
Oxide	ZnO	ord.	−46.0
Phosphate	$Zn_3(PO_4)_2$	ord.	−141.0
Sulfate	$ZnSO_4$	ord.	−45.0
Sulfate	$ZnSO_4 \cdot H_2O$	ord.	−63.0
Sulfate	$ZnSO_4 \cdot 7H_2O$	ord.	−143.0
Sulfide	ZnS	ord.	−25.0
Zirconium	Zr	293	+122.0
Zirconium	Zr	90	+119.0
Carbide	ZrC	ord.	−26.0
Nitrate	$Zr(NO_3)_4 \cdot 5H_2O$	ord.	−77.0
Oxide	ZrO_2	ord.	−13.8

(From Weast, R. C., Ed., *CRC Handbook of Chemistry and Physics,* 53rd ed., Chemical Rubber Co., Cleveland, 1972. With permission.)

Table 4.5–19
MAGNETIC INCLINATION OF DIP AND HORIZONTAL INTENSITY

State	Dip, degrees	Horizontal intensity	State	Dip, degrees	Horizontal intensity
Alabama	62–66	.23–.26	Kentucky	68–70	.20–.22
Alaska	67–74	.16–.21	Maine	74–76	.14–.16
Arizona	59	.27	Maryland	70	.20
Arkansas	63–65	.24–.25	Massachusetts	73	.17
California	58–62	.25–.27	Michigan	73–76	.15–.18
Colorado	67–68	.22–.23	Mississippi	61–66	.24–.26
Connecticut	72–73	17–.18	Missouri	67–71	.20–.22
Delaware	70–71.5	19–.20	Montana	70–72	.18–.20
Florida	57–58	27–29	Nebraska	70–71	.20
Georgia	62–66	.23–.26	New Hampshire	73–74	.16–.17
Hawaii	39	.29	New Jersey	71	.19
Idaho	69	.21	New Mexico	63–65	.24–.25
Indiana	69–72	.18–.21	New York	74	.16–.17
Iowa	71–73	.18–.20	North Carolina	66–68	.21–.23
Kansas	67–69	.21–.23	North Dakota	74–77	.15–.16

Note: The mean or limiting values are given for the territory covered by the state named. The horizontal intensity is given in gausses. The table is compiled from the results of the U.S. Coast Guard and Geodetic Survey for 1911 and 1912.

Table 4.5–19 (*Continued*)
MAGNETIC INCLINATION OF DIP AND HORIZONTAL INTENSITY

State	Dip, degrees	Horizontal intensity	State	Dip, degrees	Horizontal intensity
Ohio	71–73	.18–.20	Utah	66–67	.22–.23
Oklahoma	63–67	.23–.25	Vermont	73–75	.16–.17
Oregon	68–69	.21	Virginia	68–70	.20–.21
Pennsylvania	71–72	.18–.19	Washington	71	.19
Philippines	0–23	.37–.39	West Virginia	70.5	.20
Puerto Rico	49–50	.29–.30	Wisconsin	74–76	.15–.17
South Carolina	66–67	.23	Wyoming	68–72	.19–.22
South Dakota	71–74	.17–.19			
Tennessee	66–68	.22–.23			
Texas	57–63	.25–.29			

(From Hodgman, Charles D., Ed., *Handbook of Chemistry and Physics,* 36th ed., Chemical Rubber Co., Cleveland, 1954, 2394. With permission.)

Table 4.5–20
MAGNETIC DECLINATION

State	Station	Magnetic declination in degrees and tenths					
		1870	1880	1890	1900	1910	1920
Alabama	Ashland	4.7E	4.1E	3.4E	3.0E	2.9E	3.0E
	Tuscaloosa	6.1E	5.5E	4.8E	4.4E	4.4E	4.6E
Alaska	Sitka	29.0E	29.3E	29.5E	29.7E	30.2E	30.4E
	Kodiak	25.7E	25.2E	24.8E	24.5E	24.2E	24.2E
	Unalaska	20.1E	19.6E	19.0E	18.3E	17.5E	17.2E
	St. Michael	–	24.7E	23.1E	22.1E	21.5E	21.0E
Arizona	Holbrook	13.8E	13.6E	13.4E	13.5E	14.1E	14.5E
	Prescott	13.7E	13.7E	13.6E	13.7E	14.4E	14.9E
Arkansas	Augusta	7.1E	6.5E	5.9E	5.5E	5.6E	5.8E
	Danville	8.6E	8.1E	7.6E	7.2E	7.4E	7.7E
California	Bagdad	14.3E	14.4E	14.4E	14.6E	15.3E	15.7E
	Mojave	14.6E	14.9E	14.9E	15.1E	15.8E	16.3E
	Modesto	16.1E	16.1E	16.2E	16.6E	17.3E	17.7E
	Redding	18.1E	18.2E	18.3E	18.7E	19.4E	19.7E
Colorado	Pueblo	13.7E	13.5E	13.0E	12.8E	13.3E	13.7E
	Ouray	15.2E	15.0E	14.6E	14.6E	15.1E	15.5E
Connecticut	Hartford	8.7W	9.4W	9.8W	10.4W	11.2W	12.1W
Delaware	Dover	4.7W	5.3W	5.9W	6.5W	7.2W	8.0W
Washington, D.C.	Washington	2.4W	3.0W	3.6W	4.2W	4.9W	5.6W
Florida	Miami	3.3E	2.7E	2.2E	1.7E	1.5E	1.5E
	Bartow	3.2E	2.6E	2.1E	1.6E	1.4E	1.3E
	Jacksonville	3.0E	2.4E	1.8E	1.3E	1.1E	0.9E
	Tallahassee	4.2E	3.6E	3.0E	2.5E	2.4E	2.4E
Georgia	Millen	2.7E	2.1E	1.5E	0.9E	0.7E	0.5E
	Americus	4.1E	3.5E	2.9E	2.4E	2.2E	2.2E

Table 4.5–20 (*Continued*)
MAGNETIC DECLINATION

State	Station	Magnetic declination in degrees and tenths					
		1870	1880	1890	1900	1910	1920
Hawaii	Honolulu	9.5E	9.8E	10.1E	10.4E	10.7E	11.1E
Idaho	Pocatello	18.0E	17.9E	17.8E	17.9E	18.5E	18.8E
	Boise	18.8E	18.8E	18.6E	18.8E	19.5E	19.8E
	Pierce	21.2E	21.1E	21.2E	21.4E	22.0E	22.2E
Illinois	Kankakee	5.3E	4.8E	4.1E	3.5E	3.3E	3.1E
	Rushville	7.0E	6.4E	5.7E	5.2E	5.1E	5.1E
Indiana	Indianapolis	3.3E	2.7E	2.1E	1.5E	1.1E	0.9E
Iowa	Walker	8.2E	7.5E	6.8E	6.2E	6.2E	6.2E
	Sac City	10.2E	9.6E	8.8E	8.4E	8.6E	8.6E
Kansas	Emporia	11.2E	10.8E	10.2E	9.9E	10.1E	10.3E
	Ness City	12.2E	11.9E	11.3E	11.2E	11.4E	11.7E
Kentucky	Manchester	1.6E	1.0E	0.3E	0.3W	0.6W	0.8W
	Louisville	3.2E	2.5E	1.9E	1.5E	1.3E	1.2E
Louisiana	Princeton	5.5E	4.8E	4.2E	3.9E	3.7E	3.8E
	Winfield	8.2E	7.6E	7.1E	6.8E	7.0E	7.4E
Maine	Eastport	18.5W	18.8W	19.0W	19.3W	20.0W	21.0W
	Bangor	15.9W	16.4W	16.7W	17.1W	17.8W	18.8W
	Portland	13.1W	13.6W	14.1W	14.5W	15.3W	16.3W
Maryland	Baltimore	3.8W	4.4W	5.0W	5.6W	6.3W	7.0W
Massachusetts	Boston	11.0W	11.5W	12.0W	12.6W	13.4W	14.4W
	Pittsfield	9.3W	10.0W	10.4W	11.0W	11.8W	12.7W
Michigan	Marquette	4.7E	3.8E	3.0E	2.4E	2.1E	1.7E
	Lapeer	0.3E	0.5W	1.2W	1.8W	2.3W	2.8W
	Grand Haven	3.1E	2.4E	1.6E	1.1E	0.7E	0.3E
Minnesota	St. Paul	10.9E	10.3E	9.5E	8.9E	8.8E	8.7E
	Marshall	11.0E	10.5E	9.8E	9.3E	9.4E	9.4E
	Hibbing	9.7E	9.0E	8.2E	7.6E	7.7E	7.5E
	Bagley	12.3E	11.7E	11.0E	10.4E	10.6E	10.5E
Mississippi	Meridian	6.5E	5.9E	5.2E	4.8E	4.9E	5.1E
	Vicksburg	7.6E	7.1E	6.4E	6.0E	6.1E	6.4E
Missouri	Hermann	8.3E	7.7E	7.0E	6.5E	6.5E	6.6E
	Sedalia	9.3E	8.7E	8.0E	7.6E	7.8E	8.0E
Montana	Miles City	17.7E	17.4E	16.9E	16.9E	17.3E	17.6E
	Lewistown	20.1E	19.9E	19.6E	19.6E	20.1E	20.4E
	Ovando	21.2E	21.1E	20.9E	21.1E	21.6E	22.0E
Nebraska	Albion	12.5E	12.0E	11.4E	11.0E	11.2E	11.5E
	Valentine	13.9E	13.4E	12.8E	12.6E	12.8E	13.1E
	Alliance	15.3E	14.8E	14.3E	14.2E	14.5E	14.8E
Nevada	Elko	17.7E	17.7E	17.6E	17.8E	18.4E	18.9E
	Hawthorne	16.8E	17.0E	17.0E	17.3E	18.0E	18.4E

Table 4.5–20 (*Continued*)
MAGNETIC DECLINATION

State	Station	Magnetic declination in degrees and tenths					
		1870	1880	1890	1900	1910	1920
New Hampshire	Hanover	11.1W	11.6W	12.0W	12.6W	13.2W	14.2W
New Jersey	Trenton	6.0W	6.7W	7.2W	7.8W	8.6W	9.4W
New Mexico	Santa Rosa	12.7E	12.4E	12.0E	11.9E	12.5E	12.9E
	Laguna	13.6E	13.4E	13.0E	13.0E	13.6E	14.1E
New York	Albany	9.2W	10.0W	10.3W	10.9W	11.6W	12.5W
	Elmira	5.4W	6.3W	7.0W	7.5W	8.2W	9.0W
	Buffalo	3.8W	4.7W	5.4W	5.9W	6.5W	7.2W
North Carolina	Newbern	1.0W	1.7W	2.3W	2.9W	3.4W	4.0W
	Greensboro	1.0E	0.3E	0.3W	0.8W	1.3W	1.8W
	Asheville	2.0E	1.3E	0.7E	0.2E	0.2W	0.5W
North Dakota	Jamestown	13.7E	13.2E	12.5E	12.2E	12.4E	12.5E
	Bismarck	16.1E	15.6E	15.0E	14.7E	15.0E	15.2E
	Dickinson	17.5E	17.1E	16.5E	16.3E	16.7E	16.9E
Ohio	Canton	0.0	0.7W	1.3W	1.9W	2.5W	3.1W
	Urbana	2.4E	1.8E	1.1E	0.5E	0.1E	0.3W
Oklahoma	Okmulgee	9.8E	9.5E	9.1E	8.7E	8.9E	9.2E
	Enid	11.0E	10.6E	10.2E	9.8E	10.1E	10.5E
Oregon	Sumpter	20.0E	20.2E	20.2E	20.4E	21.1E	21.4E
	Detroit	20.1E	20.3E	20.5E	20.8E	21.6E	21.9E
Pennsylvania	Wilkes-Barre	5.3W	6.0W	6.6W	7.2W	8.0W	8.8W
	Lock Haven	4.3W	5.0W	5.6W	6.3W	7.0W	7.7W
	Indiana	2.0W	2.6W	3.3W	3.9W	4.6W	5.2W
Puerto Rico	San Juan	–	–	–	1.0W	2.0W	3.4W
Rhode Island	Newport	10.3W	10.8W	11.3W	11.9W	12.7W	13.7W
South Carolina	Marion	0.9E	0.3E	0.4W	1.0W	1.4W	1.8W
	Aiken	2.5E	1.9E	1.3E	0.7E	0.4E	0.1E
South Dakota	Huron	12.7E	12.3E	11.7E	11.2E	11.5E	11.7E
	Murdo	14.7E	14.3E	13.7E	13.4E	13.7E	13.9E
	Rapid City	16.3E	15.8E	15.3E	15.1E	15.4E	15.7E
Tennessee	Knoxville	1.8E	1.1E	0.5E	0.0	0.3W	0.5W
	Shelbyville	4.9E	4.3E	3.7E	3.2E	3.0E	2.9E
	Huntingdon	6.1E	5.5E	4.9E	4.4E	4.3E	4.4E
Texas	Houston	8.9E	8.4E	7.9E	7.7E	8.1E	8.6E
	San Antonio	9.5E	9.2E	8.7E	8.7E	9.2E	9.7E
	Pecos	11.0E	10.8E	10.4E	10.3E	10.8E	11.3E
	Wytheville	0.8E	0.1E	0.5W	1.1W	1.5W	1.9W
Utah	Manti	16.8E	16.7E	16.4E	16.5E	17.1E	17.5E
Vermont	Rutland	10.5W	11.2W	11.6W	12.1W	12.8W	13.8W

Table 4.5–20 (*Continued*)
MAGNETIC DECLINATION

State	Station	Magnetic declination in degrees and tenths 1870	1880	1890	1900	1910	1920
Virginia	Richmond	1.8W	2.5W	3.1W	3.7W	4.2W	4.9W
	Lynchburg	0.7W	1.4W	2.0W	2.6W	3.1W	3.7W
	Stanley	7.8E	7.1E	6.3E	5.8E	5.6E	5.4E
Washington	Wilson Creek	21.8E	21.9E	22.1E	22.4E	23.0E	23.3E
	Seattle	22.0E	22.2E	22.4E	22.8E	23.5E	23.8E
West Virginia	Sutton	0.4W	1.1W	1.8W	2.4W	2.9W	3.4W
Wisconsin	Shawano	5.9E	5.0E	4.3E	3.7E	3.4E	3.1E
	Floydada	11.2E	10.9E	10.4E	10.3E	10.7E	11.1E
Wyoming	Douglas	16.0E	15.8E	15.3E	15.2E	15.7E	16.0E
	Green River	17.0E	16.8E	16.5E	16.6E	17.2E	17.5E

(From Hodgman, Charles D., Ed., *Handbook of Chemistry and Physics,* 36th ed., Chemical Rubber Co., Cleveland, 1954, 2394. With permission.)

Table 4.5–21
LIQUIDS FOR INDEX BY IMMERSION METHOD

Liquid	N_D 24°C
Trimethylene chloride	1.446
Cincole	1.456
Hexahydrophenol	1.466
Decahydronaphthalene	1.477
Isoamyl phthalate	1.486
Tetrachloroethane	1.492
Pentachloroethane	1.501
Trimethylene bromide	1.513
Chlorobenzene	1.523
Ethylene bromide + chlorobenzene	1.533
o-Nitrotoluene	1.544
Xylidine	1.557
o-Toluidine	1.570
Aniline	1.584
Bromoform	1.595
Iodobenzene + bromobenzene	1.603
Iodobenzene + bromobenzene	1.613
Quinoline	1.622
α-Chloronaphthalene	1.633
α-Bromonaphthalene + α-chloronaphthalene	1.640–1.650
α-Bromonaphthalene + α-iodonaphthalene	1.660–1.690
Methylene iodide + iodobenzene	1.700–1.730
Methylene iodide	1.738
Methylene iodide saturated with sulfur	1.78
Yellow phosphorus, sulfur and methylene iodide (8:1:1 by weight)[a]	2.06

[a] Can be diluted with methylene iodide to cover range 1.74–2.06. For precautions in use, see West, *Am. Mineral,* 21, 245, 1936.

(From Weast, Robert C., Ed., *CRC Handbook of Chemistry and Physics,* 50th ed., Chemical Rubber Co., Cleveland, 1969. With permission.)

Table 4.5–22
HEAVY LIQUIDS FOR MINERAL SEPARATION

Liquid	Density
sym-Tetrabromoethane[a]	2.964, 20°/4°
Methylene iodide[b]	3.325, 20°/4°
Thallium formate,[c] aq	3.5
Thallium malonate-thallium formate,[c] aq	4.9

Note: For preparation and recovery of these liquids, see U.S. Bureau Mines, Rept. Inv. 2897, 1928.

[a] Can be diluted with carbon tetrachloride (1.595) or benzene (0.894).
[b] Can be diluted with carbon tetrachloride or benzene.
[c] Can be diluted with water.

(From Weast, Robert C., Ed., *CRC Handbook of Chemistry and Physics,* 50th ed., Chemical Rubber Co., Cleveland, 1969. With permission.)

Table 4.5–23
INDEX OF REFRACTION

Indices not otherwise indicated are for sodium light, λ = 589.3 mμ. Other wavelengths are indicated by the value in millimicrons or symbol in parentheses which follows the index. Wavelengths are indicated as follows: He, λ = 587.6 mμ; Li, λ = 670.8 mμ; Hg, λ = 579.1 mμ; A, λ = 759.4 mμ; C, λ = 656.3 mμ; D, λ = 589.3 mμ; F, λ = 486.1 mμ.

Temperatures are understood to be 20°C for liquids, or ordinary room temperatures in the case of solids. Other temperatures appear as superior figures with the index.

Indices for the elements and inorganic compounds will be understood to be for the solid form except as indicated by the abbreviation liq.

Elements

Name	Formula	Index
Bromine (liq.)	Br_2	1.661^{15}
Cadmium (liq.)	Cd	0.82 (579 mμ)
Cadmium (sol.)		1.13
Chlorine (liq.)	Cl_2	1.385
Chlorine (gas)		1.000768
Hydrogen (liq.)	H_2	$1.10974^{-252.83}$ (579 mμ)
Iodine (sol.)	I_2	3.34
Iodine (gas)		1.001920
Lead	Pb	2.6 (579 mμ)
Mercury (liq.)	Hg	1.6–1.9
Nitrogen (liq.)	N_2	1.2053^{-190}
Oxygen (liq.)	O_2	1.221^{-181}
Phosphorus (yel.) (sol.)		2.1442^{25}
Selenium	Se_8	3.00, 4.04
Selemus (amor.) (sol.)		2.92
Sodium (liq.)	Na	0.0045
Sodium (sol.)		4.22
Sulfur (liq.)	S_8	1.929^{110}
Sulfur (amor.) (sol.)		1.998
Sulfur (rhombic, α)		1.957, 2.0377, 2.2454
Tin (liq.)	Sn	2.1

Table 4.5–23 (*Continued*)
INDEX OF REFRACTION

Inorganic Compounds

Name	Formula	Index
Aluminum carbide	AlC_3	2.7, 2.75 (700 mμ)
Chloride	$AlCl_3 \cdot 6H_2O$	1.560, 1.507
Oxide	Al_2O_3	1.665–1.680, 1.63–1.65
Alums. See appropriate element.		
Ammonium antimonyl tartrate	$2(NH_4 \cdot SbO \cdot C_4H_4O_6) \cdot H_2O$	β1.6229 (C)
*Ortho*arsenate, di-H	$NH_4H_2AsO_4$	1.5766, 1.5217
Bromide	NH_4Br	1.7108
*Per*chlorate	NH_4ClO_4	1.4818, 1.4833, 1.4881
Chloroplatinate	$(NH_4)_2PtCl_6$	1.8
Fluoride	NH_4F	ω<1.328
Fluorid acid	NH_4HF_2	1.385, 1.390, 1.394
Hydrogen malate. (*d*)	$NH_4C_4H_5O_5$	β1.503
Nitrate	NH_4NO_3	1.413, 1.611(He), 1.63
Ammonium sulfate, acid	NH_4HSO_4	1.463, 1.473, 1.510
Tartrate (*dl*)	$(NH_4)_2C_4H_4O_6 \cdot 2H_2O$	β1.564
Thiocyanate	NH_4CNS	1.546, 1.685, 1.692
Uranyl acetate	$NH_4C_2H_3O_2 \cdot UO_2(C_2H_3O_2)_2$	1.4808, 1.4933
Antimony bromide	$SbBr_3$	>1.74+
Iodide, tri-	SbI_3	2.78 (Li), 2.36
Barium cadmium bromide	$BaCdBr_4 \cdot 4H_2O$	β1.702
Cadmium chloride	$BaCdCl_4 \cdot 4H_2O$	β1.651
Calcium propionate	$BaCa_2(C_3H_5O_2)_6$	1.4442
Fluochloride	$BaCl_2 \cdot BaF_2$	1.640, 1.633
Fluoride	BaF_2	1.475 also 1.4741
Barium oxide	BaO	1.980
*Ortho*phosphate, di-	$BaHPO_4$	1.617, 1.63±, 1.635
Propionate	$Ba(C_2H_5CO_2)_2 \cdot H_2O$	β1.5175
Sulfide, mono-	BaS	2.155
Cadmium ammonium chloride	$CdCl_2 \cdot 4NH_4Cl$	1.6038, 1.6042
Cesium sulate	$CdSO_4 \cdot Cs_2SO_4 \cdot 6H_2O$	1.498, 1.500, 1.506
Fluoride	CdF_2	1.56
Magnesium chloride	$(CdCl_2)_2 \cdot MgCl_2 \cdot 12H_2O$	1.49, 1.5331, 1.5769
Oxide	CdO	2.49 (Li)
Potassium chloride	$CdCl_2 \cdot 4KCl$	1.5906, 1.5907
Potassium cyanide	$Cd(CN)_2 \cdot 2KCN$	1.4213
Rubidium sulfate	$CdSO_4 \cdot Rb_2SO_4 \cdot 6H_2O$	1.4798, 1.4848, 1.4948
Calcium aluminate	$Ca_3Al_2O_6$	1.710
Borate	$CaO \cdot B_2O_3$	1.540, 1.656, 1.682
Carbide	CaC_2	>1.75
Copper acetate	$CaCu(C_2H_3O_2)_4 \cdot 6H_2O$	1.436, 1.478
Cyanamide	$CaCN_2$	1.60, >1.95
Dithionate	$CaS_2O_6 \cdot 4H_2O$	1.5516, 1.5414
*Pyro*phosphate	$Ca_2P_2O_7$	1.585, 1.60±, 1.605
Platinocyanide	$CaPt(CN)_4 \cdot 5H_2O$	1.623, 1.644, 1.767
Strontium propionate	$Ca_2Sr(C_3H_5O_2)_6$	1.4871, 1.4956
Sulfide (oldhamite)	CaS	2.137
Sulfite	$CaSO_3 \cdot 2H_2O$	1.590, 1.595, 1.628
Thiosulfate	$CaS_2O_3 \cdot 6H_2O$	1.545, 1.560, 1.605

Table 4.5–23 (*Continued*)
INDEX OF REFRACTION

Name	Formula	Index
Carbon dioxide (liq.)	CO_2	1.195^{15}
Cerium dithionate	$Ce_2(S_2O_6)_3 \cdot 15H_2O$	β1.507
Cesium *per*chlorate	$CsClO_4$	1.4752, 1.4788, 1.4804
Nitrate	$CsNO_3$	1.55, 1.56
Selenate	Cs_2SeO_4	1.5989, 1.5999, 1.6003
Thallium chloride	$Cs_3Tl_2Cl_9$	1.784, 1.774
Chromium cesium sulfate	$CrCs(SO_4)_2 \cdot 12H_2O$	1.4810
Oxide (ic)	Cr_2O_3	2.5
Potassium cyanide (ic)	$CrK_3(CN)_6$	1.5221, 1.5244, 1.5373
Sulfate (ic)	$Cr_2(SO_4)_3 \cdot 18H_2O$	1.564
Thallium sulfate	$CrTl(SO_4)_2 \cdot 12H_2O$	1.5228
Cobalt acetate	$Co(C_2H_3O_2)_2 \cdot 4H_2O$	β1.542
Aluminate (Thenard's Blue)	$Co(AlO_2)_2$	>1.78 (red), 1.74 (blue)
Ammonium selenate	$CoSeO_4 \cdot (NH_4)_2SeO_4 \cdot 6H_2O$	1.5246, 1.5311, 1.5396
Cesium sulfate	$CoCs_2(SO_4)_2 \cdot 6H_2O$	1.5057, 1.5085, 1.5132
Chloride (ous)	$CoCl_2 \cdot 2H_2O$	<1.625, <1.671, >1.67
Potassium selenate	$CoSeO_4 \cdot K_2SeO_4 \cdot 6H_2O$	1.5135, 1.5195, 1.5358
Rubidium sulfate	$CoSO_4 \cdot Rb_2SO_4 \cdot 6H_2O$	1.4859, 1.4916, 1.5014
Selenate	$CoSeO_4 \cdot 6H_2O$	β1.5225, γ1.5227
Copper ammonium selenate	$CuSeO_4 \cdot (NH_4)_2SeO_4 \cdot 6H_2O$	1.5213, 1.5355, 1.5395
Ammonium sulfate	$CuSO_4 \cdot (NH_4)_2SO_4 \cdot 6H_2O$	1.4910, 1.5007, 1.5054
Cesium sulfate	$CuSO_4 \cdot Cs_2SO_4 \cdot 6H_2O$	1.5048, 1.5061, 1.5153
Chloride (ic)	$CuCl_2 \cdot 2H_2O$	1.644, 1.684, 1.742
Formate	$Cu(CHO_2)_2 \cdot 4H_2O$	1.4133, 1.5423, 1.5571
Copper oxide (ous) (cuprite)	Cu_2O	2.705
Potassium chloride	$CuCl_2 \cdot 2KCl \cdot 2H_2O$	1.6365, 1.6148
Potassium cyanide (ous)	$CuK_3(CN)_4$	1.5215
Potassium selenate	$CuSeO_4 \cdot K_2SeO_4 \cdot 6H_2O$	1.5096, 1.5235, 1.5387
Potassium sulfate	$CuSO_4 \cdot K_2SO_4 \cdot 6H_2O$	1.4836, 1.4864, 1.5020
Strontium formate	$Cu(HCO_2)_2 \cdot 2[Sr(HCO_2)_2]$ $8H_2O$	1.4995, 1 5199, 1.5801
Sulfate (ic)	$CuSO_4$	1.724, 1.733, 1.739
Cyanogen	C_2N_2	1.327^{18} (liq.)
Germanium bromide, tetra-	$GeBr_4$	1.6269
Gold sodium chloride	$AuNaCl_4 \cdot 2H_2O$	α1.545, γ1.75+
Hafnium oxychloride	$HfOCl_2 \cdot 8H_2O$	1.557, 1.543
Ice	H_2O	1.3049, 1.3062 (A), 1.3001, 1.3104 (D), 1.3133, 1.3147 (F)
Iron ammonium chloride	$Fe(NH_4)_2Cl_4$	1.6439
Ammonium selenate	$FeSeO_4 \cdot (NH_4)_2SeO_4 \cdot 6H_2O$	1.5201, 1.5260, 1.5356
Cesium sulfate (ic)	$FeCs(SO_4)_2 \cdot 12H_2O$	1.4839
Cesium sulfate (ous)	$FeSO_4 \cdot Cs_2SO_4 \cdot 6H_2O$	1.5003, 1.5035, 1.5094
Rubidium sulfate	$FeRb(SO_4)_2 \cdot 12H_2O$	1.48234
Sulfate (ic)	$Fe_2(SO_4)_3$	1.802, 1.814, 1.818
Thallium sulfate	$FeTl(SO_4)_2 \cdot 12H_2O$	1.52365

Table 4.5–23 (*Continued*)
INDEX OF REFRACTION

Name	Formula	Index
Lanthanum sulfate	$La_2(SO_4)_3 \cdot 9H_2O$	1.564, 1.569
Lead *ortho*arsenate, di-	$PbHAsO_4$	1.8903, 1.9097, 1.9765
Nitrate	$Pb(NO_3)_2$	1.782
Lithium ammonium sulfate	$LiNH_4SO_4$	β1.437 (Li)
Ammonium tartrate (*d*)	$LiNH_4(C_4H_4O_6) \cdot H_2O$	β1.567, γ1.5673
Ammonium tartrate (*dl*)	$LiNH_4(C_4H_4O_6) \cdot H_2O$	β1.5287
Bromide	$LiBr$	1.784
Chloride	$LiCl$	1.662
Dithionate	$Li_2S_2O_6 \cdot 2H_2O$	1.5487, 1.5602, 1.5788
Oxide	Li_2O	1.644
Potassium sulfate	$LiKSO_4$	1.4723, 1.4717
Potassium tartrate	$LiK(C_4H_4O_6) \cdot H_2O$	β1.5226 (red)
Rubidium tartrate (*a*)	$LiRb(C_4H_4O_6) \cdot H_2O$	β1.552
Sodium tartrate (*dl*)	$LiNa(C_4H_4O_6) \cdot 2H_2O$	β1.4904
Magnesium ammonium selenate	$MgSeO_4 \cdot (NH_4)_2SeO_4 \cdot 6H_2O$	1.5070, 1.5093, 1.5169
Ammonium sulfate	$Mg(NH_4)_2 \cdot (SO_4)_2 \cdot 6H_2O$	1.4716, 1.4730, 1.4786
*Ortho*borate	$3MgO \cdot B_2O_3$	1.6527, 1.6537, 1.6748
Cesium sulfate	$MgCs_2(SO_4)_2 \cdot 6H_2O$	1.4857, 1.4858, 1.4916
Chlorostannate	$MgSnCl_6 \cdot 6H_2O$	1.5885, 1.5970
Fluosilicate	$MgSiF_6 \cdot 6H_2O$	1.3439, 1.3602
Platinocyanide	$MgPt(CN)_4 \cdot 7H_2O$	1.5608, 1.91
Magnesium potassium selenate	$MgK_2(SeO_4)_2 \cdot 6H_2O$	1.4969, 1.4991, 1.5139
Potassium sulfate	$MgK_2(SO_4)_2 \cdot 6H_2O$	1.4607, 1.4629, 1.4755
Rubidium sulfate	$MgRb_2(SO_4)_2 \cdot 6H_2O$	1.4672, 1.4689, 1.4779
Silicate	$MgSiO_3$	1.651, 1.654 (calc.), 1.660
Sulfide	MgS	2.271 also 2.268
Manganese borate	$Mn_3B_4O_9$	1.617, 1.738, 1.776
Cesium sulfate	$MnCs_2(SO_4)_2 \cdot 6H_2O$	1.4946, 1.4966, 1.5025
Chloride	$MnCl_2 \cdot 4H_2O$	1.555, 1.575, 1.607
Rubidium sulfate	$MnRb_2(SO_4)_2 \cdot 6H_2O$	1.4767, 1.4807, 1.4907
Sulfate (ous)	$MnSO_4 \cdot 4H_2O$	1.508, 1.518, 1.522
Sulfate (ous)	$MnSO_4 \cdot 5H_2O$	1.495, 1.508, 1.514
Mercury chloride (ic)	$HgCl_2$	1.725, 1.859, 1.965
Cyanide (ic)	$Hg(CN)_2$	1.645, 1.492
Iodide (ic) (red)	HgI_2	2.748, 2.455
Nickel ammonium selenate	$Ni(NH_4)_2 \cdot (SeO_4)_2 \cdot 6H_2O$	1.5291, 1.5372, 1.5466
Cesium sulfate	$NiCs_2(SO_4)_2 \cdot 6H_2O$	1.5087, 1.5129, 1.5162
Nickel chloride	$NiCl_2 \cdot 6H_2O$	α1.535, γ1.61
Fluoride, acid	$NiF_2 \cdot 5HF \cdot 6H_2O$	1.392, 1.408
Potassium selenate	$NiK_2(SeO_4)_2 \cdot 6H_2O$	1.5199, 1.5248, 1.5339
Rubidium sulfate	$NiRb_2(SO_4)_2 \cdot 6H_2O$	1.4895, 1.4961, 1.505
Selenate	$NiSeO_4 \cdot 6H_2O$	1.5393, 1.5125
Platinum potassium dibromonitrite	$PtK_2(NO_2)_2Br_2 \cdot H_2O$	1.626, 1.6684, 1.757
Potassium carbonate	K_2CO_3	1.426, 1.531, 1.541
Carbonate acid	$KHCO_3$	1.380, 1.482, 1.578
*Per*chlorate	$KClO_4$	1.4731, 1.4737, 1.4769
Chloroplatinate	K_2PtCl_6	1.827 (577 mμ)

Table 4.5–23 (*Continued*) INDEX OF REFRACTION

Name	Formula	Index
Chloroplatinite	K_2PtCl_4	1.64, 1.67
*Di*chromate	$K_2Cr_2O_7$	1.7202, 1.7380, 1.8197
Cyanide	KCN	1.410
Fluoborate	KBF_4	1.3239, 1.3245, 1.3247
Fluoride	KF	1.352 (1.361)
Fluoride	$KF{\cdot}2H_2O$	1.345, 1.352, 1.363
Fluosilicate	K_2SiF_6	1.3391
*Per*iodate	KIO_4	1.6205, 1.6479
Lithium ferrocyanide	$K_2Li_2Fe(CN)_6{\cdot}3H_2O$	1.5883, 1.6007, 1.6316
*Hypo*phosphate	$K_2H_2P_2O_6{\cdot}2H_2O$	1.4893, 1.5314, 1.5363
*Hypo*phosphate	$K_2H_2P_2O_6{\cdot}3H_2O$	1.4768, 1.4843, 1.4870
Ruthenium cyanide	$K_4Ru(CN)_6{\cdot}3H_2O$	β1.5837
Silicate	K_2SiO_3	1.520, 1.521, 1.528
Thiocyanate	KCNS	1.532, 1.660, 1.730
Thionate, tetra-	$K_2S_4O_6$	1.5896, 1,6057, 1.6435
Thionate, penta-	$2K_2S_5O_6{\cdot}3H_2O$	1.565, 1.63, 1.655
Rhodium cesium sulfate	$RhCs(SO_4)_2{\cdot}12H_2O$	1.5077
Rubidium *per*chlorate	$RbClO_4$	1.4692, 1.4701, 1.4731
Chromate	Rb_2CrO_4	β1.71, γ1.72
Dithionate	$Rb_2S_2O_6$	1.4574, 1.5078
Fluoride	RbF	1.396
Selenate	Rb_2SeO_4	1.5515, 1.5537, 1.5582
Ruthenium sodium nitrate	$RuNa_2(NO_2)_5{\cdot}2H_2O$	1.5889, 1.5943, 1.7163
Selenium oxide	SeO_2	>1.76
Silver cyanide	AgCN	1.685, 1.94
Nitrate	$AgNO_3$	1.729, 1.744, 1.788
Phosphate	Ag_2HPO_4	1.8036, 1.7983
Potassium cyanide	$AgK(CN)_2$	1.625, 1.63
Sodium ammonium tartrate (*d*)	$NaNH_4(C_4H_4O_6){\cdot}4H_2O$	1.495, 1.498, 1.499
Ammonium tartrate (*dl*)	$NaNH_4(C_4H_4O_6){\cdot}H_2O$	β1.473 (red)
*Ortho*arsenate	$NaH_2AsO_4{\cdot}H_2O$	1.5382, 1.5535, 1.5607
*Ortho*arsenate	$NaH_2AsO_4{\cdot}2H_2O$	1.4794, 1.5021, 1.5265
Bromide	NaBr	1.6412
Carbonate	Na_2CO_3	1.415, 1.535, 1.546
Sodium carbonate, acid	$NaHCO_3$	1.376, 1.500, 1.582
Cyanide	NaCN	1.452
Iodide	NaI	1.7745
Molybdate	$3Na_2O{\cdot}7MoO_3{\cdot}22H_2O$	β1.627
Nitrate	$NaNO_3$	1.5874, 1.3361
Phosphate	$NaH_2PO_4{\cdot}2H_2O$	1.4401, 1.4629, 1.4815
Phosphate	$Na_2HPO_4{\cdot}7H_2O$	1.4412, 1.4424, 1.4526
*Hypo*phosphate	$Na_3HP_2O_6{\cdot}9H_2O$	1.4653, 1.4738, 1.4804
Silicate	Na_2SiO_3	1.513, 1.520, 1.528
Sulfate, acid	$NaHSO_4{\cdot}H_2O$	1.43, 1.46, 1.47
Sulfite	Na_2SO_3	1.565, 1.515
Sulfite acid	$NaHSO_3$	1.474, 1.526, 1.685
Tartrate, acid (*d*)	$NaH(C_4H_4O_6){\cdot}H_2O$	β1.533
Thiocyanate	NaCNS	1.545, 1.625, 1.695
Sodium tungstate	$Na_2WO_4{\cdot}2H_2O$	1.5526, 1.5533, 1.5695
Vanadate	$Na_3VO_4{\cdot}10H_2O$	1.5305, ω1.5398, ϵ1.5475
Vanadate	$Na_3VO_4{\cdot}12H_2O$	1.5095, 1.5232

Table 4.5–23 (*Continued*)
INDEX OF REFRACTION

Name	Formula	Index
Strontium dichromate	$SrCr_2O_7 \cdot 3H_2O$	1.7146, 1.7174, 1.812
Fluoride	SrF_2	1.442 (1.438)
Oxide	SrO	1.870
*Ortho*phosphate, acid	$SrHPO_4$	1.608, 1.62±, 1.625
Sulfide, mono-	SrS	2.107
Sulfur nitride	S_4N_4	α1.908, β2.046
Thallium chloride, mono-	$TlCl$	2.247
Iodide, mono-	TlI	2.78
Tin, iodide (ic)	SnI_4	2.106
Uranyl potassium sulfate	$UO_2 \cdot SO_4 \cdot K_2SO_4 \cdot 2H_2O$	1.5144, 1.5266, 1.5705 (580 mμ)
Vanadium ammonium sulfate	$VNH_4(SO_4)_2 \cdot 12H_2O$	1.475
Zinc ammonium selenate	$Zn(SeO_4) \cdot (NH_4)_2SeO_4 \cdot 6H_2O$	1.5240, 1.5300, 1.5385
Bromate	$Zn(BrO_3)_2 \cdot 6H_2O$	1.5452
Cesium sulfate	$ZnCs_2(SO_4)_2 \cdot 6H_2O$	1.5022, 1.5048, 1.5093
Chloride	$ZnCl_2$	1.687, 1.713
Fluosilicate	$ZnSiF_6 \cdot 6H_2O$	1.3824, 1.3956
Potassium cyanide	$ZnK_2(CN)_4$	1.4115
Potassium selenate	$ZnK_2(SeO_4)_2 \cdot 6H_2O$	1.5121, 1.5181, 1.5335
Potassium sulfate	$ZnK_2(SO_4)_2 \cdot 6H_2O$	1.4775, 1.4833, 1.4969
Rubidium sulfate	$ZnRb_2(SO_4)_2 \cdot 6H_2O$	1.4833, 1.4884, 1.4975
Silicate	$ZnSiO_3$	1.616, 1.62±, 1.623
Zirconium ammonium fluoride	$Zr(NH_4)_3F_7$	1.433

Organic Compounds

Name	Index
Allantoin, solid	α1.579, γ1.660
Dimethyl thiophene (α, α′), liq	$1.51693^{13.4}$ (He)
Dimethyl thiophene (β, β′), liq	1.52217^{15} (He)
Ethyl carbylamine, liq	1.3659^{24}
Ethylidene cyanhydrin, liq	$1.40582^{18.4}$
Hexyl acetylene (n), liq	$1.4208^{12.5}$

Miscellaneous

Name	Index
Albite glass	1.4890
Amber	1.546
Anorthite glass	1.5755
Asphalt	1.635
Bell metal	1.0052
Borax, amorphous, fused	1.4630
Canada balsam	1.530
Ebonite	1.66 (red)
Fuchsin	2.70
Gelatin, Nelson's No. 1	1.530
Gelatin, various	1.516–1.534
Gum arabic	1.480 (1.514) (red)
Hoffman's violet	2.20
Ivory	1.539, 1.541
Magdala red	1.90
Obsidian	1.482–1.496
Paraffin	$1.43295^{38.3}$ (C)
Quartz, fused	1.45640 (656 mμ)
	1.45843 (589 mμ)
	1.46190 (509 mμ)
	1.47503 (361 mμ)

Table 4.5–23 (*Continued*)
INDEX OF REFRACTION

Name	Formula		Index
	1.49634 (275 mμ)	Colophony	1.548 (red)
	1.53386 (214 mμ)	Copal	1.528 (red)
	1.57464 (185 mμ)	Mastic	1.535 (red)
Resin, aloes	1.619 (red)	Peru balsam	1.593

(From Weast, Robert C., Ed., *CRC Handbook of Chemistry and Physics,* 50th ed., Chemical Rubber Co., Cleveland, 1969. With permission.)

Table 4.5–24
INDEX OF REFRACTION OF ORGANIC COMPOUNDS

Compound	N_D	Compound	N_D
Trifluoroacetic acid	1.283	2-Methylhexane	1.382
2,2,2-Trifluoroethanol	1.290	Butyronitrile	1.382
Octofluoropentanol-1	1.316	Propyl acetate	1.382
Dodecafluoroheptanol-1	1.316	Ethyl propionate	1.382
Methanol	1.326	2-Methyl-2-propanol	1.383
Acetonitrile	1.342	1-Propanol	1.383
Ethyl ether	1.352	Isobutyl formate	1.383
Acetone	1.357	Diethyl carbonate	1.383
Ethyl formate	1.358	Heptane	1.385
Ethanol	1.359	1-Methyl-2-propanol	1.385
Methyl acetate	1.360	Propionic acid	1.385
Propionitrile	1.363	3-Methylhexane	1.386
2,2-Dimethylbutane	1.366	*n*-Propyl amine	1.386
Isopropyl ether	1.367	1,1-Dimethyl-2-propanone	1.386
2-Methylpentane	1.369	1-Chloropropane	1.386
Ethyl acetate	1.370	2,2,3-Trimethylbutane	1.387
Acetic acid	1.370	Methylpropyl ketone	1.387
Propionaldehyde	1.371	*sec*-Butyl acetate	1.387
n-Hexane	1.372	Butyl formate	1.387
2,3-Dimethylbutane	1.372	β-Methylpropyl ethanoate	1.388
3-Methylpentane	1.374	2,2,4-Trimethyl pentane	1.389
2-Propanol	1.375	2,3-Dimethyl pentane	1.389
Isopropyl acetate	1.375	Acetic anhydride	1.389
Propyl formate	1.375	Diisopropyl amine	1.390
2-Chloropropane	1.376	2-Aminobutane	1.390
2-Butanone	1.377	2-Pentanone	1.390
2-Chloropropane	1.377	3-Pentanone	1.390
Methyl Butyraldehyde ethyl ketone	1.377	Nitroethane	1.390
Butyraldehyde	1.378	Methyl-b-butyrate	1.391
2,4-Dimethylpentane	1.379	Butyl acetate	1.392
Propyl ether	1.379	2-Nitropropane	1.392
Acetaldehyde-diethylacetal	1.379	4-Methyl-2-pentanone	1.394
Butylethyl ether	1.380	2-Methyl-1-propanol	1.394
Nitromethane	1.380	Octane	1.395
Trifluoropropanol	1.381	1-Amino-2-methylpropane	1.395

Note: This table contains a list of organic compounds arranged in order of increasing refractive index. Measurements were made at 25°C.

Table 4.5–25 (*Continued*)

Compound	N_D	Compound	N_D
Valeronitrile	1.395	2-Methyl-1-butanol	1.409
2-Butanol	1.395	Butyric acid anhydride	1.409
2-Hexanone	1.395	Amyl ether	1.410
5-Methyl-3-hexanone	1.395	Isoamyl isovalerate	1.410
2-Chlorobutane	1.395	1-Chloropentane	1.410
Butyric acid	1.396	2-Propene-1-ol	1.411
2,2,2-Trimethylhexane	1.397	2,4-Dimethyl dioxane	1.412
n-Dibutyl ether	1.397	Ethyl lactate	1.412
1-Butanol	1.397	Diethyl malonate	1.412
Acrolein	1.397	3-Chloropropene	1.413
1-Chloro-2-methylpropane	1.397	Ethyleneglycol diacetate	1.413
Methacrylonitrile	1.398	2-Octanone	1.414
3-Methyl-2-pentanone	1.398	3-Octanone	1.414
Triethyl amine	1.399	3-Methyl-2-heptanone	1.415
n-Butyl amine	1.399	Caproic acid	1.415
1,1,3,3-Tetramethyl-2-propanone	1.399	4-Methyldioxane	1.415
Isobutyl-*n*-butyrate	1.399	1,2-Propyleneglycol-1-monobutyl ether	1.415
1-Nitropropane	1.399	Ethylcyanoacetate	1.415
n-Dodecane	1.400	Dibutylamine	1.416
Amyl acetate	1.400	2-Pentanol	1.416
1-Chlorobutane	1.400	1,1-Dichloroethane	1.416
2-Methoxy ethanol	1.400	Heptachlorodiethyl ether	1.416
Propionic acid anhydride	1.400	1-Hexanol	1.416
2,2,3-Trimethylpentane	1.401	1-Amino-3-methoxy propane	1.417
1-Chlorobutane	1.401	Octyl nitrole	1.418
β-Methoxypropionitrile	1.401	2-Heptanol	1.418
3-Methyl butanoic acid	1.402	2-Propenyl amine	1.419
n-Nonane	1.403	1,2-Propyleneglycol carbonate	1.419
Dipropylamine	1.403	Methylpentyl carbinol	1.420
Isoamylacetate	1.403	2-Ethyl-1-butanol	1.420
Cyclopentane	1.404	1-Chloro-2-methyl-1-propene	1.420
2-Methyl-2 butanol	1.404	*p*-Dioxane	1.420
3-Methyl-1-butanol	1.404	Methylcyclohexane	1.421
Tetrahydrofuran	1.404	4-Hydroxy-4-methyl-2-pentanone	1.421
Capronitrile	1.405	1-Heptanol	1.422
2-Pentanone	1.405	3-Isopropyl-2-heptanone	1.423
2-Ethoxyethanol	1.405	Cyclohexane	1.424
2-Heptanone	1.406	2-Bromopropane	1.424
Valeric acid	1.406	3-Chloro-2-methylprop-1-ene	1.425
Diisobutylene	1.407	Caproic acid	1.426
Methylcyclopentane	1.407	Glycol carbonate	1.426
Isoamyl ether	1.407	1-Octanol	1.427
Methylpropyl carbinol	1.407	1,1-Dimethylhexanol	1.427
Tributyl borate	1.407	*N,N*-Dimethylformamide	1.427
1-Pentanol	1.408	Sulfuric acid	1.427
3-Methyl-2-butanol	1.408	1-Chlorooctane	1.428
Diethyl oxalate	1.408	Triisobutylene	1.429
n-Decane	1.409	*N*-Methylaniline nitrile	1.429
4-Methyl-2-pentanol	1.409	Ethylene glycol	1.429
3-Isopropyl-2-pentanone	1.409	1-Chloro-2-ethylhexane	1.430

Table 4.5–24 (*Continued*)

Compound	N_D
Ethylcyclohexane	1.431
1,2-Propanediol	1.431
1-Bromopropane	1.431
2-Methyl-7-ethyl-4-nonanone	1.433
Ethyleneglycol-mono-allyl ether	1.434
Butyral lactone	1.434
2-Methyl-7-ethyl-4-undecanone	1.435
4-*n*-Propyl-5-ethyldioxane	1.435
1,2-Dichloro-2-methylpropane	1.435
1,2-Propyleneglycol sulfite	1.435
N-Methylmorpholine	1.436
1-Chloro-2-methyl-2-propanol	1.436
Epichlorohydrin	1.436
Triethyleneglycol-mono-butyl ether	1.437
4-Ethyl-7,7,7-trimethyl-1-heptanol	1.438
1-Methyl-3-ethyloctan-1-ol	1.438
1-Ethyl-3-ethylhexan-1-ol	1.438
Diethyl maleate	1.438
1-Butanethiol	1.440
2-Chloroethanal	1.440
Dibutyl sebacate	1.440
1-Ethyl-3-ethyloctan-1-ol	1.441
Dimethylmaleate	1.441
3-Methylpentane-2,4-diol	1.441
Ethyl sulfide	1.442
Mesityl oxide	1.442
Butyl stearate	1.442
Cyclohexane	1.443
1,2-Dichloroethane	1.444
Chloroform	1.444
trans-1,2-Dichloroethylene	1.444
Diethyleneglycol	1.445
cis-1,2-Dichloroethylene	1.445
3-(*α*-Butyloctyl)-oxypropyl-1-amine	1.446
2-Methylmorpholine	1.446
Dipropyleneglycol-monoethyl ether	1.446
Formamide	1.446
3-Lauryloxypropyl-1-amine	1.447
Cyclohexanone	1.448
1-Aminopropan-1-ol	1.448
Diethyleneglycol-mono-*β*-oxypropyl ether	1.448
1-Amino-2-methylpentan-1-ol	1.449
Tetrahydrofurfural alcohol	1.450
2-Propylcyclohexa-1-one	1.452
2-Aminoethanol	1.452
2-Butylcyclohexan-1-one	1.453
Ethylenediamine	1.454
2-(*β*-Methyl)-propylcyclohexan-1-one	1.454
4-Methylcyclohexanol	1.454
3-Methylcyclohexanol	1.455
bis-2-Chloroethyl ether	1.455
Cyclohexylamine	1.456
1,8-Cineol	1.456
2,2′-Dimethyl-2,2′-dipropyldiethanol amine	1.456
1,1′,2,2′-Tetramethyldiethanol amine	1.459
1-Aminopropan-3-ol	1.459
Carbon tetrachloride	1.459
3-Methyl-5-ethylheptan-2,4-diol	1.459
2-(*β*-Ethyl)-butylcyclohexan-1-one	1.461
2-Methylcyclohexanol	1.461
N-(*n*-Butyl)-diethanol amine	1.461
4,5-Chloro-1,3-dioxolane-2	1.461
2-Butylcyclohexan-1-ol	1.462
N-*β*-Oxypropyl morpholine	1.462
2-(*β*-Ethyl)-hexylcyclohexanone	1.463
2-Ethylcyclohexan-1-ol	1.463
Fluorobenzene	1.463
d-*α*-Pinene	1.464
1-*α*-Pinene	1.465
Cyclohexanol	1.465
m-Fluorotoluene	1.465
p-Fluorotoluene	1.467
trans-Decahydronaphthalene	1.468
o-Fluorotoluene	1.468
3-Alloxy-2-oxypropylamine-1	1.469
Ethanol-1-methylisopropanol amine	1.470
d-Limonene	1.471
1,2,3-Trichloroisobutane	1.473
Decahydronaphthalene	1.474
1,2,3-Propanetriol	1.474
Trichloroethylene	1.475
N-*β*-Oxyethylmorpholine	1.476
Dimethylsulfoxide	1.476
cis-Decahydronaphthalene	1.479
N-*β*-Chlorallylmorpholine	1.481
n-Dodecyl-4-tertiarybutylphenyl ether	1.482
n-Dodecylphenyl ether	1.482
n-Dodecyl-4-methylphenyl ether	1.483
2-Ethylidene cyclohexanone	1.486
n-Butylbenzene	1.487
p-Cymene	1.488
iso-Propylbenzene	1.489
Furfuralcohol	1.489
tert-Butylcumene	1.490
n-Propylbenzene	1.490
sec-Butylbenzene	1.490
tert-Butylbenzene	1.490
Dibutylphthalate	1.490
tert-Butyltoluene	1.491
1-Penyl-1-oxyphenylethane	1.491
n-Hexylcumene	1.492

Table 4.5–24 (*Continued*)

Compound	N_D
n-Octyltoluene	1.492
n-Octylcumene	1.492
p-Xylene	1.493
1,31-Diethylbenzene	1.493
Ethylbenzene	1.493
1,3-Dimorpholylpropan-2-ol	1.493
1,12,2-Tetrachloroethane	1.493
Toluene	1.494
Benzylethyl ether	1.494
m-Xylene	1.495
1,4-Diethylbenzene	1.496
2,3-Dichlorodioxane	1.496
Mesitylene	1.497
2-Iodopropane	1.497
Benzene	1.498
Propyl benzoate	1.498
α-Picoline	1.499
1,2-Diethylbenzene	1.501
Pentachloroethane	1.501
1-Iodopropane	1.502
1,2-Dimethylbenzene	1.503
Ethyl benzoate	1.503
β-Picoline	1.504
Tetrachloroethylene	1.504
Phenetole	1.505
Pyridine	1.507
Iodoethane	1.512
Phenylmethallyl ether	1.514
Anisole	1.515
Methyl benzoate	1.515
Diallylphthalate	1.517
Benzylacetate	1.518
2-Methyl-4-tertiarybutylphenetol	1.521
Phenylacetonitrile	1.521
Methyl salicylate	1.522
Chlorobenzene	1.522
Furfural	1.524
Benzonitrile	1.526
Thiophene	1.526
Nonachlorodiethyl ether	1.529
Iodomethane	1.530
4-Phenyldioxane	1.530
3-Phenylpropan-1-ol	1.532
Acetophenone	1.532
Benzyl alcohol	1.538
1,2-Dibromoethane	1.538
1,2,3,4-Tetrahydronaphthalene	1.539
m-Cresol	1.542
1,3-Dichlorobenzene	1.543
Benzaldehyde	1.544
Styrene	1.545
Nitrobenzene	1.550
o-Dichlorobenzene	1.551
Bromobenzene	1.557
o-Nitroanisole	1.560
m-Toluidine	1.566
Benzyl benzoate	1.568
o-Toluidine	1.570
1-Methoxyphenyl-1-phenyl-ethane	1.571
Aniline	1.583
o-Chloroaniline	1.586
Bromoform	1.587
Benzenethiol	1.588
2,4-Bis(β-phenylethyl)-phenylmethyl ether	1.590
Carbondisulfide	1.628
1,12,2-Tetrabromomethane	1.633
Diiodomethane	1.749

(From Weast, Robert C., Ed., *CRC Handbook of Chemistry and Physics*, 50th ed., Chemical Rubber Co., Cleveland, 1969. With permission.)

Table 4.5–25
MOLAR REFRACTION OF ORGANIC COMPOUNDS

The molar refraction, R, is defined as:

$$R = \frac{n^2 - 1}{n^2 + 2} \quad \frac{M}{d}$$

where n = refractive index; M = molecular weight; d = density in g/cm^3; and (M/d) is the volume occupied by 1 g mol wt of the compound. The units of R will then be cm^3.

R is, to a first approximation, independent of temperature or physical state, and it provides an approximate measure of the actual total volume (without free space) of the molecules in one gram mole.

For a very large number of compounds R is approximately additive for the bonds present in the molecule. Using R_D based on n_D (sodium light), the following atomic, group and structural contributions to R_D are based on Vogel's extensive modern measurements published in the *Journal of the Chemical Society*, 1948.

C	2.591	Cl	5.844	=S	7.921
H	1.028	Br	8.741	C≡N	5.459
=O	2.122	I	13.954	N (primary aliphatic)	2.376
\O/	1.643	C_6H_5	25.463	N (secondary aliphatic)	2.582
OH	2.553	$C_{10}H_7$	43.00		
F	0.81	\S/	7.729		

Ethylenic bond	1.575	Four membered ring	0.317
Acetylenic bond	1.977	Three membered ring	0.614
N (aromatic)	3.550		

Example: For C_2H_5COOH: $R_{calc.}$ = 3(2.591) + 5(1.028) + 2.122 + 2.553 = 17.588

$R_{obs.}$ for this compound is 17.51

For $C_6H_5NHCH_3$: $R_{calc.}$ = 25.463 + 3.550 + 2.591 + 4(1.028) = 35.716

$R_{obs.}$ for this compound is 35.67.

(From Weast, Robert C., Ed., *CRC Handbook of Chemistry and Physics,* 50th ed., Chemical Rubber Co., Cleveland, 1969. With permission.)

Table 4.5–26
INDEX OF REFRACTION OF WATER

Alcohol and Carbon Bisulfide
For sodium light, λ = .5893

Temp, °C	Water, pure relative to air	Ethyl alcohol 99.8 relative to air	Carbon bisulfide relative to air
14	1.33348	–	–
15	1.33341	–	1.62935
16	1.33333	1.36210	1.62858
18	1.33317	1.36129	1.62704
20	1.33299	1.36048	1.62546
22	1.33281	1.35967	1.62387
24	1.33262	1.35885	1.62226
26	1,33241	1.35803	1.62064
28	1.33219	1.35721	1.61902
30	1.33192	1.35639	1.61740
32	1.33164	1.35557	1.61577
34	1.33136	1.35474	1.61413
36	1.33107	1.35390	1.61247
38	1.33079	1.35306	1.61080
40	1.33051	1.35222	1.60914
42	1.33023	1.35138	1.60748
44	1.32992	1.35054	1.60582
46	1.32959	1.34969	–
48	1.32927	1.34885	–
50	1.32894	1.34800	–
52	1.32860	1.34715	–
54	1.32827	1.34629	–
56	1.32792	1.34543	–
58	1.32755	1.34456	–
60	1.32718	1.34368	–
62	1.32678	1.34279	–
64	1.32636	1.34189	–
66	1.32596	1.34096	–
68	1.32555	1.34004	–
70	1.32511	1.33912	–
72	1.32466	1.33820	–
74	1.32421	1.33728	–
76	1.32376	1.33626	–
78	1.32332	–	–
80	1.32287	–	–
82	1.32241	–	–
84	1.32195	–	–
86	1.32148	–	–
88	1.32100	–	–
90	1.32050	–	–
92	1.32000	–	–
94	1.31949	–	–
96	1.31897	–	–
98	1.31842	–	–
100	1.31783	–	–

(From Weast, Robert C., Ed., *CRC Handbook of Chemistry and Physics,* 50th ed., Chemical Rubber Co., Cleveland, 1969. With permission.)

Table 4.5–27
ABSOLUTE INDEX FOR PURE WATER FOR SODIUM LIGHT

Temp, °C	Index	Temp °C	Index
15	1.33377	60	1.32754
20	1.33335	65	1.32652
25	1.33287	70	1.32547
30	1.33228	75	1.32434
35	1.33157	80	1.32323
40	1.33087	85	1.32208
45	1.33011	90	1.32086
50	1.32930	95	1.31959
55	1.32846	100	1.31819

(From Weast, Robert C., Ed., *CRC Handbook of Chemistry and Physics,* 50th ed., Chemical Rubber Co., Cleveland, 1969. With permission.)

Table 4.5–28
INDEX OF REFRACTION OF GLASS
Relative to Air

Variety	Wavelength in microns .361	.434	.486	.589 (Na)	.656	.768	1.20	2.00
Zinc crown	1.539	1.528	1.523	1.517	1.514	1.511	1.505	1.497
Higher dispersion crown	1.546	1.533	1.527	1.520	1.517	1.514	1.507	1.497
Light flint	1.614	1.594	1.585	1.575	1.571	1.567	1.559	1.549
Heavy flint	1.705	1.675	1.664	1.650	1.644	1.638	1.628	1.617
Heaviest flint	–	1.945	1.919	1.890	1.879	1.867	1.848	1.832

(From Weast, Robert C., Ed., *CRC Handbook of Chemistry and Physics,* 50th ed., Chemical Rubber Co., Cleveland, 1969. With permission.)

Table 4.5–29
INDEX OF REFRACTION OF ROCK SALT, SYLVINE, CALCITE, FLUORITE AND QUARTZ

Wave-length	Rock salt	Sylvine, KCl	Fluorite	Calcspar, ordinary ray	Calcspar, extraor-dinary ray	Quartz, ordinary ray	Quartz, extraor-dinary ray
0.185	1.893	1.827	–	–	–	1.676	1.690
0.198	–	–	1.496	–	1.578	1.651	1.664
0.340	–	–	–	1.701	1.506	1.567	1.577
0.589	1.544	1.490	1.434	1.658	1.486	1.544	1.553
0.760	–	–	1.431	1.650	1.483	1.539	1.548
0.884	1.534	1.481	1.430				
1.179	1.530	1.478	1.428				
1.229	–	–	–	1.639	1.479		
2.324	–	–	–	–	1.474	1.516	
2.357	1.526	1.475	1.421				
3.536	1.523	1.473	1.414				
5.893	1.516	1.469	1.387				
8.840	1.502	1.461	1.331				

(From Weast, Robert C., Ed., *CRC Handbook of Chemistry and Physics,* 50th ed., Chemical Rubber Co., Cleveland, 1969. With permission.)

Table 4.5–30
INDEX OF REFRACTION – AQUEOUS SOLUTIONS

Substance	Density	Temp, °C	Index for λ = .5893 (Na)	Observer
Ammonium chloride	1.067	27.05	1.379	Willigen
Ammonium chloride	1.025	29.75	1.351	Willigen
Calcium chloride	1.398	25.65	1.443	Willigen
Calcium chloride	1.215	22.9	1.397	Willigen
Calcium chloride	1.143	25.8	1.374	Willigen
Hydrochloric acid	1.166	20.75	1.411	Willigen
Nitric acid	1.359	18.75	1.402	Willigen
Potash (caustic)	1.416	11.0	1.403	Frauenhofer
Potassium chloride	Normal solution		1.343	Bender
Potassium chloride	Double normal		1.352	Bender
Potassium chloride	Triple normal		1.360	Bender
Soda (caustic)	1.376	21.6	1.413	Willigen
Sodium chloride	1.189	18.07	1.378	Schutt
Sodium chloride	1.109	18.07	1.360	Schutt
Sodium chloride	1.035	18.07	1.342	Schutt
Sodium nitrate	1.358	22.8	1.385	Willigen
Sulfuric acid	1.811	18.3	1.437	Willigen
Sulfuric acid	1.632	18.3	1.425	Willigen
Sulfuric acid	1.221	18.3	1.370	Willigen
Sulfuric acid	1.028	18.3	1.339	Willigen
Zinc chloride	1.359	26.6	1.402	Willigen
Zinc chloride	1.209	26.4	1.375	Willigen

(From Weast, Robert C., Ed., *CRC Handbook of Chemistry and Physics,* 50th ed. Chemical Rubber Co., Cleveland, 1969. With permission.)

Table 4.5–31
INDEX OF REFRACTION OF FUSED QUARTZ

λ mμ, 15°C	*n*, 18°C	λ mμ, 15°C	*n*, 18°C
185.467	1.57436	434.047	1.46690
193.583	1.55999	435.834	1.46675
202.55	1.54727	467.815	1.46435
214.439	1.53386	479.991	1.46355
219.462	1.52907	486.133	1.46318
226.503	1.52308	508.582	1.46191
231.288	1.51941	533.85	1.46067
250.329	1.50745	546.072	1.46013
257.304	1.50379	589.29	1.45845
274.867	1.49617	643.847	1.45674
303.412	1.48594	656.278	1.45640
340.365	1.47867	706.520	1.45517
396.848	1.47061	794.763	1.45340
404.656	1.46968		

(From Weast, Robert C., Ed., *CRC Handbook of Chemistry and Physics,* 50th ed., Chemical Rubber Co., Cleveland, 1969. With permission.)

Table 4.5–32
INDEX OF REFRACTION OF AIR

15°C, 76 cm Hg

The indices were computed from the Cauchy formula $(n - 1)10^7 = 2726.43 + 12.288/(\lambda^2 \times 10^{-8}) + 0.3555/(\lambda^4 \times 10^{-16})$. For 0°C and 76 cm Hg the constants of the equation become 2875.66, 13.412 and 0.3777 respectively, and for 30°C and 76 cm Hg 2589.72, 12.259 and 0.2576. Sellmeier's formula for but one absorption band closely fits the observations: $n^2 = 1 + 0.00057378\lambda^2/(\lambda^2 - 595260)$. If $n - 1$ were strictly proportional to the density, then $(n - 1)_0/(n - 1)t$ would equal $1 + \alpha t$ where α should be 0.00367. The following values of α were found to hold:

λ	0.85μ	0.75μ	0.65μ	0.55μ	0.45μ	0.35μ	0.25μ
α	0.003672	0.003674	0.003678	0.003685	0.003700	0.003738	0.003872

The indices are for dry air (0.05 ± % CO_2). Corrections to reduce to dry air the indices for moist air may be made for any wavelength by Lorenz's formula +0.000041 (m/760), where m is the vapor pressure in mm. The corresponding frequencies in waves per cm and the corrections to reduce wavelengths and frequencies in air at 15°C and 76 cm Hg pressure to vacuo are given. For example, a light wave of 5000 angstroms in dry air at 15°C, 76 cm Hg becomes 5001.391 A in vacuo; a frequency of 20.000 waves per cm correspondingly becomes 19994.44.

Wave-length, λ ang-stroms	Dry air $(n - 1) \times 10^7$ 15°C 76 cm Hg	Vacuo correc-tion for λ in air $(n\lambda - \lambda)$ add	Fre-quency waves/cm $\frac{1}{\lambda}$ in air	Vacuo correction for $\frac{1}{\lambda}$ in air $\left(\frac{1}{n\lambda} - \frac{1}{\lambda}\right)$ subtract	Wave-length, λ ang-stroms	Dry air $(n - 1) \times 10^7$ 15°C 76 cm Hg	Vacuo correc-tion for λ in air $(n\lambda - \lambda)$ add	Fre-quency waves/cm $\frac{1}{\lambda}$ in air	Vacuo correction for λ in air $\left(\frac{1}{n\lambda} - \frac{1}{\lambda}\right)$ subtract
2000	3256	.651	50,000	16.27	4500	2796	1.258	22,222	6.21
2100	3188	.670	47,619	15.18	4600	2792	1.284	21,739	6.07
2200	3132	.689	45,454	14.23	4700	2789	1.311	21,276	5.93
2300	3086	.710	43,478	13.41	4800	2786	1.338	20,833	5.80
2400	3047	.731	41,666	12.69	4900	2784	1.364	20,406	5.68
2500	3014	.754	40,000	12.05	5000	2781	1.391	20,000	5.56
2600	2986	.776	38,461	11.48	5100	2779	1.417	19,607	5.45
2700	2962	.800	37,037	10.97	5200	2777	1.444	19,230	5.34
2800	2941	.824	35,714	10.50	5300	2775	1.471	18,867	5.23
2900	2923	.848	34,482	10.08	5400	2773	1.497	18,518	5.13
3000	2907	.872	33,333	9.69	5500	2771	1.524	18,181	5.04
3100	2893	.897	32,258	9.33	5600	2769	1.551	17,857	4.94
3200	2880	.922	31,250	9.00	5700	2768	1.578	17,543	4.85
3300	2869	.947	30,303	8.69	5800	2766	1.604	17,241	4.77
3400	2859	.972	29,411	8.41	5900	2765	1.631	16,949	4.68
3500	2850	.998	28,571	8.14	6000	2763	1.658	16,666	4.60
3600	2842	1.023	27,777	7.89	6100	2762	1.685	16,393	4.53
3700	2835	1.049	27,027	7.66	6200	2761	1.712	16,129	4.45
3800	2829	1.075	26,315	7.44	6300	2760	1.739	15,873	4.38
3900	2823	1.101	25,641	7.24	6400	2759	1.766	15,625	4.31
4000	2817	1.127	25,000	7.04	6500	2758	1.792	15,384	4.24
4100	2812	1.153	24,390	6.86	6600	2757	1.819	15,151	4.18
4200	2808	1.179	23,809	6.68	6700	2756	1.846	14.925	4.11
4300	2803	1.205	23,255	6.52	6800	2755	1.873	14,705	4.05
4400	2799	1.232	22,727	6.36	6900	2754	1.900	14,492	3.99

Note: Corrections for reducing wavelengths and frequencies in air (15°C, 76 cm Hg) to vacuo.

Table 4.5–32 (*Continued*)

Wave-length, λ angstroms	Dry air $(n-1) \times 10^7$ 15°C 76 cm Hg	Vacuo correction for λ in air $(n\lambda - \lambda)$ add	Frequency waves/cm $\frac{1}{\lambda}$ in air	Vacuo correction for $\frac{1}{\lambda}$ in air $\left(\frac{1}{n\lambda} - \frac{1}{\lambda}\right)$ subtract	Wave-length, λ angstroms	Dry air $(n-1) \times 10^7$ 15°C 76 cm Hg	Vacuo correction for λ in air $(n\lambda - \lambda)$ add	Frequency waves/cm $\frac{1}{\lambda}$ in air	Vacuo correction for λ in air $\left(\frac{1}{n\lambda} - \frac{1}{\lambda}\right)$ substract
7000	2753	1.927	14,285	3.93	8000	2746	2.197	12,500	3.43
7100	2752	1.954	14,084	3.88	8100	2746	2.224	12,345	3.39
7200	2751	1.981	13,888	3.82	8250	2745	2.265	12,121	3.33
7300	2751	2.008	13,698	3.77	8500	2744	2.332	11,764	3.23
7400	2750	2.035	13,513	3.72	8750	2743	2.400	11,428	3.13
7500	2749	2.062	13,333	3.66	9000	2742	2.468	11,111	3.05
7600	2749	2.089	13,157	3.62	9250	2741	2.536	10,810	2.96
7700	2748	2.116	12,987	3.57	9500	2740	2.604	10,526	2.88
7800	2748	2.143	12,820	3.52	9750	2740	2.671	10,256	2.81
7900	2747	2.170	12,658	3.48	10000	2739	2.739	10,000	2.74

(From Weast, Robert C., Ed., *CRC Handbook of Chemistry and Physics,* 50th ed., Chemical Rubber Co., Cleveland, 1969. With permission.)

Table 4.5–33
INDEX OF REFRACTION – GASES

Substance	Kind of light	Indices of refraction	Observer
Acetone	*D*	1.001079–1.001100	
Air	*D*	1.0002926	Perreau
Ammonia	White	1.000381–1.000385	
Ammonia	*D*	1.000373–1.000379	
Argon	*D*	1.000281	Rayleigh
Benzene	*D*	1.001700–1.001823	
Bromine	*D*	1.001132	Mascart
Carbon dioxide	White	1.000449–1.000450	
Dioxide	*D*	1.000448–1.000454	
Disulfide	White	1.001500	Dulong
Disulfide	*D*	1.001478–1.001485	
Monoxide	White	1.000340	Dulong
Monoxide	White	1.000335	Mascart
Chlorine	White	1.000772	Dulong
Chlorine	*D*	1.000773	Mascart
Chloroform	*D*	1.001436–1.001464	
Cyanogen	White	1.000834	Dulong
Cyanogen	*D*	1.000784–1.000825	
Ethyl alcohol	*D*	1.000871–1.000885	
Ether	*D*	1.001521–1.001544	
Helium	*D*	1.000036	Ramsay
Hydrochloric acid	White	1.000449	Mascart
Hydrochloric acid	*D*	1.000447	Mascart
Hydrogen	White	1.000138–1.000143	

Note: Values are relative to a vacuum and for a temp. of 0°C and 760 mm pressure.

Table 4.5–33 (*Continued*)
INDEX OF REFRACTION – GASES

Substance	Kind of light	Indices of refraction	Observer
Hydrogen	*D*	1.000132	Burton
Sulfide	*D*	1.000644	Dulong
Sulfide	*D*	1.000623	Mascart
Methane	White	1.000443	Dulong
Methane	*D*	1.000444	Mascart
Methyl alcohol	*D*	1.000549–1.000623	
Methyl ether	*D*	1.000891	Mascart
Nitric oxide	White	1.000303	Dulong
Nitric oxide	*D*	1.000297	Mascart
Nitrogen	White	1.000295–1.000300	
Nitrogen	*D*	1.000296–1.000298	
Nitrous oxide	White	1.000503–1.000507	
Nitrous oxide	*D*	1.000516	Mascart
Oxygen	White	1.000272–1.000280	
Oxygen	*D*	1.000271–1.000272	
Pentane	*D*	1.001711	Mascart
Sulfur dioxide	White	1.000665	Dulong
Sulfur dioxide	*D*	1.000686	Ketteler
Water	White	1.000261	Jamin
Water	*D*	1.000249–1.000259	

(From Weast, Robert C., Ed., *CRC Handbook of Chemistry and Physics,* 50th ed., Chemical Rubber Co., Cleveland, 1969. With permission.)

REFERENCE

Forsythe, W. D., Ed., Smithsonian Physical Tables, Smithsonian Institution, Washington, D.C., 1954.

Table 4.5–34
COEFFICIENT OF TRANSPARENCY OF UVIOL GLASS FOR THE ULTRA-VIOLET

Wavelength, μm	0.280	0.309	0.325	0.346	0.361	0.383	0.397
Uviol crown	0.56	0.95	0.990	0.996	0.999	1.000	1.000

Note: For a thickness of 1 mm.

(From Weast, Robert C., Ed., *CRC Handbook of Chemistry and Physics,* 50th ed., Chemical Rubber Co., Cleveland, 1969. With permission.)

Table 4.5–35
SURFACE TENSION OF METALS

Substance	Symbol	Gas	Temp, °C	Surface tension	Ref
Aluminum	Al	–air	700	840	CR 1
Antimony	Sb	$-H_2$	750	368	ZA 2
Antimony	Sb	$-H_2$	640	350	PM 3
Bismuth	Bi	$-H_2$	300	388	PM 3
Bismuth	Bi	$-H_2$	583	354	ZA 2
Bismuth	Bi	–CO	700–800	346	AdP 4
Cadmium	Cd	$-H_2$	320	630	AC 5
Copper	Cu	$-H_2$	1131	1103	ZA 2
Gallium	Ga	$-CO_2$	30	358	AC 6
Gold	Au	$-H_2$	1070	580–1000	AdP 7
					AdP 4
					JI 8
Lead	Pb	$-H_2$	350	453	PM 3
Lead	Pb	$-H_2$	750	423	ZA 2
Mercury	Hg	vac.	0	480.3	AC 9
Mercury	Hg	–air	15	487	AC 10
					AdP 11
					AdP 12
					CR 13
Mercury	Hg	$-H_2$	19	470	PM 3
Mercury	Hg	–vac.	60	467.1	AC 9
Platinum	Pt	–air	2000	1819	AdP 4
Potassium	K	$-CO_2$	62	411	AdP 14
Silver	Ag	–air	970	800	AdP 4
					AdP 15
					JI 8
Sodium	Na	$-CO_2$	90	294	AdP 14
Sodium	Na	–vac.	100	206.4	PR 16
Sodium	Na	–vac.	250	199.5	PR 16
Tin	Sn	$-H_2$	253	526	PM 3
Tin	Sn	$-H_2$	878	508	ZA 2
Zinc	Zn	$-H_2$	477	753	AC 5
Zinc	Zn	–air	590	708	JI 8

(From Hodgman, Charles D., Ed., *Handbook of Chemistry and Physics,* 36th ed., Chemical Rubber Co., Cleveland, 1954, 1989. With permission.)

REFERENCES

1. **Portevin, A. and Bastien, P.,** *Comptes Rendus,* 202, 1072, 1936.
2. **Sauerwald and Drath,** *Z. anorganische allegeime Chemie,* 154, 79, 1926.
3. **Bircumshaw,** *Philos. Mag. and J. of Sci.,* 2, 341, 1926; 3, 1286, 1927.
4. **Quincke,** *Ann. Phys.,* 134, 356, 1968.
5. **Hogness,** *J. Am. Chem. Soc.,* 43, 1621, 1921.
6. **Richards and Boyer,** *J. Am. Chem. Soc.,* 43, 274, 1921.
7. **Heydweiller,** *Ann. Phys.,* 62, 694, 1897.
8. **Smith,** *J. Inst. Metals* (London), 12, 168, 1914.
9. **Harkins and Ewing,** *J. Am. Chem. Soc.,* 42, 2539, 1920.
10. **Harkins and Grafton,** *J. Am. Chem. Soc.,* 42, 2534, 1920.
11. **Meyer,** *Ann. Phys.,* 66, 523, 1898.
12. **Stöckle,** *Ann. Phys.,* 66, 499, 1898.
13. **Popesco,** *Comptes Rendus,* 172, 1474, 1921.
14. **Quincke,** *Ann. Phys.,* 135, 621, 1968.
15. **Gradenwitz,** *Ann. Phys.,* 67, 467, 1899.
16. **Poindexter,** *Phys. Rev.,* 27, 820, 1926.

Section 5

Ocean Engineering

Carl Holm (deceased), Harry DeFerrari, Ph.D.

5.1 Materials for Marine Application

Table 5.1–1
MECHANICAL PROPERTIES OF ALUMINUM ALLOYS

Material	Yield strength, psi X 10^3	Ultimate strength, psi X 10^3	Young's modulus, psi X 10^6	Elongation, %	Density, lb/in.^{3}
5052 H-38	33	39	10.1	4	0.097
2024-T4	8–46	60–65	10.6	6–17	0.100
2014-T6	57–60	63–70	10.5	2–8	0.100
7075-T6	60–72	75–80	10.5	1–5	0.100
7079-T6	57–69	72–77	10.5	2–8	0.100
6061-T6	35	42	10.1	8–10	0.096

(From Myers, J. J., Ed., *Handbook of Ocean and Underwater Engineering,* McGraw-Hill, New York, 1969. With permission.)

Table 5.1–2
COMPOSITION AND PHYSICAL PROPERTIES OF VARIOUS BRASSES

Name	Nominal composition, %		Modulus of elasticity, psi	Tensile strength, psi	Yield strength, psi
Inhibited admiralty	Cu	71	16 X 16^6	90,000 hard	70,000 hard
	Sn	1		48,000 soft	18,000 soft
	Zn	28			
Naval brass	Cu	60	15 X 10^6	70,000 hard	58,000 hard
	Sn	0.75		62,000 soft	30,000 soft
	Zn	39.25			
Leaded naval brass	Cu	60	15 X 10^6	90,000 hard	70,000 hard
	Sn	0.75		58,000 soft	20,000 soft
	Pb	1.75			
	Zn	37.5			
Aluminum brass	Cu	76	16 X 10^6	85,000 hard	60,000 hard
	Al	2		60,000 soft	27,000 soft
	Zn	22			

(From Myers, J. J. Ed., *Handbook of Ocean and Underwater Engineering,* McGraw-Hill, New York, 1969. With permission.)

Table 5.1–3
COMPOSITION AND PHYSICAL PROPERTIES OF VARIOUS BRONZES

Name	Nominal composition, %		Modulus of elasticity, psi	Tensile strength, psi	Yield strength, psi
Phosphor bronze, 5%	Cu	95	16 X 10^6	81,000 hard	75,000 hard
	Tin	5		47,000 soft	19,000 soft
Phosphor bronze, 8%	Cu	92	16 X 10^6	93,093 hard	72,000 hard
	Tin	8		55,055 soft	24,000 soft
Phosphor bronze, 10%	Cu	90	16 X 10^6	100,000 hard	
	Tin	10		66,000 soft	28,000 soft
Phosphor bronze, 1.25%	Cu	98.75	17 X 10^6	65,000 hard	50,000 hard
	Tin	1.25		40,000 soft	14,000 soft

(From Myers, J. J., Ed., *Handbook of Ocean and Underwater Engineering*, McGraw-Hill, New York, 1969. With permission.)

Table 5.1–4
MECHANICAL PROPERTIES OF STEELS

Material	Yield strength, psi X 10^3	Ultimate strength, psi X 10^3	Elongation, %	Modulus of elasticity psi X 10^6	Density, lb/in.^{3}
HY-80	80	100	14	29–30	0.28
HY-100	100	120	14	29–30	0.28
HY-140	140–160	–	16	29–30	0.28
T-1	90–110	110–130	14	29–30	0.28
A302 Grade B	70	85	27	29–30	0.28
2.25% Cr-1% Moly	100	120	19	29–30	0.28
H-11	200–220	240–260	5–9	29–30	0.28
4340	210–230	260–280	5–9	29–30	0.28
18 Ni 200	190–225	195–230	6–12	26	0.29
18 Ni 250	240–265	245–270	6–10	27	0.29
HP 9-4-25	220	250	12	29–30	0.29
HP 9-4-45	250	290	7	29–30	0.29
Stainless 301, annealed	40	105	60	28–29	0.28
Stainless 301, half-hard	95	150	54	28–29	0.28
Stainless 316, annealed	38	76	60	28–29	0.28
Stainless 410, annealed	87	110	21	28–29	0.28
Stainless 440 A	240–250	260–270	5	28–29	0.28

(From Myers, J. J., Ed., *Handbook of Ocean and Underwater Engineering*, McGraw-Hill, New York, 1969. With permission.)

Table 5.1–5
MECHANICAL PROPERTIES OF TITANIUM ALLOYS

Material	Yield strength, psi X 10^3	Ultimate strength, psi X 10^3	Young's modulus, psi X 10^6	Elongation, %	Density, lb/in.^{3}
6A1-4V, annealed	120	130	15.5	10	0.16
6A1-4V, heat-treated	150	170	16.4	6	0.16
7A1-2Cb-1Ta	107	120	16.0	13	0.16

(From Myers, J. J., Ed., *Handbook of Ocean and Underwater Engineering*, McGraw-Hill, New York, 1969. With permission.)

Table 5.1–6
MECHANICAL PROPERTIES OF PLASTICS

Material	Ultimate strength, psi X 10^3	Young's modulus, psi X 10^5	Specific gravity
Nylons	7–12	2–4	1.0–1.2
Acrylics	6–11	2–5	1.1–1.2
Acetals	10	5	1.3–1.5
Vinyls	1–9	1–4	1.2–1.8
Polyethylenes	1–4	0.5–1	0.8–1.0
Epoxies	1–30	0.5–4	1.0–2.1
Phenolics	2–10	4–50	1.2–3.0
Polyesters	1–10	1–7	1.1–1.5
Urethanes	5–8	0.5–1	1.2–1.3
Silicones	4–5	25–30	1.7–2.0

(From Myers, J. J., Ed., *Handbook of Ocean and Underwater Engineering*, McGraw-Hill, New York, 1969. With permission.)

Table 5.1–7
MECHANICAL PROPERTIES OF GLASS

Material	Tensile strength, psi X 10^3	Compressive strength, psi X 10^3	Young's modulus, psi X 10^6	Density, lb/in.^{3}
Glass	20–30	300–500 X 10^3	8–16	0.08–0.15
Tempered glass	40–50	300–500 X 10^3	8–16	0.08–0.16

(From Myers, J. J., Ed., *Handbook of Ocean and Underwater Engineering*, McGraw-Hill, New York, 1969. With permission.)

Table 5.1–8
SPECIFIC GRAVITY AND STRENGTH OF COMMONLY USED WOODS

Wood	Moisture content, %	Specific gravity, oven dry	Compressive strength parallel to grain, psi	Compressive strength perpendicular to grain, psi	Tensile strength perpendicular to grain, psi
Ash	43	0.43	2960	310	390
	12		5820	540	420
Balsa	12	0.13	1250	70	115
Hickory	57	0.78	4570	1080	
	12		8970	2310	
Oak, white	70	0.70	3520	850	760
	12		7040	1410	770
Cedar, northern	55	0.32	1990	290	240
	12		3960	380	240
Douglar fir, coast	38	0.51	3860	440	300
	12		7430	870	340
Fir, commercial white	111	0.40	2830	360	310
	12		5480	620	300
Pine, lodgepole	65	0.43	2610	310	220
	12		5370	750	290
Pine, ponderosa	91	0.42	2400	360	290
	12		5270	740	400
Pine, southern	81	0.54	3490	480	260
	12		7080	980	470

(From Myers, J. J., Ed., *Handbook of Ocean and Underwater Engineering*, McGraw-Hill, New York, 1969. With permission.)

Table 5.1–9
COMPARISON OF PROPERTIES OF LOW-DENSITY SOLIDS

Material	Density	Bulk modulus, psi × 10^5	Operating depth
Lithium metal	0.53	22	Unlimited
Wood	0.4–1.3	–	Shallow
Solid (polyethylene polypropylene)	0.9–0.95	2.6	Unlimited
Expanded plastics	Wide range	–	Shallow
Syntactic foam	0.65–0.75	5.5	Probably 20,000 ft

(From Myers, J. J., Ed., *Handbook of Ocean and Underwater Engineering*, McGraw-Hill, New York, 1969. With permission.)

Corrosion Behavior

Aluminum – Selected aluminum alloys are used successfully for long-lived marine structures, provided the proper precautions are taken. These alloys include members of the 5000 and 6000 series, but not unalloyed aluminum (1100) or the 2000 series. The very high strength 7000-series alloys (particularly 7075 and 7079) and being used successfully for intermittent or short-term marine exposures with extremely careful attention to paint coatings supplemented with cathodic protection, such as the use of anode-grade zinc, when practicable. Without such protective measures, the 7000-series alloys are susceptible to layer corrosion and to stress-corrosion cracking.

The aluminum alloy 5086 is virtually inert to clean sea water, but it usually presents a major procurement problem. The alloy 6061 will in most cases probably be selected because of its good fabricability, good balance of strength and toughness, reasonably good resistance to marine corrosion, and ready availability in a wide variety of forms. This alloy pits in sea water at the rate of about 0.01 in./yr, but the pitting can be mitigated, and perhaps even prevented altogether, by painting or providing cathodic protection (using anode-grade zinc or a reliable commercial aluminum anode having about the same potential as zinc), or both.

There are several cautions to be observed in using aluminum alloys successfully in sea water. All the aluminum alloys exhibit such active potentials in sea water that dissimilar-metal corrosion cells can be a serious problem when the aluminum alloys are connected with many of the standard marine alloys. The more common 5000- and 6000-series alloys are compatible, however, with galvanized steel as long as the galvanizing lasts. It is desirable to avoid having corrodible copper alloys in the vicinity of aluminum alloys, even where the two alloy classes are not connected by a metallic conductor; the reason is that copper-corrosion products are carried to the surface of the aluminum by convection, and the copper is reduced and remains on the surface of the aluminum, setting up galvanic cells which greatly accelerate corrosion of the aluminum. Antifouling paints that corrosion copper or mercury compounds are to be avoided for the same reason, even though a barrier coat of vinyl is interposed between the aluminum and the antifouling coat (if an antifouling paint is required, organic tin formulations are preferable to the copper or mercury formulations).

Mud can present special corrosion problems, perhaps because of bacterial action. The firm ocean floor of the Atlantic and the calcareous bottom of the Tongue of the Ocean have not presented such problems, but in an area of the Pacific just off the California coast, where the bottom is described as "green ooze," variable performance has been observed in the normally resistant aluminum alloys. Finally, if it is decided to use cathodic protection, only zinc anodes or reliable aluminum anodes with about the same potential as zinc should be used. One alloy, 5257-H25, has been observed to be more electronegative than zinc in sea water. If there is any doubt that the zinc will actually be negative (anodic) to an unfamiliar alloy, there is no safe substitute for making the determination experimentally in sea water.

Brasses and Bronzes – If a copper alloy contains more than about 15% zinc and does not contain an inhibitor additive such as arsenic, it is susceptible to dezincification in sea water and in the marine atmosphere as well. It is generally considered that the alloys of moderate zinc content, such as admiralty brass (29 percent Zn), can be made resistant to dezincification by the addition of small amounts of arsenic. The higher-zinc alloys, such as Muntz metal, Naval brass, and many manganese bronzes, cannot be satisfactorily inhibited against dezincification. There are unresolved contradictions as to whether cathodic-protection measures are effective in preventing dezincification. For these reasons it is mandatory to exclude the high-zinc alloys (those containing more than 30% zinc) from critical components intended for prolonged service in the sea.

The venerable marine alloys, such as G bronze, the phosphor bronzes, and inhibited admiralty brass (inhibited with arsenic against dezincing), have low susceptibility to crevice corrosion, pitting, and general corrosion (of the order of a 0.001 in./year) at slow relative water velocities. The more recent aluminum bronzes, containing nickel as an inhibitor against dealuminification, have comparable resistance to corrosion.

An argument of some merit for total exclusion of all brasses and bronzes where feasible is the quality-control problem in the fabricator's shops posed by the substitution of uninhibited admiralty for the required inhibited grade, the substitution of a high-zinc bronze for the specified bronze, etc. These substitutions present a problem of detection, and for this reason one would do well in many instances to consider the merits of employing an iron-bearing cupronickel instead of brass or bronze.

Cadmium – Cadmium is often used as a plating to protect steel articles against atmospheric corrosion. It is generally considered to be more compatible with aluminum than is steel or stainless steel (because of its position in the galvanic series), and for this reason it is sometimes specified as a plating for steel or stainless steel fasteners for aluminum structures. Such coatings are invariably thin and must therefore be regarded as a highly temporary measure for sea water service. There is a possibility that because of its solution potential in sea water, cadmium may prove to be a useful anode to provide a limited degree of cathodic protection to high-strength steels for critical structures.

Copper – In clean, quiet sea water, copper is reasonably resistant to corrosion, exhibiting a general surface-recession rate of the order of 0.001 in./year. For sea water moving faster than about 5 ft/sec, copper begins to corrode so rapidly that the cupronickel alloys described below are preferable.

Cupronickels – This family of alloys has two members in particular whose remarkably good corrosion resistance would repay in many cases the extra effort that may be required to procure them in the desired form. These alloys, nominally 70% copper – 30% nickel and 90% copper – 10% nickel, each with appreciable iron added, are becoming increasingly available in various forms. They are very resistant to crevice corrosion, and the pitting rate is low (of the order of 0.001 in./year). The 70–30 alloy has the added advantage of being readily distinguished by its color from the high-zinc brasses and bronzes, which as a class are unsuitable for lengthy service in the sea. Thus, part of the premium for the 70–30 alloy might be justified on the basis of quality control.

Lead – Lead is resistant to attack by sea water and corrodes uniformly at a rate of about 0.0005 in./year or less. It can act to stimulate serious dissimilar-metal-corrosion cells when coupled to structural steel or aluminum alloys. It can be corroded by excessive degrees of cathodic "protection."

Magnesium – Magnesium is useful as a galvanic-anode material. Magnesium alloys corrode so rapidly in sea water that they are not considered suitable for marine structural use. The alloy designated AZ31X, for example, was observed to undergo pitting attack at a rate of about 0.2 in./year. Alloying and surface-treatment attempts have not been found adequate to make magnesium acceptably corrosion resistant for use in the sea.

Monel® – This well-known and widely used alloy, more specifically designated as Monel alloy 400, has good corrosion resistance (general corrosion of the order of 0.001 in./year) in moving sea water. Under stagnant conditions, however, it may pit seriously (0.05 in./year or more), and it is susceptible to crevice corrosion.

Nickel and Nickel-base Alloys – Nickel in quiet sea water pits rapidly (of the order of 0.05 in./year). Two nickel-base alloys, however, are reported to be essentially inert to all forms of attack in sea water.[1] One of these is the relatively new alloy designated Inconel® alloy 625, available in various wrought forms, including sheet and tubing. The second apparently inert alloy is Hastelloy C®. The high molybdenum content of these alloys is believed responsible for their resistance to pitting and crevice corrosion. Other roughly comparable alloys are in the advanced developmental stage and may well become of interest for marine use.

Stainless Steels – The stainless steels as a group resist corrosion as long as the thin oxide film on the surface can be kept intact. In this condition they are described as being *passive.* No special acid or other chemical treatment is required to confer this passivity, and even special treatment for passivity does not confer permanent passivity in sea water. Passive films tend to break down in the pressure of chloride ions, and if there is not adequate oxygen to continuously repair the oxide film at a given point, the steel becomes active (corrodes) at that point. Crevices are especially vulnerable points for initiation of this form of attack, but particularly in the more susceptible steels, the localized attack may start on surfaces free from visible attached particles or organisms and progress as a pit.

All the stainless steels are susceptible to crevice corrosion and pitting in quiet sea water, but they differ greatly in degree of susceptibility. Generally speaking, those lower in chromium and nickel, such as AISI types 205, 304, and 410, are among the most susceptible. Type 316 is the least susceptible of the more commonly available medium-alloy stainless steels, but pits have been observed to grow even in this alloy at rates greater than 0.25 in./year. The premium low-carbon grades are no less susceptible to crevice corrosion and pitting than the standard grades.

Crevice corrosion and pitting of stainless steels in sea water can be prevented by coupling to ordinary unalloyed steel (if the unalloyed steel is not too well painted) or to anode-grade zinc. As a consequence, the unalloyed steel or zinc corrodes at an accelerated rate, but the attack on the stainless steel can thereby be prevented (when geometry and cathode-anode ratios are favorable).

In summary, all the stainless steel alloys now available commercially are susceptible to pitting and crevice corrosion to varying degrees in quiet sea water, and none should be considered for critical items for prolonged immersion unless they are cathodically protected, as by coupling to structural steel.

The successful application of stainless steel for marine propellers is useful to illustrate several corrosion-engineering points. The propellers of most ships are electrically grounded to the hull when the ships are anchored. Under these conditions the unalloyed-steel hull galvanically protects the stainless steel propeller against pitting attack, and the high conductivity of sea water and large ratio of wetted hull area to propeller area prevent disastrous attack on the hull (the principle of relative anode/cathode area). When the ship is under way, particularly in turbine-driven ships, the lubrication films insulate the propeller from the ship electrically, but when stainless steels are exposed to rapidly moving sea water the oxide film remains in repair and the steels do not pit.

The high-strength hardenable stainless steels are susceptible to stress-corrosion cracking in sea water (in addition to being susceptible to crevice corrosion and pitting). At the highest strength levels this may be so serious as to prohibit the use of these alloys. There appears to be a correlation between susceptibility to stress-corrosion cracking, susceptibility to hydrogen embrittlement, and susceptibility to fast "brittle fracture" in all these steels (though the rigorous evidence for this correlation is very scant), and the changes in heat treatment which improve fracture toughness appear to improve resistance to cracking.

There is no clear-cut dividing line according to strength levels between steels which are immune to stress-corrosion cracking and those which are susceptible, but as a very general rule, all hardenable steels at and above yield strengths of about 175,000 psi should be examined carefully for cracking. For these materials at high strength levels, cathodic-protection methods would have to be custom designed, requiring research data not now available, since coupling to a galvanic anode more electronegative than cadmium would possibly introduce hydrogen-embrittlement cracking. The technology for the use of high-strength hardenable steels (including the hardenable stainless steels) with yield strengths of about 150,000 psi or more in massive forms in sea water must be regarded as an area under development. However, steels both stainless and otherwise have long been used successfully in thin sections, as in wire rope, at even higher strengths, where this strength has been conferred by cold-drawing rather than by heat treatment, except that, again, in sea water the stainless steel is susceptible to crevice corrosion, pitting, and their consequences.

Nonstainless Steels – The corrosion rates of unalloyed steels, low-alloy (nonstainless) steels, and wrought iron in sea water are comparable and appear to be about the same regardless of geographical location. The proprietary copper-bearing grades, which are superior to the non-copper-bearing steels in resisting atmospheric corrosion, do not appear to exhibit any superiority in corrosion-resistance behavior in the sea. The *average* penetration rate is of the order of 0.005 in./year, but the rate of pit growth may be up to ten times this much. For some, applications of corrosion can be tolerated and the wastage accepted, whereas for other applications, such as in thin walled containers, pitting might produce a premature failure by perforation, as it sometimes does in ship plate. Pitting of components cyclically stressed may greatly accelerate the initiation of a corrosion-fatigue crack. Both pitting and general corrosion of steel can be readily controlled by cathodic-protection measures if geometry considerations permit.

The high-strength low-alloy steels that owe their strength to heat treatment are susceptible to stress-corrosion and hydrogen-embrittlement cracking under tensile stress. As with the hardenable stainless steels, there is no sharply defined strength level separating immune steels from susceptible ones, but careful attention is again recommended at yield strengths of 175,000 psi or greater, and at even lower yield strengths if the stresses are high. As with the hardenable stainless steels, cathodic-protection methods are not presently a practical solution to stress-corrosion cracking because of the possibility of hydrogen-embrittlement cracking. It does, however, appear practicable and safe to cathodically protect low-alloy and unalloyed steels in which the strength is conferred by cold-drawing, as, for example, in the case of wire rope.

The higher the alloy content in steels, the greater is the tendency for pitting instead of general corrosion. The maraging steels, having high nickel content, follow this rule. The main reason for interest in maraging steels, however, is their high strength and attractive toughness. At the strength levels where these steels might be reasonably justifiable, however, the corrosion phenomenon of prinicpal concern is stress-corrosion cracking. Alloy technology is changing so rapidly that, again, the answer to questions on this point will more likely have to be sought in the laboratory than in the library for a long time to come.

Titanium – Titanium, like the two nickel-base alloys cited above, appears to be essentially inert to all forms of corrosion attack in sea water at ambient temperature. Several titanium alloys, however, have recently been found to be susceptible to cracking and rapid corrosion fatigue when stressed in sea water. This subject is in a state of rapid development, and the designer would be well advised to check the current status before selecting an alloy for an application involving appreciable tensile stresses. Unalloyed titanium and the 6% aluminum – 4% vanadium alloy with low oxygen content appear to be reasonably resistant. Several other alloys which are acutely susceptible in some conditions of heat treatment can be made essentially immune by selected heat treatment, but this immunity can be removed by subsequent welding. The phenomenon apparently does not occur if the section is sufficiently thin. The critical thickness varies, depending upon composition and heat treatment, but 0.05 in. is an example for the 8% aluminum – 1% molybdenum – 1% vanadium alloy. Cathodic protection does not now appear to provide a practical safeguard against stress-corrosion cracking in susceptible titanium systems.

Zinc – Zinc not coupled to other metals corrodes in sea water at an average rate of 0.0005 to 0.001 in./year, with pitting or crevice attack up to ten times this rate. When coupled to large areas of steel or other more cathodic metals, it can corrode at a rate faster by several orders of magnitude. For successful use of zinc as a reliable galvanic anode, MIL SPEC 18001 grade zinc should be used. High purity alone is not adequate.

(From Brown, B. F., in *Handbook of Ocean and Underwater Engineering,* Myers, J. J., Ed., McGraw-Hill, New York, 1969. With permission.)

Table 5.1–10
GALVANIC SERIES IN SEA WATER FLOWING AT 13 FPS

Temperature About 25°C

Material	Steady-state electrode potential volts (Saturated Calomel half-cell)
Zinc	−1.03
Aluminum 3003-(H)	−0.79
Aluminum 6061-(T)	−0.76
Cast iron	−0.61
Carbon steel	−0.61
Stainless steel, Type 430, active	−0.57
Stainless steel, Type 304, active	−0.53
Stainless steel, Type 410, active	−0.52
Naval rolled brass	−0.40
Copper	−0.36
Red brass	−0.33
Bronze, Composition G	−0.31
Admiralty Brass	−0.29
90 Cu-40 Ni, 0.82 Fe	−0.28
70 Cu-30 Ni, 0.47 Fe	−0.25
Stainless steel, Type 430, passive	−0.22
Bronze Composition M	−0.23
Nickel	−0.20
Stainless steel, Type 410, passive	−0.15
Titanium[a]	−0.15
Silver	−0.13
Titanium[b]	−0.10
Hastelloy C	−0.08
Monel-400	−0.08
Stainless steel, Type 304, passive	−0.08
Stainless steel, Type 316, passive	−0.05
Zirconium[c]	−0.04
Platinum[c]	+0.15

[a] Prepared by powder-metallurgy techniques. Sheath-compacted powder, hot rolled, sheath removed, cold rolled in air.
[b] Prepared by iodide process.
[c] From other sources.

Crevice Attack

This form of corrosion usually is most serious under immersed conditions or in the splash zone. Metals that require plenty of oxygen to continuously repair the breaks in the oxide film and thus maintain passivity tend to be susceptible to crevice attack in sea water. The relative susceptibility to crevice attack shows stainless steels and some of the aluminum alloys to be the most sensitive.

If the oxygen in the stagnant sea water in the crevice is consumed in repairing new breaks in the passive film at a higher rate than fresh oxygen can diffuse in from the outside, rapid corrosion tends to take place under the crevice. The driving force comes from a differential aeration cell, with the surface outside the crevice in contact with oxygen-bearing sea water acting as the cathode. In accordance with electrochemical principles, the cathodic and anodic currents must be equal. In the typical case, because of the small area of the anode under the crevice, the current density or rate of local attack can be extremely high. Once such a cell has been initiated it is difficult to arrest.

(From La Que, F. L., *Proc. Am. Soc. Testing Materials,* 51, 495, 1951. With permission.)

Table 5.1–11
EXAMPLES OF GALVANIC COUPLES IN SEA WATER

Metal A	Metal B	Comments
Couples that usually give rise to undesirable results on one or both metals		
Magnesium	Low-alloy steel	Accelerated attack on **A**, danger of hydrogen damage on **B**
Aluminum	Copper	Accelerated pitting on **A**; ions from **B** attack **A**. Reduced corrosion on **B** may result in biofouling on **B**
Bronze	Stainless steel	Increased pitting on **A**
Borderline, may work, but uncertain		
Copper	Solder	Soldered joint may be attacked but may have useful life
Graphite	Titanium or Hastelloy C	
Monel-400	Type 316 SS	Both metals may pit
Generally compatible		
Titanium	Inconel 625	
Lead	Cupronickel	

(From Fink, F. W. and Boyd, W. K., The corrosion of metals in a marine environment, Defense Metals Information Center Report No. 245, Battelle Memorial Institute, Columbus, Ohio, 1970. With permission.)

Table 5.1–12
FIVE-YEAR WEIGHT LOSS AS DETERMINED GRAPHICALLY FOR STEEL

With Copper, Nickel, or Chromium Additions

	Copper			Nickel				Chromium			
Amount added, wt %	0	0.2	1	0	0.2	1	2	0	0.2	1	2
Weight loss/ paneling	>50	34	28	48	42	31	25	32	30	22	17

(From Fink, F. W. and Boyd, W. K., The corrosion of metals in a marine environment, Defense Metals Information Center Report No. 245, Battelle Memorial Institute, Columbus, Ohio, 1970. With permission.)

Table 5.1–13
CORROSION PENETRATION OF ALLOY STEELS

Immersed in the Pacific Ocean Near the Panama Canal Zone after 8 Years

		Penetration, mils							
		Mean tide[b]				14 ft below surface[b]			
Steel	Type	1	2	3	Ratio[a]	1	2	3	Ratio[a]
A	Low carbon	23.2	40	65	1.7	25.5	66	86	2.6
D	Copper bearing	24.2	45	63	1.9	27.7	63	108	2.3
E	Ni (2%)	22.9	39	50	1.7	31.7	94	179	3.0
F	Ni (5%)	20.0	39	75	2.0	32.0	117	214	3.7
G	Cr (3%)	25.7	82	93	3.2	40.5	65	78	1.6
H	Cr (5%)	24.5	88	99	3.6	32.0	63	90	2.0
I	Low alloy (Cu-Ni)	39.7	70	134	1.8	26.4	82	152	3.2
J	Low alloy (Cu-Cr-Si)	21.1	47	54	2.2	43.2	80	175	1.8
K	Low alloy (Cu-Ni-Mn-Mo)	24.8	40	94	1.6	25.5	56	139	2.2
L	Low alloy (Cr-Ni-Mn)	20.5	39	50	1.9	43.9	97	259(p)[c]	2.2

[a] Ratio of average of 20 deepest pits of weight-loss penetration. The higher the number, the greater is the pitting tendency in relation to the corrosion rate.
[b] 1 = calculated from weight loss.
2 = average of 20 deepest pits.
3 = deepest pit.
[c] p = completely perforated.

(From Southwell, C. R. and Alexander, A. L., Corrosion of structural ferrous metals in tropical environments – Sixteen years' exposure to sea and fresh water, Paper No. 14, Preprint, 1968 NACE Conference, Cleveland, Ohio.)

Table 5.1–14
COMPREHENSIVE EVALUATION OF CORROSION DAMAGE OF STAINLESS STEELS

Exposed to Marine Environments in the Panama Canal Zone

Metal	Stainless steel	Type of exposure	Corrosion rate, mpy			Avg of 20 deepest pits[a], mil			Deepest pit[a], mil			Loss in tensile strength[b], %	Type corrosion attack[c]
			1 yr	4 yr	8 yr	1 yr	4 yr	8 yr	1 yr	4 yr	8 yr	4 yr	4 yr
A	Type 410 (13 Cr)	Sea water immersion	2.98	1.97	1.75	61(11)	148	161	260(p)	260(p)	259(p)	d	KQH
		Sea water mean tide	0.50	0.41	0.42	46	67	67	66	173	152	0	JKQ
		Seashore	0.040	0.013	0.005	0(0)	3	0(0)	0(0)	5	0(0)	0	KR
B	Type 430 (17 Cr)	Seashore	0.025	0.008	0.004	0(0)	0(0)	0(0)	0(0)	0(0)	0(0)	0	KR
C	Type 301 (17 Cr, 7 Ni)	Seashore	0.00	0.001	0.001	0(0)	0(0)	0(0)	0(0)	0(0)	0(0)	0	K
D	Type 302 (18 Cr, 8 Ni)	Sea water immersion	1.46	0.88	0.69	70(12)	107	140	261(p)	286(p)	236	d	KQ
		Sea water mean tide	0.18	0.12	0.11	7(13)	26	57	16	82	110	0	JK
E	Type 316 (18-13 and Mo)	Sea water immersion	0.59	0.07	0.25	44(7)	48	154	245(p)	93	245(p)	0	KQ
		Sea water mean tide	0.06	0.03	0.02	5(9)	7(12)	16	23	22	30	1	JK
		Seashore	0.00	0.00	0.00	0(0)	0(0)	0(0)	0(0)	0(0)	0(0)	1	K
F	Type 321 (17-10 and Ti)	Sea water immersion	1.16	0.81	0.62	64(8)	175	193	270(p)	273(p)	272(p)	d	KQ
		Sea water mean tide	0.13	0.08	0.08	8(11)	37	56	26	60	93	d	JKQ
		Seashore	0.005	0.001	0.001	0(0)	0(0)	0(0)	0(0)	0(0)	0(0)	1	K

a Pit depths referred to the original surface of the metal either by measurement from an uncorroded surface or by calculation using the original and final average measured thickness of the sample. Average of 20 deepest pits represents average of the 5 deepest pits measured on each side of duplicate specimens. (Area, 2.25 ft^2 on immersed specimens, and 0.89 ft^2 on atmospheric specimens); values in parentheses indicate total number averaged when less than 20 measurable pits. Perforation of plate by deepest pit is indicated by (p).

b Changes in tensile strength calculated on basis of ¼ in. thick metal (average of 4 tests for immersed specimens, average of 3 tests on atmospheric specimens).

c H – concentration cell, J – marine fouling contact, K – no visible attack, Q – pitting attack (random), R – localized attack (random).

d Intensity and distribution of pitting prevented satisfactory tensile testing.

(From Alexander, A. L. et al., *Corrosion,* 17(7), 345t, 1961. With permission.)

Table 5.1–15
CORROSION OF NICKEL AND MONEL-400 IN MARINE ENVIRONMENTS

At Panama Canal Zone

Metal	Exposure	Weight-loss penetration, mpy			Depth of pitting, mils: Avg of 20 deepest[a]			Depth of pitting, mils: Deepest penetration			Type of corrosion attack[b]
		1 yr	4 yr	16 yr	1 yr	4 yr	16 yr	1 yr	4 yr	16 yr	16 yr
Nickel (99%)	Sea water										
	Immersion	2.40	1.30	1.21	125	121	142	245	248	249	JQHK
	Mean tide	0.35	0.33	0.27	(0)	47	61	0	105	121	JQ
	Atmospheric										
	Marine	0.01	0.01	<0.01	(0)	(0)	(0)	0	0	0	K
Monel-400® (cold rolled)	Sea water										
	Immersion	1.64	1.04	0.54	17	27	33	42	41	55	RJ
	Mean tide	0.10	0.12	0.17	(0)	(0)	14	0	00	21	JR
	Atmospheric										
	Marine	0.04	0.02	0.01	(0)	(0)	(0)	0	0	0	AK
Monel-400 (hot rolled)	Sea water										
	Immersion	2.09	1.01	0.52	43	53	56	90	82	80	RJ
	Mean tide	0.11	0.18	0.16	(0)	16(15)	24	0	20	36	JR

[a] Numbers in parentheses indicate number of measurable pits when less than 20. A measurable pit is >5 mils.
[b] A – uniform attack, H – concentration cell, J – fouling contact, K – no visible attack, Q – pitting (randomly distributed), R – local attack (randomly located).

(From Southwell, C. R. and Alexander, A. L., *Materials Protection,* 8(3), 39, 1969. With permission.)

Table 5.1–16
MARINE ATMOSPHERIC RESULTS FOR COPPER ALLOYS

After 2 and 7 Years

CDA no.[a]	Commercial designation or composition	Penetration[d], mpy 2 yr A[b]	2 yr C[c]	7 yr A	7 yr C	Appearance after 7 yr[b]
110	Touch pitch Cu	0.072	0.065	0.065	0.025	Brown film, smooth, slight patina near edges
				Tin		
505	Phos. bronze, 1.25% Sn	0.083	0.042	0.069	0.017	"Mink brown," slight patina
510	Phos. bronze, 5% Sn	0.150	0.088	0.099	–	Maroon film, heavy etch
				Aluminum		
637	Alum. bronze	0.017	0.009	0.013	–	Light tan film, smooth
				Nickel		
–	1.85 Ni, 0.03 Fe	0.134	0.145	0.044	0.036	Dark brown, mottled with green at edges
704	6.34 Ni, 0.01 Fe	0.069	0.052	0.033	–	Dark brown, plus patina streaks on panel face
707	9.16 Ni, 0.18 Fe	0.052	0.039	0.038	–	Uniform maroon with patina at edges
711	22.76 Ni, 0.04 Fe	0.036	0.024	0.031	–	Greenish brown, green near edges, slight etch
–	42.75 Ni, 0.30 Fe	0.018	0.012	0.019	0.005	Greenish brown, slight green near edges
				Zinc		
420	Tin brass	0.058	0.042	0.024	–	Dark maroon, smooth
230	Red brass	0.051	0.038	0.033	0.026	Brown-maroon film, smooth
260	Cartridge brass	0.034	0.023	0.030	0.017	Brown-maroon film, smooth, very slight patina
				Nickel-Zinc		
745	10% nickel-silver	0.030	0.020	0.024	0.010	Brown with slight patina film in center, green near edges, smooth
752	18% nickel-silver	0.030	0.020	0.021	–	Brown film in center, green near edges, smooth

[a] Copper Development Association number.
[b] 80-foot lot, Kure Beach, N.C.
[c] Point Reyes, California.
[d] Calculated from weight loss.

(From Copson, H. R. (Chairman), Atmospheric exposure of nonferrous metals and alloys, ASTM Subcommittee VI, 1957 Test Program, Reprint from American Society for Testing Materials Proc. 59, 61, 62 and 66. Published in Fink, F. W. and Boyd, W. K., The corrosion of metals in a marine environment, Defense Metals Information Center Report No. 245, Battelle Memorial Institute, Columbus, Ohio, 1970.)

Table 5.1–17
SUMMARY OF CORROSION OF TITANIUM AND TITANIUM ALLOYS IN SEA WATER

Alloy	No. exposures	Exposure time, days	Exposure depth, ft	Type of corrosion observed
Unalloyed Ti (grade unknown)	10	123–1064	2350–6780	None visible (<0.1 mpy)[a]
Unalloyed Ti (Grade RC 55)	4	90–199	4250–4500	None visible (<0.1 mpy)[a]
Unalloyed Ti (Grade 75 A)	8	123–751	5–6780	None visible (0.0 mpy)
Ti-5Al-2.5Sn	12	123–751	5–6780	None visible (<0.1 mpy)
Ti-7Al-12Zr	1	123	5640	None visible (0.0 mpy)
Ti-7Al-2Cb-1Ta	2	181	5	None visible (Fouling stains)
Ti-8Mn	1	402	2,370	
Ti-4Al-3Mo-1V	3	402–1064	2370–330	None visible (0.0 mpy)
Ti-6Al-4V	20	123–1064	5–6780	None visible (<0.1 mpy, mostly 0.0)[a]
Ti-13V-11Cr-3Al	12	123–751	5–6780	None visible (<0.1 mpy, mostly 0.0)

[a] One panel was reported as 0.19 mpy.

(From Reinhart, F. M., Corrosion of materials in hydrospace, Part III, Titanium and titanium alloys, U.S. Naval Civil Eng. Lab., Port Hueneme, Calif., Technical Note N-921, September, 1967.)

Table 5.1–18
CORROSION OF ALUMINUM ALLOYS

Exposed 16 Years in Three Tropical Environments in the Panama Canal Zone

	Average penetration[a], mils			Depth of pitting,[b] mils: Avg of 20 deepest pits			Depth of pitting,[b] mils: Deepest pits			Tensile strength loss, %[c]	Type of corrosion attack,[d]
	1 yr	8 yr	16 yr	1 yr	8 yr	16 yr	1 yr	8 yr	16 yr	8 yr	16 yr
Alloy 1100											
Immersion											
Sea water	0.28	0.61	0.97	9(13)	11	17	15	19	33	2	J
Mean tide	0.06	0.31	0.53	11(9)	14	39	29	37	67	1	JQ
Atmospheric											
Marine	0.01	0.02	0.11	N	N	N	N	N	N	0	A
Alloy 6061											
Immersion											
Sea water	0.28	0.73	0.91	N	23	14	N	49	79	0	J
Mean tide	0.04	0.13	0.29	N	N	17	N	N	41	0	J
Atmospheric											
Marine	0.03	0.03	0.11	N	N	N	N	N	N	1	A

[a] Calculated from weight loss and specific gravity.
[b] Represents depth of penetration from original surface; N – measurable pits; number in parentheses gives number of measurable pits when less than 20.
[c] Percent change in tensile strength calculated on basis of 1/4 in. thick metal and average of four tests for underwater specimens, and 1/16 in. thick metal and average of three tests for atmospheric specimens.
[d] A – uniform attack; J – marine fouling contact; Q – pitting attack (random).

(From Southwell, C. R., Alexander, A. L., and Hummer, C. W., Jr., *Materials Protection,* 4(12), 30, 1965.)

Table 5.1–19
CORROSION OF LEAD, SOLDER, TIN, AND ZINC IN SEA WATER

Metal	Days	Depth, ft	Weight loss, mpy	Pit depth, mils	Remarks
Chemical lead[a]	181	5	1.2	–	Uniform attack
	197	2340	0.3	–	Uniform attack
	123	5640	0.8	–	Uniform attack
Tellurium lead[b]	181	5	1.0	–	Uniform attack
	197	2340	0.3	–	Uniform attack
	123	5640	1.1	–	Uniform attack
Antimonial lead[c]	181	5	1.2	–	Uniform attack
	197	2340	0.3	–	Uniform attack
	123	5640	0.8	–	Uniform attack
Solder[d]	181	5	3.7	–	Uniform attack
	197	2340	0.5	–	Uniform attack
	123	5640	0.5	–	Uniform attack
Tin[e]	181	5	8.3	30	Perforated
	197	2340	1.8	2	Crevice attack
	123	5640	0.5	=	General attack
Zinc[f]	181	5	4.5	5	Pitting
	197	2340	2.3	2	Pitting
	123	5640	6.7	13	Pitting

[a] 99.9 Pb.
[b] 99+ Pb, 0.04 Te.
[c] 94.0 Pb, 6.0 Sb.
[d] 67 Pb-33 Sn.
[e] 99.9 Sn.
[f] 0.01 Fe, 0.09 Pb.

(From Reinhart, F. M., Corrosion of materials in surface sea water after 6 months exposure, Naval Civil Eng. Lab., Port Hueneme, Calif., Technical Note N-1023, March, 1969.)

Table 5.1–20

CHARACTERISTICS OF COMMERCIALLY AVAILABLE SACRIFICIAL ANODES IN SEA WATER SERVIC

Anode	Description	Max structure potential, volt	Solution potential, volt	Current efficiency, %	Ah/lb	lb/1 amp-yr	Notes
Magnesium	0.03 Cu (max), 0.003 Fe (max), and 0.10 Mn (min)	−1.15	−1.50[a]	50	500	17.5	
Zinc	–	−0.90	−1.05[a] −1.10[c]	95	354	24.7	
Al-Zn-Hg	99.9% purity Al + 0.045 Hg + 0.45 Zn	−1.00	−1.05[b] −1.1[c]	95	1280	6.1	No heat treatment required – good efficiency
Al-Zn-Sn	–	–	–	85[d]	1150	7.6	Requires precise control of heat treatment

[a] Closed-circuit potential referred to Ag/AgCl electrode.
[b] Closed-circuit potential referred to saturated calomel electrode.
[c] Closed-circuit potential referred to Cu-$CuSO_4$ electrode.
[d] Efficiencies as low as 32% have been reported with improper heat treatment.

(From Fink, F. W. and Boyd, W. K., The corrosion of metals in a marine environment, Defense Metals Information Center Report No. 245, Battelle Memorial Institute, Columbus, Ohio, 1970. With permission.)

References

1. **Lennox, T. J., Jr. et al.,** Marine corrosion studies, NRL Memorandum Report 1711, May, 1966.
2. **La Que, F. L. and May, T. P.,** Experiments relating to the mechanism and cathodic protection of steel in sea water, The 2nd Int. Cong. Metallic Corrosion, NACE, 1966, p. 789.
3. **Potosnak, C. S., Wilson, A. J., Talbot, C. J. H.,** *Corrosion Prevention and Control,* 15(2), 12, 1968.
4. **Doremus, G. L. and Davis, J. G.,** *Materials Protection,* 6(1), 30, 1967.
5. **Hine, R. A. and Wei, M. W.,** *Materials Protection,* 3(11), 49, 1964.
6. **Sansonetti, S. J.,** To prevent corrosion at sea think aluminum anodes, First Offshore Technology Conf. AIME, Houston, Texas, Preprint No. OTC 1039, May 18-21, 1969.

5.2 Ropes, Chains, and Shackles

Figure 5.2–1
WIRE-ROPE CONSTRUCTION CLASSES

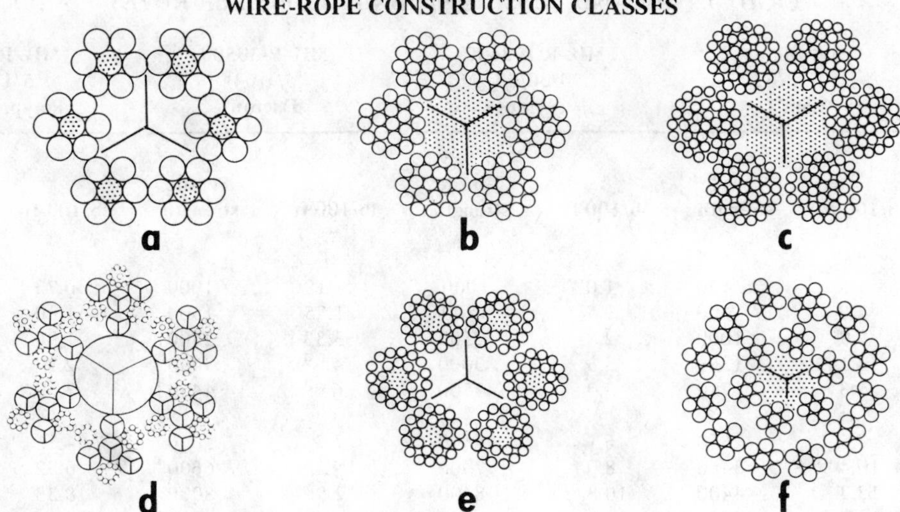

a – 6 × 7; b – 6 × 19; c – 6 × 37; d – 18 × 7; nonrotating; e – mooring lines, 6 × 12 or 6 × 24; f – spring-lay, 6 × 3 × 19.

(From Meals, W. D. in *Handbook of Ocean and Underwater Engineering,* Myers, J. J., Ed., McGraw-Hill, New York, 1969. With permission.)

Table 5.2–1
NOMINAL WIRE-ROPE BREAKING STRENGTH

in 2,000 lb Tons, for Bright Improved-plow-grade Steel

Rope diam, in.	6 × 7 FC	6 × 19 class IWRC	6 × 19 class FC	6 × 37 class IWRC	6 × 37 class FC	Non-rotating 18 × 7	Mooring line 6 × 24[a]	Spring lay 6 × 3 × 19[a]
3/8	5.86	6.56	6.10	6.20	5.77	5.59	4.77	
1/2	10.3	11.5	10.7	11.0	10.2	9.85	8.40	
5/8	15.9	18.0	16.7	17.0	15.8	15.3	13.0	
3/4	22.7	25.6	23.8	24.3	22.6	21.8	18.6	
7/8	30.7	34.6	32.2	32.9	30.6	29.5	25.3	13.5
1	39.7	45.0	41.8	42.8	39.8	38.3	32.8	17.5
1 1/8	49.8	56.6	52.6	53.9	50.1	48.2	41.2	22.1
1 1/4	61.0	65.0	64.6	66.1	61.5	59.2	50.7	27.2
1 3/8	73.1	83.5	77.7	79.7	74.1	71.8	61.0	32.8
1 1/2	86.2	98.9	92.0	94.5	87.9	84.4	72.3	38.9
1 5/8	–	115.0	107.0	111.0	103.0	98.4	84.5	45.6
1 3/4	–	134.0	124.0	128.0	119.0	114.0	97.5	52.7
2	–	172.0	160.0	166.0	154.0	–	126.0	68.5

[a] Strengths shown are for galvanized ropes. (a) For all galvanized ropes other than 6 × 24 and 6 × 3 × 19, subtract 10 percent from listed strengths unless rope is made from redrawn galvanized wire. (b) For extra-improved-plow in 6 × 19 and 6 × 37 class with IWRC add 15 percent to tabulated strength. (c) Minimum breaking strength to allow for testing variations is 97.5 percent of nominal breaking strength.

(Source: Federal Specification RR 410. From Meals W. D. in *Handbook of Ocean and Underwater Engineering,* Myers, J. J., Ed., McGraw-Hill, New York, 1969. With permission.)

Table 5.2–2
WEIGHT IN AIR AND TENSILE STRENGTH OF FIBER ROPES

Fed. Spec. Date	T-T-605b 12/13/63 Manila		MIL-R-17343C 4/30/63 Nylon		MIL-R-30500 5/1/64 Dacron		MIL-R-24049 5/11/64 Polypropylene	
Size, in.	lb/100 ft	Tensile strength	lb/100 ft	Tensile strength	lb/100 ft	Tensile strength	lb/100 ft	Tensile strength
Diam								
3/16	1.5	450	1.0	1000	1.19	1000	0.73	700
1/4	2.0	600	1.5	1500	1.75	1500	1.20	1100
5/16	2.9	1000	2.8	2500	3.33	2500	1.96	1700
3/8	4.1	1350	3.5	3000	4.4[a]	3400[a]	2.77	2150
7/16	5.3	1750	5.0	4500	6.0[a]	4450[a]	3.33	2500
1/2	7.5	2650	6.1	5500	7.7	5000	4.75	3700
9/16	10.4	3450	8.0	7000	9.5[a]	6600[a]	6.32	4800
5/8	13.3	4400	10.3	8400	12.5	8000	8.33	6000
3/4	16.7	5400	13.9	11,500	16.6[a]	11,000[a]	11.0	7000
7/8	22.5	7700	20.0	16,000	24.2[a]	15,500[a]	15.7	11,000
Circ								
3	27.0	9000	24.5	22,000	28.5	18,500	19.2	13,000
3 1/4	31.3	10,500	29.0[a]	26,000[a]	33.5[a]	21,500[a]	22.5[a]	14,800[a]
3 1/2	36.0	12,000	33.3	28,500	40.0	25,000	26.3	16,500
3 3/4	41.8	13,500	38.4	33,000	44.0[a]	28,000[a]	30.3	19,500
4	48.0	15,000	43.5	37,500	50.0	31,000	34.2	21,500
4 1/2	60.0	18,500	55.5	46,000	63.0[a]	39,000[a]	43.8	26,000
5	74.4	22,500	66.5	57,000	77.0	48,000	52.5	32,000
5 1/2	89.5	26,500	80.0	68,000	94.0[a]	57,000	63.2	38,000
6	108	31,000	100	81,000	111	68,000	79.3	44,000
6 1/2	125	36,000	111	90,000	130[a]	77,000[a]	91.0	50,000
7	146	41,000	141	110,000	152	88,000	111	60,000
7 1/2	167	46,500	162[a]	124,000[a]	175[a]	100,000[a]	127[a]	68,000[a]
8	191	52,000	182	137,000	200	110,000	142	75,000
9	242	64,000	232	170,000	250	140,000	183	94,000
10	299	77,000	294	200,000	303	165,000	232	115,000
11	367	91,000	350	240,000	375[a]	200,000[a]	272[a]	138,000[a]
12	436	105,000	416	280,000	445[a]	230,000[a]	325[a]	164,000[a]

Notes: Blend strengths are the same as polypropylene. Weight/ft is approximately 30–10% heavier than polypropylene, depending on size.

[a] These values are not included in specifications but are interpolated or extrapolated from specification figures.

(From Meals, W. D. in *Handbook of Ocean and Underwater Engineering,* Myers, J. J., Ed., McGraw-Hill, New York, 1969. With permission.)

Table 5.2–3
CHEMICAL PROPERTIES OF FIBER ROPES

Property	Manila	Nylon	Dacron	Polypropylene
Specific gravity	1.38	1.14	1.38	0.90
Resistance to mildew	Poor	Excellent	Excellent	Excellent
Resistance to acid	Poor	Fair	Good	Excellent
Resistance to alkali	Poor	Excellent	Fair	Excellent
Resistance to sunlight	Fair	Good	Good	Good
Resistance to organic solvent	Good	Good	Good	Fair
Critical temp	300°F	350°F	350°F	250°F
Melting point	–	480°F	482°F	330°F

(From Haas, F. J. in *Handbook of Ocean and Underwater Engineering,* Myers, J. J., Ed., McGraw-Hill, New York, 1969. With permission.)

Table 5.2–4
STRENGTH AND RESISTANCE PROPERTIES OF FIBER ROPES

Property	Manila	Nylon	Dacron	Polypropylene
Strength/wt ratio, avg	1.0	2.84	2.03	2.32
Relative resistance to impact load	1.0	8.6	4.0	5.2
Resistance to abrasion	Good	Excellent	Superior	Good
Water absorption, %	25.0	4.5	1.5	0

(From Haas, F. J. in *Handbook of Ocean and Underwater Engineering,* Myers, J. J., Ed., McGraw-Hill, New York, 1969. With permission.)

Figure 5.2–2

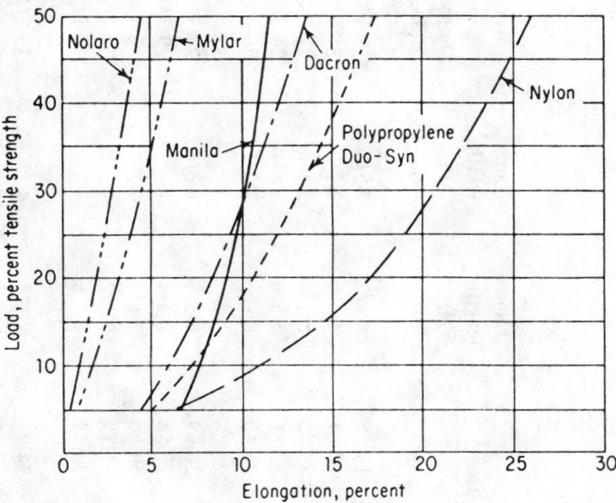

(From Haas, F. J. in *Handbook of Ocean and Underwater Engineering,* Myers, J. J., Ed., McGraw-Hill, New York, 1969. With permission.)

Table 5.2–5
STUD-LINK CHAIN DIMENSIONS AND TEST REQUIREMENTS

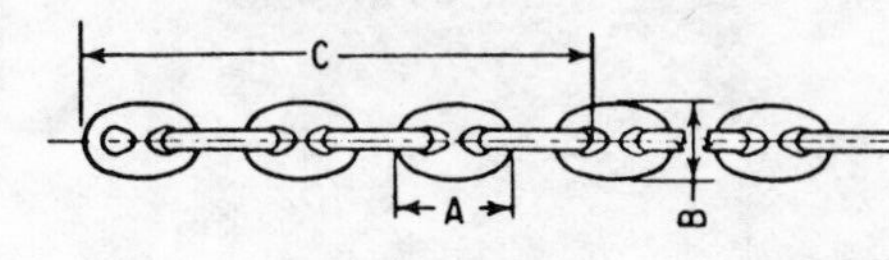

Standard

Chain size		Link length A, in.	Link width B, in.	Length over six links C, in.	Wt/15 fathom shot (approx), lb	Wrought iron		Hi-strength		Di-Lok®	
in.	mm					Proof test, lb	Break test, lb	Proof test, lb	Break test, lb	Proof test, lb	Break test, lb
3/4	19.05	4 1/2	2 5/8	19 1/2	505	22,680	33,880	34,680	48,550	48,000	75,000
13/16	20.64	4 7/8	2 7/8	21 1/8	600	26,600	39,872	40,430	56,600	56,000	86,500
7/8	22.23	5 1/4	3 1/8	22 3/4	688	30,800	46,200	46,630	65,280	64,000	98,000
15/16	23.81	5 5/8	3 5/16	24 3/8	795	35,392	53,088	53,280	74,590	74,000	113,500
1	25.40	6	3 9/16	26	900	40,320	60,480	60,360	84,500	84,000	129,000
1 1/16	26.99	6 3/8	3 3/4	27 5/8	1020	45,472	68,096	67,850	94,990	95,000	145,000
1 1/8	28.58	6 3/4	4	29 1/4	1140	50,960	76,440	75,770	106,080	106,000	161,000
1 3/16	30.16	7 1/8	4 1/4	30 7/8	1275	56,840	85,120	84,120	117,770	118,000	179,500
1 1/4	31.75	7 1/2	4 1/2	32 1/2	1415	63,000	94,360	92,910	130,070	130,000	198,000
1 5/16	33.34	7 7/8	4 3/4	34 1/8	1560	69,440	104,160	102,090	142,930	143,500	216,500
1 3/8	34.93	8 1/4	4 5/16	35 3/4	1705	76,120	114,240	111,660	156,330	157,000	235,000
1 7/16	36.51	8 5/8	5 3/16	37 3/8	1865	83,160	124,600	121,720	170,430	171,000	257,500
1 1/2	38.10	9	5 3/8	39	2035	90,720	131,488	132,190	185,060	185,000	280,000
1 9/16	39.69	9 3/8	5 5/8	40 5/8	2195	98,336	137,536	143,050	200,270	200,500	302,500
1 5/8	41.28	9 3/4	5 7/8	42 1/4	2345	106,400	148,960	154,310	216,030	216,000	325,000
1 11/16	42.86	10 1/8	6 1/16	43 7/8	2530	114,800	160,720	165,960	232,360	232,500	352,500
1 3/4	44.45	10 1/2	6 5/16	45 1/2	2720	123,480	172,760	178,000	249,210	249,000	380,000
1 13/16	46.04	10 7/8	6 1/2	47 1/8	2925	132,440	185,360	190,430	266,620	267,000	406,000
1 7/8	47.63	11 1/4	6 3/4	48 3/4	3125	141,680	198,240	203,250	284,540	285,000	432,000
1 15/16	48.21	11 5/8	7	50 3/8	3335	151,200	211,680	216,430	303,000	303,500	406,000

Table 5.2–5 (*Continued*)
STUD-LINK CHAIN DIMENSIONS AND TEST REQUIREMENTS

Chain size		Link length A, in.	Link width B, in.	Length over six links C, in.	Wt/15 fathom shot (approx), lb	Wrought iron		Hi-strength		Di-Lok®	
in.	mm					Proof test, lb	Break test, lb	Proof test, lb	Break test, lb	Proof test, lb	Break test, lb
2	50.80	12	7 3/16	52	3525	161,280	225,792	230,000	322,000	322,000	488,000
2 1/16	52.39	12 3/8	7 7/16	53 5/8	3750	171,360	239,904	243,930	341,510	342,000	518,000
2 1/8	53.98	12 3/4	7 5/8	55 1/4	3975	182,000	254,800	258,240	361,530	362,000	548,000
2 3/16	55.56	13 1/8	7 7/8	56 7/8	4215	192,920	269,920	272,910	382,060	382,500	579,100
2 1/4	57.15	13 1/2	8 1/8	58 1/2	4460	204,120	285,600	287,930	403,100	403,000	610,000
2 5/16	58.74	13 7/8	8 5/16	60 1/8	4710	215,600	301,840	303,320	424,630	425,000	642,500
2 3/8	60.33	14 1/4	8 9/16	61 3/4	4960	227,360	318,304	319,050	446,660	447,000	675,000
2 7/16	61.91	14 5/8	8 3/4	63 3/8	5210	239,456	335,160	335,130	469,180	469,500	709,500
2 1/2	63.50	15	9	65	5528	252,000	352,800	351,560	492,190	492,000	744,000
2 9/16	65.09	15 3/8	9 1/4	65 5/8	5810	261,408	365,960	368,340	515,670	516,000	778,500
2 5/8	66.68	15 3/4	9 7/16	68 1/4	6105	270,816	379,120	385,440	539,620	540,000	813,000
2 11/16	68.26	16 1/8	9 11/16	69 7/8	6410	280,224	392,280	402,890	564,040	565,000	849,000
2 3/4	69.85	16 1/2	9 7/8	71 1/2	6725	289,632	405,440	420,660	588,930	590,000	885,000
2 13/16	71.44	16 7/8	10 1/8	73 1/8	7040	298,816	418,320	438,760	614,260	615,000	925,000
2 7/8	73.03	17 1/4	10 3/8	74 3/4	7365	308,224	431,480	457,190	640,070	640,000	965,000
2 15/16	74.61	17 5/8	10 9/16	76 3/8	7696	317,408	444,360	475,940	666,310	666,500	1,005,000
3	76.20	18	10 13/16	78	8035	326,592	457,184	495,000	693,000	693,000	1,045,000
3 1/16	77.79	18 3/8	11	79 5/8	8379	335,552	469,728	514,380	720,130	720,500	1,086,500
3 1/8	79.38	18 3/4	11 1/4	81 1/4	8736	344,400	482,160	534,060	747,680	748,000	1,128,000
3 1/16	80.96	19 1/8	11 1/2	82 7/8	9093	353,248	494,480	554,050	775,670	776,050	1,169,000
3 1/4	82.55	19 1/2	11 11/16	84 1/2	9460	361,984	506,688	574,340	804,070	804,100	1,210,000
3 5/16	84.14	19 7/8	11 15/16	86 1/8	9828	370,496	518,560	594,920	832,890	833,150	1,253,000
3 3/8	85.73	20 1/4	12 1/8	87 3/4	10,210	378,840	530,320	615,800	862,130	862,200	1,296,000
3 7/16	87.31	20 5/8	12 3/8	89 3/8	10,599	386,960	541,632	636,970	891,770	892,100	1,339,550
3 1/2	88.90	21	12 5/8	91	10,998	395,136	553,056	658,440	921,810	922,000	1,383,100

(From Linnenbank, C. D. in *Handbook of Ocean and Underwater Engineering*, Myers, J. J., Ed., McGraw-Hill, New York, 1969. With permission.)

Table 5.2–6
PROOF COIL CHAIN

Trade size, in.	Material size, in.	Inside length of link, in.	Inside width of link, in.	Outside length of link, in.	Outside width of link, in.	Links/ft	Max wt/100 ft, lb	Working-load limit, lb	Trade size, in.
3/16	7/32	0.95	0.40	1.39	0.84	12 1/2	42	700	3/16
1/4	9/32	1.00	0.50	1.56	1.06	12	76	1175	1/4
5/16	11/32	1.10	0.50	1.79	1.18	11	115	1750	5/16
3/8	13/32	1.23	0.62	2.04	1.43	9 3/4	166	2450	3/8
7/16	15/32	1.37	0.75	2.31	1.68	8 3/4	225	3250	7/16
1/2	17/32	1.50	0.81	2.56	1.87	8	286	4250	1/2
9/16	19/32	1.75	0.87	2.94	2.06	6 3/4	355	5250	9/16
5/8	21/32	1.87	1.00	3.18	2.31	6 3/8	425	6375	5/8
3/4	25/32	2.12	1.12	3.68	2.68	5 5/8	605	9125	3/4
7/8	29/32	2.50	1.37	4.31	3.18	4 3/4	811	10,750	7/8
1	1 1/32	2.75	1.50	4.81	3.56	4 3/8	1045	12,400	1
1 1/8	1 5/32	3.12	1.75	5.43	4.06	3 7/8	1321	15,600	1 1/8
1 1/4	1 9/32	3.25	1.87	5.81	4.43	3 3/4	1622	19,200	1 1/4

Note: Also known as "common coil." This chain is the standard commercial quality regularly stocked by hardware and mill supply houses. Excellent elongation provides a visible warning when chain is overloaded. Sizes of 3/16 to 7/8 in. are electric-welded; sizes 1 in. and larger are fire- or electric-welded. Available hot-galvanized and in continuous lengths in fiber drums or in short lengths with or without attachments.

(From Linnenbank, C. D. in *Handbook of Ocean and Underwater Engineering,* Myers, J. J., Ed., McGraw-Hill, New York, 1969. With permission.)

Table 5.2–7
BBB-COIL CHAIN

Trade size, in.	Material size, in.	Inside length of link, in.	Inside width of link, in.	Outside length of link, in.	Outside width of link, in.	Links/ft	Max wt/100 ft, lb	Working-load limit, lb	Trade size, in.
3/16	7/32	0.78	0.37	1.21	0.81	15 1/2	46	800	3/16
1/4	9/32	0.85	0.43	1.41	0.99	14	81	1325	1/4
5/16	11/32	1.00	0.50	1.68	1.19	12	120	1950	5/16
3/8	13/32	1.09	0.62	1.90	1.43	11	173	2750	3/8
7/16	15/32	1.21	0.68	2.15	1.62	9 3/4	231	3625	7/16
1/2	17/32	1.34	0.75	2.40	1.81	9	296	4750	1/2
9/16	19/32	1.56	0.78	2.75	1.97	7 3/4	366	5875	9/16
5/8	21/32	1.68	0.87	3.00	2.18	7 1/8	447	7250	5/8
3/4	25/32	1.87	1.00	3.43	2.56	6 3/8	640	10,250	3/4
7/8	29/32	2.25	1.24	4.06	3.06	5 3/8	850	12,000	7/8
1	1 1/32	2.56	1.37	4.62	3.43	4 3/4	1087	15,500	1
1 1/8	1 5/32	2.87	1.62	5.18	3.93	4 1/8	1362	19,500	1 1/8
1 1/4	1 9/32	3.06	1.75	5.62	4.31	3 7/8	1664	24,000	1 1/4

Note: Shorter links than those of proof coil increase the working load limits. Greater number of links/ft provide added flexibility and permit wider distribution of strain and wear. Sizes of 3/16 to 7/8 in. are electric-welded; sizes 1 in. and larger are fire- or electric-welded Available hot-galvanized and in continuous lengths in fiber drums or in short lengths.

(From Linnenbank, C. D. in *Handbook of Ocean and Underwater Engineering,* Myers, J. J., Ed., McGraw-Hill, New York, 1969. With permission.)

Table 5.2–8
Conveyor Chain

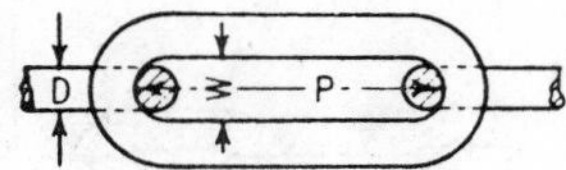

Trade size *D*, in.	Inside width *W*, in.	Inside length *P*, in.	Approx. wt/ 100 ft, lb	Working-load limit, lb	Trade size *D*, in.	Inside width *W*, in.	Inside length *P*, in.	Approx. wt/ 100 ft, lb	Working-load limit, lb
1/2	3/4	3 1/2	205	2740	7/8	2	8	630	8360
1/2	7/8	3 1/2	210	2740	1	1 1/2	5	825	10,940
1/2	1	3 1/2	215	2740	1	1 1/2	6	770	10,940
1/2	1	4	205	2740	1	1 5/8	6	785	10,940
5/8	1	4 1/2	305	4280	1	1 3/4	7	745	10,940
5/8	1	5	295	4280	1	1 3/4	8	720	10,940
5/8	1 1/8	5	300	4280	1	2	7	765	10,940
3/4	1	5	420	6140	1	2	8	735	10,940
3/4	1 1/8	5	430	6140	1 1/8	1 1/2	6	1000	12,480
3/4	1 1/2	5	450	6140	1 1/8	1 3/4	6	1025	12,480
3/4	1 1/8	6	400	6140	1 1/8	2	7	985	12,480
3/4	1 1/2	6	415	6140	1 1/8	2	8	940	12,480
7/8	1 1/8	5	595	8360	1 1/4	2 1/4	7	1260	15,360
7/8	1 1/2	5	625	8360	1 1/4	2 1/4	8	1200	15,360
7/8	1 1/4	6	570	8360	1 3/8	2 1/4	8	1450	18,400
7/8	1 1/2	6	590	8360	1 1/2	2	8	1700	21,760
7/8	1 5/8	6	600	8360	1 1/2	2 1/4	8	1750	21,760
7/8	1 1/4	7	535	8360	1 5/8	2 3/8	8	2120	25,200

Note: Links are long and straight-sided for sprocket-wheel operation. Joints are fire- or electric-welded, finish is typically asphaltum-dipped or blackened, and standard packaging is in bulk.

(From Linnenbank, C. D. in *Handbook of Ocean and Underwater Engineering,* Myers, J. J., Ed., McGraw-Hill, New York, 1969. With permission.)

Table 5.2–9
BUOY CHAIN

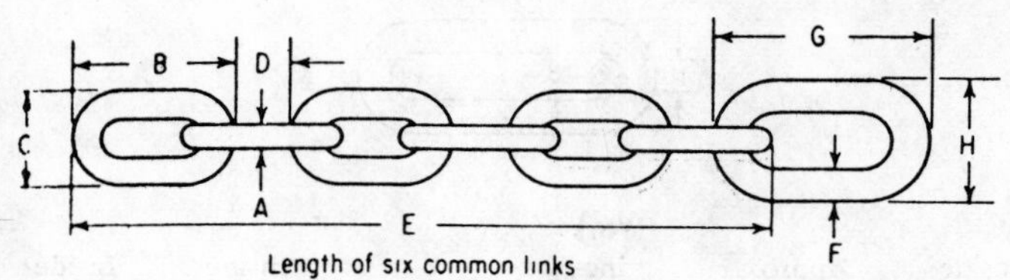

Common links: Wire diam, *A*	Length, *B*	Width, *C*	Space between ends of links, *D*	Length of 6 links, *E*	End links: Wire diam, *F*	Length, *G*	Width *H*	Link tolerance, length and width	Proof load, lb	Break load, lb	Wt / 15 fathoms, lb
1/2	3	1 7/8	1	13	3/4	4 1/2	2 5/8	1/32	7500	15,000	210
5/8	3 3/4	2 1/4	1 1/4	16 1/4	3/4	4 1/2	2 5/8	1/32	11,500	23,000	323
3/4	4 1/2	2 5/8	1 1/2	19 1/2	7/8	5 1/4	3 1/8	1/16	16,000	32,000	442
7/8	5 1/4	3 1/8	1 3/4	22 3/4	1 1/8	6 3/4	3 7/8	1/16	22,000	44,000	608
1	6	3 1/2	2	26	1 1/4	7 1/2	4 3/8	3/32	29,000	58,000	780
1 1/8	6 3/4	3 7/8	2 1/4	29 1/4	1 1/4	7 1/2	4 3/8	3/32	38,500	77,000	990
1 1/4	7 1/2	4 3/8	2 1/2	32 1/2	1 1/2	9	5 1/4	1/8	45,500	91,000	1245
1 1/2	9	5 1/4	3	39	1 7/8	11 1/4	6 1/2	5/32	65,500	131,000	1762
1 5/8	9 3/4	5 11/16	3 1/4	42 1/4	1 7/8	11 1/4	6 1/2	5/32	76,500	153,000	2040
1 3/4	10 1/2	6 1/16	3 1/2	45 1/2	2 1/8	12	7 3/16	3/16	86,500	173,000	2370
1 7/8	11 1/4	6 1/2	3 3/4	48 3/4	2 1/8	12	7 3/16	3/16	100,000	200,000	2640

(From Linnenbank, C. D. in *Handbook of Ocean and Underwater Engineering,* Myers, J. J., Ed., McGraw-Hill, New York, 1969. With permission.)

Table 5.2–10
HIGH-TEST CHAIN

Trade size, in.	Material size, in.	Inside length of link, in.	Inside width of link, in.	Outside length of link, in.	Outside width of link, in.	Links/ft	Max wt / 100 ft, lb	Working-load limit, lb	Trade size, in.
1/4	9/32	0.82	0.39	1.38	0.95	14 1/2	80	2500	1/4
5/16	11/32	1.01	0.48	1.70	1.17	12	123	4000	5/16
3/8	13/32	1.15	0.56	1.96	1.37	10 1/2	175	5100	3/8
7/16	15/32	1.29	0.65	2.23	1.59	9 1/4	235	6600	7/16
1/2	17/32	1.43	0.75	2.49	1.81	8 1/2	300	8200	1/2
5/8	21/32	1.79	0.90	3.10	2.21	6 3/4	450	11,500	5/8
3/4	25/32	1.96	1.06	3.52	2.62	6	655	16,200	3/4

Note: Chain is heat-treated and is of higher carbon content than proof coil or BBB chain. High strength-weight ratio permits the use of smaller and lighter chain for a given purpose. Available in continuous lengths in fiber drums or in short lengths. Joints are electric-welded.

(From Linnenbank, C. D. in *Handbook of Ocean and Underwater Engineering*, Myers, J. J., Ed., McGraw-Hill, New York, 1969. With permission.)

Table 5.2–11
WROUGHT-IRON CRANE CHAIN

Trade size, in.	Material size, in.	Inside length of link, in.	Inside width of link, in.	Outside length of link, in.	Outside width of link, in.	Links/ft	Wt / 100 ft, lb	Working-load limit, lb	Trade size, in.
3/8	13/32	1 3/32	5/8	1 29/32	1 7/16	11	166	2385	3/8
1/2	17/32	1 11/32	3/4	2 13/32	1 13/16	9	275	4240	1/2
5/8	21/32	1 11/16	7/8	3	2 3/16	7 1/8	430	6630	5/8
3/4	25/32	1 7/8	1	3 7/16	2 9/16	6 3/8	615	9540	3/4
7/8	29/32	2 1/4	1 1/4	4 1/16	3 1/16	5 3/8	820	12,960	7/8
1	1 1/32	2 9/16	1 3/8	4 5/8	3 7/16	4 3/4	1045	16,950	1
1 1/8	1 5/32	2 7/8	1 5/8	5 3/16	3 15/16	4 1/4	1310	20,040	1 1/8
1 1/4	1 9/32	3 1/16	1 3/4	5 5/8	4 5/16	4	1600	24,750	1 1/4
1 3/8	1 13/32	3 5/8	1 7/8	6 7/16	4 11/16	3 3/8	1930	29,910	1 3/8
1 1/2	1 17/32	3 7/8	2	6 15/16	5 1/16	3 1/8	2335	35,600	1 1/2

Note: The elastic quality of the iron permits recovery from strain produced by shock. When overloaded, the links will stretch before breaking, providing a valuable and important safety feature. Joints are fire-welded, and standard packaging is in bulk.

(From Linnenbank, C. D. in *Handbook of Ocean and Underwater Engineering*, Myers, J. J., Ed., McGraw-Hill, New York, 1969. With permission.)

Table 5.2–12
ALLOY CHAIN

Trade size, in.	Material size, in.	Inside length of link, in.	Inside width of link, in.	Outside length of link, in.	Outside width of link, in.	Links/ ft	Wt/ 100 ft, lb	Working-load limit, lb	Trade size, in.
1/4	9/32	0.85	0.39	1.41	.95	14	73	3250	1/4
5/16	11/32	0.98	0.44	1.67	1.13	12 1/4	110	4250	5/16
3/8	13/32	1.10	0.52	1.91	1.33	11	163	6600	3/8
1/2	17/32	1.49	0.72	2.55	1.78	8	270	11,250	1/2
5/8	21/32	1.74	0.91	3.05	2.22	7	422	16,500	5/8
3/4	25/32	2.05	0.97	3.61	2.53	5 3/4	590	23,000	3/4
7/8	7/8	2.25	1.09	4.00	2.84	5 1/3	730	28,750	7/8
1	1	2.62	1.25	4.62	3.25	4 1/2	965	38,750	1
1 1/8	1 1/8	3.00	1.37	5.25	3.62	4	1200	44,500	1 1/8
1 1/4	1 1/4	3.25	1.65	5.75	4.15	3 3/4	1525	57,500	1 1/4

Note: This chain, heat-treated to develop maximum strength consistent with proper ductility, has more than twice the strength of low-carbon chain of the same size. It will elongate well in excess of the minimum requirements. This safety feature provides a warning when the chain is overloaded or when it is used in applications where links are subject to extreme bending stresses. Heat treating develops a Brinell hardness of 240 to 270. This chain does not work-harden under normal conditions, making stress relief or re-heat treatment unnecessary. Min. elongation is 15%. Joints are electric-welded. Alloy chain is available in continuous lengths in fiber drums or in short lengths. Test certificates are generally available on request.

Alloys: Low-alloy heat-treatable steel[a] has enjoyed a rapid rise in popularity for chain in recent years. Such chain is sold under a variety of trade names. After heat treatment typical chain has the properties of minimum tensile strength of 125,000 psi, min. elongation of 15%, and hardness of 25-28R_c. Softer, even more ductile chain may be produced for specific application by control of the heating cycle.

[a] ASTM Specification A391-65.

(From Linnenbank, C. D. in *Handbook of Ocean and Underwater Engineering,* Myers, J. J., Ed., McGraw-Hill, New York, 1969. With permission.)

Table 5.2–13
CHAIN SWIVELS

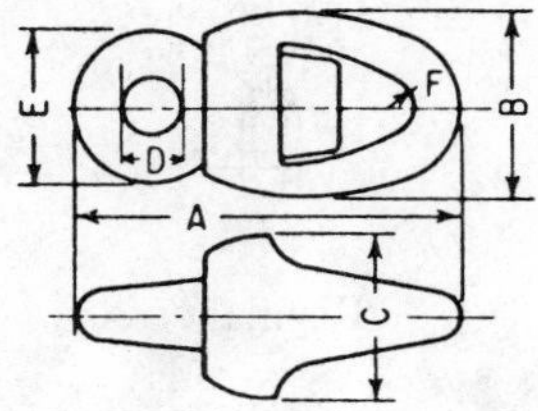

Chain size	*A*	*B*	*C*	*D*	*E*	*F*
1/2–5/8	5 3/8	2 7/16	2 7/16	13/16	2 1/16	7/16
11/16–3/4	6 25/32	3	3	1 1/16	2 9/16	3/4
3/16–7/8	7 13/16	3 1/2	3 1/2	1 3/16	2 15/16	7/8
15/16–1 1/8	10 3/16	4	4	1 3/4	3 11/16	1
1 3/16–1 1/2	14 1/4	7 3/8	6 3/4	2 1/2	5 1/2	1 1/8
1 9/16–1 7/8	15 15/16	7 7/8	7 7/8	2 5/8	6 3/8	1 1/4
1 15/16–2 3/16	19 1/8	9 7/16	9 7/16	3 1/8	7 5/8	1 3/8
2 1/4–2 3/8	21 11/16	10 13/32	9 1/4	4	8 3/4	1 1/2
2 7/16–2 13/16	25 5/16	12 1/2	10 3/4	4 5/8	10 3/8	1 3/4
2 7/8–3 3/8	30 9/16	13 11/16	12	5 1/4	11 1/16	2 1/4
3 7/16–3 3/4	34 3/4	16 1/4	14 1/2	6	13 3/8	2 3/8

Note: Sizes and dimensions in inches.

(From Linnenbank, C. D. in *Handbook of Ocean and Underwater Engineering*, Myers, J. J., Ed., McGraw-Hill, New York, 1969. With permission.)

Table 5.2–14
SWIVELS

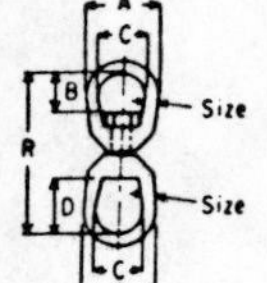

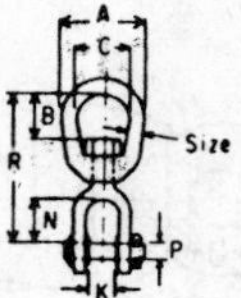

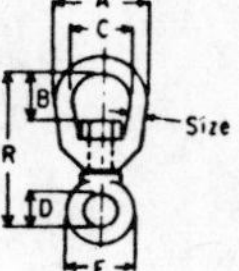

Regular

Size, in.	Est. UTS, tons	Swivel dimensions, in. A	B	C	D	R	Wt, lb
1/4	1.8	1 1/4	11/16	3/4	1 1/16	2 15/16	0.19
5/16	2.6	1 5/8	7/8	1	1 1/4	3 9/16	0.31
3/8	4.9	2	1	1 1/4	1 1/2	4 5/16	0.68
1/2	7.9	2 1/2	1 3/8	1 1/2	2	5 7/16	1.25
5/8	11.7	3	1 21/32	1 3/4	2 3/8	6 9/16	2.25
3/4	16.2	3 1/2	1 13/16	2	2 5/8	7 3/16	3.5
7/8	21.2	4	2 1/8	2 1/4	3 1/16	8 3/8	5.4
1	26.7	4 1/2	2 7/16	2 1/2	3 1/2	9 5/8	8.8
1 1/8	33.9	5	2 7/16	2 3/4	3 3/4	10 3/8	12
1 1/4	40.4	5 5/8	2 3/4	3 1/8	2 3/4	11 1/8	16
1 1/2	113.0	7	4 1/4	4	4 1/4	17 1/8	49

Jaw End

Size, in.	Est. UTS, tons	Swivel dimensions, in. A	B	C	K	N	P	R	Wt, lb
1/4	1.8	1 1/4	11/16	3/4	15/32	7/8	1/4	2 5/8	0.22
5/16	2.6	1 5/8	7/8	1	1/2	7/8	5/16	2 15/16	0.31
3/8	4.9	2	1	1 1/4	5/8	1 1/16	3/8	3 5/8	0.56
1/2	7.9	2 1/2	1 3/8	1 1/2	3/4	1 5/16	1/2	4 1/2	1.25
5/8	11.7	3	1 21/32	1 3/4	15/16	1 1/2	5/8	5 5/16	2.13
3/4	16.2	3 1/2	1 13/16	2	1 1/8	1 3/4	3/4	6 1/16	3.5
7/8	21.2	4	2 1/8	2 1/4	1 3/16	2 1/16	7/8	7	5.3
1	26.7	4 1/2	2 7/16	2 1/2	1 3/4	2 13/16	1 1/8	8 9/16	9.8
1 1/8	33.9	5	2 7/16	2 3/4	1 3/4	2 13/16	1 1/8	8 15/16	14
1 1/4	40.4	5 5/8	2 3/4	3 1/8	2 1/16	2 13/16	1 3/8	9 7/16	17
1 1/2	113.0	7	4 1/4	4	2 7/8	4 7/16	2 1/4	14 3/4	49

Chain

Size, in.	Est. UTS, tons	Swivel dimensons, in. A	B	C	D	E	R	Wt, lb
1/4	1.8	1 1/4	11/16	3/4	7/16	15/16	2 1/4	0.13
5/16	2.6	1 5/8	7/8	1	1/2	1 1/8	2 23/32	0.25
3/8	4.9	2	1	1 1/4	3/4	1 1/2	3 7/16	0.5
1/2	7.9	2 1/2	1 3/8	1 1/2	7/8	1 7/8	4 1/4	1
5/8	11.7	3	1 21/32	1 3/4	1 1/16	2 3/16	5 1/8	1.75
3/4	16.2	3 1/2	1 13/16	2	1 1/4	2 5/8	5 25/32	2.88
7/8	21.2	4	2 1/8	2 1/4	1 7/16	2 15/16	6 5/8	4.3
1	26.7	4 1/2	2 7/16	2 1/2	2	4	8 1/16	6.8

(Source: Federal Specification RRc 272a. From Linnenbank, C. D. in *Handbook of Ocean and Underwater Engineering*, Myers, J. J., Ed., McGraw-Hill, New York, 1969. With permission.)

Table 5.2–15
SCREW-PIN SHACKLES

Anchor shackles: round pin, screw pin

Safe working load, tons	Size, in.	Inside length, in.	Inside width, in. At pin	Inside width, in. At bow	Diam, in. Pin	Diam, in. Outside of eye	Tolerance, plus or minus Length	Tolerance, plus or minus Width	Wt, lb
1/3[a]	3/16	7/8	3/8	19/32	1/4	9/16	1/16	1/16	0.05
1/2	1/4	1 1/8	15/32	25/32	5/16	11/16	1/16	1/16	0.12
3/4	5/16	1 7/32	17/32	27/32	3/8	13/16	1/16	1/16	0.18
1	3/8	1 7/16	21/32	1 1/32	7/16	31/32	1/8	1/16	0.3
1 1/2	7/16	1 11/16	23/32	1 5/32	1/2	1 1/16	1/8	1/16	0.49
2	1/2	1 7/8	13/16	1 5/16	5/8	1 3/16	1/8	1/16	0.74
3 1/4	5/8	2 3/8	1 1/16	1 11/16	3/4	1 9/16	1/8	1/16	1.44
4 3/4	3/4	2 13/16	1 1/4	2	7/8	1 7/8	1/4	1/16	2.16
6 1/2	7/8	3 5/16	1 7/16	2 9/32	1	2 1/8	1/4	1/16	3.37
8 1/2	1	3 3/4	1 11/16	2 11/16	1 1/8	2 3/8	1/4	1/16	5.3
9 1/2	1 1/8	4 1/4	1 13/16	2 29/32	1 1/4	2 5/8	1/4	1/16	7
12	1 1/4	4 11/16	2 1/32	3 1/4	1 3/8	3	1/4	1/16	9.6
13 1/2	1 3/8	5 1/4	2 1/4	3 5/8	1 1/2	3 5/16	1/4	1/8	12.6
17	1 1/2	5 3/4	2 3/8	3 7/8	1 5/8	3 5/8	1/4	1/8	17.3
25	1 3/4	7	2 7/8	5	2	4 5/16	1/4	1/8	27.8
35	2	7 3/4	3 1/4	5 3/4	2 1/4	5	1/4	1/8	41.1
50	2 1/2	10 1/2	4 1/8	7 1/4	2 3/4	6	3/4	1/8	83.5
75[b]	3	13	5	7 7/8	3 1/4	6 1/2	3/4	1/8	119

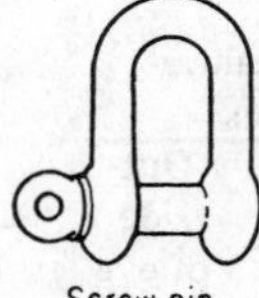

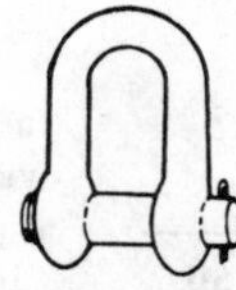

Chain shackles: round pin, screw pin

Safe working load, tons,	Size, in.	Inside length, in.	Inside width, in.	Diam, in. Pin	Diam, in. Outside of eye	Tolerance, plus or minus Length	Tolerance, plus or minus Width	Wt, lb
1/2	1/4	7/8	15/32	5/16	11/16	1/16	1/16	0.11
3/4	5/16	1 1/32	17/32	3/8	13/16	1/16	1/16	0.17
1	3/8	1 1/4	21/32	7/16	31/32	1/8	1/16	0.29
1 1/2	7/16	1 7/16	23/32	1/2	1 1/16	1/8	1/16	0.42
2	1/2	1 5/8	13/16	5/8	1 5/16	1/8	1/16	0.68
3 1/4	5/8	2	1 1/16	3/4	1 9/16	1/8	1/16	1.21

[a] Furnished in screw pin only.
[b] Furnished in round pin only.

Table 5.2–15 (*Continued*)
SCREW-PIN SHACKLES

Safe working load, tons,	Size, in.	Inside length, in.	Inside width, in.	Diam, in. Pin	Diam, in. Outside of eye	Tolerance, plus or minus Length	Tolerance, plus or minus Width	Wt, lb
4 3/4	3/4	2 3/8	1 1/4	7/8	1 7/8	1/4	1/16	2.14
6 1/2	7/8	2 13/16	1 7/16	1	2 1/8	1/4	1/16	3.1
8 1/2	1	3 3/16	1 11/16	1 1/8	2 3/8	1/4	1/16	4.5
9 1/2	1 1/8	3 9/16	1 13/16	1 1/4	2 5/8	1/4	1/16	6.6
12	1 1/4	3 15/16	2 1/32	1 3/8	3	1/4	1/8	8.9
13 1/2	1 3/8	4 7/16	2 1/4	1 1/2	3 5/16	1/4	1/8	12
17	1 1/2	4 7/8	2 3/8	1 5/8	3 5/8	1/4	1/8	16.2
25	1 3/4	5 3/4	2 7/8	2	4 5/16	1/4	1/8	25
35	2	6 3/4	3 1/4	2 1/4	5	1/4	1/8	36
50	2 1/2	8	4 1/8	2 3/4	6	3/4	1/8	74
75[b]	3	8 1/2	5	3 1/4	6 1/2	3/4	1/8	10 1/8

(Source: Federal Specification RRc 271a. From Linnenbank, C. D. in *Handbook of Ocean and Underwater Engineering*, Myers, J. J., Ed., McGraw-Hill, New York, 1969. With permission.)

Table 5.2–16
SAFETY AND TRAWLING SHACKLES

Safety-type anchor shackles with thin head bolt-nut with cotter pin

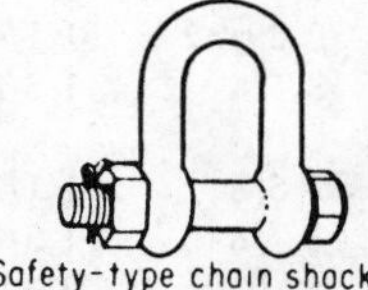

Safety-type chain shackles thin hex head bolt-nut with cotter pin

Trawling shackle with thin square head with screw pin

Safety Anchor and Chain

Safe working load, tons	Size, in.	Inside length, in. 2130	Inside length, in. 2150	Inside width at pin, in.	Diam, in. Pin	Diam, in. Outside of eye	Tolerance, plus or minus Length	Tolerance, plus or minus Width	Wt, lb 2130	Wt, lb 2150
2	1/2	1 7/8	1 5/8	13/16	5/8	1 5/16	1/8	1/16	0.82	0.76
3 1/4	5/8	2 3/8	2	1 1/16	3/4	1 9/16	1/8	1/16	1.58	1.56
4 3/4	3/4	2 13/16	2 3/8	1 1/4	7/8	1 7/8	1/4	1/16	2.82	2.62
6 1/2	7/8	3 5/16	2 13/16	1 7/16	1	2 1/8	1/4	1/16	3.95	3.65
8 1/2	1	3 3/4	3 3/16	1 11/16	1 1/8	2 3/8	1/4	1/16	5.6	5.35
9 1/2	1 1/8	4 1/4	3 9/16	1 13/16	1 1/4	2 5/8	1/4	1/16	7.85	7.27
12	1 1/4	4 11/16	3 15/16	2 1/32	1 3/8	3	1/4	1/16	11.2	10.2
13 1/2	1 3/8	5 1/4	4 7/16	2 1/4	1 1/2	3 5/16	1/4	1/8	15.2	13.35
17	1 1/2	5 3/4	4 7/8	2 3/8	1 5/8	3 5/8	1/4	1/8	19.5	18.5
25	1 3/4	7	5 3/4	2 7/8	2	4 5/16	1/4	1/8	31.3	28.5
35	2	7 3/4	6 3/4	3 1/4	2 1/4	5	1/4	1/8	46.3	41.1
50	2 1/2	10 1/2	8	4 1/8	2 3/4	6	3/4	1/8	94	84.5
75	3	13	9	5	3 1/4	6 1/2	3/4	1/8	145	123
100	3 1/2	15	10 1/2	5 3/4	3 3/4	8	1	1/4	250	218
130	4	17	12 1/2	6 1/2	4 1/4	9	1	1/4	358	310

Table 5.2–16 (*Continued*)
SAFETY AND TRAWLING SHACKLES

Trawling Shackles

Safe working load, tons	Size, in.	Inside length, in.	Inside width at pin, in.	Diam, in.		Tolerance, plus or minus		Wt, lb
				Pin	Outside of eye	Length	Width	
2	1/2	1 5/8	13/16	5/8	1 5/16	1/8	1/16	0.68
3 1/4	5/8	2	1 1/16	3/4	1 9/16	1/8	1/16	1.21
4 3/4	3/4	2 3/8	1 1/4	7/8	1 7/8	1/4	1/16	2.14
6 1/2	7/8	2 13/16	1 7/16	1	2 1/8	1/4	1/16	3.07
8 1/2	1	3 3/16	1 11/16	1 1/8	2 3/8	1/4	1/16	4.53
12	1 1/4	3 15/16	2 1/32	1 3/8	3	1/4	1/8	8.87

(Source: Federal Specification RRc 271a. From Linnenbank, C. D. in *Handbook of Ocean and Underwater Engineering*, Myers, J. J., Ed., McGraw-Hill, New York, 1969. With permission.)

5.3 Underwater Cables

Table 5.3–1
COPPER-STRAND PROPERTIES

Size AWG	Cross section, nominal: Circular mils	Cross section, nominal: in.^{2}	Cross section, nominal: mm^2	No. wires and size each, in.	Wt / 1,000 ft, lb	Diam of strand, in.	Max dc resistance uncoated S.D. strand ohms/ 1,000 ft, 20°C
20	1020	0.000804	0.519	7-0.0121	3.16	0.036	10.4
18	1620	0.00128	0.823	7-0.0152	5.01	0.046	6.51
16	2580	0.00203	1.31	7-0.0192	7.98	0.058	4.10
14	4110	0.00323	2.08	7-0.0242	12.7	0.073	2.58
12	6530	0.00513	3.31	7-0.0305	20.2	0.092	1.62
10	10,380	0.008155	5.262	7-0.0385	32	0.116	1.02
9	13,090	0.01028	6.632	7-0.0432	40.4	0.130	0.808
8	16,510	0.01297	8.367	7-0.0486	51	0.146	0.641
7	20,820	0.01635	10.55	7-0.0545	64	0.164	0.508
6	26,240	0.02061	13.30	7-0.0612	81	0.184	0.403
5	33,090	0.02599	16.77	7-0.0688	102	0.206	0.320
4	41,740	0.03278	21.15	7-0.0772	129	0.232	0.253
3	52,620	0.04133	26.67	7-0.0867	163	0.260	0.201
2	66,360	0.05212	33.62	7-0.0974	205	0.292	0.159
1	83,690	0.06573	42.41	19-0.0664	258	0.332	0.126
1/0	105,600	0.08291	53.49	19-0.0745	326	0.373	0.100
2/0	133,100	0.1045	67.43	19-0.0837	411	0.419	0.0795
3/0	167,800	0.1318	85.01	19-0.0940	518	0.470	0.0630
4/0	211,600	0.1662	107.20	19-0.1055	653	0.528	0.0500
–	250,000	0.1964	127	37-0.0822	772	0.575	0.0423
–	300,000	0.2356	152	37-0.090	926	0.630	0.0353
–	350,000	0.2749	177	37-0.0973	1081	0.681	0.0302
–	400,000	0.3142	203	37-0.104	1235	0.728	0.0264
–	500,000	0.3927	253	37-0.1162	1544	0.813	0.0212
–	600,000	0.4712	304	61-0.0992	1853	0.893	0.0176
–	700,000	0.5498	355	61-0.1071	2161	0.964	0.0151
–	750,000	0.5890	380	61-0.1109	2316	0.998	0.0141
–	800,000	0.6283	405	61-0.1145	2470	1.031	0.0132
–	900,000	0.7069	456	61-0.1215	2779	1.094	0.0118
–	1,000,000	0.7854	507	61-0.1280	3088	1.152	0.0106
–	1,250,000	0.9818	633	91-0.1172	3859	1.289	0.00846
–	1,500,000	1.178	760	91-0.1284	4631	1.412	0.00705
–	1,750,000	1.374	887	127-0.1174	5403	1.526	0.00604
–	2,000,000	1.571	1013	127-0.1255	6175	1.632	0.00529
–	2,500,000	1.964	1267	127-0.1403	7794	1.824	0.00427
–	3,000,000	2.356	1520	169-0.1332	9353	1.998	0.00356

(From Am. Steel and Wire Div., *Electrical Wire and Cable Handbook*, U.S. Steel Corp., Cleveland, 1956. With permission.)

Table 5.3–2
COPPER-STRAND BREAKING STRENGTH

Size AWG	Class of strand	No. wires	Breaking strength, lb Hard drawn, min	Medium–hard drawn, min	Soft or annealed max
4/0	B	19	9617	7479	6149
4/0	A and AA	12	9483	7378	6149
4/0	A and AA	7	9154	7269	6149
3/0	B	19	7698	5970	5074
3/0	A and AA	12	7556	5890	4876
3/0	A and AA	7	7366	5812	4876
2/0	B	19	6153	4766	4025
2/0	....	12	6049	4704	3868
2/0	A and AA	7	5927	4641	3868
1/0	B	19	4899	3803	3190
1/0	....	12	4840	3753	3190
1/0	A and AA	7	4750	3703	3066
1	B	19	3898	3037	2531
1	A	7	3804	2958	2432
1	AA	3	3620	2875	2432
2	B and A	7	3045	2361	2007
2	AA	3	2913	2299	1929
3	B and A	7	2433	1885	1591
3	AA	3	2359	1835	1529
4	B and A	7	1938	1505	1262
4	AA	3	1879	1465	1213
5	B	7	1542	1201	1001
6	B	7	1228	958.6	793.7
7	B	7	977.2	765.3	629.6
8	B	7	777.2	610.7	499.2
9	B	7	618.1	487.3	395.8
10	B	7	491.6	388.9	313.9
12	B	7	311.1	247.7	197.5
14	B	7	197.1	157.7	124.2
16	B	7	124.7	100.4	81.15
18	B	7	78.98	63.89	51.02
20	B	7	50.06	40.69	32.11

(From Am. Steel and Wire Div., *Electrical Wire and Cable Handbook,* U.S. Steel Corp., Cleveland, 1956. With permission.)

Table 5.3–3
PROPERTIES OF COMMON INSULATING MATERIALS

Property	Rubbers		Polyvinyl chloride	Polyethylene		Poly-propylene	Teflon®	Nylon
	Ethylene propylene, EPM	Natural		Low density	High density			
Specific inductive capacitance	3.1	3.5	5.0	2.3	2.3	2.2	2.0	4.6
Dissipation factor	0.01	0.01	0.05	0.0005	0.0005	0.0005	0.0003	0.04
Max. operating temp, °C	90	75	85	85	90	95	125	105
Softening temp (vicat), °C	–	–	–	98	124	150	260	195
Melting temp, °C	–	–	–	110	131	168	285	207
Tensile strength, psi	950	2500	2000	3000	3600	5000	2700	10,000
Hardness	Shore A 75	Shore A 60–65	Shore 60A–70D	Shore 45D	Shore 67D	Shore 75D	Rockwell R25	Rockwell 297
Moisture resistance, mg/in.^{2}, 70°C	3.5	25	5–15	2	2	2	nil	3.5% (by wt)
Dielectric strength, V/mil.	450–500	400	500	600	600	600	800	
Ins. resis. constant (K) $IR = K \log (D/d)$, 60°F	50,000	10,000	1000	50,000	50,000	50,000	100,000	
Relative cost/in.^{3}	1.5	1.5	1	0.8	1	1	47	5.2

(From Peirce, W. T. in *Handbook of Ocean and Underwater Engineering,* Myers, J. J., Ed., McGraw-Hill, New York, 1969. With permission.)

Table 5.3–4
PROPERTIES OF JACKET MATERIALS

Property	Neoprene	Polyvinyl chloride	Poly-ethylene	Poly-urethane	Hypalon®	Nylon
Sea water resistance	Good	Good	Excellent	Good	Good	Good
Oil resistance	Very good	Very good	Fair	Good	Very good	Very good
Moisture permeability	Poor	Poor	Very good	Very good	Good	Poor
Tensile strength, psi	2100	2000	3000	7000	2000	10,000
Tear resistance, lb/in	45	250–260	No data	400	40	
Sunlight resistance	Excellent (black)	Excellent (black)	Excellent (black)	Excellent (black)	Excellent (black)	Excellent (black)
Compression-cut resistance, lb/0.1 in	1350	>2000	>2000	Excellent	1000	Good

(From Peirce, W. T. in *Handbook of Ocean and Underwater Engineering,* Myers, J. J., Ed., McGraw-Hill, New York, 1969. With permission.)

5.4 Marine Power Sources

Figure 5.4–1
MARINE POWER-VERSUS-TIME SPECTRUM

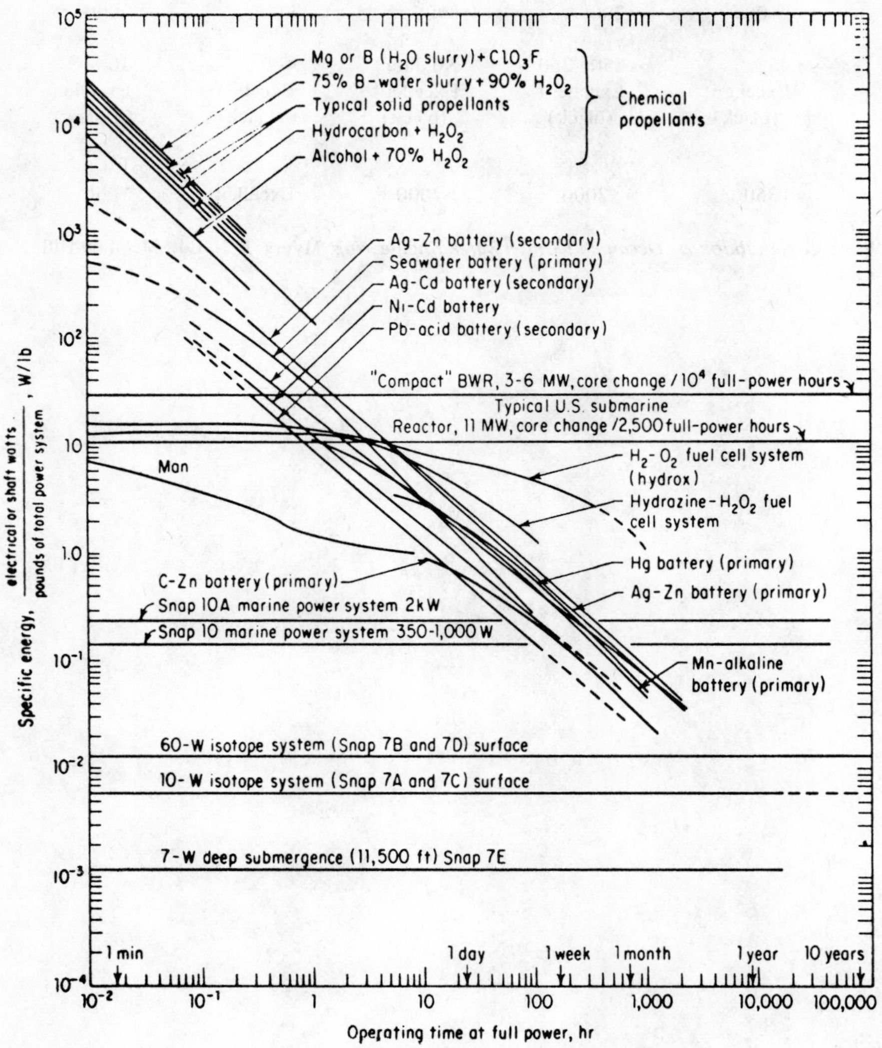

(From Cohn, P. D. and Wetch, J. R. in *Handbook of Ocean and Underwater Engineering*, Myers, J. J., Ed., McGraw-Hill, New York, 1969. With permission.)

Table 5.4–1
IDEALIZED PERFORMANCE OF COMMON DRY-CELL BATTERIES

Properties	Carbon-zinc (Leclanche)	Manganese-alkaline	Mercury	Silver-oxide-zinc
Typical size range, lb/cell (data below for 1 lb)	0.003–2.1	0.02–0.5	0.001–0.4	0.004–0.5
Cell materials				
Negative terminal	Zinc	Zinc	Zinc	Zinc
Positive terminal	MnO_2	MnO_2	HgO	Ag_2O
Electrolyte	NH_4Cl	KOH	KOH or NaOH	KOH or NaOH
Chief chemical reaction (simplified)	$Zn + 2\ MnO_2 \rightarrow ZnO + Mn_2O_3$	$Zn + MnO_2 \rightarrow ZnO + Mn_2O_3$	$Zn + HgO \rightarrow ZnO + Hg$	$Zn + Ag_2O \rightarrow ZnO + 2Ag$
Idealized performance, 1 lb cell, 70° F, continuous 1,000 hr rate, 1-V cutoff:				
Open-circuit V	1.5	1.5	1.35	1.6
Avg V to cutoff	1.25	1.3	1.3	1.5
Energy W-hr/lb	36	45	52	60+
Capacity, A-hr/lb to 1-V cutoff	30	35	40	40
Specific volume, in.^{3}/lb (complete cell and case)	15	10	7.5	6
Maintenance and life				
Charge retention, % drop/mo at 70° F for unused charged cell, approx.	0.7–2	0.2	0.1	1

(From Yeaple, F. D., *Prod. Eng.*, 36, 100, 1965. With permission.)

Table 5.4–2
RELATIONSHIP OF TEMPERATURE, DISCHARGE RATE, AND PERFORMANCE

Battery type	Cell rated capacity, A-hr	Discharge rate, A	Potential at midpoint, V			Capacity, A-hr, % rated			Energy density W-hr/lb			Energy density W-hr/in.^{3}		
			80°F	0°F	−40°F	80°F	0°F	−40°F	80°F	0°F	−40°F	80°F	0°F	−40°F
Lead-acid	5	0.5	1.95	1.89	1.85	100	54	30	10.8	5.6	3.1	0.76	0.40	0.22
		1.0	1.92	1.84	1.80	88	50	21	9.3	5.1	2.1	0.66	0.36	0.15
		10.0	1.81	1.60	1.40	46	16	3	4.7	1.4	0.24	0.33	0.10	0.02
	60	10.0	1.92	1.89	1.82	100	54	26	12.2	6.5	3.1	0.91	0.48	0.23
		25.0	1.90	1.80	1.65	87	31	10	10.5	3.5	1.0	0.78	0.26	0.07
		50.0	1.87	1.70	–	63	18	–	7.5	2.0	–	0.56	0.14	–
		100.0	1.70	–	–	39	–	–	4.1	–	–	0.31	–	–
Nickel-iron	10	2.0	1.20	0.98	–	100	67	–	10.6	7.1	–	0.91	0.61	–
	75	15.0	1.20	0.98	–	100	67	–	10.3	7.2	–	0.73	0.49	–
Nickel-cadmium	5	1.0	1.22	–	–	100	–	–	10.6	–	–	0.76	–	–
		10.0	1.11	1.05	1.05	94	67	21	9.1	6.2	2.0	0.65	0.45	0.14
	75	10.0	1.23	1.16	1.14	100	86	64	11.4	9.2	6.7	0.87	0.70	0.51
		25.0	1.20	1.14	1.06	97	82	48	10.8	8.7	4.7	0.83	0.66	0.36
		50.0	1.18	1.07	1.00	94	72	34	10.3	7.0	3.1	0.78	0.54	0.24
		100.0	1.17	–	–	82	–	–	8.4	–	–	0.64	–	–
Silver-zinc	5	0.5	1.52	1.45	–	100	75	–	43.0	31.0	–	2.2	1.6	–
		1.0	1.50	1.42	–	96	70	–	40.7	30.0	–	2.1	1.6	–
		10.0	1.40	1.26	–	85	63	–	33.7	27.0	–	1.7	1.4	–
	60	10.0	1.52	1.46	–	100	92	–	46.5	39.0	–	3.15	2.6	–
		25.0	1.49	1.42	–	97	79	–	44.7	39.0	–	3.0	2.6	–
		50.0	1.48	1.42	–	92	75	–	42.2	39.0	–	2.8	2.6	–
		100.0	1.42	1.30	–	84	69	–	36.9	35.0	–	2.5	2.4	–
Silver-cadmium	5	0.5	1.08	1.03	0.9	100	85	44	26.8	21.5	10	1.78	1.4	0.67
		5.0	1.05	0.99	0.7	95	80	40	21.0	16.0	5.6	1.4	1.05	0.37
	60	6.0	1.10	1.08	–	100	96	–	31.7	30.6	–	2.9	2.8	–
		60.0	1.00	0.94	0.9	95	80	40	24.5	22.6	13	2.2	2.0	1.2

Note: These performance data are taken at random from a variety of cells. They show pronounced effects of temperature and discharge rate on performance. Dashes indicate that heaters are needed to warm cell in cold ambients. Nickel-iron cells, however, are not usually used at temperatures below 0°F.

(From Yeaple, F. D., *Prod. Eng.*, 36, 100, 1965. With permission.)

Table 5.4–3
CELL CHARACTERISTICS: FIVE COMMON BATTERY TYPES

	Composition, charged state			Cell potential, V		Time to discharge				Shelf life in charged condition: Without maintenance	Shelf life in charged condition: With maintenance			Life in operation	
Battery type	Pos.	Neg.	Electrolyte	Open circ.	Discharging	Fastest, min	Avg, hr	Slowest, days	Shelf life if discharged, wet	Charge loss, %	Shelf life	If charged each	Shelf life	Cycles	Float
Lead-acid	PbO_2	Pb	H_2SO_4	2.14	2.1–1.46	3–5	8	>3	Not permitted	High-rate 50%/10 days Low rate 15–20%/yr	Days Months	30–45 days	Years	To 500	To 14 yr
Nickel-iron	NiO_2	Fe	KOH	1.34	1.3–0.75	10	5	>3	Decades	15–25%/mo	Weeks	30–45 days	Years	100–3000	To 30 yr
Nickel-cadmium	NiO_2	Cd	KOH	1.34	1.3–0.75	5	5	>3	Years	Pocket 20–40%/yr Sintered 10–15%/mo	Months Weeks	30–45 days	Years	100–2000 25–500	8–14 yr 4–8 yr
Silver-zinc	AgO	Zn	KOH	1.86	1.55–1.1	<0.5	5	>90	Years	15–20%/yr	3–12 mo	6 mo	1–2 yr	100–300 low dis. 5–100 high dis.	1–2 yr
Silver-cadmium	AgO	Cd	KOH	1.34	1.3–0.8	5	5	>90	Years	50%/2 yr	1–2 yr	6 mo	2–3 yr	500–1000	2–3 yr

(From Yeaple, F. D., *Prod. Eng.*, 36, 100, 1965.)

Table 5.4–4
REACTOR POWER SYSTEMS

Device	Manufacturer	Type	Approx installed cost	Power: Thermal	Power: Electric	Weight
SNAP 10	AI	Solid-state ZrH-U, T.E. conversion	–	10–30 kW	350–1000 W	3500 lb
SNAP 10A	AI	NaK-cooled ZrH-U T.E. conversion	–	20–80 kW	0.5–2 kW	7200–8200 lb
Compact	AI	High-flow BWR $ZrH-UO_2$ turbo-electric	–	15–30 MW	3–6 MW	25–80 tons[a]
Turps	Martin	P_4S_3-cooled ZrH-U fueled, thermoelect. conv.	–	1.56 MW	100 kW	18,700 lb
S2C	Comb. Engr.	PWR-turboelectric	–	–	1.9 MW[27]	–
S4W, S3W	Westinghouse	PWR-turboelectric	–	–	5.0 MW[27]	
NR-1[b]	G.E.	Small nuclear res. Submarine Reactor, PWR, thermo-electric	–	–	1.9 MW[27]	–
S5W or G	Westinghouse and G.E.	PWR-turboelectric	$9 × 10[26]	–	11.2 MW[27]	–
S3G	G.E.	PWR-turboelectric	–	–	12.7 MW[27]	–
MH1A	Martin	$PWR-UO_2$ steam turboelectric	–	45 MW	10.0 MW[27]	n.a.

Device	Length × diam, ft	Core life	Plant life, yr	New core cost	Present use or status	Design depth
SNAP 10	Cyl. 4¾ × 1¾	5 yr	5	n.a.	Conceptual	12,000 ft
SNAP 10A	Cyl. 9.5 × 5[a]	5 yr	5	n.a.	Conceptual	12,000 ft
Compact	Cyl. 39 × 7½[a]	20 MW (th)-yr	20	–	Under development	Pressure hull req.
Turps	Cyl. 19 × 4	5 yr	–	–	Under development	Pressure hull req.
S2C	–	–	–	–	*SSN Tullibee* class	Pressure hull req.
S4W, S3W						
NR-1[b]	–	–	–	–	*SSN Skate* class	Pressure hull req.
S5W or G	–	2,500 full[25] power hr	~10[25]	~$3 × 10[25]	Polaris subs	Pressure hull req.
S3G	–	–	–	–	*SSN Triton*	Pressure hull req.
MH1A	–	45 MW (th)-yr	~20	–	Barge-mounted, under construction	Surface

[a] Depending on power level and configuration; includes primary, nonpersonnel shielding.
[b] *Nucleonics Week*, April 22, 1965.

REFERENCES

1. **Cohn, P. D.,** *Power Eng.*, 17(2), 1966.
2. **Kenton, J. E.,** *Nucleonics*, 17(9), 73, 1959.
3. **Kenton, J. E.,** *Nucleonics*, 19(9), 67, 1961.
4. **Blackman, V. B., Ed.,** *Jane's Fighting Ships, 1966–1967*, McGraw-Hill, New York, 1966.

Table 5.5–1
RELATIVE FREQUENCY OF WAVES OF DIFFERENT HEIGHTS IN DIFFERENT REGIONS

Ocean region	Height of waves, ft					
	0–3	3–4	4–7	7–12	12–20	⩾20
	%	%	%	%	%	%
North Atlantic, between Newfoundland and England	20	20	20	15	10	15
Mid-equatorial Atlantic	20	30	25	15	5	5
South Atlantic, latitude of Argentina	10	20	20	20	15	10
North Pacific, latitude of Oregon and south of Alaskan Peninsula	25	20	20	15	10	10
East equatorial Pacific	25	35	25	10	5	5
West wind belt of South Pacific, latitude of southern Chile	5	20	20	20	15	15
North Indian Ocean, Northeast monsoon season	55	25	10	5	0	0
North Indian Ocean, Southwest monsoon season	15	15	25	20	15	10
Southern Indian Ocean, between Madagascar and northern Australia	35	25	20	15	5	5
West wind belt of southern Indian Ocean, on route between Cape of Good Hope and southern Australia	10	20	20	20	15	15

(From Bigelow, H. B. and Edmondson, W. T., *Wind Waves at Sea, Breakers, and Surf,* U.S. Navy Hydrographic Office, Washington, D.C., Pub. 602, 1962.)

Table 5.5–2
LENGTH OF STORM WAVES OBSERVED IN DIFFERENT OCEANS

Ocean area	Wave length, ft			No. cases
	Max	Min	Avg	
North Atlantic	559	115	303	15
South Atlantic	701	82	226	32
Pacific	765	80	242	14
Southern Indian	1121	108	360	23
China Sea	261	160	197	3

(From Bigelow, H. B. and Edmondson, W. T., *Wind Waves at Sea, Breakers, and Surf,* U.S. Navy Hydrographic Office, Washington, D.C., Pub. 602, 1962.)

Figure 5.5–1
ISOLINES OF RATIO OF CREST DISPLACEMENT TO WAVE HEIGHT, η_c/H

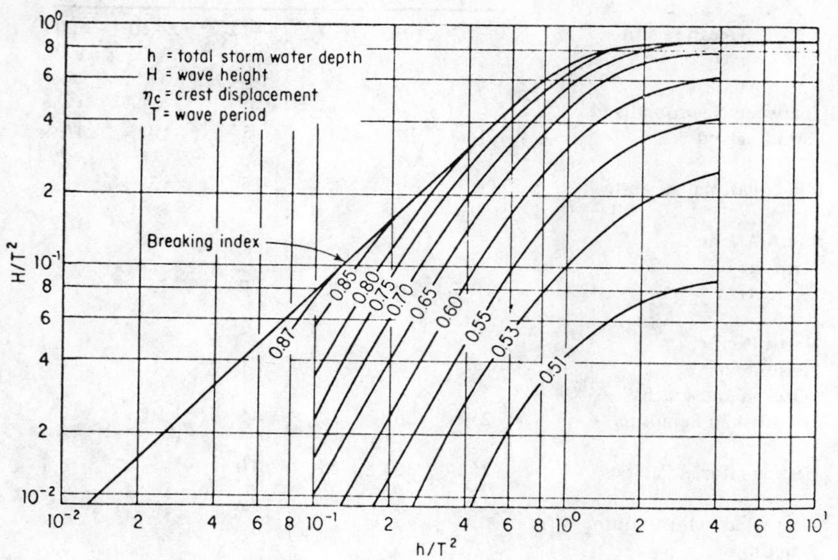

(From Dean, R. G. in *Handbook of Ocean and Underwater Engineering,* Myers, J. J., Ed., McGraw-Hill, New York, 1969. With permission.)

Table 5.5–3
AIRY WAVE

The amplitude A is found to be half the wave height, $H/2$; the coefficients a_i and b_i are unity. Hence

$$\phi_1 = -\frac{H}{2}C\frac{\cosh k(d+z)}{\sinh kd}\sin\theta$$

$$\eta = \frac{H}{2}\cos\theta$$

$$u = \frac{\pi H}{T}\frac{\cosh k(d+z)}{\sinh kd}\cos\theta$$

$$w = \frac{\pi H}{T}\frac{\sinh k(d+z)}{\sinh kd}\sin\theta$$

$$\frac{\partial u}{\partial t} = \frac{2\pi^2 H}{T^2}\frac{\cosh k(d+z)}{\sinh kd}\sin\theta$$

$$\frac{\partial w}{\partial t} = -\frac{2\pi^2 H}{T^2}\frac{\sinh k(d+z)}{\sinh kd}\cos\theta$$

$$p = \rho g\frac{H}{2}\frac{\cosh k(d+z)}{\cosh kd}\cos\theta - \rho gz$$

$$C^2 = \frac{g}{k}\tanh kd$$

where

$$\theta = kx - \omega t$$

$$k = \frac{2\pi}{L}$$

$$\omega = \frac{2\pi}{T}$$

The group velocity (coinciding with the rate of transmission of energy) is given by

$$C_g = nC \quad \text{where}$$

$$n = \frac{1}{2}\left[1 + \frac{2kd}{\sinh 2kd}\right]$$

Because of the conservation of energy, a wave traveling from infinitely deep water into water of finite depth will change height from H_0 to H, where

$$H = K_S H_0$$

and

$$K_S = \tanh kd\left(1 + \frac{2kd}{\sinh 2kd}\right)^{-1/2}$$

The relationships of wavelength, wave period, and water depth are illustrated in figure 5.5–2. A brief table of pertinent hyperbolic functions and a summary of the Airy wave theory is presented in table 5.5–4.

(From Bretschneider, C. L. in *Handbook of Ocean and Underwater Engineering,* Myers, J. J., Ed., McGraw-Hill, New York, 1969. With permission.)

Table 5.5–4
HYPERBOLIC FUNCTIONS AND SUMMARY OF AIRY THEORY

a = horizontal amplitude
b = vertical amplitude
c = wave velocity
c_g = wave group velocity
d = water depth
$k = 2\pi/L$
g = acceleration due to gravity

H = wave height
L = wavelength
p = pressure
T = wave period
U = horizontal particle velocity
V = vertical particle velocity
ρ = unit weight of water
η = height of water surface above mean

Values for deep water are given by the subscript zero. Amplitudes are measured from mean position.

Basic Formulas

$$a_{max}(z) = \frac{H \cosh k(d+z)}{2 \sinh kd}$$

$$b_{max}(z) = \frac{H \sinh k(d+z)}{2 \sinh kd}$$

$$U_{max}(z) = \frac{\pi H \sinh k(d+z)}{T \sinh kd}$$

$$V_{max}(z) = \frac{\pi H \sinh k(d+z)}{T \sinh kd}$$

$$c = \sqrt{\frac{gL}{2\pi} \tanh kd}$$

$$c_g = \frac{1}{2} C \left(1 + \frac{kd}{\sinh kd}\right)$$

$$p_{max}(z) = \rho \frac{H}{2} \frac{\cosh k(d+z)}{2 \cosh kd} + \rho g(d+z)$$

For given values of T and d

1. Calculate $L_0 = g/2\pi T^2 = 5.12T^2$ ft.
2. Calculate d/L_0.
3. Find the desired values from the tables (by linear interpolation).
4. Find L and C from $L = L_0 \tanh kd\ 0 = L/T$.

$\frac{d}{L_0}$	tanh kd	$\frac{d}{L}$	kd	sinh kd	cosh kd	$\frac{2kd}{\sinh 2kd}$	$\frac{H}{H_0}$
0.00	0.000	0.0000	0.000	0.000	1.00	1.000	
.01	.248	.0403	.253	.256	.03	0.958	1.44
.02	.347	.0576	.362	.370	.07	.918	.23
.03	.420	.0714	.448	.463	.10	.877	.12
.04	.480	.0833	.523	.548	.14	.839	.06
0.05	0.531	0.0942	0.592	0.627	1.18	0.800	1.02
.06	.575	.104	.655	.703	.22	.763	0.993
.07	.614	.114	.716	.778	.27	.725	.971
.08	.649	.123	.774	.854	.31	.690	.955
.09	.681	.132	.831	0.930	.36	.654	.942
0.10	0.709	0.141	0.886	1.01	1.42	0.621	0.933
.11	.735	.150	.940	.08	.48	.587	.926
.12	.759	.158	0.994	.16	.54	.555	.920
.13	.780	.166	1.05	.25	.60	.524	.917
.14	.800	.175	.10	.33	.67	.494	.915
0.15	0.818	0.183	1.15	1.42	1.74	0.465	0.913
.16	.835	.192	.20	.52	.82	.437	.913
.17	.850	.200	.26	.61	.90	.410	.913
.18	.864	.208	.31	.72	1.99	.384	.914
.19	.877	.217	.36	.82	2.08	.359	.916
0.20	0.888	0.225	1.41	1.94	2.18	0.335	0.918
.21	.899	.234	.47	2.06	.28	.313	.920
.22	.909	.242	.52	.18	.40	.291	.923
.23	.918	.251	.58	.31	.52	.270	.926
.24	.926	.259	.63	.45	.65	.251	.929
0.25	0.933	0.268	1.68	2.60	2.78	0.233	0.932
.26	.940	.277	.74	.76	2.93	.215	.936
.27	.946	.285	.79	2.92	3.09	.199	.939
.28	.952	.294	.85	3.10	.25	.183	.942
.29	.957	.303	.90	.28	.43	.169	.946

Table 5.5–4 (*Continued*)
HYPERBOLIC FUNCTIONS AND SUMMARY OF AIRY THEORY

$\frac{d}{L_0}$	tanh *kd*	$\frac{d}{L}$	*kd*	sinh *kd*	cosh *kd*	$\frac{2kd}{\sinh 2kd}$	$\frac{H}{H_0}$
0.30	0.961	0.312	1.96	3.48	3.62	0.155	0.949
.31	.965	.321	2.02	.69	3.83	.143	.952
.32	.969	.330	.08	3.92	4.04	.131	.955
.33	.972	.339	.13	4.16	.28	.120	.958
.34	.975	.349	.19	.41	.52	.110	.961
0.35	0.978	0.358	2.25	4.68	4.79	0.100	0.964
.36	.980	.367	.31	4.97	5.07	.091	.967
.37	.982	.377	.37	5.28	.37	.083	.969
.38	.984	.386	.42	.61	5.70	.076	.972
.39	.986	.396	.48	5.96	6.04	.069	.974
0.40	0.988	0.405	2.54	6.33	6.41	0.063	0.976
.41	.989	.414	.60	6.72	6.80	.057	.978
.42	.990	.424	.66	7.15	7.22	.052	.980
.43	.991	.434	.72	7.60	7.66	.047	.982
.44	.992	.443	.79	8.08	8.14	.042	.983
0.45	0.993	0.453	2.85	8.58	8.64	0.038	0.985
.46	.994	.463	.91	9.13	9.19	.035	.986
.47	.995	.472	2.97	9.71	9.76	.031	.987
.48	.995	.482	3.03	10.3	10.4	.028	.988
.49	.996	.492	.09	11.0	11.0	.026	.990
0.50	0.996	0.502	3.15	11.7	11.7	0.023	0.990

(From Lundgren, H., Copenhagen, Denmark, personal communication in *Handbook of Ocean and Underwater Engineering,* Myers, J. J., Ed., McGraw-Hill, New York, 1969. With permission.)

Figure 5.5–2
RELATIONSHIP OF WAVE PERIOD, LENGTH, AND DEPTH

Airy wave theory

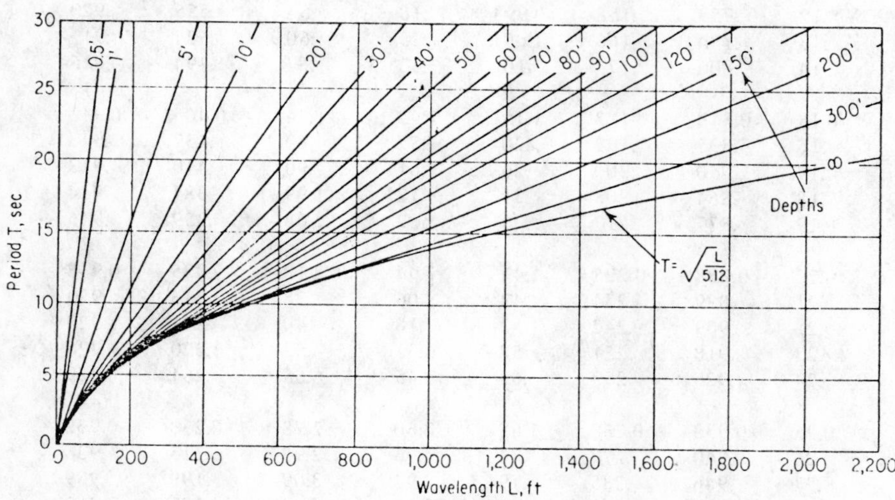

(From Bretschneider, C. L. in *Handbook of Ocean and Underwater Engineering,* Myers, J. J., Ed., McGraw-Hill, New York, 1969. With permission.)

PILINGS – DESIGN CONSIDERATIONS

For structures composed of a single vertical piling it is possible that the natural period of the structure and the vortex shedding period will be sufficiently close to cause coupling between the vortices and the piling, resulting in a self-excited resonant oscillation; that is, the lateral oscillation of the piling enhances the vortex shedding, which in turn causes larger vortex forces, and so on. This effect has been reasonably well investigated for steady flows such as wind blowing on smokestacks, but little relevant information is available for cases of unsteady flows such as water waves.

The wave-force treatment described below pertains to the deterministic forces, that is, those forces directly related to the water particle velocities and accelerations.

For a vertical circular piling of diameter D, in a wave with horizontal components of water-particle velocity u and acceleration u, the elemental horizontal force ΔF on an incremental piling length ΔS is

$$\Delta F = C_D \rho D \frac{u/u/}{2} \Delta S + C_M \frac{\rho \pi D^2}{4} \dot{u} \Delta S$$

where C_D and C_M are drag and inertia coefficients, respectively, and ρ is the mass density of the water (see figure 5.5–3). It should be emphasized that Eq. (1) and the following force and moment treatment include only the effects of wave motion; tidal, wind-driven, or other currents are not included but should be accounted for in design if they are deemed important in a specific location.

The primary problems in the calculation of wave forces are (1) the accurate description of the kinematic flow field for nonlinear waves and (2) correct values of the C_D and C_M coefficients. Wilson and Reid[1] have tabulated available published values of drag and inertia coefficients obtained from laboratory and field investigations. There is considerable discrepancy in the reported results, and it is well known that the steady-flow circular-cylinder-drag coefficient depends on Reynolds number and cylinder surface roughness. The coefficient averages of the summary are probably the most representative published values available; the averages are $\bar{C}_D$ = 1.05 and $\bar{C}_M$ = 1.40, with ranges $0.40 < C_D < 1.60$ and $0.93 < C_M < 2.30$.

These ranges indicate the difficulties in selecting valid design coefficients from the available published literature. It should be mentioned that most of the tests included in the summary were based on reasonably smooth cylinders and were conducted at Reynolds number ranges below those that would be appropriate for design. On the basis of steady-state drag-coefficient variations with Reynolds number, the larger-design Reynolds numbers would be expected to result in a design drag coefficient less than the average C_D value. Tests[2] indicate that the effect of the rougher design piling surface would result in an increased drag coefficient; these two effects would therefore tend to cancel.

The total force at one time on a single vertical piling is determined by integrating Eq. (1) over the submerged portion of the piling. The total forces and moments will vary with time as the wave passes the piling; however, it is the maximum forces and moments that are of most interest. Because of the many parameters involved in the wave-force problem, it is difficult to develop a compact graphical or tabular representation of forces and moments on a piling for all wave conditions (including nonlinearities) and piling diameters of interest. It can be shown, however, that if the drag and inertia coefficients are considered constants, then the maximum force F_m on a single vertical piling can be expressed in dimensionless form as

$$\frac{F_m}{\gamma C_D H^2 D} = \phi_m \; \frac{h}{T^2}, \frac{H}{T^2}, W$$

The maximum total moment M_m on a single vertical piling can be expressed in a corresponding dimensionless form as

$$\frac{M_m}{\gamma C_D H^2 D h} = \alpha_m \; \frac{h}{T^2}, \frac{H}{T^2}, W$$

where γ is the specific weight of water in pounds per cubic foot and W is defined as

$$W = \frac{C_M}{C_D} \frac{D}{H}$$

Figures 5.5–4 to 5.5–7 represent the dimensionless maximum total force for W values of 0.05, 0.1, 0.5, and 1.0, respectively; figures 5.5–8 to 5.5–11 represent the corresponding information for dimensionless maximum total moments. For W values different from those presented in the figures, graphical interpolation will provide a reasonable estimate. The ϕ_m and α_m value indicated at the bottom right of each of these figures is the asymptotic value as derived from small-amplitude wave theory for deep-water conditions. The isolines in these figures are believed to be accurate within 5–10%.

The wave theory employed to develop the isolines on figures 5.4–4 to 5.5–11 and 6 to 13 is a stream-function nonlinear-wave representation which has been shown to be more accurate than other available methods.[3]

To illustrate, suppose we wish to calculate the crest elevation η_c, the maximum total force F_m, and maximum total moment M_m on a single vertical piling for the following wave conditions:

Wave height H	=	40 ft
Water depth h	=	80 ft
Wave period T	=	12 sec
Piling diameter D	=	5 ft

For purposes of this example, drag and inertia coefficients will be taken as the average values (C_D = 1.05 and C_M = 1.40). The use of these average coefficients here, however, should not be interpreted as endorsement for design.

The following parameters are calculated:

$$\frac{h}{T^2} = \frac{80}{12^2} = 0.556$$

$$\frac{H}{T^2} = \frac{40}{12^2} = 0.278$$

PILING – DESIGN CONSIDERATIONS (*Continued*)

$$W = \frac{C_M D}{C_D H} = \frac{1.4 \times 5}{1.05 \times 40} = 0.164$$

(From Dean, R. G. in *Handbook of Ocean and Underwater Engineering,* Myers, J. J., Ed., McGraw-Hill, New York, 1969. With permission.)

REFERENCES

1. **Wilson, B. W. and Reid, R. O.,** *J. Waterways Harbors Div. Am. Soc. Civil Eng.,* 89(WW1), 61, 1963.
2. **Blumberg, R. and Rigg, A. M.,** Petrol. Session, Am. Soc. Met. Eng. meeting, Los Angeles, June 14, 1961.
3. **Dean, R. G.,** Am. Soc. Civil Engs. Specialty Conf. on Coastal Eng., Santa Barbara, Calif., October, 1965.

Figure 5.5–3
WAVE AND PILING SYSTEM DEFINITION SKETCH

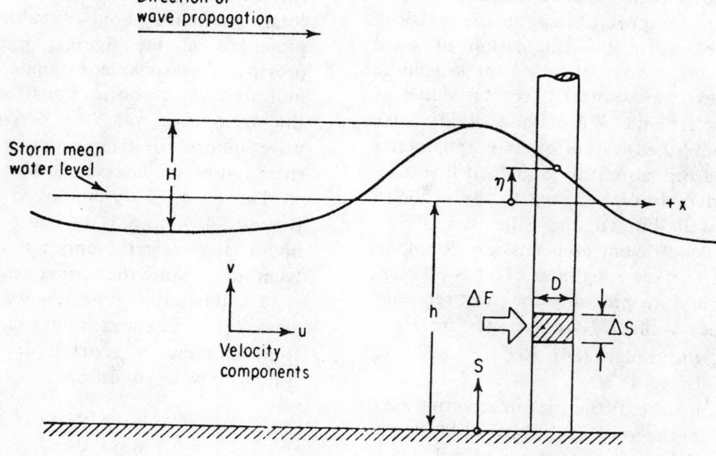

(From Dean, R. G. in *Handbook of Ocean and Underwater Engineering,* Myers, J. J., Ed., McGraw-Hill, New York, 1969. With permission.)

Figure 5.5–4
ISOLINES OF DIMENSIONLESS MAXIMUM TOTAL FORCE, ϕ_m

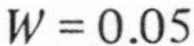

$W = 0.05$

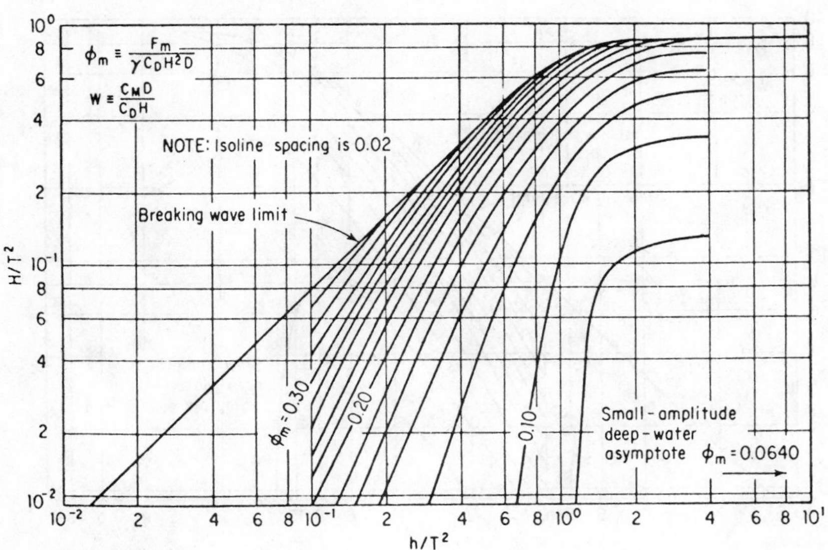

(From Dean, R. G. in *Handbook of Ocean and Underwater Engineering,* Myers, J. J., Ed., McGraw-Hill, New York, 1969. With permission.)

Figure 5.5–5
ISOLINES OF DIMENSIONLESS MAXIMUM TOTAL FORCE, ϕ_m

$W = 0.1$

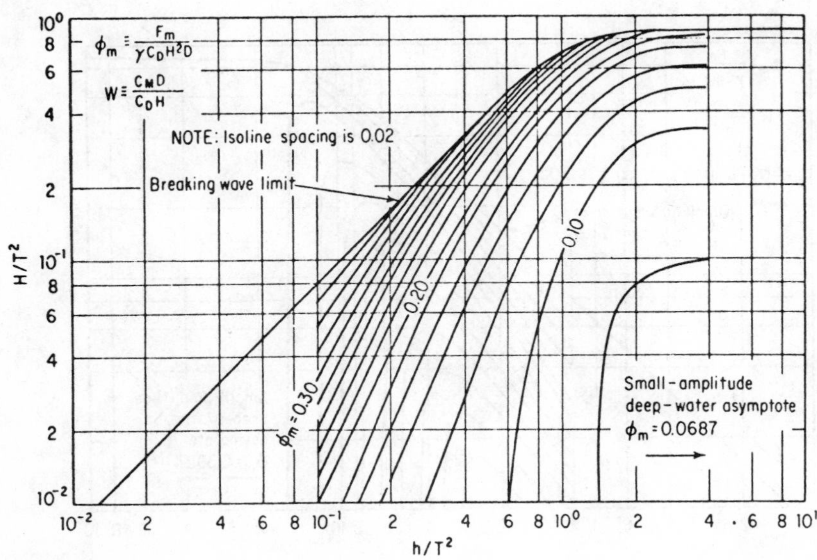

(From Dean, R. G. in *Handbook of Ocean and Underwater Engineering,* Myers, J. J., Ed., McGraw-Hill, New York, 1969. With permission.)

Figure 5.5–6
ISOLINES OF DIMENSIONLESS MAXIMUM TOTAL FORCE, ϕ_m

$W = 0.5$

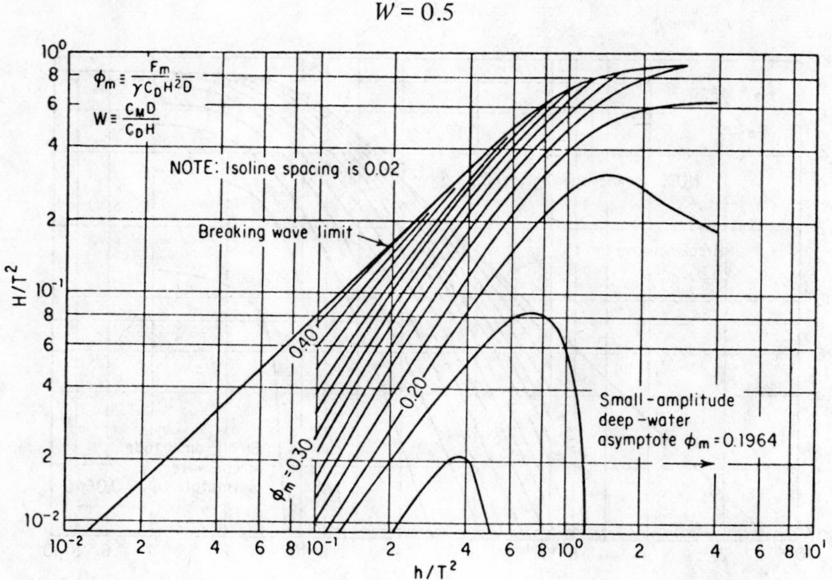

(From Dean, R. G. in *Handbook of Ocean and Underwater Engineering,* Myers, J. J., Ed., McGraw-Hill, New York, 1969. With permission.)

Figure 5.5–7
ISOLINES OF DIMENSIONLESS MAXIMUM TOTAL FORCE, ϕ_m

$W = 1.0$

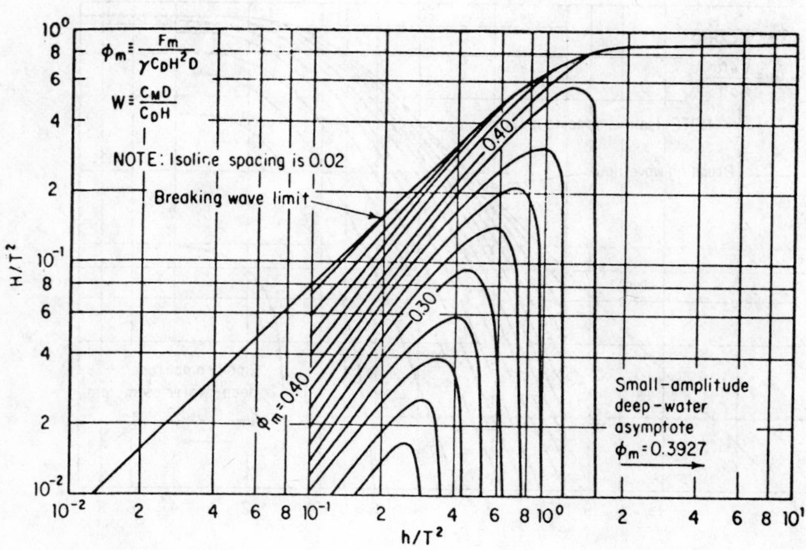

(From Dean, R. G. in *Handbook of Ocean and Underwater Engineering,* Myers, J. J., Ed., McGraw-Hill, New York, 1969. With permission.)

Figure 5.5–8
ISOLINES OF DIMENSIONLESS MAXIMUM TOTAL MOMENT, α_m

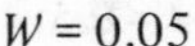

$W = 0.05$

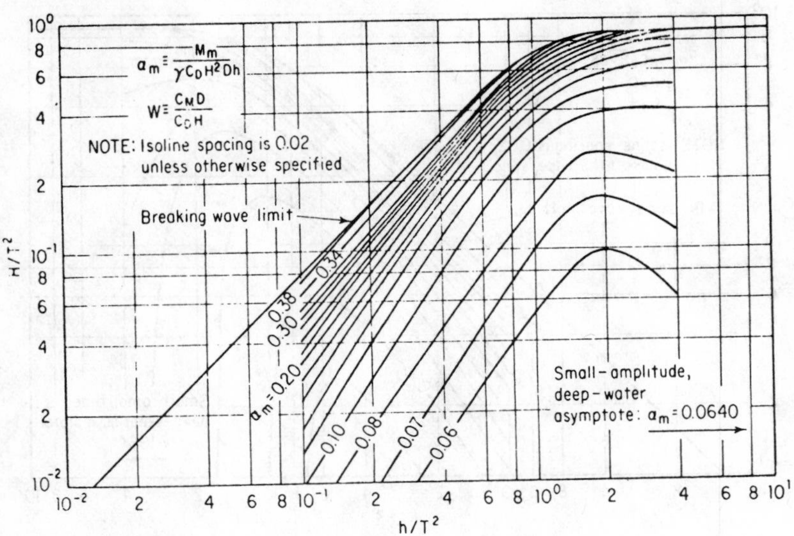

(From Dean, R. G. in *Handbook of Ocean and Underwater Engineering,* Myers, J. J., Ed., McGraw-Hill, New York, 1969. With permission.)

Figure 5.5–9
ISOLINES OF DIMENSIONLESS MAXIMUM TOTAL MOMENT, α_m

$W = 0.1$

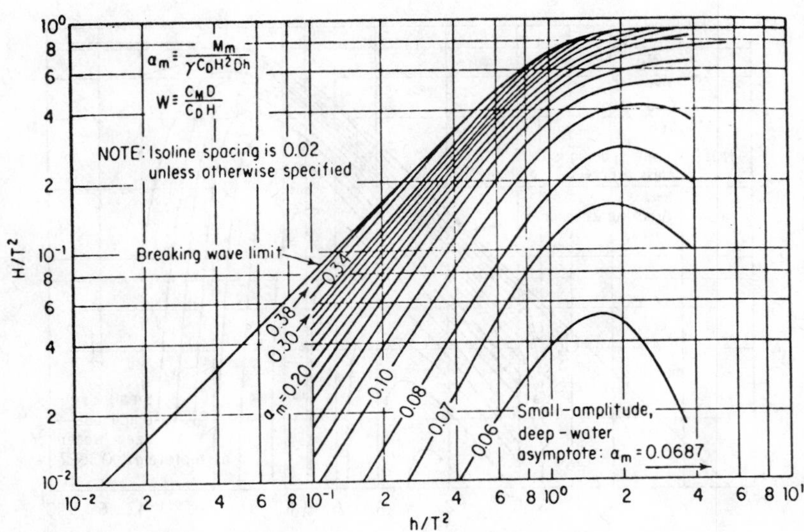

(From Dean, R. G. in *Handbook of Ocean and Underwater Engineering,* Myers, J. J., Ed., McGraw-Hill, New York, 1969. With permission.)

Figure 5.5–10
ISOLINES OF DIMENSIONLESS MAXIMUM TOTAL MOMENT, α_m

$W = 0.5$

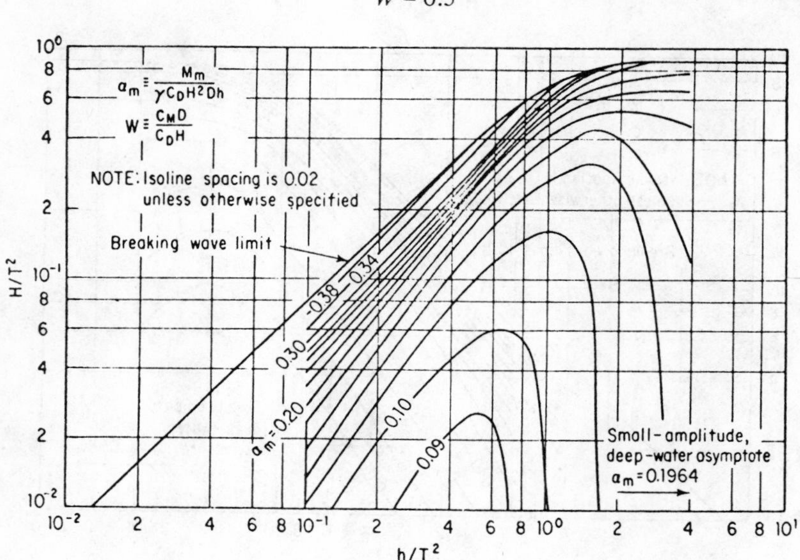

(From Dean, R. G. in *Handbook of Ocean and Underwater Engineering,* Myers, J. J., Ed., McGraw-Hill, New York, 1969. With permission.)

Figure 5.5–11
ISOLINES OF DIMENSIONLESS MAXIMUM TOTAL MOMENT, α_m

$W = 1.0$

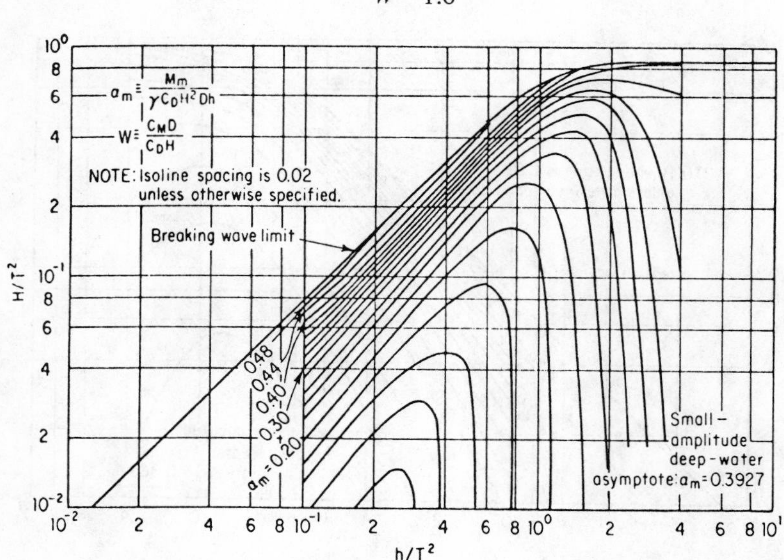

(From Dean, R. G. in *Handbook of Ocean and Underwater Engineering,* Myers, J. J., Ed., McGraw-Hill, New York, 1969. With permission.)

Table 5.5–5
SUMMARY OF DRAG AND INERTIAL COEFFICIENTS FROM EXPERIMENTS

Author and date	Type experiment	Theory used for analysis	Diam of cylinder, in.	Mean values C_D	C_M	Remarks
Morison, 1950, 1951	Laboratory	Linear	1/2, 1, 2	1.8		
Iversen and Morison, 1951	Field	Solitary	3 1/2	0.5	–	Breaking waves Monterey, Calif. (analyzed by Reid and Bretschneider)
Crook, 1955	Laboratory (Morison date)	Linear	–	1.60	2.30	Breaking waves
Keulegan and Carpenter, 1955	Laboratory	Stokes'	2, 2 1/2, 3	1.34	1.46	Avg 29 values
			1 1/4, 1 1/2	1.52	1.51	Avg 57 values
Klim, 1956	Laboratory	Accelerated flow	1/2, 1	1.00	0.93	Nonoscillatory
Dean, 1956	Laboratory	Accelerated flow	3	1.10	1.46	Nonoscillatory
Wiegel et al., 1956	Field (large and small waves)	Linear theory	13, 24	1.00	0.95	U.S. West Coast (avg many values)
Reid and Bretschneider, 1953	Field (low Reynolds number)	High order	5 5/8	1.2	1.21	Avg 54 values
Reid, 1956	Field (small waves)	Aperiodic	8 5/8	0.53	1.47	Gulf of Mexico
Bretschneider, 1956	Field (avg waves)	Stokes'	16, 30	0.40	1.10	Gulf of Mexico
Wilson, 1957	Field (small waves)	Confused	30	1.00	1.45	Gulf of Mexico
Bretschneider, 1961	Wiegel's data for all $H \gtreqless 10$ ft	Linear	13, 24	0.86, 0.68	–	Standard deviation 50% of mean values
		Second	13, 24	0.48, 0.43	–	
		Third	13, 24	0.35, 0.35	–	Avg 50 and 31 values
Goda, 1964	Laboratory		3, 5.5	1.3–0.4	1.71	R_e $1.5 \times 10^4 - 2 \times 10^5$

Note: Flow is oscillatory except as noted.

(From Bretschneider, C. L. in *Handbook of Ocean and Underwater Engineering,* Myers, J. J., Ed., McGraw-Hill, New York, 1969. With permission.)

REFERENCE

Wilson, B. W. and Reid, R. O., *J. Waterways Harbors Div. Am. Soc. Civil Eng.,* 89 (WW1), 1963.

Table 5.5–6
ESSENTIAL PROPERTIES OF SOME AMERICAN SHEET PILES

Section No.[a]							
U.S. Steel	Bethlehem Steel	Area, in.^{2}	Width, in.	Web or flange thickness, min in.	Wt, lb/ft^2 of wall	Section modulus, in.^{3}/linear ft of wall	Interlock strength, lb/in.[a]
MZ 38	ZP-38	16.77	18	3/8	38	46.8	8000
MZ 32	ZP-32	16.47	21	3/8	32	38.3	8000
MZ 27	ZP-27	11.91	18	3/8	27	30.2	8000
MP 110	DP-1	12.56	16	3/8	32	15.3	8000
MP 116	DP-2	10.59	16	3/8	27	10.7	8000
MP 115	AP-3	10.59	19 5/8	3/8	22	5.4	8000
MP 112	SP-4	8.99	16	3/8	23	2.4	12,000
MP 113	SP-5	10.98	16	1/2	28	2.5	12,000
MP 101	SP-6a	10.29	15	3/8	28	2.4	16,000
MP 102	SP-7a	11.76	15	1/2	32	2.4	16,000
MP 117	AP-8	11.41	15	–	31	7.1	10,000
	SP-9	4.38	8 1/2	13/64	21	1.4	8000

[a] See catalogs of respective companies for additional information.

(From Chellis, R. D. in *Handbook of Ocean and Underwater Engineering*, Myers, J. J., Ed., McGraw-Hill, New York, 1969. With permission.)

Table 5.5–7
H-PILE DIMENSIONS AND PROPERTIES FOR DESIGNING

Section No.[a]					Flange			Axis XX			Axis YY		
U.S. Steel	Bethlehem Steel	Wt/ft, lb	Area of section, in.^{2}	Depth of section, in.	Width, in.	Thickness, in.	Web thickness, in.	I, in.^{4}	S, in.^{3}	r, in.	I', in.^{4}	S', in.^{3}	r', in.
CBP 146	BP 14	117	34.44	14.23	14.885	0.805	0.805	1228.5	172.6	5.97	443.1	59.5	3.59
CBP 146	BP 14	102	30.01	14.03	14.784	0.704	0.704	1055.1	150.4	5.93	379.6	51.3	3.56
CBP 146	BP 14	89	26.19	13.86	14.696	0.616	0.616	909.1	131.2	5.89	326.2	44.4	3.53
CBP 146	BP 14	73	21.46	13.64	14.586	0.506	0.506	733.1	107.5	5.85	261.9	35.9	3.49
CBP 124	BP 12	74	21.76	12.12	12.217	0.607	0.607	566.5	93.5	5.10	184.7	30.2	2.91
CBP 124	BP 12	53	15.58	11.78	12.046	0.436	0.436	394.8	67.0	5.03	127.3	21.2	2.86
CBP 103	BP 10	57	16.76	10.01	10.224	0.564	0.564	294.7	58.9	4.19	100.6	19.7	2.45
CBP 103	BP 10	42	12.35	9.72	10.078	0.418	0.418	210.8	43.4	4.13	71.4	14.2	2.40
CBP 83	BP 8	36	10.60	8.03	8.158	0.446	0.446	119.8	29.9	3.36	40.4	9.9	1.95

[a] See catalogs of respective companies for additional information.

(From Chellis, R. D. in *Handbook of Ocean and Underwater Engineering*, Myers, J. J., Ed., McGraw-Hill, New York, 1969. With permission.)

Table 5.5–8
PROPERTIES OF SOME AMERICAN STEEL-PIPE-PILE SECTIONS

Nominal size, in.	Diam, in.[a] OD	ID	Wall thickness, in. Dec.	Frac.	Wt/ft, lb	Gross area of metal, in.²	Moment of inertia I, in.⁴	Section modulus I/c, in.³	Radius of gyration r	Area of concrete in.²	ft²	Effective area of metal, in.² [b]
10	10.00	**9.782**[c]	**0.109**[c]	7/64	11.52	3.39	41.37	8.47	3.50	75.15	0.5209	1.52
		9.656	**0.172**	11/64	18.05	5.31	64.13	12.82	3.48	73.29	0.5085	3.36
10	10.75	**10.532**[c]	**0.109**[c]	7/64	12.39	3.64	51.58	9.59	3.77	87.12	0.6050	1.54
		10.312[c]	**0.219**[c]	7/32	24.60	7.25	100.4	18.68	3.72	83.52	0.5800	5.15
		10.250	0.250	1/4	28.04	8.24	113.7	21.16	3.71	82.52	0.5730	6.15
		10.189	0.281	–	31.44	9.24	126.8	23.60	3.70	81.52	0.5665	7.14
		10.136	*0.307*	–	34.24	10.07	137.4	25.57	3.69	80.68	0.5603	7.97
		9.750	*0.500*	1/2	54.73	16.10	212.0	39.43	3.63	74.66	0.5184	14.02
12	12.00	**11.782**[c]	**0.109**[c]	7/64	13.84	4.07	71.98	12.00	4.21	109.03	0.7571	1.73
		11.656	**0.172**	11/64	21.73	6.39	111.8	18.64	4.19	106.70	0.7410	4.05
12	12.75	**12.532**[c]	**0.109**[c]	7/64	14.71	4.33	86.49	13.57	4.48	123.35	0.8566	1.84
		12.126[c]	**0.3125**[c]	5/16	41.51	12.19	236.3	37.06	4.40	115.49	0.8018	9.70
		12.090	*0.330*	–	43.77	12.88	248.5	38.97	4.39	114.80	0.7972	10.38
		11.750	*0.500*	1/2	65.41	19.24	361.5	56.71	4.34	108.43	0.7530	16.75
14	14.00	**13.782**[c]	**0.109**[c]	7/64	16.17	4.75	114.7	16.39	4.92	149.18	1.0360	2.01
		13.438[c]	**0.281**[c]	9/32	41.21	12.11	283.1	40.44	4.85	141.83	0.9849	9.37
		13.375[c]	0.3125[c]	5/16	45.68	13.42	314.9	44.98	4.84	140.48	0.9756	10.68
		13.250	*0.375*	3/8	54.56	16.05	372.8	53.25	4.82	137.89	0.9575	13.31
		13.000	*0.500*	1/2	72.09	21.21	483.8	69.11	4.78	132.73	0.9217	18.47

Note: Sizes in boldface type furnished, spiral-welded pipe, by the American Rolling Mill Company. Sizes in italics furnished, seamless and welded pipe, by the National Tube Company. Other sizes furnished by both companies. Pipe furnished by the American Rolling Mill Company conforms to ASTM Standard Specifications for Electric-fusion (Arc) Welded Steel Pipe (sizes 8 in. to but not including 30 in.) A139, Grade B, except that hydrostatic testing will not be required, or ASTM Standard Specifications for Welded and Seamless Steel Pipe Piles A252, for all sizes except 6, 8, 10, and 12 in. OD, which conform to ASTM Standard Specifications for Spiral-welded Steel or Iron Pipes A211 and ASTM Standard Specifications for Low Tensile Strength Carbon-steel Plates of Structural Quality for Welding A78, Grade B.

Pipe furnished by the National Tube Company conforms to ASTM Standard Specifications for Welded and Seamless Steel Pipe Piles A252.

[a] Lightest and heaviest sections of each group are shown. Full ranges of values for intermediate items appear in pipe manufacturer's catalogs.
[b] After deducting the outer 1/14 in. of pipe wall.
[c] Not carried in stock but available from the American Rolling Mill Company in minimum quantities of 10,000 lb.

Table 5.5–8 (*Continued*)
PROPERTIES OF SOME AMERICAN STEEL-PIPE-PILE SECTIONS

Nominal size, in.	Diam, in.[a]		Wall thickness, in.		Wt/ft, lb	Gross area of metal, in.^{2}	Moment of inertia I, in.^{4}	Section modulus I/c, in.^{3}	Radius of gyration r	Area of concrete		Effective area of metal, in.^{2} [b]
	OD	ID	Dec.	Frac.						in.^{2}	ft^2	
16	16.00	**15.782**[c]	**0.109**[c]	7/64	18.50	5.44	171.8	21.47	5.64	195.62	1.3585	2.31
		15.438[c]	**0.281**[c]	9/32	47.22	13.88	429.1	53.64	5.56	187.19	1.2999	10.75
		15.375[c]	0.3125[c]	5/16	52.36	15.38	473.9	59.24	5.55	185.69	1.2893	12.25
		15.125	*0.4375*	7/16	72.71	21.39	648.1	81.01	5.52	179.67	1.2477	18.26
		15.000	*0.500*	1/2	82.77	24.35	731.9	91.49	5.50	176.72	1.2271	21.22
18	18.00	**17.782**[c]	**0.109**[c]	7/64	20.83	6.13	245.1	27.24	6.35	248.34	1.7246	2.61
		17.438[c]	**0.281**[c]	9/32	53.22	15.64	614.5	68.28	6.27	238.83	1.6585	12.12
		17.375[c]	0.3125[c]	5/16	59.03	17.34	679.2	75.47	6.25	237.13	1.6466	13.81
		17.250	0.375	3/8	70.59	20.76	806.6	89.62	6.23	233.71	1.6229	17.24
		17.125	*0.4375*	7/16	82.06	24.14	931.3	103.5	6.21	230.33	1.5995	20.62
		16.750	*0.625*	5/8	115.97	34.12	1289.0	143.2	6.15	220.35	1.5302	30.59
20	20.00	**19.782**[c]	**0.109**[c]	7/64	23.15	6.81	336.9	33.69	7.02	307.35	2.1343	2.84
		19.438[c]	**0.281**[c]	9/32	59.23	17.41	847.1	84.71	6.97	296.75	2.0608	13.49
		19.375[c]	0.3125[c]	5/16	65.71	19.30	936.7	93.67	6.96	294.80	2.0474	15.38
		19.250	0.375	3/8	78.60	23.12	1113.5	111.3	6.94	291.04	2.0210	19.20
		19.125	*0.4375*	7/16	91.40	26.89	1287.0	128.7	6.92	287.27	1.9949	22.92
		18.750	*0.625*	5/8	129.33	38.04	1787.0	178.7	6.85	276.12	1.9174	34.13
22	22.00	**21.718**[c]	**0.141**[c]	9/64	32.92	9.68	578.4	52.58	7.75	370.45	2.5726	5.36
		21.438[c]	**0.281**[c]	9/32	65.18	19.17	1130.2	102.7	7.69	360.96	2.5067	14.85
		21.375[c]	0.3125[c]	5/16	72.38	21.29	1252.0	113.8	7.67	358.83	2.4919	16.97
		21.250[c]	0.375[c]	3/8	86.60	25.48	1490.0	135.4	7.65	354.66	2.4628	21.16
		21.125	*0.3475*	7/16	100.75	29.64	1723.0	156.6	7.62	350.50	2.4339	25.32
		20.750	*0.625*	5/8	142.68	41.97	2399.0	218.1	7.56	338.16	2.3483	37.65
24	24.00	**23.718**[c]	**0.141**[c]	9/64	35.83	10.57	752.1	62.67	8.45	441.82	3.0682	5.87
		23.438[c]	**0.281**[c]	9/32	71.25	20.94	1472.7	122.8	8.39	431.45	2.9962	16.24
		23.375[c]	0.3125[c]	5/16	79.06	23.22	1631.7	135.9	8.38	429.17	2.9800	18.52
		23.250	0.375	3/8	94.62	27.83	1942.0	161.9	8.35	424.56	2.9482	23.13
		23.125	*0.3475*	7/16	110.09	32.39	2248.0	187.4	8.33	420.00	2.9166	27.69
		22.750	*0.625*	5/8	156.03	45.90	3137.0	261.4	8.27	406.49	2.8228	41.20

a Lightest and heaviest sections of each group are shown. Full ranges of values for intermediate items appear in pipe manufacturer's catalogs.
b After deducting the outer 1/14 in. of pipe wall.
c Not carried in stock but available from the American Rolling Mill Company in minimum quanitites of 10,000 lb.

Table 5.5–8 (*Continued*)
PROPERTIES OF SOME AMERICAN STEEL-PIPE-PILE SECTIONS

Nominal size, in.	Diam, in.[a]		Wall thickness, in.		Wt/ft, lb	Gross area of metal, in.²	Moment of inertia I, in.⁴	Section modulus I/c, in.³	Radius of gyration r	Area of concrete		Effective area of metal, in.² [b]
	OD	ID	Dec.	Frac.						in.²	ft²	
26	26.00	25.500[c]	0.250[c]	1/4	68.76	20.22	1676.4	129.0	9.12	510.70	3.5466	15.12
		25.000[c]	0.500[c]	1/2	136.19	40.06	3257.0	250.5	9.04	490.86	3.4088	34.96
28	28.00	27.500[c]	0.250[c]	1/4	74.09	21.79	2098.1	149.9	9.83	593.96	4.1247	17.60
		27.000[c]	0.500[c]	1/2	146.88	43.20	4084.8	291.8	9.75	572.56	3.9761	37.71
30	30.00	29.500[c]	0.250[c]	1/4	79.44	23.36	2585.1	172.3	10.52	683.49	4.7465	17.49
		29.000[c]	0.500[c]	1/2	157.53	46.34	5043.0	336.1	10.43	660.52	4.5870	40.46
36	36.00	35.500[c]	0.250[c]	1/4	95.39	28.06	4485.8	249.2	12.66	989.80	6.8736	21.00
		35.000[c]	0.500[c]	1/2	189.57	55.76	8786.0	488.1	12.55	962.12	6.6813	48.70

a Lightest and heaviest sections of each group are shown. Full ranges of values for intermediate items appear in pipe manufacturer's catalogs.
b After deducting the outer 1/14 in. of pipe wall.
c Not carried in stock but available from the American Rolling Mill Company in minimum quanitites of 10,000 lb.

(From Chellis, R. D. in *Handbook of Ocean and Underwater Engineering*, Myers, J. J., Ed., McGraw-Hill, New York, 1969. With permission.)

Table 5.5–9
PROPERTIES OF PRETENSIONED-CONCRETE BEARING PILES

Diam, in.	Shape	Solid or hollow core	No. strands, strand diam, in.	Effective prestress in concrete, psi[a]	A_c, in.^{2} [b]	I, in.^{4}	I/c, in.^{3}	Perim., in.	Wt / lin. ft, lb	Allowable design load[c] Kips	Allowable design load[c] Tons	Allowable moment, kip-in.[d]	Allowable moment for earthquakes, kip-in.[e]	Allowable unsupported length, ft[f]	Normal max length, ft
10	Octag.	S	6, 3/8	839	83	547	109	33	86	91	46	124	157	32	75
12	Octag.	S	8, 3/8	780	119	1135	189	40	124	131	65	204	261	38	100
14	Octag.	S	10, 3/8	716	162	2103	300	46	169	178	89	305	395	45	130
16	Octag.	S	13, 3/8	711	212	3587	448	53	221	233	117	453	587	51	140
18	Octag.	S	16, 3/8	701	268	5746	638	60	279	295	147	637	828	58	150
20	Octag.	S	20, 3/8	701	331	8758	876	66	345	364	182	877	1140	64	160
20	Octag.	11 in. H	16, 3/8	786	236	8039	804	66	246	260	130	873	1114	73	160
20	Square	S	19, 7/16	749	398	13,146	1315	78	415	438	219	1379	1774	72	160
20	Square	11 in. H	20, 3/8	766	308	12,427	1243	78	316	333	167	1325	1698	80	160
26	Square	16 in. H	23, 7/16	760	475	32,272	2482	97	495	523	261	2631	3376	103	160
30	Round	20 in. H	19, 7/16	759	393	31,907	2127	94	409	431	216	2252	2891	113	180
36	Round	26 in. H	24, 7/16	774	487	60,016	3334	113	507	536	268	3581	4581	138	200
48	Round	38 in. H	32, 7/16	744	675	158,222	6593	151	703	743	371	6883	8861	191	225
54	Round	44 in. H	36, 7/16	734	770	233,409	8645	170	802	847	424	8939	11,532	217	250

[a] Effective prestress in based on a final effective force of 11,600 lb for 3/8-in.-diam strand and 15,700 lb for 7/16-in.-diam strand, or 145,000 psi.
[b] All holes are circular; 1-in. chamfer on 20-in.-square pile corners and 3-in. chamfer on 26-in.-square pile corners.
[c] Allowable design load is based on 1100 psi on the concrete section. Where driving and soil conditions are favorable, this may be raised accordingly.
[d] Allowable moment is based on a tension of 300 psi with an effective prestress as given in the table. Where bending resistance is critical, the allowable moment may be increased by using more strands to raise the effective prestress to about 1200 psi maximum.
[e] Allowable moment for earthquake or similar loads is based on a tension of 600 psi with an effective prestress as given in the table.
[f] Allowable unsupported length is computed for E_c = 5 million psi, with a factor of safety of 2 on the allowable direct load, assuming pin ending at both ends. If the external direct load is smaller, the length can be increased. Note that this length is for transient loads; for sustained loads the value must be revised for a modulus E_c of 2 million psi. If eccentricity is expected, allowable length should be reduced.

(From Ben C. Gerwick, Inc., in Chellis, R. D. in *Handbook of Ocean and Underwater Engineering*, Myers, J. J., Ed., McGraw-Hill, New York, 1969. With permission.)

Table 5.5–10
PROPERTIES OF TYPICAL SQUARE PRETENSIONED-CONCRETE BEARING PILES

Side diam, in.	Hole diam, in.	Min No. 7-wire strands, strand diam, in.[a]	Initial tension in each strand, lb	Concrete area, in.^{2} [b]	Section modulus, in.^{3}	Radius of gyration, in.	Max length, ft	
							Single-point pickup	Double-point pickup
12	Solid	12, 5/16	10,500	144	288	3.47	50	75
14	Solid	12, 3/8	14,000	196	457	4.05	60	85
18	Solid	16, 7/16	18,900	324	972	5.20	70	95
20	Solid	20, 7/16	18,900	400	1333	5.78	75	107
24	12	24, 7/16	18,900	576	2220	7.60	90	125

Note: Spiral ties no. 5 gage, pitch beginning at each end; 5 turns at 1 in., 16 at 3 in., balance at 9 in. through central portion. Set 2¼ in. clear from face.

[a] More strands may be required for severe driving conditions or to handle long lengths.
[b] 1-in. chamfers on corners disregarded.

(From Florida State Road Dept., Bridge Div. Published in Chellis, R. D. in *Handbook of Ocean and Underwater Engineering*, Myers, J. J., Ed., McGraw-Hill, New York, 1969. With permission.)

Table 5.5–11
PROPERTIES FOR DESIGN

Standard Sizes

O D	I D	W	No. prestressing cables
36″	28″	4″ and 4½″	8–12 or 16
54″	46″	4″ and 5″	12–16 or 24

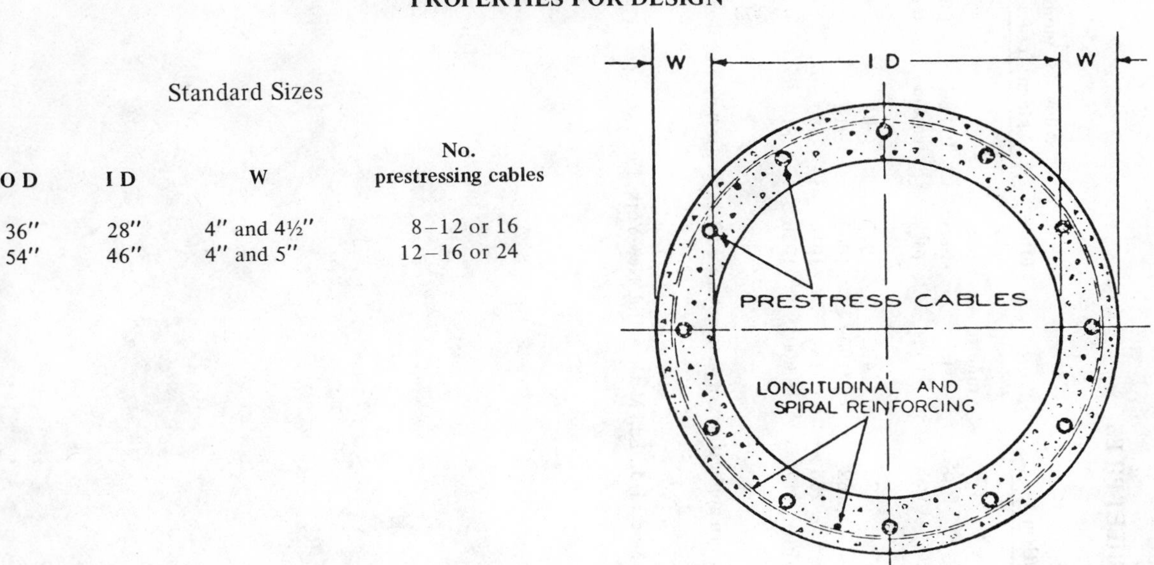

Size: O D	Size: I D	Size: Wall thickness	Area	I	S	Circum-ference	Point area	Wt/[a] ft	Concrete[b] design stress/ cable
in.	in.	in.	in.²	in.⁴	in.³	ft	ft²	lb	lb/in.²
24	16	4	251	13,070	1089	6.28	3.14	261	193.8
34	26	4	377	43,170	2540	8.90	6.30	393	129.0
	28	4	402	52,280	2900	9.43	7.07	419	121.0
36[c]	27	4½	445	56,360	3130	9.43	7.07	464	109.3
	26	5	487	60,000	3330	9.43	7.07	507	99.9
	39	4½	615	147,000	6130	12.57	12.57	641	79.1
48	38	5	675	158,200	6590	12.57	12.57	703	72.0
	36	6	792	178,100	7420	12.57	12.57	825	61.4
	45	4½	700	216,100	8000	14.14	15.90	729	69.5
54[c]	44	5	770	233,400	8640	14.14	15.90	802	63.2
	42	6	904	264,600	9800	14.14	15.90	942	53.7
66[c]	56	5	958	448,700	13,600	17.28	23.76	998	50.8
	54	6	1131	514,000	15,580	17.28	23.76	1178	43.0
72	62	5	1052	593,800	16,500	18.85	28.27	1096	46.2
	60	6	1244	683,000	18,970	18.85	28.27	1296	39.1
78	67	5½	1253	827,800	21,230	20.42	33.18	1305	38.8
	65	6½	1460	940,700	24,120	20.42	33.18	1521	33.3
84	72	6	1470	1,124,700	26,780	21.99	38.48	1531	33.1
	70	7	1693	1,265,300	30,130	21.99	38.48	1764	28.7
90	78	6	1583	1,403,600	31,190	23.56	44.18	1649	30.7
	76	7	1825	1,582,900	35,180	23.56	44.18	1901	26.6

[a] Unit weight of concrete = 150 lb/ft³.
[b] Cable = 12 ea. .192 in. diam wire stress relieved strands (140,000 lb/in.² stress).
[c] Standard sizes.

(From Raymond International Inc., Catalog CP-6, p. 31.)

Table 5.5–12
PROPERTIES OF PRETENSIONED-CONCRETE SHEET PILES

Section no.	Shape	Size, in.	Hollow or solid or core	No. strands, strand diam, in.	Area concrete, in.^{2}	Wt/ft^2 of wall, lb	I/C, in.^{3} Per pile	Per ft of wall	I about minor axis, in.^{4}	Effective prestress, psi[a]	Allowable moment, kip-in./ft of wall 300 psi tension	600 psi tension
BC-6	Rect.	6 × 24	S	12, 3/8	144	75	144	72	432	967	91	113
BC-9	Rect.	9 × 36	S	28, 3/8	324	112	487	162	2190	1002	211	259
BG-12	Rect.	12 × 36	S	28, 7/16	432	150	864	288	5180	1014	379	465
BG-18	Rect.	18 × 36	2–10-in. H	32, 7/16	491	170	1850	617	16,600	1020	814	999

[a] The effective prestress is based on a uniform distribution of strands, resulting in a uniform prestress. For special applications of sheet piles eccentric prestress may be desirable and economical.

(From Ben C. Gerwick, Inc. Published in Chellis, R. D. in *Handbook of Ocean and Underwater Engineering*, Myers J. J., Ed., McGraw-Hill, New York, 1969. With permission.)

Table 5.5–13
DRAG COEFFICIENTS FOR VARIOUS SHAPES

Underwater drag. The two types of underwater drag of consequence are pressure drag and friction drag. Pressure drag may be calculated from

$$F = ½\rho C_D A V^2$$

where

F	=	pressure drag, lb
ρ	=	mass density[a] of sea water (or air for estimating wind resistance)
C_D	=	drag coefficient as determined experimentally for various shapes and Reynolds numbers (dimensionless)
A	=	area of the shape projected onto a plane perpendicular to the direction of current flow, ft²
V	=	the current speed, ft/sec

Current-speed and Drag-coefficient Selection. The practical and difficult problems become selection of a suitable drag coefficient and current speed. Obtaining a realistic estimate of the current profile for any specific area in the world oceans is not a simple matter. More often than not unrealistically high profiles are chosen.

Note: (a) Two-dimensional; (b) three-dimensional.

[a] May be taken as 1.99 sec²/ft⁴ at standard temperature and pressure. The value may increase up to about 2.1 at 0°C and 1000 atm. Because of this and other uncertainties ρ is generally taken equal to 2. In air a value of 0.00237 sec²/ft⁴ may be used for average conditions.

(From Lampietti and Snyder, R. M., *Geo-Marine Technol.*, 1(6), 29, 1965. With permission.)

Body shape: Description	Body shape: Sketch	Reynolds number Rn	Dimension ratio L/D	Drag coefficient C_D
Circular flat-plate normal to stream		>10³	• • •	1.12
Rectangular plate normal to stream		>10³	b/h = 1	1.16
			5	1.20
			10	1.50
			∞	1.90
Circular cylinder—axis parallel to stream		>10³	L/D = 0	1.12
			1	0.91
			2	0.85
			4	0.87
			7	0.99
Circular cylinder—axis perpendicular to stream		10⁵	L/D = 1	0.63
			2	0.68
			5	0.74
			10	0.82
			20	0.90
			40	0.98
			∞	1.20
		>5x10⁵	L/D = 5	0.35
			∞	0.34

(a)

Body shape: Description	Body shape: Sketch	Reynolds number Rn	Dimension ratio L/D	Drag coefficient C_D
Sphere of diameter D		10⁵	• • •	0.50
		3x10⁵		0.20
Hemisphere concave to stream		>10³	• • •	1.33
Hemisphere convex to stream		>10³	• • •	0.34
Ellipsoid major axis perpendicular to flow		<5x10⁵	L/D = 0.75	0.60
		>5x10⁵		0.21
Ellipsoid major axis parallel to flow		>2x10⁵	L/D = 1.8	0.07
Model airship hull		>2x10⁵	• • •	0.05
Solid cone	30°	• • •	• • •	0.34
Solid cone	60°	• • •	• • •	0.51

(b)

REFERENCES

1. **Bowditch, N.,** *American Practical Navigator,* U.S. Hydrographic Office, Washington, D.C., 1958.
2. *Climatological and Oceanographic Atlas for Mariners,* U.S. Navy Hydrographic Office, U.S. Weather Bureau, Washington, D.C.
3. **Sverdrup, H. U.,** et al., *The Oceans,* Prentice-Hall, Englewood Cliffs, N.J., 1942.
4. *U.S. Navy Climatic Atlas of the World,* AVAER 50-1C-528-533, U.S. Government Printing Office, Washington, D.C.

5.6 Buoy Systems

Buoy-system Scope

Calculation of the equilibrium position of a buoy in relation to its anchor under specific conditions is generally a relatively complex calculation, particularly if the system is subsurface supported and the scope is critical. If the system is a simple surface-supported buoy using synthetic line, a simple geometric estimate is probably as meaningful as any.

Realistic evaluation of the scope of single-point moorings by the conventional catenary equations is not a straightforward process. The addition of drag forces on the mooring line introduces even more complications. Various tables are available to cover the multitude of cases possible, but their use in design problems is made unwieldy by the need for repeated interpolation. It is convenient to be able to evaluate the scope of buoy systems in terms of numerous design variables, such as cable size, buoy drag, ocean-current profiles, and water depth. This evaluation may be done with the use of a formula[1] that gives the mooring's scope directly for the range of cases where straight-line approximations are too inaccurate and catenary methods are too cumbersome. It expresses the shape of a mooring line as an exponential curve similar to the steep limb of a catenary.

The formula has a wide range of application to cases where the scope (horizontal distance from the buoy to a point vertically above the anchor) of a single mooring is of the order of one-fifth or less of the total depth of water. This proves to be a realistic situation for many deep-water oceanographic buoy systems as well as for nearly all single-line taut moorings.[a] The derivation of the formula follows, with a discussion of its applicability and some numerical examples.

The balance of horizontal forces on a vertically hanging uniform string subject to a transverse load q is given, with reference to figure 5.6–1, by

$$T_{k+1}\frac{y_{k+1}-y_k}{h} - T_k\frac{y_k - y_{k-1}}{h} + q_k h = 0$$

where $T_k + 1 = T_k + wh$, with w being the wt/unit length of cable. Sorting terms and passing to infinitesimals, the following differential equation is obtained:

$$(T_1 + wx)\frac{d^2y}{dx^2} + w\frac{dy}{dx} + q = 0$$

which has the solution

$$y = C_1 - \frac{qx}{w} + C_2 \ln \frac{T_1 + wx}{T_1} \qquad (1)$$

in which the constants C_1 and C_2 can be solved for appropriate end conditions. For a line secured at the lower end (a mooring) the general expression for the shape of the mooring line curve at any point becomes

$$y = \frac{H}{w}\ln\frac{T_1 + wx}{T_1} - \frac{qx}{w} + \frac{qT_2}{w^2}\ln\frac{T_1 + wx}{T_1}$$

and that for the scope of a buoy at $x = L$ becomes

$$y_L = \frac{H}{w}\ln\frac{T_2}{T_1} - \frac{qL}{w} + \frac{qT_2}{w^2}\ln\frac{T_2}{T_1}$$

$$= x_1 - x_3 + x_2 \qquad (2)$$

where x may be computed with the aid of the nomograms in figs. 5.6–2 to 5.6–4.

These equations rest on the assumption that drag forces are normal to the cable and that the depth of water L and cable length are approximately equal. The first assumption is conservative, but it implies that the validity is restricted to cables with moderate inclinations from the vertical. The second assumption means that for any given depth of water, a buoy would reach the scope calculated at a depth slightly less than that used in the calculation.

Equation (2) is, by suitable manipulation of the end conditions, also applicable to a variety of towing problems for heavy cables or low towing speeds. By changing the sign of w, the scope of moorings using positively buoyant lines, such as polypropylene, may also be calculated.

Equation (2) can readily be used for quick design estimates. For current profiles with several current shears, or for moorings using various types of cable, it is applied to each subsection and the displacements are added vectorially in the horizontal plane.

As a sample solution, let us calculate scope for the buoy system of fig. 5.6–5 using Eq. (2) and the following parameters:

Buoy:
- Diam = 6 ft
- Wt = 1700 lb
- Net buoyancy = 5500 lb $\cong T_2$

Cable:
- w = 0.15 lb/ft
- L = 15,000 ft
- Diam = 0.25 in.

Current:
- Velocity at buoy depth = 1.5 knots
- Velocity over cable length = 0.4 knot

Given $C_D = 1.2$, the total drag force on the cable is given by

$$qL = C_D A p \frac{v^2}{2} = 180 \text{ lb}$$

from which

$$q = 1.2 \times 10^{-2} \text{ lb/ft.}$$

[a] A taut mooring may be defined as one that will have an upward tension at the anchor with no impressed currents.

Given C_D - 0.8, the total drag force on the buoy is given by

$$H = C_D A \rho \frac{v^2}{2} = 142 \text{ lb}$$

The vertical force at the sea floor is

$$T_1 \cong T_2 - wL = 3200 \text{ lb}$$

For the mooring scope Eq. (2) and the computational aids given in figs. 5.6–2 to 5.6–4 yield

$$y = \frac{142}{0.15} \ln 1.72 - \frac{180}{0.15} + \frac{5500}{0.15^2} \times 1.2 \times 10^{-2} \ln 1.72$$

$$= 513 - 1200 + 1590$$

$$= 903 \text{ ft}$$

REFERENCES

1. **Lampietti, F. J.,** *Am. Soc. Mech. Engrs. Paper,* 63-WA-101, 1963.

(From Lampietti, F. J. and Snyder, R. M., *Geo-Marine Technol.,* 1(6), 29, 1965. With permission.)

Figure 5.6–1
SCHEMATIC OF SINGLE-POINT MOORING

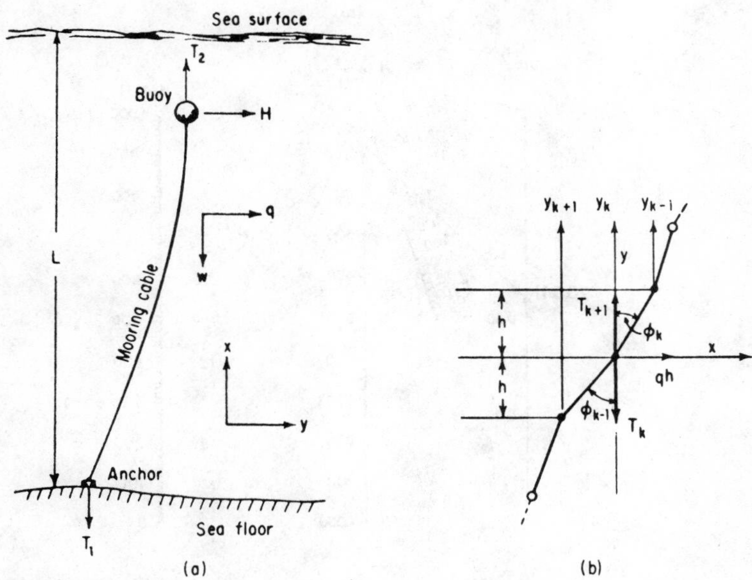

Note: (a) System; (b) force diagram in infinitesimals. x = vertical direction, y = horizontal direction, L = depth of water below buoy, ft, w = weight of cable in water, lb/ft, q = drag force on cable, lb/ft, T_1 = vertical force at sea floor, lb, T_2 = vertical force at buoy, lb, and H = horizontal drag force on buoy and all components above it.

(From Lampietti, F. J. and Synder, R. M., *Geo-Marine Technol.,* 1(6), 29, 1965. With permission.)

Figure 5.6–2
NOMOGRAM FOR USE IN SOLVING EQUATION 2

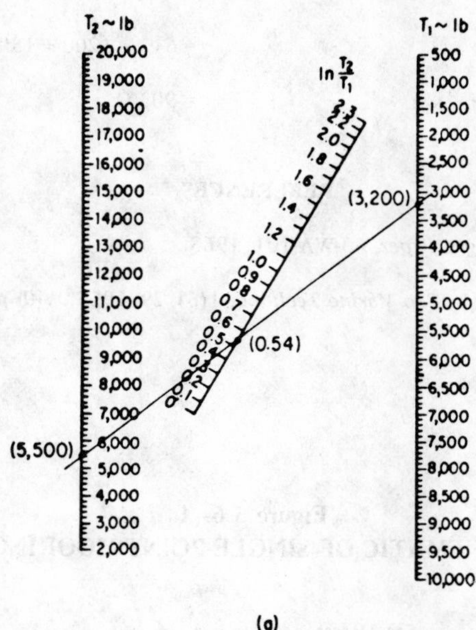

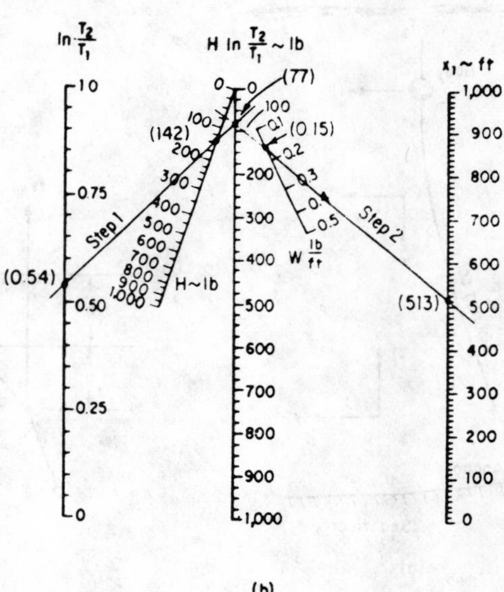

Note: (a) Solution for $\ln(T_2/T_1)$; (b) solution for $x_1 = (H/w) \ln(T_2/T_1)$. Sample lines correspond to example worked out in text.

(From Lampietti, F. J. and Snyder, R. M., *Geo-Marine Technol.*, 1(6), 29, 1965. With permission.)

Figure 5.6–3
NOMOGRAM FOR USE IN SOLVING EQUATION (2) TO OBTAIN $x_2 = (T_2\, q/w^2)\ln(T_2/T_1)$

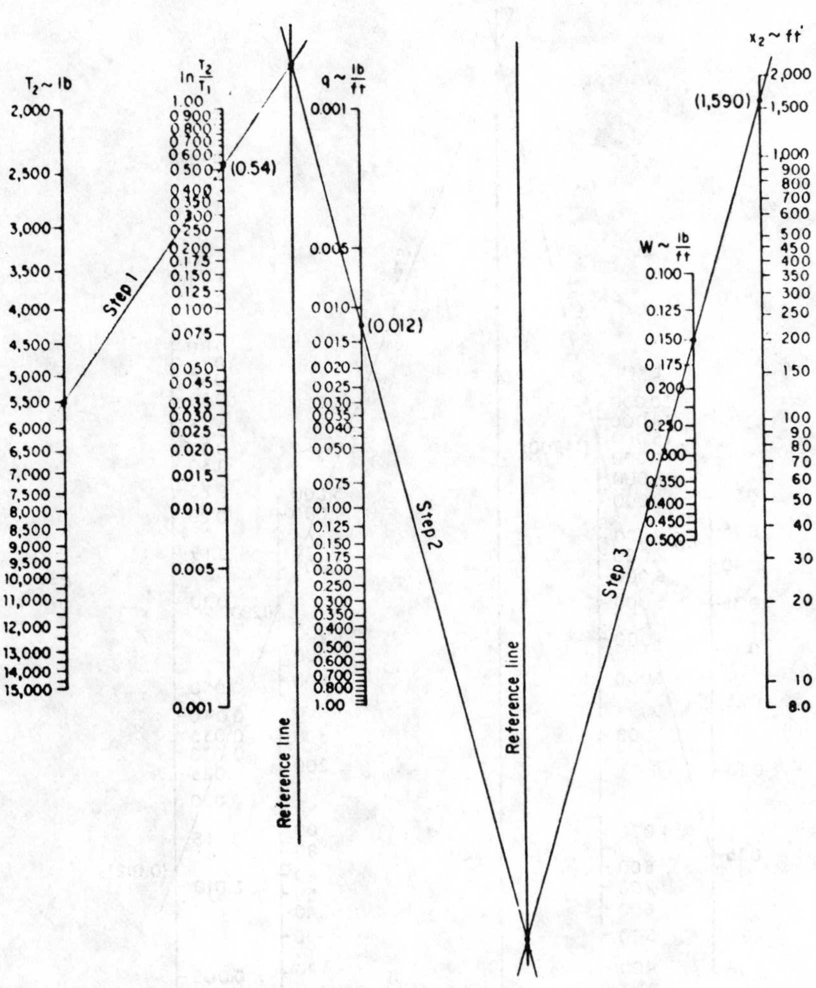

Note: Sample lines correspond to example worked out in text.

(From Lampietti, F. J. and Snyder, R. M., *Geo-Marine Technol.*, 1(6), 29, 1965. With permission.)

Figure 5.6–4
NOMOGRAM FOR USE IN SOLVING EQUATION (2) TO OBTAIN $x_3 = qL/w$.

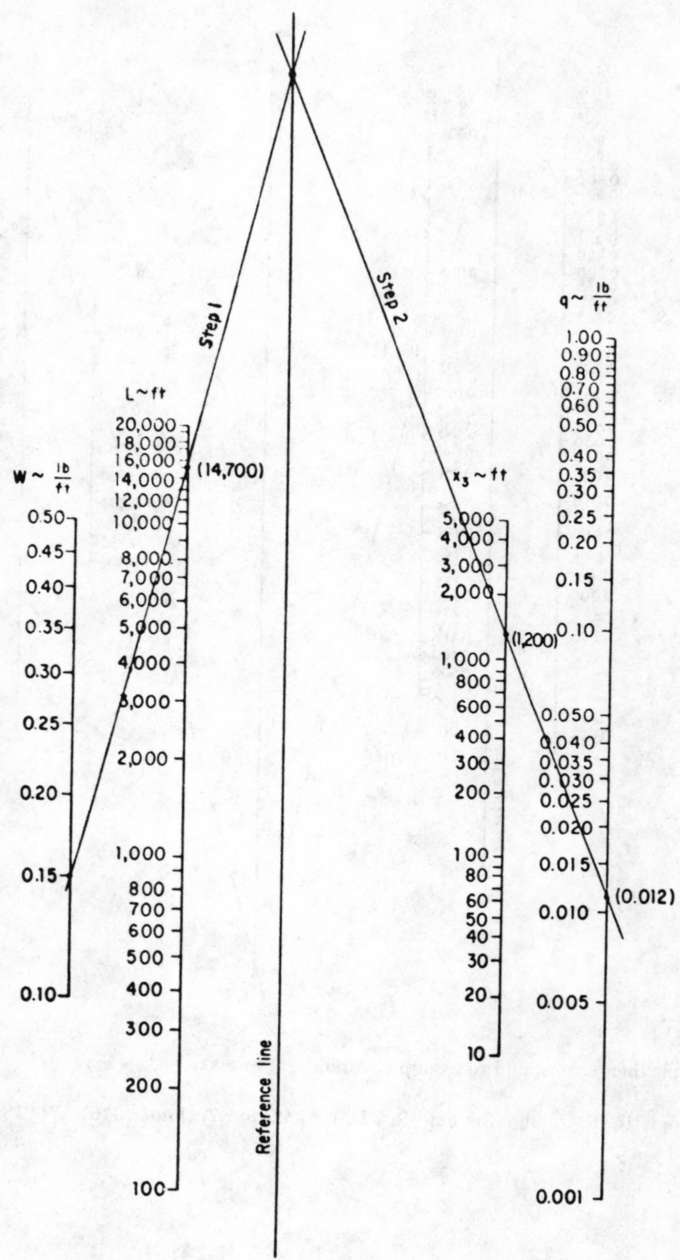

Note: Sample lines correspond to example worked out in text.

(From Lampietti, F. J. and Snyder, R. M., *Geo-Marine Technol.*, 1(6), 29, 1965. With permission.)

Buoy-system Motions

Because ocean currents are not steady but continuously shift direction and change speed, a mooring cannot remain in static equilibrium with the current and must continuously seek a new equilibrium configuration. This continual readjustment is termed *mooring motion.* Its magnitude determines the usefulness of the mooring for current measurements and position keeping.

One of the major incentives for studying mooring motion in detail is that the motion should be predictable for the measured relative flows past the mooring. Hence, in principle, the measured flows can be corrected for the motion. Also, if such corrections can be made with precision, it is not necessary to attempt to reduce the motion to a minimum by designing large rigid systems or using multiple anchoring. A relatively *soft* (compliant) mooring may be capable of giving a performance equivalent to that of a much more rigid platform for current measurements if numerical corrections can be applied precisely.

In deep water, because of the decrease of velocity with depth, the major contribution to horizontal drag is made by the upper 10 to 20 percent of the mooring. As far as displacement of the mooring is concerned, the action of the horizontal drag can be approximated by a horizontal force of the same magnitude acting on the mooring float (buoy). The restoring force for small displacements is proportional to the displacement of the float from its vertical equilibrium position.

Because both the horizontal drag and the restoring force are very large in comparison to accelerations, the inertia of the mooring can be neglected and the balance equations must be simple: the horizontal drag force is equal to the horizontal restoring force or

$$\tfrac{1}{2}\rho C_D A V^2 = F_B \frac{r}{L}$$

where ρ = water density
C_D = drag coefficient
A = effective mooring cross section
V = water speed
F_B = float buoyancy
r = horizontal displacement
L = mooring length

(see fig. 5.6–6). The displacement is in the same direction as the velocity vector.
The force equation can be rewritten in the form

$$r = KV^2 \tag{3}$$

where

$$K = \tfrac{1}{2}\rho C_D A \frac{L}{F_B} \tag{4}$$

is a measure of the softness (compliance), of a mooring. The larger the value of K, the greater the horizontal displacement of the buoy at a given current speed. In deep water a single-line mooring with good performance characteristics will have a K value of 5 to 20 sec²/cm. The complicance constant K has a usefulness beyond specifying the softness of the mooring. It can be related to the time constant or recovery time of a mooring.

Consider a mooring that is displaced a horizontal distance r_0 in still water and released at time $t = 0$. The speed of flow past the buoy is dr/dt. Hence Eq. (3) becomes

$$r = K\left(\frac{dr}{dt}\right)^2$$

or, solving for dr/dt,

$$\frac{dr}{dt} = -K^{-1/2} r^{1/2}$$

The negative sign is chosen because the motion is such as to decrease r. The equation for r is nonlinear but is easily solved to give

$$r = \frac{1}{4K}(t_0 - t)^2$$

where t_0 is a constant of integration.

The mooring reaches equilibrium in a finite time t_0 that is given by

$$r_0 = \frac{t_0^{\,2}}{4K}$$

The initial speed is

$$V_0 = \left|\frac{dr}{dt}\right|_{t-0} = \frac{t_0}{2K}$$

If the time constant τ of the mooring is defined to be $1/2t_0$, these equations can be expressed in the form

$$r_0 = Kv_0^{\,2} = V_0 r$$
$$r = Kv_0$$

Thus the compliance constant Kv specifies not only the magnitude of the displacement for a given velocity v_0, but also a typical time required to produce the displacement.

In a current of 100 cm/sec (about 2 knots) a mooring with a compliance constant of 10 sec²/cm would have a time constant of 1000 sec, or about 17 min. The horizontal displacement would be 10^5 cm, or 1 km.

The value of the single-level model as given by Eq. (3) is that explicit solutions are possible. In general, the displacement r is in the direction of the relative current v. For a changing current the equation can be written in component form as follows:

Displacement along the x axis:

$$x = r\frac{u_r}{\sqrt{u_r^{\,2} + v_r^{\,2}}} = r\frac{u - dx/dt}{(r/K)^{1/2}} = (Kr)^{1/2}\left(u - \frac{dx}{dt}\right)$$

Displacement along the y axis:

$$y = r\frac{v_r}{\sqrt{u_r^{\,2} + v_r^{\,2}}} = (Kr)^{1/2}\left(v - \frac{dy}{dt}\right)$$

where u_r and v_r are components of the relative current and u and v are components of the true current referred to the horizontal axes x and y.

Solving for the derivatives yields the mooring motion equations

$$\frac{dx}{dt} = u - \frac{x}{\sqrt{Kr}}$$

$$\frac{dy}{dt} = v - \frac{y}{\sqrt{Kr}} \qquad (5)$$

where $r = (x^2 + y^2)^{1/2}$ and u and v are assumed to be arbitrary specified functions of time t. These equations constitute the single-level approximation to mooring motion. Solutions can be obtained explicitly for a step increase or decrease in speed and for a rotating current of constant speed. Numerical solutions can be readily obtained for more complex currents.

The case of a uniformly rotating current is instructive because the mooring motion is most pronounced under these circumstances. Substituting

$$u = V_0 \cos wt, \qquad v = V_0 \sin wt$$
$$x = r \cos \theta, \qquad y = r \sin \theta$$

into Eq. (5) and equating coefficients yields the equation for mooring speed:

$$r\omega = \omega K (V_0^2 - r^2 \omega^2)$$

At low rotation rates ($t \ll 1$) the ratio of mooring speed to water speed is

$$\frac{r\omega}{V_0} \simeq \omega K V_0 = \omega r$$

$$\simeq \frac{2\pi\tau}{T} \qquad T \ll \tau$$

where T is the period of rotation of the current.

Thus, in the example given earlier, if a current of 100 cm/sec is rotary with an inertial period of 17.5 hr, the float speed would be a steady 10 cm/sec. The speed of the mooring cable would decrease approximately linearly with depth. At mid-depth (2000 to 3000 m) the speed would still be about 5 cm/sec, which is comparable to the speeds expected in deep water. Hence the degree of mooring motion must be determined before fluctuations of currents at depth can be accepted with confidence.

The compliance constant can be estimated by computing the cross section of the upper third of a moor and substituting into Eq. (4). Such a calculation yielded a value of 12 sec²/cm for a subsurface mooring launched in a depth of 2000 m. Another method is to measure the pressure (depth) overshoot during the launching transient. If the currents are weak, the change of pressure (depth) with time after the anchor reaches the sea floor can be approximated by

$$\Delta p \simeq \rho g \, \Delta Z = \frac{\frac{1}{2}\rho g r^2}{L} = \frac{1}{2} \frac{\rho g}{L} \frac{1}{(4K)^2} (t_0 - t)^4$$

$$\simeq \frac{\rho g r_0^{\,2}}{2L} \left(1 - \frac{t}{2\tau}\right)^4 = \Delta p_{max} \left(1 - \frac{t}{2\tau}\right)^4$$

as the mooring moves toward the vertical equilibrium. Therefore $(\Delta P/\Delta P_{max})^{1/4}$ is a linear function of time with a slope equal to $\frac{1}{2}\tau$. An estimate of the slope together with the maximum pressure overshoot ΔP_{max} is sufficient to determine K. For the mooring mentioned above the measured overshoot was 15.6 m and yielded an estimate of 14 sec²/cm for K. It was considered to be in good agreement with the calculated value of 12 sec²/cm. Similarly, an estimate can be made from the measured speed of the mooring during the launching transient.

If the compliance constant is known, the measured relative velocity u_r and v_r can be corrected for mooring motion with Eqs. (3) and (5) in the form

$$x = KV_r u_r$$
$$y = KV_r v_r$$
$$V_r = \sqrt{u_r^{\,2} + v_r^{\,2}}$$

to calculate the mooring motion dx/dt and dy/dt. The measured relative velocities must be filtered to remove high frequencies before differentiating; otherwise the noise level will be too high.

Multilevel extensions of this model are straightforward to derive, but the constants involved cannot be as easily estimated from measurements. However, it is fairly simple to calculate the relative magnitudes of the compliance constants for each level from the known cross section and mass distribution of a mooring. The number of levels chosen can be made to correspond with the number of current meters on the mooring.

The single-level model is a necessary first step in understanding and developing the more complex, and hopefully more precise, multilevel model. It provides a simple, concrete dynamical model of a mooring in a fluctuating current and can be used to define a single parameter to compare the motion characteristics of a wide variety of surface and subsurface moorings.

(From Fofonoff, N. P., *Geo-Marine Technol.*, 1(7), 10, 1965. With permission.)

Nonlinear Response of Buoys

Advances in the art of naval architecture and structural engineering, although of some value to the buoy system engineer, are not really in the area of his greatest concern. Essentially all practical work in fluid dynamics has been concerned with objects which are purposefully moved through the fluid. The fluid field is generally considered to be stationary even though the flow may be turbulent. Ship and airplane hulls are designed to receive flow from a single direction, with allowance for minor variations. Because the magnitude of the purposeful flow is much greater than the natural motions in the fluid, these natural motions can generally be ignored. The bodies may be streamlined or at least made to operate beyond the critical Reynolds number regime.

None of this is true for a moored buoy system. The moored buoy system must operate in the natural field, whatever it might be. Only in the major ocean-current systems can the steady component of flow be considered large in comparison with the unsteady flow. Even here it cannot be relied upon for long periods of time.

Good definitions of energy spectra for surface waves have been developed. These imput spectra have been used in analyzing the motions of ships at sea. However, the approach has generally been statistical, and with good reason. The overall length of ships is greater than their beam and they must be capable of moving in any direction. They must be considered large in relation to a wavelength. Their motions are extremely complex, with coupling between heave, roll, pitch, yaw, surge, and sway. In addition, there are torsional, lateral, and longitudinal oscillations set up in a ship's hull in response to engine torque, slamming, and cantilevering across and between waves.

With a problem this complex, it is necessary to linearize the equations of motion to keep the problem tractable. Essentially all theoretical work with ships and buoys floating on the sea surface have been pursued with the linearized equations. This work has led to an increased understanding of the problems of ship designs, and those who have attempted to analyze buoy motion have naturally borrowed on the work of the ship-motion analyst. In the limit, however, the buoy-system designer's problems are quite different. For example, with few exceptions, buoys are symmetrical about the vertical axis. Most buoys that are not symmetrical have length/beam ratios less than 2. Buoys are not required to travel through the seas in any direction; they are essentially stationary with respect to the passing seas. They can generally be considered small in comparison to a wavelength. Their motions are much less complex than the motions of a ship. This simpler nature of buoys, comforming with the flexibility of modern analog computers, opens up the possibility of performing nonlinear analyses of buoy motions. The problem remains complex, but if care is taken to proceed in a logical stepwise manner, certain tendencies can perhaps be detected and obviated by careful design.

Figure 5.6–5
BUOY SYSTEM

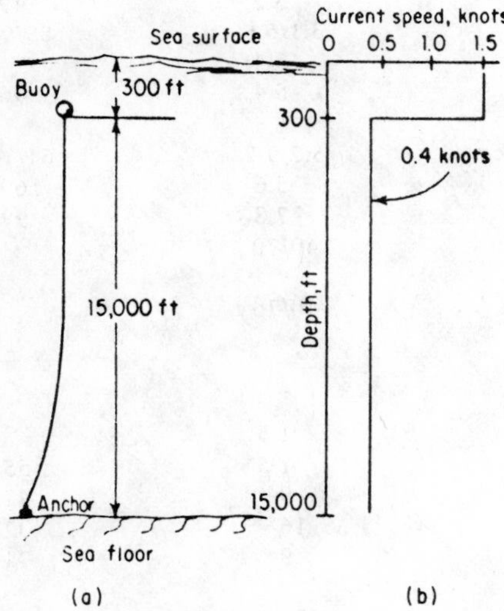

Note: For example: (a) system; (b) current velocity profile (see text for system parameters).

Figure 5.6–6
GEOMETRY FOR COMPUTING BUOY-SYSTEM MOTION

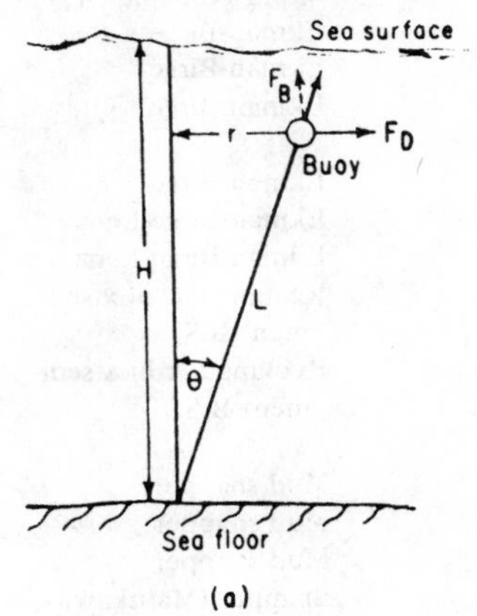

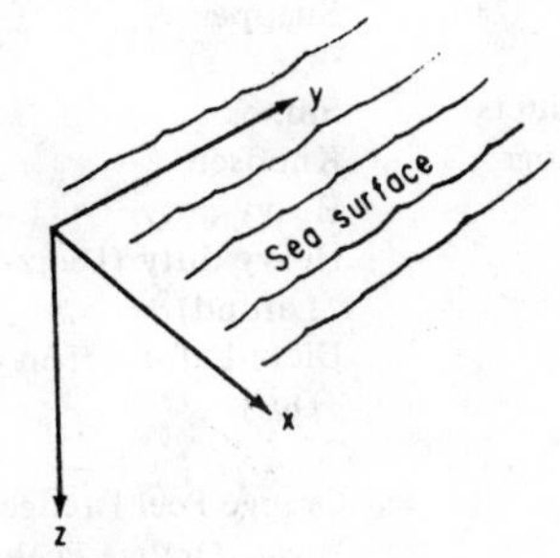

Note: (a) Buoy system; (b) coordinates.

5.7 Specifications of Oceanographic Instruments

Table 5.7–1
BOTTOM SAMPLERS, DREDGES

Bottom Grab

Manufacturer	Type	Size	Total wt, kg	Approx. price, U.S. $
Hagen	Van Veen	–	–	
Hydro-Bios	Van Veen	0.1/0.022 m²	25/12	172/166
Hydrow	Van Veen	0.1 m²	40/60	146/176
Kelvin	Van Veen	14.2 liters	–	180
Lab. Oceanogr	Van Veen	0.1/0.2 m²	32/70	138/210
GM	Emery dredge (lever type)	2 liters	5	
Bergen Nautik	Petersen	0.1/0.2 m²	41/53	133/168
Lab. Oceanogr	Petersen	0.1/0.2 m²	46/118	138/210
GM	Modified Petersen	0.023 m²	4	
Kahl	Modified Petersen	0.023 m²	4	
Mashpribor	Modified Petersen	0.025 m²	18	115
Rigosha	Modified Petersen	0.5 liters	5.2	49
Hydro-Bios	Ekman-Birge	25 × 25 × 30 cm	3.1/5.6	89/90
GM	Ekman-Birge	15 × 15 × 15 cm	5.4	
Kahl	Ekman-Birge	15 × 15 × 15 cm	5.4	96
Rigosha	Ekman-Birge	15 × 15/20 × 20 cm	5.2/9.2	61/104
Hydro-Bios	Ekman-Birge-Lenz	25 × 25 × 40 cm	5.6	169
Rigosha	Edman-Birge-Lenz	15 × 15 × 22 cm	7.8	99
GM	Rectangular box sediment B.S.	0.025/0.1 m²	40/70	
Kahl	Rectangular box sediment B.S.	0.025/0.1 m²	40/70	
Ballant	Mud snapper			
GM	Mud snapper	–	1.5	
Kahl	Mud snapper	–	1.5	55
Rigosha	Snapper (Marukawa)	300 cm³	9	42
T.S.K.	Snapper (Marukawa)	300 cm³	16	37
	Snapper	–	9	24
Hydro-Products	Shipek	20 × 20 cm	70	575
Lab. Oceanogr	Knudsen	0.1 m²	140	348
Sepine	Heavy duty	–	27	196
GM	Heavy duty (Dietz-Lafond)	–	27	
Kahl	Dietz-Lafond Heavy Duty	–	27	280
GM	Orange Peel Dredge	1.65/4.9 liters	20/-	395/-
Hayward	Dwarf Orange Peel Bucket	1.6/3.6/4.9/24.5/28.3 liters		
Hytech	Dwarf Orange Peel Bucket	1.6/3.6/4.9/24.5/28.3 liters	16/18/20/86/95	495/510/525/-/-
Mécabolier	Benne preneuse à griffe	0.1 m²	–	175
GM	Bacterial bottom sampler (Emery)	14 cm diam	–	85

Table 5.7–1 (*Continued*)
BOTTOM SAMPLERS, DREDGES

Bottom Grab

Manufacturer	Type	Size	Total wt, kg	Approx. price U.S. $
Kahl	Bacterial bottom sampler (Emery)	14 cm diam	11	
EG & G	Photo-grab system (combined with underwater camera)	60 × 100 cm	340	

Plummet Bottom Samplers

Manufacturer	Type	Size	Total wt, kg	Approx. price U.S. $
Rigosha	Single-bowl plummet	60 m liters	5.3	18
T.S.K.	Single-bowl plummet			

Dredge

Manufacturer	Type	Size: Mouth	Size: Length	Total wt, kg	Approx. price, U.S. $
GM	Pipe dredge	15 cm diam	45 cm	25	
Kahl	Pipe dredge	15 cm diam	45 cm	25	
GM	Rectangular with net and canvas	25	–	–	
Hydro-Bios	Rectangular Lubek (silk net)	30 × 40	25	1.3	41
Kahl	Rectangular with net and canvas	28	46	11	85

(From Takenouti, A. Y., reprinted from *International Marine Science,* a quarterly newsletter, Vol 4, 3, 1966, by permission of Unesco and FAO; also in *Handbook of Ocean and Underwater Engineering,* Myers, J. J., Ed., McGraw-Hill, New York, 1969.)

Table 5.7–2
CURRENT METERS

Indicator or Recorder on Instrument

Manufacturer	Type/name	Mode of use	Max depth	Max duration	Method of recording: Speed	Method of recording: Direction	Price, U.S. $	Remarks
Bergen Nautik	Ekman C.M.	From ship	No limit	No limit	Dials	Balls and cabinet	440	
Rigosha	Ekman-Merz C.M.	From ship	No limit	No limit	Dials	Balls and cabinet	182	
T.S.K.	Ekman-Merz C.M.	From ship	No limit	No limit	Dials	Balls and cabinet	152	
GM	Gemware C.M.	From ship	No limit	No limit	Dials	Balls and cabinet	–	Modified Ekman type
Kahl	Gemware C.M.	From ship	No limit	No limit	Dials	Balls and cabinet	–	Modified Ekman type
Mashpribor	BM-M Modernized C.M.	From ship	No limit	No limit	Dials	Balls and cabinet	425	Modified Ekman type
T.S.K.	T.S. Multiple C.M.	From ship	No limit	No limit	Dials	Balls and cabinet	–	For serial observation
Bergen Nautik	Fjeldstad C.M.	From ship	No limit	No limit	Printed on tinfoil		730′	Messengers excluded
GM	Fjeldstad C.M.	From ship	No limit	No limit	Printed on tinfoil			
Kahl	Fjeldstad C.M.	From ship	No limit	No limit	Printed on tinfoil			
Askania	Böhnecke C.M.	From ship	No limit	25 hr	Printed on tinfoil			
Kyowa Shoko	Ono C.M.	From buoy	300 m	15 days	Printed on paper			
Rigosha	Ono C.M.	From buoy	50 m	3 days	Printed on paper		420	
Mécabolier	Carrentograph, Type E (No. 1031)	From buoy	1000 m	8 days	Printed on paper		1850	
	Carrentograph, Type B (No. 1203)	From buoy	1000 m	20 days	Photographed on 2 × 8-mm film		3050	
T.S.K.	T.S. Self-Direction-Recording C.M.	From ship/ buoy	200 m	30 hr	Printed on paper			

5.7–2 (*Continued*)
CURRENT METERS

Indicator or Recorder on Instrument

Manufacturer	Type/name	Mode of use	Max depth	Max duration	Method of Recording: Speed	Method of Recording: Direction	Price, U.S. $	Remarks
Geodyne	Woods Hole C.M.	From buoy	6000 m	1 yr	Photographed on 16-mm film		1800	
	A850	From buoy	6000 m	No limit	Digital on magnetic tape		3000	Data-processing service available
Plessey	Recording C.M. MO21	From buoy	2000 m	80 days	Binary signal on magnetic tape		–	Acoustic link permits monitoring
Marine Adviser	Data Acquisition System Q-122	From buoy	6100 m	1 yr	Binary signal on magnetic tape		–	Temperature also
Mashpribor	Alexejev C.M. Type 2-r	From ship/buoy	250 m	1 mo	Printed on paper		6200	
	Alexejev C.M. Type 2	From ship/buoy	2000 m	1 mo	Printed on paper		6200	
Braincon	Recording C.M. Type 188	From ship/buoy	6000 m	90 days	Photographed on 16-mm film			
T.S.K.	Nanniti C.M. Type 2	From ship	–	–	Indication aboard	Balls and cabinet at the equipment		
	T.S.-N1 Type C.M.	From ship	1000/3000	–	On smoked glass			

(From Takenouti, A. Y., reprinted from *International Marine Science,* a quarterly newsletter, Vol 4, 3, 1966, by permission of Unesco and FAO; also in *Handbook of Ocean and Underwater Engineering,* Myers, J. J., Ed., McGraw-Hill, New York, 1969.)

Table 5.7–3
ECHO SOUNDER AND FISH FINDER

Vertical

Manu-facturer	Type/model	Max range		Phase scale	Frequency kHz	Recorder or indicator	Approx. price, U.S. $	Remarks
Apeico	MS-252 A	240 ft	1	240 ft	200	Ind.	215.00	12, 24, 32 V
	MS-602	360 ft/ 120 fms	1	360 ft, 120 fms	125	Ind.	395.00	12, 24, 32 V
	MS-254	60 ft/ 60 fms	1	60 ft/ 60 fms	200	Ind.	235.00	12 V (24/32 V available with VA-200 voltage adapter)
	MR-201	360 ft 240 fms	1 1	360 ft 240 ft	200	Ind. Rec.	249.50	12 V (12/110 V dc and 115-V ac accessory inverters)
	MR-603	310 ft 155 fms	1 2	160 ft 80 fms 310 ft/ 155 fms	40	Rec.	1,125.00	White line 32/24 V
ATLAS	*Navigation*							
	Monotype B	100/1000 m	1	100/1000 m	30	Ind.		
	Monotype C	100/1000 m	1	100/1000 m	30	Ind.		
	Duotype	100/1000 m	1	100/1000 m	30	Rec./ind.		
	Nereus	100/1000 m	1	100/1000 m	30	Rec.		
	Neptun/Filia	100/1000 m	1	100/1000 m	30	Rec./ind.		
	Pilot	16 m	1	16 m	200	Ind.		
	Survey							
	672 a	33/66 m	1	18/36 m	80	Rec.		
	672 atr	33/66 m		18/36 m	80	Rec.		
	Echolog 672	33/66 m depth 5 km distance	1	18/36 m	80	Rec.	–	Portable
	Isobathrecorder	Various steps			200	Rec.		
	AN 601 c	800/4000 m	4	200/1000 m	15	Rec.		
	AN 601 a	800/8000 m	4	200/2000 m	10	Rec.		
	AN 601	8000/12000 m	4	200/2000 m 300/3000 m	10	Rec.		

Table 5.7–3 (*Continued*)
ECHO SOUNDER AND FISH FINDER

Vertical

Manufacturer	Type/model	Max range	Phase scale	Frequency kHz	Recorder or indicator	Approx. price U.S. $	Remarks
	Fishery						
	Monograph 58	600 m	3 50/100/200 m	30	Rec.	–	Black/grey indic.
	Pelikan	800 m	4 200 m	30	Rec.	–	Black/grey indic.
	Pinguin	2000 m	4 200 m 2 1000 m	30	Rec.		
	Duotype	1000 m	2 200/100 m 3 200 m 1 1000 m	30	Ind.		
	Fishfinder EgK	1000 m	3 200 m 1 1000 m 1 25 m obs. range	30	Rec. Electron.	–	For fish detection up to 300 m black/grey indic.
	Fishfinder Eg	1000 m	3 200 m 1 1000 m 1 25 m obs. range	30 –	Rec. Electron.	–	For fish detection up to 600 m black/grey indic.
	Monoscop	600 m	3 200 m 1 20 m. obs. range	–	Electron.	–	Only as supplement for recorder
	Phoenix	400 m	2 50/100/200 m	30	Rec.		
	Netzsonde 684g/1200	300 m below transducer	2 50/100 m	30	Rec.	–	Up to 1200 m cable Trawl depth up to 200 m
	Netzsonde 684g/2000	300 m below transducer	2 50/100 m	30	Rec.	–	Up to 2000 m cable Trawl depth up to 400 m

(From Takenouti, A. Y., reprinted from *International Marine Science*, a quarterly newsletter, Vol 4, 3, 1966, by permission of Unesco and FAO; also in *Handbook of Ocean and Underwater Engineering*, Myers, J. J., Ed., McGraw-Hill, New York, 1969.)

Table 5.7–4
THERMOGRAPHS, SALINOMETERS

In Situ Salinity, Temperature, and Depth-measuring Instruments

Manufacturer	Salinity, %	Temp, °C	Depth, m	Indicator or recorder	Cable length, m	Approx. price, U.S. $	Remarks
Beckman RS 5-3	0–40 ± 0.3	0–40 ± 0.5	None	Digital readout	400	1,090	
Beckman RS 6	0–40 ± 0.2	0–30 ± 0.2	0–130 ± 2.5	Digital readout	130	3,325	
Beckman RS 3[a]	32–39.4 ± 0.05	None	None	Recording	30 ea. sensor		Temp corrected 12-points electrode-less salinity recorder
Geodyne	30–40 ± 0.02	–2–35 ± 0.05	0–9000 ± 0.25%	Digital tape, XY plot			
GM	0–40 ± 0.3	0–40 ± 0.5	None	Dial	15		
Hydro-Bios	0–40 ± 0.3	–1–30 ± 0.03	–	Indicator	200	1,500	
Hytech (model 9006)[b]	30–40 ± 0.01	–2–35 ± 0.05	–	X_1X_2Y recorder			Sound velocity optional
Kahl	0–40 ± 0.3	0–40 ± 0.5	None	Dial	15	890	
Kjeler	30–40 ± 0.3	–2–35 ± 0.02	0–2500	Meter readout,			
Howaldswerke		–	0–2,500 0–2500 0–200 ± 1.5%	X-2Y recorder, magnetic tape recorder, digital readout, digital printer	Up to 2000	28,700	
O.S.K.	27.2–34.3 ± 0.1	0–40 ± 0.2	None	Indicator	20		
Plessey	–	–	–	Digital, magnetic tape, punched card			Sound velocity also
T.S.K.	29–36 ± 0.03	–2–32 ± 0.2	0–100 ± 3%	XY recorder	–	11,600	
	0–40 ± 0.3	0–40 ± 0.5	None	Indicator	30	970	
Whitney	–	–	–	Meter readout	–	300	

[a] Metal-coated staballoy BT slides are supplied by Hytech at $12.50 per box of 50 slides.
[b] Including accessories (grids, viewer, etc.) and 200 smoked-glass slides.

Table 5.7–4 (*Continued*)
THERMOGRAPHS, SALINOMETERS

Bathythermograph[a] (Standard Model)

Manufacturer	Temp range, °C	Depth, m	Approx. price, U.S. $[b]	Remarks
Belfort	−1–30	60/135/250	506	Fahrenheit-feet scale is available
	−2–32	55/137/274	520	Fahrenheit-feet scale is available
GM	−2–32	60/137/274	–	Fahrenheit-feet scale is available
Jules Richard	−2–30	50/150/300		
Kahl	−2–30	60/137/274	–	Fahrenheit-feet scale is available
Mashprib	−2–30	200	1000	
Mécabolièr	–	1000	1225	
Wallace and Tiernan	−1–30	60/135/270	600	
T.S.K.	−2–32	75/150/270		

Temperature-Depth Recorder (Excluding STD)

Manufacturer	Model	Temp, °C Range	Temp, °C Accuracy, %	Depth, m Range	Depth, m Accuracy, %	Recording system	Approx. price, U.S. $	Remarks
Askania	6481	0–30	0.2	0–100	1.5	Portable temp-indicating instrument	–	Mechanical
	6433	0–30	0.15	0–300	5	Dots on chart	–	Battery 6 V, 6.5 amp-hr
Francis	Expendable BT	−2–30	0.2	0–460	2/5	Analog/digital	32.50	Ship speed 0–30 knots; price is for single probe; launcher and recorder on-board cost approx. $5000

[a] Metal-coated staballoy BT slides are supplied by Hytech at $12.50 per box of 50 slides.
[b] Including accessories (grids, viewer, etc.) and 200 smoked-glass slides.

(From Takenouti, A. Y., reprinted from *International Marine Science*, a quarterly newsletter, Vol 4, 3, 1966, by permission of Unesco and FAO; also in *Handbook of Ocean and Underwater Engineering*, Myers, J. J., Ed., McGraw-Hill, New York, 1969.)

Table 5.7–5
WATER-SAMPLING BOTTLES

Closing Water Bottles (No Thermometer Frames Attached)

Manufacturer	Name/type	Capacity, liters	Wt, kg	Material of tube (inside)	Approx. price, U.S. $	Remarks
For serial sampling:						
Hytech	Frautschy	0,5/1	–	Polyvinyl chloride	24/35	With valves
Rigosha	Doty's transparent	0,5	2,5	Plastic	42	
Hydro Products	Van Dorn	1/2/4	1,6/1,8/2,6	Plexiglass	50/60/75	
	Van Dorn	6/8	3,1/3,4	Plastic	105/120	
GM	PVC Water Bottle	2/3/6	2,7/3,1/4	Plastic transp.		
Kahl	PVC Water Bottle	2/3/6	2,7/3,1/4	Plastic transp.		
For single sampling:						
Hydro-Bios	Ruttner	0,5/1/2	–	Plexiglass	58/63/85	
Valco	Van Dorn	5	–	Plastic	81	
T.S.K.	Van Dorn	50	70	Plastic	291	
Int. Ag. 14	Insulating W.B.	0,375	10	Plexyglass/Sanyl	149	Modified Petterson
	Insulating W.B.	1	14,5	Plexyglass/Sanyl	225	Nansen bottles
Kahl	Closing W.B.	0,35	2,3	Tin-plated		
G.M.	Closing W.B.	0,35	2,3	Tin-plated		
Mécabolier	Closing W.B.	4	8	Plastic/chromed		
Rigosha	C.W.B.	10/20	15/18	Brass	126/140	
T.S.K.	C.W.B.	5/10/20	–	Plastic	87/116/181	
Lab. Oceanogr	Plankton Sampler	8	18	Nickel-plated	150	
	Steeman-Nielsen	100	–	Nylon and PVC	138	
Valco	Jitts Twin Sampler	0,35 × 2	–	Plastic	123	Transparent and brass-sheathed
T.S.K.	T.S. "TOMEI" T.R.W.B.	0,5/2	3,5/6,7	Plastic		
	T.S. "TOMEI" Kitahara W.B.	1	–	Plastic		
Horizontal closing water bottle:						
Hydro-Bios	Horizontal C.W.B.	–	16,8	–	183	With frame for reversing therm
Mécabolier	Horizontal C.W.B.	1/2/4	12/24/48	–	185/305/450	
Rigosha	Horizontal W.B.	0,5	4	Brass	70	Open and close with 2 mess. up to 50 m
T.S.K.	Horizontal W.B.	0,7/1,2	7,3/10	–	82	Open and close with piston by 1 mess.

Table 5.7–5 (*Continued*)
WATER-SAMPLING BOTTLES

Sterile Water Sampler

Manufacturer	Name/type	Capacity, ml	Material of ampule	Approx. price, U.S. $	Remarks
GM	Zo Bell sampler	230/250	Rubber/glass		
Kahl	Zo Bell sampler	230/250	Rubber/glass		
T.S.K.	Zo Bell type	200	Rubber		
Mécabolier	Reversing	250	–	105	
Hytech	ABC sampler	100	Pyrex		
Hydro Products	Cobet sampler	110/230	Neoprene	34,50	For Kit, including 1 mechanism and clamp assembly, 12 flint-sealed capillary tubes, one 4 oz bulb and inlet tube, one 8 oz bulb and inlet tube

(From Takenouti, A. Y., reprinted from *International Marine Science,* a quarterly newsletter, Vol 4, 3, 1966, by permission of Unesco and FAO; also in *Handbook of Ocean and Underwater Engineering,* Myers, J. J., Ed., McGraw-Hill, New York, 1969.)

5.8 Ship Characteristics

Table 5.8–1
TYPICAL MERCHANT VESSELS

Characteristics[b]	*Export Banner,* dry cargo	"All Hatch" ships, dry cargo	*American Challenger,* dry cargo	*Mission Capistrano,* ex-tanker[a]	*Sansinena,* tanker	*Manhattan,* tanker
Length overall	493′-0″	506′-0″	560′-6″	523′-6″	810′-0″	940′-5″
Length bet. perp	470′-0″	482′-0″	529′-0″	503′-0″	770′-0″	892′-0″
Beam	73′-0″	70′-0″	75′-0″	68′-0″	104′-0″	132′-0″
Depth	42′-2″	45′-0″	42′-6″	39′-3″	60′-0″	67′-6″
Draft	30′-6″	28′-0″	31′-6″	30′-10″	41′-9″	49′-4½″
Displacement, tons	19,350	16,800	22,000	22,380	77,000	137,068
Deadweight, tons	10,339	10,930	13,100	16,650	60,600	106,568
Cargo capacity						
Bales	670,378	657,213	670,905			
Barrels	–	–	–	140,000	478,000	910,000
Shp	12,500	10,600	16,508	10,000	25,000	39,000
Speed, knots	18.5	18	21	16.2	17.2	17.75

[a] Has a 35- by 52-ft through-hull well, 500-ton lift capacity. Operated by the Military Sea Transport Service.
[b] Steam turbine engines.

(From Miller, R. T., in *Handbook of Ocean and Underwater Engineering,* Myers, J. J., Ed., McGraw-Hill, New York, 1969. With permission.)

Table 5.8–2
TYPICAL FISHING VESSELS

Characteristics	Whale factory ship	Refrigerated fish carrier	Whale catcher	Stern trawler	Trawler	Trawler	Shrimp trawler	Purse seiner
Year built	1951	1960	1958	1960	1954	1959	1960	1960
Length overall, ft	578	273	208	230	184	145	62.5	82
Beam, ft	76.6	42	32.4	39.4	31.2	24.3	17.7	18.4
Depth, ft	41.4	21.6	17.4	27.2	16.7	13.4	8.2	8.4
Draft, light/full, ft	13.1/35.4	8/18.7	11.1/14.2	9.15/17	9.6/12.85	8.36/11	5.6/7.2	5.8/7.5
Gross tonnage	16,777	2068	758	1829	744	373	64	80
Displacement, light/full, tons	12,264/36,640	1641/4424	920/1345	1300/2955	801/1199	447/668	85.4/131.6	138/213
Fish-hold capacity, ft^3	955,000	99,000	–	69,500	19,900	12,350	1500	835
Freeze-room capacity, ft^3	–	12,300	–	6150				
Coefficients:								
Midship, light/full	.98/.99	.97/.99	.78/.83	.82/.95	.87/.90	.90/.93	.79/.85	.90/.92
Longitudinal, light/full	.76/.81	.65/.73	.56/.60	.62/.71	.61/.66	.63/.68	.65/.70	.67/.73
Waterplane, light/full	.80/.90	.72/.84	.68/.76	.72/.90	.73/.80	.76/.84	.78/.87	.83/.96
Keel to metacenter, light/full	43.1/32.2	21.4/17.9	15.8/16	19.9/18.2	15/14.5	11.6/11.4	9.7/9	9.4/9.1
Center of buoyancy, light/full	6.76/18.4	4.27/10	6.9/8.6	5.12/9.6	5.4/7.2	4.53/6.07	3.1/4.2	3.1/4.2
Center of gravity, light/full	34.5/26.6	16.7/14.3	13.9/13	18.6/15.4	13.1/12.4	10.5/9.4	7.4/6.7	7.1/6.9
Metacentric height, light/full	8.6/5.6	4.7/3.6	1.9/3	1.3/2.8	1.9/2.1	1.1/2.0	2.3/2.3	2.3/2.2
Engine	2-cycle diesel	4-cycle diesel	2-cycle diesel	2-cycle diesel[a]	2-cycle diesel	2-cycle diesel[a]	4-cycle diesel[a]	4-cycle diesel
Bhp	9500	2000	3500	2000	1200	850	200	380
Trial displ., tons	16,583	1719	966	1491	893	431	71	139
Trial speed, knots	16.2	14.98	17.93	14.39	13	12.34	9.37	10.29

Note: All hulls steel.

[a] Supercharged.

(From Miller, R. T., in *Handbook of Ocean and Underwater Engineering,* Myers, J. J., Ed., McGraw-Hill, New York, 1969. With permission.)

Table 5.8–3
PRINCIPAL DIMENSIONS OF SOME CABLE LAYERS

Name	Year built	Flag	Owner or operating company	Length overall	Breadth	Depth	Draft	Tonnage Gross	Tonnage Net	Tonnage Dead-Weight	Net cable capacity, ft^3	Speed, knots
Neptun	1962	Liberian	U.S. Underseas Cable Corp.	493′-10″	61′-8″	41′-2″	29′-5″	8909	3504	11,863	222,500	14
Long Lines	1962	U.S.	Transoceanic Cable Ship Co.	511′-6″	69′-6″	45′-6″	26′-6″	11,326	4859	9312	139,000	15
Monarch	1946	British	British Post Off.	482′-11″	55′-8″	40′-0″	27′-10″	8422	3264	7902	114,360	13
Alert	1961	British	British Post Off.	418′-0″	54′-6″	25′-3″	22′-5″	6413	2609	4765	59,300	15
Mercury	1962	British	Cable & Wire-less, Ltd.	473′-1″	58′-6″	39′-3″	24′-0″	8962	3334	5862	106,100	16

(From Pierce, G. A. and Romanelli, R. P., in *Handbook of Ocean and Underwater Engineering,* Myers, J. J., Ed., McGraw-Hill, New York, 1969. With permission.)

Table 5.8–4
PRINCIPAL DIMENSIONS OF SOME CABLE-REPAIR SHIPS

Name	Year built	Flag	Owner or operating company	Length overall	Breadth	Depth	Draft	Tonnage Gross	Tonnage Net	Tonnage Dead-weight	Net cable capacity, ft^3	Speed, knots	Max oper. depth, fath.
Lord Kelvin	1916	British	Western Union International	332′-9″	41′-0″	25′-0″	22′-3″	2641	1306	2900	32,100	12	All
Retriever	1961	British	Cable & Wireless Ltd.	367′-0″	47′-6″	29′-6″	19′-0″	4218	1443	2750	21,000	15	All
Stanley Angwin	1952	British	Cable & Wireless Ltd.	318′-3″	41′-1″	23′-8″	19′-0″	2553	816	2178	18,500	10	All
Cyrus Field	1924	British	Western Union International	223′-7″	34′-0″	18′-6″	17′-2″	1288	453	1022	7443	10	1000
Western Union	1939	U.S.	Western Union International	96′-0″	23′-6″	9′-1″	8′-6″	91	80	200	1000	8	300

(From Pierce, G. A. and Romanelli, R. P., in *Handbook of Ocean and Underwater Engineering,* Myers, J. J., Ed., McGraw-Hill, New York, 1969. With permission.)

Table 5.8–5
PRINCIPAL DIMENSIONS OF SOME AUXILIARY CABLE-REPAIR VESSELS

Name	Owner or operating company	Length	Breadth	Depth	Draft	Cable, tons	Capacity, ft^3	Remarks
Western Union	Western Union International	96′-0″	23′-6″	9′-1″	8′-6″	–	1000	Built as a cable vessel
U.S.S. Yamacraw	U.S. Navy	188′-9″	34′-0″	–	12′-6″	120	–	Converted mine layer
Omega	Hydrospace Services, Inc.	155′-0″	37′-0″	–	8′-0″	270	8600	Built as *Glassford*, renamed *Nashawena*
Cable Queen	N.Y. Telephone Co.	65′-0″	21′-11″	6′4″	6′-0″	50	–	Cable stowed on reel on deck

(From Pierce, G. A. and Romanelli, R. P., in *Handbook of Ocean and Underwater Engineering,* Myers, J. J., Ed., McGraw-Hill, New York, 1969. With permission.)

Table 5.8–6
MODERN OCEANOGRAPHIC-RESEARCH VESSELS

Characteristics	*H. V. Sverdrup*	AGOR-3 class	*Atlantis II*	*Catamaran* (proposed)
Length overall	127′-7″	208′-0″	209′-9″	141′-0″
Length at waterline	111′-6″	196′-0″	195′-0″	130′-0″
Beam	24′-11″	37′-0″	44′-0″	52′7″ max 17′-6″ ea. hull
Draft	–	14′-3″	16′-0″	8′-0″
Full-load displacement, tons	400	1373	2110	640
Gross tons	295	–	1100	
Coefficients				
Block	–	0.424	0.537	
Longitudinal	–	0.530	0.614	
Midship	–	0.800	0.875	
Engine	Diesel[a]	Diesel-elect.	Uniflow-steam	Diesel
Shp	600	1000	1400	950
Trial speed, knots	11.5	13	13	13.5
Endurance speed, knots	10	12	12	12
Endurance				
Nautical mi.	5000	12,000	8000	5000
Days	28	45		
Ship-service-generator capacity, kW	–	600	300	
Accommodations				
Officer	4	8	9	
Crew	5–7	14	19	16
Scientists	10–8	15	25	15
Laboratories, ft²	Oceanographic 65 Sound recording 160 General electronic 375	Wet 250 Dry 800	Below main deck 458 On main deck 1010 Above main deck, 1010	Main deck 1160 Below main deck 120
Winches, wire or line-haul capacity	Deep-sea anchoring 5000 m × 12 mm Hydrographic (2) 5500 m × 4 mm Cable 7000 m × 6 mm Cargo 3-ton Crane 1.5-ton Towing 4-ton Boat 1.5-ton	Deep sea 6800 lb @ 600 ft/min, 30,000 lb @ 133 ft/min, 60,000 lb static Hydrographic 2000 lb @ 350 ft/min, 4000 lb static (2)	Deep sea 30,000 ft × ½ in. Towed instrument 1800-ft chain Hydrographic 30,000 ft × 3/16 in. (2)	Trawl Hydrographic (2)

[a] Controllable reversible-pitch propeller.

Table 5.8–6 (*Continued*)
MODERN OCEANOGRAPHIC-RESEARCH VESSELS

Characteristics	*H. V. Sverdrup*	AGOR-3 class	*Atlantis II*	*Catamaran* (proposed)
Special features	All winches hydraulically operated; 360 ft^3 explosive storage	300 kW gas-turbine–electric generator for quiet operation; 10 ton crane @ 30 ft outreach, 3 ton crane @ 60 ft outreach; passive antirolling tanks; bow thruster	5 ton crane; 1 ton cranes (2); passive antirolling tanks; bow thruster; internal well; bow observation chamber	5 ton cranes (2); centerwells (3)

(From Miller, R. T., in *Handbook of Ocean and Underwater Engineering,* Myers, J. J., Ed., McGraw-Hill, New York, 1969. With permission.)

Table 5.8–7
TYPICAL SHIP CONVERSIONS FOR OCEANOGRAPHIC-RESEARCH VESSELS

Characteristics	*Paolina T.*, converted purse seiner	*Crawford*, converted Coast Guard cutter	*Atlantis*, ketch	*Horizon*, converted tug	*Chain*, converted rescue tug	*AMS-AGS*, converted minesweeper
Length overall, ft	80.25	125.0	143.25	143.0	213.5	220.92
Length bet. perp., ft	–	120.0	105.0	–	207.0	214.83
Beam, ft	22.0	24.0	28.0	33.0	41.25	31.92
(Mean) draft, ft	9.75	8.15	19.0 (max)	16.42	15.0	10.08
Full-load displacement, tons	110	304	560	768	2051	1220
Engine	Diesel	Diesel	Diesel	Diesel-elect.	Diesel-elec.	Diesel-elec.
Shp	250	800	400	1500	3000	3532
Speed, knots	9	12	8	11.5	12	16
Endurance						
Nautical mi.	2450	3000	2700	7000	10,500	7650
Days	30	90	120	45	75	30
Accommodations						
Officers	3			7	10	9
Crew	6	15	20	11	19	96
Scientists	5	7	9	18	26	4
Laboratory area, ft^2	90	300	430	600	1637	309
Special features	Hydrographic winch used for cable laying		Auxiliary ketch	Dredge winch, 22,000-ft cable	Thermistor chain winch; 5 ton crane: dredge winch; silent ship capability	Oceanographic winch

(From Miller, R. T., in *Handbook of Ocean and Underwater Engineering,* Myers, J. J., Ed., McGraw-Hill, New York, 1969. With permission.)

Table 5.8–8
TYPICAL MODERN HARBOR, COASTWISE, AND OCEANGOING TUGS

Characteristics	CL-1, harbor	*Wm. & T. Moran,* harbor	*Brave Pioneer,* coastwise	*Grace Moran,* coastwise	YTB-757 class, coastwise	*Edmund J. Moran,* ocean-going	ATA-121 class, ocean-going	ATF-67 class, ocean-going	*Zwarte Zee,* ocean-going
Length overall	56′-0″	94′-4½″	100′-0″	105′-0″	101′-0″	121′-10″	143′-0″	205′-3″	254′-3″
Length bet. perp	48′-9″	84′-2″	–	93′-4″	–	108′-4″	134′-6″	195′-0″	224′-9″
Beam	16′-6″	25′-0″	27′-0″	27′-0″	29′-0″	29′-6″	33′-0″	38′-6″	40′-6″
Depth	7′-4½″	12′-1″	–	14′-9″	–	16′-0″	17′-2″	22′-0″	22′-8″
Mean, draft	5′-1″	8′-7″	12′-0″	11′-6″	13′-6″	13′-3″	12′-9″	14′-3″	18′-10″
Drag of keel	1′-10″	1′-10″	–	3′-0″	–	1′-8″	2′-6″		
Displacement, long tons	59	268	–	406	–	611	763	1675	
Engine	Diesel, direct-rev.	Diesel	Diesel	Diesel	Diesel	Diesel	Diesel	Diesel	Diesel, direct-rev.
Drive	Geared	Electric	Rev-reduc. gear	Electric	Rev.-reduc. gear	Electric	Electric	Electric	Geared
Propeller	Open screw	Open screw	Kort nozzle	Open screw	Open screw	Open screw	Open screw	Open screw	Open screw
Bhp	250	950	1600	1750	2000	1900	1900	3800	9000
Shp	240	750	1575	1380	1940	1590	1500	3000	8700
Full speed knots	9.67	12.5	12.85 (1150 shp)	13.5	12.7	13.99	14.3	16.5	18.0
Endurance, mi. at speed	–	5035	–	4450	–	6380	7365		
Bollard pull, lb	7400	32,800	55,000	39,500 (est.)	69,000	45,650	42,000	84,000 (est.)	270,000 (est.)

(From Miller, R. T., in *Handbook of Ocean and Underwater Engineering,* Myers, J. J., Ed., McGraw-Hill, New York, 1969. With permission.)

Table 5.8–9
TYPICAL U.S. NAVY HYDROFOILS

Characteristics	PC(H)-1	AGE (H)
Length overall, ft	110	212.4
Beam max, ft	32	70.8
Draft, ft:		
Foils extended	17	25.05
Foils retracted	6	6.0
Displacement loaded, tons	110	321
Capacity, tons	10	40
Engine	Gas turbine (2)	Gas turbine (2)
Shp	6000	28,000
Speed, knots	40+	50+

(From Miller, R. T., in *Handbook of Ocean and Underwater Engineering,* Myers, J. J., Ed., McGraw-Hill, New York, 1969. With permission.)

Table 5.8–10
TYPICAL AIR-CUSHION VEHICLES

Characteristics	SR N2	SR N5[a]
Length overall	65′-3″	39′-2″
Beam, max	29′-6″	22′-9″
Height, max	24′-9″	16′-0″
Total weight, tons	27	7
Payload, tons	8[b]	2
Engines (gas turbines)	4815	1900 hp
Propellers (variable pitch)	10 ft diam (2)	9 ft diam
Lift fans (centrifugal)	12 ft, 6 in. diam (2)	7 ft diam
Speed, knots	80	70
Endurance, nmi	230	240

[a] Fitted with 4 ft flexible trunks or skirts, this vehicle can clear a 3 ft, 6 in. step or solid wall, a 4 ft rounded wall, a 5 ft to 6 ft grass bank, or a 7 ft to 8 ft scrub or sapling growth.

[b] 56 to 76 passengers, depending upon layout.

(From Miller, R. T., in *Handbook of Ocean and Underwater Engineering,* Myers, J. J., Ed., McGraw-Hill, New York, 1969. With permission.)

Table 5.8–11
REPRESENTATIVE DEEP-SUBMERSIBLE VEHICLES

Vehicle	Max op. depth, ft	Air weight, tons	Length, ft	Width, ft	Propulsion, hp	Max speed, knots	Submerged endurance, hours	Approx range, mi.	Crew	Builder/owner
Submaray	300	1.6	14	3	1½	3	5	15	2	Hydrotech Company
Ashera	600	3.5	16	5	2–2	0–4	10	9	2	Electric Boat Company for Univ. of Pa. Museum
American Submarine Model 600	600	1.6	12.5	5	1–3½	1–6	8	10	2	American Submarine Co.
Auguste Piccard	1000	160	93	18.6	80	6	8	40	3	Swiss 1964 Exposition
Denise II	1000	3.5	10	10	Pump jet	1	4	4	2	Cmdt. J. Cousteau (French)
Yomiuri	1000	35	47	–	–	4	6	24	6	Shin Mitsubishi Shipyard, Japan
Star II	1200	5	18	5	4	2	8	8	2	Electric Boat Company
Deep Diver	1350	8.3	23.4	5	10	3.8	18	9	6	Perry Submarine for Edwin Link
Deep Jeep	2000	2	8	6	–	2	4–6	10	2	USN Ordnance Test Station, China Lake
Moray TV-1A	2000	16	33	5.3	–	15	4	15	2	USN Ordnance Test Station, China Lake
PX-15	2000	120	48.6	17	100	5	1068	60	6	Grumman Aircraft Engineering Corp.
Star III	2000	10	24.5	6.5	11.5	6	10	10	2	Electric Boat Company
Deep Star 4000	4000	9	18	10	2 horiz.	3	18–12	20	3	Westinghouse Electric Corp.
Pices	5000	6.5	16	11.5	–	6	24	24	2	International Hydrodynamics Company, Ltd., Canada
Alvin	6000	15	22	8	1–15 stern 2–7½ side	6–8	10	25	2	Litton Industries for Woods Hole Oceanographic Inst.
Deep Quest	8000	54	39	19	30	4.5	24	48	4	Lockheed Aircraft Corporation
Aluminaut	15,000	73	51	8	5 horiz. (2) 5 vert.	3.8	72	150	4–6	General Dynamics Reynolds International
Trieste II	20,000	46	67	15	2–10	0–1.5	50	7.5	3	A. & J. Piccard and U.S. Navy
FNRS-3	20,000	55	52.5	11	2–1	0.5	50	5	2	French Navy
Archimede	36,000	210	70	13	30 horiz. 6 vert.	2	50	10	3	French Navy

(From Miller, R. T., in *Handbook of Ocean and Underwater Engineering,* Myers, J. J., Ed., McGraw-Hill, New York, 1969. With permission.)

Section 6

Tables of Conversion and Constants

Table 6–1
DEPTH CONVERSIONS

Table A Fathoms to Meters
1 fathom = 1.8285 Meters

Example:
Given, depth = 195 fathoms.
From table, depth = 356.6 meters.

Fathoms	0	1	2	3	4	5	6	7	8	9
0	0.0	1.8	3.7	5.5	7.3	9.1	11.0	12.8	14.6	16.5
10	18.3	20.1	21.9	23.8	25.6	27.4	29.3	31.1	32.9	34.7
20	36.6	38.4	40.2	42.1	43.9	45.7	47.5	49.4	51.2	53.0
30	54.9	56.7	58.5	60.3	62.2	64.0	65.8	67.7	69.5	71.3
40	73.2	75.0	76.8	78.6	80.5	82.3	84.1	86.0	87.8	89.6
50	91.4	93.3	95.1	96.9	98.8	100.6	102.4	104.2	106.1	107.9
60	109.7	111.6	113.4	115.2	117.0	118.9	120.7	122.5	124.4	126.2
70	128.0	129.8	131.7	133.5	135.3	137.2	139.0	140.8	142.6	144.5
80	146.3	148.1	150.0	151.8	153.6	155.4	157.3	159.1	160.9	162.8
90	164.6	166.4	168.2	170.1	171.9	173.7	175.6	177.4	179.2	181.0
100	182.9	184.7	186.5	188.4	190.2	192.0	193.8	195.7	197.5	199.3
110	201.2	203.0	204.8	206.7	208.5	210.3	212.1	214.0	215.8	217.6
120	219.5	221.3	223.1	224.9	226.8	228.6	230.4	232.3	234.1	235.9
130	237.7	239.6	241.4	243.2	245.1	246.9	248.7	250.5	252.4	254.2
140	256.0	257.9	259.7	261.5	263.3	265.2	267.0	268.8	270.7	272.5
150	274.3	276.1	278.0	279.8	281.6	283.5	285.3	287.1	288.9	290.8
160	292.6	294.4	296.3	298.1	299.9	301.7	303.6	305.4	307.2	309.1
170	310.9	312.7	314.5	316.4	318.2	320.0	321.9	323.7	325.5	327.3
180	329.2	331.0	332.8	334.7	336.5	338.3	340.2	342.0	343.8	345.6
190	347.5	349.3	351.1	353.0	354.8	356.6	358.4	360.3	362.1	363.9
200	365.8	367.6	369.4	371.2	373.1	374.9	376.7	378.6	380.4	382.2
210	384.0	385.9	387.7	389.5	391.4	393.2	395.0	396.8	398.7	400.5
220	402.3	404.2	406.0	407.8	409.6	411.5	413.3	415.1	417.0	418.8
230	420.6	422.4	424.3	426.1	427.9	429.8	431.6	433.4	435.2	437.1
240	438.9	440.7	442.6	444.4	446.2	448.0	449.9	451.7	453.5	455.4

Table 6–1 (*Continued*)
DEPTH CONVERSIONS
Table A

Fathoms	**0**	**1**	**2**	**3**	**4**	**5**	**6**	**7**	**8**	**9**
250	457.2	459.0	460.1	462.7	464.5	466.3	468.2	470.0	471.8	473.7
260	475.5	477.3	479.1	481.0	482.7	484.6	486.5	488.3	490.1	491.9
270	493.8	495.6	497.4	499.3	501.1	502.9	504.7	506.6	508.4	510.2
280	512.1	513.9	515.7	517.5	519.4	521.2	523.0	524.9	526.7	528.5
290	530.3	532.2	534.0	535.8	537.7	539.5	541.3	543.1	545.0	546.8
Fathoms	**0**	**10**	**20**	**30**	**40**	**50**	**60**	**70**	**80**	**90**
300	549	567	585	603	622	640	658	677	695	713
400	732	750	768	786	805	823	841	860	878	896
500	914	933	951	969	988	1006	1024	1042	1061	1079
600	1097	1116	1134	1152	1170	1189	1207	1225	1244	1262
700	1280	1298	1317	1335	1353	1372	1390	1408	1426	1445
800	1463	1481	1500	1518	1536	1554	1573	1591	1609	1628
900	1646	1664	1682	1701	1719	1737	1756	1774	1792	1810
Fathoms	**0**	**100**	**200**	**300**	**400**	**500**	**600**	**700**	**800**	**900**
1000	1829	2012	2195	2377	2560	2743	2926	3109	3292	3475
2000	3658	3840	4023	4206	4389	4572	4755	4938	5121	5303
3000	5486	5669	5852	6035	6218	6401	6584	6766	6949	7132
4000	7315	7498	7681	7864	8047	8229	8412	8595	8778	8961
5000	9144	9327	9510	9692	9875	10,058	10,241	10,424	10,607	10,790
6000	10,973	11,155	11,338	11,521	11,704	11,887	12,070	12,253	12,436	12,618
7000	12,801	12,984	13,167	13,350	13,533	13,716	13,899	14,082	14,264	14,447
8000	14,630	14,813	14,996	15,179	15,362	15,545	15,727	15,910	16,093	16,276
9000	16,459	16,642	16,825	17,008	17,190	17,373	17,556	17,739	17,922	18,105

Table 6–1 (*Continued*)
DEPTH CONVERSIONS

Table B Meters to Fathoms
1 Meter = 0.54681 Fathoms

Example:
Given, depth = 800 meters.
From table, depth = 437 fathoms.

Meters	0	1	2	3	4	5	6	7	8	9
0	0.0	0.5	1.1	1.6	2.2	2.7	3.3	3.8	4.4	4.9
10	5.5	6.0	6.6	7.1	7.7	8.2	8.7	9.3	9.8	10.4
20	10.9	11.5	12.0	12.6	13.1	13.7	14.2	14.8	15.3	15.9
30	16.4	17.0	17.5	18.0	18.6	19.1	19.7	20.2	20.8	21.3
40	21.9	22.4	23.0	23.5	24.1	24.6	25.2	25.7	26.2	26.8
50	27.3	27.9	28.4	29.0	29.5	30.1	30.6	31.2	31.7	32.3
60	32.8	33.4	33.9	34.4	35.0	35.5	36.1	36.6	37.2	37.7
70	38.3	38.8	39.4	39.9	40.5	41.0	41.6	42.1	42.7	43.2
80	43.7	44.3	44.8	45.4	45.9	46.5	47.0	47.6	48.1	48.7
90	49.2	49.8	50.3	50.9	51.4	51.9	52.5	53.0	53.6	54.1
100	54.7	55.2	55.8	56.3	56.9	57.4	58.0	58.5	59.1	59.6
110	60.1	60.7	61.2	61.8	62.3	62.9	63.4	64.0	64.5	65.1
120	65.6	66.2	66.7	67.3	67.8	68.4	68.9	69.4	70.0	70.5
130	71.1	71.6	72.2	72.7	73.3	73.8	74.4	74.9	75.5	76.0
140	76.6	77.1	77.6	78.2	78.7	79.3	79.8	80.4	80.9	81.5
150	82.0	82.6	83.1	83.7	84.2	84.8	85.3	85.9	86.4	86.9
160	87.5	88.0	88.6	89.1	89.7	90.2	90.8	91.3	91.9	92.4
170	93.0	93.5	94.1	94.6	95.1	95.7	96.2	96.8	97.3	97.9
180	98.4	99.0	99.5	100.1	100.6	101.2	101.7	102.3	102.8	103.3
190	103.9	104.4	105.0	105.5	106.1	106.6	107.2	107.7	108.3	108.8
200	109.4	109.9	110.5	111.0	111.6	112.1	112.6	113.2	113.7	114.3
210	114.8	115.4	115.9	116.5	117.0	117.6	118.1	118.7	119.2	119.8
220	120.3	120.8	121.4	121.9	122.5	123.0	123.6	124.1	124.7	125.2
230	125.8	126.3	126.9	127.4	128.0	128.5	129.0	129.6	130.1	130.7
240	131.2	131.8	132.3	132.9	133.4	134.0	134.5	135.1	135.6	136.2
250	136.7	137.3	137.8	138.3	138.9	139.4	140.0	140.5	141.1	141.6
260	142.2	142.7	143.3	143.8	144.4	144.9	145.5	146.0	146.5	147.1
270	147.6	148.2	148.7	149.3	149.8	150.4	150.9	151.5	152.0	152.6
280	153.1	153.7	154.2	154.7	155.3	155.8	156.4	156.9	157.5	158.0
290	158.6	159.1	159.7	160.2	160.8	161.3	161.9	162.4	163.0	163.5

Meters	0	10	20	30	40	50	60	70	80	90
300	164	170	175	180	186	191	197	202	208	213
400	219	224	230	235	241	246	252	257	262	268
500	273	279	284	290	295	301	306	312	317	323
600	328	334	339	344	350	355	361	366	372	377
700	383	388	394	399	405	410	416	421	427	432
800	437	443	448	454	459	465	470	476	481	487
900	492	498	503	509	514	519	525	530	536	541

Table 6–1 (*Continued*)
DEPTH CONVERSIONS

Meters	0	100	200	300	400	500	600	700	800	900
1000	547	601	656	711	766	820	875	930	984	1039
2000	1094	1148	1203	1258	1312	1367	1422	1476	1531	1586
3000	1640	1695	1750	1804	1859	1914	1969	2023	2078	2133
4000	2187	2242	2297	2351	2406	2461	2515	2570	2625	2679
5000	2734	2789	2843	2898	2953	3007	3062	3117	3172	3226
6000	3281	3336	3390	3445	3500	3554	3609	3664	3718	3773
7000	3828	3882	3937	3992	4046	4101	4156	4210	4265	4320
8000	4375	4429	4484	4539	4593	4648	4703	4757	4812	4867
9000	4921	4976	5031	5085	5140	5195	5249	5304	5359	5413

(From LaFond, E. C., *Processing Oceanographic Data,* U.S. Navy Hydrographic Office, Washington, D.C., Publ. No. 614, 1951.)

Table 6–2
DISTANCE CONVERSIONS

Table A Nautical Miles to Kilometers
1 Nautical Mile = 1.8532 Kilometers

Example:
Given, distance = 34 nautical miles.
From table, distance = 63.0 kilometers.

Nautical miles	0	1	2	3	4	5	6	7	8	9
0	0.0	1.8	3.7	5.6	7.4	9.3	11.1	13.0	14.8	16.7
10	18.5	20.4	22.2	24.1	25.9	27.8	29.7	31.5	33.4	35.2
20	37.1	38.9	40.8	42.6	44.5	46.3	48.2	50.0	51.9	53.7
30	55.6	57.5	59.3	61.2	63.0	64.9	66.7	68.6	70.4	72.3
40	74.1	76.0	77.8	79.7	81.5	83.4	85.2	87.1	89.0	90.8
50	92.7	94.5	96.4	98.2	100.1	101.9	103.8	105.6	107.5	109.3
60	111.2	113.0	114.9	116.8	118.6	120.5	122.3	124.2	126.0	127.9
70	129.7	131.6	133.4	135.3	137.1	139.0	140.8	142.7	144.6	146.4
80	148.3	150.1	152.0	153.8	155.7	157.5	159.4	161.2	163.1	164.9
90	166.8	168.6	170.5	172.4	174.2	176.1	177.9	179.8	181.6	183.5

Table 6–2 (*Continued*)
DISTANCE CONVERSIONS

Table B Kilometers to Nautical Miles
1 Kilometer = 0.53959 Nautical Mile

Example:
Given, distance = 105 kilometers.
From table, distance = 56.7 nautical miles.

Kilometers	0	1	2	3	4	5	6	7	8	9
0	0.0	0.5	1.1	1.6	2.2	2.7	3.2	3.8	4.3	4.9
10	5.4	5.9	6.5	7.0	7.6	8.1	8.6	9.2	9.7	10.3
20	10.8	11.3	11.9	12.4	13.0	13.5	14.0	14.6	15.1	15.6
30	16.2	16.7	17.3	17.8	18.3	18.9	19.4	20.0	20.5	21.0
40	21.6	22.1	22.7	23.2	23.7	24.3	24.8	25.4	25.9	26.4
50	27.0	27.5	28.1	28.6	29.1	29.7	30.2	30.8	31.3	31.8
60	32.4	32.9	33.5	34.0	34.5	35.1	35.6	36.2	36.7	37.2
70	37.8	38.3	38.9	39.4	39.9	40.5	41.0	41.5	42.1	42.6
80	43.2	43.7	44.2	44.8	45.3	45.9	46.4	46.9	47.5	48.0
90	48.6	49.1	49.6	50.2	50.7	51.3	51.8	52.3	52.9	53.4
100	54.0	54.5	55.0	55.6	56.1	56.7	57.2	57.7	58.3	58.8
110	59.4	59.9	60.4	61.0	61.5	62.1	62.6	63.1	63.7	64.2
120	64.8	65.3	65.8	66.4	66.9	67.4	68.0	68.5	69.1	69.6
130	70.1	70.7	71.2	71.8	72.3	72.8	73.4	73.9	74.5	75.0
140	75.5	76.1	76.6	77.2	77.7	78.2	78.8	79.3	79.9	80.4
150	80.9	81.5	82.0	82.6	83.1	83.6	84.2	84.7	85.3	85.8
160	86.3	86.9	87.4	88.0	88.5	89.0	89.6	90.1	90.7	91.2
170	91.7	92.3	92.8	93.3	93.9	94.4	95.0	95.5	96.0	96.6
180	97.1	97.7	98.2	98.7	99.3	99.8	100.4	100.9	101.4	102.0
190	102.5	103.1	103.6	104.1	104.7	105.2	105.8	106.3	106.8	107.4
200	107.9	108.5	109.0	109.5	110.1	110.6	111.2	111.7	112.2	112.8

(From LaFond, E. C., *Processing Oceanographic Data,* U.S. Navy Hydrographic Office, Washington, D.C., Publ. No. 614, 1951.)

Table 6–3
TEMPERATURE CONVERSION TABLE

This table permits one to convert from degrees Celsius to degrees Fahrenheit or from degrees Fahrenheit to degrees Celsius. The conversion is accomplished by first locating in a column printed in bold face type the number that is to be converted. If the number to be converted is in degrees Fahrenheit, one may find its equivalent in degrees Celsius by reading to the left. If the number to be converted is in degrees Celsius, one may find its equivalent in degrees Fahrenheit by reading to the right. Degrees Celsius are identical to degrees Centigrade. However, the word Celsius is preferred for international use.

The approved international symbolic abbreviation for degrees Celsius is °C, whereas for degrees Fahrenheit it is °F. Absolute zero on the Celsius scale is –273.15°C; on the Fahrenheit scale it is –459.67°F. The relation between degrees Fahrenheit and degrees Celsius may be expressed by

°C = 5/9(°F –32) or °F = 9/5(°C) +32.

To Convert			To Convert			To Convert		
To °C	←°F or °C→	To °F	To °C	←°F or °C→	To °F	To °C	←°F or °C→	To °F
−273.15	**−459.67**	—	−245.56	**−410**	—	−217.78	**−360**	—
−272.78	**−459**	—	−245	**−409**	—	−217.22	**−359**	—
−272.22	**−458**	—	−244.44	**−408**	—	−216.67	**−358**	—
−271.67	**−457**	—	−243.89	**−407**	—	−216.11	**−357**	—
−271.11	**−456**	—	−243.33	**−406**	—	−215.56	**−356**	—
−270.56	**−455**	—	−242.78	**−405**	—	−215	**−355**	—
−270	**−454**	—	−242.22	**−404**	—	−214.44	**−354**	—
−269.44	**−453**	—	−241.67	**−403**	—	−213.89	**−353**	—
−268.89	**−452**	—	−241.11	**−402**	—	−213.33	**−352**	—
−268.33	**−451**	—	−240.56	**−401**	—	−212.78	**−351**	—
−267.78	**−450**	—	−240	**−400**	—	−212.22	**−350**	—
−267.22	**−449**	—	−239.44	**−399**	—	−211.67	**−349**	—
−266.67	**−448**	—	−238.89	**−398**	—	−211.11	**−348**	—
−266.11	**−447**	—	−238.33	**−397**	—	−210.56	**−347**	—
−265.56	**−446**	—	−237.78	**−396**	—	−210	**−346**	—
−265	**−445**	—	−237.22	**−395**	—	−209.44	**−345**	—
−264.44	**−444**	—	−236.67	**−394**	—	−208.89	**−344**	—
−263.89	**−443**	—	−236.11	**−393**	—	−208.33	**−343**	—
−263.33	**−442**	—	−235.56	**−392**	—	−207.78	**−342**	—
−262.78	**−441**	—	−235	**−391**	—	−207.22	**−341**	—
−262.22	**−440**	—	−234.44	**−390**	—	−206.67	**−340**	—
−261.67	**−439**	—	−233.89	**−389**	—	−206.11	**−339**	—
−261.11	**−438**	—	−233.33	**−388**	—	−205.56	**−338**	—
−260.56	**−437**	—	−232.78	**−387**	—	−205	**−337**	—
−260	**−436**	—	−232.22	**−386**	—	−204.44	**−336**	—
−259.44	**−435**	—	−231.67	**−385**	—	−203.89	**−335**	—
−258.89	**−434**	—	−231.11	**−384**	—	−203.33	**−334**	—
−258.33	**−433**	—	−230.56	**−383**	—	−202.78	**−333**	—
−257.78	**−432**	—	−230	**−382**	—	−202.22	**−332**	—
−257.22	**−431**	—	−229.44	**−381**	—	−201.67	**−331**	—
−256.67	**−430**	—	−228.89	**−380**	—	−201.11	**−330**	—
−256.11	**−429**	—	−228.33	**−379**	—	−200.56	**−329**	—
−255.56	**−428**	—	−227.78	**−378**	—	−200	**−328**	—
−255	**−427**	—	−227.22	**−377**	—	−199.44	**−327**	—
−254.44	**−426**	—	−226.67	**−376**	—	−198.89	**−326**	—
−253.89	**−425**	—	−226.11	**−375**	—	−198.33	**−325**	—
−253.33	**−424**	—	−225.56	**−374**	—	−197.78	**−324**	—
−252.78	**−423**	—	−225	**−373**	—	−197.22	**−323**	—
−252.22	**−422**	—	−224.44	**−372**	—	−196.67	**−322**	—
−251.67	**−421**	—	−223.89	**−371**	—	−196.11	**−321**	—
−251.11	**−420**	—	−223.33	**−370**	—	−195.56	**−320**	—
−250.56	**−419**	—	−222.78	**−369**	—	−195	**−319**	—
−250	**−418**	—	−222.22	**−368**	—	−194.44	**−318**	—
−249.44	**−417**	—	−221.67	**−367**	—	−193.89	**−317**	—
−248.89	**−416**	—	−221.11	**−366**	—	−193.33	**−316**	—
−248.33	**−415**	—	−220.56	**−365**	—	−192.78	**−315**	—
−247.78	**−414**	—	−220	**−364**	—	−192.22	**−314**	—
−247.22	**−413**	—	−219.44	**−363**	—	−191.67	**−313**	—
−246.67	**−412**	—	−218.89	**−362**	—	−191.11	**−312**	—
−246.11	**−411**	—	−218.33	**−361**	—	−190.56	**−311**	—

Table 6–3 (*Continued*)
TEMPERATURE CONVERSION TABLE

To Convert			To Convert			To Convert		
To °C	←°F or °C→	To °F	To °C	←°F or °C→	To °F	To °C	←°F or °C→	To °F
−190	**−310**	—	−156.67	**−250**	−418	−123.33	**−190**	−310
−189.44	**−309**	—	−156.11	**−249**	−416.2	−122.78	**−189**	−308.2
−188.89	**−308**	—	−155.56	**−248**	−414.4	−122.22	**−188**	−306.4
−188.33	**−307**	—	−155	**−247**	−412.6	−121.67	**−187**	−304.6
−187.78	**−306**	—	−154.44	**−246**	−410.8	−121.11	**−186**	−302.8
−187.22	**−305**	—	−153.89	**−245**	−409	−120.56	**−185**	−301
−186.67	**−304**	—	−153.33	**−244**	−407.2	−120	**−184**	−299.2
−186.11	**−303**	—	−152.78	**−243**	−405.4	−119.44	**−183**	−297.4
−185.56	**−302**	—	−152.22	**−242**	−403.6	−118.89	**−182**	−295.6
−185	**−301**	—	−151.67	**−241**	−401.8	−118.33	**−181**	−293.8
−184.44	**−300**	—	−151.11	**−240**	−400	−117.78	**−180**	−292
−183.89	**−299**	—	−150.56	**−239**	−398.2	−117.22	**−179**	−290.2
−183.33	**−298**	—	−150	**−238**	−396.4	−116.67	**−178**	−288.4
−182.78	**−297**	—	−149.44	**−237**	−394.6	−116.11	**−177**	−286.6
−182.22	**−296**	—	−148.89	**−236**	−392.8	−115.56	**−176**	−284.8
−181.67	**−295**	—	−148.33	**−235**	−391	−115	**−175**	−283
−181.11	**−294**	—	−147.78	**−234**	−389.2	−114.44	**−174**	−281.2
−180.56	**−293**	—	−147.22	**−233**	−387.4	−113.89	**−173**	−279.4
−180	**−292**	—	−146.67	**−232**	−385.6	−113.33	**−172**	−277.6
−179.44	**−291**	—	−146.11	**−231**	−383.8	−112.78	**−171**	−275.8
−178.89	**−290**	—	−145.56	**−230**	−382	−112.22	**−170**	−274
−178.33	**−289**	—	−145	**−229**	−380.2	−111.67	**−169**	−272.2
−177.78	**−288**	—	−144.44	**−228**	−378.4	−111.11	**−168**	−270.4
−177.22	**−287**	—	−143.89	**−227**	−376.6	−110.56	**−167**	−268.6
−176.67	**−286**	—	−143.33	**−226**	−374.8	−110	**−166**	−266.8
−176.11	**−285**	—	−142.78	**−225**	−373	−109.44	**−165**	−265
−175.56	**−284**	—	−142.22	**−224**	−371.2	−108.89	**−164**	−263.2
−175	**−283**	—	−141.67	**−223**	−369.4	−108.33	**−163**	−261.4
−174.44	**−282**	—	−141.11	**−222**	−367.6	−107.78	**−162**	−259.6
−173.89	**−281**	—	−140.56	**−221**	−365.8	−107.22	**−161**	−257.8
−173.33	**−280**	—	−140	**−220**	−364	−106.67	**−160**	−256
−172.78	**−279**	—	−139.44	**−219**	−362.2	−106.11	**−159**	−254.2
−172.22	**−278**	—	−138.89	**−218**	−360.4	−105.56	**−158**	−252.4
−171.67	**−277**	—	−138.33	**−217**	−358.6	−105	**−157**	−250.6
−171.11	**−276**	—	−137.78	**−216**	−356.8	−104.44	**−156**	−248.8
−170.56	**−275**	—						
−170	**−274**	—	−137.22	**−215**	−355	−103.89	**−155**	−247
—	**−273.15**	−459.67	−136.67	**−214**	−353.2	−103.33	**−154**	−245.2
−169.44	**−273**	−459.4	−136.11	**−213**	−351.4	−102.78	**−153**	−243.4
−168.89	**−272**	−457.6	−135.56	**−212**	−349.6	−102.22	**−152**	−241.6
−168.33	**−271**	−455.8	−135	**−211**	−347.8	−101.67	**−151**	−239.8
−167.78	**−270**	−454	−134.44	**−210**	−346	−101.11	**−150**	−238
−167.22	**−269**	−452.2	−133.89	**−209**	−344.2	−100.56	**−149**	−236.2
−166.67	**−268**	−450.4	−133.33	**−208**	−342.4	−100	**−148**	−234.4
−166.11	**−267**	−448.6	−132.78	**−207**	−340.6	−99.44	**−147**	−232.6
−165.56	**−266**	−446.8	−132.22	**−206**	−338.8	−98.89	**−146**	−230.8
−165	**−265**	−445	−131.67	**−205**	−337	−98.33	**−145**	−229
−164.44	**−264**	−443.2	−131.11	**−204**	−335.2	−97.78	**−144**	−227.2
−163.89	**−263**	−441.4	−130.56	**−203**	−333.4	−97.22	**−143**	−225.4
−163.33	**−262**	−439.6	−130	**−202**	−331.6	−96.67	**−142**	−223.6
−162.78	**−261**	−437.8	−129.44	**−201**	−329.8	−96.11	**−141**	−221.8
−162.22	**−260**	−436	−128.89	**−200**	−328	−95.56	**−140**	−220
−161.67	**−259**	−434.2	−128.33	**−199**	−326.2	−95	**−139**	−218.2
−161.11	**−258**	−432.4	−127.78	**−198**	−324.4	−94.44	**−138**	−216.4
−160.56	**−257**	−430.6	−127.22	**−197**	−322.6	−93.89	**−137**	−214.6
−160	**−256**	−428.8	−126.67	**−196**	−320.8	−93.33	**−136**	−212.8
−159.44	**−255**	−427	−126.11	**−195**	−319	−92.78	**−135**	−211
−158.89	**−254**	−425.2	−125.56	**−194**	−317.2	−92.22	**−134**	−209.2
−158.33	**−253**	−423.4	−125	**−193**	−315.4	−91.67	**−133**	−207.4
−157.78	**−252**	−421.6	−124.44	**−192**	−313.6	−91.11	**−132**	−205.6
−157.22	**−251**	−419.8	−123.89	**−191**	−311.8	−90.56	**−131**	−203.8

Table 6–3 (*Continued*)
TEMPERATURE CONVERSION TABLE

To Convert			To Convert			To Convert		
To °C	←°F or °C→	To °F	To °C	←°F or °C→	To °F	To °C	←°F or °C→	To °F
−90	−130	−202	−56.67	−70	−94	−23.33	−10	14
−89.44	−129	−200.2	−56.11	−69	−92.2	−22.78	−9	15.8
−88.89	−128	−198.4	−55.56	−68	−90.4	−22.22	−8	17.6
−88.33	−127	−196.6	−55	−67	−88.6	−21.67	−7	19.4
−87.78	−126	−194.8	−54.44	−66	−86.8	−21.11	−6	21.2
−87.22	−125	−193	−53.89	−65	−85	−20.56	−5	23
−86.67	−124	−191.2	−53.33	−64	−83.2	−20	−4	24.8
−86.11	−123	−189.4	−52.78	−63	−81.4	−19.44	−3	26.6
−85.56	−122	−187.6	−52.22	−62	−79.6	−18.89	−2	28.4
−85	−121	−185.8	−51.67	−61	−77.8	−18.33	−1	30.2
−84.44	−120	−184	−51.11	−60	−76	−17.78	0	32
−83.89	−119	−182.2	−50.56	−59	−74.2	−17.22	1	33.8
−83.33	−118	−180.4	−50	−58	−72.4	−16.67	2	35.6
−82.78	−117	−178.6	−49.44	−57	−70.6	−16.11	3	37.4
−82.22	−116	−176.8	−48.89	−56	−68.8	−15.56	4	39.2
−81.67	−115	−175	−48.33	−55	−67	−15	5	41
−81.11	−114	−173.2	−47.78	−54	−65.2	−14.44	6	42.8
−80.56	−113	−171.4	−47.22	−53	−63.4	−13.89	7	44.6
−80	−112	−169.6	−46.67	−52	−61.6	−13.33	8	46.4
−79.44	−111	−167.8	−46.11	−51	−59.8	−12.78	9	48.2
−78.89	−110	−166	−45.56	−50	−58	−12.22	10	50
−78.33	−109	−164.2	−45	−49	−56.2	−11.67	11	51.8
−77.78	−108	−162.4	−44.44	−48	−54.4	−11.11	12	53.6
−77.22	−107	−160.6	−43.89	−47	−52.6	−10.56	13	55.4
−76.67	−106	−158.8	−43.33	−46	−50.8	−10	14	57.2
−76.11	−105	−157	−42.78	−45	−49	−9.44	15	59
−75.56	−104	−155.2	−42.22	−44	−47.2	−8.89	16	60.8
−75	−103	−153.4	−41.67	−43	−45.4	−8.33	17	62.6
−74.44	−102	−151.6	−41.11	−42	−43.6	−7.78	18	64.4
−73.89	−101	−149.8	−40.56	−41	−41.8	−7.22	19	66.2
−73.33	−100	−148	−40	−40	−40	−6.67	20	68
−72.78	−99	−146.2	−39.44	−39	−38.2	−6.11	21	69.8
−72.22	−98	−144.4	−38.89	−38	−36.4	−5.56	22	71.6
−71.67	−97	−142.6	−38.33	−37	−34.6	−5	23	73.4
−71.11	−96	−140.8	−37.78	−36	−32.8	−4.44	24	75.2
−70.56	−95	−139	−37.22	−35	−31	−3.89	25	77
−70	−94	−137.2	−36.67	−34	−29.2	−3.33	26	78.8
−69.44	−93	−135.4	−36.11	−33	−27.4	−2.78	27	80.6
−68.89	−92	−133.6	−35.56	−32	−25.6	−2.22	28	82.4
−68.33	−91	−131.8	−35	−31	−23.8	−1.67	29	84.2
−67.78	−90	−130	−34.44	−30	−22	−1.11	30	86
−67.22	−89	−128.2	−33.89	−29	−20.2	−0.56	31	87.8
−66.67	−88	−126.4	−33.33	−28	−18.4	0	32	89.6
−66.11	−87	−124.6	−32.78	−27	−16.6	.56	33	91.4
−65.56	−86	−122.8	−32.22	−26	−14.8	1.11	34	93.2
−65	−85	−121	−31.67	−25	−13	1.67	35	95
−64.44	−84	−119.2	−31.11	−24	−11.2	2.22	36	96.8
−63.89	−83	−117.4	−30.56	−23	−9.4	2.78	37	98.6
−63.33	−82	−115.6	−30	−22	−7.6	3.33	38	100.4
−62.78	−81	−113.8	−29.44	−21	−5.8	3.89	39	102.2
−62.22	−80	−112	−28.89	−20	−4	4.44	40	104
−61.67	−79	−110.2	−28.33	−19	−2.2	5	41	105.8
−61.11	−78	−108.4	−27.78	−18	−0.4	5.56	42	107.6
−60.56	−77	−106.6	−27.22	−17	1.4	6.11	43	109.4
−60	−76	−104.8	−26.67	−16	3.2	6.67	44	111.2
−59.44	−75	−103	−26.11	−15	5	7.22	45	113
−58.89	−74	−101.2	−25.56	−14	6.8	7.78	46	114.8
−58.33	−73	−99.4	−25	−13	8.6	8.33	47	116.6
−57.78	−72	−97.6	−24.44	−12	10.4	8.89	48	118.4
−57.22	−71	−95.8	−23.89	−11	12.2	9.44	49	120.2

Table 6–3 (*Continued*)
TEMPERATURE CONVERSION TABLE

To Convert			To Convert			To Convert		
To °C	←°F or °C→	To °F	To °C	←°F or °C→	To °F	To °C	←°F or °C→	To °F
10	**50**	122	43.33	**110**	230	76.67	**170**	338
10.56	**51**	123.8	43.89	**111**	231.8	77.22	**171**	339.8
11.11	**52**	125.6	44.44	**112**	233.6	77.78	**172**	341.6
11.67	**53**	127.4	45	**113**	235.4	78.33	**173**	343.4
12.22	**54**	129.2	45.56	**114**	237.2	78.89	**174**	345.2
12.78	**55**	131	46.11	**115**	239	79.44	**175**	347
13.33	**56**	132.8	46.67	**116**	240.8	80	**176**	348.8
13.89	**57**	134.6	47.22	**117**	242.6	80.56	**177**	350.6
14.44	**58**	136.4	47.78	**118**	244.4	81.11	**178**	352.4
15	**59**	138.2	48.33	**119**	246.2	81.67	**179**	354.2
15.56	**60**	140	48.89	**120**	248	82.22	**180**	356
16.11	**61**	141.8	49.44	**121**	249.8	82.78	**181**	357.8
16.67	**62**	143.6	50	**122**	251.6	83.33	**182**	359.6
17.22	**63**	145.4	50.56	**123**	253.4	83.89	**183**	361.4
17.78	**64**	147.2	51.11	**124**	255.2	84.44	**184**	363.2
18.33	**65**	149	51.67	**125**	257	85	**185**	365
18.89	**66**	150.8	52.22	**126**	258.8	85.56	**186**	366.8
19.44	**67**	152.6	52.78	**127**	260.6	86.11	**187**	368.6
20	**68**	154.4	53.33	**128**	262.4	86.67	**188**	370.4
20.56	**69**	156.2	53.89	**129**	264.2	87.22	**189**	372.2
21.11	**70**	158	54.44	**130**	266	87.78	**190**	374
21.67	**71**	159.8	55	**131**	267.8	88.33	**191**	375.8
22.22	**72**	161.6	55.56	**132**	269.6	88.89	**192**	377.6
22.78	**73**	163.4	56.11	**133**	271.4	89.44	**193**	379.4
23.33	**74**	165.2	56.67	**134**	273.2	90	**194**	381.2
23.89	**75**	167	57.22	**135**	275	90.56	**195**	383
24.44	**76**	168.8	57.78	**136**	276.8	91.11	**196**	384.8
25	**77**	170.6	58.33	**137**	278.6	91.67	**197**	386.6
25.56	**78**	172.4	58.89	**138**	280.4	92.22	**198**	388.4
26.11	**79**	174.2	59.44	**139**	282.2	92.78	**199**	390.2
26.67	**80**	176	60	**140**	284	93.33	**200**	392
27.22	**81**	177.8	60.56	**141**	285.8	93.89	**201**	393.8
27.78	**82**	179.6	61.11	**142**	287.6	94.44	**202**	395.6
28.33	**83**	181.4	61.67	**143**	289.4	95	**203**	397.4
28.89	**84**	183.2	62.22	**144**	291.2	95.56	**204**	399.2
29.44	**85**	185	62.78	**145**	293	96.11	**205**	401
30	**86**	186.8	63.33	**146**	294.8	96.67	**206**	402.8
30.56	**87**	188.6	63.89	**147**	296.6	97.22	**207**	404.6
31.11	**88**	190.4	64.44	**148**	298.4	97.78	**208**	406.4
31.67	**89**	192.2	65	**149**	300.2	98.33	**209**	408.2
32.22	**90**	194	65.56	**150**	302	98.89	**210**	410
32.78	**91**	195.8	66.11	**151**	303.8	99.44	**211**	411.8
33.33	**92**	197.6	66.67	**152**	305.6	100	**212**	413.6
33.89	**93**	199.4	67.22	**153**	307.4	100.56	**213**	415.4
34.44	**94**	201.2	67.78	**154**	309.2	101.11	**214**	417.2
35	**95**	203	68.33	**155**	311	101.67	**215**	419
35.56	**96**	204.8	68.89	**156**	312.8	102.22	**216**	420.8
36.11	**97**	206.6	69.44	**157**	314.6	102.78	**217**	422.6
36.67	**98**	208.4	70	**158**	316.4	103.33	**218**	424.4
37.22	**99**	210.2	70.56	**159**	318.2	103.89	**219**	426.2
37.78	**100**	212	71.11	**160**	320	104.44	**220**	428
38.33	**101**	213.8	71.67	**161**	321.8	105	**221**	429.8
38.89	**102**	215.6	72.22	**162**	323.6	105.56	**222**	431.6
39.44	**103**	217.4	72.78	**163**	325.4	106.11	**223**	433.4
40	**104**	219.2	73.33	**164**	327.2	106.67	**224**	435.2
40.56	**105**	221	73.89	**165**	329	107.22	**225**	437
41.11	**106**	222.8	74.44	**166**	330.8	107.78	**226**	438.8
41.67	**107**	224.6	75	**167**	332.6	108.33	**227**	440.6
42.22	**108**	226.4	75.56	**168**	334.4	108.89	**228**	442.4
42.78	**109**	228.2	76.11	**169**	336.2	109.44	**229**	444.2

Table 6–3 (*Continued*)

TEMPERATURE CONVERSION TABLE

To Convert			To Convert			To Convert		
To °C	←°F or °C→	To °F	To °C	←°F or °C→	To °F	To °C	←°F or °C→	To °F
110	**230**	446	143.33	**290**	554	176.67	**350**	662
110.56	**231**	447.8	143.89	**291**	555.8	177.22	**351**	663.8
111.11	**232**	449.6	144.44	**292**	557.6	177.78	**352**	665.6
111.67	**233**	451.4	145	**293**	559.4	178.33	**353**	667.4
112.22	**234**	453.2	145.56	**294**	561.2	178.89	**354**	669.2
112.78	**235**	455	146.11	**295**	563	179.44	**355**	671
113.33	**236**	456.8	146.67	**296**	564.8	180	**356**	672.8
113.89	**237**	458.6	147.22	**297**	566.6	180.56	**357**	674.6
114.44	**238**	460.4	147.78	**298**	568.4	181.11	**358**	676.4
115	**239**	462.2	148.33	**299**	570.2	181.67	**359**	678.2
115.56	**240**	464	148.89	**300**	572	182.22	**360**	680
116.11	**241**	465.8	149.44	**301**	573.8	182.78	**361**	681.8
116.67	**242**	467.6	150	**302**	575.6	183.33	**362**	683.6
117.22	**243**	469.4	150.56	**303**	577.4	183.89	**363**	685.4
117.78	**244**	471.2	151.11	**304**	579.2	184.44	**364**	687.2
118.33	**245**	473	151.67	**305**	581	185	**365**	689
118.89	**246**	474.8	152.22	**306**	582.8	185.56	**366**	690.8
119.44	**247**	476.6	152.78	**307**	584.6	186.11	**367**	692.6
120	**248**	478.4	153.33	**308**	586.4	186.67	**368**	694.4
120.56	**249**	480.2	153.89	**309**	588.2	187.22	**369**	696.2
121.11	**250**	482	154.44	**310**	590	187.78	**370**	698
121.67	**251**	483.8	155	**311**	591.8	188.33	**371**	699.8
122.22	**252**	485.6	155.56	**312**	593.6	188.89	**372**	701.6
122.78	**253**	487.4	156.11	**313**	595.4	189.44	**373**	703.4
123.33	**254**	489.2	156.67	**314**	597.2	190	**374**	705.2
123.89	**255**	491	157.22	**315**	599	190.56	**375**	707
124.44	**256**	492.8	157.78	**316**	600.8	191.11	**376**	708.8
125	**257**	494.6	158.33	**317**	602.6	191.67	**377**	710.6
125.56	**258**	496.4	158.89	**318**	604.4	192.22	**378**	712.4
126.11	**259**	498.2	159.44	**319**	606.2	192.78	**379**	714.2
126.67	**260**	500	160	**320**	608	193.33	**380**	716
127.22	**261**	501.8	160.56	**321**	609.8	193.89	**381**	717.8
127.78	**262**	503.6	161.11	**322**	611.6	194.44	**382**	719.6
128.33	**263**	505.4	161.67	**323**	613.4	195	**383**	721.4
128.89	**264**	507.2	162.22	**324**	615.2	195.56	**384**	723.2
129.44	**265**	509	162.78	**325**	617	196.11	**385**	725
130	**266**	510.8	163.33	**326**	618.8	196.67	**386**	726.8
130.56	**267**	512.6	163.89	**327**	620.6	197.22	**387**	728.6
131.11	**268**	514.4	164.44	**328**	622.4	197.78	**388**	730.4
131.67	**269**	516.2	165	**329**	624.2	198.33	**389**	732.2
132.22	**270**	518	165.56	**330**	626	198.89	**390**	734
132.78	**271**	519.8	166.11	**331**	627.8	199.44	**391**	735.8
133.33	**272**	521.6	166.67	**332**	629.6	200	**392**	737.6
133.89	**273**	523.4	167.22	**333**	631.4	200.56	**393**	739.4
134.44	**274**	525.2	167.78	**334**	633.2	201.11	**394**	741.2
135	**275**	527	168.33	**335**	635	201.67	**395**	743
135.56	**276**	528.8	168.89	**336**	636.8	202.22	**396**	744.8
136.11	**277**	530.6	169.44	**337**	638.6	202.78	**397**	746.6
136.67	**278**	532.4	170	**338**	640.4	203.33	**398**	748.4
137.22	**279**	534.2	170.56	**339**	642.2	203.89	**399**	750.2
137.78	**280**	536	171.11	**340**	644	204.44	**400**	752
138.33	**281**	537.8	171.67	**341**	645.8	205	**401**	753.8
138.89	**282**	539.6	172.22	**342**	647.6	205.56	**402**	755.6
139.44	**283**	541.4	172.78	**343**	649.4	206.11	**403**	757.4
140	**284**	543.2	173.33	**344**	651.2	206.67	**404**	759.2
140.56	**285**	545	173.89	**345**	653	207.22	**405**	761
141.11	**286**	546.8	174.44	**346**	654.8	207.78	**406**	762.8
141.67	**287**	548.6	175	**347**	656.6	208.33	**407**	764.6
142.22	**288**	550.4	175.56	**348**	658.4	208.89	**408**	766.4
142.78	**289**	552.2	176.11	**349**	660.2	209.44	**409**	768.2

Table 6–3 (*Continued*)
TEMPERATURE CONVERSION TABLE

To Convert			To Convert			To Convert		
To °C	←°F or °C→	To °F	To °C	←°F or °C→	To °F	To °C	←°F or °C→	To °F
210	**410**	770	243.33	**470**	878	276.67	**530**	986
210.56	**411**	771.8	243.89	**471**	879.8	277.22	**531**	987.8
211.11	**412**	773.6	244.44	**472**	881.6	277.78	**532**	989.6
211.67	**413**	775.4	245	**473**	883.4	278.33	**533**	991.4
212.22	**414**	777.2	245.56	**474**	885.2	278.89	**534**	993.2
212.78	**415**	779	246.11	**475**	887	279.44	**535**	995
213.33	**416**	780.8	246.67	**476**	888.8	280	**536**	996.8
213.89	**417**	782.6	247.22	**477**	890.6	280.56	**537**	998.6
214.44	**418**	784.4	247.78	**478**	892.4	281.11	**538**	1000.4
215	**419**	786.2	248.33	**479**	894.2	281.67	**539**	1002.2
215.56	**420**	788	248.89	**480**	896	282.22	**540**	1004
216.11	**421**	789.8	249.44	**481**	897.8	282.78	**541**	1005.8
216.67	**422**	791.6	250	**482**	899.6	283.33	**542**	1007.6
217.22	**423**	793.4	250.56	**483**	901.4	283.89	**543**	1009.4
217.78	**424**	795.2	251.11	**484**	903.2	284.44	**544**	1011.2
218.33	**425**	797	251.67	**485**	905	285	**545**	1013
218.89	**426**	798.8	252.22	**486**	906.8	285.56	**546**	1014.8
219.44	**427**	800.6	252.78	**487**	908.6	286.11	**547**	1016.6
220	**428**	802.4	253.33	**488**	910.4	286.67	**548**	1018.4
220.56	**429**	804.2	253.89	**489**	912.2	287.22	**549**	1020.2
221.11	**430**	806	254.44	**490**	914	287.78	**550**	1022
221.67	**431**	807.8	255	**491**	915.8	288.33	**551**	1023.8
222.22	**432**	809.6	255.56	**492**	917.6	288.89	**552**	1025.6
222.78	**433**	811.4	256.11	**493**	919.4	289.44	**553**	1027.4
223.33	**434**	813.2	256.67	**494**	921.2	290	**554**	1029.2
223.89	**435**	815	257.22	**495**	923	290.56	**555**	1031
224.44	**436**	816.8	257.78	**496**	924.8	291.11	**556**	1032.8
225	**437**	818.6	258.33	**497**	926.6	291.67	**557**	1034.6
225.56	**438**	820.4	258.89	**498**	928.4	292.22	**558**	1036.4
226.11	**439**	822.2	259.44	**499**	930.2	292.78	**559**	1038.2
226.67	**440**	824	260	**500**	932	293.33	**560**	1040
227.22	**441**	825.8	260.56	**501**	933.8	293.89	**561**	1041.8
227.78	**442**	827.6	261.11	**502**	935.6	294.44	**562**	1043.6
228.33	**443**	829.4	261.67	**503**	937.4	295	**563**	1045.4
228.89	**444**	831.2	262.22	**504**	939.2	295.56	**564**	1047.2
229.44	**445**	833	262.78	**505**	941	296.11	**565**	1049
230	**446**	834.8	263.33	**506**	942.8	296.67	**566**	1050.8
230.56	**447**	836.6	263.89	**507**	944.6	297.22	**567**	1052.6
231.11	**448**	838.4	264.44	**508**	946.4	297.78	**568**	1054.4
231.67	**449**	840.2	265	**509**	948.2	298.33	**569**	1056.2
232.22	**450**	842	265.56	**510**	950	298.89	**570**	1058
232.78	**451**	843.8	266.11	**511**	951.8	299.44	**571**	1059.8
233.33	**452**	845.6	266.67	**512**	953.6	300	**572**	1061.6
233.89	**453**	847.4	267.22	**513**	955.4	300.56	**573**	1063.4
234.44	**454**	849.2	267.78	**514**	957.2	301.11	**574**	1065.2
235	**455**	851	268.33	**515**	959	301.67	**575**	1067
235.56	**456**	852.8	268.89	**516**	960.8	302.22	**576**	1068.8
236.11	**457**	854.6	269.44	**517**	962.6	302.78	**577**	1070.6
236.67	**458**	856.4	270	**518**	964.4	303.33	**578**	1072.4
237.22	**459**	858.2	270.56	**519**	966.2	303.89	**579**	1074.2
237.78	**460**	860	271.11	**520**	968	304.44	**580**	1076
238.33	**461**	861.8	271.67	**521**	969.8	305	**581**	1077.8
238.89	**462**	863.6	272.22	**522**	971.6	305.56	**582**	1079.6
239.44	**463**	865.4	272.78	**523**	973.4	306.11	**583**	1081.4
240	**464**	867.2	273.33	**524**	975.2	306.67	**584**	1083.2
240.56	**465**	869	273.89	**525**	977	307.22	**585**	1085
241.11	**466**	870.8	274.44	**526**	978.8	307.78	**586**	1086.8
241.67	**467**	872.6	275	**527**	980.6	308.33	**587**	1088.6
242.22	**468**	874.4	275.56	**528**	982.4	308.89	**588**	1090.4
242.78	**469**	876.2	276.11	**529**	984.2	309.44	**589**	1092.2

Table 6–3 (*Continued*)

TEMPERATURE CONVERSION TABLE

To Convert			To Convert			To Convert		
To °C	←°F or °C→	To °F	To °C	←°F or °C→	To °F	To °C	←°F or °C→	To °F
310	**590**	1094	343.33	**650**	1202	376.67	**710**	1310
310.56	**591**	1095.8	343.89	**651**	1203.8	377.22	**711**	1311.8
311.11	**592**	1097.6	344.44	**652**	1205.6	377.78	**712**	1313.6
311.67	**593**	1099.4	345	**653**	1207.4	378.33	**713**	1315.4
312.22	**594**	1101.2	345.56	**654**	1209.2	378.89	**714**	1317.2
312.78	**595**	1103	346.11	**655**	1211	379.44	**715**	1319
313.33	**596**	1104.8	346.67	**656**	1212.8	380	**716**	1320.8
313.89	**597**	1106.6	347.22	**657**	1214.6	380.56	**717**	1322.6
314.44	**598**	1108.4	347.78	**658**	1216.4	381.11	**718**	1324.4
315	**599**	1110.2	348.33	**659**	1218.2	381.67	**719**	1326.2
315.56	**600**	1112	348.89	**660**	1220	382.22	**720**	1328
316.11	**601**	1113.8	349.44	**661**	1221.8	382.78	**721**	1329.8
316.67	**602**	1115.6	350	**662**	1223.6	383.33	**722**	1331.6
317.22	**603**	1117.4	350.56	**663**	1225.4	383.89	**723**	1333.4
317.78	**604**	1119.2	351.11	**664**	1227.2	384.44	**724**	1335.2
318.33	**605**	1121	351.67	**665**	1229	385	**725**	1337
318.89	**606**	1122.8	352.22	**666**	1230.8	385.56	**726**	1338.8
319.44	**607**	1124.6	352.78	**667**	1232.6	386.11	**727**	1340.6
320	**608**	1126.4	353.33	**668**	1234.4	386.67	**728**	1342.4
320.56	**609**	1128.2	353.89	**669**	1236.2	387.22	**729**	1344.2
321.11	**610**	1130	354.44	**670**	1238	387.78	**730**	1346
321.67	**611**	1131.8	355	**671**	1239.8	388.33	**731**	1347.8
322.22	**612**	1133.6	355.56	**672**	1241.6	388.89	**732**	1349.6
322.78	**613**	1135.4	356.11	**673**	1243.4	389.44	**733**	1351.4
323.33	**614**	1137.2	356.67	**674**	1245.2	390	**734**	1353.2
323.89	**615**	1139	357.22	**675**	1247	390.56	**735**	1355
324.44	**616**	1140.8	357.78	**676**	1248.8	391.11	**736**	1356.8
325	**617**	1142.6	358.33	**677**	1250.6	391.67	**737**	1358.6
325.56	**618**	1144.4	358.89	**678**	1252.4	392.22	**738**	1360.4
326.11	**619**	1146.2	359.44	**679**	1254.2	392.78	**739**	1362.2
326.67	**620**	1148	360	**680**	1256	393.33	**740**	1364
327.22	**621**	1149.8	360.56	**681**	1257.8	393.89	**741**	1365.8
327.78	**622**	1151.6	361.11	**682**	1259.6	394.44	**742**	1367.6
328.33	**623**	1153.4	361.67	**683**	1261.4	395	**743**	1369.4
328.89	**624**	1155.2	362.22	**684**	1263.2	395.56	**744**	1371.2
329.44	**625**	1157	362.78	**685**	1265	396.11	**745**	1373
330	**626**	1158.8	363.33	**686**	1266.8	396.67	**746**	1374.8
330.56	**627**	1160.6	363.89	**687**	1268.6	397.22	**747**	1376.6
331.11	**628**	1162.4	364.44	**688**	1270.4	397.78	**748**	1378.4
331.67	**629**	1164.2	365	**689**	1272.2	398.33	**749**	1380.2
332.22	**630**	1166	365.56	**690**	1274	398.89	**750**	1382
332.78	**631**	1167.8	366.11	**691**	1275.8	399.44	**751**	1383.8
333.33	**632**	1169.6	366.67	**692**	1277.6	400	**752**	1385.6
333.89	**633**	1171.4	367.22	**693**	1279.4	400.56	**753**	1387.4
334.44	**634**	1173.2	367.78	**694**	1281.2	401.11	**754**	1389.2
335	**635**	1175	368.33	**695**	1283	401.67	**755**	1391
335.56	**636**	1176.8	368.89	**696**	1284.8	402.22	**756**	1392.8
336.11	**637**	1178.6	369.44	**697**	1286.6	402.78	**757**	1394.6
336.67	**638**	1180.4	370	**698**	1288.4	403.33	**758**	1396.4
337.22	**639**	1182.2	370.56	**699**	1290.2	403.89	**759**	1398.2
337.78	**640**	1184	371.11	**700**	1292	404.44	**760**	1400
338.33	**641**	1185.8	371.67	**701**	1293.8	405	**761**	1401.8
338.89	**642**	1187.6	372.22	**702**	1295.6	405.56	**762**	1403.6
339.44	**643**	1189.4	372.78	**703**	1297.4	406.11	**763**	1405.4
340	**644**	1191.2	373.33	**704**	1299.2	406.67	**764**	1407.2
340.56	**645**	1193	373.89	**705**	1301	407.22	**765**	1409
341.11	**646**	1194.8	374.44	**706**	1302.8	407.78	**766**	1410.8
341.67	**647**	1196.6	375	**707**	1304.6	408.33	**767**	1412.6
342.22	**648**	1198.4	375.56	**708**	1306.4	408.89	**768**	1414.4
342.78	**649**	1200.2	376.11	**709**	1308.2	409.44	**769**	1416.2

Table 6–3 (*Continued*)
TEMPERATURE CONVERSION TABLE

To Convert			To Convert			To Convert		
To °C	←°F or °C→	To °F	To °C	←°F or °C→	To °F	To °C	←°F or °C→	To °F
410	**770**	1418	443.33	**830**	1526	476.67	**890**	1634
410.56	**771**	1419.8	443.89	**831**	1527.8	477.22	**891**	1635.8
411.11	**772**	1421.6	444.44	**832**	1529.6	477.78	**892**	1637.6
411.67	**773**	1423.4	445	**833**	1531.4	478.33	**893**	1639.4
412.22	**774**	1425.2	445.56	**834**	1533.2	478.89	**894**	1641.2
412.78	**775**	1427	446.11	**835**	1535	479.44	**895**	1643
413.33	**776**	1428.8	446.67	**836**	1536.8	480	**896**	1644.8
413.89	**777**	1430.6	447.22	**837**	1538.6	480.56	**897**	1646.6
414.44	**778**	1432.4	447.78	**838**	1540.4	481.11	**898**	1648.4
415	**779**	1434.2	448.33	**839**	1542.2	481.67	**899**	1650.2
415.56	**780**	1436	448.89	**840**	1544	482.22	**900**	1652
416.11	**781**	1437.8	449.44	**841**	1545.8	482.78	**901**	1653.8
416.67	**782**	1439.6	450	**842**	1547.6	483.33	**902**	1655.6
417.22	**783**	1441.4	450.56	**843**	1549.4	483.89	**903**	1657.4
417.78	**784**	1443.2	451.11	**844**	1551.2	484.44	**904**	1659.2
418.33	**785**	1445	451.67	**845**	1553	485	**905**	1661
418.89	**786**	1446.8	452.22	**846**	1554.8	485.56	**906**	1662.8
419.44	**787**	1448.6	452.78	**847**	1556.6	486.11	**907**	1664.6
420	**788**	1450.4	453.33	**848**	1558.4	486.67	**908**	1666.4
420.56	**789**	1452.2	453.89	**849**	1560.2	487.22	**909**	1668.2
421.11	**790**	1454	454.44	**850**	1562	487.78	**910**	1670
421.67	**791**	1455.8	455	**851**	1563.8	488.33	**911**	1671.8
422.22	**792**	1457.6	455.56	**852**	1565.6	488.89	**912**	1673.6
422.78	**793**	1459.4	456.11	**853**	1567.4	489.44	**913**	1675.4
423.33	**794**	1461.2	456.67	**854**	1569.2	490	**914**	1677.2
423.89	**795**	1463	457.22	**855**	1571	490.56	**915**	1679
424.44	**796**	1464.8	457.78	**856**	1572.8	491.11	**916**	1680.8
425	**797**	1466.6	458.33	**857**	1574.6	491.67	**917**	1682.6
425.56	**798**	1468.4	458.89	**858**	1576.4	492.22	**918**	1684.4
426.11	**799**	1470.2	459.44	**859**	1578.2	492.78	**919**	1686.2
426.67	**800**	1472	460	**860**	1580	493.33	**920**	1688
427.22	**801**	1473.8	460.56	**861**	1581.8	493.89	**921**	1689.8
427.78	**802**	1475.6	461.11	**862**	1583.6	494.44	**922**	1691.6
428.33	**803**	1477.4	461.67	**863**	1585.4	495	**923**	1693.4
428.89	**804**	1479.2	462.22	**864**	1587.2	495.56	**924**	1695.2
429.44	**805**	1481	462.78	**865**	1589	496.11	**925**	1697
430	**806**	1482.8	463.33	**866**	1590.8	496.67	**926**	1698.8
430.56	**807**	1484.6	463.89	**867**	1592.6	497.22	**927**	1700.6
431.11	**808**	1486.4	464.44	**868**	1594.4	497.78	**928**	1702.4
431.67	**809**	1488.2	465	**869**	1596.2	498.33	**929**	1704.2
432.22	**810**	1490	465.56	**870**	1598	498.89	**930**	1706
432.78	**811**	1491.8	466.11	**871**	1599.8	499.44	**931**	1707.8
433.33	**812**	1493.6	466.67	**872**	1601.6	500	**932**	1709.6
433.89	**813**	1495.4	467.22	**873**	1603.4	500.56	**933**	1711.4
434.44	**814**	1497.2	467.78	**874**	1605.2	501.11	**934**	1713.2
435	**815**	1499	468.33	**875**	1607	501.67	**935**	1715
435.56	**816**	1500.8	468.89	**876**	1608.8	502.22	**936**	1716.8
436.11	**817**	1502.6	469.44	**877**	1610.6	502.78	**937**	1718.6
436.67	**818**	1504.4	470	**878**	1612.4	503.33	**938**	1720.4
437.22	**819**	1506.2	470.56	**879**	1614.2	503.89	**939**	1722.2
437.78	**820**	1508	471.11	**880**	1616	504.44	**940**	1724
438.33	**821**	1509.8	471.67	**881**	1617.8	505	**941**	1725.8
438.89	**822**	1511.6	472.22	**882**	1619.6	505.56	**942**	1727.6
439.44	**823**	1513.4	472.78	**883**	1621.4	506.11	**943**	1729.4
440	**824**	1515.2	473.33	**884**	1623.2	506.67	**944**	1731.2
440.56	**825**	1517	473.89	**885**	1625	507.22	**945**	1733
441.11	**826**	1518.8	474.44	**886**	1626.8	507.78	**946**	1734.8
441.67	**827**	1520.6	475	**887**	1628.6	508.33	**947**	1736.6
442.22	**828**	1522.4	475.56	**888**	1630.4	508.89	**948**	1738.4
442.78	**829**	1524.2	476.11	**889**	1632.2	509.44	**949**	1740.2

Table 6–3 (*Continued*)

TEMPERATURE CONVERSION TABLE

To Convert			To Convert			To Convert		
To °C	←°F or °C→	To °F	To °C	←°F or °C→	To °F	To °C	←°F or °C→	To °F
510	**950**	1742	543.33	**1010**	1850	576.67	**1070**	1958
510.56	**951**	1743.8	543.89	**1011**	1851.8	577.22	**1071**	1959.8
511.11	**952**	1745.6	544.44	**1012**	1853.6	577.78	**1072**	1961.6
511.67	**953**	1747.4	545	**1013**	1855.4	578.33	**1073**	1963.4
512.22	**954**	1749.2	545.56	**1014**	1857.2	578.89	**1074**	1965.2
512.78	**955**	1751	546.11	**1015**	1859	579.44	**1075**	1967
513.33	**956**	1752.8	546.67	**1016**	1860.8	580	**1076**	1968.8
513.89	**957**	1754.6	547.22	**1017**	1862.6	580.56	**1077**	1970.6
514.44	**958**	1756.4	547.78	**1018**	1864.4	581.11	**1078**	1972.4
515	**959**	1758.2	548.33	**1019**	1866.2	581.67	**1079**	1974.2
515.56	**960**	1760	548.89	**1020**	1868	582.22	**1080**	1976
516.11	**961**	1761.8	549.44	**1021**	1869.8	582.78	**1081**	1977.8
516.67	**962**	1763.6	550	**1022**	1871.6	583.33	**1082**	1979.6
517.22	**963**	1765.4	550.56	**1023**	1873.4	583.89	**1083**	1981.4
517.78	**964**	1767.2	551.11	**1024**	1875.2	584.44	**1084**	1983.2
518.33	**965**	1769	551.67	**1025**	1877	585	**1085**	1985
518.89	**966**	1770.8	552.22	**1026**	1878.8	585.56	**1086**	1986.8
519.44	**967**	1772.6	552.78	**1027**	1880.6	586.11	**1087**	1988.6
520	**968**	1774.4	553.33	**1028**	1882.4	586.67	**1088**	1990.4
520.56	**969**	1776.2	553.89	**1029**	1884.2	587.22	**1089**	1992.2
521.11	**970**	1778	554.44	**1030**	1886	587.78	**1090**	1994
521.67	**971**	1779.8	555	**1031**	1887.8	588.33	**1091**	1995.8
522.22	**972**	1781.6	555.56	**1032**	1889.6	588.89	**1092**	1997.6
522.78	**973**	1783.4	556.11	**1033**	1891.4	589.44	**1093**	1999.4
523.33	**974**	1785.2	556.67	**1034**	1893.2	590	**1094**	2001.2
523.89	**975**	1787	557.22	**1035**	1895	590.56	**1095**	2003
524.44	**976**	1788.8	557.78	**1036**	1896.8	591.11	**1096**	2004.8
525	**977**	1790.6	558.33	**1037**	1898.6	591.67	**1097**	2006.6
525.56	**978**	1792.4	558.89	**1038**	1900.4	592.22	**1098**	2008.4
526.11	**979**	1794.2	559.44	**1039**	1902.2	592.78	**1099**	2010.2
526.67	**980**	1796	560	**1040**	1904	593.33	**1100**	2012
527.22	**981**	1797.8	560.56	**1041**	1905.8	593.89	**1101**	2013.8
527.78	**982**	1799.6	561.11	**1042**	1907.6	594.44	**1102**	2015.6
528.33	**983**	1801.4	561.67	**1043**	1909.4	595	**1103**	2017.4
528.89	**984**	1803.2	562.22	**1044**	1911.2	595.56	**1104**	2019.2
529.44	**985**	1805	562.78	**1045**	1913	596.11	**1105**	2021
530	**986**	1806.8	563.33	**1046**	1914.8	596.67	**1106**	2022.8
530.56	**987**	1808.6	563.89	**1047**	1916.6	597.22	**1107**	2024.6
531.11	**988**	1810.4	564.44	**1048**	1918.4	597.78	**1108**	2026.4
531.67	**989**	1812.2	565	**1049**	1920.2	598.33	**1109**	2028.2
532.22	**990**	1814	565.56	**1050**	1922	598.89	**1110**	2030
532.78	**991**	1815.8	566.11	**1051**	1923.8	599.44	**1111**	2031.8
533.33	**992**	1817.6	566.67	**1052**	1925.6	600	**1112**	2033.6
533.89	**993**	1819.4	567.22	**1053**	1927.4	600.56	**1113**	2035.4
534.44	**994**	1821.2	567.78	**1054**	1929.2	601.11	**1114**	2037.2
535	**995**	1823	568.33	**1055**	1931	601.67	**1115**	2039
535.56	**996**	1824.8	568.89	**1056**	1932.8	602.22	**1116**	2040.8
536.11	**997**	1826.6	569.44	**1057**	1934.6	602.78	**1117**	2042.6
536.67	**998**	1828.4	570	**1058**	1936.4	603.33	**1118**	2044.4
537.22	**999**	1830.2	570.56	**1059**	1938.2	603.89	**1119**	2046.2
537.78	**1000**	1832	571.11	**1060**	1940	604.44	**1120**	2048
538.33	**1001**	1833.8	571.67	**1061**	1941.8	605	**1121**	2049.8
538.89	**1002**	1835.6	572.22	**1062**	1943.6	605.56	**1122**	2051.6
539.44	**1003**	1837.4	572.78	**1063**	1945.4	606.11	**1123**	2053.4
540	**1004**	1839.2	573.33	**1064**	1947.2	606.67	**1124**	2055.2
540.56	**1005**	1841	573.89	**1065**	1949	607.22	**1125**	2057
541.11	**1006**	1842.8	574.44	**1066**	1950.8	607.78	**1126**	2058.8
541.67	**1007**	1844.6	575	**1067**	1952.6	608.33	**1127**	2060.6
542.22	**1008**	1846.4	575.56	**1068**	1954.4	608.89	**1128**	2062.4
542.78	**1009**	1848.2	576.11	**1069**	1956.2	609.44	**1129**	2064.2

Table 6–3 (*Continued*)
TEMPERATURE CONVERSION TABLE

To Convert			To Convert			To Convert		
To °C	←°F or °C→	To °F	To °C	←°F or °C→	To °F	To °C	←°F or °C→	To °F
610	**1130**	2066	643.33	**1190**	2174	676.67	**1250**	2282
610.56	**1131**	2067.8	643.89	**1191**	2175.8	677.22	**1251**	2283.8
611.11	**1132**	2069.6	644.44	**1192**	2177.6	677.78	**1252**	2285.6
611.67	**1133**	2071.4	645	**1193**	2179.4	678.33	**1253**	2287.4
612.22	**1134**	2073.2	645.56	**1194**	2181.2	678.89	**1254**	2289.2
612.78	**1135**	2075	646.11	**1195**	2183	679.44	**1255**	2291
613.33	**1136**	2076.8	646.67	**1196**	2184.8	680	**1256**	2292.8
613.89	**1137**	2078.6	647.22	**1197**	2186.6	680.56	**1257**	2294.6
614.44	**1138**	2080.4	647.78	**1198**	2188.4	681.11	**1258**	2296.4
615	**1139**	2082.2	648.33	**1199**	2190.2	681.67	**1259**	2298.2
615.56	**1140**	2084	648.89	**1200**	2192	682.22	**1260**	2300
616.11	**1141**	2085.8	649.44	**1201**	2193.8	682.78	**1261**	2301.8
616.67	**1142**	2087.6	650	**1202**	2195.6	683.33	**1262**	2303.6
617.22	**1143**	2089.4	650.56	**1203**	2197.4	683.89	**1263**	2305.4
617.78	**1144**	2091.2	651.11	**1204**	2199.2	684.44	**1264**	2307.2
618.33	**1145**	2093	651.67	**1205**	2201	685	**1265**	2309
618.89	**1146**	2094.8	652.22	**1206**	2202.8	685.56	**1266**	2310.8
619.44	**1147**	2096.6	652.78	**1207**	2204.6	686.11	**1267**	2312.6
620	**1148**	2098.4	653.33	**1208**	2206.4	686.67	**1268**	2314.4
620.56	**1149**	2100.2	653.89	**1209**	2208.2	687.22	**1269**	2316.2
621.11	**1150**	2102	654.44	**1210**	2210	687.78	**1270**	2318
621.67	**1151**	2103.8	655	**1211**	2211.8	688.33	**1271**	2319.8
622.22	**1152**	2105.6	655.56	**1212**	2213.6	688.89	**1272**	2321.6
622.78	**1153**	2107.4	656.11	**1213**	2215.4	689.44	**1273**	2323.4
623.33	**1154**	2109.2	656.67	**1214**	2217.2	690	**1274**	2325.2
623.89	**1155**	2111	657.22	**1215**	2219	690.56	**1275**	2327
624.44	**1156**	2112.8	657.78	**1216**	2220.8	691.11	**1276**	2328.8
625	**1157**	2114.6	658.33	**1217**	2222.6	691.67	**1277**	2330.6
625.56	**1158**	2116.4	658.89	**1218**	2224.4	692.22	**1278**	2332.4
626.11	**1159**	2118.2	659.44	**1219**	2226.2	692.78	**1279**	2334.2
626.67	**1160**	2120	660	**1220**	2228	693.33	**1280**	2336
627.22	**1161**	2121.8	660.56	**1221**	2229.8	693.89	**1281**	2337.8
627.78	**1162**	2123.6	661.11	**1222**	2231.6	694.44	**1282**	2339.6
628.33	**1163**	2125.4	661.67	**1223**	2233.4	695	**1283**	2341.4
628.89	**1164**	2127.2	662.22	**1224**	2235.2	695.56	**1284**	2343.2
629.44	**1165**	2129	662.78	**1225**	2237	696.11	**1285**	2345
630	**1166**	2130.8	663.33	**1226**	2238.8	696.67	**1286**	2346.8
630.56	**1167**	2132.6	663.89	**1227**	2240.6	697.22	**1287**	2348.6
631.11	**1168**	2134.4	664.44	**1228**	2242.4	697.78	**1288**	2350.4
631.67	**1169**	2136.2	665	**1229**	2244.2	698.33	**1289**	2352.2
632.22	**1170**	2138	665.56	**1230**	2246	698.89	**1290**	2354
632.78	**1171**	2139.8	666.11	**1231**	2247.8	699.44	**1291**	2355.8
633.33	**1172**	2141.6	666.67	**1232**	2249.6	700	**1292**	2357.6
633.89	**1173**	2143.4	667.22	**1233**	2251.4	700.56	**1293**	2359.4
634.44	**1174**	2145.2	667.78	**1234**	2253.2	701.11	**1294**	2361.2
635	**1175**	2147	668.33	**1235**	2255	701.67	**1295**	2363
635.56	**1176**	2148.8	668.89	**1236**	2256.8	702.22	**1296**	2364.8
636.11	**1177**	2150.6	669.44	**1237**	2258.6	702.78	**1297**	2366.6
636.67	**1178**	2152.4	670	**1238**	2260.4	703.33	**1298**	2368.4
637.22	**1179**	2154.2	670.56	**1239**	2262.2	703.89	**1299**	2370.2
637.78	**1180**	2156	671.11	**1240**	2264	704.44	**1300**	2372
638.33	**1181**	2157.8	671.67	**1241**	2265.8	705	**1301**	2373.8
638.89	**1182**	2159.6	672.22	**1242**	2267.6	705.56	**1302**	2375.6
639.44	**1183**	2161.4	672.78	**1243**	2269.4	706.11	**1303**	2377.4
640	**1184**	2163.2	673.33	**1244**	2271.2	706.67	**1304**	2379.2
640.56	**1185**	2165	673.89	**1245**	2273	707.22	**1305**	2381
641.11	**1186**	2166.8	674.44	**1246**	2274.8	707.78	**1306**	2382.8
641.67	**1187**	2168.6	675	**1247**	2276.6	708.33	**1307**	2384.6
642.22	**1188**	2170.4	675.56	**1248**	2278.4	708.89	**1308**	2386.4
642.78	**1189**	2172.2	676.11	**1249**	2280.2	709.44	**1309**	2388.2

Table 6–3 (*Continued*)
TEMPERATURE CONVERSION TABLE

To Convert			To Convert			To Convert		
To °C	←°F or °C→	To °F	To °C	←°F or °C→	To °F	To °C	←°F or °C→	To °F
710	**1310**	2390	743.33	**1370**	2498	776.67	**1430**	2606
710.56	**1311**	2391.8	743.89	**1371**	2499.8	777.22	**1431**	2607.8
711.11	**1312**	2393.6	744.44	**1372**	2501.6	777.78	**1432**	2609.6
711.67	**1313**	2395.4	745	**1373**	2503.4	778.33	**1433**	2611.4
712.22	**1314**	2397.2	745.56	**1374**	2505.2	778.89	**1434**	2613.2
712.78	**1315**	2399	746.11	**1375**	2507	779.44	**1435**	2615
713.33	**1316**	2400.8	746.67	**1376**	2508.8	780	**1436**	2616.8
713.89	**1317**	2402.6	747.22	**1377**	2510.6	780.56	**1437**	2618.6
714.44	**1318**	2404.4	747.78	**1378**	2512.4	781.11	**1438**	2620.4
715	**1319**	2406.2	748.33	**1379**	2514.2	781.67	**1439**	2622.2
715.56	**1320**	2408	748.89	**1380**	2516	782.22	**1440**	2624
716.11	**1321**	2409.8	749.44	**1381**	2517.8	782.78	**1441**	2625.8
716.67	**1322**	2411.6	750	**1382**	2519.6	783.33	**1442**	2627.6
717.22	**1323**	2413.4	750.56	**1383**	2521.4	783.89	**1443**	2629.4
717.78	**1324**	2415.2	751.11	**1384**	2523.2	784.44	**1444**	2631.2
718.33	**1325**	2417	751.67	**1385**	2525	785	**1445**	2633
718.89	**1326**	2418.8	752.22	**1386**	2526.8	785.56	**1446**	2634.8
719.44	**1327**	2420.6	752.78	**1387**	2528.6	786.11	**1447**	2636.6
720	**1328**	2422.4	753.33	**1388**	2530.4	786.67	**1448**	2638.4
720.56	**1329**	2424.2	753.89	**1389**	2532.2	787.22	**1449**	2640.2
721.11	**1330**	2426	754.44	**1390**	2534	787.78	**1450**	2642
721.67	**1331**	2427.8	755	**1391**	2535.8	788.33	**1451**	2443.8
722.22	**1332**	2429.6	755.56	**1392**	2537.6	788.89	**1452**	2645.6
722.78	**1333**	2431.4	756.11	**1393**	2539.4	789.44	**1453**	2647.4
723.33	**1334**	2433.2	756.67	**1394**	2541.2	790	**1454**	2649.2
723.89	**1335**	2435	757.22	**1395**	2543	790.56	**1455**	2651
724.44	**1336**	2436.8	757.78	**1396**	2544.8	791.11	**1456**	2652.8
725	**1337**	2438.6	758.33	**1397**	2546.6	791.67	**1457**	2654.6
725.56	**1338**	2440.4	758.89	**1398**	2548.4	792.22	**1458**	2656.4
726.11	**1339**	2442.2	759.44	**1399**	2550.2	792.78	**1459**	2658.2
726.67	**1340**	2444	760	**1400**	2552	793.33	**1460**	2660
727.22	**1341**	2445.8	760.56	**1401**	2553.8	793.89	**1461**	2661.8
727.78	**1342**	2447.6	761.11	**1402**	2555.6	794.44	**1462**	2663.6
728.33	**1343**	2449.4	761.67	**1403**	2557.4	795	**1463**	2665.4
728.89	**1344**	2451.2	762.22	**1404**	2559.2	795.56	**1464**	2667.2
729.44	**1345**	2453	762.78	**1405**	2561	796.11	**1465**	2669
730	**1346**	2454.8	763.33	**1406**	2562.8	796.67	**1466**	2670.8
730.56	**1347**	2456.6	763.89	**1407**	2564.6	797.22	**1467**	2672.6
731.11	**1348**	2458.4	764.44	**1408**	2566.4	797.78	**1468**	2674.4
731.67	**1349**	2460.2	765	**1409**	2568.2	798.33	**1469**	2676.2
732.22	**1350**	2462	765.56	**1410**	2570	798.89	**1470**	2678
732.78	**1351**	2463.8	766.11	**1411**	2571.8	799.44	**1471**	2679.8
733.33	**1352**	2465.6	766.67	**1412**	2573.6	800	**1472**	2681.6
733.89	**1353**	2467.4	767.22	**1413**	2575.4	800.56	**1473**	2683.4
734.44	**1354**	2469.2	767.78	**1414**	2577.2	801.11	**1474**	2685.2
735	**1355**	2471	768.33	**1415**	2579	801.67	**1475**	2687
735.56	**1356**	2472.8	768.89	**1416**	2580.8	802.22	**1476**	2688.8
736.11	**1357**	2474.6	769.44	**1417**	2582.6	802.78	**1477**	2690.6
736.67	**1358**	2476.4	770	**1418**	2584.4	803.33	**1478**	2692.4
737.22	**1359**	2478.2	770.56	**1419**	2586.2	803.89	**1479**	2694.2
737.78	**1360**	2480	771.11	**1420**	2588	804.44	**1480**	2696
738.33	**1361**	2481.8	771.67	**1421**	2589.8	805	**1481**	2697.8
738.89	**1362**	2483.6	772.22	**1422**	2591.6	805.56	**1482**	2699.6
739.44	**1363**	2485.4	772.78	**1423**	2593.4	806.11	**1483**	2701.4
740	**1364**	2487.2	773.33	**1424**	2595.2	806.67	**1484**	2703.2
740.56	**1365**	2489	773.89	**1425**	2597	807.22	**1485**	2705
741.11	**1366**	2490.8	774.44	**1426**	2598.8	807.78	**1486**	2706.8
741.67	**1367**	2492.6	775	**1427**	2600.6	808.33	**1487**	2708.6
742.22	**1368**	2494.4	775.56	**1428**	2602.4	808.89	**1488**	2710.4
742.78	**1369**	2496.2	776.11	**1429**	2604.2	809.44	**1489**	2712.2

Table 6–3 (*Continued*)
TEMPERATURE CONVERSION TABLE

To Convert			To Convert			To Convert		
To °C	←°F or °C→	To °F	To °C	←°F or °C→	To °F	To °C	←°F or °C→	To °F
810	**1490**	2714	843.33	**1550**	2822	876.67	**1610**	2930
810.56	**1491**	2715.8	843.89	**1551**	2823.8	877.22	**1611**	2931.8
811.11	**1492**	2717.6	844.44	**1552**	2825.6	877.78	**1612**	2933.6
811.67	**1493**	2719.4	845	**1553**	2827.4	878.33	**1613**	2935.4
812.22	**1494**	2721.2	845.56	**1554**	2829.2	878.89	**1614**	2937.2
812.78	**1495**	2723	846.11	**1555**	2831	879.44	**1615**	2939
813.33	**1496**	2724.8	846.67	**1556**	2832.8	880	**1616**	2940.8
813.89	**1497**	2726.6	847.22	**1557**	2834.6	880.56	**1617**	2942.6
814.44	**1498**	2728.4	847.78	**1558**	2836.4	881.11	**1618**	2944.4
815	**1499**	2730.2	848.33	**1559**	2838.2	881.67	**1619**	2946.2
815.56	**1500**	2732	848.89	**1560**	2840	882.22	**1620**	2948
816.11	**1501**	2733.8	849.44	**1561**	2841.8	882.78	**1621**	2949.8
816.67	**1502**	2735.6	850	**1562**	2843.6	883.33	**1622**	2951.6
817.22	**1503**	2737.4	850.56	**1563**	2845.4	883.89	**1623**	2953.4
817.78	**1504**	2739.2	851.11	**1564**	2847.2	884.44	**1624**	2955.2
818.33	**1505**	2741	851.67	**1565**	2849	885	**1625**	2957
818.89	**1506**	2742.8	852.22	**1566**	2850.8	885.56	**1626**	2958.8
819.44	**1507**	2744.6	852.78	**1567**	2852.6	886.11	**1627**	2960.6
820	**1508**	2746.4	853.33	**1568**	2854.4	886.67	**1628**	2962.4
820.56	**1509**	2748.2	853.89	**1569**	2856.2	887.22	**1629**	2964.2
821.11	**1510**	2750	854.44	**1570**	2858	887.78	**1630**	2966
821.67	**1511**	2751.8	855	**1571**	2859.8	888.33	**1631**	2967.8
822.22	**1512**	2753.6	855.56	**1572**	2861.6	888.89	**1632**	2969.6
822.78	**1513**	2755.4	856.11	**1573**	2863.4	889.44	**1633**	2971.4
823.33	**1514**	2757.2	856.67	**1574**	2865.2	890	**1634**	2973.2
823.89	**1515**	2759	857.22	**1575**	2867	890.56	**1635**	2975
824.44	**1516**	2760.8	857.78	**1576**	2868.8	891.11	**1636**	2976.8
825	**1517**	2762.6	858.33	**1577**	2870.6	891.67	**1637**	2978.6
825.56	**1518**	2764.4	858.89	**1578**	2872.4	892.22	**1638**	2980.4
826.11	**1519**	2766.2	859.44	**1579**	2874.2	892.78	**1639**	2982.2
826.67	**1520**	2768	860	**1580**	2876	893.33	**1640**	2984
827.22	**1521**	2769.8	860.56	**1581**	2877.8	893.89	**1641**	2985.8
827.78	**1522**	2771.6	861.11	**1582**	2879.6	894.44	**1642**	2987.6
828.33	**1523**	2773.4	861.67	**1583**	2881.4	895	**1643**	2989.4
828.89	**1524**	2775.2	862.22	**1584**	2883.2	895.56	**1644**	2991.2
829.44	**1525**	2777	862.78	**1585**	2885	896.11	**1645**	2993
830	**1526**	2778.8	863.33	**1586**	2886.8	896.67	**1646**	2994.8
830.56	**1527**	2780.6	863.89	**1587**	2888.6	897.22	**1647**	2996.6
831.11	**1528**	2782.4	864.44	**1588**	2890.4	897.78	**1648**	2998.4
831.67	**1529**	2784.2	865	**1589**	2892.2	898.33	**1649**	3000.2
832.22	**1530**	2786	865.56	**1590**	2894	898.89	**1650**	3002
832.78	**1531**	2787.8	866.11	**1591**	2895.8	899.44	**1651**	3003.8
833.33	**1532**	2789.6	866.67	**1592**	2897.6	900	**1652**	3005.6
833.89	**1533**	2791.4	867.22	**1593**	2899.4	900.56	**1653**	3007.4
834.44	**1534**	2793.2	867.78	**1594**	2901.2	901.11	**1654**	3009.2
835	**1535**	2795	868.33	**1595**	2903	901.67	**1655**	3011
835.56	**1536**	2796.8	868.89	**1596**	2904.8	902.22	**1656**	3012.8
836.11	**1537**	2798.6	869.44	**1597**	2906.6	902.78	**1657**	3014.6
836.67	**1538**	2800.4	870	**1598**	2908.4	903.33	**1658**	3016.4
837.22	**1539**	2802.2	870.56	**1599**	2910.2	903.89	**1659**	3018.2
837.78	**1540**	2804	871.11	**1600**	2912	904.44	**1660**	3020
838.33	**1541**	2805.8	871.67	**1601**	2913.8	905	**1661**	3021.8
838.89	**1542**	2807.6	872.22	**1602**	2915.6	905.56	**1662**	3023.6
839.44	**1543**	2809.4	872.78	**1603**	2917.4	906.11	**1663**	3025.4
840	**1544**	2811.2	873.33	**1604**	2919.2	906.67	**1664**	3027.2
840.56	**1545**	2813	873.89	**1605**	2921	907.22	**1665**	3029
841.11	**1546**	2814.8	874.44	**1606**	2922.8	907.78	**1666**	3030.8
841.67	**1547**	2816.6	875	**1607**	2924.6	908.33	**1667**	3032.6
842.22	**1548**	2818.4	875.56	**1608**	2926.4	908.89	**1668**	3034.4
842.78	**1549**	2820.2	876.11	**1609**	2928.2	909.44	**1669**	3036.2

Table 6–3 (*Continued*)
TEMPERATURE CONVERSION TABLE

To Convert			To Convert			To Convert		
To °C	←°F or °C→	To °F	To °C	←°F or °C→	To °F	To °C	←°F or °C→	To °F
910	**1670**	3038	943.33	**1730**	3146	976.67	**1790**	3254
910.56	**1671**	3039.8	943.89	**1731**	3147.8	977.22	**1791**	3255.8
911.11	**1672**	3041.6	944.44	**1732**	3149.6	977.78	**1792**	3257.6
911.67	**1673**	3043.4	945	**1733**	3151.4	978.33	**1793**	3259.4
912.22	**1674**	3045.2	945.56	**1734**	3153.2	978.89	**1794**	3261.2
912.78	**1675**	3047	946.11	**1735**	3155	979.44	**1795**	3263
913.33	**1676**	3048.8	946.67	**1736**	3156.8	980	**1796**	3264.8
913.89	**1677**	3050.6	947.22	**1737**	3158.6	980.56	**1797**	3266.6
914.44	**1678**	3052.4	947.78	**1738**	3160.4	981.11	**1798**	3268.4
915	**1679**	3054.2	948.33	**1739**	3162.2	981.67	**1799**	3270.2
915.56	**1680**	3056	948.89	**1740**	3164	982.22	**1800**	3272
916.11	**1681**	3057.8	949.44	**1741**	3165.8	982.78	**1801**	3273.8
916.67	**1682**	3059.6	950	**1742**	3167.6	983.33	**1802**	3275.6
917.22	**1683**	3061.4	950.56	**1743**	3169.4	983.89	**1803**	3277.4
917.78	**1684**	3063.2	951.11	**1744**	3171.2	984.44	**1804**	3279.2
918.33	**1685**	3065	951.67	**1745**	3173	985	**1805**	3281
918.89	**1686**	3066.8	952.22	**1746**	3174.8	985.56	**1806**	3282.8
919.44	**1687**	3068.6	952.78	**1747**	3176.6	986.11	**1807**	3284.6
920	**1688**	3070.4	953.33	**1748**	3178.4	986.67	**1808**	3286.4
920.56	**1689**	3072.2	953.89	**1749**	3180.2	987.22	**1809**	3288.2
921.11	**1690**	3074	954.44	**1750**	3182	987.78	**1810**	3290
921.67	**1691**	3075.8	955	**1751**	3183.8	988.33	**1811**	3291.8
922.22	**1692**	3077.6	955.56	**1752**	3185.6	988.89	**1812**	3293.6
922.78	**1693**	3079.4	956.11	**1753**	3187.4	989.44	**1813**	3295.4
923.33	**1694**	3081.2	956.67	**1754**	3189.2	990	**1814**	3297.2
923.89	**1695**	3083	957.22	**1755**	3191	990.56	**1815**	3299
924.44	**1696**	3084.8	957.78	**1756**	3192.8	991.11	**1816**	3300.8
925	**1697**	3086.6	958.33	**1757**	3194.6	991.67	**1817**	3302.6
925.56	**1698**	3088.4	958.89	**1758**	3196.4	992.22	**1818**	3304.4
926.11	**1699**	3090.2	959.44	**1759**	3198.2	992.78	**1819**	3306.2
926.67	**1700**	3092	960	**1760**	3200	993.33	**1820**	3308
927.22	**1701**	3093.8	960.56	**1761**	3201.8	993.89	**1821**	3309.8
927.78	**1702**	3095.6	961.11	**1762**	3203.6	994.44	**1822**	3311.6
928.33	**1703**	3097.4	961.67	**1763**	3205.4	995	**1823**	3313.4
928.89	**1704**	3099.2	962.22	**1764**	3207.2	995.56	**1824**	3315.2
929.44	**1705**	3101	962.78	**1765**	3209	996.11	**1825**	3317
930	**1706**	3102.8	963.33	**1766**	3210.8	996.67	**1826**	3318.8
930.56	**1707**	3104.6	963.89	**1767**	3212.6	997.22	**1827**	3320.6
931.11	**1708**	3106.4	964.44	**1768**	3214.4	997.78	**1828**	3322.4
931.67	**1709**	3108.2	965	**1769**	3216.2	998.33	**1829**	3324.2
932.22	**1710**	3110	965.56	**1770**	3218	998.89	**1830**	3326
932.78	**1711**	3111.8	966.11	**1771**	3219.8	999.44	**1831**	3327.8
933.33	**1712**	3113.6	966.67	**1772**	3221.6	1000	**1832**	3329.6
933.89	**1713**	3115.4	967.22	**1773**	3223.4	1000.56	**1833**	3331.4
934.44	**1714**	3117.2	967.78	**1774**	3225.2	1001.11	**1834**	3333.2
935	**1715**	3119	968.33	**1775**	3227	1001.67	**1835**	3335
935.56	**1716**	3120.8	968.89	**1776**	3228.8	1002.22	**1836**	3336.8
936.11	**1717**	3122.6	969.44	**1777**	3230.6	1002.78	**1837**	3338.6
936.67	**1718**	3124.4	970	**1778**	3232.4	1003.33	**1838**	3340.4
937.22	**1719**	3126.2	970.56	**1779**	3234.2	1003.89	**1839**	3342.2
937.78	**1720**	3128	971.11	**1780**	3236	1004.44	**1840**	3344
938.33	**1721**	3129.8	971.67	**1781**	3237.8	1005	**1841**	3345.8
938.89	**1722**	3131.6	972.22	**1782**	3239.6	1005.56	**1842**	3347.6
939.44	**1723**	3133.4	972.78	**1783**	3241.4	1006.11	**1843**	3349.4
940	**1724**	3135.2	973.33	**1784**	3243.2	1006.67	**1844**	3351.2
940.56	**1725**	3137	973.89	**1785**	3245	1007.22	**1845**	3353
941.11	**1726**	3138.8	974.44	**1786**	3246.8	1007.78	**1846**	3354.8
941.67	**1727**	3140.6	975	**1787**	3248.6	1008.33	**1847**	3356.6
942.22	**1728**	3142.4	975.56	**1788**	3250.4	1008.89	**1848**	3358.4
942.78	**1729**	3144.2	976.11	**1789**	3252.2	1009.44	**1849**	3360.2

Table 6–3 (*Continued*)
TEMPERATURE CONVERSION TABLE

To Convert			To Convert			To Convert		
To °C	←°F or °C→	To °F	To °C	←°F or °C→	To °F	To °C	←°F or °C→	To °F
1010	**1850**	3362	1043.33	**1910**	3470	1076.67	**1970**	3578
1010.56	**1851**	3363.8	1043.89	**1911**	3471.8	1077.22	**1971**	3579.8
1011.11	**1852**	3365.6	1044.44	**1912**	3473.6	1077.78	**1972**	3581.6
1011.67	**1853**	3367.4	1045	**1913**	3475.4	1078.33	**1973**	3583.4
1012.22	**1854**	3369.2	1045.56	**1914**	3477.2	1078.89	**1974**	3585.2
1012.78	**1855**	3371	1046.11	**1915**	3479	1079.44	**1975**	3587
1013.33	**1856**	3372.8	1046.67	**1916**	3480.8	1080	**1976**	3588.8
1013.89	**1857**	3374.6	1047.22	**1917**	3482.6	1080.56	**1977**	3590.6
1014.44	**1858**	3376.4	1047.78	**1918**	3484.4	1081.11	**1978**	3592.4
1015	**1859**	3378.2	1048.33	**1919**	3486.2	1081.67	**1979**	3594.2
1015.56	**1860**	3380	1048.89	**1920**	3488	1082.22	**1980**	3596
1016.11	**1861**	3381.8	1049.44	**1921**	3489.8	1082.78	**1981**	3597.8
1016.67	**1862**	3383.6	1050	**1922**	3491.6	1083.33	**1982**	3599.6
1017.22	**1863**	3385.4	1050.56	**1923**	3493.4	1083.89	**1983**	3601.4
1017.78	**1864**	3387.2	1051.11	**1924**	3495.2	1084.44	**1984**	3603.2
1018.33	**1865**	3389	1051.67	**1925**	3497	1085	**1985**	3605
1018.89	**1866**	3390.8	1052.22	**1926**	3498.8	1085.56	**1986**	3606.8
1019.44	**1867**	3392.6	1052.78	**1927**	3500.6	1086.11	**1987**	3608.6
1020	**1868**	3394.4	1053.33	**1928**	3502.4	1086.67	**1988**	3610.4
1020.56	**1869**	3396.2	1053.89	**1929**	3504.2	1087.22	**1989**	3612.2
1021.11	**1870**	3398	1054.44	**1930**	3506	1087.78	**1990**	3614
1021.67	**1871**	3399.8	1055	**1931**	3507.8	1088.33	**1991**	3615.8
1022.22	**1872**	3401.6	1055.56	**1932**	3509.6	1088.89	**1992**	3617.6
1022.78	**1873**	3403.4	1056.11	**1933**	3511.4	1089.44	**1993**	3619.4
1023.33	**1874**	3405.2	1056.67	**1934**	3513.2	1090	**1994**	3621.2
1023.89	**1875**	3407	1057.22	**1935**	3515	1090.56	**1995**	3623
1024.44	**1876**	3408.8	1057.78	**1936**	3516.8	1091.11	**1996**	3624.8
1025	**1877**	3410.6	1058.33	**1937**	3518.6	1091.67	**1997**	3626.6
1025.56	**1878**	3412.4	1058.89	**1938**	3520.4	1092.22	**1998**	3628.4
1026.11	**1879**	3414.2	1059.44	**1939**	3522.2	1092.78	**1999**	3630.2
1026.67	**1880**	3416	1060	**1940**	3524	1093.33	**2000**	3632
1027.22	**1881**	3417.8	1060.56	**1941**	3525.8	1093.89	**2001**	3633.8
1027.78	**1882**	3419.6	1061.11	**1942**	3527.6	1094.44	**2002**	3635.6
1028.33	**1883**	3421.4	1061.67	**1943**	3529.4	1095	**2003**	3637.4
1028.89	**1884**	3423.2	1062.22	**1944**	3531.2	1095.56	**2004**	3639.2
1029.44	**1885**	3425	1062.78	**1945**	3533	1096.11	**2005**	3641
1030	**1886**	3426.8	1063.33	**1946**	3534.8	1096.67	**2006**	3642.8
1030.56	**1887**	3428.6	1063.89	**1947**	3536.6	1097.22	**2007**	3644.6
1031.11	**1888**	3430.4	1064.44	**1948**	3538.4	1097.78	**2008**	3646.4
1031.67	**1889**	3432.2	1065	**1949**	3540.2	1098.33	**2009**	3648.2
1032.22	**1890**	3434	1065.56	**1950**	3542	1098.89	**2010**	3650
1032.78	**1891**	3435.8	1066.11	**1951**	3543.8	1099.44	**2011**	3651.8
1033.33	**1892**	3437.6	1066.67	**1952**	3545.6	1100	**2012**	3653.6
1033.89	**1893**	3439.4	1067.22	**1953**	3547.4	1100.56	**2013**	3655.4
1034.44	**1894**	3441.2	1067.78	**1954**	3549.2	1101.11	**2014**	3657.2
1035	**1895**	3443	1068.33	**1955**	3551	1101.67	**2015**	3659
1035.56	**1896**	3444.8	1068.89	**1956**	3552.8	1102.22	**2016**	3660.8
1036.11	**1897**	3446.6	1069.44	**1957**	3554.6	1102.78	**2017**	3662.6
1036.67	**1898**	3448.4	1070	**1958**	3556.4	1103.33	**2018**	3664.4
1037.22	**1899**	3450.2	1070.56	**1959**	3558.2	1103.89	**2019**	3666.2
1037.78	**1900**	3452	1071.11	**1960**	3560	1104.44	**2020**	3668
1038.33	**1901**	3453.8	1071.67	**1961**	3561.8	1105	**2021**	3669.8
1038.89	**1902**	3455.6	1072.22	**1962**	3563.6	1105.56	**2022**	3671.6
1039.44	**1903**	3457.4	1072.78	**1963**	3565.4	1106.11	**2023**	3673.4
1040	**1904**	3459.2	1073.33	**1964**	3567.2	1106.67	**2024**	3675.2
1040.56	**1905**	3461	1073.89	**1965**	3569	1107.22	**2025**	3677
1041.11	**1906**	3462.8	1074.44	**1966**	3570.8	1107.78	**2026**	3678.8
1041.67	**1907**	3464.6	1075	**1967**	3572.6	1108.33	**2027**	3680.6
1042.22	**1908**	3466.4	1075.56	**1968**	3574.4	1108.89	**2028**	3682.4
1042.78	**1909**	3468.2	1076.11	**1969**	3576.2	1109.44	**2029**	3684.2

Table 6–3 (*Continued*)
TEMPERATURE CONVERSION TABLE

To Convert			To Convert			To Convert		
To °C	←°F or °C→	To °F	To °C	←°F or °C→	To °F	To °C	←°F or °C→	To °F
1110	**2030**	3686	1143.33	**2090**	3794	1176.67	**2150**	3902
1110.56	**2031**	3687.8	1143.89	**2091**	3795.8	1177.22	**2151**	3903.8
1111.11	**2032**	3689.6	1144.44	**2092**	3797.6	1177.78	**2152**	3905.6
1111.67	**2033**	3691.4	1145	**2093**	3799.4	1178.33	**2153**	3907.4
1112.22	**2034**	3693.2	1145.56	**2094**	3801.2	1178.89	**2154**	3909.2
1112.78	**2035**	3695	1146.11	**2095**	3803	1179.44	**2155**	3911
1113.33	**2036**	3696.8	1146.67	**2096**	3804.8	1180	**2156**	3912.8
1113.89	**2037**	3698.6	1147.22	**2097**	3806.6	1180.56	**2157**	3914.6
1114.44	**2038**	3700.4	1147.78	**2098**	3808.4	1181.11	**2158**	3916.4
1115	**2039**	3702.2	1148.33	**2099**	3810.2	1181.67	**2159**	3918.2
1115.56	**2040**	3704	1148.89	**2100**	3812	1182.22	**2160**	3920
1116.11	**2041**	3705.8	1149.44	**2101**	3813.8	1182.78	**2161**	3921.8
1116.67	**2042**	3707.6	1150	**2102**	3815.6	1183.33	**2162**	3923.6
1117.22	**2043**	3709.4	1150.56	**2103**	3817.4	1183.89	**2163**	3925.4
1117.78	**2044**	3711.2	1151.11	**2104**	3819.2	1184.44	**2164**	3927.2
1118.33	**2045**	3713	1151.67	**2105**	3821	1185	**2165**	3929
1118.89	**2046**	3714.8	1152.22	**2106**	3822.8	1185.56	**2166**	3930.8
1119.44	**2047**	3716.6	1152.78	**2107**	3824.6	1186.11	**2167**	3932.6
1120	**2048**	3718.4	1153.33	**2108**	3826.4	1186.67	**2168**	3934.4
1120.56	**2049**	3720.2	1153.89	**2109**	3828.2	1187.22	**2169**	3936.2
1121.11	**2050**	3722	1154.44	**2110**	3830	1187.78	**2170**	3938
1121.67	**2051**	3723.8	1155	**2111**	3831.8	1188.33	**2171**	3939.8
1122.22	**2052**	3725.6	1155.56	**2112**	3833.6	1188.89	**2172**	3941.6
1122.78	**2053**	3727.4	1156.11	**2113**	3835.4	1189.44	**2173**	3943.4
1123.33	**2054**	3729.2	1156.67	**2114**	3837.2	1190	**2174**	3945.2
1123.89	**2055**	3731	1157.22	**2115**	3839	1190.56	**2175**	3947
1124.44	**2056**	3732.8	1157.78	**2116**	3840.8	1191.11	**2176**	3948.8
1125	**2057**	3734.6	1158.33	**2117**	3842.6	1191.67	**2177**	3950.6
1125.56	**2058**	3736.4	1158.89	**2118**	3844.4	1192.22	**2178**	3952.4
1126.11	**2059**	3738.2	1159.44	**2119**	3846.2	1192.78	**2179**	3954.2
1126.67	**2060**	3740	1160	**2120**	3848	1193.33	**2180**	3956
1127.22	**2061**	3741.8	1160.56	**2121**	3849.8	1193.89	**2181**	3957.8
1127.78	**2062**	3743.6	1161.11	**2122**	3851.6	1194.44	**2182**	3959.6
1128.33	**2063**	3745.4	1161.67	**2123**	3853.4	1195	**2183**	3961.4
1128.89	**2064**	3747.2	1162.22	**2124**	3855.2	1195.56	**2184**	3963.2
1129.44	**2065**	3749	1162.78	**2125**	3857	1196.11	**2185**	3965
1130	**2066**	3750.8	1163.33	**2126**	3858.8	1196.67	**2186**	3966.8
1130.56	**2067**	3752.6	1163.89	**2127**	3860.6	1197.22	**2187**	3968.6
1131.11	**2068**	3754.4	1164.44	**2128**	3862.4	1197.78	**2188**	3970.4
1131.67	**2069**	3756.2	1165	**2129**	3864.2	1198.33	**2189**	3972.2
1132.22	**2070**	3758	1165.56	**2130**	3866	1198.89	**2190**	3974
1132.78	**2071**	3759.8	1166.11	**2131**	3867.8	1199.44	**2191**	3975.8
1133.33	**2072**	3761.6	1166.67	**2132**	3869.6	1200	**2192**	3977.6
1133.89	**2073**	3763.4	1167.22	**2133**	3871.4	1200.56	**2193**	3979.4
1134.44	**2074**	3765.2	1167.78	**2134**	3873.2	1201.11	**2194**	3981.2
1135	**2075**	3767	1168.33	**2135**	3875	1201.67	**2195**	3983
1135.56	**2076**	3768.8	1168.89	**2136**	3876.8	1202.22	**2196**	3984.8
1136.11	**2077**	3770.6	1169.44	**2137**	3878.6	1202.78	**2197**	3986.6
1136.67	**2078**	3772.4	1170	**2138**	3880.4	1203.33	**2198**	3988.4
1137.22	**2079**	3774.2	1170.56	**2139**	3882.2	1203.89	**2199**	3990.2
1137.78	**2080**	3776	1171.11	**2140**	3884	1204.44	**2200**	3992
1138.33	**2081**	3777.8	1171.67	**2141**	3885.8	1205	**2201**	3993.8
1138.89	**2082**	3779.6	1172.22	**2142**	3887.6	1205.56	**2202**	3995.6
1139.44	**2083**	3781.4	1172.78	**2143**	3889.4	1206.11	**2203**	3997.4
1140	**2084**	3783.2	1173.33	**2144**	3891.2	1206.67	**2204**	3999.2
1140.56	**2085**	3785	1173.89	**2145**	3893	1207.22	**2205**	4001
1141.11	**2086**	3786.8	1174.44	**2146**	3894.8	1207.78	**2206**	4002.8
1141.67	**2087**	3788.6	1175	**2147**	3896.6	1208.33	**2207**	4004.6
1142.22	**2088**	3790.4	1175.56	**2148**	3898.4	1208.89	**2208**	4006.4
1142.78	**2089**	3792.2	1176.11	**2149**	3900.2	1209.44	**2209**	4008.2

Table 6–3 (*Continued*)
TEMPERATURE CONVERSION TABLE

To Convert			To Convert			To Convert		
To °C	←°F or °C→	To °F	To °C	←°F or °C→	To °F	To °C	←°F or °C→	To °F
1210	**2210**	4010	1243.33	**2270**	4118	1276.67	**2330**	4226
1210.56	**2211**	4011.8	1243.89	**2271**	4119.8	1277.22	**2331**	4227.8
1211.11	**2212**	4013.6	1244.44	**2272**	4121.6	1277.78	**2332**	4229.6
1211.67	**2213**	4015.4	1245	**2273**	4123.4	1278.33	**2333**	4231.4
1212.22	**2214**	4017.2	1245.56	**2274**	4125.2	1278.89	**2334**	4233.2
1212.78	**2215**	4019	1246.11	**2275**	4127	1279.44	**2335**	4235
1213.33	**2216**	4020.8	1246.67	**2276**	4128.8	1280	**2336**	4236.8
1213.89	**2217**	4022.6	1247.22	**2277**	4130.6	1280.56	**2337**	4238.6
1214.44	**2218**	4024.4	1247.78	**2278**	4132.4	1281.11	**2338**	4240.4
1215	**2219**	4026.2	1248.33	**2279**	4134.2	1281.67	**2339**	4242.2
1215.56	**2220**	4028	1248.89	**2280**	4136	1282.22	**2340**	4244
1216.11	**2221**	4029.8	1249.44	**2281**	4137.8	1282.78	**2341**	4245.8
1216.67	**2222**	4031.6	1250	**2282**	4139.6	1283.33	**2342**	4247.6
1217.22	**2223**	4033.4	1250.56	**2283**	4141.4	1283.89	**2343**	4249.4
1217.78	**2224**	4035.2	1251.11	**2284**	4143.2	1284.44	**2344**	4251.2
1218.33	**2225**	4037	1251.67	**2285**	4145	1285	**2345**	4253
1218.89	**2226**	4038.8	1252.22	**2286**	4146.8	1285.56	**2346**	4254.8
1219.44	**2227**	4040.6	1252.78	**2287**	4148.6	1286.11	**2347**	4256.6
1220	**2228**	4042.4	1253.33	**2288**	4150.4	1286.67	**2348**	4258.4
1220.56	**2229**	4044.2	1253.89	**2289**	4152.2	1287.22	**2349**	4260.2
1221.11	**2230**	4046	1254.44	**2290**	4154	1287.78	**2350**	4262
1221.67	**2231**	4047.8	1255	**2291**	4155.8	1288.33	**2351**	4263.8
1222.22	**2232**	4049.6	1255.56	**2292**	4157.6	1288.89	**2352**	4265.6
1222.78	**2233**	4051.4	1256.11	**2293**	4159.4	1289.44	**2353**	4267.4
1223.33	**2234**	4053.2	1256.67	**2294**	4161.2	1290	**2354**	4269.2
1223.89	**2235**	4055	1257.22	**2295**	4163	1290.56	**2355**	4271
1224.44	**2236**	4056.8	1257.78	**2296**	4164.8	1291.11	**2356**	4272.8
1225	**2237**	4058.6	1258.33	**2297**	4166.6	1291.67	**2357**	4274.6
1225.56	**2238**	4060.4	1258.89	**2298**	4168.4	1292.22	**2358**	4276.4
1226.11	**2239**	4062.2	1259.44	**2299**	4170.2	1292.78	**2359**	4278.2
1226.67	**2240**	4064	1260	**2300**	4172	1293.33	**2360**	4280
1227.22	**2241**	4065.8	1260.56	**2301**	4173.8	1293.89	**2361**	4281.8
1227.78	**2242**	4067.6	1261.11	**2302**	4175.6	1294.44	**2362**	4283.6
1228.33	**2243**	4069.4	1261.67	**2303**	4177.4	1295	**2363**	4285.4
1228.89	**2244**	4071.2	1262.22	**2304**	4179.2	1295.56	**2364**	4287.2
1229.44	**2245**	4073	1262.78	**2305**	4181	1296.11	**2365**	4289
1230	**2246**	4074.8	1263.33	**2306**	4182.8	1296.67	**2366**	4290.8
1230.56	**2247**	4076.6	1263.89	**2307**	4184.6	1297.22	**2367**	4292.6
1231.11	**2248**	4078.4	1264.44	**2308**	4186.4	1297.78	**2368**	4294.4
1231.67	**2249**	4080.2	1265	**2309**	4188.2	1298.33	**2369**	4296.2
1232.22	**2250**	4082	1265.56	**2310**	4190	1298.89	**2370**	4298
1232.78	**2251**	4083.8	1266.11	**2311**	4191.8	1299.44	**2371**	4299.8
1233.33	**2252**	4085.6	1266.67	**2312**	4193.6	1300	**2372**	4301.6
1233.89	**2253**	4087.4	1267.22	**2313**	4195.4	1300.56	**2373**	4303.4
1234.44	**2254**	4089.2	1267.78	**2314**	4197.2	1301.11	**2374**	4305.2
1235	**2255**	4091	1268.33	**2315**	4199	1301.67	**2375**	4307
1235.56	**2256**	4092.8	1268.89	**2316**	4200.8	1302.22	**2376**	4308.8
1236.11	**2257**	4094.6	1269.44	**2317**	4202.6	1302.78	**2377**	4310.6
1236.67	**2258**	4096.4	1270	**2318**	4204.4	1303.33	**2378**	4312.4
1237.22	**2259**	4098.2	1270.56	**2319**	4206.2	1303.89	**2379**	4314.2
1237.78	**2260**	4100	1271.11	**2320**	4208	1304.44	**2380**	4316
1238.33	**2261**	4101.8	1271.67	**2321**	4209.8	1305	**2381**	4317.8
1238.89	**2262**	4103.6	1272.22	**2322**	4211.6	1305.56	**2382**	4319.6
1239.44	**2263**	4105.4	1272.78	**2323**	4213.4	1306.11	**2383**	4321.4
1240	**2264**	4107.2	1273.33	**2324**	4215.2	1306.67	**2384**	4323.2
1240.56	**2265**	4109	1273.89	**2325**	4217	1307.22	**2385**	4325
1241.11	**2267**	4110.8	1274.44	**2326**	4218.8	1307.78	**2386**	4326.8
1241.67	**2267**	4112.6	1275	**2327**	4220.6	1308.33	**2387**	4328.6
1242.22	**2268**	4114.4	1275.56	**2328**	4222.4	1308.89	**2388**	4330.4
1242.78	**2269**	4116.2	1276.11	**2329**	4224.2	1309.44	**2389**	4332.2

Table 6–3 (*Continued*)
TEMPERATURE CONVERSION TABLE

To Convert			To Convert			To Convert		
To °C	←°F or °C→	To °F	To °C	←°F or °C→	To °F	To °C	←°F or °C→	To °F
1310	**2390**	4334	1343.33	**2450**	4442	1376.67	**2510**	4550
1310.56	**2391**	4335.8	1343.89	**2451**	4443.8	1377.22	**2511**	4551.8
1311.11	**2392**	4337.6	1344.44	**2452**	4445.6	1377.78	**2512**	4553.6
1311.67	**2393**	4339.4	1345	**2453**	4447.4	1378.33	**2513**	4555.4
1312.22	**2394**	4341.2	1345.56	**2454**	4449.2	1378.89	**2514**	4557.2
1312.78	**2395**	4343	1346.11	**2455**	4451	1379.44	**2515**	4559
1313.33	**2396**	4344.8	1346.67	**2456**	4452.8	1380	**2516**	4560.8
1313.89	**2397**	4346.6	1347.22	**2457**	4454.6	1380.56	**2517**	4562.6
1314.44	**2398**	4348.4	1347.78	**2458**	4456.4	1381.11	**2518**	4564.4
1315	**2399**	4350.2	1348.33	**2459**	4458.2	1381.67	**2519**	4566.2
1315.56	**2400**	4352	1348.89	**2460**	4460	1382.22	**2520**	4568
1316.11	**2401**	4353.8	1349.44	**2461**	4461.8	1382.78	**2521**	4569.8
1316.67	**2402**	4355.6	1350	**2462**	4463.6	1383.33	**2522**	4571.6
1317.22	**2403**	4357.4	1350.56	**2463**	4465.4	1383.89	**2523**	4573.4
1317.78	**2404**	4359.2	1351.11	**2464**	4467.2	1384.44	**2524**	4575.2
1318.33	**2405**	4361	1351.67	**2465**	4469	1385	**2525**	4577
1318.89	**2406**	4362.8	1352.22	**2466**	4470.8	1385.56	**2526**	4578.8
1319.44	**2407**	4364.6	1352.78	**2467**	4472.6	1386.11	**2527**	4580.6
1320	**2408**	4366.4	1353.33	**2468**	4474.4	1386.67	**2528**	4582.4
1320.56	**2409**	4368.2	1353.89	**2469**	4476.2	1387.22	**2529**	4584.2
1321.11	**2410**	4370	1354.44	**2470**	4478	1387.78	**2530**	4586
1321.67	**2411**	4371.8	1355	**2471**	4479.8	1388.33	**2531**	4587.8
1322.22	**2412**	4373.6	1355.56	**2472**	4481.6	1388.89	**2532**	4589.6
1322.78	**2413**	4375.4	1356.11	**2473**	4483.4	1389.44	**2533**	4591.4
1323.33	**2414**	4377.2	1356.67	**2474**	4485.2	1390	**2534**	4593.2
1323.89	**2415**	4379	1357.22	**2475**	4487	1390.56	**2535**	4595
1324.44	**2416**	4380.8	1357.78	**2476**	4488.8	1391.11	**2536**	4596.8
1325	**2417**	4382.6	1358.33	**2477**	4490.6	1391.67	**2537**	4598.6
1325.56	**2418**	4384.4	1358.89	**2478**	4492.4	1392.22	**2538**	4600.4
1326.11	**2419**	4386.2	1359.44	**2479**	4494.2	1392.78	**2539**	4602.2
1326.67	**2420**	4388	1360	**2480**	4496	1393.33	**2540**	4604
1327.22	**2421**	4389.8	1360.56	**2481**	4497.8	1393.89	**2541**	4605.8
1327.78	**2422**	4391.6	1361.11	**2482**	4499.6	1394.44	**2542**	4607.6
1328.33	**2423**	4393.4	1361.67	**2483**	4501.4	1395	**2543**	4609.4
1328.89	**2424**	4395.2	1362.22	**2484**	4503.2	1395.56	**2544**	4611.2
1329.44	**2425**	4397	1362.78	**2485**	4505	1396.11	**2545**	4613
1330	**2426**	4398.8	1363.33	**2486**	4506.8	1396.67	**2546**	4614.8
1330.56	**2427**	4400.6	1363.89	**2487**	4508.6	1397.22	**2547**	4616.6
1331.11	**2428**	4402.4	1364.44	**2488**	4510.4	1397.78	**2548**	4618.4
1331.67	**2429**	4404.2	1365	**2489**	4512.2	1398.33	**2549**	4620.2
1332.22	**2430**	4406	1365.56	**2490**	4514	1398.89	**2550**	4622
1332.78	**2431**	4407.8	1366.11	**2491**	4515.8	1399.44	**2551**	4623.8
1333.33	**2432**	4409.6	1366.67	**2492**	4517.6	1400	**2552**	4625.6
1333.89	**2433**	4411.4	1367.22	**2493**	4519.4	1400.56	**2553**	4627.4
1334.44	**2434**	4413.2	1367.78	**2494**	4521.2	1401.11	**2554**	4629.2
1335	**2435**	4415	1368.33	**2495**	4523	1401.67	**2555**	4631
1335.56	**2436**	4416.8	1368.89	**2496**	4524.8	1402.22	**2556**	4632.8
1336.11	**2437**	4418.6	1369.44	**2497**	4526.6	1402.78	**2557**	4634.6
1336.67	**2438**	4420.4	1370	**2498**	4528.4	1403.33	**2558**	4636.4
1337.22	**2439**	4422.2	1370.56	**2499**	4530.2	1403.89	**2559**	4638.2
1337.78	**2440**	4424	1371.11	**2500**	4532	1404.44	**2560**	4640
1338.33	**2441**	4425.8	1371.67	**2501**	4533.8	1405	**2561**	4641.8
1338.89	**2442**	4427.6	1372.22	**2502**	4535.6	1405.56	**2562**	4643.6
1339.44	**2443**	4429.4	1372.78	**2503**	4537.4	1406.11	**2563**	4645.4
1340	**2444**	4431.2	1373.33	**2504**	4539.2	1406.67	**2564**	4647.2
1340.56	**2445**	4433	1373.89	**2505**	4541	1407.22	**2565**	4649
1341.11	**2446**	4434.8	1374.44	**2506**	4542.8	1407.78	**2566**	4650.8
1341.67	**2447**	4436.6	1375	**2507**	4544.6	1408.33	**2567**	4652.6
1342.22	**2448**	4438.4	1375.56	**2508**	4546.4	1408.89	**2568**	4654.4
1342.78	**2449**	4440.2	1376.11	**2509**	4548.2	1409.44	**2569**	4656.2

Table 6–3 (*Continued*)
TEMPERATURE CONVERSION TABLE

To Convert			To Convert			To Convert		
To °C	←°F or °C→	To °F	To °C	←°F or °C→	To °F	To °C	←°F or °C→	To °F
1410	**2570**	4658	1443.33	**2630**	4766	1476.67	**2690**	4874
1410.56	**2571**	4659.8	1443.89	**2631**	4767.8	1477.22	**2691**	4875.8
1411.11	**2572**	4661.6	1444.44	**2632**	4769.6	1477.78	**2692**	4877.6
1411.67	**2573**	4663.4	1445	**2633**	4771.4	1478.33	**2693**	4879.4
1412.22	**2574**	4665.2	1445.56	**2634**	4773.2	1478.89	**2694**	4881.2
1412.78	**2575**	4667	1446.11	**2635**	4775	1479.44	**2695**	4883
1413.33	**2576**	4668.8	1446.67	**2636**	4776.8	1480	**2696**	4884.8
1413.89	**2577**	4670.6	1447.22	**2637**	4778.6	1480.56	**2697**	4886.6
1414.44	**2578**	4672.4	1447.78	**2638**	4780.4	1481.11	**2698**	4888.4
1415	**2579**	4674.2	1448.33	**2639**	4782.2	1481.67	**2699**	4890.2
1415.56	**2580**	4676	1448.89	**2640**	4784	1482.22	**2700**	4892
1416.11	**2581**	4677.8	1449.44	**2641**	4785.8	1482.78	**2701**	4893.8
1416.67	**2582**	4679.6	1450	**2642**	4787.6	1483.33	**2702**	4895.6
1417.22	**2583**	4681.4	1450.56	**2643**	4789.4	1483.89	**2703**	4897.4
1417.78	**2584**	4683.2	1451.11	**2644**	4791.2	1484.44	**2704**	4899.2
1418.33	**2585**	4685	1451.67	**2645**	4793	1485	**2705**	4901
1418.89	**2586**	4686.8	1452.22	**2646**	4794.8	1485.56	**2706**	4902.8
1419.44	**2587**	4688.6	1452.78	**2647**	4796.6	1486.11	**2707**	4904.6
1420	**2588**	4690.4	1453.33	**2648**	4798.4	1486.67	**2708**	4906.4
1420.56	**2589**	4692.2	1453.89	**2649**	4800.2	1487.22	**2709**	4908.2
1421.11	**2590**	4694	1454.44	**2650**	4802	1487.78	**2710**	4910
1421.67	**2591**	4695.8	1455	**2651**	4803.8	1488.33	**2711**	4911.8
1422.22	**2592**	4697.6	1455.56	**2652**	4805.6	1488.89	**2712**	4913.6
1422.78	**2593**	4699.4	1456.11	**2653**	4807.4	1489.44	**2713**	4915.4
1423.33	**2594**	4701.2	1456.67	**2654**	4809.2	1490	**2714**	4917.2
1423.89	**2595**	4703	1457.22	**2655**	4811	1490.56	**2715**	4919
1424.44	**2596**	4704.8	1457.78	**2656**	4812.8	1491.11	**2716**	4920.8
1425	**2597**	4706.6	1458.33	**2657**	4814.6	1491.67	**2717**	4922.6
1425.56	**2598**	4708.4	1458.89	**2658**	4816.4	1492.22	**2718**	4924.4
1426.11	**2599**	4710.2	1459.44	**2659**	4818.2	1492.78	**2719**	4926.2
1426.67	**2600**	4712	1460	**2660**	4820	1493.33	**2720**	4928
1427.22	**2601**	4713.8	1460.56	**2661**	4821.8	1493.89	**2721**	4929.8
1427.78	**2602**	4715.6	1461.11	**2662**	4823.6	1494.44	**2722**	4931.6
1428.33	**2603**	4717.4	1461.67	**2663**	4825.4	1495	**2723**	4933.4
1428.89	**2604**	4719.2	1462.22	**2664**	4827.2	1495.56	**2724**	4935.2
1429.44	**2605**	4721	1462.78	**2665**	4829	1496.11	**2725**	4937
1430	**2606**	4722.8	1463.33	**2666**	4830.8	1496.67	**2726**	4938.8
1430.56	**2607**	4724.6	1463.89	**2667**	4832.6	1497.22	**2727**	4940.6
1431.11	**2608**	4726.4	1464.44	**2668**	4834.4	1497.78	**2728**	4942.4
1431.67	**2609**	4728.2	1465	**2669**	4836.2	1498.33	**2729**	4944.2
1432.22	**2610**	4730	1465.56	**2670**	4838	1498.89	**2730**	4946
1432.78	**2611**	4731.8	1466.11	**2671**	4839.8	1499.44	**2731**	4947.8
1433.33	**2612**	4733.6	1466.67	**2672**	4841.6	1500	**2732**	4949.6
1433.89	**2613**	4735.4	1467.22	**2673**	4843.4	1500.56	**2733**	4951.4
1434.44	**2614**	4737.2	1467.78	**2674**	4845.2	1501.11	**2734**	4953.2
1435	**2615**	4739	1468.33	**2675**	4847	1501.67	**2735**	4955
1435.56	**2616**	4740.8	1468.89	**2676**	4848.8	1502.22	**2736**	4956.8
1436.11	**2617**	4742.6	1469.44	**2677**	4850.6	1502.78	**2737**	4958.6
1436.67	**2618**	4744.4	1470	**2678**	4852.4	1503.33	**2738**	4960.4
1437.22	**2619**	4746.2	1470.56	**2679**	4854.2	1503.89	**2739**	4962.2
1437.78	**2620**	4748	1471.11	**2680**	4856	1504.44	**2740**	4964
1438.33	**2621**	4749.8	1471.67	**2681**	4857.8	1505	**2741**	4965.8
1438.89	**2622**	4751.6	1472.22	**2682**	4859.6	1505.56	**2742**	4967.6
1439.44	**2623**	4753.4	1472.78	**2683**	4861.4	1506.11	**2743**	4969.4
1440	**2624**	4755.2	1473.33	**2684**	4863.2	1506.67	**2744**	4971.2
1440.56	**2625**	4757	1473.89	**2685**	4865	1507.22	**2745**	4973
1441.11	**2626**	4758.8	1474.44	**2686**	4866.8	1507.78	**2746**	4974.8
1441.67	**2627**	4760.6	1475	**2687**	4868.6	1508.33	**2747**	4976.6
1442.22	**2628**	4762.4	1475.56	**2688**	4870.4	1508.89	**2748**	4978.4
1442.78	**2629**	4764.2	1476.11	**2689**	4872.2	1509.44	**2749**	4980.2

Table 6–3 (*Continued*)
TEMPERATURE CONVERSION TABLE

To Convert			To Convert			To Convert		
To °C	←°F or °C→	To °F	To °C	←°F or °C→	To °F	To °C	←°F or °C→	To °F
1510	**2750**	4982	1543.33	**2810**	5090	1576.67	**2870**	5198
1510.56	**2751**	4983.8	1543.89	**2811**	5091.8	1577.22	**2871**	5199.8
1511.11	**2752**	4985.6	1544.44	**2812**	5093.6	1577.78	**2872**	5201.6
1511.67	**2753**	4987.4	1545	**2813**	5095.4	1578.33	**2873**	5203.4
1512.22	**2754**	4989.2	1545.56	**2814**	5097.2	1578.89	**2874**	5205.2
1512.78	**2755**	4991	1546.11	**2815**	5099	1579.44	**2875**	5207
1513.33	**2756**	4992.8	1546.67	**2816**	5100.8	1580	**2876**	5208.8
1513.89	**2757**	4994.6	1547.22	**2817**	5102.6	1580.56	**2877**	5210.6
1514.44	**2758**	4996.4	1547.78	**2818**	5104.4	1581.11	**2878**	5212.4
1515	**2759**	4998.2	1548.33	**2819**	5106.2	1581.67	**2879**	5214.2
1515.56	**2760**	5000	1548.89	**2820**	5108	1582.22	**2880**	5216
1516.11	**2761**	5001.8	1549.44	**2821**	5109.8	1582.78	**2881**	5217.8
1516.67	**2762**	5003.6	1550	**2822**	5111.6	1583.33	**2882**	5219.6
1517.22	**2763**	5005.4	1550.56	**2823**	5113.4	1583.89	**2883**	5221.4
1517.78	**2764**	5007.2	1551.11	**2824**	5115.2	1584.44	**2884**	5223.2
1518.33	**2765**	5009	1551.67	**2825**	5117	1585	**2885**	5225
1518.89	**2766**	5010.8	1552.22	**2826**	5118.8	1585.56	**2886**	5226.8
1519.44	**2767**	5012.6	1552.78	**2827**	5120.6	1586.11	**2887**	5228.6
1520	**2768**	5014.4	1553.33	**2828**	5122.4	1586.67	**2888**	5230.4
1520.56	**2769**	5016.2	1553.89	**2829**	5124.2	1587.22	**2889**	5232.2
1521.11	**2770**	5018	1554.44	**2830**	5126	1587.78	**2890**	5234
1521.67	**2771**	5019.8	1555	**2831**	5127.8	1588.33	**2891**	5235.8
1522.22	**2772**	5021.6	1555.56	**2832**	5129.6	1588.89	**2892**	5237.6
1522.78	**2773**	5023.4	1556.11	**2833**	5131.4	1589.44	**2893**	5239.4
1523.33	**2774**	5025.2	1556.67	**2834**	5133.2	1590	**2894**	5241.2
1523.89	**2775**	5027	1557.22	**2835**	5135	1590.56	**2895**	5243
1524.44	**2776**	5028.8	1557.78	**2836**	5136.8	1591.11	**2896**	5244.8
1525	**2777**	5030.6	1558.33	**2837**	5138.6	1591.67	**2897**	5246.6
1525.56	**2778**	5032.4	1558.89	**2838**	5140.4	1592.22	**2898**	5248.4
1526.11	**2779**	5034.2	1559.44	**2839**	5142.2	1592.78	**2899**	5250.2
1526.67	**2780**	5036	1560	**2840**	5144	1593.33	**2900**	5252
1527.22	**2781**	5037.8	1560.56	**2841**	5145.8	1593.89	**2901**	5253.8
1527.78	**2782**	5039.6	1561.11	**2842**	5147.6	1594.44	**2902**	5255.6
1528.33	**2783**	5041.4	1561.67	**2843**	5149.4	1595	**2903**	5257.4
1528.89	**2784**	5043.2	1562.22	**2844**	5151.2	1595.56	**2904**	5259.2
1529.44	**2785**	5045	1562.78	**2845**	5153	1596.11	**2905**	5261
1530	**2786**	5046.8	1563.33	**2846**	5154.8	1596.67	**2906**	5262.8
1530.56	**2787**	5048.6	1563.89	**2847**	5156.6	1597.22	**2907**	5264.6
1531.11	**2788**	5050.4	1564.44	**2848**	5158.4	1597.78	**2908**	5266.4
1531.67	**2789**	5052.2	1565	**2849**	5160.2	1598.33	**2909**	5268.2
1532.22	**2790**	5054	1565.56	**2850**	5162	1598.89	**2910**	5270
1532.78	**2791**	5055.8	1566.11	**2851**	5163.8	1599.44	**2911**	5271.8
1533.33	**2792**	5057.6	1566.67	**2852**	5165.6	1600	**2912**	5273.6
1533.89	**2793**	5059.4	1567.22	**2853**	5167.4	1600.56	**2913**	5275.4
1534.44	**2794**	5061.2	1567.78	**2854**	5169.2	1601.11	**2914**	5277.2
1535	**2795**	5063	1568.33	**2855**	5171	1601.67	**2915**	5279
1535.56	**2796**	5064.8	1568.89	**2856**	5172.8	1602.22	**2916**	5280.8
1536.11	**2797**	5066.6	1569.44	**2857**	5174.6	1602.78	**2917**	5282.6
1536.67	**2798**	5068.4	1570	**2858**	5776.4	1603.33	**2918**	5284.4
1537.22	**2799**	5070.2	1570.56	**2859**	5178.2	1603.89	**2919**	5286.2
1537.78	**2800**	5072	1571.11	**2860**	5180	1604.44	**2920**	5288
1538.33	**2801**	5073.8	1571.67	**2861**	5181.8	1605	**2921**	5289.8
1538.89	**2802**	5075.6	1572.22	**2862**	5183.6	1605.56	**2922**	5291.6
1539.44	**2803**	5077.4	1572.78	**2863**	5185.4	1606.11	**2923**	5293.4
1540	**2804**	5079.2	1573.33	**2864**	5187.2	1606.67	**2924**	5295.2
1540.56	**2805**	5081	1573.89	**2865**	5189	1607.22	**2925**	5297
1541.11	**2806**	5082.8	1574.44	**2866**	5190.8	1607.78	**2926**	5298.8
1541.67	**2807**	5084.6	1575	**2867**	5192.6	1608.33	**2927**	5300.6
1542.22	**2808**	5086.4	1575.56	**2868**	5194.4	1608.89	**2928**	5302.4
1542.78	**2809**	5088.2	1576.11	**2869**	5196.2	1609.44	**2929**	5304.2

Table 6–3 (*Continued*)
TEMPERATURE CONVERSION TABLE

To Convert			To Convert			To Convert		
To °C	←°F or °C→	To °F	To °C	←°F or °C→	To °F	To °C	←°F or °C→	To °F
1610	**2930**	5306	1643.33	**2990**	5414	1676.67	**3050**	5522
1610.56	**2931**	5307.8	1643.89	**2991**	5415.8	1677.22	**3051**	5523.8
1611.11	**2932**	5309.6	1644.44	**2992**	5417.6	1677.78	**3052**	5525.6
1611.67	**2933**	5311.4	1645	**2993**	5419.4	1678.33	**3053**	5527.4
1612.22	**2934**	5313.2	1645.56	**2994**	5421.2	1678.89	**3054**	5529.2
1612.78	**2935**	5315	1646.11	**2995**	5423	1679.44	**3055**	5531
1613.33	**2936**	5316.8	1646.67	**2996**	5424.8	1680	**3056**	5532.8
1613.89	**2937**	5318.6	1647.22	**2997**	5426.6	1680.56	**3057**	5534.6
1614.44	**2938**	5320.4	1647.78	**2998**	5428.4	1681.11	**3058**	5536.4
1615	**2939**	5322.2	1648.33	**2999**	5430.2	1681.67	**3059**	5538.2
1615.56	**2940**	5324	1648.89	**3000**	5432	1682.22	**3060**	5540
1616.11	**2941**	5325.8	1649.44	**3001**	5433.8	1682.78	**3061**	5541.8
1616.67	**2942**	5327.6	1650	**3002**	5435.6	1683.33	**3062**	5543.6
1617.22	**2943**	5329.4	1650.56	**3003**	5437.4	1683.89	**3063**	5545.4
1617.78	**2944**	5331.2	1651.11	**3004**	5439.2	1684.44	**3064**	5547.2
1618.33	**2945**	5333	1651.67	**3005**	5441	1685	**3065**	5549
1618.89	**2946**	5334.8	1652.22	**3006**	5442.8	1685.56	**3066**	5550.8
1619.44	**2947**	5336.6	1652.78	**3007**	5444.6	1686.11	**3067**	5552.6
1620	**2948**	5338.4	1653.33	**3008**	5446.4	1686.67	**3068**	5554.4
1620.56	**2949**	5340.2	1653.89	**3009**	5448.2	1687.22	**3069**	5556.2
1621.11	**2950**	5342	1654.44	**3010**	5450	1687.78	**3070**	5558
1621.67	**2951**	5343.8	1655	**3011**	5451.8	1688.33	**3071**	5559.8
1622.22	**2952**	5345.6	1655.56	**3012**	5453.6	1688.89	**3072**	5561.6
1622.78	**2953**	5347.4	1656.11	**3013**	5455.4	1689.44	**3073**	5563.4
1623.33	**2954**	5349.2	1656.67	**3014**	5457.2	1690	**3074**	5565.2
1623.89	**2955**	5351	1657.22	**3015**	5459	1690.56	**3075**	5567
1624.44	**2956**	5352.8	1657.78	**3016**	5460.8	1691.11	**3076**	5568.8
1625	**2957**	5354.6	1658.33	**3017**	5462.6	1691.67	**3077**	5570.6
1625.56	**2958**	5356.4	1658.89	**3018**	5464.4	1692.22	**3078**	5572.4
1626.11	**2959**	5358.2	1659.44	**3019**	5466.2	1692.78	**3079**	5574.2
1626.67	**2960**	5360	1660	**3020**	5468	1693.33	**3080**	5576
1627.22	**2961**	5361.8	1660.56	**3021**	5469.8	1693.89	**3081**	5577.8
1627.78	**2962**	5363.6	1661.11	**3022**	5471.6	1694.44	**3082**	5579.6
1628.33	**2963**	5365.4	1661.67	**3023**	5473.4	1695	**3083**	5581.4
1628.89	**2964**	5367.2	1662.22	**3024**	5475.2	1695.56	**3084**	5583.2
1629.44	**2965**	5369	1662.78	**3025**	5477	1696.11	**3085**	5585
1630	**2966**	5370.8	1663.33	**3026**	5478.8	1696.67	**3086**	5586.8
1630.56	**2967**	5372.6	1663.89	**3027**	5480.6	1697.22	**3087**	5588.6
1631.11	**2968**	5374.4	1664.44	**3028**	5482.4	1697.78	**3088**	5590.4
1631.67	**2969**	5376.2	1665	**3029**	5484.2	1698.33	**3089**	5592.2
1632.22	**2970**	5378	1665.56	**3030**	5486	1698.89	**3090**	5594
1632.78	**2971**	5379.8	1666.11	**3031**	5487.8	1699.44	**3091**	5595.8
1633.33	**2972**	5381.6	1666.67	**3032**	5489.6	1700	**3092**	5597.6
1633.89	**2973**	5383.4	1667.22	**3033**	5491.4	1700.56	**3093**	5599.4
1634.44	**2974**	5385.2	1667.78	**3034**	5493.2	1701.11	**3094**	5601.2
1635	**2975**	5387	1668.33	**3035**	5495	1701.67	**3095**	5603
1635.56	**2976**	5388.8	1668.89	**3036**	5496.8	1702.22	**3096**	5604.8
1636.11	**2977**	5390.6	1669.44	**3037**	5498.6	1702.78	**3097**	5606.6
1636.67	**2978**	5392.4	1670	**3038**	5500.4	1703.33	**3098**	5608.4
1637.22	**2979**	5394.2	1670.56	**3039**	5502.2	1703.89	**3099**	5610.2
1637.78	**2980**	5396	1671.11	**3040**	5504	1704.44	**3100**	5612
1638.33	**2981**	5397.8	1671.67	**3041**	5505.8	1705	**3101**	5613.8
1638.89	**2982**	5399.6	1672.22	**3042**	5507.6	1705.56	**3102**	5615.6
1639.44	**2983**	5401.4	1672.78	**3043**	5509.4	1706.11	**3103**	5617.4
1640	**2984**	5403.2	1673.33	**3044**	5511.2	1706.67	**3104**	5619.2
1640.56	**2985**	5405	1673.89	**3045**	5513	1707.22	**3105**	5621
1641.11	**2986**	5406.8	1674.44	**3046**	5514.8	1707.78	**3106**	5622.8
1641.67	**2987**	5408.6	1675	**3047**	5516.6	1708.33	**3107**	5624.6
1642.22	**2988**	5410.4	1675.56	**3048**	5518.4	1708.89	**3108**	5626.4
1642.78	**2989**	5412.2	1676.11	**3049**	5520.2	1709.44	**3109**	5628.2

Table 6–3 (*Continued*)
TEMPERATURE CONVERSION TABLE

To Convert			To Convert			To Convert		
To °C	←°F or °C→	To °F	To °C	←°F or °C→	To °F	To °C	←°F or °C→	To °F
1710	**3110**	5630	1743.33	**3170**	5738	1776.67	**3230**	5846
1710.56	**3111**	5631.8	1743.89	**3171**	5739.8	1777.22	**3231**	5847.8
1711.11	**3112**	5633.6	1744.44	**3172**	5741.6	1777.78	**3232**	5849.6
1711.67	**3113**	5635.4	1745	**3173**	5743.4	1778.33	**3233**	5851.4
1712.22	**3114**	5637.2	1745.56	**3174**	5745.2	1778.89	**3234**	5853.2
1712.78	**3115**	5639	1746.11	**3175**	5747	1779.44	**3235**	5855
1713.33	**3116**	5640.8	1746.67	**3176**	5748.8	1780	**3236**	5856.8
1713.89	**3117**	5642.6	1747.22	**3177**	5750.6	1780.56	**3237**	5858.6
1714.44	**3118**	5644.4	1747.78	**3178**	5752.4	1781.11	**3238**	5860.4
1715	**3119**	5646.2	1748.33	**3179**	5754.2	1781.67	**3239**	5862.2
1715.56	**3120**	5648	1748.89	**3180**	5756	1782.22	**3240**	5864
1716.11	**3121**	5649.8	1749.44	**3181**	5757.8	1782.78	**3241**	5865.8
1716.67	**3122**	5651.6	1750	**3182**	5759.6	1783.33	**3242**	5867.6
1717.22	**3123**	5653.4	1750.56	**3183**	5761.4	1783.89	**3243**	5869.4
1717.78	**3124**	5655.2	1751.11	**3184**	5763.2	1784.44	**3244**	5871.2
1718.33	**3125**	5657	1751.67	**3185**	5765	1785	**3245**	5873
1718.89	**3126**	5658.8	1752.22	**3186**	5766.8	1785.56	**3246**	5874.8
1719.44	**3127**	5660.6	1752.78	**3187**	5768.6	1786.11	**3247**	5876.6
1720	**3128**	5662.4	1753.33	**3188**	5770.4	1786.67	**3248**	5878.4
1720.56	**3129**	5664.2	1753.89	**3189**	5772.2	1787.22	**3249**	5880.2
1721.11	**3130**	5666	1754.44	**3190**	5774	1787.78	**3250**	5882
1721.67	**3131**	5667.8	1755	**3191**	5775.8	1788.33	**3251**	5883.8
1722.22	**3132**	5669.6	1755.56	**3192**	5777.6	1788.89	**3252**	5885.6
1722.78	**3133**	5671.4	1756.11	**3193**	5779.4	1789.44	**3253**	5887.4
1723.33	**3134**	5673.2	1756.67	**3194**	5781.2	1790	**3254**	5889.2
1723.89	**3135**	5675	1757.22	**3195**	5783	1790.56	**3255**	5891
1724.44	**3136**	5676.8	1757.78	**3196**	5784.8	1791.11	**3256**	5892.8
1725	**3137**	5678.6	1758.33	**3197**	5786.6	1791.67	**3257**	5894.6
1725.56	**3138**	5680.4	1758.89	**3198**	5788.4	1792.22	**3258**	5896.4
1726.11	**3139**	5682.2	1759.44	**3199**	5790.2	1792.78	**3259**	5898.2
1726.67	**3140**	5684	1760	**3200**	5792	1793.33	**3260**	5900
1727.22	**3141**	5685.8	1760.56	**3201**	5793.8	1793.89	**3261**	5901.8
1727.78	**3142**	5687.6	1761.11	**3202**	5795.6	1794.44	**3262**	5903.6
1728.33	**3143**	5689.4	1761.67	**3203**	5797.4	1795	**3263**	5905.4
1728.89	**3144**	5691.2	1762.22	**3204**	5799.2	1795.56	**3264**	5907.2
1729.44	**3145**	5693	1762.78	**3205**	5801	1796.11	**3265**	5909
1730	**3146**	5694.8	1763.33	**3206**	5802.8	1796.67	**3266**	5910.8
1730.56	**3147**	5696.6	1763.89	**3207**	5804.6	1797.22	**3267**	5912.6
1731.11	**3148**	5698.4	1764.44	**3208**	5806.4	1797.78	**3268**	5914.4
1731.67	**3149**	5700.2	1765	**3209**	5808.2	1798.33	**3269**	5916.2
1732.22	**3150**	5702	1765.56	**3210**	5810	1798.89	**3270**	5918
1732.78	**3151**	5703.8	1766.11	**3211**	5811.8	1799.44	**3271**	5919.8
1733.33	**3152**	5705.6	1766.67	**3212**	5813.6	1800	**3272**	5921.6
1733.89	**3153**	5707.4	1767.22	**3213**	5815.4	1800.56	**3273**	5923.4
1734.44	**3154**	5709.2	1767.78	**3214**	5817.2	1801.11	**3274**	5925.2
1735	**3155**	5711	1768.33	**3215**	5819	1801.67	**3275**	5927
1735.56	**3156**	5712.8	1768.89	**3216**	5820.8	1802.22	**3276**	5928.8
1736.11	**3157**	5714.6	1769.44	**3217**	5822.6	1802.78	**3277**	5930.6
1736.67	**3158**	5716.4	1770	**3218**	5824.4	1803.33	**3278**	5932.4
1737.22	**3159**	5718.2	1770.56	**3219**	5826.2	1803.89	**3279**	5934.2
1737.78	**3160**	5720	1771.11	**3220**	5828	1804.44	**3280**	5936
1738.33	**3161**	5721.8	1771.67	**3221**	5829.8	1805	**3281**	5937.8
1738.89	**3162**	5723.6	1772.22	**3222**	5831.6	1805.56	**3282**	5939.6
1739.44	**3163**	5725.4	1772.78	**3223**	5833.4	1806.11	**3283**	5941.4
1740	**3164**	5727.2	1773.33	**3224**	5835.2	1806.67	**3284**	5943.2
1740.56	**3165**	5729	1773.89	**3225**	5837	1807.22	**3285**	5945
1741.11	**3166**	5730.8	1774.44	**3226**	5838.8	1807.78	**3286**	5946.8
1741.67	**3167**	5732.6	1775	**3227**	5840.6	1808.33	**3287**	5948.6
1742.22	**3168**	5734.4	1775.56	**3228**	5842.4	1808.89	**3288**	5950.4
1742.78	**3169**	5736.2	1776.11	**3229**	5844.2	1809.44	**3289**	5952.2

Table 6–3 (*Continued*)
TEMPERATURE CONVERSION TABLE

To Convert			To Convert			To Convert		
To °C	←°F or °C→	To °F	To °C	←°F or °C→	To °F	To °C	←°F or °C→	To °F
1810	**3290**	5954	1954.44	**3550**	6422	2121.11	**3850**	6962
1810.56	**3291**	5955.8	1957.22	**3555**	6431	2123.89	**3855**	6971
1811.11	**3292**	5957.6	1960.00	**3560**	6440	2126.67	**3860**	6980
1811.67	**3293**	5959.4	1962.78	**3565**	6449	2129.44	**3865**	6989
1812.22	**3294**	5961.2	1965.56	**3570**	6458	2132.22	**3870**	6998
1812.78	**3295**	5963	1968.33	**3575**	6467	2135.00	**3875**	7007
1813.33	**3296**	5964.8	1971.11	**3580**	6476	2137.78	**3880**	7016
1813.89	**3297**	5966.6	1973.89	**3585**	6485	2140.56	**3885**	7025
1814.44	**3298**	5968.4	1976.67	**3590**	6494	2143.33	**3890**	7034
1815	**3299**	5970.2	1979.44	**3595**	6503	2145.11	**3895**	7043
1815.56	**3300**	5972	1982.22	**3600**	6512	2148.89	**3900**	7052
1818.33	**3305**	5981	1985.00	**3605**	6521	2151.67	**3905**	7061
1821.11	**3310**	5990	1987.78	**3610**	6530	2154.44	**3910**	7070
1823.89	**3315**	5999	1990.56	**3615**	6539	2157.22	**3915**	7079
1826.67	**3320**	6008	1993.33	**3620**	6548	2160.00	**3920**	7088
1829.44	**3325**	6017	1996.11	**3625**	6557	2162.78	**3925**	7097
1832.22	**3330**	6026	1998.89	**3630**	6566	2165.56	**3930**	7106
1835.00	**3335**	6035	2001.67	**3635**	6575	2168.33	**3935**	7115
1837.78	**3340**	6044	2004.44	**3640**	6584	2171.11	**3940**	7124
1840.56	**3345**	6053	2007.22	**3645**	6593	2173.89	**3945**	7133
1843.33	**3350**	6062	2010.00	**3650**	6602	2176.67	**3950**	7142
1846.11	**3355**	6071	2012.78	**3655**	6611	2179.44	**3955**	7151
1848.89	**3360**	6080	2015.56	**3660**	6620	2182.22	**3960**	7160
1851.67	**3365**	6089	2018.33	**3665**	6629	2185.00	**3965**	7169
1854.44	**3370**	6098	2021.11	**3670**	6638	2187.78	**3970**	7178
1857.22	**3375**	6107	2023.89	**3675**	6647	2190.56	**3975**	7187
1860.00	**3380**	6116	2026.67	**3680**	6656	2193.33	**3980**	7196
1862.78	**3385**	6125	2029.44	**3685**	6665	2196.11	**3985**	7205
1865.56	**3390**	6134	2032.22	**3690**	6674	2198.89	**3990**	7214
1868.33	**3395**	6143	2035.00	**3695**	6683	2201.67	**3995**	7223
1871.11	**3400**	6152	2037.78	**3700**	6692	2204.44	**4000**	7232
1873.89	**3405**	6161	2040.56	**3705**	6701	2207.22	**4005**	7241
1876.67	**3410**	6170	2043.33	**3710**	6710	2210.00	**4010**	7250
1879.44	**3415**	6179	2046.11	**3715**	6719	2212.78	**4015**	7259
1882.22	**3420**	6188	2048.89	**3720**	6728	2215.56	**4020**	7268
1885.00	**3425**	6197	2051.67	**3725**	6737	2218.33	**4025**	7277
1887.78	**3430**	6206	2054.44	**3730**	6746	2221.11	**4030**	7286
1890.56	**3435**	6215	2057.22	**3735**	6755	2223.89	**4035**	7295
1893.33	**3440**	6224	2060.00	**3740**	6764	2226.67	**4040**	7304
1896.11	**3445**	6233	2062.78	**3745**	6773	2229.44	**4045**	7313
1898.89	**3450**	6242	2065.56	**3750**	6782	2232.22	**4050**	7322
1901.67	**3455**	6251	2068.33	**3755**	6791	2235.00	**4055**	7331
1904.44	**3460**	6260	2071.11	**3760**	6800	2237.78	**4060**	7340
1907.22	**3465**	6269	2073.89	**3765**	6809	2240.56	**4065**	7349
1910.00	**3470**	6278	2076.67	**3770**	6818	2243.33	**4070**	7358
1912.78	**3475**	6287	2079.44	**3775**	6827	2246.11	**4075**	7367
1915.56	**3480**	6296	2082.22	**3780**	6836	2248.89	**4080**	7376
1918.33	**3485**	6305	2085.00	**3785**	6845	2251.67	**4085**	7385
1921.11	**3490**	6314	2087.78	**3790**	6854	2254.44	**4090**	7394
1923.89	**3495**	6323	2090.56	**3795**	6863	2257.22	**4095**	7403
1926.67	**3500**	6332	2093.33	**3800**	6872	2260.00	**4100**	7412
1929.44	**3505**	6341	2096.11	**3805**	6881	2262.78	**4105**	7421
1932.22	**3510**	6350	2098.89	**3810**	6890	2265.56	**4110**	7430
1935.00	**3515**	6359	2101.67	**3815**	6899	2268.33	**4115**	7439
1937.78	**3520**	6368	2104.44	**3820**	6908	2271.11	**4120**	7448
1940.56	**3525**	6377	2107.22	**3825**	6917	2273.89	**4125**	7457
1943.33	**3530**	6386	2110.00	**3830**	6926	2276.67	**4130**	7466
1946.11	**3535**	6395	2112.78	**3835**	6935	2279.44	**4135**	7475
1948.89	**3540**	6404	2115.56	**3840**	6944	2282.22	**4140**	7484
1951.67	**3545**	6413	2118.33	**3845**	6953	2285.00	**4145**	7493

Table 6–3 (*Continued*)
TEMPERATURE CONVERSION TABLE

To Convert			To Convert			To Convert		
To °C	←°F or °C→	To °F	To °C	←°F or °C→	To °F	To °C	←°F or °C→	To °F
2287.78	**4150**	7502	2354.44	**4270**	7718	2421.11	**4390**	7934
2290.56	**4155**	7511	2357.22	**4275**	7727	2423.89	**4395**	7943
2293.33	**4160**	7520	2360.00	**4280**	7736	2426.67	**4400**	7952
2296.11	**4165**	7529	2362.78	**4285**	7745	2429.44	**4405**	7961
2298.89	**4170**	7538	2365.56	**4290**	7754	2432.22	**4410**	7970
2301.67	**4175**	7547	2368.33	**4295**	7763	2435.00	**4415**	7979
2304.44	**4180**	7556	2371.11	**4300**	7772	2437.78	**4420**	7988
2307.22	**4185**	7565	2373.89	**4305**	7781	2440.56	**4425**	7997
2310.00	**4190**	7574	2376.67	**4310**	7790	2443.33	**4430**	8006
2312.78	**4195**	7583	2379.44	**4315**	7799	2446.11	**4435**	8015
2315.56	**4200**	7592	2382.22	**4320**	7808	2448.89	**4440**	8024
2318.33	**4205**	7601	2385.00	**4325**	7817	2451.67	**4445**	8033
2321.11	**4210**	7610	2387.78	**4330**	7826	2454.44	**4450**	8042
2323.89	**4215**	7619	2390.56	**4335**	7835	2457.22	**4455**	8051
2326.67	**4220**	7628	2393.33	**4340**	7844	2460.00	**4460**	8060
2329.44	**4225**	7637	2396.11	**4345**	7853	2462.78	**4465**	8069
2332.22	**4230**	7646	2398.89	**4350**	7862	2465.56	**4470**	8078
2335.00	**4235**	7655	2401.67	**4355**	7871	2468.33	**4475**	8087
2337.78	**4240**	7664	2404.44	**4360**	7880	2471.11	**4480**	8096
2340.56	**4245**	7673	2407.22	**4365**	7889	2473.89	**4485**	8105
2343.33	**4250**	7682	2410.00	**4370**	7898	2476.67	**4490**	8114
2346.11	**4255**	7691	2412.78	**4375**	7907	2479.44	**4495**	8123
2348.89	**4260**	7700	2415.56	**4380**	7916	2482.22	**4500**	8132
2351.67	**4265**	7709	2418.33	**4385**	7925			

(From Weast, R. C., Ed., CRC Handbook of Chemistry and Physics, 54th Ed., CRC Press, Cleveland, 1973, pp. F118–F140. With permission.)

Table 6–4
VELOCITY CONVERSIONS

Table A Knots to Centimeters per Second

Example:
Given, velocity 1.5 knots.
From Table A, velocity 77.2 cm/sec

Knots	0.0	0.1	0.2	0.3	0.4	0.5	0.6	0.7	0.8	0.9
0	0.0	5.1	10.3	15.4	20.6	25.7	30.9	36.0	41.2	46.3
1	51.5	56.6	61.8	66.9	72.1	77.2	82.4	87.5	92.7	97.8
2	103.0	108.1	113.3	118.4	123.5	128.7	133.8	139.0	144.1	149.3
3	154.4	159.6	164.7	169.9	175.0	180.2	185.3	190.5	195.6	200.8
4	205.9	211.1	216.2	221.4	226.5	231.7	236.8	242.0	247.1	252.2
5	257.4	262.5	267.7	272.8	278.0	283.1	288.3	293.4	298.6	303.7
6	308.9	314.0	319.2	324.3	329.5	334.6	339.8	344.9	350.1	355.2
7	360.4	365.5	370.6	375.8	380.9	386.1	391.2	396.4	401.5	406.7
8	411.8	417.0	422.1	427.3	432.4	437.6	442.7	447.9	453.0	458.2
9	463.3	468.5	473.6	478.8	483.9	489.1	494.2	499.3	504.5	509.6

Table B Centimeters per Second to Knots

Example:
Given, velocity 84 cm/sec.
From Table B, velocity 1.63 knots.

cm/sec	0	1	2	3	4	5	6	7	8	9
0	0.0	0.02	0.04	0.06	0.08	0.10	0.12	0.14	0.16	0.17
10	0.19	0.21	0.23	0.25	0.27	0.29	0.31	0.33	0.35	0.37
20	0.39	0.41	0.43	0.45	0.47	0.49	0.51	0.52	0.54	0.56
30	0.58	0.60	0.62	0.64	0.66	0.68	0.70	0.72	0.74	0.76
40	0.78	0.80	0.82	0.84	0.85	0.87	0.89	0.91	0.93	0.95
50	.97	.99	1.01	1.03	1.05	1.07	1.09	1.11	1.13	1.15
60	1.17	1.18	1.20	1.22	1.24	1.26	1.28	1.30	1.32	1.34
70	1.36	1.38	1.40	1.42	1.44	1.46	1.48	1.50	1.52	1.53
80	1.55	1.57	1.59	1.61	1.63	1.65	1.67	1.69	1.71	1.73
90	1.75	1.77	1.79	1.81	1.83	1.85	1.86	1.88	1.90	1.92
100	1.94	1.96	1.98	2.00	2.02	2.04	2.06	2.08	2.10	2.12
110	2.14	2.16	2.18	2.20	2.21	2.23	2.25	2.27	2.29	2.31
120	2.33	2.35	2.37	2.39	2.41	2.43	2.45	2.47	2.49	2.51
130	1.53	2.54	2.56	2.58	1.60	2.62	2.64	2.66	2.68	2.70
140	2.72	2.74	2.76	2.78	2.80	2.82	2.84	2.86	2.87	2.89
150	2.91	2.93	2.95	2.97	2.99	3.01	3.03	3.05	3.07	3.09
160	3.11	3.13	3.15	3.17	3.19	3.21	3.22	3.24	3.26	3.28
170	3.30	3.32	3.34	3.36	3.38	3.40	3.42	3.44	3.46	3.48
180	3.50	3.52	3.54	3.55	3.57	3.59	3.61	3.63	3.65	3.67
190	3.69	3.71	3.73	3.75	3.77	3.79	3.81	3.83	3.85	3.87
200	3.89	3.90	3.92	3.94	3.96	3.98	4.00	4.02	4.04	4.06
210	4.08	4.10	4.12	4.14	4.16	4.18	4.20	4.22	4.23	4.25
220	4.27	4.29	4.31	4.33	4.35	4.37	4.39	4.41	4.43	4.45
230	4.47	4.49	4.51	4.53	4.55	4.56	4.58	4.60	4.62	4.64
240	4.66	4.68	4.70	4.72	4.74	4.76	4.78	4.80	4.82	4.84

Table 6–4 (*Continued*)

cm/sec	0	1	2	3	4	5	6	7	8	9
250	4.86	4.88	4.90	4.91	4.93	4.95	4.97	4.99	5.01	5.03
260	5.05	5.07	5.09	5.11	5.13	5.15	5.17	5.19	5.21	5.23
270	5.24	5.26	5.28	5.30	5.32	5.34	5.36	5.38	5.40	5.42
280	5.44	5.46	5.48	5.50	5.52	5.54	5.56	5.58	5.59	5.61
290	5.63	5.65	5.67	5.69	5.71	5.73	5.75	5.77	5.79	5.81

(From LaFond, E. C., *Processing Oceanographic Data,* U.S. Navy Hydrographic Office, Washington, D.C., Publ. No. 614, 1951.)

Table 6–5
CURRENT FACTORS FOR VALUES OF LATITUDE

$$c = \frac{1}{2\omega \sin \phi \, 10^5}$$

where

ω = angular velocity of earth's rotation, equal to 0.729 × 10^{-4} rad/sec,

ϕ = latitude in degrees.

Example:

Given, latitude of 30°N.
From above equation, c = 0.1371

Current factor, c, is used in the following equation to obtain current velocity.

$$V = \frac{c(D_A - D_B)(n)}{L}$$

where

V = average current velocity normal to a line between stations A and B,

$D_A - D_B$ = dynamic height difference between stations A and B,

L = distance between stations A and B,

n = unit conversion factor, dependent upon the units of the other variables. If units of V, $D_A - D_B$, and L are as shown, then n will have the indicated values.

V	$D_A - D_B$	L	n
m/sec	dyn. m	meters	10^6
cm/sec	dyn. m	kilometers	10^5
cm/sec	dyn. m	nautical miles	53,959
knots	dyn. m	kilometers	31,942.6
knots	dyn. m	nautical miles	1048.2

Current Factor

Latitude (degrees)	0	1	2	3	4	5	6	7	8	9
0			1.9646	1.3101	0.9829	0.7867	0.6560	0.5626	0.4927	0.4383
10	0.3949	0.3594	1.3298	1.3048	0.2834	0.2649	0.2488	0.2345	0.2219	0.2106
20	0.2005	0.1913	1.1830	1.1755	0.1686	0.1622	0.1564	0.1510	0.1461	0.1414
30	0.1371	0.1331	1.1294	1.1259	0.1226	0.1195	0.1167	0.1139	0.1114	0.1090
40	0.1067	0.1045	1.1025	1.1005	0.0987	0.0970	0.0953	0.0938	0.0923	0.0909
50	0.0895	0.0882	1.0870	1.0859	0.0848	0.0837	0.0827	0.0817	0.0809	0.0800
60	0.0792	0.0784	1.0777	1.0770	0.0763	0.0757	0.0751	0.0745	0.0740	0.0735
70	0.0730	0.0725	1.0721	1.0717	0.0713	0.0710	0.0707	0.0704	0.0701	0.0699
80	0.0696	0.0694	1.0692	1.0691	0.0690	0.0688	0.0687	0.0687	0.0686	0.0686

(From LaFond, E. C., *Processing Oceanographic Data,* U.S. Navy Hydrographic Office, Washington, D.C., Publ. No. 614, 1951.)

Table 6–6
LENGTH OF A DEGREE OF LATITUDE AND LONGITUDE

	Degree of latitude				Degree of longitude				
Lat. °	Nautical mi.	Statute mi.	Ft	Meters	Nautical mi.	Statute mi.	Ft	Meters	Lat. °
0	59.702	68.703	362,752	110,567	60.109	69.172	365,226	111,321	0
1	59.702	68.704	362,755	110,568	60.100	69.161	365,170	111,304	1
2	59.703	68.704	362,758	110,569	60.072	69.129	365,003	111,253	2
3	59.703	68.705	362,762	110,570	60.027	69.077	364,727	111,169	3
4	59.705	68.707	362,772	110,573	59.963	69.004	364,340	111,051	4
5	59.707	68.709	362,781	110,576	59.882	68.910	363,844	110,900	5
6	59.709	68.711	362,795	110,580	59.782	68.795	363,237	110,715	6
7	59.711	68.714	362,808	110,584	59.664	68.660	362,522	110,497	7
8	59.714	68.717	362,824	110,589	59.528	68.503	361,695	110,245	8
9	59.717	68.720	362,844	110,595	59.373	68.325	360,757	109,959	9
10	59.720	68.724	362,863	110,601	59.202	68.128	359,714	109,641	10
11	59.724	68.728	362,886	110,608	59.012	67.909	358,559	109,289	11
12	59.728	68.733	362,913	110,616	58.804	67.670	357,296	108,904	12
13	59.733	68.738	362,939	110,624	58.578	67.410	355,924	108,486	13
14	59.737	68.744	362,968	110,633	58.335	67.130	354,448	108,036	14
15	59.743	68.750	363,001	110,643	58.074	66.830	352,863	107,553	15
16	59.748	68.756	363,034	110,653	57.795	66.509	351,167	107,036	16
17	59.754	68.763	363,067	110,663	57.499	66.168	349,366	106,487	17
18	59.760	68.770	363,106	110,675	57.185	65.807	347,460	105,906	18
19	59.766	68.777	363,142	110,686	56.855	65.427	345,452	105,294	19
20	59.773	68.785	363,185	110,699	56.506	65.026	343,336	104,649	20
21	59.780	68.793	363,228	110,712	56.141	64.605	341,115	103,972	21
22	59.787	68.801	363,270	110,725	55.758	64.165	338,792	103,264	22
23	59.795	68.810	363,316	110,739	55.359	63.705	336,364	102,524	23
24	59.802	68.819	363,362	110,753	54.943	63.227	333,838	101,754	24
25	59.810	68.828	363,411	110,768	54.510	62.729	331,207	100,952	25
26	59.818	68.837	363,461	110,783	54.060	62.211	328,474	100,119	26
27	59.827	68.847	363,513	110,799	53.595	61.675	325,646	99,257	27
28	59.836	68.857	363,566	110,815	53.113	61.120	322,716	98,364	28
29	59.845	68.868	363,621	110,832	52.614	60.547	319,688	97,441	29
30	59.853	68.878	363,674	110,848	52.100	59.955	316,561	96,488	30
31	59.863	68.889	363,733	110,866	51.569	59.345	313,339	95,506	31
32	59.872	68.899	363,789	110,883	51.024	58.716	310,022	94,495	32
33	59.882	68.911	363,848	110,901	50.462	58.070	306,610	93,455	33
34	59.892	68.922	363,907	110,919	49.885	57.407	303,106	92,387	34
35	59.902	68.934	363,969	110,938	49.293	56.725	299,507	91,290	35
36	59.912	68.945	364,028	110,956	48.686	56.026	295,820	90,166	36
37	59.922	68.957	364,090	110,975	48.064	55.311	292,040	89,014	37
38	59.932	68.968	364,153	110,994	47.427	54.578	288,172	87,835	38
39	59.943	68.980	364,215	111,013	46.776	53.829	284,215	86,629	39
40	59.953	68.995	364,281	111,033	46.110	53.063	280,170	85,396	40
41	59.964	69.004	364,343	111,052	45.431	52.280	276,039	84,137	41
42	59.974	69.017	364,409	111,072	44.737	51.482	271,827	82,853	42
43	59.985	69.029	364,471	111,091	44.030	50.668	267,529	81,543	43
44	59.995	69.041	364,537	111,111	43.309	49.839	263,149	80,208	44

Table 6–6 (*Continued*)

	Degree of latitude				Degree of longitude				
Lat. °	Nautical mi.	Statute mi.	Ft.	Meters	Nautical mi.	Statute mi.	Ft	Meters	Lat. °
45	60.006	69.053	364,602	111,131	42.575	48.994	258,690	78,849	45
46	60.017	69.066	364,668	111,151	41.829	48.135	254,153	77,466	46
47	60.027	69.078	364,730	111,170	41.068	47.260	249,534	76,058	47
48	60.038	69.090	364,796	111,190	40.296	46.372	244,842	74,628	48
49	60.049	69.103	364,861	111,210	39.511	45.468	240,072	73,174	49
50	60.059	69.114	364,924	111,229	38.714	44.551	235,229	71,698	50
51	60.070	69.127	364,989	111,249	37.905	43.620	230,314	70,200	51
52	60.080	69.139	365,052	111,268	37.084	42.676	225,328	68,680	52
53	60.091	69.150	365,114	111,287	36.253	41.719	220,275	67,140	53
54	60.101	69.162	365,176	111,306	35.409	40.748	215,150	65,578	54
55	60.111	69.174	365,239	111,325	34.555	39.765	209,960	63,996	55
56	60.121	69.185	365,298	111,343	33.691	38.770	204,708	62,395	56
57	60.130	69.196	365,357	111,361	32.816	37.763	199,389	60,774	57
58	60.140	69.208	365,416	111,379	31.931	36.745	194,012	59,135	58
59	60.150	69.219	365,475	111,397	31.036	35.715	188,576	57,478	59
60	60.159	69.229	365,531	111,414	30.131	34.674	183,077	55,802	60
61	60.169	69.241	365,590	111,432	29.217	33.622	177,526	54,110	61
62	60.177	69.250	365,642	111,448	28.294	32.560	171,916	52,400	62
63	60.186	69.260	365,695	111,464	27.362	31.488	166,256	50,675	63
64	60.195	69.270	365,747	111,480	26.422	30.406	160,544	48,934	64
65	60.203	69.280	365,800	111,496	25.474	29.314	154,780	47,177	65
66	60.211	69.290	365,849	111,511	24.518	28.215	148,973	45,407	66
67	60.219	69.298	365,895	111,525	23.554	27.105	143,117	43,622	67
68	60.227	69.307	365,941	111,539	22.583	25.988	137,214	41,823	68
69	60.234	69.316	365,987	111,553	21.605	24.862	131,273	40,012	69
70	60.241	69.324	366,029	111,566	20.620	23.729	125,288	38,188	70
71	60.248	69.331	366,069	111,578	19.629	22.589	119,268	36,535	71
72	60.254	69.339	366,108	111,590	18.632	21.441	113,208	34,506	72
73	60.261	69.346	366,148	111,602	17.629	20.286	107,113	32,648	73
74	60.267	69.353	366,184	111,613	16.621	19.126	100,987	30,781	74
75	60.272	69.359	366,216	111,623	15.606	17.959	94,826	28,903	75
76	60.277	69.365	366,246	111,632	14.588	16.788	88,638	27,017	76
77	60.282	69.371	366,279	111,642	13.565	15.611	82,424	25,123	77
78	60.287	69.376	366,305	111,650	12.538	14.428	76,181	23,220	78
79	60.291	69.381	366,331	111,658	11.507	13.242	69,918	21,311	79
80	60.295	69.385	366,354	111,665	10.472	12.051	63,628	19,394	80
81	60.298	69.389	366,374	111,671	9.434	10.857	57,323	17,472	81
82	60.301	69.393	366,394	111,677	8.394	9.659	51,001	15,545	82
83	60.304	69.396	366,410	111,682	7.350	8.458	44,695	13,612	83
84	60.307	69.399	366,426	111,687	6.304	7.254	38,304	11,675	84
85	60.309	69.401	366,440	111,691	5.257	6.049	31,939	9,735	85
86	60.310	69.403	366,449	111,694	4.207	4.842	25,564	7,792	86
87	60.311	69.405	366,450	111,696	3.157	3.633	19,180	5,846	87
88	60.312	69.406	366,463	111,698	2.105	2.422	12,789	3,898	88
89	60.313	69.406	366,466	111,699	1.052	1.211	6,394	1,949	89
90	60.313	69.406	366,466	111,699	0.000	0.000	0	0	90

Table 6–7
CONVERSION OF COMPASS POINTS TO DEGREES

North to East

	Points 32	Angular measure ° ′ ″	Points 8
North	0	0 00 00	
N ¼ E	¼	2 48 45	
N ½ E	½	5 37 30	
N ¾ E	¾	8 26 15	
N by E	1	11 15 00	8
N by E ¼ E	1¼	14 03 45	
N by E ½ E	1½	16 52 30	
N by E ¾ E	1¾	19 41 15	
NNE	2	22 30 00	
NNE ¼ E	2¼	25 18 45	
NNE ½ E	2½	28 07 30	
NNE ¾ E	2¾	30 56 15	
NE by N	3	33 45 00	
NE ¾ N	3¼	33 36 45	
NE ½ N	3½	39 22 30	
NE ¾ N	3¾	42 11 15	
NE	4	45 00 00	1
NE ¼ E	4¼	47 48 45	
NE ½ E	4½	50 37 30	
NE ¾ E	4¾	53 26 15	
NE by E	5	56 15 00	
NE by E ¼ E	5¼	59 03 45	
NE by E ½ E	5½	61 52 30	
NE by E ¾ E	5¾	64 41 15	
ENE	6	67 30 00	
ENE ¼ E	6¼	70 18 45	
ENE ½ E	6½	73 07 30	
ENE ¾ E	6¾	75 56 15	
E by N	7	78 45 00	2
E ¾ N	7¼	81 33 45	
E ½ N	7½	84 22 30	
E ¼ N	7¾	87 11 15	

East to South

	Points 32	Angular measure ° ′ ″	Points 8
East	8¼	90 00 00	
E ¼ S	8¼	92 48 45	
E ½ S	8½	95 37 30	
E ¾ S	8¾	98 26 15	
E by S	9	101 15 00	2
ESE ¾ E	9¼	104 03 45	
ESE ½ E	9½	106 52 30	
ESE ¼ E	9¾	109 41 15	
ESE	10	112 30 00	
SE by E ¾ E	10¼	115 18 45	
SE by E ½ E	10½	118 07 30	
SE by E ¼ E	10¾	120 56 15	
SE by E	11	123 45 00	
SE ¾ E	11¼	126 33 45	
SE ½ E	11½	129 22 30	
SE ¼ E	11¾	132 11 15	
SE	12	135 00 00	3
SE ¼ S	12¼	137 48 45	
SE ½ S	12½	140 37 30	
SE ¾ S	12¾	143 26 15	
SE by S	13	146 15 00	
SSE ¾ E	13¼	149 03 45	
SSE ½ E	13½	151 52 30	
SSE ¼ E	13¾	154 41 15	
SSE	14	157 30 00	
S by E ¾ E	14¼	160 18 45	
S by E ½ E	14½	163 07 30	
S by E ¼ E	14¾	165 56 15	
S by E	15	168 45 00	4
S ¾ E	15¼	171 33 45	
2 ½ E	15½	174 22 30	
S ¼ E	15¾	177 11 15	
South	16	180 00 00	

South to West

	Points 32	Angular measure ° ′ ″	Points 8
South	16	180 00 00	
S ¼ W	16¼	182 48 45	
S ½ W	16½	185 37 30	
S ¾ W	16¾	188 26 15	
S by W	17	191 15 00	4
S by W ¼ W	17¼	194 03 45	
S by W ½ W	17½	196 52 30	
S by W ¾ W	17¾	199 41 15	
SSW	18	202 30 00	
SSW ¼ W	18¼	205 18 45	
SSW ½ W	18½	208 07 30	
SSW ¾ W	18¾	210 56 15	
SW by S	19	213 45 00	5
SW ¾ S	19¼	216 33 45	
SW ½ S	19½	219 22 30	
SW ¼ S	19¾	222 11 15	
SW	20	225 00 00	

West to North

	Points 32	Angular measure ° ′ ″	Points 8
West	24	270 00 00	
W ¼ N	24¼	272 48 45	
W ½ N	24½	275 37 30	
W ¾ N	24¾	278 26 15	
W by N	25	281 15 00	6
WNW ¾ W	25¼	284 03 45	
WNW ½ W	25½	286 52 30	
WNW ¼ W	25¾	289 41 15	
WNW	26	292 30 00	
NW by W ¾ W	16¼	295 18 45	
NW by W ½ W	26½	298 07 30	
NW by W ¼ W	26¾	300 56 15	
NW by W	27	303 45 00	7
NW ¾ W	27¼	306 33 45	
Nw ½ W	27½	309 22 30	
NW ¼ W	27¾	312 11 15	
NW	27	303 45 00	

Table 6–7 (*Continued*)
CONVERSION OF COMPASS POINTS TO DEGREES

	Points 32	Angular measure	Points 8
SW ¼ W	20¼	227 48 45	5
SW ½ W	20½	230 37 30	
SW ¾ W	20¾	233 26 15	
SW by W	21	236 15 00	
SW by W ¼ W	21¼	239 03 45	
SW by W ½ W	21½	241 52 30	
SW by W ¾ W	21¾	244 41 15	
WSW	22	247 30 00	6
WSW ¼ W	22¼	250 18 45	
WSW ½ W	22½	253 07 30	
WSW ¾ W	22¾	255 56 15	
W by S	23	258 45 00	
W ¾ S	23¼	261 33 45	
W ½ S	23½	264 22 30	
W ¼ S	23¾	267 11 15	
NW ¼ N	28¼	317 48 45	7
NW ½ N	28½	320 37 30	
NW ¾ N	28¾	323 26 15	
NW by N	29	326 15 00	
NNW ¾ W	29¼	329 03 45	
NNW ½ W	29½	331 52 30	
NNW ¼ W	29¾	334 41 15	
NNW	30	337 30 00	8
N by W ¾ W	30¼	340 18 45	
N by W ½ W	30½	343 07 30	
N by W ¼ W	30¾	345 56 15	
N by W	31	348 45 00	
N ¾ W	31¼	351 33 45	
N ½ W	31½	354 22 30	
N ¼ W	31¾	357 11 15	
North	32	360 00 00	

Table 6–8
TIME TO ARC

Min of time	Arc		Min of time	Arc		Min of time	Arc		Sec of time	Arc		Sec of time	Arc		Sec of time	Arc	
1	0°	15′	21	5°	15′	41	10°	15′	1	0′	15″	21	5′	15″	41	10′	15″
2	0	30	22	5	30	42	10	30	2	0	30	22	5	30	42	10	30
3	0	45	23	5	45	43	10	45	3	0	45	23	5	45	43	10	45
4	1	0	24	6	0	44	11	0	4	1	0	24	6	0	44	11	0
5	1	15	25	6	15	45	11	15	5	1	15	25	6	15	45	11	15
6	1	30	26	6	30	46	11	30	6	1	30	26	6	30	46	11	30
7	1	45	27	6	45	47	11	45	7	1	45	27	6	45	47	11	45
8	2	0	28	7	0	48	12	0	8	2	0	28	7	0	48	12	0
9	2	15	29	7	15	49	12	15	9	2	15	29	7	15	49	12	15
10	2	30	30	7	30	50	12	30	10	2	30	30	7	30	50	12	30
11	2	45	31	7	45	51	12	45	11	2	45	31	7	45	51	12	45
12	3	0	32	8	0	52	13	0	12	3	0	32	8	0	52	13	0
13	3	15	33	8	15	53	13	15	13	3	15	33	8	15	53	13	15
14	3	30	34	8	30	54	13	30	14	3	30	34	8	30	54	13	30
15	3	45	35	8	45	55	13	45	15	3	45	35	8	45	55	13	45
16	4	0	36	9	0	56	14	0	16	4	0	36	9	0	56	14	0
17	4	15	37	9	15	57	14	15	17	4	15	37	9	15	57	14	15
18	4	30	38	9	30	58	14	30	18	4	30	38	9	30	58	14	30
19	4	45	39	9	45	59	14	45	19	4	45	39	9	45	59	14	45
20	5	0	40	10	0	60	15	0	20	5	0	40	10	0	60	15	0

Note: 1 hour = 15 degrees of arc.

(From List, R. J., Ed., *Smithsonian Meteorological Tables,* 6th rev. ed., Smithsonian Institution Press, Washington, D.C., 1971.)

Table 6–9
HOURS, MINUTES, AND SECONDS TO DECIMALS OF A DAY

Hr	Day	Min	Day	Min	Day	Sec	Day	Sec	Day
1	0.041667	1	0.000694	31	0.021528	1	0.000012	31	0.000359
2	0.083333	2	0.001389	32	0.022222	2	0.000023	32	0.000370
3	0.125000	3	0.002083	33	0.022917	3	0.000035	33	0.000382
4	0.166667	4	0.002778	34	0.023611	4	0.000046	34	0.000394
5	0.208333	5	0.003472	35	0.024305	5	0.000058	35	0.000405
6	0.250000	6	0.004167	36	0.025000	6	0.000069	36	0.000417
7	0.291667	7	0.004861	37	0.025694	7	0.000081	37	0.000428
8	0.333333	8	0.005556	38	0.026389	8	0.000093	38	0.000440
9	0.375000	9	0.006250	39	0.027083	9	0.000104	39	0.000451
10	0.416667	10	0.006944	40	0.027778	10	0.000116	40	0.000463
11	0.458333	11	0.007639	41	0.028472	11	0.000127	41	0.000475
12	0.500000	12	0.008333	42	0.029167	12	0.000139	42	0.000486
13	0.541667	13	0.009028	43	0.029861	13	0.000150	43	0.000498
14	0.583333	14	0.009722	44	0.030556	14	0.000162	44	0.000509
15	0.625000	15	0.010417	45	0.031250	15	0.000174	45	0.000521
16	0.666667	16	0.011111	46	0.031944	16	0.000185	46	0.000532
17	0.708333	17	0.011806	47	0.032639	17	0.000197	47	0.000544
18	0.750000	18	0.012500	48	0.033333	18	0.000208	48	0.000556
19	0.791667	19	0.013194	49	0.034028	19	0.000220	49	0.000567
20	0.833333	20	0.013889	50	0.034722	20	0.000231	50	0.000579
21	0.875000	21	0.014583	51	0.035417	21	0.000243	51	0.000590
22	0.916667	22	0.015278	52	0.036111	22	0.000255	52	0.000602
23	0.958333	23	0.015972	53	0.036806	23	0.000266	53	0.000613
24	1.000000	24	0.016667	54	0.037500	24	0.000278	54	0.000625
		25	0.017361	55	0.038194	25	0.000289	55	0.000637
		26	0.018056	56	0.038889	26	0.000301	56	0.000648
		27	0.018750	57	0.039583	27	0.000313	57	0.000660
		28	0.019444	58	0.040278	28	0.000324	58	0.000671
		29	0.020139	59	0.040972	29	0.000336	59	0.000683
		30	0.020833	60	0.041667	30	0.000347	60	0.000694

(From List, R. J., Ed., *Smithsonian Meteorological Tables,* 6th rev. ed., Smithsonian Institution Press, Washington, D.C., 1971.)

Table 6–10
MINUTES AND SECONDS TO DECIMALS OF AN HOUR

Min	Decimals of hr	Min	Decimals of hr	Sec	Decimals of hr	Sec	Decimals of hr
1	0.016667	31	0.516667	1	0.000278	31	0.008611
2	0.033333	32	0.533333	2	0.000556	32	0.008889
3	0.050000	33	0.550000	3	0.000833	33	0.009167
4	0.066667	34	0.566667	4	0.001111	34	0.009144
5	0.083333	35	0.583333	5	0.001389	35	0.009722
6	0.100000	36	0.600000	6	0.001667	36	0.010000
7	0.116667	37	0.616667	7	0.001944	37	0.010278
8	0.133333	38	0.633333	8	0.002222	38	0.010556
9	0.150000	39	0.650000	9	0.002500	39	0.010833
10	0.166667	40	0.666667	10	0.002778	40	0.011111
11	0.183333	41	0.683333	11	0.003056	41	0.011389
12	0.200000	42	0.700000	12	0.003333	42	0.011667
13	0.216667	43	0.716667	13	0.003611	43	0.011944
14	0.233333	44	0.733333	14	0.003889	44	0.012222
15	0.250000	45	0.750000	15	0.004167	45	0.012500
16	0.266667	46	0.766667	16	0.004444	46	0.012778
17	0.283333	47	0.783333	17	0.004722	47	0.013056
18	0.300000	48	0.800000	18	0.005000	48	0.013333
19	0.316667	49	0.816667	19	0.005278	49	0.013611
20	0.333333	50	0.833333	20	0.005556	50	0.013889
21	0.350000	51	0.850000	21	0.005833	51	0.014167
22	0.366667	52	0.866667	22	0.006111	52	0.014444
23	0.383333	53	0.883333	23	0.006389	53	0.014722
24	0.400000	54	0.900000	24	0.006667	54	0.015000
25	0.416667	55	0.916667	25	0.006944	55	0.015278
26	0.433333	56	0.933333	26	0.007222	56	0.015556
27	0.450000	57	0.950000	27	0.007500	57	0.015833
28	0.466667	58	0.966667	28	0.007778	58	0.016111
29	0.483333	59	0.983333	29	0.008056	59	0.016389
30	0.500000	60	1.000000	30	0.008333	60	0.016667

(From List, R. J., Ed., *Smithsonian Meteorological Tables,* 6th rev. ed., Smithsonian Institution Press, Washington, D.C., 1971.)

Table 6–11

Conversion Factors

Multiply	By	To obtain
Atmospheres	76.0	cm mercury
Atm	29.92	in. mercury
Atm	33.90	Water, ft
Atm	1.0333	kg/cm^2
Atm	14.70	$lb/in.^2$
Atm	1.058	$tons/ft^2$
Barrels-oil	42	gal-oil
British thermal units	0.2520	kg-cal
Btu	777.5	ft-lb
Btu	3.927×10^{-4}	hp-hr
Btu	107.5	kg-m
Btu	2.928×10^{-4}	kWh
Btu minutes	12.96	ft-lb/sec
Btu/min	0.02356	hp
Btu/min	0.0175	kW
Btu/min	17.57	W
Centares (Centiares)	1	m^2
Centigrams	0.01	grams
Centiliters	0.01	liters
Centimeters	0.3937	inches
Centimeters	0.01	meters
Centimeters	10	millimeters
Centimeters of mercury	0.01316	atm
cm mercury	0.4461	Water, ft
cm mercury	136.0	kg/m^2
cm mercury	27.85	lb/ft^2
cm mercury	0.1934	$lb/in.^2$
Centimeters/second	1.969	ft/min
cm/sec	0.03281	ft/sec
cm/sec	0.036	km/hr
cm/sec	0.6	m/min
cm/sec	0.02237	mi./hr
cm/sec	3.728×10	mi./min
C.M.S./sec/sec	0.03281	ft/sec/sec
Cubic centimeters	3.531×10^{-5}	ft^3
cm^3	6.102×10^{-2}	$in.^3$
cm^3	10^{-6}	m^3
cm^3	1.308×10^{-6}	yd^3
cm^3	2.642×10^{-4}	gal
cm^3	10-3	liters
cm^3	2.113×10^{-3}	pints (liq)
cm^3	1.057×10^{-3}	quarts (liq)

Table 6–11 (*Continued*)
CONVERSION FACTORS

Multiply	By	To obtain
Cubic feet	2.832×10^{-4}	cm^3
ft^3	1728	$in.^3$
ft^3	0.02832	m^3
ft^3	0.03704	yd^3
ft^3	7.48052	gal
ft^3	28.32	liters
ft^3	59.84	pints (liq)
ft^3	29.92	quarts (liq)
Cubic feet/minute	472.0	cm^3/sec
ft^3/min	0.1247	gal/sec
ft^3/min	0.4720	liters/sec
ft^3/min	62.43	water/min
Cubic feet/second	0.646317	mil/gal/day
ft^3/sec	448.831	gal/min
Cubic inches	16.39	cm^3
$in.^3$	5.787×10^{-4}	ft^3
$in.^3$	1.639×10^{-5}	m^3
$in.^3$	2.143×10^{-5}	yd^3
$in.^3$	4.329×10^{-3}	gal
$in.^3$	1.639×10^{-2}	liters
$in.^3$	0.03463	pints (liq)
$in.^3$	0.01732	quarts (liq)
Cubic meters	10^6	cm^3
m^3	35.31	ft^3
m^3	61,023	$in.^3$
m^3	1.308	yd^3
m^3	264.2	gal
m^3	10^3	liters
m^3	2113	pints (liq)
m^3	1057	quarts (liq)
Cubic yards	7.646×10^5	cm^3
yd^3	27	ft^3
yd^3	46,656	$in.^3$
yd^3	0.7646	m^3
yd^3	202.0	gal
yd^3	764.6	liters
yd^3	1616	pints (liq)
yd^3	807.9	quarts (liq)
Cubic yards/min	0.45	ft^3
yd^3/min	3.367	gal/sec
yd^3/min	12.74	l/sec
Decigrams	0.1	grams
Deciliters	0.1	liters
Decimeters	0.1	meters
Degrees (angle)	60	min
Degrees (angle)	0.01745	radians
Degrees (angle)	3600	sec

Table 6–11 (*Continued*)

CONVERSION FACTORS

Multiply	By	To obtain
Degrees/sec	0.01745	rad/sec
Degrees/sec	0.1667	r/min
Degrees/sec	0.002778	r/sec
Dekagrams	10	grams
Dekaliters	10	liters
Dekameters	10	meters
Fathoms	6	ft
Feet	30.48	cm
ft	12	in.
ft	0.3048	m
ft	1/3	yd
Feet of water	0.02950	atm
ft water	0.8826	in. mercury
ft water	0.03048	kg/cm^2
ft water	62.43	lb/ft^2
ft water	0.4335	$lb/in.^2$
Feet/min	0.5080	cm/sec
ft/min	0.01667	ft/sec
ft/min	0.01829	km/hr
ft/min	0.3048	m/min
ft/min	0.01136	mi./hr
Feet/sec/sec	30.48	cm/sec/sec
ft/sec/sec	0.3048	m/sec/sec
Foot-pounds	1.268×10^{-3}	Btu
ft-lb	5.050×10^{-7}	hp-hr
ft-lb	3.241×10^{-4}	kg-cal
ft-lb	0.1383	kg-m
ft-lb	3.766×10^{-7}	kWh
Foot-pounds/min	1.286×10^{-3}	Btu/min
ft-lb/min	0.01667	ft-lb/sec
ft-lb/min	5.050×10^{-7}	hp
ft-lb/min	3.241×10^{-4}	kg-cal/min
ft-lb/min	2.260×10^{-5}	kW
Foot-pounds/sec	7.717×10^{-2}	Btu/min
ft-lb/sec	1.818×10^{-3}	hp
ft-lb/sec	1.945×10^{-2}	kg-cal/min
ft-lb/sec	1.356×10^{-3}	kW
Gallons	3785	cm^3
gal	0.1337	ft^3
gal	231	$in.^3$
gal	3.785×10^{-3}	m^3
gal	4.951×10^{-3}	yd^3
gal	3.785	liters
gal	8	pints (liq)
gal	4	quarts (liq)

Table 6–11 (*Continued*)

CONVERSION FACTORS

Multiply	By	To obtain
Gallons, imperial	1.20095	U.S. gal
gal, U.S.	0.83267	Imp. gal
Gallons water	8.3453	lb water
Gallons/min	2.228×10^{-3}	ft^3/sec
gal/min	0.06308	l/sec
gal/min	8.0208	ft^3/hr
Gallons water/min	6.0086	tons water/24 hr
Grams	980.7	dyn
grams	15.43	grains
grams	10^{-3}	kg
grams	10^{-3}	mg
grams	0.03527	oz
grams	0.03215	oz (troy)
grams	2.205×10^{-3}	lb
Grams/cm	5.600×10^{-3}	lb/in.
Grams cm³	62.43	lb/ft^3
g/cm^3	0.03613	$lb/in.^3$
Grams/liter	58.417	gr/gal
g/l	8.345	lb/1000 gal
g/l	0.062427	lb/ft^3
g/l	1000	ppm
Hectograms	100	g
Hectoliters	100	liters
Hectometers	100	meters
Hectowatts	100	watts
Inches	2.540	centimeters
Inches of mercury	0.03342	atm
in. mercury	1.133	ft water
in. mercury	0.03453	kg/cm^2
in. mercury	70.73	lb/ft^2
in. mercury	0.4912	$lb/in.^2$
Inches of water	0.002458	atm
in. water	0.07355	in. mercury
in. water	0.002540	kg/cm^2
in. water	0.5781	$oz/in.^2$
in. water	5.202	lb/ft^2
in. water	0.03613	$lb/in.^2$
Joules (abs)	9.480×10^{-4}	Btu (mean)
Joules (abs)	0.23895	grain cal (mean)
Joules (abs)	0.23918	grain cal (20°C)
Joules (abs)	2.3889×10^{-4}	kg cal (mean)
Joules (abs)	1×10^7	erg

Table 6–11 (*Continued*)
CONVERSION FACTORS

Multiply	By	To obtain
Joules (abs)	0.73756	ft lb
Joules (abs)	1.0197×10^{-4}	g cm
Joules (abs)	3.72508×10^{-7}	hp-hr
Joules (abs)	0.999680	Joules (international)
Joules (abs)	2.77778×10^{-7}	kilowatt hr
Kilograms	980.665	dyn
kg	2.205	lb
kg	1.102×10^{-3}	tons (short)
kg	10^3	grams
Kilograms/meter	0.6720	lb/ft
Kilograms/square centimeter	0.9678	Atm
kg/cm^2	32.81	Water, ft
kg/cm^2	28.96	in. mercury
kg/cm^2	2048	lb/ft^2
kg/cm^2	14.22	$lb/in.^2$
Kilograms/square	10^6	kg/m^2
Kiloliters	10^3	liters
Kilometers	10^5	cm
km	3281	ft
km	10^3	meters
km	0.6214	mi.
km	1094	yd
Kilometers/hour	27.78	cm/sec
km/hr	54.68	ft/min
km/hr	0.9113	ft/sec
km/hr	0.5396	knots
km/hr	16.67	m/min
km/hr	0.6214	mi./hr
Kilometers/hour/sec	27.78	cm/sec/sec
km/hr/sec	0.9113	ft/sec/sec
km/hr/sec	0.2778	m/sec/sec
Kilowatts	56.92	Btu/min
kW	4.425×10^4	ft-lb/min
kW	737.6	ft-lb/sec
kW	1.341	hp
kW	14.34	kg-cal/min
kW	10^3	watts
Kilowatt hours	3415	Btu
kWh	2.655×10^6	ft-lb
kWh	1.341	hp-hr
kWh	860.5	kg-cal
kWh	3.671×10^5	kg-m
Liters	10^3	cm^3
liters	0.03531	ft^3
liters	61.02	$in.^3$
liters	10^{-2}	m^3

Table 6–11 (*Continued*)
CONVERSION FACTORS

Multiply	By	To obtain
liters	1308×10^{-3}	yd^3
liters	0.2642	gal
liters	2.113	pints (liq)
liters	1.057	quarts (liq)
Liters/min	5.886×10^{-4}	ft^3/sec
liters/min	4.403×10^{-3}	gal/sec
Meters	100	cm
meters	3.281	ft
meters	39.37	in.
meters	10^{-3}	km
meters	10^3	mm
meters	1.094	yd
Meters/min	1.667	cm/sec
m/min	3.281	ft/min
m/min	0.05468	ft/sec
m/min	0.06	km/hr
m/min	0.03728	mi./hr
Meters/sec	196.8	ft/min
m/sec	3.281	ft/sec
m/sec	3.6	km/hr
m/sec	0.06	km/min
m/sec	2.237	mi./hr
m/sec	0.03728	mi./min
Microns	10^{-6}	meters
Miles	1.609×10^5	cm
m	5280	ft
m	1.609	km
m	1760	yd
Miles/hr	44.70	cm/sec
mi./hr	88	ft/min
mi./hr	1.467	ft/sec
mi./hr	1.609	km/hr
mi./hr	0.8684	knots
mi./hr	26.82	m/min
Miles/min	2682	cm/sec
mi./min	88	ft/sec
mi./min	1.609	km/min
mi./min	60	mi./hr
Milliers	10^3	kg
Milligrams	10^{-3}	grams
Milliliters	10^{-3}	liters
Millimeters	0.1	cm
Millimeters	0.03937	in.
Milligrams/liter	1	ppm

Table 6–11 (*Continued*)
CONVERSION FACTORS

Multiply	By	To obtain
Million gal/day	1.54723	ft^3/sec
Minutes (angle)	2.909×10^{-4}	rad
Ounces	16	drams
oz	137.5	grains
oz	0.0625	lb
oz	28.349527	grams
oz	0.9115	oz (troy)
oz	2.790×10^{-5}	tons (long)
oz	2.835×10^{-5}	tons (metric)
Ounces (fluid)	1.805	in.^{3}
oz (fluid)	0.02957	liters
Ounces/in.^{2}	0.0625	lb/in.^{2}
Parts/million	0.0584	gr/U.S. gal
ppm	0.07016	gr/imp. gal
ppm	8.345	lb/mil gal
Pounds	16	oz
lb	256	drams
lb	7000	grains
lb	0.0005	tons (short)
lb	453.5924	grams
lb	1.21528	pounds (troy)
lb	14.5833	ounces (troy)
Pounds of water	0.01602	ft^3
lb water	27.68	in.^{3}
lb water	0.1198	gal
Pounds of water/min	2.670×10^{-4}	ft^3/sec
Pounds/cubic foot	0.01602	g/cm^3
lb/ft^3	16.02	kg/m^3
lb/ft^3	5.787×10^{-4}	lb/in.^{3}
Pounds/cubic inch	27.68	g/cm^3
lb/in.^{3}	2.768×10^4	kg/m^3
lb/in.^{3}	1728	lb/ft^3
Pounds/foot	1.488	kg/m
lb/in.	178.6	g/cm
Pounds/square foot	0.01602	ft. water
lb/ft^2	4.883×10^{-4}	kg/cm^2
lb/ft^2	6.945×10^{-3}	lb/in.^{2}
Pounds/square inch	0.06804	atm
lb/in.^{2}	2.307	ft water
lb/in.^{2}	2.036	in. mercury
lb/in.^{2}	0.07031	kg/cm^2
Quarts (dry)	67.20	in.^{3}

Table 6–11 (*Continued*)
CONVERSION FACTORS

Multiply	By	To obtain
Quarts (liq.)	57.75	in.^{3}
$\frac{1}{ft^2/gal/min}$	8.0208	Overflow rate (ft/hr)
Temperature, °C 273	1	abs. temp, °C
temp, °C 17.78	1.8	temp, °F
temp, °F 460	1	abs. temp °F
temp, °F −32	5/9	temp, °C
Tons (long)	1016	kg
tons (long)	2240	lb
tons (long)	1.12000	tons (short)
Tons (metric)	10^3	kg
tons, metric	2205	lb
Tons (short)	2000	lb
tons, short	32000	oz
tons, short	907.18486	kg
tons, short	2430.56	lb, troy
tons, short	0.89287	tons, long
tons, short	29166.66	oz, troy
tons, short	0.90718	tons, metric
Tons of water/24 hr	83.333	lb/water/hr
tons water/24 hr	0.16643	gal/min
tons water/24 hr	1.3349	ft^3/hr
Volts (abs)	1×10^8	Abvolts
volts/°C	1.0000	J/coulomb/°C
volts, abs	0.0033356	statvolts
volts, abs	0.099955	volts (international)
Watts	0.05692	Btu/min
watts	44.26	ft-lb/min
watts	0.7376	ft-lb/sec
watts	1.341×10^{-3}	hp
watts	0.01434	kg-cal/min
watts	10^{-3}	kW
Watt-hours	3.415	Btu
watt-hours	2655	ft-lb
watt-hours	1.341×10^{-3}	hp
watt-hours	0.8605	kg-cal
watt-hours	367.1	kg-m
watt-hours	10^{-3}	kWh

(From *Handbook of Oceanographic Tables,* SP-68, Bialek, E. L., Compiler, U.S. Naval Oceanographic Office, Washington, D.C., 1966.)

Table 6–12
FUNDAMENTAL PHYSICAL CONSTANTS

Quantity	Symbol	Value[a]	Error, ppm	Units: SI	Units: cgs
Velocity of light	c	2.9979250(10)	0.33	10^{8} m sec^{-1}	10^{10} cm sec^{-1}
Fine-structure constant,	α	7.297351(11)	1.5	10^{-3}	10^{-3}
$[\mu_0 c^2/4\pi](e^2/\hbar c)$	α^{-1}	137.03602(21)	1.5		
Electron charge	e	1.6021917(70)	4.4	10^{-19} C	10^{-20} emu
		4.803250(21)	4.4		10^{-10} esu
Planck's constant	h	6.626196(50)	7.6	10^{-34} J·sec	10^{-27} erg·sec
	$\hbar = h/2\pi$	1.0545919(80)	7.6	10^{-34} J·sec	10^{-27} erg·sec
Avogadro's number	N	6.022169(40)	6.6	10^{26} kmole^{-1}	10^{23} mole^{-1}
Atomic mass unit	amu	1.660531(11)	6.6	10^{-27} kg	10^{-24} g
Electron rest mass	m_e	9.109558(54)	6.0	10^{-31} kg	10^{-28} g
	$m_e{}^*$	5.485930(34)	6.2	10^{-4} amu	10^{-4} amu
Proton rest mass	M_p	1.672614(11)	6.6	10^{-27} kg	10^{-24} g
	$M_p{}^*$	1.00727661(8)	0.08	amu	amu
Neutron rest mass	M_n	1.674920(11)	6.6	10^{-27} kg	10^{-24} g
	$M_n{}^*$	1.00866520(10)	0.10	amu	amu
Ratio of proton mass to electron mass	M_p/m_e	1836.109(11)	6.2		
Electron charge to mass ratio	e/m_e	1.7588028(54)	3.1	10^{11} C kg^{-1}	10^{7} emu g^{-1}
		5.272759(16)	3.1		10^{17} esu g^{-1}
Magnetic flux quantum,	Φ_0	2.0678538(69)	3.3	10^{-15} T·m^2	10^{-7} G·cm^2
$[c]^{-1}(hc/2e)$	h/e	4.135708(14)	3.3	10^{-15} J·sec C^{-1}	10^{-7} erg·sec emu^{-1}
		1.3795234(46)	3.3		10^{-17} erg·sec esu^{-1}
Quantum of circulation	$h/2m_e$	3.636947(11)	3.1	10^{-4} J·sec kg^{-1}	erg·sec g^{-1}
	h/m_e	7.273894(22)	3.1	10^{-4} J·sec kg^{-1}	erg·sec g^{-1}
Faraday constant, Ne	F	9.648670(54)	5.5	10^{7} C kmole^{-1}	10^{3} emu mole^{-1}
		2.892599(16)	5.5		10^{14} esu mole^{-1}
Rydberg constant, $[\mu_0 c^2/4\pi]^2(m_e e^4/4\pi\hbar^3 c)$	R_∞	1.09737312(11)	0.10	10^{7} m^{-1}	10^{5} cm^{-1}

Note: The unified atomic mass scale $^{12}C \equiv 12$ has been used throughout, amu = atomic mass unit, C = coulomb, G = gauss, Hz = hertz = cycles/sec, J = joule, K = kelvin (degrees kelvin), T = tesla (10^4 G), V = volt, and W = watt. In cases where formulas for constants are given (e.g., R_∞), the relations are written as the product of two factors. The second factor, in parentheses, is the expression to be used when all quantities are expressed in cgs units, with the electron charge in electrostatic units. The first factor, in brackets, is to be included only if all quantities are expressed in SI units. We remind the reader that with the exception of the auxiliary constants which have been taken to be exact, the uncertainties of these constants are correlated, and therefore the general law of error propagation must be used in calculating additional quantities requiring two or more of these constants.

[a] The numbers in parentheses are the standard deviation uncertainties in the last digits of the quoted value, computed on the basis of internal consistency.

Table 6–12 (*Continued*)
FUNDAMENTAL PHYSICAL CONSTANTS

Quantity	Symbol	Value[a]	Error, ppm	Units: SI	Units: cgs
Bohr radius, $[\mu_0 c^2/4\pi]^{-1}(\hbar^2/m_e e^2) = \alpha/4\pi R_\infty$	a_0	5.2917715(81)	1.5	10^{-11} m	10^{-9} cm
Classical electron radius, $[\mu_0 c^2/4\pi](e^2/m_e c^2) = \alpha^3/4\pi R_\infty$	r_0	2.817939(13)	4.6	10^{-15} m	10^{-13} cm
Electron magnetic moment in Bohr magnetons	μ_e/μ_B	1.0011596389(31)	0.0031		
Bohr magneton, $[c](e\hbar/2m_e c)$	μ_B	9.274096(65)	7.0	10^{-24} J T^{-1}	10^{-21} erg G^{-1}
Electron magnetic moment	μ_e	9.284851(65)	7.0	10^{-24} J T^{-1}	10^{-21} erg G^{-1}
Gyromagnetic ratio of protons in H_2O	γ_p'	2.6751270(82)	3.1	10^8 rad $sec^{-1}\cdot T^{-1}$	10^4 rad $sec^{-1}\cdot G^{-1}$
	$\gamma_p'/2\pi$	4.257597(13)	3.1	10^7 Hz T^{-1}	10^3 Hz G^{-1}
γ_p' corrected for diamagnetism of H_2O	γ_p	2.6751965(82)	3.1	10^8 rad $sec^{-1}\cdot T^{-1}$	10^4 rad $sec^{-1}\cdot G^{-1}$
	$\gamma_p/2\pi$	4.257707(13)	3.1	10^7 Hz T^{-1}	10^3 Hz G^{-1}
Magnetic moment of protons in H_2O in Bohr magnetons	μ_p'/μ_B	1.52099312(10)	0.066	10^{-3}	10^{-3}
Proton magnetic moment in Bohr magnetons	μ_p/μ_B	1.52103264(46)	0.30	10^{-3}	10^{-3}
Proton magnetic moment	μ_p	1.4106203(99)	7.0	10^{-26} J T^{-1}	10^{-23} erg G^{-1}
Magnetic moment of protons in H_2O in nuclear magnetons	μ_p'/μ_n	2.792709(17)	6.2		
μ_p'/μ_n corrected for diamagnetism of H_2O	μ_p/μ_n	2.792782(17)	6.2		
Nuclear magneton, $[c](e\hbar/2M_p c)$	μ_n	5.050951(50)	10	10^{-27} J T^{-1}	10^{-24} erg G^{-1}
Compton wavelength of the electron, $h/m_e c$	λ_c	2.4263096(74)	3.1	10^{-12} m	10^{-10} cm
	$\lambda_c/2\pi$	3.861592(12)	3.1	10^{-12} m	10^{-10} cm
Compton wavelength of the proton, $h/M_p c$	$\lambda_{c.p}$	1.3214409(90)	6.8	10^{-15} m	10^{-13} cm
	$\lambda_{c.p}/2\pi$	2.103139(14)	6.8	10^{-16} m	10^{-14} cm
Compton wavelength of the neutron, $h/M_n c$	$\lambda_{c.n}$	1.3196217(90)	6.8	10^{-15} m	10^{-13} cm
	$\lambda_{c.n}/2\pi$	2.100243(14)	6.8	10^{-16} m	10^{-14} cm
Gas constant	R_0	8.31434(35)	42	10^3 J $kmole^{-1}\cdot K^{-1}$	10^7 erg $mole^{-1}\cdot K^{-1}$
Boltzman's constant, R_0/N	k	1.380622(59)	43	10^{-23} J K^{-1}	10^{-16} erg K^{-1}
Stefan-Boltzman constant, $\pi^2 k^4/60\hbar^3 c^2$	σ	5.66961(96)	170	10^{-8} W m^{-2} K^4	10^{-5} erg $sec^{-1}\cdot cm^{-2}\cdot K^{-4}$
First radiation constant, $8\pi hc$	c_1	4.992579(38)	7.6	10^{-24} J·m	10^{-15} erg·cm

[a] The numbers in parentheses are the standard deviation uncertainties in the last digits of the quoted value, computed on the basis of internal consistency.

Table 6–12 (*Continued*)
FUNDAMENTAL PHYSICAL CONSTANTS

Quantity	Symbol	Value[a]	Error, ppm	Units: SI	Units: cgs
Second radiation constant, hc/k	c_2	1.438833(61)	43	10^{-2} m·K	cm·K
Gravitational constant	G	6.6732(31)	460	10^{-11} N·m² kg^{-2}	10^{-8} dyn·cm²g^{-2}
kx-unit-to-angstrom conversion factor, $\Lambda = \lambda(Å)/\lambda(kxu); \lambda(CuK\alpha_1) \equiv$ 1.537400 kxu	Λ	1.0020764(53)	5.3		
Å*-to-angstrom conversion factor, $\Lambda = \lambda(Å)/\lambda(Å^*); \lambda(WK\alpha_1) \equiv$ 0.2090100 Å*	Λ^*	1.0000197(56)	5.6		

[a] The numbers in parentheses are the standard deviation uncertainties in the last digits of the quoted value, computed on the basis of internal consistency.

(From Taylor, B.N., Parker, W.H., and Langenberg, D.N., *Rev. Mod. Phys.*, 41, 375, 1969. With permission.)

INDEX

INDEX

A

B

C

D

E

F

G

H

I

J

L

M

Q

R

S

W

Z